*Calculus*

# Tom M. Apostol

# CALCULUS

## VOLUME I

## One-Variable Calculus, with an Introduction to Linear Algebra

### SECOND EDITION

**WILEY-INDIA**

CONSULTING EDITOR

George Springer, *Indiana University*

**CALCULUS**
**Volume I : One Variable Calculus, with an Introduction to Linear Algebra**
*Second Edition*

Bicentennial logo designer: Richard J. Pacifico

Wiley also publishes its books in a variety of electronic formats. Some content that appears in print may not be available in electronic books. For more information about Wiley products, visit our website at www.wiley.com.

Reprint: 2007

Printed at: Sheel Print-N-Pack, Noida

ISBN   978-81-265-1519-6

*To*
*Jane and Stephen*

# PREFACE

## Excerpts from the Preface to the First Edition

There seems to be no general agreement as to what should constitute a first course in calculus and analytic geometry. Some people insist that the only way to really understand calculus is to start off with a thorough treatment of the real-number system and develop the subject step by step in a logical and rigorous fashion. Others argue that calculus is primarily a tool for engineers and physicists; they believe the course should stress applications of the calculus by appeal to intuition and by extensive drill on problems which develop manipulative skills. There is much that is sound in both these points of view. Calculus is a deductive science and a branch of pure mathematics. At the same time, it is very important to remember that calculus has strong roots in physical problems and that it derives much of its power and beauty from the variety of its applications. It is possible to combine a strong theoretical development with sound training in technique; this book represents an attempt to strike a sensible balance between the two. While treating the calculus as a deductive science, the book does not neglect applications to physical problems. Proofs of all the important theorems are presented as an essential part of the growth of mathematical ideas; the proofs are often preceded by a geometric or intuitive discussion to give the student some insight into why they take a particular form. Although these intuitive discussions will satisfy readers who are not interested in detailed proofs, the complete proofs are also included for those who prefer a more rigorous presentation.

The approach in this book has been suggested by the historical and philosophical development of calculus and analytic geometry. For example, integration is treated before differentiation. Although to some this may seem unusual, it is historically correct and pedagogically sound. Moreover, it is the best way to make meaningful the true connection between the integral and the derivative.

The concept of the integral is defined first for step functions. Since the integral of a step function is merely a finite sum, integration theory in this case is extremely simple. As the student learns the properties of the integral for step functions, he gains experience in the use of the summation notation and at the same time becomes familiar with the notation for integrals. This sets the stage so that the transition from step functions to more general functions seems easy and natural.

## Preface to the Second Edition

The second edition differs from the first in many respects. Linear algebra has been incorporated, the mean-value theorems and routine applications of calculus are introduced at an earlier stage, and many new and easier exercises have been added. A glance at the table of contents reveals that the book has been divided into smaller chapters, each centering on an important concept. Several sections have been rewritten and reorganized to provide better motivation and to improve the flow of ideas.

As in the first edition, a historical introduction precedes each important new concept, tracing its development from an early intuitive physical notion to its precise mathematical formulation. The student is told something of the struggles of the past and of the triumphs of the men who contributed most to the subject. Thus the student becomes an active participant in the evolution of ideas rather than a passive observer of results.

The second edition, like the first, is divided into two volumes. The first two thirds of Volume I deals with the calculus of functions of one variable, including infinite series and an introduction to differential equations. The last third of Volume I introduces linear algebra with applications to geometry and analysis. Much of this material leans heavily on the calculus for examples that illustrate the general theory. It provides a natural blending of algebra and analysis and helps pave the way for the transition from one-variable calculus to multivariable calculus, discussed in Volume II. Further development of linear algebra will occur as needed in the second edition of Volume II.

Once again I acknowledge with pleasure my debt to Professors H. F. Bohnenblust, A. Erdélyi, F. B. Fuller, K. Hoffman, G. Springer, and H. S. Zuckerman. Their influence on the first edition continued into the second. In preparing the second edition, I received additional help from Professor Basil Gordon, who suggested many improvements. Thanks are also due George Springer and William P. Ziemer, who read the final draft. The staff of the Blaisdell Publishing Company has, as always, been helpful; I appreciate their sympathetic consideration of my wishes concerning format and typography.

Finally, it gives me special pleasure to express my gratitude to my wife for the many ways she has contributed during the preparation of both editions. In grateful acknowledgment I happily dedicate this book to her.

T. M. A.

*Pasadena, California*
*September* 16, 1966

# CONTENTS

## I. INTRODUCTION

### Part 1. Historical Introduction

### Part 2. Some Basic Concepts of the Theory of Sets

### Part 3. A Set of Axioms for the Real-Number System

## Part 4.  Mathematical Induction, Summation Notation, and Related Topics

## 1. THE CONCEPTS OF INTEGRAL CALCULUS

## 2. SOME APPLICATIONS OF INTEGRATION

## 3. CONTINUOUS FUNCTIONS

# 4. DIFFERENTIAL CALCULUS

# 5. THE RELATION BETWEEN INTEGRATION AND DIFFERENTIATION

# 6. THE LOGARITHM, THE EXPONENTIAL, AND THE INVERSE TRIGONOMETRIC FUNCTIONS

# 7. POLYNOMIAL APPROXIMATIONS TO FUNCTIONS

# 8. INTRODUCTION TO DIFFERENTIAL EQUATIONS

# 9. COMPLEX NUMBERS

# 10. SEQUENCES, INFINITE SERIES, IMPROPER INTEGRALS

# 11. SEQUENCES AND SERIES OF FUNCTIONS

# 12. VECTOR ALGEBRA

# 13. APPLICATIONS OF VECTOR ALGEBRA
# TO ANALYTIC GEOMETRY

# 14. CALCULUS OF VECTOR-VALUED FUNCTIONS

# 15. LINEAR SPACES

# 16. LINEAR TRANSFORMATIONS AND MATRICES

*Calculus*

# INTRODUCTION

## Part 1.  Historical Introduction

### I 1.1   The two basic concepts of calculus

The remarkable progress that has been made in science and technology during the last century is due in large part to the development of mathematics. That branch of mathematics known as integral and differential calculus serves as a natural and powerful tool for attacking a variety of problems that arise in physics, astronomy, engineering, chemistry, geology, biology, and other fields including, rather recently, some of the social sciences.

To give the reader an idea of the many different types of problems that can be treated by the methods of calculus, we list here a few sample questions selected from the exercises that occur in later chapters of this book.

With what speed should a rocket be fired upward so that it never returns to earth? What is the radius of the smallest circular disk that can cover every isosceles triangle of a given perimeter $L$? What volume of material is removed from a solid sphere of radius $2r$ if a hole of radius $r$ is drilled through the center? If a strain of bacteria grows at a rate proportional to the amount present and if the population doubles in one hour, by how much will it increase at the end of two hours? If a ten-pound force stretches an elastic spring one inch, how much work is required to stretch the spring one foot?

These examples, chosen from various fields, illustrate some of the technical questions that can be answered by more or less routine applications of calculus.

Calculus is more than a technical tool—it is a collection of fascinating and exciting ideas that have interested thinking men for centuries. These ideas have to do with *speed, area, volume, rate of growth, continuity, tangent line,* and other concepts from a variety of fields. Calculus forces us to stop and think carefully about the meanings of these concepts. Another remarkable feature of the subject is its unifying power. Most of these ideas can be formulated so that they revolve around two rather specialized problems of a geometric nature. We turn now to a brief description of these problems.

Consider a curve $C$ which lies above a horizontal base line such as that shown in Figure I.1. We assume this curve has the property that every vertical line intersects it once at most.

1

The shaded portion of the figure consists of those points which lie below the curve *C*, above the horizontal base, and between two parallel vertical segments joining *C* to the base. The first fundamental problem of calculus is this: *To assign a number which measures the area of this shaded region.*

Consider next a line drawn tangent to the curve, as shown in Figure I.1. The second fundamental problem may be stated as follows: *To assign a number which measures the steepness of this line.*

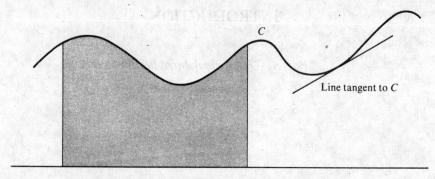

FIGURE I.1

Basically, calculus has to do with the precise formulation and solution of these two special problems. It enables us to *define* the concepts of area and tangent line and *to calculate* the area of a given region or the steepness of a given tangent line. *Integral calculus* deals with the problem of area and will be discussed in Chapter 1. *Differential calculus* deals with the problem of tangents and will be introduced in Chapter 4.

The study of calculus requires a certain mathematical background. The present chapter deals with this background material and is divided into four parts: Part 1 provides historical perspective; Part 2 discusses some notation and terminology from the mathematics of sets; Part 3 deals with the real-number system; Part 4 treats mathematical induction and the summation notation. If the reader is acquainted with these topics, he can proceed directly to the development of integral calculus in Chapter 1. If not, he should become familiar with the material in the unstarred sections of this Introduction before proceeding to Chapter 1.

## I 1.2  Historical background

The birth of integral calculus occurred more than 2000 years ago when the Greeks attempted to determine areas by a process which they called the *method of exhaustion*. The essential ideas of this method are very simple and can be described briefly as follows: Given a region whose area is to be determined, we inscribe in it a polygonal region which approximates the given region and whose area we can easily compute. Then we choose another polygonal region which gives a better approximation, and we continue the process, taking polygons with more and more sides in an attempt to exhaust the given region. The method is illustrated for a semicircular region in Figure I.2. It was used successfully by Archimedes (287–212 B.C.) to find exact formulas for the area of a circle and a few other special figures.

The development of the method of exhaustion beyond the point to which Archimedes carried it had to wait nearly eighteen centuries until the use of algebraic symbols and techniques became a standard part of mathematics. The elementary algebra that is familiar to most high-school students today was completely unknown in Archimedes' time, and it would have been next to impossible to extend his method to any general class of regions without some convenient way of expressing rather lengthy calculations in a compact and simplified form.

A slow but revolutionary change in the development of mathematical notations began in the 16th century A.D. The cumbersome system of Roman numerals was gradually displaced by the Hindu-Arabic characters used today, the symbols $+$ and $-$ were introduced for the first time, and the advantages of the decimal notation began to be recognized. During this same period, the brilliant successes of the Italian mathematicians Tartaglia,

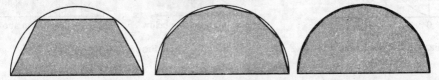

FIGURE I.2   The method of exhaustion applied to a semicircular region.

Cardano, and Ferrari in finding algebraic solutions of cubic and quartic equations stimulated a great deal of activity in mathematics and encouraged the growth and acceptance of a new and superior algebraic language. With the widespread introduction of well-chosen algebraic symbols, interest was revived in the ancient method of exhaustion and a large number of fragmentary results were discovered in the 16th century by such pioneers as Cavalieri, Toricelli, Roberval, Fermat, Pascal, and Wallis.

Gradually the method of exhaustion was transformed into the subject now called integral calculus, a new and powerful discipline with a large variety of applications, not only to geometrical problems concerned with areas and volumes but also to problems in other sciences. This branch of mathematics, which retained some of the original features of the method of exhaustion, received its biggest impetus in the 17th century, largely due to the efforts of Isaac Newton (1642–1727) and Gottfried Leibniz (1646–1716), and its development continued well into the 19th century before the subject was put on a firm mathematical basis by such men as Augustin-Louis Cauchy (1789–1857) and Bernhard Riemann (1826–1866). Further refinements and extensions of the theory are still being carried out in contemporary mathematics.

### I 1.3   The method of exhaustion for the area of a parabolic segment

Before we proceed to a systematic treatment of integral calculus, it will be instructive to apply the method of exhaustion directly to one of the special figures treated by Archimedes himself. The region in question is shown in Figure I.3 and can be described as follows: If we choose an arbitrary point on the base of this figure and denote its distance from 0 by $x$, then the vertical distance from this point to the curve is $x^2$. In particular, if the length of the base itself is $b$, the altitude of the figure is $b^2$. The vertical distance from $x$ to the curve is called the "ordinate" at $x$. The curve itself is an example of what is known

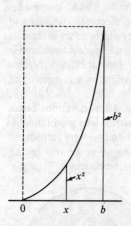

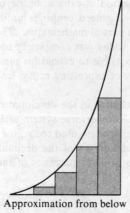

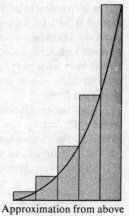

Approximation from below          Approximation from above

FIGURE I.3   A parabolic                    FIGURE I.4
                  segment.

as a *parabola*. The region bounded by it and the two line segments is called a *parabolic segment*.

This figure may be enclosed in a rectangle of base $b$ and altitude $b^2$, as shown in Figure I.3. Examination of the figure suggests that the area of the parabolic segment is less than half the area of the rectangle. Archimedes made the surprising discovery that the area of the parabolic segment is exactly *one-third* that of the rectangle; that is to say, $A = b^3/3$, where $A$ denotes the area of the parabolic segment. We shall show presently how to arrive at this result.

It should be pointed out that the parabolic segment in Figure I.3 is not shown exactly as Archimedes drew it and the details that follow are not exactly the same as those used by him.

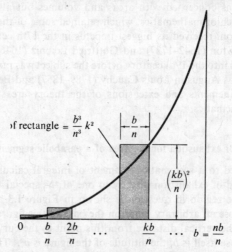

FIGURE I.5   Calculation of the area of a parabolic segment.

Nevertheless, the essential *ideas* are those of Archimedes; what is presented here is the method of exhaustion in modern notation.

The method is simply this: We slice the figure into a number of strips and obtain two approximations to the region, one from below and one from above, by using two sets of rectangles as illustrated in Figure I.4. (We use rectangles rather than arbitrary polygons to simplify the computations.) The area of the parabolic segment is larger than the total area of the inner rectangles but smaller than that of the outer rectangles.

If each strip is further subdivided to obtain a new approximation with a larger number of strips, the total area of the inner rectangles *increases*, whereas the total area of the outer rectangles *decreases*. Archimedes realized that an approximation to the area within any desired degree of accuracy could be obtained by simply taking enough strips.

Let us carry out the actual computations that are required in this case. For the sake of simplicity, we subdivide the base into $n$ *equal* parts, each of length $b/n$ (see Figure I.5). The points of subdivision correspond to the following values of $x$:

$$0, \frac{b}{n}, \frac{2b}{n}, \frac{3b}{n}, \ldots, \frac{(n-1)b}{n}, \frac{nb}{n} = b \, .$$

A typical point of subdivision corresponds to $x = kb/n$, where $k$ takes the successive values $k = 0, 1, 2, 3, \ldots, n$. At each point $kb/n$ we construct the outer rectangle of altitude $(kb/n)^2$ as illustrated in Figure I.5. The area of this rectangle is the product of its base and altitude and is equal to

$$\left(\frac{b}{n}\right)\left(\frac{kb}{n}\right)^2 = \frac{b^3}{n^3} k^2.$$

Let us denote by $S_n$ the sum of the areas of all the outer rectangles. Then since the $k$th rectangle has area $(b^3/n^3)k^2$, we obtain the formula

(I.1)
$$S_n = \frac{b^3}{n^3}(1^2 + 2^2 + 3^2 + \cdots + n^2) \, .$$

In the same way we obtain a formula for the sum $s_n$ of all the inner rectangles:

(I.2)
$$s_n = \frac{b^3}{n^3}[1^2 + 2^2 + 3^2 + \cdots + (n-1)^2] \, .$$

This brings us to a very important stage in the calculation. Notice that the factor multiplying $b^3/n^3$ in Equation (I.1) is the sum of the squares of the first $n$ integers:

$$1^2 + 2^2 + \cdots + n^2 \, .$$

[The corresponding factor in Equation (I.2) is similar except that the sum has only $n-1$ terms.] For a large value of $n$, the computation of this sum by direct addition of its terms is tedious and inconvenient. Fortunately there is an interesting identity which makes it possible to evaluate this sum in a simpler way, namely,

(I.3)
$$1^2 + 2^2 + \cdots + n^2 = \frac{n^3}{3} + \frac{n^2}{2} + \frac{n}{6} \, .$$

This identity is valid for every integer $n \geq 1$ and can be proved as follows: Start with the formula $(k + 1)^3 = k^3 + 3k^2 + 3k + 1$ and rewrite it in the form

$$3k^2 + 3k + 1 = (k + 1)^3 - k^3.$$

Taking $k = 1, 2, \ldots, n - 1$, we get $n - 1$ formulas

$$3 \cdot 1^2 + 3 \cdot 1 + 1 = 2^3 - 1^3$$

$$3 \cdot 2^2 + 3 \cdot 2 + 1 = 3^3 - 2^3$$

$$\cdot$$
$$\cdot$$
$$\cdot$$

$$3(n - 1)^2 + 3(n - 1) + 1 = n^3 - (n - 1)^3.$$

When we add these formulas, all the terms on the right cancel except two and we obtain

$$3[1^2 + 2^2 + \cdots + (n - 1)^2] + 3[1 + 2 + \cdots + (n - 1)] + (n - 1) = n^3 - 1^3.$$

The second sum on the left is the sum of terms in an arithmetic progression and it simplifies to $\frac{1}{2}n(n - 1)$. Therefore this last equation gives us

(I.4) $$1^2 + 2^2 + \cdots + (n - 1)^2 = \frac{n^3}{3} - \frac{n^2}{2} + \frac{n}{6}.$$

Adding $n^2$ to both members, we obtain (I.3).

For our purposes, we do not need the exact expressions given in the right-hand members of (I.3) and (I.4). All we need are the two *inequalities*

(I.5) $$1^2 + 2^2 + \cdots + (n - 1)^2 < \frac{n^3}{3} < 1^2 + 2^2 + \cdots + n^2$$

which are valid for every integer $n \geq 1$. These inequalities can de deduced easily as consequences of (I.3) and (I.4), or they can be proved directly by induction. (A proof by induction is given in Section I 4.1.)

If we multiply both inequalities in (I.5) by $b^3/n^3$ and make use of (I.1) and (I.2), we obtain

(I.6) $$s_n < \frac{b^3}{3} < S_n$$

for every $n$. The inequalities in (I.6) tell us that $b^3/3$ is a number which lies between $s_n$ and $S_n$ for every $n$. We will now prove that $b^3/3$ is the *only* number which has this property. In other words, we assert that if $A$ is any number which satisfies the inequalities

(I.7) $$s_n < A < S_n$$

for every positive integer $n$, then $A = b^3/3$. It is because of this fact that Archimedes concluded that the area of the parabolic segment is $b^3/3$.

To prove that $A = b^3/3$, we use the inequalities in (I.5) once more. Adding $n^2$ to both sides of the leftmost inequality in (I.5), we obtain

$$1^2 + 2^2 + \cdots + n^2 < \frac{n^3}{3} + n^2.$$

Multiplying this by $b^3/n^3$ and using (I.1), we find

(I.8)
$$S_n < \frac{b^3}{3} + \frac{b^3}{n}.$$

Similarly, by subtracting $n^2$ from both sides of the rightmost inequality in (I.5) and multiplying by $b^3/n^3$, we are led to the inequality

(I.9)
$$\frac{b^3}{3} - \frac{b^3}{n} < s_n.$$

Therefore, any number $A$ satisfying (I.7) must also satisfy

(I.10)
$$\frac{b^3}{3} - \frac{b^3}{n} < A < \frac{b^3}{3} + \frac{b^3}{n}$$

for every integer $n \geq 1$. Now there are only three possibilities:

$$A > \frac{b^3}{3}, \qquad A < \frac{b^3}{3}, \qquad A = \frac{b^3}{3}.$$

If we show that each of the first two leads to a contradiction, then we must have $A = b^3/3$, since, in the manner of Sherlock Holmes, this exhausts all the possibilities.

Suppose the inequality $A > b^3/3$ were true. From the second inequality in (I.10) we obtain

(I.11)
$$A - \frac{b^3}{3} < \frac{b^3}{n}$$

for every integer $n \geq 1$. Since $A - b^3/3$ is positive, we may divide both sides of (I.11) by $A - b^3/3$ and then multiply by $n$ to obtain the equivalent statement

$$n < \frac{b^3}{A - b^3/3}$$

for every $n$. But this inequality is obviously false when $n \geq b^3/(A - b^3/3)$. Hence the inequality $A > b^3/3$ leads to a contradiction. By a similar argument, we can show that the inequality $A < b^3/3$ also leads to a contradiction, and therefore we must have $A = b^3/3$, as asserted.

## *I 1.4   Exercises

1. (a) Modify the region in Figure I.3 by assuming that the ordinate at each $x$ is $2x^2$ instead of $x^2$. Draw the new figure. Check through the principal steps in the foregoing section and find what effect this has on the calculation of the area. Do the same if the ordinate at each $x$ is (b) $3x^2$, (c) $\frac{1}{4}x^2$, (d) $2x^2 + 1$, (e) $ax^2 + c$.

2. Modify the region in Figure I.3 by assuming that the ordinate at each $x$ is $x^3$ instead of $x^2$. Draw the new figure.

   (a) Use a construction similar to that illustrated in Figure I.5 and show that the outer and inner sums $S_n$ and $s_n$ are given by

   $$S_n = \frac{b^4}{n^4}(1^3 + 2^3 + \cdots + n^3), \qquad s_n = \frac{b^4}{n^4}[1^3 + 2^3 + \cdots + (n-1)^3].$$

   (b) Use the inequalities (which can be proved by mathematical induction; see Section I4.2)

   (I.12)  $$1^3 + 2^3 + \cdots + (n-1)^3 < \frac{n^4}{4} < 1^3 + 2^3 + \cdots + n^3$$

   to show that $s_n < b^4/4 < S_n$ for every $n$, and prove that $b^4/4$ is the *only* number which lies between $s_n$ and $S_n$ for every $n$.

   (c) What number takes the place of $b^4/4$ if the ordinate at each $x$ is $ax^3 + c$?

3. The inequalities (I.5) and (I.12) are special cases of the more general inequalities

   (I.13)  $$1^k + 2^k + \cdots + (n-1)^k < \frac{n^{k+1}}{k+1} < 1^k + 2^k + \cdots + n^k$$

   that are valid for every integer $n \geq 1$ and every integer $k \geq 1$. Assume the validity of (I.13) and generalize the results of Exercise 2.

## I 1.5   A critical analysis of Archimedes' method

From calculations similar to those in Section I 1.3, Archimedes concluded that the area of the parabolic segment in question is $b^3/3$. This fact was generally accepted as a mathematical theorem for nearly 2000 years before it was realized that one must re-examine the result from a more critical point of view. To understand why anyone would question the validity of Archimedes' conclusion, it is necessary to know something about the important changes that have taken place in the recent history of mathematics.

Every branch of knowledge is a collection of ideas described by means of words and symbols, and one cannot understand these ideas unless one knows the exact meanings of the words and symbols that are used. Certain branches of knowledge, known as *deductive systems*, are different from others in that a number of "undefined" concepts are chosen in advance and all other concepts in the system are defined in terms of these. Certain statements about these undefined concepts are taken as *axioms* or *postulates* and other statements that can be deduced from the axioms are called *theorems*. The most familiar example of a deductive system is the Euclidean theory of elementary geometry that has been studied by well-educated men since the time of the ancient Greeks.

The spirit of early Greek mathematics, with its emphasis on the theoretical and postulational approach to geometry as presented in Euclid's *Elements*, dominated the thinking of mathematicians until the time of the Renaissance. A new and vigorous phase in the development of mathematics began with the advent of algebra in the 16th century, and the next 300 years witnessed a flood of important discoveries. Conspicuously absent from this period was the logically precise reasoning of the deductive method with its use of axioms, definitions, and theorems. Instead, the pioneers in the 16th, 17th, and 18th centuries resorted to a curious blend of deductive reasoning combined with intuition, pure guesswork, and mysticism, and it is not surprising to find that some of their work was later shown to be incorrect. However, a surprisingly large number of important discoveries emerged from this era, and a great deal of the work has survived the test of history—a tribute to the unusual skill and ingenuity of these pioneers.

As the flood of new discoveries began to recede, a new and more critical period emerged. Little by little, mathematicians felt forced to return to the classical ideals of the deductive method in an attempt to put the new mathematics on a firm foundation. This phase of the development, which began early in the 19th century and has continued to the present day, has resulted in a degree of logical purity and abstraction that has surpassed all the traditions of Greek science. At the same time, it has brought about a clearer understanding of the foundations of not only calculus but of all of mathematics.

There are many ways to develop calculus as a deductive system. One possible approach is to take the real numbers as the undefined objects. Some of the rules governing the operations on real numbers may then be taken as axioms. One such set of axioms is listed in Part 3 of this Introduction. New concepts, such as *integral*, *limit*, *continuity*, *derivative*, must then be defined in terms of real numbers. Properties of these concepts are then deduced as theorems that follow from the axioms.

Looked at as part of the deductive system of calculus, Archimedes' result about the area of a parabolic segment cannot be accepted as a theorem until a satisfactory definition of area is given first. It is not clear whether Archimedes had ever formulated a precise definition of what he meant by area. He seems to have taken it for granted that every region has an area associated with it. On this assumption he then set out to calculate areas of particular regions. In his calculations he made use of certain facts about area that cannot be proved until we know what is *meant* by area. For instance, he assumed that if one region lies inside another, the area of the smaller region cannot exceed that of the larger region. Also, if a region is decomposed into two or more parts, the sum of the areas of the individual parts is equal to the area of the whole region. All these are properties we would like area to possess, and we shall insist that any definition of area should imply these properties. It is quite possible that Archimedes himself may have taken area to be an undefined concept and then used the properties we just mentioned as *axioms* about area.

Today we consider the work of Archimedes as being important not so much because it helps us to compute areas of particular figures, but rather because it suggests a reasonable way to *define* the concept of area for more or less *arbitrary* figures. As it turns out, the method of Archimedes suggests a way to define a much more general concept known as the *integral*. The integral, in turn, is used to compute not only area but also quantities such as arc length, volume, work and others.

If we look ahead and make use of the terminology of integral calculus, the result of the calculation carried out in Section I 1.3 for the parabolic segment is often stated as follows:

"The integral of $x^2$ from 0 to $b$ is $b^3/3$."

It is written symbolically as

$$\int_0^b x^2 \, dx = \frac{b^3}{3}.$$

The symbol $\int$ (an elongated $S$) is called an *integral sign*, and it was introduced by Leibniz in 1675. The process which produces the number $b^3/3$ is called *integration*. The numbers 0 and $b$ which are attached to the integral sign are referred to as the *limits of integration*. The symbol $\int_0^b x^2 \, dx$ must be regarded as a whole. Its definition will treat it as such, just as the dictionary describes the word "lapidate" without reference to "lap," "id," or "ate."

Leibniz' symbol for the integral was readily accepted by many early mathematicians because they liked to think of integration as a kind of "summation process" which enabled them to add together infinitely many "infinitesimally small quantities." For example, the area of the parabolic segment was conceived of as a sum of infinitely many infinitesimally thin rectangles of height $x^2$ and base $dx$. The integral sign represented the process of adding the areas of all these thin rectangles. This kind of thinking is suggestive and often very helpful, but it is not easy to assign a precise meaning to the idea of an "infinitesimally small quantity." Today the integral is defined in terms of the notion of real number without using ideas like "infinitesimals." This definition is given in Chapter 1.

### I 1.6 The approach to calculus to be used in this book

A thorough and complete treatment of either integral or differential calculus depends ultimately on a careful study of the real number system. This study in itself, when carried out in full, is an interesting but somewhat lengthy program that requires a small volume for its complete exposition. The approach in this book is to begin with the real numbers as *undefined objects* and simply to list a number of fundamental properties of real numbers which we shall take as *axioms*. These axioms and some of the simplest theorems that can be deduced from them are discussed in Part 3 of this chapter.

Most of the properties of real numbers discussed here are probably familiar to the reader from his study of elementary algebra. However, there are a few properties of real numbers that do not ordinarily come into consideration in elementary algebra but which play an important role in the calculus. These properties stem from the so-called *least-upper-bound axiom* (also known as the *completeness* or *continuity axiom*) which is dealt with here in some detail. The reader may wish to study Part 3 before proceeding with the main body of the text, or he may postpone reading this material until later when he reaches those parts of the theory that make use of least-upper-bound properties. Material in the text that depends on the least-upper-bound axiom will be clearly indicated.

To develop calculus as a complete, formal mathematical theory, it would be necessary to state, in addition to the axioms for the real number system, a list of the various "methods of proof" which would be permitted for the purpose of deducing theorems from the axioms. Every statement in the theory would then have to be justified either as an "established law" (that is, an axiom, a definition, or a previously proved theorem) or as the result of applying one of the acceptable methods of proof to an established law. A program of this sort would be extremely long and tedious and would add very little to a beginner's understanding of the subject. Fortunately, it is not necessary to proceed in this fashion in order to get a good understanding and a good working knowledge of calculus. In this book the subject is introduced in an informal way, and ample use is made of geometric intuition whenever it is convenient to do so. At the same time, the discussion proceeds in a manner that is consistent with modern standards of precision and clarity of thought. All the important theorems of the subject are explicitly stated and rigorously proved.

To avoid interrupting the principal flow of ideas, some of the proofs appear in separate starred sections. For the same reason, some of the chapters are accompanied by supplementary material in which certain important topics related to calculus are dealt with in detail. Some of these are also starred to indicate that they may be omitted or postponed without disrupting the continuity of the presentation. The extent to which the starred sections are taken up or not will depend partly on the reader's background and skill and partly on the depth of his interests. A person who is interested primarily in the basic techniques may skip the starred sections. Those who wish a more thorough course in calculus, including theory as well as technique, should read some of the starred sections.

## Part 2.  Some Basic Concepts of the Theory of Sets

### I 2.1  Introduction to set theory

In discussing any branch of mathematics, be it analysis, algebra, or geometry, it is helpful to use the notation and terminology of set theory. This subject, which was developed by Boole and Cantor† in the latter part of the 19th century, has had a profound influence on the development of mathematics in the 20th century. It has unified many seemingly disconnected ideas and has helped to reduce many mathematical concepts to their logical foundations in an elegant and systematic way. A thorough treatment of the theory of sets would require a lengthy discussion which we regard as outside the scope of this book. Fortunately, the basic notions are few in number, and it is possible to develop a working knowledge of the methods and ideas of set theory through an informal discussion. Actually, we shall discuss not so much a new theory as an agreement about the precise terminology that we wish to apply to more or less familiar ideas.

In mathematics, the word "set" is used to represent a collection of objects viewed as a single entity. The collections called to mind by such nouns as "flock," "tribe," "crowd," "team," and "electorate" are all examples of sets. The individual objects in the collection are called *elements* or *members* of the set, and they are said to *belong to* or to be *contained in* the set. The set, in turn, is said to *contain* or be *composed of* its elements.

---

† George Boole (1815–1864) was an English mathematician and logician. His book, *An Investigation of the Laws of Thought*, published in 1854, marked the creation of the first workable system of symbolic logic. Georg F. L. P. Cantor (1845–1918) and his school created the modern theory of sets during the period 1874–1895.

We shall be interested primarily in sets of mathematical objects: sets of numbers, sets of curves, sets of geometric figures, and so on. In many applications it is convenient to deal with sets in which nothing special is assumed about the nature of the individual objects in the collection. These are called *abstract sets*. Abstract set theory has been developed to deal with such collections of arbitrary objects, and from this generality the theory derives its power.

## I 2.2  Notations for designating sets

Sets usually are denoted by capital letters: $A, B, C, \ldots, X, Y, Z$; elements are designated by lower-case letters: $a, b, c, \ldots, x, y, z$. We use the special notation

$$x \in S$$

to mean that "$x$ is an element of $S$" or "$x$ belongs to $S$." If $x$ does not belong to $S$, we write $x \notin S$. When convenient, we shall designate sets by displaying the elements in braces; for example, the set of positive even integers less than 10 is denoted by the symbol $\{2, 4, 6, 8\}$ whereas the set of all positive even integers is displayed as $\{2, 4, 6, \ldots\}$, the three dots taking the place of "and so on." The dots are used only when the meaning of "and so on" is clear. The method of listing the members of a set within braces is sometimes referred to as *the roster notation*.

The first basic concept that relates one set to another is *equality* of sets:

DEFINITION OF SET EQUALITY. *Two sets A and B are said to be equal (or identical) if they consist of exactly the same elements, in which case we write $A = B$. If one of the sets contains an element not in the other, we say the sets are unequal and we write $A \neq B$.*

EXAMPLE 1. According to this definition, the two sets $\{2, 4, 6, 8\}$ and $\{2, 8, 6, 4\}$ are equal since they both consist of the four integers 2, 4, 6, and 8. Thus, when we use the roster notation to describe a set, the order in which the elements appear is irrelevant.

EXAMPLE 2. The sets $\{2, 4, 6, 8\}$ and $\{2, 2, 4, 4, 6, 8\}$ are equal even though, in the second set, each of the elements 2 and 4 is listed twice. Both sets contain the four elements 2, 4, 6, 8 and no others; therefore, the definition requires that we call these sets equal. This example shows that we do not insist that the objects listed in the roster notation be distinct. A similar example is the set of letters in the word *Mississippi*, which is equal to the set $\{M, i, s, p\}$, consisting of the four distinct letters $M, i, s,$ and $p$.

## I 2.3  Subsets

From a given set $S$ we may form new sets, called *subsets* of $S$. For example, the set consisting of those positive integers less than 10 which are divisible by 4 (the set $\{4, 8\}$) is a subset of the set of all even integers less than 10. In general, we have the following definition.

DEFINITION OF A SUBSET. *A set A is said to be a subset of a set B, and we write*

$$A \subseteq B,$$

*whenever every element of A also belongs to B. We also say that A is contained in B or that B contains A. The relation $\subseteq$ is referred to as set inclusion.*

The statement $A \subseteq B$ does not rule out the possibility that $B \subseteq A$. In fact, we may have both $A \subseteq B$ and $B \subseteq A$, but this happens only if $A$ and $B$ have the same elements. In other words,

$$A = B \quad \text{if and only if} \quad A \subseteq B \text{ and } B \subseteq A.$$

This theorem is an immediate consequence of the foregoing definitions of equality and inclusion. If $A \subseteq B$ but $A \neq B$, then we say that $A$ is a *proper subset* of $B$; we indicate this by writing $A \subset B$.

In all our applications of set theory, we have a fixed set $S$ given in advance, and we are concerned only with subsets of this given set. The underlying set $S$ may vary from one application to another; it will be referred to as the *universal set* of each particular discourse. The notation

$$\{x \mid x \in S \quad \text{and} \quad x \text{ satisfies } P\}$$

will designate the set of all elements $x$ in $S$ which satisfy the property $P$. When the universal set to which we are referring is understood, we omit the reference to $S$ and write simply $\{x \mid x \text{ satisfies } P\}$. This is read "the set of all $x$ such that $x$ satisfies $P$." Sets designated in this way are said to be described by a defining property. For example, the set of all positive real numbers could be designated as $\{x \mid x > 0\}$; the universal set $S$ in this case is understood to be the set of all real numbers. Similarly, the set of all even positive integers $\{2, 4, 6, \ldots\}$ can be designated as $\{x \mid x \text{ is a positive even integer}\}$. Of course, the letter $x$ is a dummy and may be replaced by any other convenient symbol. Thus, we may write

$$\{x \mid x > 0\} = \{y \mid y > 0\} = \{t \mid t > 0\}$$

and so on.

It is possible for a set to contain no elements whatever. This set is called the *empty set* or the *void set*, and will be denoted by the symbol $\varnothing$. We will consider $\varnothing$ to be a subset of every set. Some people find it helpful to think of a set as analogous to a container (such as a bag or a box) containing certain objects, its elements. The empty set is then analogous to an empty container.

To avoid logical difficulties, we must distinguish between the element $x$ and the set $\{x\}$ whose only element is $x$. (A box with a hat in it is conceptually distinct from the hat itself.) In particular, the empty set $\varnothing$ is not the same as the set $\{\varnothing\}$. In fact, the empty set $\varnothing$ contains no elements, whereas the set $\{\varnothing\}$ has one element, $\varnothing$. (A box which contains an empty box is not empty.) Sets consisting of exactly one element are sometimes called *one-element sets*.

Diagrams often help us visualize relations between sets. For example, we may think of a set $S$ as a region in the plane and each of its elements as a point. Subsets of $S$ may then be thought of as collections of points within $S$. For example, in Figure I.6(b) the shaded portion is a subset of $A$ and also a subset of $B$. Visual aids of this type, called *Venn diagrams*, are useful for testing the validity of theorems in set theory or for suggesting methods to prove them. Of course, the proofs themselves must rely only on the definitions of the concepts and not on the diagrams.

## I 2.4 Unions, intersections, complements

From two given sets $A$ and $B$, we can form a new set called the *union* of $A$ and $B$. This new set is denoted by the symbol

$$A \cup B \quad (\text{read: "} A \text{ union } B \text{"})$$

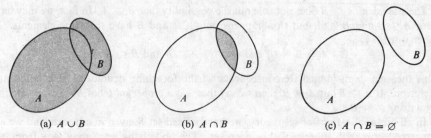

FIGURE I.6 Unions and intersections.

and is defined as the set of those elements which are in $A$, in $B$, or in both. That is to say, $A \cup B$ is the set of all elements which belong to at least one of the sets $A$, $B$. An example is illustrated in Figure I.6(a), where the shaded portion represents $A \cup B$.

Similarly, the *intersection* of $A$ and $B$, denoted by

$$A \cap B \quad (\text{read: "}A \text{ intersection } B\text{"}),$$

is defined as the set of those elements common to *both* $A$ and $B$. This is illustrated by the shaded portion of Figure I.6(b). In Figure I.6(c), the two sets $A$ and $B$ have no elements in common; in this case, their intersection is the empty set $\varnothing$. Two sets $A$ and $B$ are said to be *disjoint* if $A \cap B = \varnothing$.

If $A$ and $B$ are sets, the *difference* $A - B$ (also called the *complement of B relative to A*) is defined to be the set of all elements of $A$ which are not in $B$. Thus, by definition,

$$A - B = \{x \mid x \in A \text{ and } x \notin B\}.$$

In Figure I.6(b) the unshaded portion of $A$ represents $A - B$; the unshaded portion of $B$ represents $B - A$.

The operations of union and intersection have many formal similarities to (as well as differences from) ordinary addition and multiplication of real numbers. For example, since there is no question of order involved in the definitions of union and intersection, it follows that $A \cup B = B \cup A$ and that $A \cap B = B \cap A$. That is to say, union and intersection are *commutative* operations. The definitions are also phrased in such a way that the operations are *associative*:

$$(A \cup B) \cup C = A \cup (B \cup C) \quad \text{and} \quad (A \cap B) \cap C = A \cap (B \cap C).$$

These and other theorems related to the "algebra of sets" are listed as Exercises in Section I 2.5. One of the best ways for the reader to become familiar with the terminology and notations introduced above is to carry out the proofs of each of these laws. A sample of the type of argument that is needed appears immediately after the Exercises.

The operations of union and intersection can be extended to finite or infinite collections of sets as follows: Let $\mathscr{F}$ be a nonempty class† of sets. The union of all the sets in $\mathscr{F}$ is

---

† To help simplify the language, we call a collection of sets a *class*. Capital script letters $\mathscr{A}, \mathscr{B}, \mathscr{C}, \ldots$ are used to denote classes. The usual terminology and notation of set theory applies, of course, to classes. Thus, for example, $A \in \mathscr{F}$ means that $A$ is one of the sets in the class $\mathscr{F}$, and $\mathscr{A} \subseteq \mathscr{B}$ means that every set in $\mathscr{A}$ is also in $\mathscr{B}$, and so forth.

defined as the set of those elements which belong to at least one of the sets in $\mathscr{F}$ and is denoted by the symbol

$$\bigcup_{A \in \mathscr{F}} A.$$

If $\mathscr{F}$ is a finite collection of sets, say $\mathscr{F} = \{A_1, A_2, \ldots, A_n\}$, we write

$$\bigcup_{A \in \mathscr{F}} A = \bigcup_{k=1}^{n} A_k = A_1 \cup A_2 \cup \cdots \cup A_n.$$

Similarly, the intersection of all the sets in $\mathscr{F}$ is defined to be the set of those elements which belong to every one of the sets in $\mathscr{F}$; it is denoted by the symbol

$$\bigcap_{A \in \mathscr{F}} A.$$

For finite collections (as above), we write

$$\bigcap_{A \in \mathscr{F}} A = \bigcap_{k=1}^{n} A_k = A_1 \cap A_2 \cap \cdots \cap A_n.$$

Unions and intersections have been defined in such a way that the associative laws for these operations are automatically satisfied. Hence, there is no ambiguity when we write $A_1 \cup A_2 \cup \cdots \cup A_n$ or $A_1 \cap A_2 \cap \cdots \cap A_n$.

## I 2.5 Exercises

1. Use the roster notation to designate the following sets of real numbers.

$$A = \{x \mid x^2 - 1 = 0\}. \qquad D = \{x \mid x^3 - 2x^2 + x = 2\}.$$

$$B = \{x \mid (x - 1)^2 = 0\}. \qquad E = \{x \mid (x + 8)^2 = 9^2\}.$$

$$C = \{x \mid x + 8 = 9\}. \qquad F = \{x \mid (x^2 + 16x)^2 = 17^2\}.$$

2. For the sets in Exercise 1, note that $B \subseteq A$. List all the inclusion relations $\subseteq$ that hold among the sets $A$, $B$, $C$, $D$, $E$, $F$.
3. Let $A = \{1\}$, $B = \{1, 2\}$. Discuss the validity of the following statements (prove the ones that are true and explain why the others are not true).
   (a) $A \subset B$.      (d) $1 \in A$.
   (b) $A \subseteq B$.      (e) $1 \subseteq A$.
   (c) $A \in B$.      (f) $1 \subset B$.
4. Solve Exercise 3 if $A = \{1\}$ and $B = \{\{1\}, 1\}$.
5. Given the set $S = \{1, 2, 3, 4\}$. Display all subsets of $S$. There are 16 altogether, counting $\varnothing$ and $S$.
6. Given the following four sets

$$A = \{1, 2\}, \qquad B = \{\{1\}, \{2\}\}, \qquad C = \{\{1\}, \{1, 2\}\}, \qquad D = \{\{1\}, \{2\}, \{1, 2\}\},$$

discuss the validity of the following statements (prove the ones that are true and explain why the others are not true).

(a) $A = B$.     (d) $A \in C$.     (g) $B \subset D$.

(b) $A \subseteq B$.     (e) $A \subset D$.     (h) $B \in D$.

(c) $A \subset C$.     (f) $B \subset C$.     (i) $A \in D$.

7. Prove the following properties of set equality.

(a) $\{a, a\} = \{a\}$.

(b) $\{a, b\} = \{b, a\}$.

(c) $\{a\} = \{b, c\}$ if and only if $a = b = c$.

Prove the set relations in Exercises 8 through 19. (Sample proofs are given at the end of this section).

8. *Commutative laws:* $A \cup B = B \cup A, \quad A \cap B = B \cap A$.

9. *Associative laws:* $A \cup (B \cup C) = (A \cup B) \cup C, \quad A \cap (B \cap C) = (A \cap B) \cap C$.

10. *Distributive laws:* $A \cap (B \cup C) = (A \cap B) \cup (A \cap C), \quad A \cup (B \cap C) = (A \cup B) \cap (A \cup C)$.

11. $A \cup A = A, \quad A \cap A = A$,

12. $A \subseteq A \cup B, \quad A \cap B \subseteq A$.

13. $A \cup \varnothing = A, \quad A \cap \varnothing = \varnothing$.

14. $A \cup (A \cap B) = A, \quad A \cap (A \cup B) = A$.

15. If $A \subseteq C$ and $B \subseteq C$, then $A \cup B \subseteq C$.

16. If $C \subseteq A$ and $C \subseteq B$, then $C \subseteq A \cap B$.

17. (a) If $A \subset B$ and $B \subset C$, prove that $A \subset C$.

(b) If $A \subseteq B$ and $B \subseteq C$, prove that $A \subseteq C$.

(c) What can you conclude if $A \subset B$ and $B \subseteq C$?

(d) If $x \in A$ and $A \subseteq B$, is it necessarily true that $x \in B$?

(e) If $x \in A$ and $A \in B$, is it necessarily true that $x \in B$?

18. $A - (B \cap C) = (A - B) \cup (A - C)$.

19. Let $\mathscr{F}$ be a class of sets. Then

$$B - \bigcup_{A \in \mathscr{F}} A = \bigcap_{A \in \mathscr{F}} (B - A) \quad \text{and} \quad B - \bigcap_{A \in \mathscr{F}} A = \bigcup_{A \in \mathscr{F}} (B - A).$$

20. (a) Prove that one of the following two formulas is always right and the other one is sometimes wrong:

$$\text{(i)} \quad A - (B - C) = (A - B) \cup C,$$

$$\text{(ii)} \quad A - (B \cup C) = (A - B) - C.$$

(b) State an additional necessary and sufficient condition for the formula which is sometimes incorrect to be always right.

*Proof of the commutative law* $A \cup B = B \cup A$. Let $X = A \cup B$, $Y = B \cup A$. To prove that $X = Y$ we prove that $X \subseteq Y$ and $Y \subseteq X$. Suppose that $x \in X$. Then $x$ is in at least one of $A$ or $B$. Hence, $x$ is in at least one of $B$ or $A$; so $x \in Y$. Thus, every element of $X$ is also in $Y$, so $X \subseteq Y$. Similarly, we find that $Y \subseteq X$, so $X = Y$.

*Proof of* $A \cap B \subseteq A$. If $x \in A \cap B$, then $x$ is in both $A$ and $B$. In particular, $x \in A$. Thus, every element of $A \cap B$ is also in $A$; therefore, $A \cap B \subseteq A$.

## Part 3. A Set of Axioms for the Real-Number System

### I 3.1 Introduction

There are many ways to introduce the real-number system. One popular method is to begin with the positive integers 1, 2, 3, ... and use them as building blocks to construct a more comprehensive system having the properties desired. Briefly, the idea of this method is to take the positive integers as undefined concepts, state some axioms concerning them, and then use the positive integers to build a larger system consisting of the positive *rational* numbers (quotients of positive integers). The positive rational numbers, in turn, may then be used as a basis for constructing the positive *irrational* numbers (real numbers like $\sqrt{2}$ and $\pi$ that are not rational). The final step is the introduction of the negative real numbers and zero. The most difficult part of the whole process is the transition from the rational numbers to the irrational numbers.

Although the need for irrational numbers was apparent to the ancient Greeks from their study of geometry, satisfactory methods for constructing irrational numbers from rational numbers were not introduced until late in the 19th century. At that time, three different theories were outlined by Karl Weierstrass (1815–1897), Georg Cantor (1845–1918), and Richard Dedekind (1831–1916). In 1889, the Italian mathematician Guiseppe Peano (1858–1932) listed five axioms for the positive integers that could be used as the starting point of the whole construction. A detailed account of this construction, beginning with the Peano postulates and using the method of Dedekind to introduce irrational numbers, may be found in a book by E. Landau, *Foundations of Analysis* (New York, Chelsea Publishing Co., 1951).

The point of view we shall adopt here is nonconstructive. We shall start rather far out in the process, taking the real numbers themselves as undefined objects satisfying a number of properties that we use as axioms. That is to say, we shall assume there exists a set **R** of objects, called real numbers, which satisfy the 10 axioms listed in the next few sections. All the properties of real numbers can be deduced from the axioms in the list. When the real numbers are defined by a constructive process, the properties we list as axioms must be proved as theorems.

In the axioms that appear below, lower-case letters $a, b, c, \ldots, x, y, z$ represent arbitrary real numbers unless something is said to the contrary. The axioms fall in a natural way into three groups which we refer to as the *field axioms*, the *order axioms*, and the *least-upper-bound axiom* (also called the *axiom of continuity* or the *completeness axiom*).

### I 3.2 The field axioms

Along with the set **R** of real numbers we assume the existence of two operations called *addition* and *multiplication*, such that for every pair of real numbers $x$ and $y$ we can form the *sum* of $x$ and $y$, which is another real number denoted by $x + y$, and the *product* of $x$ and $y$, denoted by $xy$ or by $x \cdot y$. It is assumed that the sum $x + y$ and the product $xy$ are *uniquely determined* by $x$ and $y$. In other words, given $x$ and $y$, there is exactly one real number $x + y$ and exactly one real number $xy$. We attach no special meanings to the symbols $+$ and $\cdot$ other than those contained in the axioms.

AXIOM 1.   COMMUTATIVE LAWS.   $x + y = y + x,$     $xy = yx.$

AXIOM 2.   ASSOCIATIVE LAWS.   $x + (y + z) = (x + y) + z,$     $x(yz) = (xy)z.$

AXIOM 3.   DISTRIBUTIVE LAW.   $x(y + z) = xy + xz.$

AXIOM 4.   EXISTENCE OF IDENTITY ELEMENTS.   *There exist two distinct real numbers, which we denote by* 0 *and* 1, *such that for every real x we have* $x + 0 = x$ *and* $1 \cdot x = x.$

AXIOM 5.   EXISTENCE OF NEGATIVES.   *For every real number x there is a real number y such that* $x + y = 0.$

AXIOM 6.   EXISTENCE OF RECIPROCALS.   *For every real number* $x \neq 0$ *there is a real number y such that* $xy = 1.$

   *Note:*   The numbers 0 and 1 in Axioms 5 and 6 are those of Axiom 4.

From the above axioms we can deduce all the usual laws of elementary algebra. The most important of these laws are collected here as a list of theorems. In all these theorems the symbols *a, b, c, d* represent arbitrary real numbers.

THEOREM I.1.   CANCELLATION LAW FOR ADDITION.   *If* $a + b = a + c,$ *then* $b = c.$ (*In particular, this shows that the number* 0 *of Axiom* 4 *is unique.*)

THEOREM I.2.   POSSIBILITY OF SUBTRACTION.   *Given a and b, there is exactly one x such that* $a + x = b.$ *This x is denoted by* $b - a.$ *In particular,* $0 - a$ *is written simply* $-a$ *and is called the negative of a.*

THEOREM I.3.   $b - a = b + (-a).$

THEOREM I.4.   $-(-a) = a.$

THEOREM I.5.   $a(b - c) = ab - ac.$

THEOREM I.6.   $0 \cdot a = a \cdot 0 = 0.$

THEOREM I.7.   CANCELLATION LAW FOR MULTIPLICATION.   *If* $ab = ac$ *and* $a \neq 0,$ *then* $b = c.$ (*In particular, this shows that the number* 1 *of Axiom* 4 *is unique.*)

THEOREM I.8.   POSSIBILITY OF DIVISION.   *Given a and b with* $a \neq 0,$ *there is exactly one x such that* $ax = b.$ *This x is denoted by* $b/a$ *or* $\frac{b}{a}$ *and is called the quotient of b and a. In particular,* $1/a$ *is also written* $a^{-1}$ *and is called the reciprocal of a.*

THEOREM I.9.   *If* $a \neq 0,$ *then* $b/a = b \cdot a^{-1}.$

THEOREM I.10.   *If* $a \neq 0,$ *then* $(a^{-1})^{-1} = a.$

THEOREM I.11.   *If* $ab = 0,$ *then* $a = 0$ *or* $b = 0.$

THEOREM I.12.   $(-a)b = -(ab)$ *and* $(-a)(-b) = ab.$

THEOREM I.13.   $(a/b) + (c/d) = (ad + bc)/(bd)$ *if* $b \neq 0$ *and* $d \neq 0.$

THEOREM I.14.   $(a/b)(c/d) = (ac)/(bd)$ *if* $b \neq 0$ *and* $d \neq 0.$

THEOREM I.15.   $(a/b)/(c/d) = (ad)/(bc)$ *if* $b \neq 0,$ $c \neq 0,$ *and* $d \neq 0.$

To illustrate how these statements may be obtained as consequences of the axioms, we shall present proofs of Theorems I.1 through I.4. Those readers who are interested may find it instructive to carry out proofs of the remaining theorems.

*Proof of* I.1. Given $a + b = a + c$. By Axiom 5, there is a number $y$ such that $y + a = 0$. Since sums are uniquely determined, we have $y + (a + b) = y + (a + c)$. Using the associative law, we obtain $(y + a) + b = (y + a) + c$ or $0 + b = 0 + c$. But by Axiom 4 we have $0 + b = b$ and $0 + c = c$, so that $b = c$. Notice that this theorem shows that there is only one real number having the property of 0 in Axiom 4. In fact, if 0 and 0' both have this property, then $0 + 0' = 0$ and $0 + 0 = 0$. Hence $0 + 0' = 0 + 0$ and, by the cancellation law, $0 = 0'$.

*Proof of* I.2. Given $a$ and $b$, choose $y$ so that $a + y = 0$ and let $x = y + b$. Then $a + x = a + (y + b) = (a + y) + b = 0 + b = b$. Therefore there is at least one $x$ such that $a + x = b$. But by Theorem I.1 there is at most one such $x$. Hence there is *exactly* one.

*Proof of* I.3. Let $x = b - a$ and let $y = b + (-a)$. We wish to prove that $x = y$. Now $x + a = b$ (by the definition of $b - a$) and

$$y + a = [b + (-a)] + a = b + [(-a) + a] = b + 0 = b.$$

Therefore $x + a = y + a$ and hence, by Theorem I.1, $x = y$.

*Proof of* I.4. We have $a + (-a) = 0$ by the definition of $-a$. But this equation tells us that $a$ is the negative of $-a$. That is, $a = -(-a)$, as asserted.

## *I 3.3  Exercises

1. Prove Theorems I.5 through I.15, using Axioms 1 through 6 and Theorems I.1 through I.4.

In Exercises 2 through 10, prove the given statements or establish the given equations. You may use Axioms 1 through 6 and Theorems I.1 through I.15.

2. $-0 = 0$.
3. $1^{-1} = 1$.
4. Zero has no reciprocal.
5. $-(a + b) = -a - b$.
6. $-(a - b) = -a + b$.
7. $(a - b) + (b - c) = a - c$.
8. If $a \neq 0$ and $b \neq 0$, then $(ab)^{-1} = a^{-1}b^{-1}$.
9. $-(a/b) = (-a/b) = a/(-b)$ if $b \neq 0$.
10. $(a/b) - (c/d) = (ad - bc)/(bd)$ if $b \neq 0$ and $d \neq 0$.

## I 3.4  The order axioms

This group of axioms has to do with a concept which establishes an *ordering* among the real numbers. This ordering enables us to make statements about one real number being larger or smaller than another. We choose to introduce the order properties as a set of axioms about a new undefined concept called *positiveness* and then to define terms like *less than* and *greater than* in terms of positiveness.

We shall assume that there exists a certain subset $\mathbf{R}^+ \subset \mathbf{R}$, called the set of *positive* numbers, which satisfies the following three order axioms:

AXIOM 7.   *If x and y are in* $\mathbf{R}^+$, *so are* $x + y$ *and* $xy$.

AXIOM 8.   *For every real* $x \neq 0$, *either* $x \in \mathbf{R}^+$ *or* $-x \in \mathbf{R}^+$, *but not both.*

AXIOM 9.   $0 \notin \mathbf{R}^+$.

Now we can define the symbols $<, >, \leq$, and $\geq$, called, respectively, *less than, greater than, less than or equal to,* and *greater than or equal to,* as follows:

$$x < y \text{ means that } y - x \text{ is positive;}$$
$$y > x \text{ means that } x < y;$$
$$x \leq y \text{ means that either } x < y \text{ or } x = y;$$
$$y \geq x \text{ means that } x \leq y.$$

Thus, we have $x > 0$ if and only if $x$ is positive. If $x < 0$, we say that $x$ is *negative*; if $x \geq 0$, we say that $x$ is *nonnegative*. A pair of simultaneous inequalities such as $x < y$, $y < z$ is usually written more briefly as $x < y < z$; similar interpretations are given to the compound inequalities $x \leq y < z$, $x < y \leq z$, and $x \leq y \leq z$.

From the order axioms we can derive all the usual rules for calculating with inequalities. The most important of these are listed here as theorems.

THEOREM I.16.   TRICHOTOMY LAW.   *For arbitrary real numbers a and b, exactly one of the three relations* $a < b$, $b < a$, $a = b$ *holds.*

THEOREM I.17.   TRANSITIVE LAW.   *If* $a < b$ *and* $b < c$, *then* $a < c$.

THEOREM I.18.   *If* $a < b$, *then* $a + c < b + c$.

THEOREM I.19.   *If* $a < b$ *and* $c > 0$, *then* $ac < bc$.

THEOREM I.20.   *If* $a \neq 0$, *then* $a^2 > 0$.

THEOREM I.21.   $1 > 0$.

THEOREM I.22.   *If* $a < b$ *and* $c < 0$, *then* $ac > bc$.

THEOREM I.23.   *If* $a < b$, *then* $-a > -b$. *In particular, if* $a < 0$, *then* $-a > 0$.

THEOREM I.24.   *If* $ab > 0$, *then both a and b are positive or both are negative.*

THEOREM I.25.   *If* $a < c$ *and* $b < d$, *then* $a + b < c + d$.

Again, we shall prove only a few of these theorems as samples to indicate how the proofs may be carried out. Proofs of the others are left as exercises.

*Proof of* I.16. Let $x = b - a$. If $x = 0$, then $b - a = a - b = 0$, and hence, by Axiom 9, we cannot have $a > b$ or $b > a$. If $x \neq 0$, Axiom 8 tells us that either $x > 0$ or $x < 0$, but not both; that is, either $a < b$ or $b < a$, but not both. Therefore, exactly one of the three relations, $a = b$, $a < b$, $b < a$, holds.

*Proof of* I.17. If $a < b$ and $b < c$, then $b - a > 0$ and $c - b > 0$. By Axiom 7 we may add to obtain $(b - a) + (c - b) > 0$. That is, $c - a > 0$, and hence $a < c$.

*Proof of* I.18. Let $x = a + c$, $y = b + c$. Then $y - x = b - a$. But $b - a > 0$ since $a < b$. Hence $y - x > 0$, and this means that $x < y$.

*Proof of* I.19. If $a < b$, then $b - a > 0$. If $c > 0$, then by Axiom 7 we may multiply $c$ by $(b - a)$ to obtain $(b - a)c > 0$. But $(b - a)c = bc - ac$. Hence $bc - ac > 0$, and this means that $ac < bc$, as asserted.

*Proof of* I.20. If $a > 0$, then $a \cdot a > 0$ by Axiom 7. If $a < 0$, then $-a > 0$, and hence $(-a) \cdot (-a) > 0$ by Axiom 7. In either case we have $a^2 > 0$.

*Proof of* I.21. Apply Theorem I.20 with $a = 1$.

## *I 3.5   Exercises

1. Prove Theorems I.22 through I.25, using the earlier theorems and Axioms 1 through 9.

In Exercises 2 through 10, prove the given statements or establish the given inequalities. You may use Axioms 1 through 9 and Theorems I.1 through I.25.

2. There is no real number $x$ such that $x^2 + 1 = 0$.
3. The sum of two negative numbers is negative.
4. If $a > 0$, then $1/a > 0$; if $a < 0$, then $1/a < 0$.
5. If $0 < a < b$, then $0 < b^{-1} < a^{-1}$.
6. If $a \leq b$ and $b \leq c$, then $a \leq c$.
7. If $a \leq b$ and $b \leq c$, and $a = c$, then $b = c$.
8. For all real $a$ and $b$ we have $a^2 + b^2 \geq 0$. If $a$ and $b$ are not both 0, then $a^2 + b^2 > 0$.
9. There is no real number $a$ such that $x \leq a$ for all real $x$.
10. If $x$ has the property that $0 \leq x < h$ for *every* positive real number $h$, then $x = 0$.

## I 3.6   Integers and rational numbers

There exist certain subsets of **R** which are distinguished because they have special properties not shared by all real numbers. In this section we shall discuss two such subsets, the *integers* and the *rational numbers*.

To introduce the positive integers we begin with the number 1, whose existence is guaranteed by Axiom 4. The number $1 + 1$ is denoted by 2, the number $2 + 1$ by 3, and so on. The numbers $1, 2, 3, \ldots$, obtained in this way by repeated addition of 1 are all positive, and they are called the *positive integers*. Strictly speaking, this description of the positive integers is not entirely complete because we have not explained in detail what we mean by the expressions "and so on," or "repeated addition of 1." Although the intuitive meaning of these expressions may seem clear, in a careful treatment of the real-number system it is necessary to give a more precise definition of the positive integers. There are many ways to do this. One convenient method is to introduce first the notion of an *inductive set*.

DEFINITION OF AN INDUCTIVE SET.    *A set of real numbers is called an inductive set if it has the following two properties:*
   (a) *The number 1 is in the set.*
   (b) *For every x in the set, the number x + 1 is also in the set.*

For example, **R** is an inductive set. So is the set **R**⁺. Now we shall define the positive integers to be those real numbers which belong to every inductive set.

DEFINITION OF POSITIVE INTEGERS.    *A real number is called a positive integer if it belongs to every inductive set.*

Let **P** denote the set of all positive integers. Then **P** is itself an inductive set because (a) it contains 1, and (b) it contains $x + 1$ whenever it contains $x$. Since the members of **P** belong to every inductive set, we refer to **P** as the *smallest* inductive set. This property of the set **P** forms the logical basis for a type of reasoning that mathematicians call *proof by induction*, a detailed discussion of which is given in Part 4 of this Introduction.

The negatives of the positive integers are called the *negative integers*. The positive integers, together with the negative integers and 0 (zero), form a set **Z** which we call simply the *set of integers*.

In a thorough treatment of the real-number system, it would be necessary at this stage to prove certain theorems about integers. For example, the sum, difference, or product of two integers is an integer, but the quotient of two integers need not be an integer. However, we shall not enter into the details of such proofs.

Quotients of integers $a/b$ (where $b \neq 0$) are called *rational numbers*. The set of rational numbers, denoted by **Q**, contains **Z** as a subset. The reader should realize that all the field axioms and the order axioms are satisfied by **Q**. For this reason, we say that the set of rational numbers is an *ordered field*. Real numbers that are not in **Q** are called *irrational*.

## I 3.7  Geometric interpretation of real numbers as points on a line

The reader is undoubtedly familiar with the geometric representation of real numbers by means of points on a straight line. A point is selected to represent 0 and another, to the right of 0, to represent 1, as illustrated in Figure I.7. This choice determines the scale. If one adopts an appropriate set of axioms for Euclidean geometry, then each real number corresponds to exactly one point on this line and, conversely, each point on the line corresponds to one and only one real number. For this reason the line is often called the *real line* or the *real axis*, and it is customary to use the words *real number* and *point* interchangeably. Thus we often speak of the *point x* rather than the point corresponding to the real number $x$.

The ordering relation among the real numbers has a simple geometric interpretation. If $x < y$, the point $x$ lies to the left of the point $y$, as shown in Figure I.7. Positive numbers lie to the right of 0 and negative numbers to the left of 0. If $a < b$, a point $x$ satisfies the inequalities $a < x < b$ if and only if $x$ is *between* $a$ and $b$.

This device for representing real numbers geometrically is a very worthwhile aid that helps us to discover and understand better certain properties of real numbers. However, the reader should realize that all properties of real numbers that are to be accepted as theorems must be deducible from the axioms without any reference to geometry. This does not mean that one should not make use of geometry in studying properties of real numbers. On the contrary, the geometry often suggests the method of proof of a particular theorem, and sometimes a geometric argument is more illuminating than a purely *analytic* proof (one depending entirely on the axioms for the real numbers). In this book, geometric

0          1          x          y

FIGURE I.7   Real numbers represented geometrically on a line.

arguments are used to a large extent to help motivate or clarify a particular discussion. Nevertheless, the proofs of all the important theorems are presented in analytic form.

### I 3.8   Upper bound of a set, maximum element, least upper bound (supremum)

The nine axioms listed above contain all the properties of real numbers usually discussed in elementary algebra. There is another axiom of fundamental importance in calculus that is ordinarily not discussed in elementary algebra courses. This axiom (or some property equivalent to it) is used to establish the existence of irrational numbers.

Irrational numbers arise in elementary algebra when we try to solve certain quadratic equations. For example, it is desirable to have a real number $x$ such that $x^2 = 2$. From the nine axioms above, we cannot prove that such an $x$ exists in $\mathbf{R}$, because these nine axioms are also satisfied by $\mathbf{Q}$, and there is no rational number $x$ whose square is 2. (A proof of this statement is outlined in Exercise 11 of Section I 3.12.) Axiom 10 allows us to introduce irrational numbers in the real-number system, and it gives the real-number system a property of continuity that is a keystone in the logical structure of calculus.

Before we describe Axiom 10, it is convenient to introduce some more terminology and notation. Suppose $S$ is a nonempty set of real numbers and suppose there is a number $B$ such that

$$x \leq B$$

for every $x$ in $S$. Then $S$ is said to be *bounded above* by $B$. The number $B$ is called an *upper bound* for $S$. We say *an* upper bound because every number greater than $B$ will also be an upper bound. If an upper bound $B$ is also a member of $S$, then $B$ is called the *largest member* or the *maximum element* of $S$. There can be at most one such $B$. If it exists, we write

$$B = \max S.$$

Thus, $B = \max S$ if $B \in S$ and $x \leq B$ for all $x$ in $S$. A set with no upper bound is said to be *unbounded above*.

The following examples serve to illustrate the meaning of these terms.

EXAMPLE 1. Let $S$ be the set of all positive real numbers. This set is unbounded above. It has no upper bounds and it has no maximum element.

EXAMPLE 2. Let $S$ be the set of all real $x$ satisfying $0 \leq x \leq 1$. This set is bounded above by 1. In fact, 1 is its maximum element.

EXAMPLE 3. Let $T$ be the set of all real $x$ satisfying $0 \leq x < 1$. This is like the set in Example 2 except that the point 1 is not included. This set is bounded above by 1 but it has no maximum element.

Some sets, like the one in Example 3, are bounded above but have no maximum element. For these sets there is a concept which takes the place of the maximum element. This is called the *least upper bound* of the set and it is defined as follows:

DEFINITION OF LEAST UPPER BOUND. *A number $B$ is called a least upper bound of a nonempty set $S$ if $B$ has the following two properties*:
(a) *$B$ is an upper bound for $S$.*
(b) *No number less than $B$ is an upper bound for $S$.*

If $S$ has a maximum element, this maximum is also a least upper bound for $S$. But if $S$ does not have a maximum element, it may still have a least upper bound. In Example 3 above, the number 1 is a least upper bound for $T$ although $T$ has no maximum element. (See Figure I.8.)

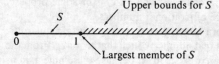
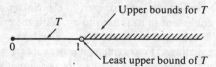

(a) $S$ has a largest member:
     max $S = 1$

(b) $T$ has no largest member, but it has
     a least upper bound: sup $T = 1$

FIGURE I.8   Upper bounds, maximum element, supremum.

THEOREM I.26. *Two different numbers cannot be least upper bounds for the same set.*

*Proof.* Suppose that $B$ and $C$ are two least upper bounds for a set $S$. Property (b) implies that $C \geq B$ since $B$ is a least upper bound; similarly, $B \geq C$ since $C$ is a least upper bound. Hence, we have $B = C$.

This theorem tells us that if there is a least upper bound for a set $S$, there is *only* one and we may speak of *the* least upper bound.

It is common practice to refer to the least upper bound of a set by the more concise term *supremum*, abbreviated *sup*. We shall adopt this convention and write

$$B = \sup S$$

to express the fact that $B$ is the least upper bound, or supremum, of $S$.

## I 3.9 The least-upper-bound axiom (completeness axiom)

Now we are ready to state the least-upper-bound axiom for the real-number system.

AXIOM 10. *Every nonempty set S of real numbers which is bounded above has a supremum; that is, there is a real number B such that $B = \sup S$.*

We emphasize once more that the supremum of $S$ need not be a member of $S$. In fact, $\sup S$ belongs to $S$ if and only if $S$ has a maximum element, in which case $\max S = \sup S$.

Definitions of the terms *lower bound, bounded below, smallest member* (or *minimum element*) may be similarly formulated. The reader should formulate these for himself. If $S$ has a minimum element, we denote it by $\min S$.

A number $L$ is called a *greatest lower bound* (or *infimum*) of $S$ if (a) $L$ is a lower bound for $S$, and (b) no number greater than $L$ is a lower bound for $S$. The infimum of $S$, when it exists, is uniquely determined and we denote it by $\inf S$. If $S$ has a minimum element, then $\min S = \inf S$.

Using Axiom 10, we can prove the following.

THEOREM I.27. *Every nonempty set S that is bounded below has a greatest lower bound; that is, there is a real number L such that $L = \inf S$.*

*Proof.* Let $-S$ denote the set of negatives of numbers in $S$. Then $-S$ is nonempty and bounded above. Axiom 10 tells us that there is a number $B$ which is a supremum for $-S$. It is easy to verify that $-B = \inf S$.

Let us refer once more to the examples in the foregoing section. In Example 1, the set of all positive real numbers, the number 0 is the infimum of $S$. This set has no minimum element. In Examples 2 and 3, the number 0 is the minimum element.

In all these examples it was easy to decide whether or not the set $S$ was bounded above or below, and it was also easy to determine the numbers $\sup S$ and $\inf S$. The next example shows that it may be difficult to determine whether upper or lower bounds exist.

EXAMPLE 4. Let $S$ be the set of all numbers of the form $(1 + 1/n)^n$, where $n = 1, 2, 3, \ldots$. For example, taking $n = 1$, 2, and 3, we find that the numbers 2, $\frac{9}{4}$, and $\frac{64}{27}$ are in $S$. Every number in the set is greater than 1, so the set is bounded below and hence has an infimum. With a little effort we can show that 2 is the smallest element of $S$ so $\inf S = \min S = 2$. The set $S$ is also bounded above, although this fact is not as easy to prove. (Try it!) Once we know that $S$ is bounded above, Axiom 10 tells us that there is a number which is the supremum of $S$. In this case it is not easy to determine the value of $\sup S$ from the description of $S$. In a later chapter we will learn that $\sup S$ is an irrational number approximately equal to 2.718. It is an important number in calculus called the Euler number $e$.

## I 3.10 The Archimedean property of the real-number system

This section contains a number of important properties of the real-number system which are consequences of the least-upper-bound axiom.

THEOREM I.28.    *The set* **P** *of positive integers* 1, 2, 3, . . . *is unbounded above.*

*Proof.* Assume **P** is bounded above. We shall show that this leads to a contradiction. Since **P** is nonempty, Axiom 10 tells us that **P** has a least upper bound, say $b$. The number $b - 1$, being less than $b$, cannot be an upper bound for **P**. Hence, there is at least one positive integer $n$ such that $n > b - 1$. For this $n$ we have $n + 1 > b$. Since $n + 1$ is in **P**, this contradicts the fact that $b$ is an upper bound for **P**.

As corollaries of Theorem I.28, we immediately obtain the following consequences:

THEOREM I.29.    *For every real $x$ there exists a positive integer $n$ such that $n > x$.*

*Proof.* If this were not so, some $x$ would be an upper bound for **P**, contradicting Theorem I.28.

THEOREM I.30.    *If $x > 0$ and if $y$ is an arbitrary real number, there exists a positive integer $n$ such that $nx > y$.*

*Proof.* Apply Theorem I.29 with $x$ replaced by $y/x$.

The property described in Theorem I.30 is called the *Archimedean property* of the real-number system. Geometrically it means that any line segment, no matter how long, may be covered by a finite number of line segments of a given positive length, no matter how small. In other words, a small ruler used often enough can measure arbitrarily large distances. Archimedes realized that this was a fundamental property of the straight line and stated it explicitly as one of the axioms of geometry. In the 19th and 20th centuries, non-Archimedean geometries have been constructed in which this axiom is rejected.

From the Archimedean property, we can prove the following theorem, which will be useful in our discussion of integral calculus.

THEOREM I.31.    *If three real numbers $a$, $x$, and $y$ satisfy the inequalities*

(I.14)
$$a \leq x \leq a + \frac{y}{n}$$

*for every integer $n \geq 1$, then $x = a$.*

*Proof.* If $x > a$, Theorem I.30 tells us that there is a positive integer $n$ satisfying $n(x - a) > y$, contradicting (I.14). Hence we cannot have $x > a$, so we must have $x = a$.

### I 3.11  Fundamental properties of the supremum and infimum

This section discusses three fundamental properties of the supremum and infimum that we shall use in our development of calculus. The first property states that any set of numbers with a supremum contains points arbitrarily close to its supremum; similarly, a set with an infimum contains points arbitrarily close to its infimum.

THEOREM I.32.   *Let h be a given positive number and let S be a set of real numbers.*

(a) *If S has a supremum, then for some x in S we have*

$$x > \sup S - h.$$

(b) *If S has an infimum, then for some x in S we have*

$$x < \inf S + h.$$

*Proof of* (a). If we had $x \leq \sup S - h$ for *all* x in S, then sup $S - h$ would be an upper bound for $S$ smaller than its least upper bound. Therefore we must have $x > \sup S - h$ for at least one x in S. This proves (a). The proof of (b) is similar.

THEOREM I.33. ADDITIVE PROPERTY.   *Given nonempty subsets A and B of* **R**, *let C denote the set*

$$C = \{a + b \mid a \in A, b \in B\}.$$

(a) *If each of A and B has a supremum, then C has a supremum, and*

$$\sup C = \sup A + \sup B.$$

(b) *If each of A and B has an infimum, then C has an infimum, and*

$$\inf C = \inf A + \inf B.$$

*Proof.* Assume each of A and B has a supremum. If $c \in C$, then $c = a + b$, where $a \in A$ and $b \in B$. Therefore $c \leq \sup A + \sup B$; so sup $A + \sup B$ is an upper bound for C. This shows that C has a supremum and that

$$\sup C \leq \sup A + \sup B.$$

Now let $n$ be any positive integer. By Theorem I.32 (with $h = 1/n$) there is an a in A and a b in B such that

$$a > \sup A - \frac{1}{n}, \qquad b > \sup B - \frac{1}{n}.$$

Adding these inequalities, we obtain

$$a + b > \sup A + \sup B - \frac{2}{n}, \qquad \text{or} \qquad \sup A + \sup B < a + b + \frac{2}{n} \leq \sup C + \frac{2}{n},$$

since $a + b \leq \sup C$. Therefore we have shown that

$$\sup C \leq \sup A + \sup B < \sup C + \frac{2}{n}$$

for every integer $n \geq 1$. By Theorem I.31, we must have sup $C = \text{sup } A + \text{sup } B$. This proves (a), and the proof of (b) is similar.

THEOREM I.34.    *Given two nonempty subsets S and T of* **R** *such that*

$$s \leq t$$

*for every s in S and every t in T. Then S has a supremum, and T has an infimum, and they satisfy the inequality*

$$\text{sup } S \leq \text{inf } T .$$

*Proof.* Each $t$ in $T$ is an upper bound for $S$. Therefore $S$ has a supremum which satisfies the inequality sup $S \leq t$ for all $t$ in $T$. Hence sup $S$ is a lower bound for $T$, so $T$ has an infimum which cannot be less than sup $S$. In other words, we have sup $S \leq \text{inf } T$, as asserted.

## *I 3.12  Exercises

1. If $x$ and $y$ are arbitrary real numbers with $x < y$, prove that there is at least one real $z$ satisfying $x < z < y$.
2. If $x$ is an arbitrary real number, prove that there are integers $m$ and $n$ such that $m < x < n$.
3. If $x > 0$, prove that there is a positive integer $n$ such that $1/n < x$.
4. If $x$ is an arbitrary real number, prove that there is exactly one integer $n$ which satisfies the inequalities $n \leq x < n + 1$. This $n$ is called the greatest integer in $x$ and is denoted by $[x]$. For example, $[5] = 5$, $[\frac{5}{2}] = 2$, $[-\frac{8}{3}] = -3$.
5. If $x$ is an arbitrary real number, prove that there is exactly one integer $n$ which satisfies $x \leq n < x + 1$.
6. If $x$ and $y$ are arbitrary real numbers, $x < y$, prove that there exists at least one rational number $r$ satisfying $x < r < y$, and hence infinitely many. This property is often described by saying that the rational numbers are *dense* in the real-number system.
7. If $x$ is rational, $x \neq 0$, and $y$ irrational, prove that $x + y$, $x - y$, $xy$, $x/y$, and $y/x$ are all irrational.
8. Is the sum or product of two irrational numbers always irrational?
9. If $x$ and $y$ are arbitrary real numbers, $x < y$, prove that there exists at least one irrational number $z$ satisfying $x < z < y$, and hence infinitely many.
10. An integer $n$ is called *even* if $n = 2m$ for some integer $m$, and *odd* if $n + 1$ is even. Prove the following statements:
    (a) An integer cannot be both even and odd.
    (b) Every integer is either even or odd.
    (c) The sum or product of two even integers is even. What can you say about the sum or product of two odd integers?
    (d) If $n^2$ is even, so is $n$. If $a^2 = 2b^2$, where $a$ and $b$ are integers, then both $a$ and $b$ are even.
    (e) Every rational number can be expressed in the form $a/b$, where $a$ and $b$ are integers, at least one of which is odd.
11. Prove that there is no rational number whose square is 2.

    [*Hint:* Argue by contradiction. Assume $(a/b)^2 = 2$, where $a$ and $b$ are integers, at least one of which is odd. Use parts of Exercise 10 to deduce a contradiction.]

12. The Archimedean property of the real-number system was deduced as a consequence of the least-upper-bound axiom. Prove that the set of rational numbers satisfies the Archimedean property but not the least-upper-bound property. This shows that the Archimedean property does not imply the least-upper-bound axiom.

## *I 3.13   Existence of square roots of nonnegative real numbers

It was pointed out earlier that the equation $x^2 = 2$ has no solutions among the rational numbers. With the help of Axiom 10, we can prove that the equation $x^2 = a$ has a solution among the *real* numbers if $a \geq 0$. Each such $x$ is called a *square root* of $a$.

First, let us see what we can say about square roots without using Axiom 10. Negative numbers cannot have square roots because if $x^2 = a$, then $a$, being a square, must be nonnegative (by Theorem I.20). Moreover, if $a = 0$, then $x = 0$ is the only square root (by Theorem I.11). Suppose, then, that $a > 0$. If $x^2 = a$, then $x \neq 0$ and $(-x)^2 = a$, so both $x$ and its negative are square roots. In other words, if $a$ has a square root, then it has two square roots, one positive and one negative. Also, it has *at most two* because if $x^2 = a$ and $y^2 = a$, then $x^2 = y^2$ and $(x - y)(x + y) = 0$, and so, by Theorem I.11, either $x = y$ or $x = -y$. Thus, if $a$ has a square root, it has *exactly* two.

The existence of at least one square root can be deduced from an important theorem in calculus known as the intermediate-value theorem for continuous functions, but it may be instructive to see how the existence of a square root can be proved directly from Axiom 10.

THEOREM I.35.   *Every nonnegative real number $a$ has a unique nonnegative square root.*

*Note:* If $a \geq 0$, we denote its nonnegative square root by $a^{1/2}$ or by $\sqrt{a}$. If $a > 0$, the negative square root is $-a^{1/2}$ or $-\sqrt{a}$.

*Proof.* If $a = 0$, then 0 is the only square root. Assume, then, that $a > 0$. Let $S$ be the set of all positive $x$ such that $x^2 \leq a$. Since $(1 + a)^2 > a$, the number $1 + a$ is an upper bound for $S$. Also, $S$ is nonempty because the number $a/(1 + a)$ is in $S$; in fact, $a^2 \leq a(1 + a)^2$ and hence $a^2/(1 + a)^2 \leq a$. By Axiom 10, $S$ has a least upper bound which we shall call $b$. Note that $b \geq a/(1 + a)$ so $b > 0$. There are only three possibilities: $b^2 > a$, $b^2 < a$, or $b^2 = a$.

Suppose $b^2 > a$ and let $c = b - (b^2 - a)/(2b) = \frac{1}{2}(b + a/b)$. Then $0 < c < b$ and $c^2 = b^2 - (b^2 - a) + (b^2 - a)^2/(4b^2) = a + (b^2 - a)^2/(4b^2) > a$. Therefore $c^2 > x^2$ for each $x$ in $S$, and hence $c > x$ for each $x$ in $S$. This means that $c$ is an upper bound for $S$. Since $c < b$, we have a contradiction because $b$ was the *least* upper bound for $S$. Therefore the inequality $b^2 > a$ is impossible.

Suppose $b^2 < a$. Since $b > 0$, we may choose a positive number $c$ such that $c < b$ and such that $c < (a - b^2)/(3b)$. Then we have

$$(b + c)^2 = b^2 + c(2b + c) < b^2 + 3bc < b^2 + (a - b^2) = a .$$

Therefore $b + c$ is in $S$. Since $b + c > b$, this contradicts the fact that $b$ is an upper bound for $S$. Therefore the inequality $b^2 < a$ is impossible, and the only remaining alternative is $b^2 = a$.

## *I 3.14  Roots of higher order.  Rational powers

The least-upper-bound axiom can also be used to show the existence of roots of higher order. For example, if $n$ is a positive *odd* integer, then for each real $x$ there is exactly one real $y$ such that $y^n = x$. This $y$ is called the *n*th *root* of $x$ and is denoted by

(I.15) $$y = x^{1/n} \quad \text{or} \quad y = \sqrt[n]{x}.$$

When $n$ is *even*, the situation is slightly different. In this case, if $x$ is negative, there is no real $y$ such that $y^n = x$ because $y^n \geq 0$ for all real $y$. However, if $x$ is positive, it can be shown that there is one and only one positive $y$ such that $y^n = x$. This $y$ is called the *positive nth root* of $x$ and is denoted by the symbols in (I.15). Since $n$ is even, $(-y)^n = y^n$ and hence each $x > 0$ has two real $n$th roots, $y$ and $-y$. However, the symbols $x^{1/n}$ and $\sqrt[n]{x}$ are reserved for the *positive nth* root. We do not discuss the proofs of these statements here because they will be deduced later as consequences of the intermediate-value theorem for continuous functions (see Section 3.10).

If $r$ is a positive rational number, say $r = m/n$, where $m$ and $n$ are positive integers, we define $x^r$ to be $(x^m)^{1/n}$, the $n$th root of $x^m$, whenever this exists. If $x \neq 0$, we define $x^{-r} = 1/x^r$ whenever $x^r$ is defined. From these definitions, it is easy to verify that the usual laws of exponents are valid for rational exponents: $x^r \cdot x^s = x^{r+s}$, $(x^r)^s = x^{rs}$, and $(xy)^r = x^r y^r$.

## *I 3.15  Representation of real numbers by decimals

A real number of the form

(I.16) $$r = a_0 + \frac{a_1}{10} + \frac{a_2}{10^2} + \cdots + \frac{a_n}{10^n},$$

where $a_0$ is a nonnegative integer and $a_1, a_2, \ldots, a_n$ are integers satisfying $0 \leq a_i \leq 9$, is usually written more briefly as follows:

$$r = a_0.a_1a_2 \cdots a_n.$$

This is said to be a *finite decimal representation* of $r$. For example,

$$\frac{1}{2} = \frac{5}{10} = 0.5, \quad \frac{1}{50} = \frac{2}{10^2} = 0.02, \quad \frac{29}{4} = 7 + \frac{2}{10} + \frac{5}{10^2} = 7.25.$$

Real numbers like these are necessarily rational and, in fact, they all have the form $r = a/10^n$, where $a$ is an integer. However, not all rational numbers can be expressed with finite decimal representations. For example, if $\frac{1}{3}$ could be so expressed, then we would have $\frac{1}{3} = a/10^n$ or $3a = 10^n$ for some integer $a$. But this is impossible since 3 is not a factor of any power of 10.

Nevertheless, we can approximate an arbitrary real number $x > 0$ to any desired degree of accuracy by a sum of the form (I.16) if we take $n$ large enough. The reason for this may be seen by the following geometric argument: If $x$ is not an integer, then $x$ lies between two consecutive integers, say $a_0 < x < a_0 + 1$. The segment joining $a_0$ and $a_0 + 1$ may be subdivided into ten equal parts. If $x$ is not one of the subdivision points, then $x$ must lie between two consecutive subdivision points. This gives us a pair of inequalities of the form

$$a_0 + \frac{a_1}{10} < x < a_0 + \frac{a_1 + 1}{10},$$

where $a_1$ is an integer ($0 \leq a_1 \leq 9$). Next we divide the segment joining $a_0 + a_1/10$ and $a_0 + (a_1 + 1)/10$ into ten equal parts (each of length $10^{-2}$) and continue the process. If after a finite number of steps a subdivision point coincides with $x$, then $x$ is a number of the form (I.16). Otherwise the process continues indefinitely, and it generates an infinite set of integers $a_1, a_2, a_3, \ldots$ . In this case, we say that $x$ has the infinite decimal representation

$$x = a_0.a_1a_2a_3 \cdots .$$

At the $n$th stage, $x$ satisfies the inequalities

$$a_0 + \frac{a_1}{10} + \cdots + \frac{a_n}{10^n} < x < a_0 + \frac{a_1}{10} + \cdots + \frac{a_n + 1}{10^n}.$$

This gives us two approximations to $x$, one from above and one from below, by finite decimals that differ by $10^{-n}$. Therefore we can achieve any desired degree of accuracy in our approximations by taking $n$ large enough.

When $x = \frac{1}{3}$, it is easy to verify that $a_0 = 0$ and $a_n = 3$ for all $n \geq 1$, and hence the corresponding infinite decimal expansion is

$$\tfrac{1}{3} = 0.333 \cdots .$$

Every irrational number has an infinite decimal representation. For example, when $x = \sqrt{2}$ we may calculate by trial and error as many digits in the expansion as we wish. Thus, $\sqrt{2}$ lies between 1.4 and 1.5, because $(1.4)^2 < 2 < (1.5)^2$. Similarly, by squaring and comparing with 2, we find the following further approximations:

$$1.41 < \sqrt{2} < 1.42, \qquad 1.414 < \sqrt{2} < 1.415, \qquad 1.4142 < \sqrt{2} < 1.4143 .$$

Note that the foregoing process generates a succession of intervals of lengths $10^{-1}$, $10^{-2}$, $10^{-3}, \ldots$, each contained in the preceding and each containing the point $x$. This is an example of what is known as a sequence of *nested intervals*, a concept that is sometimes used as a basis for constructing the irrational numbers from the rational numbers.

Since we shall do very little with decimals in this book, we shall not develop their properties in any further detail except to mention how decimal expansions may be defined analytically with the help of the least-upper-bound axiom.

If $x$ is a given positive real number, let $a_0$ denote the largest integer $\leq x$. Having chosen $a_0$, we let $a_1$ denote the largest integer such that

$$a_0 + \frac{a_1}{10} \leq x .$$

More generally, having chosen $a_0$, $a_1$, ..., $a_{n-1}$, we let $a_n$ denote the largest integer such that

(I.17)
$$a_0 + \frac{a_1}{10} + \frac{a_2}{10^2} + \cdots + \frac{a_n}{10^n} \leq x \, .$$

Let $S$ denote the set of all numbers

(I.18)
$$a_0 + \frac{a_1}{10} + \frac{a_2}{10^2} + \cdots + \frac{a_n}{10^n}$$

obtained in this way for $n = 0, 1, 2, \ldots$ . Then $S$ is nonempty and bounded above, and it is easy to verify that $x$ is actually the least upper bound of $S$. The integers $a_0$, $a_1$, $a_2$, ... so obtained may be used to define a decimal expansion of $x$ if we write

$$x = a_0.a_1a_2a_3 \cdots$$

to mean that the $n$th digit $a_n$ is the largest integer satisfying (I.17). For example, if $x = \tfrac{1}{8}$, we find $a_0 = 0$, $a_1 = 1$, $a_2 = 2$, $a_3 = 5$, and $a_n = 0$ for all $n \geq 4$. Therefore we may write

$$\tfrac{1}{8} = 0.125000 \cdots .$$

If in (I.17) we replace the inequality sign $\leq$ by $<$, we obtain a slightly different definition of decimal expansions. The least upper bound of all numbers of the form (I.18) is again $x$, although the integers $a_0$, $a_1$, $a_2$, ... . need not be the same as those which satisfy (I.17). For example, if this second definition is applied to $x = \tfrac{1}{8}$, we find $a_0 = 0$, $a_1 = 1$, $a_2 = 2$, $a_3 = 4$, and $a_n = 9$ for all $n \geq 4$. This leads to the infinite decimal representation

$$\tfrac{1}{8} = 0.124999 \cdots .$$

The fact that a real number might have two different decimal representations is merely a reflection of the fact that two different sets of real numbers can have the same supremum.

## Part 4.   *Mathematical Induction, Summation Notation, and Related Topics*

### I 4.1   An example of a proof by mathematical induction

There is no *largest* integer because when we add 1 to an integer $k$, we obtain $k + 1$, which is larger than $k$. Nevertheless, starting with the number 1, we can reach any positive integer whatever in a finite number of steps, passing successively from $k$ to $k + 1$ at each step. This is the basis for a type of reasoning that mathematicians call *proof by induction*. We shall illustrate the use of this method by proving the pair of inequalities used in Section

I 1.3 in the computation of the area of a parabolic segment, namely

(I.19) $$1^2 + 2^2 + \cdots + (n-1)^2 < \frac{n^3}{3} < 1^2 + 2^2 + \cdots + n^2.$$

Consider the leftmost inequality first, and let us refer to this formula as $A(n)$ (an assertion involving $n$). It is easy to verify this assertion directly for the first few values of $n$. Thus, for example, when $n$ takes the values 1, 2, and 3, the assertion becomes

$$A(1): 0 < \frac{1^3}{3}, \qquad A(2): 1^2 < \frac{2^3}{3}, \qquad A(3): 1^2 + 2^2 < \frac{3^3}{3},$$

provided we agree to interpret the sum on the left as 0 when $n = 1$.

Our object is to prove that $A(n)$ is true for every positive integer $n$. The procedure is as follows: Assume the assertion has been proved for a particular value of $n$, say for $n = k$. That is, assume we have proved

$$A(k): 1^2 + 2^2 + \cdots + (k-1)^2 < \frac{k^3}{3}$$

for a fixed $k \geq 1$. Now *using this*, we shall deduce the corresponding result for $k + 1$:

$$A(k+1): 1^2 + 2^2 + \cdots + k^2 < \frac{(k+1)^3}{3}.$$

Start with $A(k)$ and add $k^2$ to both sides. This gives the inequality

$$1^2 + 2^2 + \cdots + k^2 < \frac{k^3}{3} + k^2.$$

To obtain $A(k+1)$ as a consequence of this, it suffices to show that

$$\frac{k^3}{3} + k^2 < \frac{(k+1)^3}{3}.$$

But this follows at once from the equation

$$\frac{(k+1)^3}{3} = \frac{k^3 + 3k^2 + 3k + 1}{3} = \frac{k^3}{3} + k^2 + k + \frac{1}{3}.$$

Therefore we have shown that $A(k+1)$ follows from $A(k)$. Now, since $A(1)$ has been verified directly, we conclude that $A(2)$ is also true. Knowing that $A(2)$ is true, we conclude that $A(3)$ is true, and so on. Since every integer can be reached in this way, $A(n)$ is true for all positive integers $n$. This proves the leftmost inequality in (I.19). The rightmost inequality can be proved in the same way.

## I 4.2   The principle of mathematical induction

The reader should make certain that he understands the *pattern* of the foregoing proof. First we proved the assertion $A(n)$ for $n = 1$. Next we showed that *if* the assertion is true for a particular integer, *then* it is also true for the next integer. From this, we concluded that the assertion is true for all positive integers.

The idea of induction may be illustrated in many nonmathematical ways. For example, imagine a row of toy soldiers, numbered consecutively, and suppose they are so arranged that if any one of them falls, say the one labeled $k$, it will knock over the next one, labeled $k + 1$. Then anyone can visualize what would happen if soldier number 1 were toppled backward. It is also clear that if a later soldier were knocked over first, say the one labeled $n_1$, then all soldiers behind *him* would fall. This illustrates a slight generalization of the method of induction which can be described in the following way.

*Method of proof by induction.* Let $A(n)$ be an assertion involving an integer $n$. We conclude that $A(n)$ is true for every $n \geq n_1$ if we can perform the following two steps:
   (a) Prove that $A(n_1)$ is true.
   (b) Let $k$ be an arbitrary but fixed integer $\geq n_1$. Assume that $A(k)$ is true and prove that $A(k + 1)$ is also true.

In actual practice $n_1$ is usually 1. The logical justification for this method of proof is the following theorem about real numbers.

THEOREM I.36.   PRINCIPLE OF MATHEMATICAL INDUCTION.   *Let $S$ be a set of positive integers which has the following two properties*:
   (a) *The number 1 is in the set $S$.*
   (b) *If an integer $k$ is in $S$, then so is $k + 1$.*
*Then every positive integer is in the set $S$.*

*Proof.* Properties (a) and (b) tell us that $S$ is an inductive set. But the positive integers were defined to be exactly those real numbers which belong to every inductive set. (See Section I 3.6.) Therefore $S$ contains every positive integer.

Whenever we carry out a proof of an assertion $A(n)$ for all $n \geq 1$ by mathematical induction, we are applying Theorem I.36 to the set $S$ of all the integers for which the assertion is true. If we want to prove that $A(n)$ is true only for $n \geq n_1$, we apply Theorem I.36 to the set of $n$ for which $A(n + n_1 - 1)$ is true.

## *I 4.3   The well-ordering principle

There is another important property of the positive integers, called the well-ordering principle, that is also used as a basis for proofs by induction. It can be stated as follows.

THEOREM I.37.   WELL-ORDERING PRINCIPLE.   *Every nonempty set of positive integers contains a smallest member.*

Note that the well-ordering principle refers to sets of *positive* integers. The theorem is not true for arbitrary sets of integers. For example, the set of all integers has no smallest member.

The well-ordering principle can be deduced from the principle of induction. This is demonstrated in Section I 4.5. We conclude this section with an example showing how the well-ordering principle can be used to prove theorems about positive integers.

Let $A(n)$ denote the following assertion:

$$A(n): 1^2 + 2^2 + \cdots + n^2 = \frac{n^3}{3} + \frac{n^2}{2} + \frac{n}{6}.$$

Again, we note that $A(1)$ is true, since

$$1^2 = \tfrac{1}{3} + \tfrac{1}{2} + \tfrac{1}{6}.$$

Now there are only two possibilities. We have either
  (i) $A(n)$ is true for every positive integer $n$, or
  (ii) there is at least one positive integer $n$ for which $A(n)$ is false.
We shall prove that alternative (ii) leads to a contradiction. Assume (ii) holds. Then by the well-ordering principle, there must be a *smallest* positive integer, say $k$, for which $A(k)$ is false. (We apply the well-ordering principle to the set of all positive integers $n$ for which $A(n)$ is false. Statement (ii) says that this set is nonempty.) This $k$ must be greater than 1, because we have verified that $A(1)$ is true. Also, the assertion must be true for $k - 1$, since $k$ was the smallest integer for which $A(k)$ is false; therefore we may write

$$A(k - 1): 1^2 + 2^2 + \cdots + (k - 1)^2 = \frac{(k - 1)^3}{3} + \frac{(k - 1)^2}{2} + \frac{k - 1}{6}.$$

Adding $k^2$ to both sides and simplifying the right-hand side, we find

$$1^2 + 2^2 + \cdots + k^2 = \frac{k^3}{3} + \frac{k^2}{2} + \frac{k}{6}.$$

But this equation states that $A(k)$ is true; therefore we have a contradiction, because $k$ is an integer for which $A(k)$ is false. In other words, statement (ii) leads to a contradiction. Therefore (i) holds, and this proves that the identity in question is valid for all values of $n \geq 1$. An immediate consequence of this identity is the rightmost inequality in (I.19).

A proof like this which makes use of the well-ordering principle is also referred to as a proof by induction. Of course, the proof could also be put in the more usual form in which we verify $A(1)$ and then pass from $A(k)$ to $A(k + 1)$.

## I 4.4 Exercises

1. Prove the following formulas by induction:

   (a) $1 + 2 + 3 + \cdots + n = n(n + 1)/2.$

   (b) $1 + 3 + 5 + \cdots + (2n - 1) = n^2.$

   (c) $1^3 + 2^3 + 3^3 + \cdots + n^3 = (1 + 2 + 3 + \cdots + n)^2.$

   (d) $1^3 + 2^3 + \cdots + (n - 1)^3 < n^4/4 < 1^3 + 2^3 + \cdots + n^3.$

2. Note that
$$1 = 1,$$
$$1 - 4 = -(1 + 2),$$
$$1 - 4 + 9 = 1 + 2 + 3,$$
$$1 - 4 + 9 - 16 = -(1 + 2 + 3 + 4).$$

Guess the general law suggested and prove it by induction.

3. Note that
$$1 + \tfrac{1}{2} = 2 - \tfrac{1}{2},$$
$$1 + \tfrac{1}{2} + \tfrac{1}{4} = 2 - \tfrac{1}{4},$$
$$1 + \tfrac{1}{2} + \tfrac{1}{4} + \tfrac{1}{8} = 2 - \tfrac{1}{8}.$$

Guess the general law suggested and prove it by induction.

4. Note that
$$1 - \tfrac{1}{2} = \tfrac{1}{2},$$
$$(1 - \tfrac{1}{2})(1 - \tfrac{1}{3}) = \tfrac{1}{3},$$
$$(1 - \tfrac{1}{2})(1 - \tfrac{1}{3})(1 - \tfrac{1}{4}) = \tfrac{1}{4}.$$

Guess the general law suggested and prove it by induction.

5. Guess a general law which simplifies the product

$$\left(1 - \frac{1}{4}\right)\left(1 - \frac{1}{9}\right)\left(1 - \frac{1}{16}\right) \cdots \left(1 - \frac{1}{n^2}\right)$$

and prove it by induction.

6. Let $A(n)$ denote the statement: $1 + 2 + \cdots + n = \tfrac{1}{8}(2n + 1)^2$.
   (a) Prove that if $A(k)$ is true for an integer $k$, then $A(k + 1)$ is also true.
   (b) Criticize the statement: "By induction it follows that $A(n)$ is true for all $n$."
   (c) Amend $A(n)$ by changing the equality to an inequality that is true for all positive integers $n$.

7. Let $n_1$ be the smallest positive integer $n$ for which the inequality $(1 + x)^n > 1 + nx + nx^2$ is true for all $x > 0$. Compute $n_1$, and prove that the inequality is true for all integers $n \geq n_1$.

8. Given positive real numbers $a_1, a_2, a_3, \ldots$, such that $a_n \leq c a_{n-1}$ for all $n \geq 2$, where $c$ is a fixed positive number, use induction to prove that $a_n \leq a_1 c^{n-1}$ for all $n \geq 1$.

9. Prove the following statement by induction: If a line of unit length is given, then a line of length $\sqrt{n}$ can be constructed with straightedge and compass for each positive integer $n$.

10. Let $b$ denote a fixed positive integer. Prove the following statement by induction: For every integer $n \geq 0$, there exist nonnegative integers $q$ and $r$ such that

$$n = qb + r, \qquad 0 \leq r < b.$$

11. Let $n$ and $d$ denote integers. We say that $d$ is a *divisor* of $n$ if $n = cd$ for some integer $c$. An integer $n$ is called a *prime* if $n > 1$ and if the only positive divisors of $n$ are 1 and $n$. Prove, by induction, that every integer $n > 1$ is either a prime or a product of primes.

12. Describe the fallacy in the following "proof" by induction:

*Statement.* Given any collection of $n$ blonde girls. If at least one of the girls has blue eyes, then all $n$ of them have blue eyes.

"*Proof.*" The statement is obviously true when $n = 1$. The step from $k$ to $k + 1$ can be illustrated by going from $n = 3$ to $n = 4$. Assume, therefore, that the statement is true when $n = 3$ and let $G_1, G_2, G_3, G_4$ be four blonde girls, at least one of which, say $G_1$, has blue eyes. Taking $G_1, G_2,$ and $G_3$ together and using the fact that the statement is true when $n = 3$, we find that $G_2$ and $G_3$ also have blue eyes. Repeating the process with $G_1, G_2,$ and $G_4$, we find that $G_4$ has blue eyes. Thus all four have blue eyes. A similar argument allows us to make the step from $k$ to $k + 1$ in general.

*Corollary.* All blonde girls have blue eyes.

*Proof.* Since there exists at least one blonde girl with blue eyes, we can apply the foregoing result to the collection consisting of all blonde girls.

*Note:* This example is from G. Pólya, who suggests that the reader may want to test the validity of the statement by experiment.

## *I 4.5 Proof of the well-ordering principle

In this section we deduce the well-ordering principle from the principle of induction.

Let $T$ be a nonempty collection of positive integers. We want to prove that $T$ has a smallest member, that is, that there is a positive integer $t_0$ in $T$ such that $t_0 \leq t$ for all $t$ in $T$.

Suppose $T$ has no smallest member. We shall show that this leads to a contradiction. The integer 1 cannot be in $T$ (otherwise it would be the smallest member of $T$). Let $S$ denote the collection of all positive integers $n$ such that $n < t$ for all $t$ in $T$. Now 1 is in $S$ because $1 < t$ for all $t$ in $T$. Next, let $k$ be a positive integer in $S$. Then $k < t$ for all $t$ in $T$. We shall prove that $k + 1$ is also in $S$. If this were not so, then for some $t_1$ in $T$ we would have $t_1 \leq k + 1$. Since $T$ has no smallest member, there is an integer $t_2$ in $T$ such that $t_2 < t_1$, and hence $t_2 < k + 1$. But this means that $t_2 \leq k$, contradicting the fact that $k < t$ for all $t$ in $T$. Therefore $k + 1$ is in $S$. By the induction principle, $S$ contains all positive integers. Since $T$ is nonempty, there is a positive integer $t$ in $T$. But this $t$ must also be in $S$ (since $S$ contains all positive integers). It follows from the definition of $S$ that $t < t$, which is a contradiction. Therefore, the assumption that $T$ has no smallest member leads to a contradiction. It follows that $T$ must have a smallest member, and in turn this proves that the well-ordering principle is a consequence of the principle of induction.

## I 4.6 The summation notation

In the calculations for the area of the parabolic segment, we encountered the sum

(I.20) $$1^2 + 2^2 + 3^2 + \cdots + n^2 .$$

Note that a typical term in this sum is of the form $k^2$, and we get all the terms by letting $k$ run through the values $1, 2, 3, \ldots, n$. There is a very useful and convenient notation which enables us to write sums like this in a more compact form. This is called the *summation notation* and it makes use of the Greek letter sigma, $\Sigma$. Using summation notation, we can write the sum in (I.20) as follows:

$$\sum_{k=1}^{n} k^2.$$

This symbol is read: "The sum of $k^2$ for $k$ running from 1 to $n$." The numbers appearing under and above the sigma tell us the range of values taken by $k$. The letter $k$ itself is referred to as the *index of summation*. Of course, it is not important that we use the letter $k$; any other convenient letter may take its place. For example, instead of $\sum_{k=1}^{n} k^2$ we could write $\sum_{i=1}^{n} i^2$, $\sum_{j=1}^{n} j^2$, $\sum_{m=1}^{n} m^2$, etc., all of which are considered as alternative notations for the same thing. The letters $i, j, k, m$, etc. that are used in this way are called *dummy indices*. It would not be a good idea to use the letter $n$ for the dummy index in this particular example because $n$ is already being used for the number of terms.

More generally, when we want to form the sum of several real numbers, say $a_1, a_2, \ldots, a_n$, we denote such a sum by the symbol

(I.21) $$a_1 + a_2 + \cdots + a_n$$

which, using summation notation, can be written as follows:

(I.22) $$\sum_{k=1}^{n} a_k.$$

For example, we have

$$\sum_{k=1}^{4} a_k = a_1 + a_2 + a_3 + a_4,$$

$$\sum_{i=1}^{5} x_i = x_1 + x_2 + x_3 + x_4 + x_5.$$

Sometimes it is convenient to begin summations from 0 or from some value of the index beyond 1. For example, we have

$$\sum_{i=0}^{4} x_i = x_0 + x_1 + x_2 + x_3 + x_4,$$

$$\sum_{n=2}^{5} n^3 = 2^3 + 3^3 + 4^3 + 5^3.$$

Other uses of the summation notation are illustrated below:

$$\sum_{m=0}^{4} x^{m+1} = x + x^2 + x^3 + x^4 + x^5,$$

$$\sum_{j=1}^{6} 2^{j-1} = 1 + 2 + 2^2 + 2^3 + 2^4 + 2^5.$$

To emphasize once more that the choice of dummy index is unimportant, we note that the last sum may also be written in each of the following forms:

$$\sum_{q=1}^{6} 2^{q-1} = \sum_{r=0}^{5} 2^r = \sum_{n=0}^{5} 2^{5-n} = \sum_{k=1}^{6} 2^{6-k}.$$

*Note:* From a strictly logical standpoint, the symbols in (I.21) and (I.22) do not appear among the primitive symbols for the real-number system. In a more careful treatment, we could define these new symbols in terms of the primitive undefined symbols of our system.

This may be done by a process known as *definition by induction* which, like proof by induction, consists of two parts:

(a) We define

$$\sum_{k=1}^{1} a_k = a_1.$$

(b) Assuming that we have defined $\sum_{k=1}^{n} a_k$ for a fixed $n \geq 1$, we further define

$$\sum_{k=1}^{n+1} a_k = \left( \sum_{k=1}^{n} a_k \right) + a_{n+1}.$$

To illustrate, we may take $n = 1$ in (b) and use (a) to obtain

$$\sum_{k=1}^{2} a_k = \sum_{k=1}^{1} a_k + a_2 = a_1 + a_2.$$

Now, having defined $\sum_{k=1}^{2} a_k$, we can use (b) again with $n = 2$ to obtain

$$\sum_{k=1}^{3} a_k = \sum_{k=1}^{2} a_k + a_3 = (a_1 + a_2) + a_3.$$

By the associative law for addition (Axiom 2), the sum $(a_1 + a_2) + a_3$ is the same as $a_1 + (a_2 + a_3)$, and therefore there is no danger of confusion if we drop the parentheses and simply write $a_1 + a_2 + a_3$ for $\sum_{k=1}^{3} a_k$. Similarly, we have

$$\sum_{k=1}^{4} a_k = \sum_{k=1}^{3} a_k + a_4 = (a_1 + a_2 + a_3) + a_4.$$

In this case we can *prove* that the sum $(a_1 + a_2 + a_3) + a_4$ is the same as $(a_1 + a_2) + (a_3 + a_4)$ or $a_1 + (a_2 + a_3 + a_4)$, and therefore the parentheses can be dropped again without danger of ambiguity, and we agree to write

$$\sum_{k=1}^{4} a_k = a_1 + a_2 + a_3 + a_4.$$

Continuing in this way, we find that (a) and (b) together give us a complete definition of the symbol in (I.22). The notation in (I.21) is considered to be merely an alternative way of writing (I.22). It is justified by a general associative law for addition which we shall not attempt to state or to prove here.

The reader should notice that *definition by induction* and *proof by induction* involve the same underlying idea. A definition by induction is also called a *recursive definition*.

## I 4.7  Exercises

1. Find the numerical values of the following sums:

(a) $\sum_{k=1}^{4} k$,  (c) $\sum_{r=0}^{3} 2^{2r+1}$,  (e) $\sum_{i=0}^{5} (2i + 1)$,

(b) $\sum_{n=2}^{5} 2^{n-2}$,  (d) $\sum_{n=1}^{4} n^n$,  (f) $\sum_{k=1}^{5} \frac{1}{k(k + 1)}$.

2. Establish the following properties of the summation notation:

$$\text{(a)} \sum_{k=1}^{n} (a_k + b_k) = \sum_{k=1}^{n} a_k + \sum_{k=1}^{n} b_k \qquad \text{(additive property)}.$$

$$\text{(b)} \sum_{k=1}^{n} (ca_k) = c \sum_{k=1}^{n} a_k \qquad \text{(homogeneous property)}.$$

$$\text{(c)} \sum_{k=1}^{n} (a_k - a_{k-1}) = a_n - a_0 \qquad \text{(telescoping property)}.$$

Use the properties in Exercise 2 whenever possible to derive the formulas in Exercises 3 through 8.

3. $\sum_{k=1}^{n} 1 = n.$ (This means $\sum_{k=1}^{n} a_k$, where each $a_k = 1$.)

4. $\sum_{k=1}^{n} (2k - 1) = n^2.$   [*Hint:* $2k - 1 = k^2 - (k - 1)^2.$]

5. $\sum_{k=1}^{n} k = \dfrac{n^2}{2} + \dfrac{n}{2}.$   [*Hint:* Use Exercises 3 and 4.]

6. $\sum_{k=1}^{n} k^2 = \dfrac{n^3}{3} + \dfrac{n^2}{2} + \dfrac{n}{6}.$   [*Hint:* $k^3 - (k - 1)^3 = 3k^2 - 3k + 1.$]

7. $\sum_{k=1}^{n} k^3 = \dfrac{n^4}{4} + \dfrac{n^3}{2} + \dfrac{n^2}{4}.$

8. (a) $\sum_{k=0}^{n} x^k = \dfrac{1 - x^{n+1}}{1 - x}$   if $x \neq 1$.   *Note:* $x^0$ is defined to be 1.

   [*Hint:* Apply Exercise 2 to $(1 - x) \sum_{k=0}^{n} x^k$.]
   (b) What is the sum equal to when $x = 1$?

9. Prove, by induction, that the sum $\sum_{k=1}^{2n} (-1)^k (2k + 1)$ is proportional to $n$, and find the constant of proportionality.

10. (a) Give a reasonable definition of the symbol $\sum_{k=m}^{m+n} a_k$.
    (b) Prove, by induction, that for $n \geq 1$ we have

$$\sum_{k=n+1}^{2n} \frac{1}{k} = \sum_{m=1}^{2n} \frac{(-1)^{m+1}}{m}.$$

11. Determine whether each of the following statements is true or false. In each case give a reason for your decision.

(a) $\sum_{n=0}^{100} n^4 = \sum_{n=1}^{100} n^4.$   (d) $\sum_{i=1}^{100} (i + 1)^2 = \sum_{i=0}^{99} i^2.$

(b) $\sum_{j=0}^{100} 2 = 200.$   (e) $\sum_{k=1}^{100} k^3 = \left( \sum_{k=1}^{100} k \right) \cdot \left( \sum_{k=1}^{100} k^2 \right).$

(c) $\sum_{k=0}^{100} (2 + k) = 2 + \sum_{k=0}^{100} k.$   (f) $\sum_{k=0}^{100} k^3 = \left( \sum_{k=0}^{100} k \right)^3.$

12. Guess and prove a general rule which simplifies the sum

$$\sum_{k=1}^{n} \frac{1}{k(k+1)}.$$

13. Prove that $2(\sqrt{n+1} - \sqrt{n}) < \dfrac{1}{\sqrt{n}} < 2(\sqrt{n} - \sqrt{n-1})$ if $n \geq 1$. Then use this to prove that

$$2\sqrt{m} - 2 < \sum_{n=1}^{m} \frac{1}{\sqrt{n}} < 2\sqrt{m} - 1$$

if $m \geq 2$. In particular, when $m = 10^6$, the sum lies between 1998 and 1999.

## I 4.8  Absolute values and the triangle inequality

Calculations with inequalities arise quite frequently in calculus. They are of particular importance in dealing with the notion of *absolute value*. If $x$ is a real number, the absolute value of $x$ is a nonnegative real number denoted by $|x|$ and defined as follows:

$$|x| = \begin{cases} x & \text{if } x \geq 0, \\ -x & \text{if } x \leq 0. \end{cases}$$

Note that $-|x| \leq x \leq |x|$. When real numbers are represented geometrically on a real axis, the number $|x|$ is called the *distance* of $x$ from 0. If $a > 0$ and if a point $x$ lies between $-a$ and $a$, then $|x|$ is nearer to 0 than $a$ is. The analytic statement of this fact is given by the following theorem.

THEOREM I.38.  *If $a \geq 0$, then $|x| \leq a$ if and only if $-a \leq x \leq a$.*

*Proof.* There are two statements to prove: first, that the inequality $|x| \leq a$ implies the two inequalities $-a \leq x \leq a$ and, conversely, that $-a \leq x \leq a$ implies $|x| \leq a$.

Suppose $|x| \leq a$. Then we also have $-a \leq -|x|$. But either $x = |x|$ or $x = -|x|$ and hence $-a \leq -|x| \leq x \leq |x| \leq a$. This proves the first statement.

To prove the converse, assume $-a \leq x \leq a$. Then if $x \geq 0$, we have $|x| = x \leq a$, whereas if $x \leq 0$, we have $|x| = -x \leq a$. In either case we have $|x| \leq a$, and this completes the proof.

Figure I.9 illustrates the geometrical significance of this theorem.

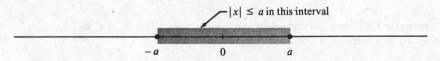

FIGURE I.9   Geometrical significance of Theorem I.38.

As a consequence of Theorem I.38, it is easy to derive an important inequality which states that the absolute value of a sum of two real numbers cannot exceed the sum of their absolute values.

THEOREM I.39.    *For arbitrary real numbers x and y, we have*

$$|x + y| \leq |x| + |y|.$$

*Note:* This property is called the *triangle inequality*, because when it is generalized to vectors it states that the length of any side of a triangle is less than or equal to the sum of the lengths of the other two sides.

*Proof.* Adding the inequalities $-|x| \leq x \leq |x|$ and $-|y| \leq y \leq |y|$, we obtain

$$-(|x| + |y|) \leq x + y \leq |x| + |y|,$$

and hence, by Theorem I.38, we conclude that $|x + y| \leq |x| + |y|$.

If we take $x = a - c$ and $y = c - b$, then $x + y = a - b$ and the triangle inequality becomes

$$|a - b| \leq |a - c| + |b - c|.$$

This form of the triangle inequality is often used in practice.

Using mathematical induction, we may extend the triangle inequality as follows:

THEOREM I.40.    *For arbitrary real numbers $a_1, a_2, \ldots, a_n$, we have*

$$\left| \sum_{k=1}^{n} a_k \right| \leq \sum_{k=1}^{n} |a_k|.$$

*Proof.* When $n = 1$ the inequality is trivial, and when $n = 2$ it is the triangle inequality. Assume, then, that it is true for $n$ real numbers. Then for $n + 1$ real numbers $a_1, a_2, \ldots, a_{n+1}$, we have

$$\left| \sum_{k=1}^{n+1} a_k \right| = \left| \sum_{k=1}^{n} a_k + a_{n+1} \right| \leq \left| \sum_{k=1}^{n} a_k \right| + |a_{n+1}| \leq \sum_{k=1}^{n} |a_k| + |a_{n+1}| = \sum_{k=1}^{n+1} |a_k|.$$

Hence the theorem is true for $n + 1$ numbers if it is true for $n$. By induction, it is true for every positive integer $n$.

The next theorem describes an important inequality that we shall use later in connection with our study of vector algebra.

THEOREM I.41.    THE CAUCHY–SCHWARZ INEQUALITY.    *If $a_1, \ldots, a_n$ and $b_1, \ldots, b_n$ are arbitrary real numbers, we have*

(I.23)                          $$\left( \sum_{k=1}^{n} a_k b_k \right)^2 \leq \left( \sum_{k=1}^{n} a_k^2 \right) \left( \sum_{k=1}^{n} b_k^2 \right).$$

*The equality sign holds if and only if there is a real number x such that $a_k x + b_k = 0$ for each $k = 1, 2, \ldots, n$.*

*Proof.* We have $\sum_{k=1}^{n} (a_k x + b_k)^2 \geq 0$ for every real $x$ because a sum of squares can never be negative. This may be written in the form

(I.24)
$$Ax^2 + 2Bx + C \geq 0,$$

where

$$A = \sum_{k=1}^{n} a_k^2, \qquad B = \sum_{k=1}^{n} a_k b_k, \qquad C = \sum_{k=1}^{n} b_k^2.$$

We wish to prove that $B^2 \leq AC$. If $A = 0$, then each $a_k = 0$, so $B = 0$ and the result is trivial. If $A \neq 0$, we may complete the square and write

$$Ax^2 + 2Bx + C = A\left(x + \frac{B}{A}\right)^2 + \frac{AC - B^2}{A}.$$

The right side has its smallest value when $x = -B/A$. Putting $x = -B/A$ in (I.24), we obtain $B^2 \leq AC$. This proves (I.23). The reader should verify that the equality sign holds if and only if there is an $x$ such that $a_k x + b_k = 0$ for each $k$.

## I 4.9 Exercises

1. Prove each of the following properties of absolute values.
   (a) $|x| = 0$ if and only if $x = 0$.    (f) $|xy| = |x|\,|y|$.
   (b) $|-x| = |x|$.    (g) $|x/y| = |x|/|y|$ if $y \neq 0$.
   (c) $|x - y| = |y - x|$.    (h) $|x - y| \leq |x| + |y|$.
   (d) $|x|^2 = x^2$.    (i) $|x| - |y| \leq |x - y|$.
   (e) $|x| = \sqrt{x^2}$.    (j) $\big|\,|x| - |y|\,\big| \leq |x - y|$.

2. Each inequality $(a_i)$, listed below, is equivalent to exactly one inequality $(b_j)$. For example, $|x| < 3$ if and only if $-3 < x < 3$, and hence $(a_1)$ is equivalent to $(b_2)$. Determine all equivalent pairs.
   ($a_1$) $|x| < 3$.    ($b_1$) $4 < x < 6$.
   ($a_2$) $|x - 1| < 3$.    ($b_2$) $-3 < x < 3$.
   ($a_3$) $|3 - 2x| < 1$.    ($b_3$) $x > 3$ or $x < -1$.
   ($a_4$) $|1 + 2x| \leq 1$.    ($b_4$) $x > 2$.
   ($a_5$) $|x - 1| > 2$.    ($b_5$) $-2 < x < 4$.
   ($a_6$) $|x + 2| \geq 5$.    ($b_6$) $-\sqrt{3} \leq x \leq -1$ or $1 \leq x \leq \sqrt{3}$.
   ($a_7$) $|5 - x^{-1}| < 1$.    ($b_7$) $1 < x < 2$.
   ($a_8$) $|x - 5| < |x + 1|$.    ($b_8$) $x \leq -7$ or $x \geq 3$.
   ($a_9$) $|x^2 - 2| \leq 1$.    ($b_9$) $\frac{1}{6} < x < \frac{1}{4}$.
   ($a_{10}$) $x < x^2 - 12 < 4x$.    ($b_{10}$) $-1 \leq x \leq 0$.

3. Determine whether each of the following is true or false. In each case give a reason for your decision.
   (a) $x < 5$ implies $|x| < 5$.
   (b) $|x - 5| < 2$ implies $3 < x < 7$.
   (c) $|1 + 3x| \leq 1$ implies $x \geq -\frac{2}{3}$.
   (d) There is no real $x$ for which $|x - 1| = |x - 2|$.
   (e) For every $x > 0$ there is a $y > 0$ such that $|2x + y| = 5$.

4. Show that the equality sign holds in the Cauchy–Schwarz inequality if and only if there is a real number $x$ such that $a_k x + b_k = 0$ for every $k = 1, 2, \ldots, n$.

## *I 4.10 Miscellaneous exercises involving induction

In this section we assemble a number of miscellaneous facts whose proofs are good exercises in the use of mathematical induction. Some of these exercises may serve as a basis for supplementary classroom discussion.

*Factorials and binomial coefficients.* The symbol $n!$ (read "*n factorial*") may be defined by induction as follows: $0! = 1$, $n! = (n - 1)! \, n$ if $n \geq 1$. Note that $n! = 1 \cdot 2 \cdot 3 \cdots n$.

If $0 \leq k \leq n$, the *binomial coefficient* $\binom{n}{k}$ is defined as follows:

$$\binom{n}{k} = \frac{n!}{k! \, (n - k)!} \, .$$

*Note:* Sometimes $_nC_k$ is written for $\binom{n}{k}$. These numbers appear as coefficients in the binomial theorem. (See Exercise 4 below.)

1. Compute the values of the following binomial coefficients:
   (a) $\binom{5}{3}$,  (b) $\binom{7}{0}$,  (c) $\binom{7}{1}$,  (d) $\binom{7}{2}$,  (e) $\binom{17}{14}$,  (f) $\binom{0}{0}$.
2. (a) Show that $\binom{n}{k} = \binom{n}{n-k}$.  (c) Find $k$, given that $\binom{14}{k} = \binom{14}{k-4}$.
   (b) Find $n$, given that $\binom{n}{10} = \binom{n}{7}$.  (d) Is there a $k$ such that $\binom{12}{k} = \binom{12}{k-3}$?
3. Prove that $\binom{n+1}{k} = \binom{n}{k-1} + \binom{n}{k}$. This is called the *law of Pascal's triangle* and it provides a rapid way of computing binomial coefficients successively. Pascal's triangle is illustrated here for $n \leq 6$.

$$
\begin{array}{ccccccccccccc}
 &  &  &  &  & 1 &  &  &  &  &  \\
 &  &  &  & 1 &  & 1 &  &  &  &  \\
 &  &  & 1 &  & 2 &  & 1 &  &  &  \\
 &  & 1 &  & 3 &  & 3 &  & 1 &  &  \\
 & 1 &  & 4 &  & 6 &  & 4 &  & 1 &  \\
1 &  & 5 &  & 10 &  & 10 &  & 5 &  & 1 \\
\end{array}
$$
$$1 \quad 6 \quad 15 \quad 20 \quad 15 \quad 6 \quad 1$$

4. Use induction to prove the binomial theorem

$$(a + b)^n = \sum_{k=0}^{n} \binom{n}{k} a^k b^{n-k} \, .$$

Then use the theorem to derive the formulas

$$\sum_{k=0}^{n} \binom{n}{k} = 2^n \quad \text{and} \quad \sum_{k=0}^{n} (-1)^k \binom{n}{k} = 0, \quad \text{if} \quad n > 0.$$

*The product notation.* The product of $n$ real numbers $a_1, a_2, \ldots, a_n$ is denoted by the symbol $\prod_{k=1}^{n} a_k$, which may be defined by induction. The symbol $a_1 a_2 \cdots a_n$ is an alternative notation for this product. Note that

$$n! = \prod_{k=1}^{n} k.$$

5. Give a definition by induction for the product $\prod_{k=1}^{n} a_k$.

Prove the following properties of products by induction:

6. $\prod_{k=1}^{n} (a_k b_k) = \left( \prod_{k=1}^{n} a_k \right) \left( \prod_{k=1}^{n} b_k \right)$     (multiplicative property).

An important special case is the relation $\prod_{k=1}^{n} (ca_k) = c^n \prod_{k=1}^{n} a_k$.

7. $\prod_{k=1}^{n} \dfrac{a_k}{a_{k-1}} = \dfrac{a_n}{a_0}$     if each $a_k \neq 0$     (telescoping property).

8. If $x \neq 1$, show that

$$\prod_{k=1}^{n} (1 + x^{2^{k-1}}) = \frac{1 - x^{2^n}}{1 - x}.$$

What is the value of the product when $x = 1$?

9. If $a_k < b_k$ for each $k = 1, 2, \ldots, n$, it is easy to prove by induction that $\sum_{k=1}^{n} a_k < \sum_{k=1}^{n} b_k$. Discuss the corresponding inequality for products:

$$\prod_{k=1}^{n} a_k < \prod_{k=1}^{n} b_k.$$

*Some special inequalities*

10. If $x > 1$, prove by induction that $x^n > x$ for every integer $n \geq 2$. If $0 < x < 1$, prove that $x^n < x$ for every integer $n \geq 2$.

11. Determine all positive integers $n$ for which $2^n < n!$.

12. (a) Use the binomial theorem to prove that for $n$ a positive integer we have

$$\left( 1 + \frac{1}{n} \right)^n = 1 + \sum_{k=1}^{n} \left\{ \frac{1}{k!} \prod_{r=0}^{k-1} \left( 1 - \frac{r}{n} \right) \right\}.$$

(b) If $n > 1$, use part (a) and Exercise 11 to deduce the inequalities

$$2 < \left( 1 + \frac{1}{n} \right)^n < 1 + \sum_{k=1}^{n} \frac{1}{k!} < 3.$$

13. (a) Let $p$ be a positive integer. Prove that

$$b^p - a^p = (b - a)(b^{p-1} + b^{p-2}a + b^{p-3}a^2 + \cdots + ba^{p-2} + a^{p-1}).$$

[*Hint:* Use the telescoping property for sums.]

(b) Let $p$ and $n$ denote positive integers. Use part (a) to show that

$$n^p < \frac{(n + 1)^{p+1} - n^{p+1}}{p + 1} < (n + 1)^p.$$

(c) Use induction to prove that

$$\sum_{k=1}^{n-1} k^p < \frac{n^{p+1}}{p+1} < \sum_{k=1}^{n} k^p .$$

Part (b) will assist in making the inductive step from $n$ to $n + 1$.

14. Let $a_1, \ldots, a_n$ be $n$ real numbers, all having the same sign and all greater than $-1$. Use induction to prove that

$$(1 + a_1)(1 + a_2) \cdots (1 + a_n) \geq 1 + a_1 + a_2 + \cdots + a_n .$$

In particular, when $a_1 = a_2 = \cdots = a_n = x$, where $x > -1$, this yields

(I.25)                    $(1 + x)^n \geq 1 + nx$      (*Bernoulli's inequality*).

Show that when $n > 1$ the equality sign holds in (I.25) only for $x = 0$.

15. If $n \geq 2$, prove that $n!/n^n \leq (\frac{1}{2})^k$, where $k$ is the greatest integer $\leq n/2$.

16. The numbers 1, 2, 3, 5, 8, 13, 21, $\ldots$, in which each term after the second is the sum of its two predecessors, are called *Fibonacci numbers*. They may be defined by induction as follows:

$$a_1 = 1, \qquad a_2 = 2, \qquad a_{n+1} = a_n + a_{n-1} \qquad \text{if} \quad n \geq 2 .$$

Prove that

$$a_n < \left( \frac{1 + \sqrt{5}}{2} \right)^n$$

for every $n \geq 1$.

*Inequalities relating different types of averages.* Let $x_1, x_2, \ldots, x_n$ be $n$ positive real numbers. If $p$ is a nonzero integer, the *pth-power mean* $M_p$ of the $n$ numbers is defined as follows:

$$M_p = \left( \frac{x_1^p + \cdots + x_n^p}{n} \right)^{1/p} .$$

The number $M_1$ is also called the *arithmetic mean*, $M_2$ the *root mean square*, and $M_{-1}$ the *harmonic mean*.

17. If $p > 0$, prove that $M_p < M_{2p}$ when $x_1, x_2, \ldots, x_n$ are not all equal.

[*Hint:*   Apply the Cauchy–Schwarz inequality with $a_k = x_k^p$ and $b_k = 1$.]

18. Use the result of Exercise 17 to prove that

$$a^4 + b^4 + c^4 \geq \tfrac{64}{3}$$

if $a^2 + b^2 + c^2 = 8$ and $a > 0, b > 0, c > 0$.

19. Let $a_1, \ldots, a_n$ be $n$ positive real numbers whose product is equal to 1. Prove that $a_1 + \cdots + a_n \geq n$ and that the equality sign holds only if every $a_k = 1$.

[*Hint:*   Consider two cases: (a) All $a_k = 1$; (b) not all $a_k = 1$. Use induction. In case (b) notice that if $a_1 a_2 \cdots a_{n+1} = 1$, then at least one factor, say $a_1$, exceeds 1 and at least one factor, say $a_{n+1}$, is less than 1. Let $b_1 = a_1 a_{n+1}$ and apply the induction hypothesis to the product $b_1 a_2 \cdots a_n$, using the fact that $(a_1 - 1)(a_{n+1} - 1) < 0$.]

20. The *geometric mean* $G$ of $n$ positive real numbers $x_1, \ldots, x_n$ is defined by the formula $G = (x_1 x_2 \cdots x_n)^{1/n}$.

(a) Let $M_p$ denote the $p$th power mean. Prove that $G \leq M_1$ and that $G = M_1$ only when $x_1 = x_2 = \cdots = x_n$.

(b) Let $p$ and $q$ be integers, $q < 0 < p$. From part (a) deduce that $M_q < G < M_p$ when $x_1$, $x_2, \ldots, x_n$ are not all equal.

21. Use the result of Exercise 20 to prove the following statement: If $a$, $b$, and $c$ are positive real numbers such that $abc = 8$, then $a + b + c \geq 6$ and $ab + ac + bc \geq 12$.

22. If $x_1, \ldots, x_n$ are positive numbers and if $y_k = 1/x_k$, prove that

$$\left( \sum_{k=1}^{n} x_k \right) \left( \sum_{k=1}^{n} y_k \right) \geq n^2 .$$

23. If $a$, $b$, and $c$ are positive and if $a + b + c = 1$, prove that $(1 - a)(1 - b)(1 - c) \geq 8abc$.

# 1

# THE CONCEPTS OF INTEGRAL CALCULUS

In this chapter we present the definition of the integral and some of its basic properties. To understand the definition one must have some acquaintance with the function concept; the next few sections are devoted to an explanation of this and related ideas.

## 1.1 The basic ideas of Cartesian geometry

As mentioned earlier, one of the applications of the integral is the calculation of area. Ordinarily we do not talk about area by itself. Instead, we talk about the area *of something*. This means that we have certain objects (polygonal regions, circular regions, parabolic segments, etc.) whose areas we wish to measure. If we hope to arrive at a treatment of area that will enable us to deal with many different kinds of objects, we must first find an effective way to describe these objects.

The most primitive way of doing this is by drawing figures, as was done by the ancient Greeks. A much better way was suggested by René Descartes (1596–1650), who introduced the subject of analytic geometry (also known as *Cartesian geometry*). Descartes' idea was to represent geometric points by *numbers*. The procedure for points in a plane is this:

Two perpendicular reference lines (called *coordinate axes*) are chosen, one horizontal (called the "*x*-axis"), the other vertical (the "*y*-axis"). Their point of intersection, denoted by 0, is called the *origin*. On the *x*-axis a convenient point is chosen to the right of 0 and its distance from 0 is called the *unit distance*. Vertical distances along the *y*-axis are usually measured with the same unit distance, although sometimes it is convenient to use a different scale on the *y*-axis. Now each point in the plane (sometimes called the *xy*-plane) is assigned a pair of numbers, called its *coordinates*. These numbers tell us how to locate the point. Figure 1.1 illustrates some examples. The point with coordinates (3, 2) lies three units to the right of the *y*-axis and two units above the *x*-axis. The number 3 is called the *x*-coordinate of the point, 2 its *y*-coordinate. Points to the left of the *y*-axis have a negative *x*-coordinate; those below the *x*-axis have a negative *y*-coordinate. The *x*-coordinate of a point is sometimes called its *abscissa* and the *y*-coordinate is called its *ordinate*.

When we write a pair of numbers such as (*a*, *b*) to represent a point, we agree that the abscissa or *x*-coordinate, *a*, is written first. For this reason, the pair (*a*, *b*) is often referred to as an *ordered pair*. It is clear that two ordered pairs (*a*, *b*) and (*c*, *d*) represent the same point if and only if we have $a = c$ and $b = d$. Points (*a*, *b*) with both *a* and *b* positive are said to lie in the *first quadrant*; those with $a < 0$ and $b > 0$ are in the *second quadrant*;

those with $a < 0$ and $b < 0$ are in the *third quadrant*; and those with $a > 0$ and $b < 0$ are in the *fourth quadrant*. Figure 1.1 shows one point in each quadrant.

The procedure for points in space is similar. We take three mutually perpendicular lines in space intersecting at a point (the origin). These lines determine three mutually perpendicular planes, and each point in space can be completely described by specifying, with appropriate regard for signs, its distances from these planes. We shall discuss three-dimensional Cartesian geometry in more detail later on; for the present we confine our attention to plane analytic geometry.

A geometric figure, such as a curve in the plane, is a collection of points satisfying one or more special conditions. By translating these conditions into expressions involving the

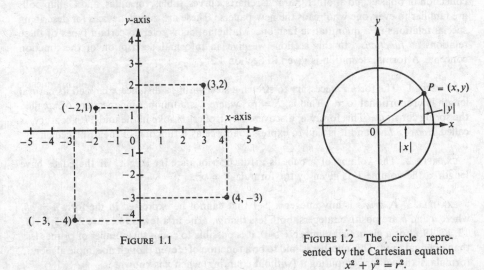

FIGURE 1.1

FIGURE 1.2 The circle represented by the Cartesian equation $x^2 + y^2 = r^2$.

coordinates $x$ and $y$, we obtain one or more equations which characterize the figure in question. For example, consider a circle of radius $r$ with its center at the origin, as shown in Figure 1.2. Let $P$ be an arbitrary point on this circle, and suppose $P$ has coordinates $(x, y)$. Then the line segment $OP$ is the hypotenuse of a right triangle whose legs have lengths $|x|$ and $|y|$ and hence, by the theorem of Pythagoras,

$$x^2 + y^2 = r^2.$$

This equation, called a *Cartesian equation* of the circle, is satisfied by all points $(x, y)$ on the circle and by no others, so the equation completely characterizes the circle. This example illustrates how analytic geometry is used to reduce geometrical statements about points to analytical statements about real numbers.

Throughout their historical development, calculus and analytic geometry have been intimately intertwined. New discoveries in one subject led to improvements in the other. The development of calculus and analytic geometry in this book is similar to the historical development, in that the two subjects are treated together. However, our primary purpose is to discuss calculus. Concepts from analytic geometry that are required for this purpose will be discussed as needed. Actually, only a few very elementary concepts of plane analytic geometry are required to understand the rudiments of calculus. A deeper study of analytic geometry is needed to extend the scope and applications of calculus, and this study will be carried out in later chapters using vector methods as well as the methods of calculus. Until then, all that is required from analytic geometry is a little familiarity with drawing graphs of functions.

## 1.2 Functions. Informal description and examples

Various fields of human endeavor have to do with relationships that exist between one collection of objects and another. Graphs, charts, curves, tables, formulas, and Gallup polls are familiar to everyone who reads the newspapers. These are merely devices for describing special relations in a quantitative fashion. Mathematicians refer to certain types of these relations as *functions*. In this section, we give an informal description of the function concept. A formal definition is given in Section 1.3.

EXAMPLE 1. The force $F$ necessary to stretch a steel spring a distance $x$ beyond its natural length is proportional to $x$. That is, $F = cx$, where $c$ is a number independent of $x$ called the spring constant. This formula, discovered by Robert Hooke in the mid-17th century, is called *Hooke's law*, and it is said to express the force as a function of the displacement.

EXAMPLE 2. The volume of a cube is a function of its edge-length. If the edges have length $x$, the volume $V$ is given by the formula $V = x^3$.

EXAMPLE 3. A *prime* is any integer $n > 1$ that cannot be expressed in the form $n = ab$, where $a$ and $b$ are positive integers, both less than $n$. The first few primes are 2, 3, 5, 7, 11, 13, 17, 19. For a given real number $x > 0$, it is possible to count the number of primes less than or equal to $x$. This number is said to be a function of $x$ even though no simple algebraic formula is known for computing it (without counting) when $x$ is known.

The word "function" was introduced into mathematics by Leibniz, who used the term primarily to refer to certain kinds of mathematical formulas. It was later realized that Leibniz's idea of function was much too limited in its scope, and the meaning of the word has since undergone many stages of generalization. Today, the meaning of function is essentially this: Given two sets, say $X$ and $Y$, a *function* is a correspondence which associates with each element of $X$ one and only one element of $Y$. The set $X$ is called the *domain* of the function. Those elements of $Y$ associated with the elements in $X$ form a set called the *range* of the function. (This may be all of $Y$, but it need not be.)

Letters of the English and Greek alphabets are often used to denote functions. The particular letters $f$, $g$, $h$, $F$, $G$, $H$, and $\varphi$ are frequently used for this purpose. If $f$ is a given function and if $x$ is an object of its domain, the notation $f(x)$ is used to designate that object in the range which is associated to $x$ by the function $f$, and it is called the *value of f at x* or the *image of x under f*. The symbol $f(x)$ is read as "$f$ of $x$."

The function idea may be illustrated schematically in many ways. For example, in Figure 1.3(a) the collections $X$ and $Y$ are thought of as sets of points and an arrow is used to suggest a "pairing" of a typical point $x$ in $X$ with the image point $f(x)$ in $Y$. Another scheme is shown in Figure 1.3(b). Here the function $f$ is imagined to be like a machine into

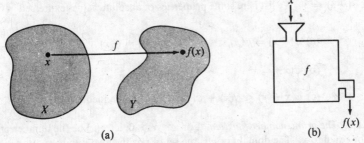

(a)            (b)

FIGURE 1.3   Schematic representations of the function idea.

which objects of the collection $X$ are fed and objects of $Y$ are produced. When an object $x$ is fed into the machine, the output is the object $f(x)$.

Although the function idea places no restriction on the nature of the objects in the domain $X$ and in the range $Y$, in elementary calculus we are primarily interested in functions whose domain and range are sets of real numbers. Such functions are called *real-valued functions of a real variable*, or, more briefly, *real functions*, and they may be illustrated geometrically by a graph in the $xy$-plane. We plot the domain $X$ on the $x$-axis, and above each point $x$ in $X$ we plot the point $(x, y)$, where $y = f(x)$. The totality of such points $(x, y)$ is called the *graph* of the function.

Now we consider some more examples of real functions.

EXAMPLE 4. *The identity function.* Suppose that $f(x) = x$ for all real $x$. This function is often called the *identity function*. Its domain is the real line, that is, the set of all real numbers. Here $x = y$ for each point $(x, y)$ on the graph of $f$. The graph is a straight line making equal angles with the coordinates axes (see Figure 1.4). The range of $f$ is the set of all real numbers.

EXAMPLE 5. *The absolute-value function.* Consider the function which assigns to each real number $x$ the nonnegative number $|x|$. A portion of its graph is shown in Figure 1.5.

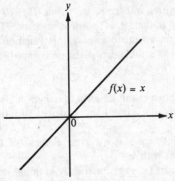

FIGURE 1.4   Graph of the identity function $f(x) = x$.

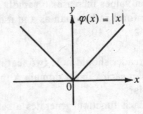

FIGURE 1.5   Absolute-value function $\varphi(x) = |x|$.

Denoting this function by $\varphi$, we have $\varphi(x) = |x|$ for all real $x$. For example, $\varphi(0) = 0$, $\varphi(2) = 2$, $\varphi(-3) = 3$. We list here some properties of absolute values expressed in function notation.

(a) $\varphi(-x) = \varphi(x)$.  (d) $\varphi[\varphi(x)] = \varphi(x)$.

(b) $\varphi(x^2) = x^2$.  (e) $\varphi(x) = \sqrt{x^2}$.

(c) $\varphi(x + y) \leq \varphi(x) + \varphi(y)$  (the triangle inequality).

EXAMPLE 6. *The prime-number function.* For any $x > 0$, let $\pi(x)$ be the number of primes less than or equal to $x$. The domain of $\pi$ is the set of positive real numbers. Its range is the set of nonnegative integers $\{0, 1, 2, \ldots\}$. A portion of the graph of $\pi$ is shown in Figure 1.6.

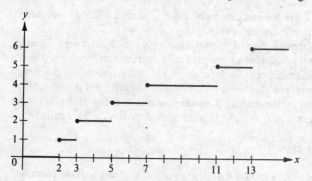

| $n$ | $n!$ | $n$ | $n!$ |
|---|---|---|---|
| 1 | 1 | 6 | 720 |
| 2 | 2 | 7 | 5,040 |
| 3 | 6 | 8 | 40,320 |
| 4 | 24 | 9 | 362,880 |
| 5 | 120 | 10 | 3,628,800 |

FIGURE 1.6   The prime-number function.        FIGURE 1.7   The factorial function.

(Different scales are used on the $x$- and $y$-axes.) As $x$ increases, the function value $\pi(x)$ remains constant until $x$ reaches a prime, at which point the function value jumps by 1. Therefore the graph of $\pi$ consists of horizontal line segments. This is an example of a class of functions called *step functions*; they play a fundamental role in the theory of the integral.

EXAMPLE 7. *The factorial function.* For every positive integer $n$, we define $f(n)$ to be $n! = 1 \cdot 2 \cdots n$. In this example, the domain of $f$ is the set of positive integers. The function values increase so rapidly that it is more convenient to display this function in tabular form rather than as a graph. Figure 1.7 shows a table listing the pairs $(n, n!)$ for $n = 1, 2, \ldots, 10$.

The reader should note two features that all the above examples have in common.

(1) For each $x$ in the domain $X$ there is one and only one image $y$ that is paired with that particular $x$.

(2) Each function generates a set of pairs $(x, y)$, where $x$ is a typical element of the domain $X$, and $y$ is the unique element of $Y$ that goes with $x$.

In most of the above examples, we displayed the pairs $(x, y)$ geometrically as points on a graph. In Example 7 we displayed them as entries in a table. In each case, to know the function is to know, in one way or another, *all* the pairs $(x, y)$ that it generates. This simple observation is the motivation behind the formal definition of the function concept that is given in the next section.

## *1.3 Functions. Formal definition as a set of ordered pairs

In the informal discussion of the foregoing section, a function was described as a correspondence which associates with each object in a set $X$ one and only one object in a set $Y$. The words "correspondence" and "associates with" may not convey exactly the same meaning to all people, so we shall reformulate the whole idea in a different way, basing it on the set concept. First we require the notion of an *ordered pair* of objects.

In the definition of set equality, no mention is made of the *order* in which elements appear. Thus, the sets $\{2,5\}$ and $\{5, 2\}$ are equal because they consist of exactly the same elements. Sometimes the order *is* important. For example, in plane analytic geometry the coordinates $(x, y)$ of a point represent an ordered pair of numbers. The point with coordinates $(2, 5)$ is not the same as the point with coordinates $(5, 2)$, although the *sets* $\{2, 5\}$ and $\{5, 2\}$ are equal. In the same way, if we have a pair of objects $a$ and $b$ (not necessarily distinct) and if we wish to distinguish one of the objects, say $a$, as the *first* member and the other, $b$, as the *second*, we enclose the objects in parentheses, $(a, b)$. We refer to this as an ordered pair. We say that two ordered pairs $(a, b)$ and $(c, d)$ are equal if and only if their first members are equal and their second members are equal. That is to say, we have

$$(a, b) = (c, d) \qquad \text{if and only if} \quad a = c \quad \text{and} \quad b = d.$$

Now we may state the formal definition of function.

DEFINITION OF FUNCTION.    *A function $f$ is a set of ordered pairs $(x, y)$ no two of which have the same first member.*

If $f$ is a function, the set of all elements $x$ that occur as first members of pairs $(x, y)$ in $f$ is called the *domain* of $f$. The set of second members $y$ is called the *range* of $f$, or the set of *values* of $f$.

Intuitively, a function can be thought of as a table consisting of two columns. Each entry in the table is an ordered pair $(x, y)$; the column of $x$'s is the domain of $f$, and the column of $y$'s, the range. If two entries $(x, y)$ and $(x, z)$ appear in the table with the same $x$-value, then for the table to be a function it is necessary that $y = z$. In other words, a function cannot take two different values at a given point $x$. Therefore, for every $x$ in the domain of $f$ there is exactly one $y$ such that $(x, y) \in f$. Since this $y$ is uniquely determined once $x$ is known, we can introduce a special symbol for it. It is customary to write

$$y = f(x)$$

instead of $(x, y) \in f$ to indicate that the pair $(x, y)$ is in the set $f$.

As an alternative to describing a function $f$ by specifying explicitly the pairs it contains, it is usually preferable to describe the domain of $f$, and then, for each $x$ in the domain, to describe how the function value $f(x)$ is obtained. In this connection, we have the following theorem whose proof is left as an exercise for the reader.

THEOREM 1.1.    *Two functions f and g are equal if and only if*
(a) *f and g have the same domain, and*
(b) $f(x) = g(x)$ *for every x in the domain of f.*

It is important to realize that the objects $x$ and $f(x)$ which appear in the ordered pairs $(x, f(x))$ of a function need not be numbers but may be arbitrary objects of any kind. Occasionally we shall use this degree of generality, but for the most part we shall be interested in real functions, that is, functions whose domain and range are subsets of the real line.

Some of the functions that arise in calculus are described in the next few examples.

## 1.4   More examples of real functions

1. *Constant functions.* A function whose range consists of a single number is called a constant function. An example is shown in Figure 1.8, where $f(x) = 3$ for every real $x$. The graph is a horizontal line cutting the $y$-axis at the point $(0, 3)$.

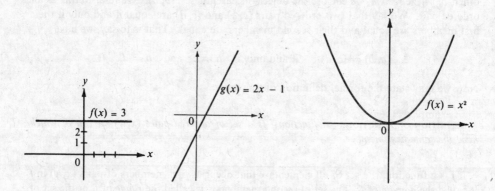

FIGURE 1.8  A constant        FIGURE 1.9  A linear function        FIGURE 1.10  A quadratic
  function $f(x) = 3$.                $g(x) = 2x - 1$.                  polynomial $f(x) = x^2$.

2. *Linear functions.* A function $g$ defined for all real $x$ by a formula of the form

$$g(x) = ax + b$$

is called a linear function because its graph is a straight line. The number $b$ is called the $y$-intercept of the line; it is the $y$-coordinate of the point $(0, b)$ where the line cuts the $y$-axis. The number $a$ is called the slope of the line. One example, $g(x) = x$, is shown in Figure 1.4. Another, $g(x) = 2x - 1$, is shown in Figure 1.9.

3. *The power functions.* For a fixed positive integer $n$, let $f$ be defined by the equation $f(x) = x^n$ for all real $x$. When $n = 1$, this is the identity function, shown in Figure 1.4. For $n = 2$, the graph is a parabola, part of which is shown in Figure 1.10. For $n = 3$, the graph is a cubic curve and has the appearance of that in Figure 1.11 (p. 56).

4. *Polynomial functions.* A polynomial function $P$ is one defined for all real $x$ by an equation of the form

$$P(x) = c_0 + c_1 x + \cdots + c_n x^n = \sum_{k=0}^{n} c_k x^k$$

The numbers $c_0, c_1, \ldots, c_n$ are called the *coefficients* of the polynomial, and the nonnegative integer $n$ is called its *degree* (if $c_n \neq 0$). They include the constant functions and the power functions as special cases. Polynomials of degree 2, 3, and 4 are called *quadratic*, *cubic*, and *quartic* polynomials, respectively. Figure 1.12 shows a portion of the graph of a quartic polynomial $P$ given by $P(x) = \frac{1}{2}x^4 - 2x^2$.

5. *The circle.* Suppose we return to the Cartesian equation of a circle, $x^2 + y^2 = r^2$ and solve this equation for $y$ in terms of $x$. There are two solutions given by

$$y = \sqrt{r^2 - x^2} \quad \text{and} \quad y = -\sqrt{r^2 - x^2}.$$

(We remind the reader that if $a > 0$, the symbol $\sqrt{a}$ denotes the positive square root of $a$. The negative square root is $-\sqrt{a}$.) There was a time when mathematicians would say that $y$ is a *double-valued function* of $x$ given by $y = \pm\sqrt{r^2 - x^2}$. However, the more modern point of view does not admit "double-valuedness" as a property of functions. The definition of function requires that for each $x$ in the domain, there corresponds one and only one $y$ in the range. Geometrically, this means that vertical lines which intersect the graph do so at exactly one point. Therefore to make this example fit the theory, we say that the two solutions for $y$ define *two* functions, say $f$ and $g$, where

$$f(x) = \sqrt{r^2 - x^2} \quad \text{and} \quad g(x) = -\sqrt{r^2 - x^2}$$

for each $x$ satisfying $-r \leq x \leq r$. Each of these functions has for its domain the interval extending from $-r$ to $r$. If $|x| > r$, there is no real $y$ such that $x^2 + y^2 = r^2$, and we say that the functions $f$ and $g$ are *not defined* for such $x$. Since $f(x)$ is the nonnegative square root of $r^2 - x^2$, the graph of $f$ is the upper semicircle shown in Figure 1.13. The function values of $g$ are $\leq 0$, and hence the graph of $g$ is the lower semicircle shown in Figure 1.13.

6. *Sums, products, and quotients of functions.* Let $f$ and $g$ be two real functions having the same domain $D$. We can construct new functions from $f$ and $g$ by adding, multiplying, or dividing the function values. The function $u$ defined by the equation

$$u(x) = f(x) + g(x) \quad \text{if} \quad x \in D$$

is called the *sum* of $f$ and $g$ and is denoted by $f + g$. Similarly, the *product* $v = f \cdot g$ and the *quotient* $w = f/g$ are the functions defined by the respective formulas

$$v(x) = f(x)g(x) \quad \text{if} \quad x \in D, \qquad w(x) = f(x)/g(x) \quad \text{if} \quad x \in D \text{ and } g(x) \neq 0.$$

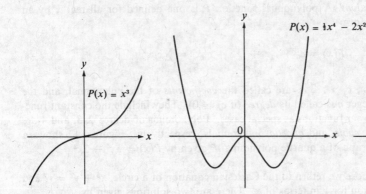

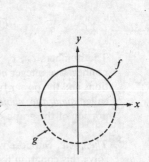

FIGURE 1.11 A cubic polynomial: $P(x) = x^3$.

FIGURE 1.12 A quartic polynomial: $P(x) = \frac{1}{2}x^4 - 2x^2$.

FIGURE 1.13 Graphs of two functions:
$$f(x) = \sqrt{r^2 - x^2},$$
$$g(x) = -\sqrt{r^2 - x^2}.$$

The next set of exercises is intended to give the reader some familiarity with the use of the function notation.

## 1.5 Exercises

1. Let $f(x) = x + 1$ for all real $x$. Compute the following: $f(2)$, $f(-2)$, $-f(2)$, $f(\frac{1}{2})$, $1/f(2)$, $f(a + b)$, $f(a) + f(b)$, $f(a)f(b)$.

2. Let $f(x) = 1 + x$ and let $g(x) = 1 - x$ for all real $x$. Compute the following: $f(2) + g(2)$, $f(2) - g(2)$, $f(2)g(2)$, $f(2)/g(2)$, $f[g(2)]$, $g[f(2)]$, $f(a) + g(-a)$, $f(t)g(-t)$.

3. Let $\varphi(x) = |x - 3| + |x - 1|$ for all real $x$. Compute the following: $\varphi(0)$, $\varphi(1)$, $\varphi(2)$, $\varphi(3)$, $\varphi(-1)$, $\varphi(-2)$. Find all $t$ for which $\varphi(t + 2) = \varphi(t)$.

4. Let $f(x) = x^2$ for all real $x$. Verify each of the following formulas. In each case describe the set of real $x$, $y$, $t$, etc., for which the given formula is valid.
   (a) $f(-x) = f(x)$.
   (b) $f(y) - f(x) = (y - x)(y + x)$.
   (c) $f(x + h) - f(x) = 2xh + h^2$.
   (d) $f(2y) = 4f(y)$.
   (e) $f(t^2) = f(t)^2$.
   (f) $\sqrt{f(a)} = |a|$.

5. Let $g(x) = \sqrt{4 - x^2}$ for $|x| \leq 2$. Verify each of the following formulas and tell for which values of $x$, $y$, $s$, and $t$ the given formula is valid.
   (a) $g(-x) = g(x)$.
   (b) $g(2y) = 2\sqrt{1 - y^2}$.
   (c) $g\left(\dfrac{1}{t}\right) = \dfrac{\sqrt{4t^2 - 1}}{|t|}$.
   (d) $g(a - 2) = \sqrt{4a - a^2}$.
   (e) $g\left(\dfrac{s}{2}\right) = \frac{1}{2}\sqrt{16 - s^2}$.
   (f) $\dfrac{1}{2 + g(x)} = \dfrac{2 - g(x)}{x^2}$.

6. Let $f$ be defined as follows: $f(x) = 1$ for $0 \leq x \leq 1$; $f(x) = 2$ for $1 < x \leq 2$. The function is not defined if $x < 0$ or if $x > 2$.
   (a) Draw the graph of $f$.
   (b) Let $g(x) = f(2x)$. Describe the domain of $g$ and draw its graph.
   (c) Let $h(x) = f(x - 2)$. Describe the domain of $h$ and draw its graph.
   (d) Let $k(x) = f(2x) + f(x - 2)$. Describe the domain of $k$ and draw its graph.

7. The graphs of the two polynomials $g(x) = x$ and $f(x) = x^3$ intersect at three points. Draw enough of their graphs to show how they intersect.

8. The graphs of the two quadratic polynomials $f(x) = x^2 - 2$ and $g(x) = 2x^2 + 4x + 1$ intersect at two points. Draw the portions of the two graphs between the points of intersection.

9. This exercise develops some fundamental properties of polynomials. Let $f(x) = \sum_{k=0}^{n} c_k x^k$ be a polynomial of degree $n$. Prove each of the following:

   (a) If $n \geq 1$ and $f(0) = 0$, then $f(x) = xg(x)$, where $g$ is a polynomial of degree $n - 1$.

   (b) For each real $a$, the function $p$ given by $p(x) = f(x + a)$ is a polynomial of degree $n$.

   (c) If $n \geq 1$ and $f(a) = 0$ for some real $a$, then $f(x) = (x - a)h(x)$, where $h$ is a polynomial of degree $n - 1$. [*Hint:* Consider $p(x) = f(x + a)$.]

   (d) If $f(x) = 0$ for $n + 1$ distinct real values of $x$, then every coefficient $c_k$ is zero and $f(x) = 0$ for all real $x$.

   (e) Let $g(x) = \sum_{k=0}^{m} b_k x^k$ be a polynomial of degree $m$, where $m \geq n$. If $g(x) = f(x)$ for $m + 1$ distinct real values of $x$, then $m = n$, $b_k = c_k$ for each $k$, and $g(x) = f(x)$ for all real $x$.

10. In each case, find all polynomials $p$ of degree $\leq 2$ which satisfy the given conditions.

    (a) $p(0) = p(1) = p(2) = 1$.    (c) $p(0) = p(1) = 1$.

    (b) $p(0) = p(1) = 1, p(2) = 2$.    (d) $p(0) = p(1)$.

11. In each case, find all polynomials $p$ of degree $\leq 2$ which satisfy the given conditions for all real $x$.

    (a) $p(x) = p(1 - x)$.    (c) $p(2x) = 2p(x)$.

    (b) $p(x) = p(1 + x)$.    (d) $p(3x) = p(x + 3)$.

12. Show that the following are polynomials by converting them to the form $\sum_{k=0}^{m} a_k x^k$ for a suitable $m$. In each case $n$ is a positive integer.

    (a) $(1 + x)^{2n}$.    (b) $\dfrac{1 - x^{n+1}}{1 - x}$,    $x \neq 1$.    (c) $\prod_{k=0}^{n} (1 + x^{2^k})$.

## 1.6 The concept of area as a set function

When a mathematician attempts to develop a general theory encompassing many different concepts, he tries to isolate common properties which seem to be basic to each of the particular applications he has in mind. He then uses these properties as fundamental building blocks of his theory. Euclid used this process when he developed elementary geometry as a deductive system based on a set of axioms. We used the same process in our axiomatic treatment of the real number system, and we shall use it once more in our discussion of area.

When we assign an area to a plane region, we associate a number with a set $S$ in the plane. From a purely mathematical viewpoint, this means that we have a function $a$ (an area function) which assigns a real number $a(S)$ (the area of $S$) to each set $S$ in some given collection of sets. A function of this kind, whose domain is a collection of sets and whose function values are real numbers, is called a *set function*. The basic problem is this: Given a plane set $S$, what area $a(S)$ shall we assign to $S$?

Our approach to this problem is to start with a number of properties we feel area should have and take these as *axioms* for area. Any set function which satisfies these axioms will be called an area function. To make certain we are not discussing an empty theory, it is necessary to show that an area function actually exists. We shall not attempt to do this here. Instead, we assume the existence of an area function and deduce further properties from the axioms. An elementary construction of an area function may be found in Chapters 14 and 22 of Edwin E. Moise, *Elementary Geometry From An Advanced Standpoint*, Addison-Wesley Publishing Co., 1963.

Before we state the axioms for area, we will make a few remarks about the collection of sets in the plane to which an area can be assigned. These sets will be called *measurable* sets; the collection of all measurable sets will be denoted by $\mathcal{M}$. The axioms contain enough information about the sets in $\mathcal{M}$ to enable us to prove that all geometric figures arising in the usual applications of calculus are in $\mathcal{M}$ and that their areas can be calculated by integration.

One of the axioms (Axiom 5) states that every rectangle is measurable and that its area is the product of the lengths of its edges. The term "rectangle" as used here refers to any set congruent† to a set of the form

$$\{(x, y) \mid 0 \leq x \leq h, 0 \leq y \leq k\},$$

where $h \geq 0$ and $k \geq 0$. The numbers $h$ and $k$ are called the lengths of the edges of the rectangle. We consider a line segment or a point to be a special case of a rectangle by allowing $h$ or $k$ (or both) to be zero.

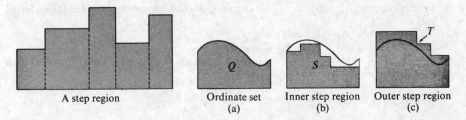

A step region

FIGURE 1.14

Ordinate set
(a)

Inner step region
(b)

Outer step region
(c)

FIGURE 1.15   An ordinate set enclosed by two step regions.

From rectangles we can build up more complicated sets. The set shown in Figure 1.14 is the union of a finite collection of adjacent rectangles with their bases resting on the $x$-axis and is called a *step region*. The axioms imply that each step region is measurable and that its area is the sum of the areas of the rectangular pieces.

The region $Q$ shown in Figure 1.15(a) is an example of an *ordinate set*. Its upper boundary is the graph of a nonnegative function. Axiom 6 will enable us to prove that many ordinate sets are measurable and that their areas can be calculated by approximating such sets by inner and outer step regions, as shown in Figure 1.15(b) and (c).

We turn now to the axioms themselves.

AXIOMATIC DEFINITION OF AREA. *We assume there exists a class $\mathcal{M}$ of measurable sets in the plane and a set function $a$, whose domain is $\mathcal{M}$, with the following properties:*

*1. Nonnegative property. For each set $S$ in $\mathcal{M}$, we have $a(S) \geq 0$.*

---

† Congruence is used here in the same sense as in elementary Euclidean geometry. Two sets are said to be congruent if their points can be put in one-to-one correspondence in such a way that distances are preserved. That is, if two points $p$ and $q$ in one set correspond to $p'$ and $q'$ in the other, the distance from $p$ to $q$ must be equal to the distance from $p'$ to $q'$; this must be true for all choices of $p$ and $q$.

2. *Additive property. If S and T are in $\mathcal{M}$, then $S \cup T$ and $S \cap T$ are in $\mathcal{M}$, and we have*

$$a(S \cup T) = a(S) + a(T) - a(S \cap T).$$

3. *Difference property. If S and T are in $\mathcal{M}$ with $S \subseteq T$, then $T - S$ is in $\mathcal{M}$, and we have $a(T - S) = a(T) - a(S)$.*

4. *Invariance under congruence. If a set S is in $\mathcal{M}$ and if T is congruent to S, then T is also in $\mathcal{M}$ and we have $a(S) = a(T)$.*

5. *Choice of scale. Every rectangle R is in $\mathcal{M}$. If the edges of R have lengths h and k, then $a(R) = hk$.*

6. *Exhaustion property. Let Q be a set that can be enclosed between two step regions S and T, so that*

(1.1) $$S \subseteq Q \subseteq T.$$

*If there is one and only one number c which satisfies the inequalities*

$$a(S) \leq c \leq a(T)$$

*for all step regions S and T satisfying (1.1), then Q is measurable and $a(Q) = c$.*

Axiom 1 simply states that the area of a plane measurable set is either a positive number or zero. Axiom 2 tells us that when a set is formed from two pieces (which may overlap), the area of the union is the sum of the areas of the two parts minus the area of their intersection. In particular, if the intersection has zero area, the area of the whole is the sum of the areas of the two parts.

If we remove a measurable set $S$ from a larger measurable set $T$, Axiom 3 states that the remaining part, $T - S$, is measurable and its area is obtained by subtraction, $a(T - S) = a(T) - a(S)$. In particular, this axiom implies that the empty set $\varnothing$ is measurable and has zero area. Since $a(T - S) \geq 0$, Axiom 3 also implies the *monotone property*:

$$a(S) \leq a(T), \qquad \text{for sets } S \text{ and } T \text{ in } \mathcal{M} \text{ with } S \subseteq T.$$

In other words, a set which is part of another cannot have a larger area.

Axiom 4 assigns equal areas to sets having the same size and shape. The first four axioms would be trivially satisfied if we assigned the number 0 as the area of every set in $\mathcal{M}$. Axiom 5 assigns a nonzero area to some rectangles and thereby excludes this trivial case. Finally, Axiom 6 incorporates the Greek method of exhaustion; it enables us to extend the class of measurable sets from step regions to more general regions.

Axiom 5 assigns zero area to each line segment. Repeated use of the additive property shows that every step region is measurable and that its area is the sum of the areas of the rectangular pieces. Further elementary consequences of the axioms are discussed in the next set of exercises.

## 1.7 Exercises

The properties of area in this set of exercises are to be deduced from the axioms for area stated in the foregoing section.

1. Prove that each of the following sets is measurable and has zero area: (a) A set consisting of a single point. (b) A set consisting of a finite number of points in a plane. (c) The union of a finite collection of line segments in a plane.

2. Every right triangular region is measurable because it can be obtained as the intersection of two rectangles. Prove that every triangular region is measurable and that its area is one half the product of its base and altitude.

3. Prove that every trapezoid and every parallelogram is measurable and derive the usual formulas for their areas.

4. A point $(x, y)$ in the plane is called a *lattice point* if both coordinates $x$ and $y$ are integers. Let $P$ be a polygon whose vertices are lattice points. The area of $P$ is $I + \frac{1}{2}B - 1$, where $I$ denotes the number of lattice points inside the polygon and $B$ denotes the number on the boundary.
   (a) Prove that the formula is valid for rectangles with sides parallel to the coordinate axes.
   (b) Prove that the formula is valid for right triangles and parallelograms.
   (c) Use induction on the number of edges to construct a proof for general polygons.

5. Prove that a triangle whose vertices are lattice points cannot be equilateral.

   [*Hint:* Assume there is such a triangle and compute its area in two ways, using Exercises 2 and 4.]

6. Let $A = \{1, 2, 3, 4, 5\}$, and let $\mathscr{M}$ denote the class of all subsets of $A$. (There are 32 altogether, counting $A$ itself and the empty set $\varnothing$.) For each set $S$ in $\mathscr{M}$, let $n(S)$ denote the number of distinct elements in $S$. If $S = \{1, 2, 3, 4\}$ and $T = \{3, 4, 5\}$, compute $n(S \cup T)$, $n(S \cap T)$, $n(S - T)$, and $n(T - S)$. Prove that the set function $n$ satisfies the first three axioms for area.

## 1.8 Intervals and ordinate sets

In the theory of integration we are concerned primarily with real functions whose domains are intervals on the $x$-axis. Sometimes it is important to distinguish between intervals which include their endpoints and those which do not. This distinction is made by introducing the following definitions.

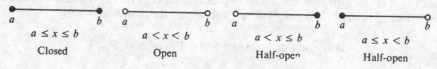

$$a \leq x \leq b \qquad a < x < b \qquad a < x \leq b \qquad a \leq x < b$$
$$\text{Closed} \qquad\qquad \text{Open} \qquad\qquad \text{Half-open} \qquad\qquad \text{Half-open}$$

FIGURE 1.16  Examples of intervals.

If $a < b$, we denote by $[a, b]$ the set of all $x$ satisfying the inequalities $a \leq x \leq b$ and refer to this set as the *closed interval* from $a$ to $b$. The corresponding *open interval*, written $(a, b)$, is the set of all $x$ satisfying $a < x < b$. The closed interval $[a, b]$ includes the endpoints $a$ and $b$, whereas the open interval does not. (See Figure 1.16.) The open interval $(a, b)$ is also called the *interior* of $[a, b]$. Half-open intervals $(a, b]$ and $[a, b)$, which include just one endpoint are defined by the inequalities $a < x \leq b$ and $a \leq x < b$, respectively.

Let $f$ be a nonnegative function whose domain is a closed interval $[a, b]$. The portion of the plane between the graph of $f$ and the $x$-axis is called the *ordinate set* of $f$. More precisely, the ordinate set of $f$ is the collection of all points $(x, y)$ satisfying the inequalities

$$a \leq x \leq b, \quad 0 \leq y \leq f(x).$$

In each of the examples shown in Figure 1.17 the shaded portion represents the ordinate set of the corresponding function.

Ordinate sets are the geometric objects whose areas we want to compute by means of the integral calculus. We shall define the concept of integral first for step functions and then use the integral of a step function to formulate the definition of integral for more general

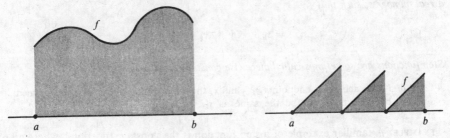

FIGURE 1.17 Examples of ordinate sets.

functions. Integration theory for step functions is extremely simple and leads in a natural way to the corresponding theory for more general functions. To start this program, it is necessary to have an analytic definition of a step function. This may be given most simply in terms of the concept of a *partition*, to which we turn now.

## 1.9 Partitions and step functions

Suppose we decompose a given closed interval $[a, b]$ into $n$ subintervals by inserting $n - 1$ points of subdivision, say $x_1, x_2, \ldots, x_{n-1}$, subject only to the restriction

$$(1.2) \qquad a < x_1 < x_2 < \cdots < x_{n-1} < b.$$

It is convenient to denote the point $a$ itself by $x_0$ and the point $b$ by $x_n$. A collection of points satisfying (1.2) is called a *partition* $P$ of $[a, b]$, and we use the symbol

$$P = \{x_0, x_1, \ldots, x_n\}$$

to designate this partition. The partition $P$ determines $n$ closed subintervals

$$[x_0, x_1], [x_1, x_2], \ldots, [x_{n-1}, x_n].$$

A typical closed subinterval is $[x_{k-1}, x_k]$, and it is referred to as the $k$th closed subinterval of $P$; an example is shown in Figure 1.18. The corresponding open interval $(x_{k-1}, x_k)$ is called the $k$th open subinterval of $P$.

Now we are ready to formulate an analytic definition of a step function.

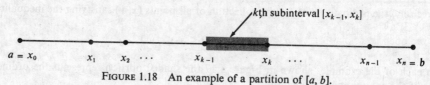

FIGURE 1.18    An example of a partition of $[a, b]$.

DEFINITION OF A STEP FUNCTION.    *A function s, whose domain is a closed interval $[a, b]$, is called a step function if there is a partition $P = \{x_0, x_1, \ldots, x_n\}$ of $[a, b]$ such that s is constant on each open subinterval of P.    That is to say, for each $k = 1, 2, \ldots, n$, there is a real number $s_k$ such that*

$$s(x) = s_k \quad if \quad x_{k-1} < x < x_k.$$

*Step functions are sometimes called piecewise constant functions.*

> *Note:*  At each of the endpoints $x_{k-1}$ and $x_k$ the function must have some well-defined value, but this need not be the same as $s_k$.

EXAMPLE.    A familiar example of a step function is the "postage function," whose graph is shown in Figure 1.19. Assume that the charge for first-class mail for parcels weighing up to 20 pounds is 5 cents for every ounce or fraction thereof.  The graph shows the number of 5-cent stamps required for mail weighing up to 4 ounces.  In this case the line segments on the graph are half-open intervals containing their right endpoints.  The domain of the function is the interval $[0, 320]$.

From a given partition $P$ of $[a, b]$, we can always form a new partition $P'$ by adjoining more subdivision points to those already in $P$.  Such a partition $P'$ is called a *refinement* of $P$ and is said to be *finer than P*.  For example, $P = \{0, 1, 2, 3, 4\}$ is a partition of the interval $[0, 4]$. If we adjoin the points $3/4$, $\sqrt{2}$, and $7/2$, we obtain a new partition $P'$ of

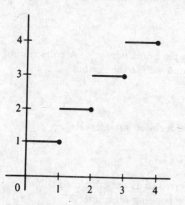

FIGURE 1.19    The postage function.

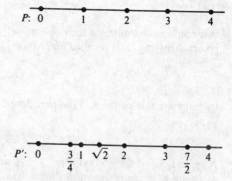

FIGURE 1.20    A partition $P$ of $[0, 4]$ and a refinement $P'$.

[0, 4], namely, $P' = \{0, 3/4, 1, \sqrt{2}, 2, 3, 7/2, 4\}$, which is a refinement of $P$. (See Figure 1.20.) If a step function is constant on the open subintervals of $P$, then it is also constant on the open subintervals of every refinement $P'$.

## 1.10 Sum and product of step functions

New step functions may be formed from given step functions by adding corresponding function values. For example, suppose $s$ and $t$ are step functions, both defined on the same interval $[a, b]$. Let $P_1$ and $P_2$ be partitions of $[a, b]$ such that $s$ is constant on the open subintervals of $P_1$ and $t$ is constant on the open subintervals of $P_2$. Let $u = s + t$ be the function defined by the equation

$$u(x) = s(x) + t(x) \quad \text{if} \quad a \leq x \leq b.$$

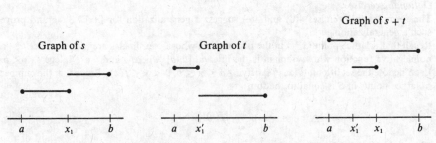

FIGURE 1.21 The sum of two step functions.

To show that $u$ is actually a step function, we must exhibit a partition $P$ such that $u$ is constant on the open subintervals of $P$. For the new partition $P$, we take all the points of $P_1$ along with all the points of $P_2$. This partition, the union of $P_1$ and $P_2$, is called the *common refinement* of $P_1$ and $P_2$. Since both $s$ and $t$ are constant on the open subintervals of the common refinement, the same is true of $u$. An example is illustrated in Figure 1.21. The partition $P_1$ is $\{a, x_1, b\}$, the partition $P_2$ is $\{a, x_1', b\}$, and the common refinement is $\{a, x_1', x_1, b\}$.

Similarly, the product $v = s \cdot t$ of two step functions is another step function. An important special case occurs when one of the factors, say $t$, is constant throughout $[a, b]$. If $t(x) = c$ for each $x$ in $[a, b]$, then each function value $v(x)$ is obtained by multiplying the step function $s(x)$ by the constant $c$.

## 1.11 Exercises

In this set of exercises, $[x]$ denotes the greatest integer $\leq x$.

1. Let $f(x) = [x]$ and let $g(x) = [2x]$ for all real $x$. In each case, draw the graph of the function $h$ defined over the interval $[-1, 2]$ by the formula given.
   (a) $h(x) = f(x) + g(x)$.   (c) $h(x) = f(x)g(x)$.
   (b) $h(x) = f(x) + g(x/2)$.   (d) $h(x) = \frac{1}{4}f(2x)g(x/2)$.
2. In each case, $f$ is a function defined over the interval $[-2, 2]$ by the formula given. Draw the graph of $f$. If $f$ is a step function, find a partition $P$ of $[-2, 2]$ such that $f$ is constant on the open subintervals of $P$.

(a) $f(x) = x + [x]$.      (d) $f(x) = 2[x]$.

(b) $f(x) = x - [x]$.      (e) $f(x) = [x + \frac{1}{2}]$.

(c) $f(x) = [-x]$.         (f) $f(x) = [x] + [x + \frac{1}{2}]$.

3. In each case, sketch the graph of the function $f$ defined by the formula given.

   (a) $f(x) = [\sqrt{x}]$   for   $0 \le x \le 10$.   (c) $f(x) = \sqrt{[x]}$   for   $0 \le x \le 10$.

   (b) $f(x) = [x^2]$   for   $0 \le x \le 3$.   (d) $f(x) = [x]^2$   for   $0 \le x \le 3$.

4. Prove that the greatest-integer function has the properties indicated.

   (a) $[x + n] = [x] + n$ for every integer $n$.

   (b) $[-x] = \begin{cases} -[x] & \text{if } x \text{ is an integer,} \\ -[x] - 1 & \text{otherwise.} \end{cases}$

   (c) $[x + y] = [x] + [y]$   or   $[x] + [y] + 1$.

   (d) $[2x] = [x] + [x + \frac{1}{2}]$.

   (e) $[3x] = [x] + [x + \frac{1}{3}] + [x + \frac{2}{3}]$.

*Optional exercises.*

5. The formulas in Exercises 4(d) and 4(e) suggest a generalization for $[nx]$. State and prove such a generalization.

6. Recall that a lattice point $(x, y)$ in the plane is one whose coordinates are integers. Let $f$ be a nonnegative function whose domain is the interval $[a, b]$, where $a$ and $b$ are integers, $a < b$. Let $S$ denote the set of points $(x, y)$ satisfying $a \le x \le b, 0 < y \le f(x)$. Prove that the number of lattice points in $S$ is equal to the sum

$$\sum_{n=a}^{b} [f(n)].$$

7. If $a$ and $b$ are positive integers with no common factor, we have the formula

$$\sum_{n=1}^{b-1} \left[ \frac{na}{b} \right] = \frac{(a - 1)(b - 1)}{2}.$$

When $b = 1$, the sum on the left is understood to be 0.

   (a) Derive this result by a geometric argument, counting lattice points in a right triangle.

   (b) Derive the result analytically as follows: By changing the index of summation, note that $\sum_{n=1}^{b-1} [na/b] = \sum_{n=1}^{b-1} [a(b - n)/b]$. Now apply Exercises 4(a) and (b) to the bracket on the right.

8. Let $S$ be a set of points on the real line. The *characteristic function* of $S$ is, by definition, the function $\chi_S$ such that $\chi_S(x) = 1$ for every $x$ in $S$, and $\chi_S(x) = 0$ for those $x$ not in $S$. Let $f$ be a step function which takes the constant value $c_k$ on the $k$th open subinterval $I_k$ of some partition of an interval $[a, b]$. Prove that for each $x$ in the union $I_1 \cup I_2 \cup \cdots \cup I_n$ we have

$$f(x) = \sum_{k=1}^{n} c_k \chi_{I_k}(x).$$

This property is described by saying that every step function is a linear combination of characteristic functions of intervals.

## 1.12   The definition of the integral for step functions

In this section we introduce the integral for step functions. The definition is constructed so that the integral of a nonnegative step function is equal to the area of its ordinate set.

Let $s$ be a step function defined on $[a, b]$, and let $P = \{x_0, x_1, \ldots, x_n\}$ be a partition of $[a, b]$ such that $s$ is constant on the open subintervals of $P$. Denote by $s_k$ the constant value that $s$ takes in the $k$th open subinterval, so that

$$s(x) = s_k \quad \text{if} \quad x_{k-1} < x < x_k, \quad k = 1, 2, \ldots, n.$$

DEFINITION OF THE INTEGRAL OF STEP FUNCTIONS. *The integral of $s$ from $a$ to $b$, denoted by the symbol $\int_a^b s(x)\, dx$, is defined by the following formula:*

(1.3)
$$\int_a^b s(x)\, dx = \sum_{k=1}^n s_k \cdot (x_k - x_{k-1}).$$

That is to say, to compute the integral, we multiply each constant value $s_k$ by the length of the $k$th subinterval, and then we add together all these products.

Note that the values of $s$ at the subdivision points are immaterial since they do not appear on the right-hand side of (1.3). In particular, if $s$ is constant on the open interval $(a, b)$, say $s(x) = c$ if $a < x < b$, then we have

$$\int_a^b s(x)\, dx = c \sum_{k=1}^n (x_k - x_{k-1}) = c(b - a),$$

regardless of the values $s(a)$ and $s(b)$. If $c > 0$ and if $s(x) = c$ for all $x$ in the closed interval $[a, b]$, the ordinate set of $s$ is a rectangle of base $b - a$ and altitude $c$; the integral of $s$ is $c(b - a)$, the area of this rectangle. Changing the value of $s$ at one or both endpoints $a$ or $b$ changes the ordinate set but does not alter the integral of $s$ or the area of its ordinate set. For example, the two ordinate sets shown in Figure 1.22 have equal areas.

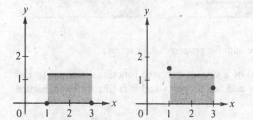
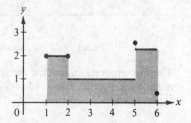

FIGURE 1.22 Changes in function values at two points do not alter area of ordinate set.

FIGURE 1.23 The ordinate set of a step function.

The ordinate set of any nonnegative step function $s$ consists of a finite number of rectangles, one for each interval of constancy; the ordinate set may also contain or lack certain vertical line segments, depending on how $s$ is defined at the subdivision points. The integral of $s$ is equal to the sum of the areas of the individual rectangles, regardless of the values $s$ takes at the subdivision points. This is consistent with the fact that the vertical segments have zero area and make no contribution to the area of the ordinate set. In Figure 1.23, the step function $s$ takes the constant values 2, 1, and $\frac{9}{4}$ in the open intervals $(1, 2)$, $(2, 5)$, and $(5, 6)$, respectively. Its integral is equal to

$$\int_1^6 s(x)\, dx = 2 \cdot (2 - 1) + 1 \cdot (5 - 2) + \tfrac{9}{4} \cdot (6 - 5) = \tfrac{29}{4}.$$

It should be noted that the formula for the integral in (1.3) is independent of the choice of the partition $P$ as long as $s$ is constant on the open subintervals of $P$. For example, suppose we change from $P$ to a finer partition $P'$ by inserting exactly one new subdivision point $t$, where $x_0 < t < x_1$. Then the first term on the right of (1.3) is replaced by the two terms $s_1 \cdot (t - x_0)$ and $s_1 \cdot (x_1 - t)$, and the rest of the terms are unchanged. Since

$$s_1 \cdot (t - x_0) + s_1 \cdot (x_1 - t) = s_1 \cdot (x_1 - x_0),$$

the value of the entire sum is unchanged. We can proceed from $P$ to any finer partition $P'$ by inserting the new subdivision points one at a time. At each stage, the sum in (1.3) remains unchanged, so the integral is the same for all refinements of $P$.

### 1.13   Properties of the integral of a step function

In this section we describe a number of fundamental properties satisfied by the integral of a step function. Most of these properties seem obvious when they are interpreted geometrically, and some of them may even seem trivial. All these properties carry over to integrals of more general functions, and it will be a simple matter to prove them in the general case once we have established them for step functions. The properties are listed below as theorems, and in each case a geometric interpretation for nonnegative step functions is given in terms of areas. Analytic proofs of the theorems are outlined in Section 1.15.

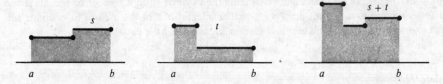

FIGURE 1.24   Illustrating the additive property of the integral.

The first property states that the integral of a sum of two step functions is equal to the sum of the integrals. This is known as the *additive* property and it is illustrated in Figure 1.24.

THEOREM 1.2.   ADDITIVE PROPERTY.

$$\int_a^b [s(x) + t(x)] \, dx = \int_a^b s(x) \, dx + \int_a^b t(x) \, dx.$$

The next property, illustrated in Figure 1.25, is called the *homogeneous* property. It states that if all the function values are multiplied by a constant $c$, then the integral is also multiplied by $c$.

THEOREM 1.3.   HOMOGENEOUS PROPERTY.   *For every real number $c$, we have*

$$\int_a^b c \cdot s(x) \, dx = c \int_a^b s(x) \, dx.$$

These two theorems can be combined into one formula known as the linearity property.

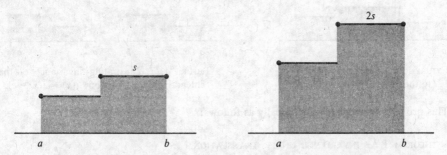

FIGURE 1.25   Illustrating the homogeneous property of the integral (with $c = 2$).

THEOREM 1.4.   LINEARITY PROPERTY.   *For every real $c_1$ and $c_2$, we have*

$$\int_a^b [c_1 s(x) + c_2 t(x)]\, dx = c_1 \int_a^b s(x)\, dx + c_2 \int_a^b t(x)\, dx\,.$$

Next, we have a *comparison* theorem which tells us that if one step function has larger values than another throughout $[a, b]$, its integral over this interval is also larger.

THEOREM 1.5.   COMPARISON THEOREM.   *If $s(x) < t(x)$ for every $x$ in $[a, b]$, then*

$$\int_a^b s(x)\, dx < \int_a^b t(x)\, dx\,.$$

Interpreted geometrically, this theorem reflects the monotone property of area. If the ordinate set of a nonnegative step function lies inside another, the area of the smaller region is less than that of the larger.

The foregoing properties all refer to step functions defined on a common interval. The integral has further important properties that relate integrals over different intervals. Among these we have the following.

THEOREM 1.6.   ADDITIVITY WITH RESPECT TO THE INTERVAL OF INTEGRATION.

$$\int_a^c s(x)\, dx + \int_c^b s(x)\, dx = \int_a^b s(x)\, dx \qquad if \qquad a < c < b\,.$$

This theorem reflects the additive property of area, illustrated in Figure 1.26. If an ordinate set is decomposed into two ordinate sets, the sum of the areas of the two parts is equal to the area of the whole.

The next theorem may be described as *invariance under translation*. If the ordinate set of a step function $s$ is "shifted" by an amount $c$, the resulting ordinate set is that of another step function $t$ related to $s$ by the equation $t(x) = s(x - c)$. If $s$ is defined on $[a, b]$, then $t$ is defined on $[a + c, b + c]$, and their ordinate sets, being congruent, have equal areas.

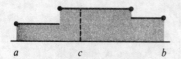

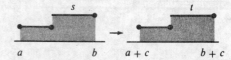

FIGURE 1.26   Additivity with respect
to the interval of integration.

FIGURE 1.27   Illustrating invariance of the
integral under translation: $t(x) = s(x - c)$.

This property is expressed analytically as follows:

THEOREM 1.7.   INVARIANCE UNDER TRANSLATION.

$$\int_a^b s(x)\, dx = \int_{a+c}^{b+c} s(x - c)\, dx \qquad for\ every\ real\ c\,.$$

Its geometric meaning is illustrated in Figure 1.27 for $c > 0$. When $c < 0$, the ordinate set is shifted to the left.

The homogeneous property (Theorem 1.3) explains what happens to an integral under a change of scale on the $y$-axis. The following theorem deals with a change of scale on the $x$-axis. If $s$ is a step function defined on an interval $[a, b]$ and if we distort the scale in the horizontal direction by multiplying all $x$-coordinates by a factor $k > 0$, then the new graph is that of another step function $t$ defined on the interval $[ka, kb]$ and related to $s$ by the equation

$$t(x) = s\left(\frac{x}{k}\right) \qquad if \qquad ka \leq x \leq kb\,.$$

An example with $k = 2$ is shown in Figure 1.28 and it suggests that the distorted figure has an area twice that of the original figure. More generally, distortion by a positive factor $k$

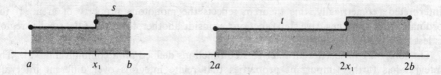

FIGURE 1.28   Change of scale on the $x$-axis: $t(x) = s(x/2)$.

has the effect of multiplying the integral by $k$. Expressed analytically, this property assumes the following form:

THEOREM 1.8.   EXPANSION OR CONTRACTION OF THE INTERVAL OF INTEGRATION.

$$\int_{ka}^{kb} s\left(\frac{x}{k}\right) dx = k \int_a^b s(x)\, dx \qquad for\ every\ k > 0\,.$$

Until now, when we have used the symbol $\int_a^b$, it has been understood that the lower limit $a$ was less than the upper limit $b$. It is convenient to extend our ideas somewhat and consider integrals with a lower limit larger than the upper limit. This is done by defining

(1.4) $$\int_b^a s(x)\, dx = -\int_a^b s(x)\, dx \qquad if \qquad a < b\,.$$

We also define

$$\int_a^a s(x)\,dx = 0\,,$$

a definition that is suggested by putting $a = b$ in (1.4). These conventions allow us to conclude that Theorem 1.6 is valid not only when $c$ is between $a$ and $b$ but for any arrangement of the points $a$, $b$, $c$. Theorem 1.6 is sometimes written in the form

$$\int_a^c s(x)\,dx + \int_c^b s(x)\,dx + \int_b^a s(x)\,dx = 0\,.$$

Similarly, we can extend the range of validity of Theorem 1.8 and allow the constant $k$ to be negative. In particular, when $k = -1$, Theorem 1.8 and Equation (1.4) give us

$$\int_a^b s(x)\,dx = \int_{-b}^{-a} s(-x)\,dx\,.$$

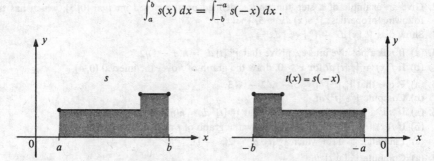

FIGURE 1.29  Illustrating the reflection property of the integral.

We shall refer to this as the *reflection property* of the integral, since the graph of the function $t$ given by $t(x) = s(-x)$ is obtained from that of $s$ by reflection through the $y$-axis. An example is shown in Figure 1.29.

### 1.14  Other notations for integrals

The letter $x$ that appears in the symbol $\int_a^b s(x)\,dx$ plays no essential role in the definition of the integral. Any other letter would serve equally well. The letters $t$, $u$, $v$, $z$ are frequently used for this purpose, and it is agreed that instead of $\int_a^b s(x)\,dx$ we may write $\int_a^b s(t)\,dt$, $\int_a^b s(u)\,du$, etc., all these being considered as alternative notations for the same thing. The symbols $x$, $t$, $u$, etc. that are used in this way are called "dummy variables." They are analogous to dummy indices used in the summation notation.

There is a tendency among some authors of calculus textbooks to omit the dummy variable and the $d$-symbol altogether and to write simply $\int_a^b s$ for the integral. One good reason for using this abbreviated symbol is that it suggests more strongly that the integral depends only on the *function s* and on the *interval* $[a, b]$. Also, certain formulas appear simpler in this notation. For example, the additive property becomes $\int_a^b (s + t) = \int_a^b s + \int_a^b t$. On the other hand, it becomes awkward to write formulas like Theorems 1.7 and 1.8 in the abbreviated notation. More important than this, we shall find later that the original Leibniz notation has certain practical advantages. The symbol $dx$, which appears to be rather superfluous at this stage, turns out to be an extremely useful computational device in connection with many routine calculations with integrals.

## 1.15  Exercises

1. Compute the value of each of the following integrals. You may use the theorems of Section 1.13 whenever it is convenient to do so. The notation $[x]$ denotes the greatest integer $\le x$.

   (a) $\int_{-1}^{3} [x]\, dx.$          (d) $\int_{-1}^{3} 2[x]\, dx.$

   (b) $\int_{-1}^{3} [x + \frac{1}{2}]\, dx.$        (e) $\int_{-1}^{3} [2x]\, dx.$

   (c) $\int_{-1}^{3} ([x] + [x + \frac{1}{2}])\, dx.$    (f) $\int_{-1}^{3} [-x]\, dx.$

2. Give an example of a step function $s$, defined on the closed interval $[0, 5]$, which has the following properties: $\int_{0}^{3} s(x)\, dx = 5$, $\int_{0}^{5} s(x)\, dx = 2$.

3. Show that $\int_{a}^{b} [x]\, dx + \int_{a}^{b} [-x]\, dx = a - b.$

4. (a) If $n$ is a positive integer, prove that $\int_{0}^{n} [t]\, dt = n(n - 1)/2.$

   (b) If $f(x) = \int_{0}^{x} [t]\, dt$ for $x \ge 0$, draw the graph of $f$ over the interval $[0, 4]$.

5. (a) Prove that $\int_{0}^{2} [t^2]\, dt = 5 - \sqrt{2} - \sqrt{3}.$

   (b) Compute $\int_{-3}^{3} [t^2]\, dt.$

6. (a) If $n$ is a positive integer, prove that $\int_{0}^{n} [t]^2\, dt = n(n - 1)(2n - 1)/6.$

   (b) If $f(x) = \int_{0}^{x} [t]^2\, dt$ for $x \ge 0$, draw the graph of $f$ over the interval $[0, 3]$.

   (c) Find all $x > 0$ for which $\int_{0}^{x} [t]^2\, dt = 2(x - 1).$

7. (a) Compute $\int_{0}^{9} [\sqrt{t}]\, dt.$

   (b) If $n$ is a positive integer, prove that $\int_{0}^{n^2} [\sqrt{t}]\, dt = n(n - 1)(4n + 1)/6.$

8. Show that the translation property (Theorem 1.7) may be expressed in the equivalent form

$$\int_{a+c}^{b+c} f(x)\, dx = \int_{a}^{b} f(x + c)\, dx .$$

9. Show that the following property is equivalent to Theorem 1.8:

$$\int_{ka}^{kb} f(x)\, dx = k \int_{a}^{b} f(kx)\, dx .$$

10. Given a positive integer $p$. A step function $s$ is defined on the interval $[0, p]$ as follows: $s(x) = (-1)^n n$ if $x$ lies in the interval $n \le x < n + 1$, where $n = 0, 1, 2, \ldots, p - 1$; $s(p) = 0$. Let $f(p) = \int_{0}^{p} s(x)\, dx.$

    (a) Calculate $f(3)$, $f(4)$, and $f(f(3))$.

    (b) For what value (or values) of $p$ is $|f(p)| = 7$?

11. If, instead of defining integrals of step functions by using formula (1.3), we used the definition

$$\int_{a}^{b} s(x)\, dx = \sum_{k=1}^{n} s_k^3 \cdot (x_k - x_{k-1}) ,$$

a new and different theory of integration would result. Which of the following properties would remain valid in this new theory?

(a) $\int_a^b s + \int_b^c s = \int_a^c s.$   (c) $\int_a^b c \cdot s = c \int_a^b s.$

(b) $\int_a^b (s + t) = \int_a^b s + \int_a^b t.$   (d) $\int_{a+c}^{b+c} s(x)\, dx = \int_a^b s(x + c)\, dx.$

(e) If $s(x) < t(x)$ for each $x$ in $[a, b]$, then $\int_a^b s < \int_a^b t.$

12. Solve Exercise 11 if we use the definition

$$\int_a^b s(x)\, dx = \sum_{k=1}^n s_k \cdot (x_k^2 - x_{k-1}^2).$$

Analytic proofs of the properties of the integral given in Section 1.13 are requested in the following exercises. The proofs of Theorems 1.3 and 1.8 are worked out here as samples. Hints are given for the others.

*Proof of Theorem 1.3:* $\int_a^b c \cdot s(x)\, dx = c \int_a^b s(x)\, dx$ for every real $c$.

Let $P = \{x_0, x_1, \ldots, x_n\}$ be a partition of $[a, b]$ such that $s$ is constant on the open subintervals of $P$. Assume $s(x) = s_k$ if $x_{k-1} < x < x_k$ ($k = 1, 2, \ldots, n$). Then $c \cdot s(x) = c \cdot s_k$ if $x_{k-1} < x < x_k$, and hence by the definition of an integral we have

$$\int_a^b c \cdot s(x)\, dx = \sum_{k=1}^n c \cdot s_k \cdot (x_k - x_{k-1}) = c \sum_{k=1}^n s_k \cdot (x_k - x_{k-1}) = c \int_a^b s(x)\, dx.$$

*Proof of Theorem 1.8:*

$$\int_{ka}^{kb} s\left(\frac{x}{k}\right) dx = k \int_a^b s(x)\, dx \qquad \text{if} \quad k > 0.$$

Let $P = \{x_0, x_1, \ldots, x_n\}$ be a partition of the interval $[a, b]$ such that $s$ is constant on the open subintervals of $P$. Assume that $s(x) = s_i$ if $x_{i-1} < x < x_i$. Let $t(x) = s(x/k)$ if $ka \leq x \leq kb$. Then $t(x) = s_i$ if $x$ lies in the open interval $(kx_{i-1}, kx_i)$; hence $P' = \{kx_0, kx_1, \ldots, kx_n\}$ is a partition of $[ka, kb]$ and $t$ is constant on the open subintervals of $P'$. Therefore $t$ is a step function whose integral is

$$\int_{ka}^{kb} t(x)\, dx = \sum_{i=1}^n s_i \cdot (kx_i - kx_{i-1}) = k \sum_{i=1}^n s_i \cdot (x_i - x_{i-1}) = k \int_a^b s(x)\, dx.$$

13. Prove Theorem 1.2 (the additive property).

   [*Hint:* Use the additive property for sums: $\sum_{k=1}^n (a_k + b_k) = \sum_{k=1}^n a_k + \sum_{k=1}^n b_k.$]

14. Prove Theorem 1.4 (the linearity property).

   [*Hint:* Use the additive property and the homogeneous property.]

15. Prove Theorem 1.5 (the comparison theorem).

   [*Hint:* Use the corresponding property for sums: $\sum_{k=1}^n a_k < \sum_{k=1}^n b_k$ if $a_k < b_k$ for $k = 1, 2, \ldots, n.$]

16. Prove Theorem 1.6 (additivity with respect to the interval).

   [*Hint:*   If $P_1$ is a partition of $[a, c]$ and $P_2$ a partiton of $[c, b]$, then the points of $P_1$ along with those of $P_2$ form a partition of $[a, b]$.]

17. Prove Theorem 1.7 (invariance under translation).

   [*Hint:*   If $P = \{x_0, x_1, \ldots, x_n\}$ is a partition of $[a, b]$, then $P' = \{x_0 + c, x_1 + c, \ldots, x_n + c\}$ is a partition of $[a + c, b + c]$.]

### 1.16   The integral of more general functions

The integral $\int_a^b s(x)\, dx$ has been defined when $s$ is a step function. In this section we shall formulate a definition of $\int_a^b f(x)\, dx$ that will apply to more general functions $f$. The definition will be constructed so that the resulting integral has all the properties listed in Section 1.13.

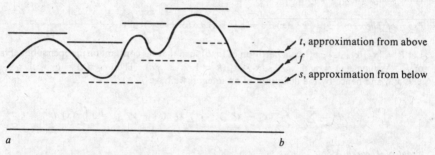

FIGURE 1.30   Approximating a function $f$ from above and below by step functions.

The approach will be patterned somewhat after the method of Archimedes, which was explained above in Section I 1.3. The idea is simply this: We begin by approximating the function $f$ from below and from above by step functions, as suggested in Figure 1.30. That is, we choose an arbitrary step function, say $s$, whose graph lies below that of $f$, and a arbitrary step function, say $t$, whose graph lies above that of $f$. Next, we consider the collection of all the numbers $\int_a^b s(x)\, dx$ and $\int_a^b t(x)\, dx$ obtained by choosing $s$ and $t$ in all possible ways. In general, we have

$$\int_a^b s(x)\, dx < \int_a^b t(x)\, dx$$

because of the comparison theorem. If the integral of $f$ is to obey the comparison theorem, then it must be a number which falls between $\int_a^b s(x)\, dx$ and $\int_a^b t(x)\, dx$ for every pair of approximating functions $s$ and $t$. If there is *only one* number which has this property we define the integral of $f$ to be this number.

There is only one thing that can cause trouble in this procedure, and it occurs in the very first step. Unfortunately, it is not possible to approximate *every* function from above and from below by step functions. For example, the function $f$ given by the equations

$$f(x) = \frac{1}{x} \quad \text{if} \quad x \neq 0, \quad f(0) = 0,$$

is defined for all real $x$, but on any interval $[a, b]$ containing the origin we cannot surround $f$ by step functions. This is due to the fact that $f$ has arbitrarily large values near the origin or, as we say, $f$ is *unbounded* in every neighborhood of the origin (see Figure 1.31). Therefore, we shall first restrict ourselves to those functions that are *bounded* on $[a, b]$, that is, to those functions $f$ for which there exists a number $M > 0$ such that

$$(1.5) \qquad -M \leq f(x) \leq M$$

for every $x$ in $[a, b]$. Geometrically, the graph of such a function lies between the graphs of two constant step functions $s$ and $t$ having the values $-M$ and $+M$, respectively. (See

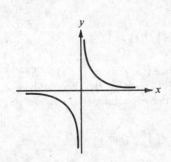

FIGURE 1.31   An unbounded function.          FIGURE 1.32   A bounded function.

Figure 1.32.) In a case like this, we say that $f$ is bounded by $M$. The two inequalities in (1.5) can also be written as

$$|f(x)| \leq M.$$

With this point taken care of, we can proceed to carry out the plan described above and to formulate the definition of the integral.

DEFINITION OF THE INTEGRAL OF A BOUNDED FUNCTION. *Let $f$ be a function defined and bounded on $[a, b]$. Let $s$ and $t$ denote arbitrary step functions defined on $[a, b]$ such that*

$$(1.6) \qquad s(x) \leq f(x) \leq t(x)$$

*for every $x$ in $[a, b]$. If there is one and only one number $I$ such that*

$$(1.7) \qquad \int_a^b s(x)\, dx \leq I \leq \int_a^b t(x)\, dx$$

*for every pair of step functions $s$ and $t$ satisfying (1.6), then this number $I$ is called the integral of $f$ from $a$ to $b$, and is denoted by the symbol $\int_a^b f(x)\, dx$ or by $\int_a^b f$. When such an $I$ exists, the function $f$ is said to be integrable on $[a, b]$.*

If $a < b$, we define $\int_b^a f(x)\, dx = -\int_a^b f(x)\, dx$, provided $f$ is integrable on $[a, b]$. We also define $\int_a^a f(x)\, dx = 0$. If $f$ is integrable on $[a, b]$, we say that the integral $\int_a^b f(x)\, dx$ exists. The function $f$ is called the *integrand*, the numbers $a$ and $b$ are called the *limits of integration*, and the interval $[a, b]$ the *interval of integration*.

## 1.17  Upper and lower integrals

Assume $f$ is bounded on $[a, b]$. If $s$ and $t$ are step functions satisfying (1.6), we say $s$ is *below* $f$, and $t$ is *above* $f$, and we write $s \le f \le t$.

Let $S$ denote the set of all numbers $\int_a^b s(x)\, dx$ obtained as $s$ runs through all step functions below $f$, and let $T$ be the set of all numbers $\int_a^b t(x)\, dx$ obtained as $t$ runs through all step functions above $f$. That is, let

$$S = \left\{ \int_a^b s(x)\, dx \,\middle|\, s \le f \right\}, \qquad T = \left\{ \int_a^b t(x)\, dx \,\middle|\, f \le t \right\}.$$

Both sets $S$ and $T$ are nonempty since $f$ is bounded. Also, $\int_a^b s(x)\, dx \le \int_a^b t(x)\, dx$ if $s \le f \le t$, so every number in $S$ is less than every number in $T$. Therefore, by Theorem I.34, $S$ has a supremum, and $T$ has an infimum, and they satisfy the inequalities

$$\int_a^b s(x)\, dx \le \sup S \le \inf T \le \int_a^b t(x)\, dx$$

for all $s$ and $t$ satisfying $s \le f \le t$. This shows that both numbers $\sup S$ and $\inf T$ satisfy (1.7). Therefore, $f$ is integrable on $[a, b]$ if and only if $\sup S = \inf T$, in which case we have

$$\int_a^b f(x)\, dx = \sup S = \inf T.$$

The number $\sup S$ is called the *lower integral* of $f$ and is denoted by $\underline{I}(f)$. The number $\inf T$ is called the *upper* integral of $f$ and is denoted by $\overline{I}(f)$. Thus, we have

$$\underline{I}(f) = \sup \left\{ \int_a^b s(x)\, dx \,\middle|\, s \le f \right\}, \qquad \overline{I}(f) = \inf \left\{ \int_a^b t(x)\, dx \,\middle|\, f \le t \right\}.$$

The foregoing argument proves the following theorem.

THEOREM 1.9.  *Every function $f$ which is bounded on $[a, b]$ has a lower integral $\underline{I}(f)$ and an upper integral $\overline{I}(f)$ satisfying the inequalities*

$$\int_a^b s(x)\, dx \le \underline{I}(f) \le \overline{I}(f) \le \int_a^b t(x)\, dx$$

*for all step functions $s$ and $t$ with $s \le f \le t$. The function $f$ is integrable on $[a, b]$ if and only if its upper and lower integrals are equal, in which case we have*

$$\int_a^b f(x)\, dx = \underline{I}(f) = \overline{I}(f).$$

## 1.18 The area of an ordinate set expressed as an integral

The concept of area was introduced axiomatically in Section 1.6 as a set function having certain properties. From these properties we proved that the area of the ordinate set of a nonnegative step function is equal to the integral of the function. Now we show that the same is true for any integrable nonnegative function. We recall that the ordinate set of a nonnegative function $f$ over an interval $[a, b]$ is the set of all points $(x, y)$ satisfying the inequalities $0 \leq y \leq f(x)$, $a \leq x \leq b$.

THEOREM 1.10. *Let f be a nonnegative function, integrable on an interval* $[a, b]$, *and let Q denote the ordinate set of f over* $[a, b]$. *Then Q is measurable and its area is equal to the integral* $\int_a^b f(x)\, dx$.

*Proof.* Let $S$ and $T$ be two step regions satisfying $S \subseteq Q \subseteq T$. Then there are two step functions $s$ and $t$ satisfying $s \leq f \leq t$ on $[a, b]$, such that

$$a(S) = \int_a^b s(x)\, dx \quad \text{and} \quad a(T) = \int_a^b t(x)\, dx .$$

Since $f$ is integrable on $[a, b]$, the number $I = \int_a^b f(x)\, dx$ is the only number satisfying the inequalities

$$\int_a^b s(x)\, dx \leq I \leq \int_a^b t(x)\, dx$$

for all step functions $s$ and $t$ with $s \leq f \leq t$. Therefore this is also the only number satisfying $a(S) \leq I \leq a(T)$ for all step regions $S$ and $T$ with $S \subseteq Q \subseteq T$. By the exhaustion property, this proves that $Q$ is measurable and that $a(Q) = I$.

Let $Q$ denote the ordinate set of Theorem 1.10, and let $Q'$ denote the set that remains if we remove from $Q$ those points on the graph of $f$. That is, let

$$Q' = \{(x, y) \mid a \leq x \leq b, 0 \leq y < f(x)\} .$$

The argument used to prove Theorem 1.10 also shows that $Q'$ is measurable and that $a(Q') = a(Q)$. Therefore, by the difference property of area, the set $Q - Q'$ is measurable and

$$a(Q - Q') = a(Q) - a(Q') = 0 .$$

In other words, we have proved the following theorem.

THEOREM 1.11. *Let f be a nonnegative function, integrable on an interval* $[a, b]$. *Then the graph of f, that is, the set*

$$\{(x, y) \mid a \leq x \leq b, y = f(x)\} ,$$

*is measurable and has area equal to* 0.

## 1.19 Informal remarks on the theory and technique of integration

Two fundamental questions arise at this stage: (1) *Which bounded functions are integrable?* (2) *Given that a function f is integrable, how do we compute the integral of f?*

The first question comes under the heading "Theory of Integration" and the second under the heading "Technique of Integration." A complete answer to question (1) lies beyond the scope of an introductory course and will not be given in this book. Instead, we shall give partial answers which require only elementary ideas.

First we introduce an important class of functions known as *monotonic functions*. In the following section we define these functions and give a number of examples. Then we prove that all bounded monotonic functions are integrable. Fortunately, most of the functions that occur in practice are monotonic or sums of monotonic functions, so the results of this miniature theory of integration are quite comprehensive.

The discussion of "Technique of Integration" begins in Section 1.23, where we calculate the integral $\int_0^b x^p \, dx$, when $p$ is a positive integer. Then we develop general properties of the integral, such as linearity and additivity, and show how these properties help us to extend our knowledge of integrals of specific functions.

## 1.20 Monotonic and piecewise monotonic functions. Definitions and examples

A function $f$ is said to be *increasing* on a set $S$ if $f(x) \leq f(y)$ for every pair of points $x$ and $y$ in $S$ with $x < y$. If the strict inequality $f(x) < f(y)$ holds for all $x < y$ in $S$, the function is said to be *strictly increasing* on $S$. Similarly, $f$ is called *decreasing* on $S$ if

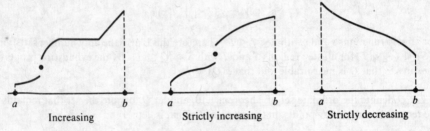

| Increasing | Strictly increasing | Strictly decreasing |

FIGURE 1.33   Monotonic functions.

$f(x) \geq f(y)$ for all $x < y$ in $S$. If $f(x) > f(y)$ for all $x < y$ in $S$, then $f$ is called *strictly decreasing* on $S$. A function is called *monotonic* on $S$ if it is increasing on $S$ or if it is decreasing on $S$. The term *strictly monotonic* means that $f$ is strictly increasing on $S$ or strictly decreasing on $S$. Ordinarily, the set $S$ under consideration is either an open interval or a closed interval. Examples are shown in Figure 1.33.

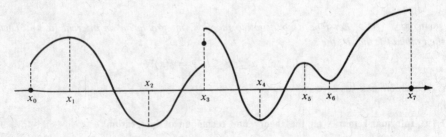

FIGURE 1.34   A piecewise monotonic function.

A function $f$ is said to be *piecewise monotonic* on an interval if its graph consists of a finite number of monotonic pieces. That is to say, $f$ is piecewise monotonic on $[a, b]$ if there is a partition $P$ of $[a, b]$ such that $f$ is monotonic on each of the open subintervals of $P$. In particular, step functions are piecewise monotonic, as are all the examples shown in Figures 1.33 and 1.34.

EXAMPLE 1. *The power functions.* If $p$ is a positive integer, we have the inequality

$$x^p < y^p \qquad \text{if} \quad 0 \le x < y,$$

which is easily proved by mathematical induction. This shows that the power function $f$, defined for all real $x$ by the equation $f(x) = x^p$, is strictly increasing on the nonnegative real axis. It is also strictly monotonic on the negative real axis (it is decreasing if $p$ is even and increasing if $p$ is odd). Therefore, $f$ is piecewise monotonic on every finite interval.

EXAMPLE 2. *The square-root function.* Let $f(x) = \sqrt{x}$ for $x \ge 0$. This function is strictly increasing on the nonnegative real axis. In fact, if $0 \le x < y$, we have

$$\sqrt{y} - \sqrt{x} = \frac{y - x}{\sqrt{y} + \sqrt{x}} \, ;$$

hence, $\sqrt{y} - \sqrt{x} > 0$.

EXAMPLE 3. The graph of the function $g$ defined by the equation

$$g(x) = \sqrt{r^2 - x^2} \qquad \text{if} \quad -r \le x \le r$$

is a semicircle of radius $r$. This function is strictly increasing on the interval $-r \le x \le 0$ and strictly decreasing on the interval $0 \le x \le r$. Hence, $g$ is piecewise monotonic on $[-r, r]$.

## 1.21 Integrability of bounded monotonic functions

The importance of monotonic functions in integration theory is due to the following theorem.

THEOREM 1.12. *If $f$ is monotonic on a closed interval $[a, b]$, then $f$ is integrable on $[a, b]$.*

*Proof.* We shall prove the theorem for increasing functions. The proof for decreasing functions is analogous. Assume $f$ is increasing and let $\underline{I}(f)$ and $\overline{I}(f)$ denote its lower and upper integrals, respectively. We shall prove that $\underline{I}(f) = \overline{I}(f)$.

Let $n$ be a positive integer and construct two special approximating step functions $s_n$ and $t_n$ as follows: Let $P = \{x_0, x_1, \ldots, x_n\}$ be a partition of $[a, b]$ into $n$ *equal* subintervals, that is, subintervals $[x_{k-1}, x_k]$ with $x_k - x_{k-1} = (b - a)/n$ for each $k$. Now define $s_n$ and $t_n$ by the formulas

$$s_n(x) = f(x_{k-1}), \qquad t_n(x) = f(x_k) \qquad \text{if} \quad x_{k-1} < x < x_k.$$

At the subdivision points, define $s_n$ and $t_n$ so as to preserve the relations $s_n(x) \leq f(x) \leq t_n(x)$ throughout $[a, b]$. An example is shown in Figure 1.35(a). For this choice of step functions, we have

$$\int_a^b t_n - \int_a^b s_n = \sum_{k=1}^n f(x_k)(x_k - x_{k-1}) - \sum_{k=1}^n f(x_{k-1})(x_k - x_{k-1})$$

$$= \frac{b-a}{n} \sum_{k=1}^n [f(x_k) - f(x_{k-1})] = \frac{(b-a)[f(b) - f(a)]}{n},$$

where the last equation is a consequence of the telescoping property of finite sums. This last relation has a simple geometric interpretation. The difference $\int_a^b t_n - \int_a^b s_n$ is equal to the sum of the areas of the shaded rectangles in Figure 1.35(a). By sliding these rectangles to the right so that they rest on a common base as in Figure 1.35(b), we see that they fill out a

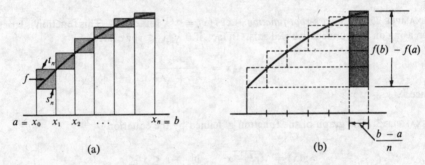

FIGURE 1.35   Proof of integrability of an increasing function.

rectangle of base $(b - a)/n$ and altitude $f(b) - f(a)$; the sum of the areas is therefore $C/n$, where $C = (b - a)[f(b) - f(a)]$.

Now we rewrite the foregoing relation in the form

$$(1.8) \qquad \int_a^b t_n - \int_a^b s_n = \frac{C}{n}.$$

The lower and upper integrals of $f$ satisfy the inequalities

$$\int_a^b s_n \leq \underline{I}(f) \leq \int_a^b t_n \quad \text{and} \quad \int_a^b s_n \leq \overline{I}(f) \leq \int_a^b t_n.$$

Multiplying the first set of inequalities by $(-1)$ and adding the result to the second set, we obtain

$$\overline{I}(f) - \underline{I}(f) \leq \int_a^b t_n - \int_a^b s_n.$$

Using (1.8) and the relation $\underline{I}(f) \leq \overline{I}(f)$, we obtain

$$0 \leq \overline{I}(f) - \underline{I}(f) \leq \frac{C}{n}$$

for every integer $n \geq 1$. Therefore, by Theorem I.31, we must have $\underline{I}(f) = \overline{I}(f)$. This proves that $f$ is integrable on $[a, b]$.

## 1.22 Calculation of the integral of a bounded monotonic function

The proof of Theorem 1.12 not only shows that the integral of a bounded increasing function *exists*, but it also suggests a method for computing the value of the integral. This is described by the following theorem.

THEOREM 1.13.    *Assume $f$ is increasing on a closed interval $[a, b]$. Let $x_k = a + k(b - a)/n$ for $k = 0, 1, \ldots, n$. If $I$ is any number which satisfies the inequalities*

$$(1.9) \qquad \frac{b - a}{n} \sum_{k=0}^{n-1} f(x_k) \leq I \leq \frac{b - a}{n} \sum_{k=1}^{n} f(x_k)$$

*for every integer $n \geq 1$, then $I = \int_a^b f(x)\, dx$.*

*Proof.* Let $s_n$ and $t_n$ be the special approximating step functions obtained by subdivision of the interval $[a, b]$ into $n$ equal parts, as described in the proof of Theorem 1.12. Then, inequalities (1.9) state that

$$\int_a^b s_n \leq I \leq \int_a^b t_n$$

for every $n \geq 1$. But the integral $\int_a^b f(x)\, dx$ satisfies the same inequalities as $I$. Using Equation (1.8) we see that

$$0 \leq \left| I - \int_a^b f(x)\, dx \right| \leq \frac{C}{n}$$

for every integer $n \geq 1$. Therefore, by Theorem I.31, we have $I = \int_a^b f(x)\, dx$, as asserted.

An analogous argument gives a proof of the corresponding theorem for decreasing functions.

THEOREM 1.14.    *Assume $f$ is decreasing on $[a, b]$. Let $x_k = a + k(b - a)/n$ for $k = 0, 1, \ldots, n$. If $I$ is any number which satisfies the inequalities*

$$\frac{b - a}{n} \sum_{k=1}^{n} f(x_k) \leq I \leq \frac{b - a}{n} \sum_{k=0}^{n-1} f(x_k)$$

*for every integer $n \geq 1$, then $I = \int_a^b f(x)\, dx$.*

## 1.23 Calculation of the integral $\int_0^b x^p\, dx$ when $p$ is a positive integer

To illustrate the use of Theorem 1.13 we shall calculate the integral $\int_0^b x^p\, dx$ where $b > 0$ and $p$ is any positive integer. The integral exists because the integrand is bounded and increasing on $[0, b]$.

THEOREM 1.15. *If p is a positive integer and b > 0, we have*

$$\int_0^b x^p \, dx = \frac{b^{p+1}}{p+1}.$$

*Proof.* We begin with the inequalities

$$\sum_{k=1}^{n-1} k^p < \frac{n^{p+1}}{p+1} < \sum_{k=1}^{n} k^p$$

valid for every integer $n \geq 1$ and every integer $p \geq 1$. These inequalities may be easily proved by mathematical induction. (A proof is outlined in Exercise 13 of Section I 4.10.) Multiplication of these inequalities by $b^{p+1}/n^{p+1}$ gives us

$$\frac{b}{n} \sum_{k=1}^{n-1} \left(\frac{kb}{n}\right)^p < \frac{b^{p+1}}{p+1} < \frac{b}{n} \sum_{k=1}^{n} \left(\frac{kb}{n}\right)^p.$$

If we let $f(x) = x^p$ and $x_k = kb/n$, for $k = 0, 1, 2, \ldots, n$, these inequalities become

$$\frac{b}{n} \sum_{k=0}^{n-1} f(x_k) < \frac{b^{p+1}}{p+1} < \frac{b}{n} \sum_{k=1}^{n} f(x_k).$$

Therefore, the inequalities (1.9) of Theorem 1.13 are satisfied with $f(x) = x^p$, $a = 0$, and $I = b^{p+1}/(p+1)$. It follows that $\int_0^b x^p \, dx = b^{p+1}/(p+1)$.

## 1.24 The basic properties of the integral

From the definition of the integral, it is possible to deduce the following properties. Proofs are given in Section 1.27.

THEOREM 1.16. LINEARITY WITH RESPECT TO THE INTEGRAND. *If both f and g are integrable on [a, b], so is $c_1 f + c_2 g$ for every pair of constants $c_1$ and $c_2$. Furthermore, we have*

$$\int_a^b [c_1 f(x) + c_2 g(x)] \, dx = c_1 \int_a^b f(x) \, dx + c_2 \int_a^b g(x) \, dx.$$

*Note:* By use of mathematical induction, the linearity property can be generalized as follows: If $f_1, \ldots, f_n$ are integrable on $[a, b]$, then so is $c_1 f_1 + \cdots + c_n f_n$ for all real $c_1, \ldots, c_n$, and

$$\int_a^b \sum_{k=1}^{n} c_k f_k(x) \, dx = \sum_{k=1}^{n} c_k \int_a^b f_k(x) \, dx.$$

THEOREM 1.17. ADDITIVITY WITH RESPECT TO THE INTERVAL OF INTEGRATION. *If two of the following three integrals exist, the third also exists, and we have*

$$\int_a^b f(x) \, dx + \int_b^c f(x) \, dx = \int_a^c f(x) \, dx.$$

*Note:* In particular, if $f$ is monotonic on $[a, b]$ and also on $[b, c]$, then both integrals $\int_a^b f$ and $\int_b^c f$ exist, so $\int_a^c f$ also exists and is equal to the sum of the other two integrals.

THEOREM 1.18. INVARIANCE UNDER TRANSLATION. *If $f$ is integrable on $[a, b]$, then for every real $c$ we have*

$$\int_a^b f(x)\, dx = \int_{a+c}^{b+c} f(x - c)\, dx\,.$$

THEOREM 1.19. EXPANSION OR CONTRACTION OF THE INTERVAL OF INTEGRATION. *If $f$ is integrable on $[a, b]$, then for every real $k \neq 0$ we have*

$$\int_a^b f(x)\, dx = \frac{1}{k} \int_{ka}^{kb} f\left(\frac{x}{k}\right) dx\,.$$

*Note:* In both Theorems 1.18 and 1.19, the existence of one of the integrals implies the existence of the other. When $k = -1$, Theorem 1.19 is called the *reflection property*.

THEOREM 1.20. COMPARISON THEOREM. *If both $f$ and $g$ are integrable on $[a, b]$ and if $g(x) \leq f(x)$ for every $x$ in $[a, b]$, then we have*

$$\int_a^b g(x)\, dx \leq \int_a^b f(x)\, dx\,.$$

An important special case of Theorem 1.20 occurs when $g(x) = 0$ for every $x$. In this case, the theorem states that if $f(x) \geq 0$ everywhere on $[a, b]$, then $\int_a^b f(x)\, dx \geq 0$. In other words, a nonnegative function has a nonnegative integral. It can also be shown that if we have the *strict* inequality $g(x) < f(x)$ for all $x$ in $[a, b]$, then the same strict inequality holds for the integrals, but the proof is not easy to give at this stage.

In Chapter 5 we shall discuss various methods for calculating the value of an integral without the necessity of using the definition in each case. These methods, however, are applicable to only a relatively small number of functions, and for most integrable functions the actual numerical value of the integral can only be estimated. This is usually done by approximating the integrand above and below by step functions or by other simple functions whose integrals can be evaluated exactly. Then the comparison theorem is used to obtain corresponding approximations for the integral of the function in question. This idea will be explored more fully in Chapter 7.

## 1.25 Integration of polynomials

In Section 1.23 we established the integration formula

(1.10) $$\int_0^b x^p\, dx = \frac{b^{p+1}}{p + 1}$$

for $b > 0$ and $p$ any positive integer. The formula is also valid if $b = 0$, since both members are zero. We can use Theorem 1.19 to show that (1.10) also holds for negative $b$. We simply take $k = -1$ in Theorem 1.19 to obtain

$$\int_0^{-b} x^p \, dx = -\int_0^b (-x)^p \, dx = (-1)^{p+1} \int_0^b x^p \, dx = \frac{(-b)^{p+1}}{p+1},$$

which shows that (1.10) holds for negative $b$. The additive property $\int_a^b x^p \, dx = \int_0^b x^p \, dx - \int_0^a x^p \, dx$ now leads to the more general formula

$$\int_a^b x^p \, dx = \frac{b^{p+1} - a^{p+1}}{p+1},$$

valid for all real $a$ and $b$, and any integer $p \geq 0$.

Sometimes the special symbol

$$P(x) \Big|_a^b$$

is used to designate the difference $P(b) - P(a)$. Thus the foregoing formula may also be written as follows:

$$\int_a^b x^p \, dx = \frac{x^{p+1}}{p+1} \Big|_a^b = \frac{b^{p+1} - a^{p+1}}{p+1}.$$

This formula, along with the linearity property, enables us to integrate every polynomial. For example, to compute the integral $\int_1^3 (x^2 - 3x + 5) \, dx$, we find the integral of each term and then add the results. Thus, we have

$$\int_1^3 (x^2 - 3x + 5) \, dx = \int_1^3 x^2 \, dx - 3 \int_1^3 x \, dx + 5 \int_1^3 dx = \frac{x^3}{3} \Big|_1^3 - 3 \frac{x^2}{2} \Big|_1^3 + 5x \Big|_1^3$$

$$= \frac{3^3 - 1^3}{3} - 3 \frac{3^2 - 1^2}{2} + 5 \frac{3^1 - 1^1}{1} = \frac{26}{3} - 12 + 10 = \frac{20}{3}.$$

More generally, to compute the integral of any polynomial we integrate term by term:

$$\int_a^b \sum_{k=0}^n c_k x^k \, dx = \sum_{k=0}^n c_k \int_a^b x^k \, dx = \sum_{k=0}^n c_k \frac{b^{k+1} - a^{k+1}}{k+1}.$$

We can also integrate more complicated functions formed by piecing together various polynomials. For example, consider the integral $\int_0^1 |x(2x - 1)| \, dx$. Because of the absolute-value signs, the integrand is not a polynomial. However, by considering the sign of

$x(2x - 1)$, we can split the interval $[0, 1]$ into two subintervals, in each of which the integrand is a polynomial. As $x$ varies from 0 to 1, the product $x(2x - 1)$ changes sign at the point $x = \frac{1}{2}$; it is negative if $0 < x < \frac{1}{2}$ and positive if $\frac{1}{2} < x < 1$. Therefore, we use the additive property to write

$$\int_0^1 |x(2x - 1)| \, dx = -\int_0^{1/2} x(2x - 1) \, dx + \int_{1/2}^1 x(2x - 1) \, dx$$

$$= \int_0^{1/2} (x - 2x^2) \, dx + \int_{1/2}^1 (2x^2 - x) \, dx$$

$$= (\tfrac{1}{8} - \tfrac{1}{12}) + (\tfrac{7}{12} - \tfrac{3}{8}) = \tfrac{1}{4}.$$

## 1.26 Exercises

Compute each of the following integrals.

1. $\int_0^3 x^2 \, dx$.

2. $\int_{-3}^3 x^2 \, dx$.

3. $\int_0^2 4x^3 \, dx$.

4. $\int_{-2}^2 4x^3 \, dx$.

5. $\int_0^1 5t^4 \, dt$.

6. $\int_{-1}^1 5t^4 \, dt$.

7. $\int_0^1 (5x^4 - 4x^3) \, dx$.

8. $\int_{-1}^1 (5x^4 - 4x^3) \, dx$.

9. $\int_{-1}^2 (t^2 + 1) \, dt$.

10. $\int_2^3 (3x^2 - 4x + 2) \, dx$.

11. $\int_0^{1/2} (8t^3 + 6t^2 - 2t + 5) \, dt$.

12. $\int_{-2}^4 (u - 1)(u - 2) \, du$.

13. $\int_{-1}^0 (x + 1)^2 \, dx$.

14. $\int_0^{-1} (x + 1)^2 \, dx$.

15. $\int_0^2 (x - 1)(3x - 1) \, dx$.

16. $\int_0^2 |(x - 1)(3x - 1)| \, dx$.

17. $\int_0^3 (2x - 5)^3 \, dx$.

18. $\int_{-3}^3 (x^2 - 3)^3 \, dx$.

19. $\int_0^5 x^2(x - 5)^4 \, dx$.

20. $\int_{-2}^{-4} (x + 4)^{10} \, dx$.   [*Hint:* Theorem 1.18.]

21. Find all values of $c$ for which

(a) $\int_0^c x(1 - x) \, dx = 0$,     (b) $\int_0^c |x(1 - x)| \, dx = 0$.

22. Compute each of the following integrals. Draw the graph of $f$ in each case.

(a) $\int_0^2 f(x) \, dx$   where $f(x) = \begin{cases} x^2 & \text{if } 0 \le x \le 1, \\ 2 - x & \text{if } 1 \le x \le 2. \end{cases}$

(b) $\int_0^1 f(x) \, dx$   where $f(x) = \begin{cases} x & \text{if } 0 \le x \le c, \\ c\dfrac{1 - x}{1 - c} & \text{if } c \le x \le 1; \end{cases}$

$c$ is a fixed real number, $0 < c < 1$.

23. Find a quadratic polynomial $P$ for which $P(0) = P(1) = 0$ and $\int_0^1 P(x) \, dx = 1$.

24. Find a cubic polynomial $P$ for which $P(0) = P(-2) = 0$, $P(1) = 15$, and $3 \int_{-2}^0 P(x) \, dx = 4$.

*Optional exercises*

25. Let $f$ be a function whose domain contains $-x$ whenever it contains $x$. We say that $f$ is an *even* function if $f(-x) = f(x)$ and an *odd* function if $f(-x) = -f(x)$ for all $x$ in the domain of $f$. If $f$ is integrable on $[0, b]$, prove that

   (a) $\int_{-b}^{b} f(x)\,dx = 2\int_{0}^{b} f(x)\,dx$     if $f$ is even;

   (b) $\int_{-b}^{b} f(x)\,dx = 0$     if $f$ is odd.

26. Use Theorems 1.18 and 1.19 to derive the formula

$$\int_{a}^{b} f(x)\,dx = (b - a)\int_{0}^{1} f[a + (b - a)x]\,dx\,.$$

27. Theorems 1.18 and 1.19 suggest a common generalization for the integral $\int_{a}^{b} f(Ax + B)\,dx$. Guess the formula suggested and prove it with the help of Theorems 1.18 and 1.19. Discuss also the case $A = 0$.

28. Use Theorems 1.18 and 1.19 to derive the formula

$$\int_{a}^{b} f(c - x)\,dx = \int_{c-b}^{c-a} f(x)\,dx\,.$$

## 1.27  Proofs of the basic properties of the integral

This section contains proofs of the basic properties of the integral listed in Theorems 1.16 through 1.20 in Section 1.24. We make repeated use of the fact that every function $f$ which is bounded on an interval $[a, b]$ has a lower integral $\underline{I}(f)$ and an upper integral $\overline{I}(f)$ given by

$$\underline{I}(f) = \sup\left\{ \int_{a}^{b} s \mid s \le f \right\}, \qquad \overline{I}(g) = \inf\left\{ \int_{a}^{b} t \mid f \le t \right\},$$

where $s$ and $t$ denote arbitrary step functions below and above $f$, respectively. We know, by Theorem 1.9, that $f$ is integrable if and only if $\underline{I}(f) = \overline{I}(f)$, in which case the value of the integral of $f$ is the common value of the upper and lower integrals.

*Proof of the Linearity Property* (*Theorem* 1.16). We decompose the linearity property into two parts:

(A)                                $$\int_{a}^{b}(f + g) = \int_{a}^{b} f + \int_{a}^{b} g\,,$$

(B)                                $$\int_{a}^{b} cf = c\int_{a}^{b} f\,.$$

To prove (A), let $I(f) = \int_{a}^{b} f$ and let $I(g) = \int_{a}^{b} g$. We shall prove that $I(f + g) = \overline{I}(f + g) = I(f) + I(g)$.

Let $s_1$ and $s_2$ denote arbitrary step functions below $f$ and $g$, respectively. Since $f$ and $g$ are integrable, we have

$$I(f) = \sup\left\{ \int_{a}^{b} s_1 \mid s_1 \le f \right\}, \qquad I(g) = \sup\left\{ \int_{a}^{b} s_2 \mid s_2 \le g \right\}.$$

By the additive property of the supremum (Theorem I.33), we also have

(1.11) $$I(f) + I(g) = \sup \left\{ \int_a^b s_1 + \int_a^b s_2 \,\Big|\, s_1 \leq f,\, s_2 \leq g \right\}.$$

But if $s_1 \leq f$ and $s_2 \leq g$, then the sum $s = s_1 + s_2$ is a step function below $f + g$, and we have

$$\int_a^b s_1 + \int_a^b s_2 = \int_a^b s \leq I(f + g).$$

Therefore, the number $I(f + g)$ is an upper bound for the set appearing on the right of (1.11). This upper bound cannot be less than the least upper bound of the set, so we have

(1.12) $$I(f) + I(g) \leq I(f + g).$$

Similarly, if we use the relations

$$I(f) = \inf \left\{ \int_a^b t_1 \,\Big|\, f \leq t_1 \right\}, \qquad I(g) = \inf \left\{ \int_a^b t_2 \,\Big|\, g \leq t_2 \right\},$$

where $t_1$ and $t_2$ denote arbitrary step functions above $f$ and $g$, respectively, we obtain the inequality

(1.13) $$\bar{I}(f + g) \leq \bar{I}(f) + \bar{I}(g).$$

Inequalities (1.12) and (1.13) together show that $I(f + g) = \bar{I}(f + g) = I(f) + I(g)$. Therefore $f + g$ is integrable and relation (A) holds.

Relation (B) is trivial if $c = 0$. If $c > 0$, we note that every step function $s_1$ below $cf$ is of the form $s_1 = cs$, where $s$ is a step function below $f$. Similarly, every step function $t_1$ above $cf$ is of the form $t_1 = ct$, where $t$ is a step function above $f$. Therefore we have

$$I(cf) = \sup \left\{ \int_a^b s_1 \,\Big|\, s_1 \leq cf \right\} = \sup \left\{ c \int_a^b s \,\Big|\, s \leq f \right\} = cI(f)$$

and

$$\bar{I}(cf) = \inf \left\{ \int_a^b t_1 \,\Big|\, cf \leq t_1 \right\} = \inf \left\{ c \int_a^b t \,\Big|\, f \leq t \right\} = c\bar{I}(f).$$

Therefore $I(cf) = \bar{I}(cf) = cI(f)$. Here we have used the following properties of the supremum and infimum:

(1.14) $\sup \{cx \mid x \in A\} = c \sup \{x \mid x \in A\}$, $\quad \inf \{cx \mid x \in A\} = c \inf \{x \mid x \in A\}$,

which hold if $c > 0$. This proves (B) if $c > 0$.

If $c < 0$, the proof of (B) is basically the same, except that every step function $s_1$ below $cf$ is of the form $s_1 = ct$, where $t$ is a step function *above* $f$, and every step function $t_1$ above $cf$ is of the form $t_1 = cs$, where $s$ is a step function *below* $f$. Also, instead of (1.14) we use the relations

$$\sup \{cx \mid x \in A\} = c \inf \{x \mid x \in A\}, \qquad \inf \{cx \mid x \in A\} = c \sup \{x \mid x \in A\},$$

which hold if $c < 0$. We now have

$$I(cf) = \sup\left\{\int_a^b s_1 \mid s_1 \le cf\right\} = \sup\left\{c\int_a^b t \mid f \le t\right\} = c\inf\left\{\int_a^b t \mid f \le t\right\} = cI(f).$$

Similarly, we find $I(cf) = cI(f)$. Therefore (B) holds for all real $c$.

*Proof of Additivity with Respect to the Interval of Integration (Theorem 1.17).* Suppose that $a < b < c$, and assume that the two integrals $\int_a^b f$ and $\int_b^c f$ exist. Let $\bar I(f)$ and $I(f)$ denote the upper and lower integrals of $f$ over the interval $[a, c]$. We shall prove that

(1.15)                     $$\bar I(f) = I(f) = \int_a^b f + \int_b^c f.$$

If $s$ is any step function below $f$ on $[a, c]$, we have

$$\int_a^c s = \int_a^b s + \int_b^c s.$$

Conversely, if $s_1$ and $s_2$ are step functions below $f$ on $[a, b]$ and on $[b, c]$, respectively, then the function $s$ which is equal to $s_1$ on $[a, b)$ and equal to $s_2$ on $[b, c]$ is a step function below $f$ on $[a, c]$ for which we have

$$\int_a^c s = \int_a^b s_1 + \int_b^c s_2.$$

Therefore, by the additive property of the supremum (Theorem 1.33), we have

$$I(f) = \sup\left\{\int_a^c s \mid s \le f\right\} = \sup\left\{\int_a^b s_1 \mid s_1 \le f\right\} + \sup\left\{\int_b^c s_2 \mid s_2 \le f\right\} = \int_a^b f + \int_b^c f.$$

Similarly, we find

$$\bar I(f) = \int_a^b f + \int_b^c f,$$

which proves (1.15) when $a < b < c$. The proof is similar for any other arrangement of the points $a, b, c$.

*Proof of the Translation Property (Theorem 1.18).* Let $g$ be the function defined on the interval $[a + c, b + c]$ by the equation $g(x) = f(x - c)$. Let $I(g)$ and $\bar I(g)$ denote the lower and upper integrals of $g$ on the interval $[a + c, b + c]$. We shall prove that

(1.16)                     $$I(g) = \bar I(g) = \int_a^b f(x)\, dx.$$

Let $s$ be any step function below $g$ on the interval $[a + c, b + c]$. Then the function $s_1$ defined on $[a, b]$ by the equation $s_1(x) = s(x + c)$ is a step function below $f$ on $[a, b]$. Moreover, every step function $s_1$ below $f$ on $[a, b]$ has this form for some $s$ below $g$. Also, by the translation property for integrals of step functions, we have

$$\int_{a+c}^{b+c} s(x)\, dx = \int_a^b s(x + c)\, dx = \int_a^b s_1(x)\, dx.$$

Therefore we have

$$I(g) = \sup\left\{\int_{a+c}^{b+c} s \mid s \le g\right\} = \sup\left\{\int_a^b s_1 \mid s_1 \le f\right\} = \int_a^b f(x)\,dx\,.$$

Similarly, we find $\bar{I}(g) = \int_a^b f(x)\,dx$, which proves (1.16).

*Proof of the Expansion Property* (*Theorem* 1.19). Assume $k > 0$ and define $g$ on the interval $[ka, kb]$ by the equation $g(x) = f(x/k)$. Let $I(g)$ and $\bar{I}(g)$ denote the lower and upper integrals of $g$ on $[ka, kb]$. We shall prove that

(1.17) $$I(g) = \bar{I}(g) = k\int_a^b f(x)\,dx\,.$$

Let $s$ be any step function below $g$ on $[ka, kb]$. Then the function $s_1$ defined on $[a, b]$ by the equation $s_1(x) = s(kx)$ is a step function below $f$ on $[a, b]$. Moreover, every step function $s_1$ below $f$ on $[a, b]$ has this form. Also, by the expansion property for integrals of step functions, we have

$$\int_{ka}^{kb} s(x)\,dx = k\int_a^b s(kx)\,dx = k\int_a^b s_1(x)\,dx\,.$$

Therefore we have

$$I(g) = \sup\left\{\int_{ka}^{kb} s \mid s \le g\right\} = \sup\left\{k\int_a^b s_1 \mid s_1 \le f\right\} = k\int_a^b f(x)\,dx\,.$$

Similarly, we find $\bar{I}(g) = k\int_a^b f(x)\,dx$, which proves (1.17) if $k > 0$. The same type of proof can be used if $k < 0$.

*Proof of the Comparison Theorem* (*Theorem* 1.20). Assume $g \le f$ on the interval $[a, b]$. Let $s$ be any step function below $g$, and let $t$ be any step function above $f$. Then we have $\int_a^b s \le \int_a^b t$, and hence Theorem I.34 gives us

$$\int_a^b g = \sup\left\{\int_a^b s \mid s \le g\right\} \le \inf\left\{\int_a^b t \mid f \le t\right\} = \int_a^b f\,.$$

This proves that $\int_a^b g \le \int_a^b f$, as required.

# 2

# SOME APPLICATIONS OF INTEGRATION

## 2.1 Introduction

In Section 1.18 we expressed the area of the ordinate set of a nonnegative function as an integral. In this chapter we will show that areas of more general regions can also be expressed as integrals. We will also discuss further applications of the integral to concepts such as volume, work, and averages. Then, at the end of the chapter, we will study properties of functions defined by integrals.

## 2.2 The area of a region between two graphs expressed as an integral

If two functions $f$ and $g$ are related by the inequality $f(x) \leq g(x)$ for all $x$ in an interval $[a, b]$, we write $f \leq g$ on $[a, b]$. Figure 2.1 shows two examples. If $f \leq g$ on $[a, b]$, the set $S$ consisting of all points $(x, y)$ satisfying the inequalities

$$f(x) \leq y \leq g(x), \qquad a \leq x \leq b,$$

is called the region between the graphs of $f$ and $g$. The following theorem tells us how to express the area of $S$ as an integral.

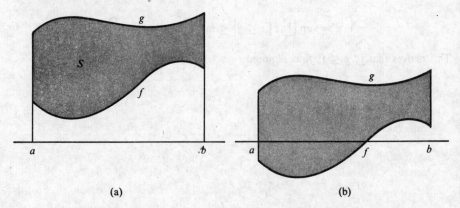

(a)                                    (b)

FIGURE 2.1  The area of a region between two graphs expressed as an integral:

$$a(S) = \int_a^b [g(x) - f(x)]\, dx.$$

THEOREM 2.1. *Assume f and g are integrable and satisfy $f \leq g$ on $[a, b]$. Then the region S between their graphs is measurable and its area $a(S)$ is given by the integral*

$$(2.1) \qquad a(S) = \int_a^b [g(x) - f(x)]\, dx \,.$$

*Proof.* Assume first that $f$ and $g$ are nonnegative, as shown in Figure 2.1(a). Let $F$ and $G$ denote the following sets:

$$F = \{(x, y) \mid a \leq x \leq b,\, 0 \leq y < f(x)\}, \qquad G = \{(x, y) \mid a \leq x \leq b,\, 0 \leq y \leq g(x)\} \,.$$

That is, $G$ is the ordinate set of $g$, and $F$ is the ordinate set of $f$, minus the graph of $f$. The region $S$ between the graphs of $f$ and $g$ is the difference $S = G - F$. By Theorems 1.10 and 1.11, both $F$ and $G$ are measurable. Since $F \subseteq G$, the difference $S = G - F$ is also measurable, and we have

$$a(S) = a(G) - a(F) = \int_a^b g(x)\, dx - \int_a^b f(x)\, dx = \int_a^b [g(x) - f(x)]\, dx \,.$$

This proves (2.1) when $f$ and $g$ are nonnegative.

Now consider the general case where $f \leq g$ on $[a, b]$, but $f$ and $g$ are not necessarily nonnegative. An example is shown in Figure 2.1(b). We can reduce this to the previous case by sliding the region upward until it lies above the $x$-axis. That is, we choose a positive number $c$ large enough to ensure that $0 \leq f(x) + c \leq g(x) + c$ for all $x$ in $[a, b]$. By what we have already proved, the new region $T$ between the graphs of $f + c$ and $g + c$ is measurable, and its area is given by the integral

$$a(T) = \int_a^b [(g(x) + c) - (f(x) + c)]\, dx = \int_a^b [g(x) - f(x)]\, dx \,.$$

But $T$ is congruent to $S$; so $S$ is also measurable and we have

$$a(S) = a(T) = \int_a^b [g(x) - f(x)]\, dx \,.$$

This completes the proof.

## 2.3 Worked examples

EXAMPLE 1. Compute the area of the region $S$ between the graphs of $f$ and $g$ over the interval $[0, 2]$ if $f(x) = x(x - 2)$ and $g(x) = x/2$.

*Solution.* The two graphs are shown in Figure 2.2. The shaded portion represents $S$. Since $f \leq g$ over the interval $[0, 2]$, we use Theorem 2.1 to write

$$a(S) = \int_0^2 [g(x) - f(x)]\, dx = \int_0^2 \left(\frac{5}{2}x - x^2\right) dx = \frac{5}{2}\frac{2^2}{2} - \frac{2^3}{3} = \frac{7}{3} \,.$$

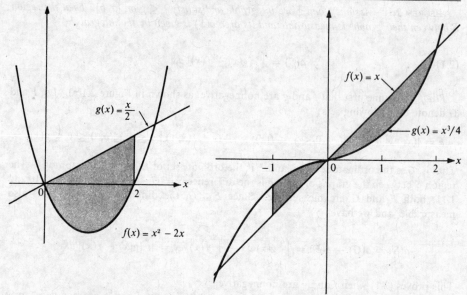

FIGURE 2.2   Example 1.                    FIGURE 2.3   Example 2.

EXAMPLE 2. Compute the area of the region $S$ between the graphs of $f$ and $g$ over the interval $[-1, 2]$ if $f(x) = x$ and $g(x) = x^3/4$.

*Solution.*   The region $S$ is shown in Figure 2.3. Here we do not have $f \leq g$ throughout the interval $[-1, 2]$. However, we do have $f \leq g$ over the subinterval $[-1, 0]$ and $g \leq f$ over the subinterval $[0, 2]$. Applying Theorem 2.1 to each subinterval, we have

$$a(S) = \int_{-1}^{0} [g(x) - f(x)] \, dx + \int_{0}^{2} [f(x) - g(x)] \, dx$$

$$= \int_{-1}^{0} \left( \frac{x^3}{4} - x \right) dx + \int_{0}^{2} \left( x - \frac{x^3}{4} \right) dx$$

$$= -\frac{1}{4} \frac{(-1)^4}{4} + \frac{(-1)^2}{2} + \frac{2^2}{2} - \frac{1}{4} \frac{2^4}{4} = \frac{23}{16} .$$

In examples like this one, where the interval $[a, b]$ can be broken up into a finite number of subintervals such that either $f \leq g$ or $g \leq f$ in each subinterval, formula (2.1) of Theorem 2.1 becomes

$$a(S) = \int_{a}^{b} |g(x) - f(x)| \, dx .$$

EXAMPLE 3. *Area of a circular disk.* A circular disk of radius $r$ is the set of all points inside or on the boundary of a circle of radius $r$. Such a disk is congruent to the region between the graphs of the two functions $f$ and $g$ defined on the interval $[-r, r]$ by the formulas

$$g(x) = \sqrt{r^2 - x^2} \quad \text{and} \quad f(x) = -\sqrt{r^2 - x^2}.$$

Each function is bounded and piecewise monotonic so each is integrable on $[-r, r]$. Theorem 2.1 tells us that the region between their graphs is measurable and that its area is $\int_{-r}^{r} [g(x) - f(x)]\, dx$. Let $A(r)$ denote the area of the disk. We will prove that

$$A(r) = r^2 A(1).$$

That is, *the area of a disk of radius $r$ is $r^2$ times the area of a unit disk* (a disk of radius 1). Since $g(x) - f(x) = 2g(x)$, Theorem 2.1 gives us

$$A(r) = \int_{-r}^{r} 2g(x)\, dx = 2 \int_{-r}^{r} \sqrt{r^2 - x^2}\, dx.$$

In particular, when $r = 1$, we have the formula

$$A(1) = 2 \int_{-1}^{1} \sqrt{1 - x^2}\, dx.$$

Now we change the scale on the $x$-axis, using Theorem 1.19 with $k = 1/r$, to obtain

$$A(r) = 2 \int_{-r}^{r} g(x)\, dx = 2r \int_{-1}^{1} g(rx)\, dx = 2r \int_{-1}^{1} \sqrt{r^2 - (rx)^2}\, dx$$

$$= 2r^2 \int_{-1}^{1} \sqrt{1 - x^2}\, dx = r^2 A(1).$$

This proves that $A(r) = r^2 A(1)$, as asserted.

DEFINITION. *We define the number $\pi$ to be the area of a unit disk.*

The formula just proved states that $A(r) = \pi r^2$.

The foregoing example illustrates the behavior of area under expansion or contraction of plane regions. Suppose $S$ is a given set of points in the plane and consider a new set of points obtained by multiplying the coordinates of each point of $S$ by a constant factor $k > 0$. We denote this set by $kS$ and say that it is *similar to S*. The process which produces $kS$ from $S$ is called a *similarity transformation*. Each point is moved along a straight line which passes through the origin to $k$ times its original distance from the origin. If $k > 1$, the transformation is also called a *stretching* or an *expansion* (from the origin) and, if $0 < k < 1$, it is called a *shrinking* or a *contraction* (toward the origin).

For example, if $S$ is the region bounded by a unit circle with center at the origin, then $kS$ is a concentric circular region of radius $k$. In Example 3 we showed that for circular regions, the area of $kS$ is $k^2$ times the area of $S$. Now we prove that this property of area holds for any ordinate set.

EXAMPLE 4. *Behavior of the area of an ordinate set under a similarity transformation.*
Let $f$ be nonnegative and integrable on $[a, b]$ and let $S$ be its ordinate set. An example is
shown in Figure 2.4(a). If we apply a similarity transformation with a positive factor $k$,
then $kS$ is the ordinate set of a new function, say $g$, over the interval $[ka, kb]$. [See Figure
2.4(b).] A point $(x, y)$ is on the graph of $g$ if and only if the point $(x/k, y/k)$ is on the graph
of $f$. Hence $y/k = f(x/k)$, so $y = kf(x/k)$. In other words, the new function $g$ is related to
$f$ by the formula

$$g(x) = kf(x/k)$$

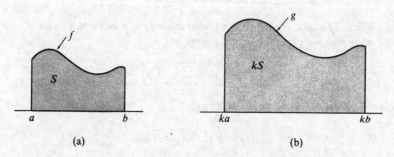

(a)                                                  (b)

FIGURE 2.4   The area of $kS$ is $k^2$ times that of $S$.

for each $x$ in $[ka, kb]$. Therefore, the area of $kS$ is given by

$$a(kS) = \int_{ka}^{kb} g(x)\,dx = k \int_{ka}^{kb} f(x/k)\,dx = k^2 \int_{a}^{b} f(x)\,dx\,,$$

where in the last step we used the expansion property for integrals (Theorem 1.19). Since
$\int_{a}^{b} f(x)\,dx = a(S)$, this proves that $a(kS) = k^2 a(S)$. In other words, the area of $kS$ is $k^2$ times
that of $S$.

EXAMPLE 5. *Calculation of the integral $\int_{0}^{a} x^{1/2}\,dx$.* The integral for area is a two-edged
sword. Although we ordinarily use the integral to calculate areas, sometimes we can use
our knowledge of area to calculate integrals. We illustrate by computing the value of the
integral $\int_{0}^{a} x^{1/2}\,dx$, where $a > 0$. (The integral exists since the integrand is increasing and
bounded on $[0, a]$.)

Figure 2.5 shows the graph of the function $f$ given by $f(x) = x^{1/2}$ over the interval $[0, a]$.
Its ordinate set $S$ has an area given by

$$a(S) = \int_{0}^{a} x^{1/2}\,dx\,.$$

Now we compute this area another way. We simply observe that in Figure 2.5 the region
$S$ and the shaded region $T$ together fill out a rectangle of base $a$ and altitude $a^{1/2}$. Therefore,
$a(S) + a(T) = a^{3/2}$, so we have

$$a(S) = a^{3/2} - a(T)\,.$$

But $T$ is the ordinate set of a function $g$ defined over the interval $[0, a^{1/2}]$ on the $y$-axis by the equation $g(y) = y^2$. Thus, we have

$$a(T) = \int_0^{a^{1/2}} g(y)\, dy = \int_0^{a^{1/2}} y^2\, dy = \tfrac{1}{3} a^{3/2} \,,$$

so $a(S) = a^{3/2} - \tfrac{1}{3} a^{3/2} = \tfrac{2}{3} a^{3/2}$. This proves that

$$\int_0^a x^{1/2}\, dx = \tfrac{2}{3}\, a^{3/2} \,.$$

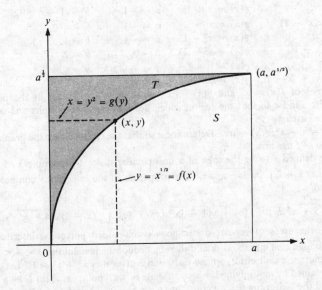

FIGURE 2.5 Calculation of the integral $\int_0^a x^{1/2}\, dx$.

More generally, if $a > 0$ and $b > 0$, we may use the additive property of the integral to obtain the formula

$$\int_a^b x^{1/2}\, dx = \tfrac{2}{3}(b^{3/2} - a^{3/2}) \,.$$

The foregoing argument can also be used to compute the integral $\int_a^b x^{1/n}\, dx$, if $n$ is a positive integer. We state the result as a theorem.

THEOREM 2.2. *For $a > 0$, $b > 0$ and $n$ a positive integer, we have*

$$(2.2) \qquad \int_a^b x^{1/n}\, dx = \frac{b^{1+1/n} - a^{1+1/n}}{1 + 1/n} \,.$$

The proof is so similar to that in Example 5 that we leave the details to the reader.

## 2.4　Exercises

In Exercises 1 through 14, compute the area of the region $S$ between the graphs of $f$ and $g$ over the interval $[a, b]$ specified in each case.　Make a sketch of the two graphs and indicate $S$ by shading.

1. $f(x) = 4 - x^2$,　　　　　$g(x) = 0$,　　　　　$a = -2$,　　　$b = 2$.
2. $f(x) = 4 - x^2$,　　　　　$g(x) = 8 - 2x^2$,　　　$a = -2$,　　　$b = 2$.
3. $f(x) = x^3 + x^2$,　　　　$g(x) = x^3 + 1$,　　　$a = -1$,　　　$b = 1$.
4. $f(x) = x - x^2$,　　　　　$g(x) = -x$,　　　　$a = 0$,　　　$b = 2$.
5. $f(x) = x^{1/3}$,　　　　　$g(x) = x^{1/2}$,　　　$a = 0$,　　　$b = 1$.
6. $f(x) = x^{1/3}$,　　　　　$g(x) = x^{1/2}$,　　　$a = 1$,　　　$b = 2$.
7. $f(x) = x^{1/3}$,　　　　　$g(x) = x^{1/2}$,　　　$a = 0$,　　　$b = 2$.
8. $f(x) = x^{1/2}$,　　　　　$g(x) = x^2$,　　　　$a = 0$,　　　$b = 2$.
9. $f(x) = x^2$,　　　　　　$g(x) = x + 1$,　　　$a = -1$,　　　$b = (1 + \sqrt{5})/2$.
10. $f(x) = x(x^2 - 1)$,　　　$g(x) = x$,　　　　$a = -1$,　　　$b = \sqrt{2}$.
11. $f(x) = |x|$,　　　　　　$g(x) = x^2 - 1$,　　　$a = -1$,　　　$b = 1$.
12. $f(x) = |x - 1|$,　　　　$g(x) = x^2 - 2x$,　　　$a = 0$,　　　$b = 2$.
13. $f(x) = 2|x|$,　　　　　$g(x) = 1 - 3x^3$,　　　$a = -\sqrt{3}/3$,　$b = \frac{1}{3}$.
14. $f(x) = |x| + |x - 1|$,　$g(x) = 0$,　　　　$a = -1$,　　　$b = 2$.

15. The graphs of $f(x) = x^2$ and $g(x) = cx^3$, where $c > 0$, intersect at the points $(0, 0)$ and $(1/c, 1/c^2)$. Find $c$ so that the region which lies between these graphs and over the interval $[0, 1/c]$ has area $\frac{2}{3}$.

16. Let $f(x) = x - x^2, g(x) = ax$. Determine $a$ so that the region above the graph of $g$ and below the graph of $f$ has area $\frac{9}{2}$.

17. We have defined $\pi$ to be the area of a unit circular disk. In Example 3 of Section 2.3, we proved that $\pi = 2\int_{-1}^{1}\sqrt{1 - x^2}\,dx$. Use properties of the integral to compute the following in terms of $\pi$:

   (a) $\int_{-3}^{3}\sqrt{9 - x^2}\,dx$;　　(b) $\int_{0}^{2}\sqrt{1 - \frac{1}{4}x^2}\,dx$;　　(c) $\int_{-2}^{2}(x - 3)\sqrt{4 - x^2}\,dx$.

18. Calculate the areas of regular dodecagons (twelve-sided polygons) inscribed and circumscribed about a unit circular disk and thereby deduce the inequalities $3 < \pi < 12(2 - \sqrt{3})$.

19. Let $C$ denote the unit circle, whose Cartesian equation is $x^2 + y^2 = 1$. Let $E$ be the set of points obtained by multiplying the $x$-coordinate of each point $(x, y)$ on $C$ by a constant factor $a > 0$ and the $y$-coordinate by a constant factor $b > 0$. The set $E$ is called an ellipse. (When $a = b$, the ellipse is another circle.)
   (a) Show that each point $(x, y)$ on $E$ satisfies the Cartesian equation $(x/a)^2 + (y/b)^2 = 1$.
   (b) Use properties of the integral to prove that the region enclosed by this ellipse is measurable and that its area is $\pi ab$.

20. Exercise 19 is a generalization of Example 3 of Section 2.3. State and prove a corresponding generalization of Example 4 of Section 2.3.

21. Use an argument similar to that in Example 5 of Section 2.3 to prove Theorem 2.2.

## 2.5　The trigonometric functions

Before we introduce further applications of integration, we will digress briefly to discuss the trigonometric functions. We assume that the reader has some knowledge of the properties of the six trigonometric functions, sine, cosine, tangent, cotangent, secant, and cosecant; and their inverses, arc sine, arc cosine, arc tangent, etc. These functions are discussed in elementary trigonometry courses in connection with various problems involving the sides and angles of triangles.

The trigonometric functions are important in calculus, not so much because of their relation to the sides and angles of a triangle, but rather because of the properties they possess as *functions*. The six trigonometric functions have in common an important property known as periodicity.

A function $f$ is said to be *periodic* with period $p \neq 0$ if its domain contains $x + p$ whenever it contains $x$ and if $f(x + p) = f(x)$ for every $x$ in the domain of $f$. The sine and cosine functions are periodic with period $2\pi$, where $\pi$ is the area of a unit circular disk. Many problems in physics and engineering deal with periodic phenomena (such as vibrations, planetary and wave motion) and the sine and cosine functions form the basis for the mathematical analysis of such problems.

The sine and cosine functions can be introduced in many different ways. For example, there are geometric definitions which relate the sine and cosine functions to angles, and there are analytic definitions which introduce these functions without any reference whatever to geometry. All these methods are equivalent, in the sense that they all lead to the same functions.

Ordinarily, when we work with the sine and cosine we are not concerned so much with their definitions as we are with the properties that can be deduced from the definitions. Some of these properties, which are of importance in calculus, are listed below. As usual, we denote the values of the sine and cosine functions at $x$ by sin $x$, cos $x$, respectively.

FUNDAMENTAL PROPERTIES OF THE SINE AND COSINE.

1. *Domain of definition. The sine and cosine functions are defined everywhere on the real line.*

2. *Special values. We have* $\cos 0 = \sin \frac{1}{2}\pi = 1$, $\cos \pi = -1$.

3. *Cosine of a difference. For all $x$ and $y$, we have*

$$(2.3) \qquad \cos (y - x) = \cos y \cos x + \sin y \sin x.$$

4. *Fundamental inequalities. For $0 < x < \frac{1}{2}\pi$, we have*

$$(2.4) \qquad 0 < \cos x < \frac{\sin x}{x} < \frac{1}{\cos x}.$$

From these four properties we can deduce all the properties of the sine and cosine that are of importance in calculus. This suggests that we might introduce the trigonometric functions axiomatically. That is, we could take properties 1 through 4 as axioms about the sine and cosine and deduce all further properties as theorems. To make certain we are not discussing an empty theory, it is necessary to show that there are functions satisfying the above properties. We shall by-pass this problem for the moment. First we assume that functions exist which satisfy these fundamental properties and show how further properties can then be deduced. Then, in Section 2.7, we indicate a geometric method of defining the sine and cosine so as to obtain functions with the desired properties. In Chapter 11 we also outline an analytic method for defining the sine and cosine.

THEOREM 2.3.    *If two functions* sin *and* cos *satisfy properties 1 through 4, then they also satisfy the following properties:*

(a) *Pythagorean identity.* $\sin^2 x + \cos^2 x = 1$ *for all* $x$.

(b) *Special values.* $\sin 0 = \cos \frac{1}{2}\pi = \sin \pi = 0$.

(c) *Even and odd properties. The cosine is an even function and the sine is an odd function. That is, for all* $x$ *we have*

$$\cos(-x) = \cos x, \qquad \sin(-x) = -\sin x.$$

(d) *Co-relations. For all* $x$, *we have*

$$\sin(\tfrac{1}{2}\pi + x) = \cos x, \qquad \cos(\tfrac{1}{2}\pi + x) = -\sin x.$$

(e) *Periodicity. For all* $x$, *we have* $\sin(x + 2\pi) = \sin x$, $\cos(x + 2\pi) = \cos x$.

(f) *Addition formulas. For all* $x$ *and* $y$, *we have*

$$\cos(x + y) = \cos x \cos y - \sin x \sin y,$$
$$\sin(x + y) = \sin x \cos y + \cos x \sin y.$$

(g) *Difference formulas. For all* $a$ *and* $b$, *we have*

$$\sin a - \sin b = 2 \sin \frac{a-b}{2} \cos \frac{a+b}{2},$$

$$\cos a - \cos b = -2 \sin \frac{a-b}{2} \sin \frac{a+b}{2}.$$

(h) *Monotonicity. In the interval* $[0, \frac{1}{2}\pi]$, *the sine is strictly increasing and the cosine is strictly decreasing.*

*Proof.*    Part (a) follows at once if we take $x = y$ in (2.3) and use the relation $\cos 0 = 1$. Property (b) follows from (a) by taking $x = 0$, $x = \frac{1}{2}\pi$, $x = \pi$ and using the relation $\sin \frac{1}{2}\pi = 1$. The even property of the cosine also follows from (2.3) by taking $y = 0$. Next we deduce the formula

(2.5)                    $$\cos(\tfrac{1}{2}\pi - x) = \sin x,$$

by taking $y = \frac{1}{2}\pi$ in (2.3). From this and (2.3), we find that the sine is odd, since

$$\sin(-x) = \cos\left(\frac{\pi}{2} + x\right) = \cos\left[\pi - \left(\frac{\pi}{2} - x\right)\right]$$

$$= \cos \pi \cos\left(\frac{\pi}{2} - x\right) + \sin \pi \sin\left(\frac{\pi}{2} - x\right) = -\sin x.$$

This proves (c). To prove (d), we again use (2.5), first with $x$ replaced by $\frac{1}{2}\pi + x$ and then with $x$ replaced by $-x$. Repeated use of (d) then gives us the periodicity relations (e).

To prove the addition formula for the cosine, we simply replace $x$ by $-x$ in (2.3) and use the even and odd properties. Then we use part (d) and the addition formula for the cosine to obtain

$$\sin (x + y) = -\cos \left(x + y + \frac{\pi}{2}\right) = -\cos x \cos \left(y + \frac{\pi}{2}\right) + \sin x \sin \left(y + \frac{\pi}{2}\right)$$

$$= \cos x \sin y + \sin x \cos y \, .$$

This proves (f). To deduce the difference formulas (g), we first replace $y$ by $-y$ in the addition formula for $\sin (x + y)$ to obtain

$$\sin (x - y) = \sin x \cos y - \cos x \sin y \, .$$

Subtracting this from the formula for $\sin (x + y)$ and doing the same for the cosine function, we get

$$\sin (x + y) - \sin (x - y) = 2 \sin y \cos x \, ,$$

$$\cos (x + y) - \cos (x - y) = -2 \sin y \sin x \, .$$

Taking $x = (a + b)/2$, $y = (a - b)/2$, we find that these become the difference formulas in (g).

Properties (a) through (g) were deduced from properties 1 through 3 alone. Property 4 is used to prove (h). The inequalities (2.4) show that $\cos x$ and $\sin x$ are positive if $0 < x < \frac{1}{2}\pi$. Now, if $0 < b < a < \frac{1}{2}\pi$, the numbers $(a + b)/2$ and $(a - b)/2$ are in the interval $(0, \frac{1}{2}\pi)$, and the difference formulas (g) show that $\sin a > \sin b$ and $\cos a < \cos b$. This completes the proof of Theorem 2.3.

Further properties of the sine and cosine functions are discussed in the next set of exercises (page 104). We mention, in particular, two formulas that are used frequently in calculus. These are called the *double-angle* or *duplication formulas*. We have

$$\sin 2x = 2 \sin x \cos x \, , \qquad \cos 2x = \cos^2 x - \sin^2 x = 1 - 2 \sin^2 x \, .$$

These are, of course, merely special cases of the addition formulas obtained by taking $y = x$. The second formula for $\cos 2x$ follows from the first by use of the Pythagorean identity. The Pythagorean identity also shows that $|\cos x| \leq 1$ and $|\sin x| \leq 1$ for all $x$.

## 2.6 Integration formulas for the sine and cosine

The monotonicity properties in part (h) of Theorem 2.3, along with the co-relations and the periodicity properties, show that the sine and cosine functions are piecewise monotonic on every interval. Therefore, by repeated use of Theorem 1.12, we see that the sine and cosine are integrable on every finite interval. Now we shall calculate their integrals by applying Theorem 1.14. This calculation makes use of a pair of inequalities which we state as a separate theorem.

THEOREM 2.4. *If $0 < a \leq \frac{1}{2}\pi$ and $n \geq 1$, we have*

$$(2.6) \qquad \frac{a}{n} \sum_{k=1}^{n} \cos \frac{ka}{n} < \sin a < \frac{a}{n} \sum_{k=0}^{n-1} \cos \frac{ka}{n} \, .$$

*Proof.* The inequalities in (2.6) will be deduced from the trigonometric identity

$$(2.7) \qquad 2 \sin \tfrac{1}{2}x \sum_{k=1}^{n} \cos kx = \sin (n + \tfrac{1}{2})x - \sin \tfrac{1}{2}x,$$

which is valid for $n \geq 1$ and all real $x$. To prove (2.7), we use one of the difference formulas (g) of Theorem 2.3 to write

$$2 \sin \tfrac{1}{2}x \cos kx = \sin (k + \tfrac{1}{2})x - \sin (k - \tfrac{1}{2})x.$$

Taking $k = 1, 2, \ldots, n$ and adding these equations, we find that the sum on the right telescopes and we obtain (2.7).

If $\tfrac{1}{2}x$ is not an integer multiple of $\pi$ we can divide both members of (2.7) by $2 \sin \tfrac{1}{2}x$ to obtain

$$\sum_{k=1}^{n} \cos kx = \frac{\sin (n + \tfrac{1}{2})x - \sin \tfrac{1}{2}x}{2 \sin \tfrac{1}{2}x}.$$

Replacing $n$ by $n - 1$ and adding 1 to both members we also obtain

$$\sum_{k=0}^{n-1} \cos kx = \frac{\sin (n - \tfrac{1}{2})x + \sin \tfrac{1}{2}x}{2 \sin \tfrac{1}{2}x}.$$

Both these formulas are valid if $x \neq 2m\pi$, where $m$ is an integer. Taking $x = a/n$, where $0 < a \leq \tfrac{1}{2}\pi$ we find that the pair of inequalities in (2.6) is equivalent to the pair

$$\frac{a}{n} \frac{\sin (n + \tfrac{1}{2}) \dfrac{a}{n} - \sin \left( \dfrac{a}{2n} \right)}{2 \sin \left( \dfrac{a}{2n} \right)} < \sin a < \frac{a}{n} \frac{\sin (n - \tfrac{1}{2}) \dfrac{a}{n} + \sin \left( \dfrac{a}{2n} \right)}{2 \sin \left( \dfrac{a}{2n} \right)}.$$

This pair, in turn, is equivalent to the pair

$$(2.8) \qquad \sin (n + \tfrac{1}{2}) \frac{a}{n} - \sin \left( \frac{a}{2n} \right) < \frac{\sin \left( \dfrac{a}{2n} \right)}{\left( \dfrac{a}{2n} \right)} \sin a < \sin (n - \tfrac{1}{2}) \frac{a}{n} + \sin \left( \frac{a}{2n} \right).$$

Therefore, proving (2.6) is equivalent to proving (2.8). We shall prove that we have

$$(2.9) \qquad \sin (2n + 1)\theta - \sin \theta < \frac{\sin \theta}{\theta} \sin 2n\theta < \sin (2n - 1)\theta + \sin \theta$$

for $0 < 2n\theta \leq \tfrac{1}{2}\pi$. When $\theta = a/(2n)$ this reduces to (2.8).

To prove the leftmost inequality in (2.9), we use the addition formula for the sine to write

$$(2.10) \quad \sin(2n+1)\theta = \sin 2n\theta \cos \theta + \cos 2n\theta \sin \theta < \sin 2n\theta \, \frac{\sin \theta}{\theta} + \sin \theta,$$

where we have also used the inequalities

$$\cos \theta < \frac{\sin \theta}{\theta}, \quad 0 < \cos 2n\theta \leq 1, \quad \sin \theta > 0,$$

all of which are valid since $0 < 2n\theta \leq \frac{1}{2}\pi$. Inequality (2.10) is equivalent to the leftmost inequality in (2.9).

To prove the rightmost inequality in (2.9), we again use the addition formula for the sine and write

$$\sin(2n-1)\theta = \sin 2n\theta \cos \theta - \cos 2n\theta \sin \theta.$$

Adding $\sin \theta$ to both members, we obtain

$$(2.11) \quad \sin(2n-1)\theta + \sin \theta = \sin 2n\theta \left( \cos \theta + \sin \theta \, \frac{1 - \cos 2n\theta}{\sin 2n\theta} \right).$$

But since we have

$$\frac{1 - \cos 2n\theta}{\sin 2n\theta} = \frac{2 \sin^2 n\theta}{2 \sin n\theta \cos n\theta} = \frac{\sin n\theta}{\cos n\theta},$$

the right member of (2.11) is equal to

$$\sin 2n\theta \left( \cos \theta + \sin \theta \, \frac{\sin n\theta}{\cos n\theta} \right) = \sin 2n\theta \, \frac{\cos \theta \cos n\theta + \sin \theta \sin n\theta}{\cos n\theta}$$

$$= \sin 2n\theta \, \frac{\cos(n-1)\theta}{\cos n\theta}.$$

Therefore, to complete the proof of (2.9), we need only show that

$$(2.12) \quad \frac{\cos(n-1)\theta}{\cos n\theta} > \frac{\sin \theta}{\theta}.$$

But we have

$$\cos n\theta = \cos(n-1)\theta \cos \theta - \sin(n-1)\theta \sin \theta$$

$$< \cos(n-1)\theta \cos \theta < \cos(n-1)\theta \, \frac{\theta}{\sin \theta},$$

where we have again used the fundamental inequality $\cos \theta < \theta/(\sin \theta)$. This last relation implies (2.12), so the proof of Theorem 2.4 is complete.

THEOREM 2.5.   *If two functions* sin *and* cos *satisfy the fundamental properties* 1 *through* 4, *then for every real a we have*

(2.13)
$$\int_0^a \cos x \, dx = \sin a \, ,$$

(2.14)
$$\int_0^a \sin x \, dx = 1 - \cos a \, .$$

*Proof.*   First we prove (2.13), and then we use (2.13) to deduce (2.14). Assume that $0 < a \le \frac{1}{2}\pi$. Since the cosine is decreasing on $[0, a]$, we can apply Theorem 1.14 in conjunction with the inequalities of Theorem 2.4 to obtain (2.13). The formula also holds trivially for $a = 0$, since both members are zero. The general properties of the integral can now be used to extend its validity to all real $a$.

For example, if $-\frac{1}{2}\pi \le a \le 0$, then $0 \le -a \le \frac{1}{2}\pi$, and the reflection property gives us

$$\int_0^a \cos x \, dx = -\int_0^{-a} \cos(-x) \, dx = -\int_0^{-a} \cos x \, dx = -\sin(-a) = \sin a \, .$$

Thus (2.13) is valid in the interval $[-\frac{1}{2}\pi, \frac{1}{2}\pi]$. Now suppose that $\frac{1}{2}\pi \le a \le \frac{3}{2}\pi$. Then $-\frac{1}{2}\pi \le a - \pi \le \frac{1}{2}\pi$, so we have

$$\int_0^a \cos x \, dx = \int_0^{\pi/2} \cos x \, dx + \int_{\pi/2}^a \cos x \, dx = \sin \tfrac{1}{2}\pi + \int_{-\pi/2}^{a-\pi} \cos(x + \pi) \, dx$$

$$= 1 - \int_{-\pi/2}^{a-\pi} \cos x \, dx = 1 - \sin(a - \pi) + \sin(-\tfrac{1}{2}\pi) = \sin a \, .$$

Thus (2.13) holds for all $a$ in the interval $[-\frac{1}{2}\pi, \frac{3}{2}\pi]$. But this interval has length $2\pi$, so formula (2.13) holds for all $a$ since both members are periodic in $a$ with period $2\pi$.

Now we use (2.13) to deduce (2.14). First we prove that (2.14) holds when $a = \pi/2$. Applying, in succession, the translation property, the co-relation $\sin(x + \frac{1}{2}\pi) = \cos x$, and the reflection property, we find

$$\int_0^{\pi/2} \sin x \, dx = \int_{-\pi/2}^0 \sin\left(x + \frac{\pi}{2}\right) dx = \int_{-\pi/2}^0 \cos x \, dx = \int_0^{\pi/2} \cos(-x) \, dx \, .$$

Using the relation $\cos(-x) = \cos x$ and Equation (2.13), we obtain

$$\int_0^{\pi/2} \sin x \, dx = 1 \, .$$

Now, for any real $a$, we may write

$$\int_0^a \sin x \, dx = \int_0^{\pi/2} \sin x \, dx + \int_{\pi/2}^a \sin x \, dx = 1 + \int_0^{a-\pi/2} \sin\left(x + \frac{\pi}{2}\right) dx$$

$$= 1 + \int_0^{a-\pi/2} \cos x \, dx = 1 + \sin\left(a - \frac{\pi}{2}\right) = 1 - \cos a \, .$$

This shows that Equation (2.13) implies (2.14).

EXAMPLE 1. Using (2.13) and (2.14) in conjunction with the additive property

$$\int_a^b f(x)\,dx = \int_0^b f(x)\,dx - \int_0^a f(x)\,dx,$$

we get the more general integration formulas

$$\int_a^b \cos x\,dx = \sin b - \sin a$$

and

$$\int_a^b \sin x\,dx = (1 - \cos b) - (1 - \cos a) = -(\cos b - \cos a)\,.$$

If again we use the special symbol $f(x)\,\big|_a^b$ to denote the difference $f(b) - f(a)$, we can write these integration formulas in the form

$$\int_a^b \cos x\,dx = \sin x\,\Big|_a^b \qquad \text{and} \qquad \int_a^b \sin x\,dx = -\cos x\,\Big|_a^b\,.$$

EXAMPLE 2. Using the results of Example 1 and the expansion property

$$\int_a^b f(x)\,dx = \frac{1}{c}\int_{ca}^{cb} f(x/c)\,dx\,,$$

we obtain the following formulas, valid for $c \neq 0$:

$$\int_a^b \cos cx\,dx = \frac{1}{c}\int_{ca}^{cb} \cos x\,dx = \frac{1}{c}(\sin cb - \sin ca)\,,$$

and

$$\int_a^b \sin cx\,dx = \frac{1}{c}\int_{ca}^{cb} \sin x\,dx = -\frac{1}{c}(\cos cb - \cos ca)\,.$$

EXAMPLE 3. The identity $\cos 2x = 1 - 2\sin^2 x$ implies $\sin^2 x = \frac{1}{2}(1 - \cos 2x)$ so, from Example 2, we obtain

$$\int_0^a \sin^2 x\,dx = \frac{1}{2}\int_0^a (1 - \cos 2x)\,dx = \frac{a}{2} - \frac{1}{4}\sin 2a\,.$$

Since $\sin^2 x + \cos^2 x = 1$, we also find

$$\int_0^a \cos^2 x\,dx = \int_0^a (1 - \sin^2 x)\,dx = a - \int_0^a \sin^2 x\,dx = \frac{a}{2} + \frac{1}{4}\sin 2a\,.$$

### 2.7 A geometric description of the sine and cosine functions

In this section we indicate a geometric method for defining the sine and cosine functions, and we give a geometric interpretation of the fundamental properties listed in the Section 2.5.

Consider a circle of radius $r$ with its center at the origin. Denote the point $(r, 0)$ by $A$, and let $P$ be any other point on the circle. The two line segments $OA$ and $OP$ determine a geometric configuration called an angle which we denote by the symbol $\angle AOP$. An example is shown in Figure 2.6. We wish to assign to this angle a nonnegative real number $x$ which can be used as a measurement of its size. The most common way of doing this is to take a circle of radius 1 and let $x$ be the length of the circular arc $AP$, traced counterclockwise

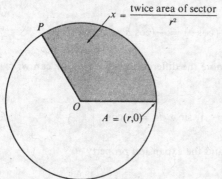
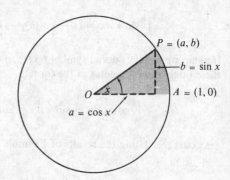

FIGURE 2.6  An angle $\angle AOP$ consisting of $x$ radians.

FIGURE 2.7  Geometric description of sin $x$ and cos $x$.

from $A$ to $P$, and to say that the measure of $\angle AOP$ is $x$ radians. From a logical point of view, this is unsatisfactory at the present stage because we have not yet discussed the concept of arc length. Arc length will be discussed later in Chapter 14. Since the concept of area has already been discussed, we prefer to use the area of the circular sector $AOP$ rather than the length of the arc $AP$ as a measure of the size of $\angle AOP$. It is understood that the sector $AOP$ is the smaller portion of the circular disk when $P$ is above the real axis, and the larger portion when $P$ is below the real axis.

Later, when arc length is discussed, we shall find that the length of arc $AP$ is exactly twice the area of sector $AOP$. Therefore, to get the same scale of measurement for angles by both methods, we shall use *twice* the area of the sector $AOP$ as a measure of the angle $\angle AOP$. However, to obtain a "dimensionless" measure of angles, that is, a measure independent of the unit of distance in our coordinate system, we shall define the measure of $\angle AOP$ to be *twice the area of sector AOP divided by the square of the radius.* This ratio does not change if we expand or contract the circle, and therefore there is no loss in generality in restricting our considerations to a unit circle. The unit of measure so obtained is called the *radian.* Thus, we say the measure of an angle $\angle AOP$ is $x$ radians if $x/2$ is the area of the sector $AOP$ cut from a unit circular disk.

We have already introduced the symbol $\pi$ to denote the area of a unit circular disk. When $P = (-1, 0)$, the sector $AOP$ is a semicircular disk of area $\frac{1}{2}\pi$, so it subtends an angle of $\pi$ radians. The entire disk is a sector consisting of $2\pi$ radians. If $P$ is initially at $(1, 0)$ and if

$P$ moves once around the circle in a counterclockwise direction, the area of sector $AOP$ increases from 0 to $\pi$, taking every value in the interval $[0, \pi]$ exactly once. This property, which is geometrically plausible, can be proved by expressing the area as an integral, but we shall not discuss the proof.

The next step is to define the sine and cosine of an angle. Actually, we prefer to speak of the sine and cosine of a *number* rather than of an *angle*, so that the sine and cosine will be *functions* defined on the real line. We proceed as follows: Choose a number $x$ satisfying $0 < x < 2\pi$ and let $P$ be the point on the unit circle such that the area of sector $AOP$ is equal to $x/2$. Let $(a, b)$ denote the coordinates of $P$. An example is shown in Figure 2.7. The numbers $a$ and $b$ are completely determined by $x$. We define the sine and cosine of $x$ as follows:

$$\cos x = a, \qquad \sin x = b.$$

In other words, $\cos x$ is the abscissa of $P$ and $\sin x$ is its ordinate.

For example, when $x = \pi$, we have $P = (-1, 0)$ so that $\cos \pi = -1$ and $\sin \pi = 0$. Similarly, when $x = \frac{1}{2}\pi$ we have $P = (0, 1)$ and hence $\cos \frac{1}{2}\pi = 0$ and $\sin \frac{1}{2}\pi = 1$. This procedure describes the sine and cosine as functions defined in the open interval $(0, 2\pi)$. We extend the definitions to the whole real axis by means of the following equations:

$$\sin 0 = 0, \qquad \cos 0 = 1, \qquad \sin (x + 2\pi) = \sin x, \qquad \cos (x + 2\pi) = \cos x.$$

The other four trigonometric functions are now defined in terms of the sine and cosine by the usual formulas,

$$\tan x = \frac{\sin x}{\cos x}, \qquad \cot x = \frac{\cos x}{\sin x}, \qquad \sec x = \frac{1}{\cos x}, \qquad \csc x = \frac{1}{\sin x}.$$

These functions are defined for all real $x$ except for certain isolated points where the denominators may be zero. They all satisfy the periodicity property $f(x + 2\pi) = f(x)$. The tangent and cotangent have the smaller period $\pi$.

Now we give geometric arguments to indicate how these definitions lead to the fundamental properties listed in Section 2.5. Properties 1 and 2 have already been taken care of by the way we have defined the sine and cosine. The Pythagorean identity becomes evident when we refer to Figure 2.7. The line segment $OP$ is the hypotenuse of a right triangle whose legs have lengths $|\cos x|$ and $|\sin x|$. Hence the Pythagorean theorem for right triangles implies the identity $\cos^2 x + \sin^2 x = 1$.

Now we use the Pythagorean theorem for right triangles again to give a geometric proof of formula (2.3) for $\cos (y - x)$. Refer to the two right triangles $PAQ$ and $PBQ$ shown in Figure 2.8. In triangle $PAQ$, the length of side $AQ$ is $|\sin y - \sin x|$, the absolute value of the difference of the ordinates of $Q$ and $P$. Similarly, $AP$ has length $|\cos x - \cos y|$. If $d$ denotes the length of the hypotenuse $PQ$, we have, by the Pythagorean theorem,

$$d^2 = (\sin y - \sin x)^2 + (\cos x - \cos y)^2.$$

On the other hand, in right triangle $PBQ$ the leg $BP$ has length $|1 - \cos (y - x)|$ and the leg $BQ$ has length $|\sin (y - x)|$. Therefore, the Pythagorean theorem gives us

$$d^2 = [1 - \cos (y - x)]^2 + \sin^2 (y - x).$$

Equating the two expressions for $d^2$ and solving for $\cos(y - x)$, we obtain the desired formula (2.3) for $\cos(y - x)$.

Finally, geometric proofs of the fundamental inequalities in property 4 may be given by referring to Figure 2.9. We simply compare the area of sector $OAP$ with that of triangles $OQP$ and $OAB$. Because of the way we have defined angular measure, the area of sector $OAP$ is $\frac{1}{2}x$. Triangle $OAB$ has base 1 and altitude $h$, say. By similar triangles, we find $h/1 = (\sin x)/(\cos x)$, so the area of triangle $OAB$ is $\frac{1}{2}h = \frac{1}{2}(\sin x)/(\cos x)$. Therefore, comparison of areas gives us the inequalities

$$\frac{1}{2}\sin x \cos x < \frac{1}{2}x < \frac{1}{2}\frac{\sin x}{\cos x}.$$

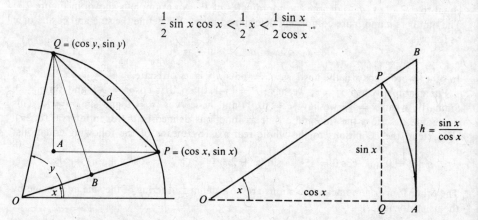

FIGURE 2.8   Geometric proof of the formula       FIGURE 2.9   Geometric proof of the inequalities
for $\cos(y - x)$.

$$0 < \cos x < \frac{\sin x}{x} < \frac{1}{\cos x}.$$

Dividing by $\frac{1}{2}\sin x$ and taking reciprocals, we obtain the fundamental inequalities (2.4).

We remind the reader once more that the discussion of this section is intended to provide a geometric interpretation of the sine and cosine and their fundamental properties. An analytic treatment of these functions, making no use of geometry, will be described in Section 11.11.

Extensive tables of values of the sine, cosine, tangent, and cotangent appear in most mathematical handbooks. The graphs of the six trigonometric functions are shown in Figure 2.10 (page 107) as they appear over one complete period-interval. The rest of the graph in each case is obtained by appealing to periodicity.

## 2.8   Exercises

In this set of exercises, you may use the properties of the sine and cosine listed in Sections 2.5 through 2.7.

1. (a) Prove that $\sin n\pi = 0$ for every integer $n$ and that these are the only values of $x$ for which $\sin x = 0$.
   (b) Find all real $x$ such that $\cos x = 0$.
2. Find all real $x$ such that (a) $\sin x = 1$; (b) $\cos x = 1$; (c) $\sin x = -1$; (d) $\cos x = -1$.
3. Prove that $\sin(x + \pi) = -\sin x$ and $\cos(x + \pi) = -\cos x$ for all $x$.
4. Prove that $\sin 3x = 3\sin x - 4\sin^3 x$ and $\cos 3x = \cos x - 4\sin^2 x \cos x$ for all real $x$. Prove also that $\cos 3x = 4\cos^3 x - 3\cos x$.

5. (a) Prove that $\sin \frac{1}{6}\pi = \frac{1}{2}$, $\cos \frac{1}{6}\pi = \frac{1}{2}\sqrt{3}$. [*Hint:* Use Exercise 4.]
   (b) Prove that $\sin \frac{1}{3}\pi = \frac{1}{2}\sqrt{3}$, $\cos \frac{1}{3}\pi = \frac{1}{2}$.
   (c) Prove that $\sin \frac{1}{4}\pi = \cos \frac{1}{4}\pi = \frac{1}{2}\sqrt{2}$.
6. Prove that $\tan (x - y) = (\tan x - \tan y)/(1 + \tan x \tan y)$ for all $x$ and $y$ with $\tan x \tan y \ne -1$. Obtain corresponding formulas for $\tan (x + y)$ and $\cot (x + y)$.
7. Find numbers $A$ and $B$ such that $3 \sin (x + \frac{1}{3}\pi) = A \sin x + B \cos x$ for all $x$.
8. Prove that if $C$ and $\alpha$ are given real numbers, there exist real numbers $A$ and $B$ such that $C \sin (x + \alpha) = A \sin x + B \cos x$ for all $x$.
9. Prove that if $A$ and $B$ are given real numbers, there exist numbers $C$ and $\alpha$, with $C \ge 0$, such that the formula of Exercise 8 holds.
10. Determine $C$ and $\alpha$, with $C > 0$, such that $C \sin (x + \alpha) = -2 \sin x - 2 \cos x$ for all $x$.
11. Prove that if $A$ and $B$ are given real numbers, there exist numbers $C$ and $\alpha$, with $C \ge 0$, such that $C \cos (x + \alpha) = A \sin x + B \cos x$. Determine $C$ and $\alpha$ if $A = B = 1$.
12. Find all real $x$ such that $\sin x = \cos x$.
13. Find all real $x$ such that $\sin x - \cos x = 1$.
14. Prove that the following identities hold for all $x$ and $y$.
    (a) $2 \cos x \cos y = \cos (x - y) + \cos (x + y)$.
    (b) $2 \sin x \sin y = \cos (x - y) - \cos (x + y)$.
    (c) $2 \sin x \cos y = \sin (x - y) + \sin (x + y)$.
15. If $h \ne 0$, prove that the following identities hold for all $x$:

$$\frac{\sin (x + h) - \sin x}{h} = \frac{\sin (h/2)}{h/2} \cos \left(x + \frac{h}{2}\right),$$

$$\frac{\cos (x + h) - \cos x}{h} = -\frac{\sin (h/2)}{h/2} \sin \left(x + \frac{h}{2}\right).$$

These formulas are used in differential calculus.
16. Prove or disprove each of the following statements.
    (a) For all $x \ne 0$, we have $\sin 2x \ne 2 \sin x$.
    (b) For every $x$, there is a $y$ such that $\cos (x + y) = \cos x + \cos y$.
    (c) There is an $x$ such that $\sin (x + y) = \sin x + \sin y$ for all $y$.
    (d) There is a $y \ne 0$ such that $\int_0^y \sin x \, dx = \sin y$.
17. Calculate the integral $\int_a^b \sin x \, dx$ for each of the following values of $a$ and $b$. In each case interpret your result geometrically in terms of areas.
    (a) $a = 0, b = \pi/6$.          (e) $a = 0, b = \pi$.
    (b) $a = 0, b = \pi/4$.          (f) $a = 0, b = 2\pi$.
    (c) $a = 0, b = \pi/3$.          (g) $a = -1, b = 1$.
    (d) $a = 0, b = \pi/2$.          (h) $a = -\pi/6, b = \pi/4$.

Evaluate the integrals in Exercises 18 through 27.

18. $\int_0^\pi (x + \sin x) \, dx$.

19. $\int_0^{\pi/2} (x^2 + \cos x) \, dx$.

20. $\int_0^{\pi/2} (\sin x - \cos x) \, dx$.

21. $\int_0^{\pi/2} |\sin x - \cos x| \, dx$.

22. $\int_0^\pi (\frac{1}{2} + \cos t) \, dt$.

23. $\int_0^\pi |\frac{1}{2} + \cos t| \, dt$.

24. $\int_{-\pi}^x |\frac{1}{2} + \cos t| \, dt$, if $0 \le x \le \pi$.

25. $\int_x^{x^2} (t^2 + \sin t) \, dt$.

26. $\int_0^{\pi/2} \sin 2x \, dx$.

27. $\int_0^{\pi/3} \cos \frac{x}{2} \, dx$.

28. Prove the following integration formulas, valid for $b \neq 0$:

$$\int_0^x \cos(a + bt)\, dt = \frac{1}{b}\left[\sin(a + bx) - \sin a\right],$$

$$\int_0^x \sin(a + bt)\, dt = -\frac{1}{b}\left[\cos(a + bx) - \cos a\right].$$

29. (a) Use the identity $\sin 3t = 3 \sin t - 4 \sin^3 t$ to deduce the integration formula

$$\int_0^x \sin^3 t\, dt = \tfrac{2}{3} - \tfrac{1}{3}(2 + \sin^2 x)\cos x\,.$$

(b) Derive the identity $\cos 3t = 4 \cos^3 t - 3 \cos t$ and use it to prove that

$$\int_0^x \cos^3 t\, dt = \tfrac{1}{3}(2 + \cos^2 x)\sin x\,.$$

30. If a function $f$ is periodic with period $p > 0$ and integrable on $[0, p]$, prove that $\int_0^p f(x)\, dx = \int_a^{a+p} f(x)\, dx$ for all $a$.

31. (a) Prove that $\int_0^{2\pi} \sin nx\, dx = \int_0^{2\pi} \cos nx\, dx = 0$ for all integers $n \neq 0$.

(b) Use part (a) and the addition formulas for the sine and cosine to establish the following formulas, valid for integers $m$ and $n$, $m^2 \neq n^2$;

$$\int_0^{2\pi} \sin nx \cos mx\, dx = \int_0^{2\pi} \sin nx \sin mx\, dx = \int_0^{2\pi} \cos nx \cos mx\, dx = 0\,,$$

$$\int_0^{2\pi} \sin^2 nx\, dx = \int_0^{2\pi} \cos^2 nx\, dx = \pi\,, \qquad \text{if} \quad n \neq 0\,.$$

These formulas are known as the orthogonality relations for the sine and cosine.

32. Use the identity

$$2 \sin \frac{x}{2} \cos kx = \sin(2k + 1)\frac{x}{2} - \sin(2k - 1)\frac{x}{2}$$

and the telescoping property of finite sums to prove that if $x \neq 2m\pi$ ($m$ an integer), we have

$$\sum_{k=1}^{n} \cos kx = \frac{\sin \frac{1}{2}nx \cos \frac{1}{2}(n + 1)x}{\sin \frac{1}{2}x}\,.$$

33. If $x \neq 2m\pi$ ($m$ an integer), prove that

$$\sum_{k=1}^{n} \sin kx = \frac{\sin \frac{1}{2}nx \sin \frac{1}{2}(n + 1)x}{\sin \frac{1}{2}x}\,.$$

34. Refer to Figure 2.7. By comparing the area of triangle $OAP$ with that of the circular sector $OAP$, prove that $\sin x < x$ if $0 < x < \tfrac{1}{2}\pi$. Then use the fact that $\sin(-x) = -\sin x$ to prove that $|\sin x| < |x|$ if $0 < |x| < \tfrac{1}{2}\pi$.

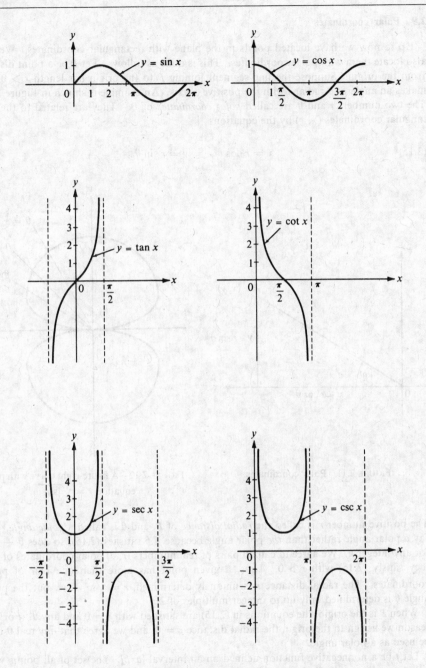

FIGURE 2.10 Graphs of the trigonometric functions as they appear over one period-interval.

## 2.9  Polar coordinates

Up to now we have located points in the plane with rectangular coordinates. We can also locate them with polar coordinates. This is done as follows. Let $P$ be a point distinct from the origin. Suppose the line segment joining $P$ to the origin has length $r > 0$ and makes an angle of $\theta$ radians with the positive $x$-axis. An example is shown in Figure 2.11. The two numbers $r$ and $\theta$ are called *polar coordinates* of $P$. They are related to the rectangular coordinates $(x, y)$ by the equations

(2.15)                    $$x = r \cos \theta, \qquad y = r \sin \theta.$$

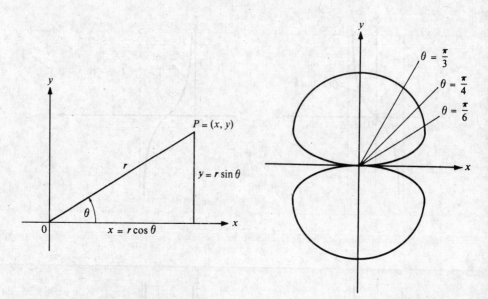

FIGURE 2.11  Polar coordinates.          FIGURE 2.12  A figure-eight curve with polar
                                         equation $r = \sqrt{|\sin \theta|}$.

The positive number $r$ is called the *radial distance* of $P$, and $\theta$ is called a *polar angle*. We say *a* polar angle rather than *the* polar angle because if $\theta$ satisfies (2.15), so does $\theta + 2n\pi$ for any integer $n$. We agree to call all pairs of real numbers $(r, \theta)$ polar coordinates of $P$ if they satisfy (2.15) with $r > 0$. Thus, a given point has more than one pair of polar coordinates. The radial distance $r$ is uniquely determined, $r = \sqrt{x^2 + y^2}$, but the polar angle $\theta$ is determined only up to integer multiples of $2\pi$.

When $P$ is the origin, the equations in (2.15) are satisfied with $r = 0$ and any $\theta$. For this reason we assign to the origin the radial distance $r = 0$, and we agree that *any* real $\theta$ may be used as a polar angle.

Let $f$ be a nonnegative function defined on an interval $[a, b]$. The set of all points with polar coordinates $(r, \theta)$ satisfying $r = f(\theta)$ is called the graph of $f$ in polar coordinates. The equation $r = f(\theta)$ is called a polar equation of this graph. For some curves, polar equations may be simpler and more convenient to use than Cartesian equations. For example, the circle with Cartesian equation $x^2 + y^2 = 4$ has the simpler polar equation $r = 2$. The equations in (2.15) show how to convert from rectangular to polar coordinates.

EXAMPLE. Figure 2.12 shows a curve in the shape of a figure eight whose Cartesian equation is $(x^2 + y^2)^3 = y^2$. Using (2.15), we find $x^2 + y^2 = r^2$, so the polar coordinates of the points on this curve satisfy the equation $r^6 = r^2 \sin^2 \theta$, or $r^2 = |\sin \theta|$, $r = \sqrt{|\sin \theta|}$. It is not difficult to sketch this curve from the polar equation. For example, in the interval $0 \leq \theta \leq \pi/2$, $\sin \theta$ increases from 0 to 1, so $r$ also increases from 0 to 1. Plotting a few values which are easy to calculate, for example, those corresponding to $\theta = \pi/6$, $\pi/4$, and $\pi/3$, we quickly sketch the portion of the curve in the first quadrant. The rest of the curve is obtained by appealing to symmetry in the Cartesian equation, or to the symmetry and periodicity of $|\sin \theta|$. It would be a more difficult task to sketch this curve from its Cartesian equation alone.

## 2.10 The integral for area in polar coordinates

Let $f$ be a nonnegative function defined on an interval $[a, b]$, where $0 \leq b - a \leq 2\pi$. The set of all points with polar coordinates $(r, \theta)$ satisfying the inequalities

$$0 \leq r \leq f(\theta), \qquad a \leq \theta \leq b,$$

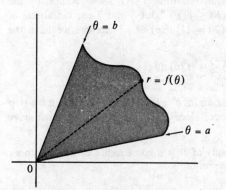

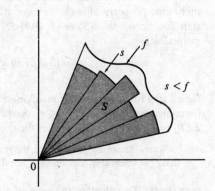

FIGURE 2.13 The radial set of $f$ over an interval $[a, b]$.

FIGURE 2.14 The radial set of a step function $s$ is a union of circular sectors. Its area is $\frac{1}{2} \int_a^b s^2(\theta)\, d\theta$.

is called the *radial set* of $f$ over $[a, b]$. The shaded region shown in Figure 2.13 is an example. If $f$ is constant on $[a, b]$, its radial set is a circular sector subtending an angle of $b - a$ radians. Figure 2.14 shows the radial set $S$ of a step function $s$. Over each of the $n$ open subintervals $(\theta_{k-1}, \theta_k)$ of $[a, b]$ in which $s$ is constant, say $s(\theta) = s_k$, the graph of $s$ in polar coordinates is a circular arc of radius $s_k$, and its radial set is a circular sector subtending an angle of $\theta_k - \theta_{k-1}$ radians. Because of the way we have defined angular measure, the area of this sector is $\frac{1}{2}(\theta_k - \theta_{k-1})s_k^2$. Since $b - a \leq 2\pi$, none of these sectors overlap so, by additivity, the area of the radial set of $s$ over the full interval $[a, b]$ is given by

$$a(S) = \tfrac{1}{2} \sum_{k=1}^{n} s_k^2 \cdot (\theta_k - \theta_{k-1}) = \tfrac{1}{2} \int_a^b s^2(\theta)\, d\theta \,,$$

where $s^2(\theta)$ means the square of $s(\theta)$. Thus, for step functions, the area of the radial set has been expressed as an integral. Now we prove that this integral formula holds more generally.

THEOREM 2.6. *Let $R$ denote the radial set of a nonnegative function $f$ over an interval $[a, b]$, where $0 \le b - a \le 2\pi$, and assume that $R$ is measurable. If $f^2$ is integrable on $[a, b]$ the area of $R$ is given by the integral*

$$a(R) = \tfrac{1}{2} \int_a^b f^2(\theta)\, d\theta \,.$$

*Proof.* Choose two step functions $s$ and $t$ satisfying

$$0 \le s(\theta) \le f(\theta) \le t(\theta)$$

for all $\theta$ in $[a, b]$, and let $S$ and $T$ denote their radial sets, respectively. Since $s \le f \le t$ on $[a, b]$, the radial sets are related by the inclusion relations $S \subseteq R \subseteq T$. Hence, by the monotone property of area, we have $a(S) \le a(R) \le a(T)$. But $S$ and $T$ are radial sets of step functions, so $a(S) = \tfrac{1}{2}\int_a^b s^2(\theta)\, d\theta$ and $a(T) = \tfrac{1}{2}\int_a^b t^2(\theta)\, d\theta$. Therefore we have the inequalities

$$\int_a^b s^2(\theta)\, d\theta \le 2a(R) \le \int_a^b t^2(\theta)\, d\theta \,,$$

for all step functions $s$ and $t$ satisfying $s \le f \le t$ on $[a, b]$. But $s^2$ and $t^2$ are arbitrary step functions satisfying $s^2 \le f^2 \le t^2$ on $[a, b]$ hence, since $f^2$ is integrable, we must have $2a(R) = \int_a^b f^2(\theta)\, d\theta$. This proves the theorem.

*Note:* It can be proved that the measurability of $R$ is a consequence of the hypothesis that $f^2$ is integrable, but we shall not discuss the proof.

EXAMPLE. To calculate the area of the radial set $R$ enclosed by the figure-eight curve shown in Figure 2.12, we calculate the area of the portion in the first quadrant and multiply by four. For this curve, we have $f^2(\theta) = |\sin \theta|$ and, since $\sin \theta \ge 0$ for $0 \le \theta \le \pi/2$, we find

$$a(R) = 4 \int_0^{\pi/2} \tfrac{1}{2} f^2(\theta)\, d\theta = 2 \int_0^{\pi/2} \sin \theta \, d\theta = 2\left(\cos 0 - \cos \frac{\pi}{2}\right) = 2 \,.$$

## 2.11 Exercises

In each of Exercises 1 through 4, show that the set of points whose rectangular coordinates $(x, y)$ satisfy the given Cartesian equation is equal to the set of all points whose polar coordinates $(r, \theta)$ satisfy the corresponding polar equation.

1. $(x - 1)^2 + y^2 = 1$;    $r = 2 \cos \theta$,  $\cos \theta > 0$.
2. $x^2 + y^2 - x = \sqrt{x^2 + y^2}$;    $r = 1 + \cos \theta$.
3. $(x^2 + y^2)^2 = x^2 - y^2, y^2 \leq x^2$;    $r = \sqrt{\cos 2\theta}$,  $\cos 2\theta \geq 0$.
4. $(x^2 + y^2)^2 = |x^2 - y^2|$;    $r = \sqrt{|\cos 2\theta|}$.

In each of Exercises 5 through 15, sketch the graph of $f$ in polar coordinates and compute the area of the radial set of $f$ over the interval specified. You may assume each set is measurable.

5. *Spiral of Archimedes:* $f(\theta) = \theta$,  $0 \leq \theta \leq 2\pi$.
6. *Circle tangent to y-axis:*  $f(\theta) = 2 \cos \theta$,  $-\pi/2 \leq \theta \leq \pi/2$.
7. *Two circles tangent to y-axis:* $f(\theta) = 2 |\cos \theta|$,  $0 \leq \theta \leq 2\pi$.
8. *Circle tangent to x-axis:* $f(\theta) = 4 \sin \theta$,  $0 \leq \theta \leq \pi$.
9. *Two circles tangent to x-axis:* $f(\theta) = 4 |\sin \theta|$,  $0 \leq \theta \leq 2\pi$.
10. *Rose petal:* $f(\theta) = \sin 2\theta$,  $0 \leq \theta \leq \pi/2$.
11. *Four-leaved rose:* $f(\theta) = |\sin 2\theta|$,  $0 \leq \theta \leq 2\pi$.
12. *Lazy eight:* $f(\theta) = \sqrt{|\cos \theta|}$,  $0 \leq \theta \leq 2\pi$.
13. *Four-leaf clover:* $f(\theta) = \sqrt{|\cos 2\theta|}$,  $0 \leq \theta \leq 2\pi$.
14. *Cardioid:* $f(\theta) = 1 + \cos \theta$,  $0 \leq \theta \leq 2\pi$.
15. *Limaçon:* $f(\theta) = 2 + \cos \theta$,  $0 \leq \theta \leq 2\pi$.

### 2.12 Application of integration to the calculation of volume

In Section 1.6 we introduced the concept of area as a set function satisfying certain properties which we took as axioms for area. Then, in Sections 1.18 and 2.2, we showed that the areas of many regions could be calculated by integration. The same approach can be used to discuss the concept of volume.

We assume there exist certain sets $S$ of points in three-dimensional space, which we call *measurable sets*, and a set function $v$, called a *volume function*, which assigns to each measurable set $S$ a number $v(S)$, called the volume of $S$. We use the symbol $\mathscr{A}$ to denote the class of all measurable sets in three-dimensional space, and we call each set $S$ in $\mathscr{A}$ a *solid*.

As in the case of area, we list a number of properties we would like volume to have and take these as axioms for volume. The choice of axioms enables us to prove that the volumes of many solids can be computed by integration.

The first three axioms, like those for area, describe the nonnegative, additive, and difference properties. Instead of an axiom of invariance under congruence, we use a different type of axiom, called *Cavalieri's principle*. This assigns equal volumes to congruent solids and also to certain solids which, though not congruent, have equal cross-sectional areas cut by planes perpendicular to a given line. More precisely, suppose $S$ is a given solid and $L$ a given line. If a plane $F$ is perpendicular to $L$, the intersection $F \cap S$ is called a cross-section perpendicular to $L$. If every cross-section perpendicular to $L$ is a measurable set in its own plane, we call $S$ a *Cavalieri solid*. Cavalieri's principle assigns equal volumes to two Cavalieri solids, $S$ and $T$, if $a(S \cap F) = a(T \cap F)$ for every plane $F$ perpendicular to the given line $L$.

Cavalieri's principle can be illustrated intuitively as follows. Imagine a Cavalieri solid as being a stack of thin sheets of material, like a deck of cards, each sheet being perpendicular to a given line $L$. If we slide each sheet in its own plane we can change the shape of the solid but not its volume.

The next axiom states that the volume of a rectangular parallelepiped is the product of the lengths of its edges. A rectangular parallelepiped is any set congruent to a set of the form

(2.16)                    $\{(x, y, z) \mid 0 \leq x \leq a, \quad 0 \leq y \leq b, \quad 0 \leq z \leq c\}.$

We shall use the shorter term "box" rather than "rectangular parallelepiped." The non-negative numbers $a$, $b$, $c$ in (2.16) are called the lengths of the edges of the box.

Finally, we include an axiom which states that every convex set is measurable. A set is called *convex* if, for every pair of points $P$ and $Q$ in the set, the line segment joining $P$ and $Q$ is also in the set. This axiom, along with the additive and difference properties, ensures that all the elementary solids that occur in the usual applications of calculus are measurable.

The axioms for volume can now be stated as follows.

AXIOMATIC DEFINITION OF VOLUME.  *We assume there exists a class $\mathscr{A}$ of solids and a set function $v$, whose domain is $\mathscr{A}$, with the following properties:*

*1. Nonnegative property.  For each set $S$ in $\mathscr{A}$ we have $v(S) \geq 0$.*

*2. Additive property.  If $S$ and $T$ are in $\mathscr{A}$, then $S \cup T$ and $S \cap T$ are in $\mathscr{A}$, and we have*

$$v(S \cup T) = v(S) + v(T) - v(S \cap T).$$

*3. Difference property.  If $S$ and $T$ are in $\mathscr{A}$ with $S \subseteq T$, then $T - S$ is in $\mathscr{A}$, and we have $v(T - S) = v(T) - v(S)$.*

*4. Cavalieri's principle.  If $S$ and $T$ are two Cavalieri solids in $\mathscr{A}$ with $a(S \cap F) \leq a(T \cap F)$ for every plane $F$ perpendicular to a given line, then $v(S) \leq v(T)$.*

*5. Choice of scale.  Every box $B$ is in $\mathscr{A}$.  If the edges of $B$ have lengths $a$, $b$, and $c$, then $v(B) = abc$.*

*6. Every convex set is in $\mathscr{A}$.*

Axiom 3 shows that the empty set $\varnothing$ is in $\mathscr{A}$ and has zero volume. Since $v(T - S) \geq 0$, Axiom 3 also implies the following monotone property:

$$v(S) \leq v(T), \qquad \text{for sets } S \text{ and } T \text{ in } \mathscr{A} \text{ with } S \subseteq T.$$

The monotone property, in turn, shows that every bounded plane set $S$ in $\mathscr{A}$ has zero volume. A plane set is called *bounded* if it is a subset of some square in the plane. If we consider a box $B$ of altitude $c$ having this square as its base, then $S \subseteq B$ so that we have $v(S) \leq v(B) = a^2 c$, where $a$ is the length of each edge of the square base. If we had $v(S) > 0$, we could choose $c$ so that $c < v(S)/a^2$, contradicting the inequality $v(S) \leq a^2 c$. This shows that $v(S)$ cannot be positive, so $v(S) = 0$, as asserted.

Note that Cavalieri's principle has been stated in the form of inequalities. If $a(S \cap F) = a(T \cap F)$ for every plane $F$ perpendicular to a given line, we may apply Axiom 5 twice to deduce $v(S) \leq v(T)$ and $v(T) \leq v(S)$, and hence we have $v(T) = v(S)$.

Next we show that the volume of a right cylindrical solid is equal to the area of its base multiplied by its altitude. By a right cylindrical solid we mean a set congruent to a set $S$ of the form

$$S = \{(x, y, z) \mid (x, y) \in B, \quad a \leq z \leq b\},$$

where $B$ is a bounded plane measurable set. The areas of the cross sections of $S$ perpendicular to the $z$-axis determine a cross-sectional area function $a_S$ which takes the constant value $a(B)$ on the interval $a \leq z \leq b$, and the value 0 outside $[a, b]$.

Now let $T$ be a box with cross-sectional area function $a_T$ equal to $a_S$. Axiom 5 tells us that $v(T) = a(B)(b - a)$, where $a(B)$ is the area of the base of $T$, and $b - a$ is its altitude. Cavalieri's principle states that $v(S) = v(T)$, so the volume of $S$ is the area of its base, $a(B)$, multiplied by its altitude, $b - a$. Note that the product $a(B)(b - a)$ is the integral of the function $a_S$ over the interval $[a, b]$. In other words, the volume of a right cylindrical solid is equal to the integral of its cross-sectional area function,

$$v(S) = \int_a^b a_S(z)\, dz\ .$$

We can extend this formula to more general Cavalieri solids. Let $R$ be a Cavalieri solid with measurable cross-sections perpendicular to a given line $L$. Introduce a coordinate axis along $L$ (call it the $u$-axis), and let $a_R(u)$ be the area of the cross section cut by a plane perpendicular to $L$ at the point $u$. The volume of $R$ can be computed by the following theorem.

THEOREM 2.7.    *Let $R$ be a Cavalieri solid in $\mathscr{A}$ with a cross-sectional area function $a_R$ which is integrable on an interval $[a, b]$ and zero outside $[a, b]$. Then the volume of $R$ is equal to the integral of the cross-sectional area:*

$$v(R) = \int_a^b a_R(u)\, du\ .$$

*Proof.* Choose step functions $s$ and $t$ such that $s \leq a_R \leq t$ on $[a, b]$ and define $s$ and $t$ to be zero outside $[a, b]$. For each subinterval of $[a, b]$ on which $s$ is constant, we can imagine a cylindrical solid (for example, a right circular cylinder) constructed so that its cross-sectional area on this subinterval has the same constant value as $s$. The union of these cylinders over all intervals of constancy of $s$ is a solid $S$ whose volume $v(S)$ is, by additivity, equal to the integral $\int_a^b s(u)\, du$. Similarly, there is a solid $T$, a union of cylinders, whose volume $v(T) = \int_a^b t(u)\, du$. But $a_S(u) = s(u) \leq a_R(u) \leq t(u) = a_T(u)$ for all $u$ in $[a, b]$, so Cavalieri's principle implies that $v(S) \leq v(R) \leq v(T)$. In other words, $v(R)$ satisfies the inequalities

$$\int_a^b s(u)\, du \leq v(R) \leq \int_a^b t(u)\, du$$

for all step functions $s$ and $t$ satisfying $s \leq a_S \leq t$ on $[a, b]$. Since $a_S$ is integrable on $[a, b]$, it follows that $v(R) = \int_a^b a_S(u)\, du$.

EXAMPLE.    *Volume of a solid of revolution.* Let $f$ be a function which is nonnegative and integrable on an interval $[a, b]$. If the ordinate set of this function is revolved about the $x$-axis, it sweeps out a solid of revolution. Each cross section cut by a plane perpendicular to the $x$-axis is a circular disk. The area of the circular disk cut at the point $x$ is $\pi f^2(x)$, where $f^2(x)$ means the square of $f(x)$. Therefore, by Theorem 2.7, the volume of the solid (if the solid is in $\mathscr{A}$) is equal to the integral $\int_a^b \pi f^2(x)\, dx$, if the integral exists. In particular, if $f(x) = \sqrt{r^2 - x^2}$ for $-r \leq x \leq r$, the ordinate set of $f$ is a semicircular disk of radius $r$ and the solid swept out is a sphere of radius $r$. The sphere is convex. Its volume is equal to

$$\int_{-r}^{r} \pi f^2(x)\, dx = \pi \int_{-r}^{r} (r^2 - x^2)\, dx = 2\pi \int_{0}^{r} (r^2 - x^2)\, dx = \tfrac{4}{3}\pi r^3\,.$$

More generally, suppose we have two nonnegative functions $f$ and $g$ which are integrable on an interval $[a, b]$ and satisfy $f \leq g$ on $[a, b]$. When the region between their graphs is rotated about the $x$-axis, it sweeps out a solid of revolution such that each cross section cut by a plane perpendicular to the $x$-axis at the point $x$ is an annulus (a region bounded by two concentric circles) with area $\pi g^2(x) - \pi f^2(x)$. Therefore, if $g^2 - f^2$ is integrable, the volume of such a solid (if the solid is in $\mathscr{A}$) is given by the integral

$$\int_{a}^{b} \pi [g^2(x) - f^2(x)]\, dx\,.$$

## 2.13 Exercises

1. Use integration to compute the volume of a right circular cone generated by revolving the ordinate set of a linear function $f(x) = cx$ over the interval $0 \leq x \leq b$. Show that the result is one-third the area of the base times the altitude of the cone.

In each of Exercises 2 through 7, compute the volume of the solid generated by revolving the ordinate set of the function $f$ over the interval indicated. Sketch each of the ordinate sets.

2. $f(x) = \sqrt{x}, \quad 0 \leq x \leq 1$.
3. $f(x) = x^{1/4}, \quad 0 \leq x \leq 1$.
4. $f(x) = x^2, \quad -1 \leq x \leq 2$.
5. $f(x) = \sin x, \quad 0 \leq x \leq \pi$.
6. $f(x) = \cos x, \quad 0 \leq x \leq \pi/2$.
7. $f(x) = \sin x + \cos x, \quad 0 \leq x \leq \pi$.

In each of Exercises 8 through 11, sketch the region between the graphs of $f$ and $g$ and compute the volume of the solid obtained by rotating this region about the $x$-axis.

8. $f(x) = \sqrt{x}, \quad g(x) = 1, \quad 0 \leq x \leq 1$.
9. $f(x) = \sqrt{x}, \quad g(x) = x^2, \quad 0 \leq x \leq 1$.
10. $f(x) = \sin x, \quad g(x) = \cos x, \quad 0 \leq x \leq \pi/4$.
11. $f(x) = \sqrt{4 - x^2}, \quad g(x) = 1, \quad 0 \leq x \leq \sqrt{3}$.
12. Sketch the graphs of $f(x) = \sqrt{x}$ and $g(x) = x/2$ over the interval $[0, 2]$. Find a number $t$, $1 < t < 2$, so that when the region between the graphs of $f$ and $g$ over the interval $[0, t]$ is rotated about the $x$-axis, it sweeps out a solid of revolution whose volume is equal to $\pi t^3/3$.
13. What volume of material is removed from a solid sphere of radius $2r$ by drilling a hole of radius $r$ through the center?
14. A napkin-ring is formed by drilling a cylindrical hole symmetrically through the center of a solid sphere. If the length of the hole is $2h$, prove that the volume of the napkin-ring is $\pi a h^3$, where $a$ is a rational number.
15. A solid has a circular base of radius 2. Each cross section cut by a plane perpendicular to a fixed diameter is an equilateral triangle. Compute the volume of the solid.
16. The cross sections of a solid are squares perpendicular to the $x$-axis with their centers on the axis. If the square cut off at $x$ has edge $2x^2$, find the volume of the solid between $x = 0$ and $x = a$. Make a sketch.
17. Find the volume of a solid whose cross section, made by a plane perpendicular to the $x$-axis, has the area $ax^2 + bx + c$ for each $x$ in the interval $0 \leq x \leq h$. Express the volume in terms of the areas $B_1$, $M$, and $B_2$ of the cross sections corresponding to $x = 0$, $x = h/2$, and $x = h$, respectively. The resulting formula is known as the *prismoid formula*.

18. Make a sketch of the region in the $xy$-plane consisting of all points $(x, y)$ satisfying the simultaneous inequalities $0 \leq x \leq 2$, $\frac{1}{4}x^2 \leq y \leq 1$. Compute the volume of the solid obtained by rotating this region about (a) the $x$-axis; (b) the $y$-axis; (c) the vertical line passing through $(2, 0)$; (d) the horizontal line passing through $(0, 1)$.

## 2.14 Application of integration to the concept of work

Thus far our applications of integration have been to area and volume, concepts from geometry. Now we discuss an application to *work*, a concept from physics.

Work is a measure of the energy expended by a force in moving a particle from one point to another. In this section we consider only the simplest case, linear motion. That is, we assume that the motion takes place along a line (which we take as the $x$-axis) from one point, say $x = a$, to another point, $x = b$, and we also assume that the force acts along this line. We permit either $a < b$ or $b < a$. We assume further that the force acting on the particle is a function of the position. If the particle is at $x$, we denote by $f(x)$ the force acting on it, where $f(x) > 0$ if the force acts in the direction of the positive $x$-axis, and $f(x) < 0$ if the force acts in the opposite direction. When the force is constant, say $f(x) = c$ for all $x$ between $a$ and $b$, we define the work done by $f$ to be the number $c \cdot (b - a)$, force times displacement. The work may be positive or negative.

If force is measured in pounds and distance in feet, we measure work in *foot-pounds*; if force is in *dynes* and distance in *centimeters* (the *cgs* system), work is measured in *dyne-centimeters*. One dyne-centimeter of work is called an *erg*. If force is in *newtons* and distance in *meters* (the *mks* system), work is in *newton-meters*. One newton-meter of work is called a *joule*. One newton is $10^5$ dynes, and one joule is $10^7$ ergs.

EXAMPLE. A stone weighing 3 pounds (lb) is thrown upward along a straight line, rising to a height of 15 feet (ft) and returning to the ground. We take the $x$-axis pointing up along the line of motion. The constant force of gravity acts downward, so $f(x) = -3$ lb for each $x$, $0 \leq x \leq 15$. The work done by gravity in moving the stone from, say, $x = 6$ ft to $x = 15$ ft is $-3 \cdot (15 - 6) = -27$ foot-pounds (ft-lb). When the same stone falls from $x = 15$ ft to $x = 6$ ft, the work done by gravity is $-3(6 - 15) = 27$ ft-lb.

Now suppose the force is not necessarily constant but is a given function of position defined on the interval joining $a$ and $b$. How do we define the work done by $f$ in moving a particle from $a$ to $b$? We proceed much as we did for area and volume. We state some properties of work which are dictated by physical requirements. Then we prove that for any definition of work which has these properties, the work done by an integrable force function $f$ is equal to the integral $\int_a^b f(x)\, dx$.

FUNDAMENTAL PROPERTIES OF WORK. *Let* $W_a(f)$ *denote the work done by a force function* $f$ *in moving a particle from* $a$ *to* $b$. *Then work has the following properties:*

1. *Additive property.* If $a < c < b$, then $W_a^b(f) = W_a^c(f) + W_c^b(f)$.
2. *Monotone property.* If $f \leq g$ on $[a, b]$, then $W_a^b(f) \leq W_a^b(g)$. *That is, a greater force does greater work.*
3. *Elementary formula.* If $f$ is constant, say $f(x) = c$ for all $x$ in the open interval $(a, b)$, then $W_a^b(f) = c \cdot (b - a)$.

The additive property can be extended by induction to any finite number of intervals.

That is, if $a = x_0 < x_1 < \cdots < x_n = b$, we have

$$W_a^b(f) = \sum_{k=1}^{n} W_k,$$

where $W_k$ is the work done by $f$ from $x_{k-1}$ to $x_k$. In particular, if the force is a step function $s$ which takes a constant value $s_k$ on the open interval $(x_{k-1}, x_k)$, property 3 states that $W_k = s_k \cdot (x_k - x_{k-1})$, so we have

$$W_a^b(s) = \sum_{k=1}^{n} s_k \cdot (x_k - x_{k-1}) = \int_a^b s(x)\, dx.$$

Thus, for step functions, work has been expressed as an integral. Now it is an easy matter to prove that this holds true more generally.

THEOREM 2.8. *Suppose work has been defined for a class of force functions f in such a way that it satisfies properties 1, 2, and 3. Then the work done by an integrable force function f in moving a particle from a to b is equal to the integral of f,*

$$W_a^b(f) = \int_a^b f(x)\, dx.$$

*Proof.* Let $s$ and $t$ be two step functions satisfying $s \leq f \leq t$ on $[a, b]$. The monotone property of work states that $W_a^b(s) \leq W_a^b(f) \leq W_a^b(t)$. But $W_a^b(s) = \int_a^b s(x)\, dx$ and $W_a^b(t) = \int_a^b t(x)\, dx$, so the number $W_a^b(f)$ satisfies the inequalities

$$\int_a^b s(x)\, dx \leq W_a^b(f) \leq \int_a^b t(x)\, dx$$

for all step functions $s$ and $t$ satisfying $s \leq f \leq t$ on $[a, b]$. Since $f$ is integrable on $[a, b]$, it follows that $W_a^b(f) = \int_a^b f(x)\, dx$.

*Note:* Many authors simply define work to be the integral of the force function. The foregoing discussion serves as motivation for this definition.

EXAMPLE. *Work required to stretch a spring.* Assume that the force $f(x)$ needed to stretch a steel spring a distance $x$ beyond its natural length is proportional to $x$ (*Hooke's law*). We place the $x$-axis along the axis of the spring. If the stretching force acts in the positive direction of the axis, we have $f(x) = cx$, where the spring constant $c$ is positive. (The value of $c$ can be determined if we know the force $f(x)$ for a particular value of $x \neq 0$.) The work required to stretch the spring a distance $a$ is $\int_0^a f(x)\, dx = \int_0^a cx\, dx = ca^2/2$, a number proportional to the square of the displacement.

A discussion of work for motion along curves other than straight lines is carried out in Volume II with the aid of line integrals.

## 2.15 Exercises

In Exercises 1 and 2 assume the force on the spring obeys Hooke's law.
1. If a ten-pound force stretches an elastic spring one inch, how much work is done in stretching the spring one foot?

2. A spring has a natural length of 1 meter (m). A force of 100 newtons compresses it to 0.9 m. How many joules of work are required to compress it to half its natural length? What is the length of the spring when 20 joules of work have been expended?

3. A particle is moved along the $x$-axis by a propelling force $f(x) = 3x^2 + 4x$ newtons. Calculate how many joules of work are done by the force to move the particle (a) from $x = 0$ to $x = 7$ m; (b) from $x = 2$ m to $x = 7$ m.

4. A particle is to be moved along the $x$-axis by a quadratic propelling force $f(x) = ax^2 + bx$ dynes. Calculate $a$ and $b$ so that 900 ergs of work are required to move the particle 10 centimeters (cm) from the origin, if the force is 65 dynes when $x = 5$ cm.

5. A cable 50 feet in length and weighing 4 pounds per foot (lb/ft) hangs from a windlass. Calculate the work done in winding up 25 ft of the cable. Neglect all forces except gravity.

6. Solve Exercise 5 if a 50 pound weight is attached to the end of the cable.

7. A weight of 150 pounds is attached at one end of a long flexible chain weighing 2 lb/ft. The weight is initially suspended with 10 feet of chain over the edge of a building 100 feet in height. Neglect all forces except gravity and calculate the amount of work done by the force of gravity when the load is lowered to a position 10 feet above the ground.

8. In Exercise 7, suppose that the chain is only 60 feet long and that the load and chain are allowed to drop to the ground, starting from the same initial position as before. Calculate the amount of work done by the force of gravity when the weight reaches the ground.

9. Let $V(q)$ denote the voltage required to place a charge $q$ on the plates of a condensor. The work required to charge a condensor from $q = a$ to $q = b$ is defined to be the integral $\int_a^b V(q)\, dq$. If the voltage is proportional to the charge, prove that the work done to place a charge $Q$ on an uncharged condensor is $\frac{1}{2}QV(Q)$.

## 2.16 Average value of a function

In scientific work it is often necessary to make several measurements under similar conditions and then compute an *average* or *mean* for the purpose of summarizing the data. There are many useful types of averages, the most common being the *arithmetic mean*. If $a_1, a_2, \ldots, a_n$ are $n$ real numbers, their arithmetic mean $\bar{a}$ is defined by the equation

$$(2.17) \qquad \bar{a} = \frac{1}{n}\sum_{k=1}^{n} a_k .$$

If the numbers $a_k$ are the values of a function $f$ at $n$ distinct points, say $a_k = f(x_k)$, then the number

$$\frac{1}{n}\sum_{k=1}^{n} f(x_k)$$

is the arithmetic mean of the function values $f(x_1), \ldots, f(x_n)$. We can extend this concept to compute an average value not only for a finite number of values of $f(x)$ but for all values of $f(x)$ where $x$ runs through an interval. The following definition serves this purpose.

DEFINITION OF AVERAGE VALUE OF A FUNCTION ON AN INTERVAL. *If $f$ is integrable on an interval $[a, b]$, we define $A(f)$, the average value of $f$ on $[a, b]$, by the formula*

$$(2.18) \qquad A(f) = \frac{1}{b-a}\int_a^b f(x)\, dx .$$

When $f$ is nonnegative, this formula has a simple geometric interpretation. Written in the form $(b-a)A(f) = \int_a^b f(x)\, dx$, it states that the rectangle of altitude $A(f)$ and base $[a, b]$ has an area equal to that of the ordinate set of $f$ over $[a, b]$.

Now we can show that formula (2.18) is actually an extension of the concept of the arithmetic mean. Let $f$ be a step function which is constant on $n$ equal subintervals of $[a, b]$. Specifically, let $x_k = a + k(b-a)/n$ for $k = 0, 1, 2, \ldots, n$, and suppose that $f(x) = f(x_k)$, if $x_{k-1} < x < x_k$. Then $x_k - x_{k-1} = (b-a)/n$, so we have

$$A(f) = \frac{1}{b-a}\int_a^b f(x)\, dx = \frac{1}{b-a}\sum_{k=1}^{n} f(x_k)\frac{b-a}{n} = \frac{1}{n}\sum_{k=1}^{n} f(x_k).$$

Thus, for step functions, the average $A(f)$ is the same as the arithmetic mean of the values $f(x_1), \ldots, f(x_n)$ taken on the intervals of constancy.

Weighted arithmetic means are often used in place of the ordinary arithmetic mean in (2.17). If $w_1, w_2, \ldots, w_n$ are $n$ nonnegative numbers (called *weights*), not all zero, the weighted arithmetic mean $\bar{a}$ of $a_1, a_2, \ldots, a_n$ is defined by the formula

$$\bar{a} = \frac{\displaystyle\sum_{k=1}^{n} w_k a_k}{\displaystyle\sum_{k=1}^{n} w_k}.$$

When the weights are all equal, this reduces to the ordinary arithmetic mean. The extension of this concept to integrable functions is given by the formula

$$(2.19) \qquad A(f) = \frac{\displaystyle\int_a^b w(x) f(x)\, dx}{\displaystyle\int_a^b w(x)\, dx},$$

where $w$ is a nonnegative weight function with $\int_a^b w(x)\, dx \neq 0$.

Weighted averages are widely used in physics and engineering, as well as in mathematics. For example, consider a straight rod of length $a$ made of a material of varying density. Place the rod along the positive $x$-axis with one end at the origin 0, and let $m(x)$ denote the mass of a portion of the rod of length $x$, measured from 0. If $m(x) = \int_0^x \rho(t)\, dt$ for some integrable function $\rho$ ($\rho$ is the Greek letter *rho*), then $\rho$ is called the *mass density* of the rod. A *uniform* rod is one whose mass density is constant. The integral $\int_0^a x\rho(x)\, dx$ is called the *first moment* of the rod about 0, and the *center of mass* is the point whose $x$-coordinate is

$$\bar{x} = \frac{\displaystyle\int_0^a x\rho(x)\, dx}{\displaystyle\int_0^a \rho(x)\, dx}.$$

This is an example of a weighted average. We are averaging the distance function $f(x) = x$ with the mass density $\rho$ as weight function.

The integral $\int_0^a x^2 \rho(x)\, dx$ is called the *second moment*, or *moment of inertia*, of the rod about 0, and the positive number $r$ given by the formula

$$r^2 = \frac{\displaystyle\int_0^a x^2 \rho(x)\, dx}{\displaystyle\int_0^a \rho(x)\, dx}$$

is called the *radius of gyration* of the rod. In this case, the function being averaged is the square of the distance function, $f(x) = x^2$, with the mass density $\rho$ as the weight function.

Weighted averages like these also occur in the mathematical theory of probability where the concepts of *expectation* and *variance* play the same role as center of mass and moment of inertia.

## 2.17  Exercises

In Exercises 1 through 10, compute the average $A(f)$ for the given function $f$ over the specified interval.

1. $f(x) = x^2, \quad a \le x \le b.$
2. $f(x) = x^2 + x^3, \quad 0 \le x \le 1.$
3. $f(x) = x^{1/2}, \quad 0 \le x \le 4.$
4. $f(x) = x^{1/3}, \quad 1 \le x \le 8.$
5. $f(x) = \sin x, \quad 0 \le x \le \pi/2.$
6. $f(x) = \cos x, \quad -\pi/2 \le x \le \pi/2.$
7. $f(x) = \sin 2x, \quad 0 \le x \le \pi/2.$
8. $f(x) = \sin x \cos x, \quad 0 \le x \le \pi/4.$
9. $f(x) = \sin^2 x, \quad 0 \le x \le \pi/2.$
10. $f(x) = \cos^2 x, \quad 0 \le x \le \pi.$

11. (a) If $f(x) = x^2$ for $0 \le x \le a$, find a number $c$ satisfying $0 < c < a$ such that $f(c)$ is equal to the average of $f$ in $[0, a]$.
    (b) Solve part (a) if $f(x) = x^n$, where $n$ is any positive integer.
12. Let $f(x) = x^2$ for $0 \le x \le 1$. The average value of $f$ on $[0, 1]$ is $\frac{1}{3}$. Find a nonnegative weight function $w$ such that the weighted average of $f$ on $[0, 1]$, as defined by Equation (2.19) is (a) $\frac{1}{2}$; (b) $\frac{3}{5}$; (c) $\frac{2}{3}$.
13. Let $A(f)$ denote the average of $f$ over an interval $[a, b]$. Prove that the average has the following properties:
    (a) *Additive property:* $A(f + g) = A(f) + A(g)$.
    (b) *Homogenous property:* $A(cf) = cA(f) \quad$ if $c$ is any real number.
    (c) *Monotone property:* $A(f) \le A(g) \quad$ if $f \le g$ on $[a, b]$.
14. Which of the properties in Exercise 13 are valid for weighted averages as defined by Equation (2.19)?
15. Let $A_a^b(f)$ denote the average of $f$ on an interval $[a, b]$.
    (a) If $a < c < b$, prove that there is a number $t$ satisfying $0 < t < 1$ such that $A_a^b(f) = tA_a^c(f) + (1 - t)A_c^b(f)$. Thus, $A_a^b(f)$ is a weighted arithmetic mean of $A_a^c(f)$ and $A_c^b(f)$.
    (b) Prove that the result of part (a) also holds for weighted averages as defined by Equation (2.19).

Each of Exercises 16 through 21 refers to a rod of length $L$ placed on the $x$-axis with one end at the origin. For the mass density $\rho$ as described in each case, calculate (a) the center of mass of the rod, (b) the moment of inertia about the origin, and (c) the radius of gyration.

16. $\rho(x) = 1 \quad$ for $0 \le x \le L.$
17. $\rho(x) = 1 \quad$ for $0 \le x \le \dfrac{L}{2}, \quad \rho(x) = 2 \quad$ for $\dfrac{L}{2} < x \le L.$
18. $\rho(x) = x \quad$ for $0 \le x \le L.$
19. $\rho(x) = x \quad$ for $0 \le x \le \dfrac{L}{2}, \quad \rho(x) = \dfrac{L}{2} \quad$ for $\dfrac{L}{2} \le x \le L.$

20. $\rho(x) = x^2$    for   $0 \leq x \leq L$.

21. $\rho(x) = x^2$    for   $0 \leq x \leq \dfrac{L}{2}$,    $\rho(x) = \dfrac{L^2}{4}$    for   $\dfrac{L}{2} \leq x \leq L$.

22. Determine a mass density $\rho$ so that the center of mass of a rod of length $L$ will be at a distance $L/4$ from one end of the rod.

23. In an electrical circuit, the voltage $e(t)$ at time $t$ is given by the formula $e(t) = 3 \sin 2t$. Calculate the following: (a) the average voltage over the time interval $[0, \pi/2]$; (b) the root-mean-square of the voltage; that is, the square root of the average of the function $e^2$ in the interval $[0, \pi/2]$.

24. In an electrical circuit, the voltage $e(t)$ and the current $i(t)$ at time $t$ are given by the formulas $e(t) = 160 \sin t$, $i(t) = 2 \sin (t - \pi/6)$. The average power is defined to be

$$\frac{1}{T} \int_0^T e(t)i(t) \, dt \, ,$$

where $T$ is the period of both the voltage and the current. Determine $T$ and calculate the average power.

## 2.18 The integral as a function of the upper limit. Indefinite integrals

In this section we assume that $f$ is a function such that the integral $\int_a^x f(t) \, dt$ exists for each $x$ in an interval $[a, b]$. We shall keep $a$ and $f$ fixed and study this integral as a function of $x$. We denote the value of the integral by $A(x)$, so that we have

(2.20)            $A(x) = \displaystyle\int_a^x f(t) \, dt$    if   $a \leq x \leq b$ .

An equation like this enables us to construct a new function $A$ from a given function $f$, the value of $A$ at each point in $[a, b]$ being determined by Equation (2.20). The function $A$ is sometimes referred to as an *indefinite integral* of $f$, and it is said to be obtained from $f$ by integration. We say *an* indefinite integral rather than *the* indefinite integral because $A$ also depends on the lower limit $a$. Different values of $a$ will lead to different functions $A$. If we use a different lower limit, say $c$, and define another indefinite integral $F$ by the equation

$$F(x) = \int_c^x f(t) \, dt \, ,$$

then the additive property tells us that

$$A(x) - F(x) = \int_a^x f(t) \, dt - \int_c^x f(t) \, dt = \int_a^c f(t) \, dt \, ,$$

and hence the difference $A(x) - F(x)$ is *independent* of $x$. Therefore any two indefinite integrals of the same function differ only by a constant (the constant depends on the choice of $a$ and $c$).

When an indefinite integral of $f$ is known, the value of an integral such as $\int_a^b f(t) \, dt$ may be evaluated by a simple subtraction. For example, if $n$ is a nonnegative integer, we have the formula of Theorem 1.15,

$$\int_0^x t^n \, dt = \frac{x^{n+1}}{n + 1} \, ,$$

and the additive property implies that

$$\int_a^b t^n \, dt = \int_0^b t^n \, dt - \int_0^a t^n \, dt = \frac{b^{n+1} - a^{n+1}}{n + 1}.$$

In general, if $F(x) = \int_c^x f(t) \, dt$, then we have

(2.21) $$\int_a^b f(t) \, dt = \int_c^b f(t) \, dt - \int_c^a f(t) \, dt = F(b) - F(a).$$

A different choice of $c$ merely changes $F(x)$ by a constant; this does not alter the difference $F(b) - F(a)$, because the constant cancels out in the subtraction.

If we use the special symbol

$$F(x)\big|_a^b$$

to denote the difference $F(b) - F(a)$, Equation (2.21) may be written as

$$\int_a^b f(x) \, dx = F(x)\big|_a^b = F(b) - F(a).$$

There is, of course, a very simple geometric relationship between a function $f$ and its indefinite integrals. An example is illustrated in Figure 2.15(a), where $f$ is a nonnegative function and the number $A(x)$ is equal to the area of the shaded region under the graph of $f$ from $a$ to $x$. If $f$ assumes both positive and negative values, as in Figure 2.15(b), the integral $A(x)$ gives the sum of the areas of the regions above the $x$-axis minus the sum of the areas below the $x$-axis.

Many of the functions that occur in various branches of science arise exactly in this way, as indefinite integrals of other functions. This is one of the reasons that a large part of calculus is devoted to the study of indefinite integrals.

Sometimes a knowledge of a special property of $f$ implies a corresponding special property of the indefinite integral. For example, if $f$ is nonnegative on $[a, b]$, then the indefinite integral $A$ is increasing, since we have

$$A(y) - A(x) = \int_a^y f(t) \, dt - \int_a^x f(t) \, dt = \int_x^y f(t) \, dt \geq 0,$$

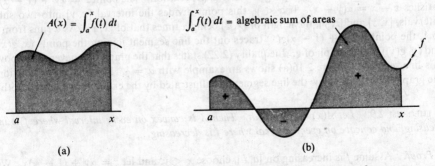

FIGURE 2.15 Indefinite integral interpreted geometrically in terms of area.

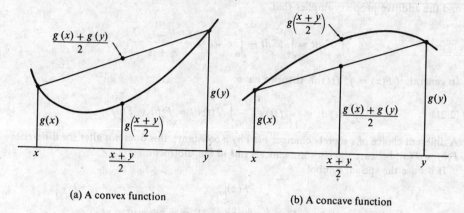

(a) A convex function                    (b) A concave function

FIGURE 2.16   Geometric interpretation of convexity and concavity.

whenever $a \leq x \leq y \leq b$. Interpreted geometrically, this means that the area under the graph of a nonnegative function from $a$ to $x$ cannot decrease as $x$ increases.

Now we discuss another property which is not immediately evident geometrically. Suppose $f$ is increasing on $[a, b]$. We can prove that the indefinite integral $A$ has a property known as *convexity*. Its graph bends upward, as illustrated in Figure 2.16(a); that is, the chord joining any two points on the graph always lies above the graph. An analytic definition of convexity may be given as follows.

DEFINITION OF A CONVEX FUNCTION.   *A function $g$ is said to be convex on an interval $[a, b]$ if, for all $x$ and $y$ in $[a, b]$ and for every $\alpha$ satisfying $0 < \alpha < 1$, we have*

$$(2.22) \qquad g(z) \leq \alpha g(y) + (1 - \alpha)g(x), \qquad where \quad z = \alpha y + (1 - \alpha)x .$$

*We say $g$ is concave on $[a, b]$ if the reverse inequality holds,*

$$g(z) \geq \alpha g(y) + (1 - \alpha)g(x), \qquad where \quad z = \alpha y + (1 - \alpha)x .$$

These inequalities have a simple geometric interpretation. The point $z = \alpha y + (1 - \alpha)x$ satisfies $z - x = \alpha(y - x)$. If $x < y$, this point divides the interval $[x, y]$ into two subintervals, $[x, z]$ and $[z, y]$, the length of $[x, z]$ being $\alpha$ times that of $[x, y]$. As $\alpha$ runs from 0 to 1, the point $\alpha g(y) + (1 - \alpha)g(x)$ traces out the line segment joining the points $(x, g(x))$ and $(y, g(y))$ on the graph of $g$. Inequality (2.22) states that the graph of $g$ never goes above this line segment. Figure 2.16(a) shows an example with $\alpha = \frac{1}{2}$. For a concave function, the graph never goes below the line segment, as illustrated by the example in Figure 2.16(b).

THEOREM 2.9.   *Let $A(x) = \int_a^x f(t) \, dt$. Then $A$ is convex on every interval where $f$ is increasing, and concave on every interval where $f$ is decreasing.*

*Proof.*   Assume $f$ is increasing on $[a, b]$, choose $x < y$, and let $z = \alpha y + (1 - \alpha)x$. We are to prove that $A(z) \leq \alpha A(y) + (1 - \alpha)A(x)$. Since $A(z) = \alpha A(z) + (1 - \alpha)A(z)$, this is the same as proving that $\alpha A(z) + (1 - \alpha)A(z) \leq \alpha A(y) + (1 - \alpha)A(x)$, or that

$$(1 - \alpha)[A(z) - A(x)] \leq \alpha[A(y) - A(z)].$$

Since we have $A(z) - A(x) = \int_x^z f(t)\,dt$ and $A(y) - A(z) = \int_z^y f(t)\,dt$, we are to prove that

(2.23) $$\qquad (1 - \alpha)\int_x^z f(t)\,dt \leq \alpha \int_z^y f(t)\,dt.$$

But $f$ is increasing, so we have the inequalities

$$f(t) \leq f(z) \quad \text{if} \quad x \leq t \leq z, \quad \text{and} \quad f(z) \leq f(t) \quad \text{if} \quad z \leq t \leq y.$$

Integrating these inequalities we find

$$\int_x^z f(t)\,dt \leq f(z)(z - x), \quad \text{and} \quad f(z)(y - z) \leq \int_z^y f(t)\,dt.$$

But $(1 - \alpha)(z - x) = \alpha(y - z)$, so these inequalities give us

$$(1 - \alpha)\int_x^z f(t)\,dt \leq (1 - \alpha)f(z)(z - x) = \alpha f(z)(y - z) \leq \alpha \int_z^y f(t)\,dt,$$

which proves (2.23). This proves that $A$ is convex when $f$ is increasing. When $f$ is decreasing, we may apply the result just proved to $-f$.

EXAMPLE. The cosine function decreases in the interval $[0, \pi]$. Since $\sin x = \int_0^x \cos t\,dt$, the graph of the sine function is concave in the interval $[0, \pi]$. In the interval $[\pi, 2\pi]$, the cosine increases and the sine function is convex.

Figure 2.17 illustrates further properties of indefinite integrals. The graph on the left is that of the greatest-integer function, $f(x) = [x]$; the graph on the right is that of the indefinite integral $A(x) = \int_0^x [t]\,dt$. On those intervals where $f$ is constant, the function $A$ is linear. We describe this by saying that *the integral of a step function is piecewise linear.*

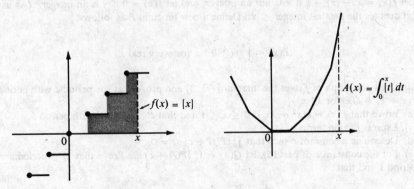

$f(x) = [x]$

$A(x) = \int_0^x [t]\,dt$

FIGURE 2.17   The indefinite integral of a step function is piecewise linear.

Observe also that the graph of $f$ is made up of disconnected line segments. There are points on the graph of $f$ where a small change in $x$ produces a sudden jump in the value of the function. Note, however, that the corresponding indefinite integral does not exhibit this behavior. A small change in $x$ produces only a small change in $A(x)$. That is why the graph of $A$ is not disconnected. This illustrates a general property of indefinite integrals known as *continuity*. In the next chapter we shall discuss the concept of continuity in detail and prove that the indefinite integral is always a continuous function.

## 2.19 Exercises

Evaluate the integrals in Exercises 1 through 16.

1. $\int_0^x (1 + t + t^2)\, dt.$

2. $\int_0^{2y} (1 + t + t^2)\, dt.$

3. $\int_{-1}^{2x} (1 + t + t^2)\, dt.$

4. $\int_1^{1-x} (1 - 2t + 3t^2)\, dt.$

5. $\int_{-2}^x t^2(t^2 + 1)\, dt.$

6. $\int_x^{x^2} (t^2 + 1)^2\, dt.$

7. $\int_1^x (t^{1/2} + 1)\, dt, \quad x > 0.$

8. $\int_x^{x^2} (t^{1/2} + t^{1/4})\, dt, \quad x > 0.$

9. $\int_{-\pi}^x \cos t\, dt.$

10. $\int_0^{x^2} (\tfrac{1}{2} + \cos t)\, dt.$

11. $\int_x^{x^2} (\tfrac{1}{2} - \sin t)\, dt.$

12. $\int_0^x (u^2 + \sin 3u)\, du.$

13. $\int_x^{x^2} (v^2 + \sin 3v)\, dv.$

14. $\int_0^y (\sin^2 x + x)\, dx.$

15. $\int_0^x \left(\sin 2w + \cos \dfrac{w}{2}\right) dw.$

16. $\int_{-\pi}^x (\tfrac{1}{2} + \cos t)^2\, dt.$

17. Find all real values of $x$ such that

$$\int_0^x (t^3 - t)\, dt = \tfrac{1}{3}\int_{\sqrt{2}}^x (t - t^3)\, dt.$$

Draw a suitable figure and interpret the equation geometrically.

18. Let $f(x) = x - [x] - \tfrac{1}{2}$ if $x$ is not an integer, and let $f(x) = 0$ if $x$ is an integer. (As usual, $[x]$ denotes the greatest integer $\le x$.) Define a new function $P$ as follows:

$$P(x) = \int_0^x f(t)\, dt \qquad \text{for every real } x.$$

(a) Draw the graph of $f$ over the interval $[-3, 3]$ and prove that $f$ is periodic with period 1: $f(x + 1) = f(x)$ for all $x$.
(b) Prove that $P(x) = \tfrac{1}{2}(x^2 - x)$, if $0 \le x \le 1$ and that $P$ is periodic with period 1.
(c) Express $P(x)$ in terms of $[x]$.
(d) Determine a constant $c$ such that $\int_0^1 (P(t) + c)\, dt = 0$.
(e) For the constant $c$ of part (d), let $Q(x) = \int_0^x (P(t) + c)\, dt$. Prove that $Q$ is periodic with period 1 and that

$$Q(x) = \frac{x^3}{6} - \frac{x^2}{4} + \frac{x}{12} \qquad \text{if } 0 \le x \le 1.$$

19. Given an odd function $f$, defined everywhere, periodic with period 2, and integrable on every interval. Let $g(x) = \int_0^x f(t)\, dt$.
    (a) Prove that $g(2n) = 0$ for every integer $n$.
    (b) Prove that $g$ is even and periodic with period 2.

20. Given an even function $f$, defined everywhere, periodic with period 2, and integrable on every interval. Let $g(x) = \int_0^x f(t)\, dt$, and let $A = g(1)$.
    (a) Prove that $g$ is odd and that $g(x + 2) - g(x) = g(2)$.
    (b) Compute $g(2)$ and $g(5)$ in terms of $A$.
    (c) For what value of $A$ will $g$ be periodic with period 2?

21. Given two functions $f$ and $g$, integrable on every interval and having the following properties: $f$ is odd, $g$ is even, $f(5) = 7$, $f(0) = 0$, $g(x) = f(x + 5)$, $f(x) = \int_0^x g(t)\, dt$ for all $x$. Prove that (a) $f(x - 5) = -g(x)$ for all $x$; (b) $\int_0^5 f(t)\, dt = 7$; (c) $\int_0^x f(t)\, dt = g(0) - g(x)$.

# 3

# CONTINUOUS FUNCTIONS

## 3.1 Informal description of continuity

This chapter deals with the concept of continuity, one of the most important and also one of the most fascinating ideas in all of mathematics. Before we give a precise technical definition of continuity, we shall briefly discuss the concept in an informal and intuitive way to give the reader a feeling for its meaning.

Roughly speaking, the situation is this: Suppose a function $f$ has the value $f(p)$ at a certain point $p$. Then $f$ is said to be continuous at $p$ if at every nearby point $x$ the function

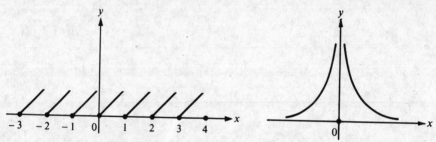

(a) A jump discontinuity at each integer.

(b) An infinite discontinuity at 0.

FIGURE 3.1    Illustrating two kinds of discontinuities.

value $f(x)$ is close to $f(p)$. Another way of putting it is as follows: If we let $x$ move toward $p$, we want the corresponding function values $f(x)$ to become arbitrarily close to $f(p)$, regardless of the manner in which $x$ approaches $p$. We do *not* want sudden jumps in the values of a continuous function, as in the examples in Figure 3.1.

Figure 3.1(a) shows the graph of the function $f$ defined by the equation $f(x) = x - [x]$, where $[x]$ denotes the greatest integer $\leq x$. At each integer we have what is known as a *jump discontinuity*. For example, $f(2) = 0$, but as $x$ approaches 2 from the left, $f(x)$ approaches the value 1, which is not equal to $f(2)$. Therefore we have a discontinuity at 2. Note that $f(x)$ *does* approach $f(2)$ if we let $x$ approach 2 *from the right*, but this by itself is not enough to establish continuity at 2. In a case like this, the function is called *continuous from the right* at 2 and *discontinuous from the left* at 2. Continuity at a point requires both continuity from the left and from the right.

126

In the early development of calculus almost all functions that were dealt with were continuous and there was no real need at that time for a penetrating look into the exact meaning of continuity. It was not until late in the 18th century that discontinuous functions began appearing in connection with various kinds of physical problems. In particular, the work of J. B. J. Fourier (1758–1830) on the theory of heat forced mathematicians of the early 19th century to examine more carefully the exact meaning of such concepts as *function* and *continuity*. Although the meaning of the word "continuous" seems intuitively clear to most people, it is not obvious how a good definition of this idea should be formulated. One popular dictionary explains continuity as follows:

*Continuity:* Quality or state of being continuous.

*Continuous:* Having continuity of parts.

Trying to learn the meaning of continuity from these two statements alone is like trying to learn Chinese with only a Chinese dictionary. A satisfactory mathematical definition of continuity, expressed entirely in terms of properties of the real-number system, was first formulated in 1821 by the French mathematician, Augustin-Louis Cauchy (1789–1857). His definition, which is still used today, is most easily explained in terms of the limit concept to which we turn now.

## 3.2 The definition of the limit of a function

Let $f$ be a function defined in some open interval containing a point $p$, although we do not insist that $f$ be defined at the point $p$ itself. Let $A$ be a real number. The equation

$$\lim_{x \to p} f(x) = A$$

is read: "The limit of $f(x)$, as $x$ approaches $p$, is equal to $A$," or "$f(x)$ approaches $A$ as $x$ approaches $p$." It is also written without the limit symbol, as follows:

$$f(x) \to A \quad \text{as} \quad x \to p .$$

This symbolism is intended to convey the idea that we can make $f(x)$ as close to $A$ as we please, provided we choose $x$ sufficiently close to $p$.

Our first task is to explain the meaning of these symbols entirely in terms of real numbers. We shall do this in two stages. First we introduce the concept of a *neighborhood* of a point, then we define limits in terms of neighborhoods.

DEFINITION OF NEIGHBORHOOD OF A POINT. *Any open interval containing a point $p$ as its midpoint is called a neighborhood of $p$.*

*Notation.* We denote neighborhoods by $N(p)$, $N_1(p)$, $N_2(p)$, etc. Since a neighborhood $N(p)$ is an open interval symmetric about $p$, it consists of all real $x$ satisfying $p - r < x < p + r$ for some $r > 0$. The positive number $r$ is called the *radius* of the neighborhood. We designate $N(p)$ by $N(p; r)$ if we wish to specify its radius. The inequalities $p - r < x < p + r$ are equivalent to $-r < x - p < r$, and to $|x - p| < r$. Thus, $N(p; r)$ consists of all points $x$ whose distance from $p$ is less than $r$.

In the next definition, we assume that $A$ is a real number and that $f$ is a function defined on some neighborhood of a point $p$ (except possibly at $p$). The function $f$ may also be defined at $p$ but this is irrelevant in the definition.

DEFINITION OF LIMIT OF A FUNCTION. *The symbolism*

$$\lim_{x \to p} f(x) = A \qquad [or \quad f(x) \to A \quad as \quad x \to p]$$

*means that for every neighborhood* $N_1(A)$ *there is some neighborhood* $N_2(p)$ *such that*

(3.1) $\qquad f(x) \in N_1(A) \qquad whenever \quad x \in N_2(p) \quad and \quad x \neq p$.

The first thing to note about this definition is that it involves *two* neighborhoods, $N_1(A)$ and $N_2(p)$. The neighborhood $N_1(A)$ is specified *first;* it tells us how close we wish $f(x)$ to

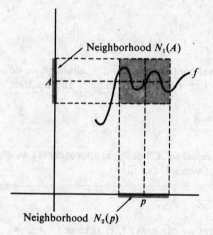

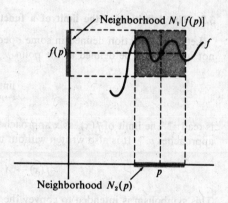

FIGURE 3.2 Here $\lim\limits_{x \to p} f(x) = A$, but there is no assertion about $f$ at $p$.

FIGURE 3.3 Here $f$ is defined at $p$ and $\lim\limits_{x \to p} f(x) = f(p)$, hence $f$ is continuous at $p$.

be to the limit $A$. The second neighborhood, $N_2(p)$, tells us how close $x$ should be to $p$ so that $f(x)$ will be within the first neighborhood $N_1(A)$. The essential part of the definition is that, for *every* $N_1(A)$, *no matter how small*, there is *some* neighborhood $N_2(p)$ to satisfy (3.1). In general, the neighborhood $N_2(p)$ will depend on the choice of $N_1(A)$. A neighborhood $N_2(p)$ that works for one particular $N_1(A)$ will also work, of course, for every larger $N_1(A)$, but it may not be suitable for any smaller $N_1(A)$.

The definition of limit may be illustrated geometrically as in Figure 3.2. A neighborhood $N_1(A)$ is shown on the $y$-axis. A neighborhood $N_2(p)$ corresponding to $N_1(A)$ is shown on the $x$-axis. The shaded rectangle consists of all points $(x, y)$ for which $x \in N_2(p)$ and $y \in N_1(A)$. The definition of limit asserts that the entire graph of $f$ above the interval $N_2(p)$ lies within this rectangle, except possibly for the point on the graph above $p$ itself.

The definition of limit can also be formulated in terms of the *radii* of the neighborhoods $N_1(A)$ and $N_2(p)$. It is customary to denote the radius of $N_1(A)$ by $\epsilon$ (the Greek letter *epsilon*) and the radius of $N_2(p)$ by $\delta$ (the Greek letter *delta*). The statement $f(x) \in N_1(A)$ is equivalent to the inequality $|f(x) - A| < \epsilon$, and the statement $x \in N_2(p)$, $x \neq p$, is equivalent to the inequalities $0 < |x - p| < \delta$. Therefore, the definition of limit can also be expressed as follows:

*The symbol* $\lim_{x \to p} f(x) = A$ *means that for every* $\epsilon > 0$, *there is a* $\delta > 0$ *such that*

(3.2)  $\qquad\qquad |f(x) - A| < \epsilon \qquad$ *whenever* $\quad 0 < |x - p| < \delta$ .

We note that the three statements,

$$\lim_{x \to p} f(x) = A , \qquad \lim_{x \to p} (f(x) - A) = 0 , \qquad \lim_{x \to p} |f(x) - A| = 0 ,$$

are all equivalent. This equivalence becomes apparent as soon as we write each of these statements in the $\epsilon$, $\delta$-terminology (3.2).

In dealing with limits as $x \to p$, we sometimes find it convenient to denote the difference $x - p$ by a new symbol, say $h$, and to let $h \to 0$. This simply amounts to a change in notation, because, as can be easily verified, the following two statements are equivalent:

$$\lim_{x \to p} f(x) = A , \qquad \lim_{h \to 0} f(p + h) = A .$$

EXAMPLE 1. *Limit of a constant function.* Let $f(x) = c$ for all $x$. It is easy to prove that for every $p$, we have $\lim_{x \to p} f(x) = c$. In fact, given any neighborhood $N_1(c)$, relation (3.1) is trivially satisfied for any choice of $N_2(p)$ because $f(x) = c$ for all $x$ and $c \in N_1(c)$ for all neighborhoods $N_1(c)$. In limit notation, we write

$$\lim_{x \to p} c = c .$$

EXAMPLE 2. *Limit of the identity function.* Here $f(x) = x$ for all $x$. We can easily prove that $\lim_{x \to p} f(x) = p$. Choose any neighborhood $N_1(p)$ and take $N_2(p) = N_1(p)$. Then relation (3.1) is trivially satisfied. In limit notation, we write

$$\lim_{x \to p} x = p .$$

"One-sided" limits may be defined in a similar way. For example, if $f(x) \to A$ as $x \to p$ through values greater than $p$, we say that $A$ is the *right-hand limit* of $f$ at $p$, and we indicate this by writing

$$\lim_{x \to p+} f(x) = A .$$

In neighborhood terminology this means that for every neighborhood $N_1(A)$, there is some neighborhood $N_2(p)$ such that

(3.3)  $\qquad\qquad f(x) \in N_1(A) \qquad$ whenever $\quad x \in N_2(p) \quad$ and $\quad x > p$ .

Left-hand limits, denoted by writing $x \to p-$, are similarly defined by restricting $x$ to values less than $p$.

If $f$ has a limit $A$ at $p$, then it also has a right-hand limit and a left-hand limit at $p$, both of these being equal to $A$. But a function can have a right-hand limit at $p$ different from the left-hand limit, as indicated in the next example.

EXAMPLE 3. Let $f(x) = [x]$ for all $x$, and let $p$ be any integer. For $x$ near $p$, $x < p$, we have $f(x) = p - 1$, and for $x$ near $p$, $x > p$, we have $f(x) = p$. Therefore we see that

$$\lim_{x \to p-} f(x) = p - 1 \quad \text{and} \quad \lim_{x \to p+} f(x) = p .$$

In an example like this one, where the right- and left-hand limits are unequal, the limit of $f$ at $p$ *does not exist.*

EXAMPLE 4. Let $f(x) = 1/x^2$ if $x \neq 0$, and let $f(0) = 0$. The graph of $f$ near zero is shown in Figure 3.1(b). In this example, $f$ takes arbitrarily large values near 0 so it has no right-hand limit and no left-hand limit at 0. To prove rigorously that there is no real number $A$ such that $\lim_{x \to 0+} f(x) = A$, we may argue as follows: Suppose there were such an $A$, say $A \geq 0$. Choose a neighborhood $N_1(A)$ of length 1. In the interval $0 < x < 1/(A + 2)$, we have $f(x) = 1/x^2 > (A + 2)^2 > A + 2$, so $f(x)$ cannot lie in the neighborhood $N_1(A)$. Thus, every neighborhood $N(0)$ contains points $x > 0$ for which $f(x)$ is outside $N_1(A)$, so (3.3) is violated for this choice of $N_1(A)$. Hence $f$ has no right-hand limit at 0.

EXAMPLE 5. Let $f(x) = 1$ if $x \neq 0$, and let $f(0) = 0$. This function takes the constant value 1 everywhere except at 0, where it has the value 0. Both the right- and left-hand limits are 1 at every point $p$, so the limit of $f(x)$, as $x$ approaches $p$, exists and equals 1. Note that the limit of $f$ is 1 at the point 0, even though $f(0) = 0$.

## 3.3 The definition of continuity of a function

In the definition of limit we made no assertion about the behavior of $f$ at the point $p$ itself. Statement (3.1) refers to those $x \neq p$ which lie in $N_2(p)$, so it is not necessary that $f$ be defined at $p$. Moreover, even if $f$ is defined at $p$, its value there need not be equal to the limit $A$. However, if it happens that $f$ is defined at $p$ and if it also happens that $f(p) = A$, then we say the function $f$ is continuous at $p$. In other words, we have the following definition.

DEFINITION OF CONTINUITY OF A FUNCTION AT A POINT. *A function $f$ is said to be continuous at a point $p$ if*

(a) *$f$ is defined at $p$, and*

(b) $\lim_{x \to p} f(x) = f(p) .$

This definition can also be formulated in terms of neighborhoods. A function $f$ is continuous at $p$ if for every neighborhood $N_1[f(p)]$ there is a neighborhood $N_2(p)$ such that

(3.4)     $f(x) \in N_1[f(p)] \quad \text{whenever} \quad x \in N_2(p) .$

Since $f(p)$ always belongs to $N_1[f(p)]$, we do not need the condition $x \neq p$ in (3.4). In the $\epsilon$, $\delta$-terminology, where we specify the radii of the neighborhoods, the definition of continuity can be restated as follows:

A function $f$ is continuous at $p$ if for every $\epsilon > 0$ there is a $\delta > 0$ such that

$$|f(x) - f(p)| < \epsilon \qquad \text{whenever} \quad |x - p| < \delta.$$

The definition of continuity is illustrated geometrically in Figure 3.3. This is like Figure 3.2 except that the limiting value, $A$, is equal to the function value $f(p)$ so the entire graph of $f$ above $N_2(p)$ lies in the shaded rectangle.

EXAMPLE 1. *Constant functions are continuous everywhere.* If $f(x) = c$ for all $x$, then

$$\lim_{x \to p} f(x) = \lim_{x \to p} c = c = f(p)$$

for every $p$, so $f$ is continuous everywhere.

EXAMPLE 2. *The identity function is continuous everywhere.* If $f(x) = x$ for all $x$, we have

$$\lim_{x \to p} f(x) = \lim_{x \to p} x = p = f(p)$$

for every $p$, so the identity function is continuous everywhere.

EXAMPLE 3. Let $f(x) = [x]$ for all $x$. This function is continuous at every point $p$ which is not an integer. At the integers it is discontinuous, since the limit of $f$ does not exist, the right- and left-hand limits being unequal. A discontinuity of this type, where the right- and left-hand limits exist but are unequal, is called a *jump discontinuity*. However, since the right-hand limit equals $f(p)$ at each integer $p$, we say that $f$ is *continuous from the right* at $p$.

EXAMPLE 4. The function $f$ for which $f(x) = 1/x^2$ for $x \neq 0$, $f(0) = 0$, is discontinuous at 0. [See Figure 3.1(b).] We say there is an *infinite discontinuity* at 0 because the function takes arbitrarily large values near 0.

EXAMPLE 5. Let $f(x) = 1$ for $x \neq 0$, $f(0) = 0$. This function is continuous everywhere except at 0. It is discontinuous at 0 because $f(0)$ is not equal to the limit of $f(x)$ as $x \to 0$. In this example, the discontinuity could be removed by redefining the function at 0 to have the value 1 instead of 0. For this reason, a discontinuity of this type is called a *removable discontinuity*. Note that jump discontinuities, such as those possessed by the greatest-integer function, cannot be removed by simply changing the value of $f$ at one point.

## 3.4 The basic limit theorems. More examples of continuous functions

Calculations with limits may often be simplified by the use of the following theorem which provides basic rules for operating with limits.

THEOREM 3.1.  *Let f and g be functions such that*

$$\lim_{x \to p} f(x) = A, \qquad \lim_{x \to p} g(x) = B.$$

*Then we have*

(i)  $\lim_{x \to p} [f(x) + g(x)] = A + B,$

(ii)  $\lim_{x \to p} [f(x) - g(x)] = A - B,$

(iii)  $\lim_{x \to p} f(x) \cdot g(x) = A \cdot B,$

(iv)  $\lim_{x \to p} f(x)/g(x) = A/B \qquad \text{if } B \neq 0.$

*Note:* An important special case of (iii) occurs when $f$ is constant, say $f(x) = A$ for all $x$. In this case, (iii) is written as $\lim_{x \to p} A \cdot g(x) = A \cdot B$.

The proof of Theorem 3.1 is not difficult but it is somewhat lengthy so we have placed it in a separate section (Section 3.5). We discuss here some simple consequences of the theorem.

First we note that the statements in the theorem may be written in a slightly different form. For example, (i) can be written as follows:

$$\lim_{x \to p} [f(x) + g(x)] = \lim_{x \to p} f(x) + \lim_{x \to p} g(x).$$

It tells us that the limit of a sum is the sum of the limits.

It is customary to denote by $f + g, f - g, f \cdot g$, and $f/g$ the functions whose values at each $x$ under consideration are

$$f(x) + g(x), \qquad f(x) - g(x), \qquad f(x) \cdot g(x), \qquad \text{and} \qquad f(x)/g(x),$$

respectively. These functions are called the *sum, difference, product,* and *quotient* of $f$ and $g$. Of course, the quotient $f/g$ is defined only at those points for which $g(x) \neq 0$. The following corollary to Theorem 3.1 is stated in this terminology and notation and is concerned with continuous functions.

THEOREM 3.2.  *Let f and g be continuous at a point p. Then the sum $f + g$, the difference $f - g$, and the product $f \cdot g$ are also continuous at p. The same is true of the quotient $f/g$ if $g(p) \neq 0$.*

*Proof.*  Since $f$ and $g$ are continuous at $p$, we have $\lim_{x \to p} f(x) = f(p)$ and $\lim_{x \to p} g(x) = g(p)$. Therefore we may apply the limit formulas in Theorem 3.1 with $A = f(p)$ and $B = g(p)$ to deduce Theorem 3.2.

We have already seen that the identity function and constant functions are continuous everywhere. Using these examples and Theorem 3.2, we may construct many more examples of continuous functions.

EXAMPLE 1. *Continuity of polynomials.* If we take $f(x) = g(x) = x$, the result on continuity of products proves the continuity at each point for the function whose value at each $x$ is $x^2$. By mathematical induction, it follows that for every real $c$ and every positive integer $n$, the function $f$ for which $f(x) = cx^n$ is continuous for all $x$. Since the sum of two continuous functions is itself continuous, by induction it follows that the same is true for the sum of any finite number of continuous functions. Therefore every polynomial $p(x) = \sum_{k=0}^{n} c_k x^k$ is continuous at all points.

EXAMPLE 2. *Continuity of rational functions.* The quotient of two polynomials is called a *rational function.* If $r$ is a rational function, then we have

$$r(x) = \frac{p(x)}{q(x)},$$

where $p$ and $q$ are polynomials. The function $r$ is defined for all real $x$ for which $q(x) \neq 0$. Since quotients of continuous functions are continuous, we see that every rational function is continuous wherever it is defined. A simple example is $r(x) = 1/x$ if $x \neq 0$. This function is continuous everywhere except at $x = 0$, where it fails to be defined.

The next theorem shows that if a function $g$ is squeezed between two other functions which have equal limits as $x \to p$, then $g$ also has this limit as $x \to p$.

THEOREM 3.3. SQUEEZING PRINCIPLE. *Suppose that $f(x) \leq g(x) \leq h(x)$ for all $x \neq p$ in some neighborhood $N(p)$. Suppose also that*

$$\lim_{x \to p} f(x) = \lim_{x \to p} h(x) = a .$$

*Then we also have $\lim_{x \to p} g(x) = a$.*

*Proof.* Let $G(x) = g(x) - f(x)$, and $H(x) = h(x) - f(x)$. The inequalities $f \leq g \leq h$ imply $0 \leq g - f \leq h - f$, or

$$0 \leq G(x) \leq H(x)$$

for all $x \neq p$ in $N(p)$. To prove the theorem, it suffices to show that $G(x) \to 0$ as $x \to p$, given that $H(x) \to 0$ as $x \to p$.

Let $N_1(0)$ be any neighborhood of 0. Since $H(x) \to 0$ as $x \to p$, there is a neighborhood $N_2(p)$ such that

$$H(x) \in N_1(0) \quad \text{whenever} \quad x \in N_2(p) \quad \text{and} \quad x \neq p .$$

We can assume that $N_2(p) \subseteq N(p)$. Then the inequality $0 \leq G \leq H$ states that $G(x)$ is no further from 0 than $H(x)$ if $x$ is in $N_2(p)$, $x \neq p$. Therefore $G(x) \in N_1(0)$ for such $x$, and hence $G(x) \to 0$ as $x \to p$. This proves the theorem. The same proof is valid if all the limits are one-sided limits.

The squeezing principle is useful in practice because it is often possible to find squeezing functions $f$ and $h$ which are easier to deal with than $g$. We shall use the result now to prove that every indefinite integral is a continuous function.

THEOREM 3.4.  CONTINUITY OF INDEFINITE INTEGRALS.  *Assume $f$ is integrable on $[a, x]$ for every $x$ in $[a, b]$, and let*

$$A(x) = \int_a^x f(t) \, dt \,.$$

*Then the indefinite integral $A$ is continuous at each point of $[a, b]$. (At each endpoint we have one-sided continuity.)*

*Proof.*  Choose $p$ in $[a, b]$. We are to prove that $A(x) \to A(p)$ as $x \to p$. We have

(3.5) $$A(x) - A(p) = \int_p^x f(t) \, dt \,.$$

Now we estimate the size of this integral. Since $f$ is bounded on $[a, b]$, there is a constant $M > 0$ such that $-M \leq f(t) \leq M$ for all $t$ in $[a, b]$. If $x > p$, we integrate these inequalities over the interval $[p, x]$ to obtain

$$-M(x - p) \leq A(x) - A(p) \leq M(x - p) \,.$$

If $x < p$, we obtain the same inequalities with $x - p$ replaced by $p - x$. Therefore, in either case we can let $x \to p$ and apply the squeezing principle to find that $A(x) \to A(p)$. This proves the theorem. If $p$ is an endpoint of $[a, b]$, we must let $x \to p$ from inside the interval, so the limits are one-sided.

EXAMPLE 3.  *Continuity of the sine and cosine.* Since the sine function is an indefinite integral, $\sin x = \int_0^x \cos t \, dt$, the foregoing theorem tells us that the sine is continuous everywhere. Similarly, the cosine is everywhere continuous since $\cos x = 1 - \int_0^x \sin t \, dt$. The continuity of these functions can also be deduced without making use of the fact that they are indefinite integrals. An alternate proof is outlined in Exercise 26 of Section 3.6.

EXAMPLE 4.  In this example we prove an important limit formula,

(3.6) $$\lim_{x \to 0} \frac{\sin x}{x} = 1 \,,$$

that is needed later in our discussion of differential calculus. Since the denominator of the quotient $(\sin x)/x$ approaches 0 as $x \to 0$, we cannot apply the quotient theorem on limits to deduce (3.6). Instead, we use the squeezing principle. From Section 2.5 we have the fundamental inequalities

$$0 < \cos x < \frac{\sin x}{x} < \frac{1}{\cos x},$$

valid for $0 < x < \frac{1}{2}\pi$. They are also valid for $-\frac{1}{2}\pi < x < 0$ since $\cos(-x) = \cos x$ and $\sin(-x) = -\sin x$, and hence they hold for all $x \neq 0$ in the neighborhood $N(0; \frac{1}{2}\pi)$. When $x \to 0$, we find $\cos x \to 1$ since the cosine is continuous at 0, and hence $1/(\cos x) \to 1$. Therefore, by the squeezing principle, we deduce (3.6). If we define $f(x) = (\sin x)/x$ for $x \neq 0$, $f(0) = 1$, then $f$ is continuous everywhere. Its graph is shown in Figure 3.4.

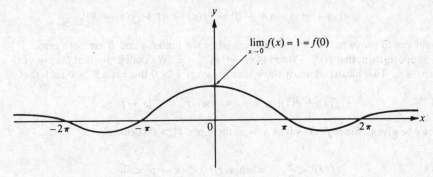

FIGURE 3.4 $f(x) = (\sin x)/x$ if $x \neq 0$, $f(0) = 1$. This function is continuous everywhere.

EXAMPLE 5. *Continuity of f when $f(x) = x^r$ for $x > 0$, where r is a positive rational number.* From Theorem 2.2 we have the integration formula

$$\int_0^x t^{1/n}\, dt = \frac{x^{1+1/n}}{1 + 1/n},$$

valid for all $x > 0$ and every integer $n \geq 1$. Using Theorems 3.4 and 3.1, we find that the function $A$ given by $A(x) = x^{1+1/n}$ is continuous at all points $p > 0$. Now let $g(x) = x^{1/n} = A(x)/x$ for $x > 0$. Since $g$ is a quotient of two continuous functions it, too, is continuous at all points $p > 0$. More generally, if $f(x) = x^{m/n}$, where $m$ is a positive integer, then $f$ is a product of continuous functions and hence is continuous at all points $p > 0$. This establishes the continuity of the $r$th-power function, $f(x) = x^r$, when $r$ is any positive rational number, at all points $p > 0$. At $p = 0$ we have right-hand continuity.

The continuity of the $r$th-power function for rational $r$ can also be deduced without using integrals. An alternate proof is given in Section 3.13.

## 3.5 Proofs of the basic limit theorems

In this section we prove Theorem 3.1 which describes the basic rules for dealing with limits of sums, products, and quotients. The principal algebraic tools used in the proof are two properties of absolute values that were mentioned earlier in Sections I4.8 and I4.9. They are (1) the triangle inequality, which states that $|a + b| \leq |a| + |b|$ for all real $a$ and $b$, and (2) the equation $|ab| = |a|\,|b|$, which states that the absolute value of a product is the product of absolute values.

*Proofs of* (i) *and* (ii).   Since the two statements

$$\lim_{x \to p} f(x) = A \qquad \text{and} \qquad \lim_{x \to p} [f(x) - A] = 0$$

are equivalent, and since we have

$$f(x) + g(x) - (A + B) = [f(x) - A] + [g(x) - B],$$

it suffices to prove part (i) of the theorem when the limits $A$ and $B$ are both zero.

Suppose, then, that $f(x) \to 0$ and $g(x) \to 0$ as $x \to p$. We shall prove that $f(x) + g(x) \to 0$ as $x \to p$. This means we must show that for every $\epsilon > 0$ there is a $\delta > 0$ such that

(3.7)                    $|f(x) + g(x)| < \epsilon$      whenever   $0 < |x - p| < \delta$.

Let $\epsilon$ be given. Since $f(x) \to 0$ as $x \to p$, there is a $\delta_1 > 0$ such that

(3.8)                    $|f(x)| < \dfrac{\epsilon}{2}$      whenever   $0 < |x - p| < \delta_1$.

Similarly, since $g(x) \to 0$ as $x \to p$, there is a $\delta_2 > 0$ such that

(3.9)                    $|g(x)| < \dfrac{\epsilon}{2}$      whenever   $0 < |x - p| < \delta_2$.

If we let $\delta$ denote the smaller of the two numbers $\delta_1$ and $\delta_2$, then both inequalities (3.8) and (3.9) are valid if $0 < |x - p| < \delta$ and hence, by the triangle inequality, we find that

$$|f(x) + g(x)| \leq |f(x)| + |g(x)| < \frac{\epsilon}{2} + \frac{\epsilon}{2} = \epsilon.$$

This proves (3.7) which, in turn, proves (i). The proof of (ii) is entirely similar, except that in the last step we use the inequality $|f(x) - g(x)| \leq |f(x)| + |g(x)|$.

*Proof of* (iii).   Suppose that we have proved part (iii) for the special case in which one of the limits is 0. Then the general case follows easily from this special case. In fact, all we need to do is write

$$f(x)g(x) - AB = f(x)[g(x) - B] + B[f(x) - A].$$

The special case implies that each term on the right approaches 0 as $x \to p$ and, by property (i), the sum of the two terms also approaches 0. Therefore, it remains to prove (iii) in the special case where one of the limits, say $B$, is 0.

Suppose, then, that $f(x) \to A$ and $g(x) \to 0$ as $x \to p$. We wish to prove that $f(x)g(x) \to 0$ as $x \to p$. To do this we must show that if a positive $\epsilon$ is given, there is a $\delta > 0$ such that

$$(3.10) \qquad |f(x)g(x)| < \epsilon \qquad \text{whenever} \quad 0 < |x - p| < \delta.$$

Since $f(x) \to A$ as $x \to p$, there is a $\delta_1$ such that

$$(3.11) \qquad |f(x) - A| < 1 \qquad \text{whenever} \quad 0 < |x - p| < \delta_1.$$

For such $x$, we have $|f(x)| = |f(x) - A + A| \leq |f(x) - A| + |A| < 1 + |A|$, and hence

$$(3.12) \qquad |f(x)g(x)| = |f(x)| \, |g(x)| < (1 + |A|) \, |g(x)|.$$

Since $g(x) \to 0$ as $x \to p$, for every $\epsilon > 0$ there is a $\delta_2$ such that

$$(3.13) \qquad |g(x)| < \frac{\epsilon}{1 + |A|} \qquad \text{whenever} \quad 0 < |x - p| < \delta_2.$$

Therefore, if we let $\delta$ be the smaller of the two numbers $\delta_1$ and $\delta_2$, then both inequalities (3.12) and (3.13) are valid whenever $0 < |x - p| < \delta$, and for such $x$ we deduce (3.10). This completes the proof of (iii).

*Proof of* (iv). Since the quotient $f(x)/g(x)$ is the product of $f(x)/B$ with $B/g(x)$, it suffices to prove that $B/g(x) \to 1$ as $x \to p$ and then appeal to (iii). Let $h(x) = g(x)/B$. Then $h(x) \to 1$ as $x \to p$, and we wish to prove that $1/h(x) \to 1$ as $x \to p$.

Let $\epsilon > 0$ be given. We must show that there is a $\delta > 0$ such that

$$(3.14) \qquad \left| \frac{1}{h(x)} - 1 \right| < \epsilon \qquad \text{whenever} \quad 0 < |x - p| < \delta.$$

The difference to be estimated may be written as follows.

$$(3.15) \qquad \left| \frac{1}{h(x)} - 1 \right| = \frac{|h(x) - 1|}{|h(x)|}.$$

Since $h(x) \to 1$ as $x \to p$, we can choose a $\delta > 0$ such that both inequalities

$$(3.16) \qquad |h(x) - 1| < \frac{\epsilon}{2} \quad \text{and} \quad |h(x) - 1| < \frac{1}{2}$$

are satisfied whenever $0 < |x - p| < \delta$. The second of these inequalities implies $h(x) > \frac{1}{2}$ so $1/|h(x)| = 1/h(x) < 2$ for such $x$. Using this in (3.15) along with the first inequality in (3.16), we obtain (3.14). This completes the proof of (iv).

## 3.6 Exercises

In Exercises 1 through 10, compute the limits and explain which limit theorems you are using in each case.

1. $\lim\limits_{x\to 2} \dfrac{1}{x^2}$.

2. $\lim\limits_{x\to 0} \dfrac{25x^3 + 2}{75x^7 - 2}$.

3. $\lim\limits_{x\to 2} \dfrac{x^2 - 4}{x - 2}$.

4. $\lim\limits_{x\to 1} \dfrac{2x^2 - 3x + 1}{x - 1}$.

5. $\lim\limits_{h\to 0} \dfrac{(t + h)^2 - t^2}{h}$.

6. $\lim\limits_{x\to 0} \dfrac{x^2 - a^2}{x^2 + 2ax + a^2}$, $\quad a \neq 0$.

7. $\lim\limits_{a\to 0} \dfrac{x^2 - a^2}{x^2 + 2ax + a^2}$, $\quad x \neq 0$.

8. $\lim\limits_{x\to a} \dfrac{x^2 - a^2}{x^2 + 2ax + a^2}$, $\quad a \neq 0$.

9. $\lim\limits_{t\to 0} \tan t$.

10. $\lim\limits_{t\to 0} (\sin 2t + t^2 \cos 5t)$.

11. $\lim\limits_{x\to 0+} \dfrac{|x|}{x}$.

12. $\lim\limits_{x\to 0-} \dfrac{|x|}{x}$.

13. $\lim\limits_{x\to 0+} \dfrac{\sqrt{x^2}}{x}$.

14. $\lim\limits_{x\to 0-} \dfrac{\sqrt{x^2}}{x}$.

Use the relation $\lim_{x\to 0} (\sin x)/x = 1$ to establish the limit formulas in Exercises 15 through 20.

15. $\lim\limits_{x\to 0} \dfrac{\sin 2x}{x} = 2$.

16. $\lim\limits_{x\to 0} \dfrac{\tan 2x}{\sin x} = 2$.

17. $\lim\limits_{x\to 0} \dfrac{\sin 5x}{\sin x} = 5$.

18. $\lim\limits_{x\to 0} \dfrac{\sin 5x - \sin 3x}{x} = 2$.

19. $\lim\limits_{x\to 0} \dfrac{\sin x - \sin a}{x - a} = \cos a$.

20. $\lim\limits_{x\to 0} \dfrac{1 - \cos x}{x^2} = \tfrac{1}{2}$.

21. Show that $\lim\limits_{x\to 0} \dfrac{1 - \sqrt{1 - x^2}}{x^2} = \tfrac{1}{2}$. [*Hint:* $(1 - \sqrt{u})(1 + \sqrt{u}) = 1 - u$.]

22. A function $f$ is defined as follows:

$$f(x) = \begin{cases} \sin x & \text{if } x \leq c, \\ ax + b & \text{if } x > c, \end{cases}$$

where $a, b, c$ are constants. If $b$ and $c$ are given, find all values of $a$ (if any exist) for which $f$ is continuous at the point $x = c$.

23. Solve Exercise 22 if $f$ is defined as follows:

$$f(x) = \begin{cases} 2 \cos x & \text{if } x \leq c, \\ ax^2 + b & \text{if } x > c. \end{cases}$$

24. At what points are the tangent and cotangent functions continuous?

25. Let $f(x) = (\tan x)/x$ if $x \neq 0$. Sketch the graph of $f$ over the half-open intervals $[-\tfrac{1}{4}\pi, 0)$ and $(0, \tfrac{1}{4}\pi]$. What happens to $f(x)$ as $x \to 0$? Can you define $f(0)$ so that $f$ becomes continuous at 0?

26. This exercise outlines an alternate proof of the continuity of the sine and cosine functions.

    (a) The inequality $|\sin x| < |x|$, valid for $0 < |x| < \frac{1}{2}\pi$, was proved in Exercise 34 of Section 2.8. Use this inequality to prove that the sine function is continuous at 0.

    (b) Use part (a) and the identity $\cos 2x = 1 - 2\sin^2 x$ to prove that the cosine is continuous at 0.

    (c) Use the addition formulas for $\sin(x + h)$ and $\cos(x + h)$ to prove that the sine and cosine are continuous at any real $x$.

27. Figure 3.5 shows a portion of the graph of the function $f$ defined as follows:

$$f(x) = \sin \frac{1}{x} \quad \text{if} \quad x \neq 0.$$

For $x = 1/(n\pi)$, where $n$ is an integer, we have $\sin(1/x) = \sin(n\pi) = 0$. Between two such points, the function values rise to $+1$ and drop back to 0 or else drop to $-1$ and rise back to 0.

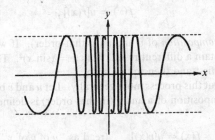

FIGURE 3.5 $f(x) = \sin(1/x)$ if $x \neq 0$. This function is discontinuous at 0 no matter how $f(0)$ is defined.

Therefore, between any such point and the origin, the curve has an infinite number of oscillations. This suggests that the function values do not approach any fixed value as $x \to 0$. Prove that there is no real number $A$ such that $f(x) \to A$ as $x \to 0$. This shows that it is not possible to define $f(0)$ in such a way that $f$ becomes continuous at 0.

[*Hint:* Assume such an $A$ exists and obtain a contradiction.]

28. For $x \neq 0$, let $f(x) = [1/x]$, where $[t]$ denotes the greatest integer $\leq t$. Sketch the graph of $f$ over the intervals $[-2, -\frac{1}{5}]$ and $[\frac{1}{5}, 2]$. What happens to $f(x)$ as $x \to 0$ through positive values? through negative values? Can you define $f(0)$ so that $f$ becomes continuous at 0?

29. Same as Exercise 28, when $f(x) = (-1)^{[1/x]}$ for $x \neq 0$.

30. Same as Exercise 28, when $f(x) = x(-1)^{[1/x]}$ for $x \neq 0$.

31. Give an example of a function that is continuous at one point of an interval and discontinuous at all other points of the interval, or prove that there is no such function.

32. Let $f(x) = x\sin(1/x)$ if $x \neq 0$. Define $f(0)$ so that $f$ will be continuous at 0.

33. Let $f$ be a function such that $|f(u) - f(v)| \leq |u - v|$ for all $u$ and $v$ in an interval $[a, b]$.

    (a) Prove that $f$ is continuous at each point of $[a, b]$.

    (b) Assume that $f$ is integrable on $[a, b]$. Prove that

$$\left| \int_a^b f(x)\, dx - (b - a)f(a) \right| \leq \frac{(b - a)^2}{2}.$$

(c) More generally, prove that for any $c$ in $[a, b]$, we have

$$\left| \int_a^b f(x)\, dx - (b - a)f(c) \right| \leq \frac{(b - a)^2}{2}.$$

## 3.7  Composite functions and continuity

We can create new functions from given ones by addition, subtraction, multiplication, and division. In this section we learn a new way to construct functions by an operation known as composition. We illustrate with an example.

Let $f(x) = \sin(x^2)$. To compute $f(x)$, we first square $x$ and then take the sine of $x^2$. Thus, $f(x)$ is obtained by combining two other functions, the squaring function and the sine function. If we let $v(x) = x^2$ and $u(x) = \sin x$, we can express $f(x)$ in terms of $u$ and $v$ by writing

$$f(x) = u[v(x)].$$

We say that $f$ is the *composition* of $u$ and $v$ (in that order). If we compose $v$ and $u$ in the opposite order, we obtain a different result, $v[u(x)] = (\sin x)^2$. That is, to compute $v[u(x)]$, we take the sine of $x$ first and then square $\sin x$.

Now we can carry out this process more generally. Let $u$ and $v$ be any two given functions. The composite or composition of $u$ and $v$ (in that order) is defined to be the function $f$ for which

$$f(x) = u[v(x)] \qquad \text{(read as ``u of v of x'')}.$$

That is, to evaluate $f$ at $x$ we first compute $v(x)$ and then evaluate $u$ at the point $v(x)$. Of course, this presupposes that it makes sense to evaluate $u$ at $v(x)$, and therefore $f$ will be defined only at those points $x$ for which $v(x)$ is in the domain of $u$.

For example, if $u(x) = \sqrt{x}$ and $v(x) = 1 - x^2$, then the composite $f$ is given by $f(x) = \sqrt{1 - x^2}$. Note that $v$ is defined for all real $x$, whereas $u$ is defined only for $x \geq 0$. Therefore the composite $f$ is defined only for those $x$ satisfying $1 - x^2 \geq 0$.

Formally, $f(x)$ is obtained by substituting $v(x)$ for $x$ in the expression $u(x)$. For this reason, the function $f$ is sometimes denoted by the symbol $f = u(v)$ (read as "u of v"). Another notation that we shall use to denote composition is $f = u \circ v$ (read as "u circle v"). This resembles the notation for the product $u \cdot v$. In fact, we shall see in a moment that the operation of composition has some of the properties possessed by multiplication.

The composite of three or more functions may be found by composing them two at a time. Thus, the function $f$ given by

$$f(x) = \cos[\sin(x^2)]$$

is a composition, $f = u \circ (v \circ w)$, where

$$u(x) = \cos x, \qquad v(x) = \sin x, \qquad \text{and} \qquad w(x) = x^2.$$

Notice that the same $f$ can be obtained by composing $u$ and $v$ first and then composing $u \circ v$

with $w$, thus: $f = (u \circ v) \circ w$. This illustrates the *associative law* for composition which states that

$$(3.17) \qquad\qquad u \circ (v \circ w) = (u \circ v) \circ w$$

for all functions $u$, $v$, $w$, provided it makes sense to form all the composites in question. The reader will find that the proof of (3.17) is a straightforward exercise.

It should be noted that the *commutative law*, $u \circ v = v \circ u$, does not always hold for composition. For example, if $u(x) = \sin x$ and $v(x) = x^2$, the composite $f = u \circ v$ is given by $f(x) = \sin x^2$ (which means $\sin (x^2)$]), whereas the composition $g = v \circ u$ is given by $g(x) = \sin^2 x$ [which means $(\sin x)^2$].

Now we shall prove a theorem which tells us that the property of continuity is preserved under the operation of composition. More precisely, we have the following.

THEOREM 3.5.    *Assume $v$ is continuous at $p$ and that $u$ is continuous at $q$, where $q = v(p)$. Then the composite function $f = u \circ v$ is continuous at $p$.*

*Proof.* Since $u$ is continuous at $q$, for every neighborhood $N_1[u(q)]$ there is a neighborhood $N_2(q)$ such that

$$(3.18) \qquad\qquad u(y) \in N_1[u(q)] \quad \text{whenever} \quad y \in N_2(q).$$

But $q = v(p)$ and $v$ is continuous at $p$, so for the neighborhood $N_2(q)$ there is another neighborhood $N_3(p)$ such that

$$(3.19) \qquad\qquad v(x) \in N_2(q) \quad \text{whenever} \quad x \in N_3(p).$$

If we let $y = v(x)$ and combine (3.18) with (3.19), we find that for every neighborhood $N_1(u[v(p)])$ there is a neighborhood $N_3(p)$ such that

$$u[v(x)] \in N_1(u[v(p)]) \quad \text{whenever} \quad x \in N_3(p),$$

or, in other words, since $f(x) = u[v(x)]$,

$$f(x) \in N_1[f(p)] \quad \text{whenever} \quad x \in N_3(p).$$

This means that $f$ is continuous at $p$, as asserted.

EXAMPLE 1. Let $f(x) = \sin x^2$. This is the composition of two functions continuous everywhere so $f$ is continuous everywhere.

EXAMPLE 2. Let $f(x) = \sqrt{1 - x^2} = u[v(x)]$, where $u(x) = \sqrt{x}$, $v(x) = 1 - x^2$. The function $v$ is continuous everywhere but $u$ is continuous only for points $x \geq 0$. Hence $f$ is continuous at those points $x$ for which $v(x) \geq 0$, that is at all points satisfying $x^2 \leq 1$.

## 3.8   Exercises

In Exercises 1 through 10, the functions $f$ and $g$ are defined by the formulas given. Unless otherwise noted, the domains of $f$ and $g$ consist of all real numbers. Let $h(x) = f[g(x)]$ whenever $g(x)$ lies in the domain of $f$. In each case, describe the domain of $h$ and give one or more formulas for determining $h(x)$.

1. $f(x) = x^2 - 2x$,                   $g(x) = x + 1$.
2. $f(x) = x + 1$,                      $g(x) = x^2 - 2x$.
3. $f(x) = \sqrt{x}$    if   $x \geq 0$,         $g(x) = x^2$.
4. $f(x) = \sqrt{x}$    if   $x \geq 0$,         $g(x) = -x^2$.
5. $f(x) = x^2$,                       $g(x) = \sqrt{x}$    if   $x \geq 0$.
6. $f(x) = -x^2$,                     $g(x) = \sqrt{x}$    if   $x \geq 0$.
7. $f(x) = \sin x$,                    $g(x) = \sqrt{x}$    if   $x \geq 0$.
8. $f(x) = \sqrt{x}$    if   $x \geq 0$,         $g(x) = \sin x$.
9. $f(x) = \sqrt{x}$    if   $x > 0$,         $g(x) = x + \sqrt{x}$    if   $x > 0$.
10. $f(x) = \sqrt{x + \sqrt{x}}$   if   $x > 0$,    $g(x) = x + \sqrt{x}$    if   $x > 0$.

Calculate the limits in Exercises 11 through 20 and explain which limit theorems you are using in each case.

11. $\lim\limits_{x \to -2} \dfrac{x^3 + 8}{x^2 - 4}$.

12. $\lim\limits_{x \to 4} \sqrt{1 + \sqrt{x}}$.

13. $\lim\limits_{t \to 0} \dfrac{\sin(\tan t)}{\sin t}$.

14. $\lim\limits_{x \to \pi/2} \dfrac{\sin(\cos x)}{\cos x}$.

15. $\lim\limits_{t \to \pi} \dfrac{\sin(t - \pi)}{t - \pi}$.

16. $\lim\limits_{x \to 1} \dfrac{\sin(x^2 - 1)}{x - 1}$.

17. $\lim\limits_{x \to 0} x \sin \dfrac{1}{x}$.

18. $\lim\limits_{x \to 0} \dfrac{1 - \cos 2x}{x^2}$.

19. $\lim\limits_{x \to 0} \dfrac{\sqrt{1 + x} - \sqrt{1 - x}}{x}$.

20. $\lim\limits_{x \to 0} \dfrac{1 - \sqrt{1 - 4x^2}}{x^2}$.

21. Let $f$ and $g$ be two functions defined as follows:

$$f(x) = \frac{x + |x|}{2} \quad \text{for all } x, \qquad g(x) = \begin{cases} x & \text{for } x < 0, \\ x^2 & \text{for } x \geq 0. \end{cases}$$

Find a formula (or formulas) for computing the composite function $h(x) = f[g(x)]$. For what values of $x$ is $h$ continuous?

22. Solve Exercise 21 when $f$ and $g$ are defined as follows:

$$f(x) = \begin{cases} 1 & \text{if } |x| \leq 1, \\ 0 & \text{if } |x| > 1, \end{cases} \qquad g(x) = \begin{cases} 2 - x^2 & \text{if } |x| \leq 2, \\ 2 & \text{if } |x| > 2. \end{cases}$$

23. Solve Exercise 21 when $h(x) = g[f(x)]$.

## 3.9   Bolzano's theorem for continuous functions

In the rest of this chapter we shall discuss certain special properties of continuous functions that are used quite frequently. Most of these properties appear obvious when interpreted geometrically; consequently many people are inclined to accept them as self-evident.

However, it is important to realize that these statements are no more self-evident than the definition of continuity itself, and therefore they require proof if they are to be used with any degree of generality. The proofs of most of these properties make use of the least-upper-bound axiom for the real number system.

Bernard Bolzano (1781–1848), a Catholic priest who made many important contributions to mathematics in the first half of the 19th century, was one of the first to recognize that many "obvious" statements about continuous functions require proof. His observations concerning continuity were published posthumously in 1850 in an important book, *Paradoxien des Unendlichen*. One of his results, now known as the theorem of Bolzano, is illustrated in Figure 3.6, where the graph of a continuous function *f* is shown. The graph lies below the *x*-axis at $x = a$ and above the axis at $x = b$. Bolzano's theorem asserts that the curve must cross the axis somewhere between *a* and *b*. This property, first published by Bolzano in 1817, may be stated formally as follows.

THEOREM 3.6. BOLZANO'S THEOREM. *Let f be continuous at each point of a closed interval* [a, b] *and assume that f(a) and f(b) have opposite signs. Then there is at least one c in the open interval (a, b) such that f(c) = 0.*

We shall base our proof of Bolzano's theorem on the following property of continuous functions which we state here as a separate theorem.

THEOREM 3.7. SIGN-PRESERVING PROPERTY OF CONTINUOUS FUNCTIONS. *Let f be continuous at c and suppose that f(c) ≠ 0. Then there is an interval (c − δ, c + δ) about c in which f has the same sign as f(c).*

*Proof of Theorem 3.7.* Suppose $f(c) > 0$. By continuity, for every $\epsilon > 0$ there is a $\delta > 0$ such that

$$(3.20) \qquad f(c) - \epsilon < f(x) < f(c) + \epsilon \qquad \text{whenever} \quad c - \delta < x < c + \delta.$$

If we take the δ corresponding to $\epsilon = f(c)/2$ (this ε is *positive*), then (3.20) becomes

$$\tfrac{1}{2}f(c) < f(x) < \tfrac{3}{2}f(c) \qquad \text{whenever} \quad c - \delta < x < c + \delta.$$

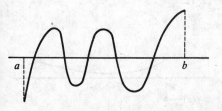

FIGURE 3.6 Illustrating Bolzano's theorem.

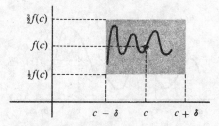

FIGURE 3.7 Here $f(x) > 0$ for $x$ near $c$ because $f(c) > 0$.

(See Figure 3.7). Therefore $f(x) > 0$ in this interval, and hence $f(x)$ and $f(c)$ have the same sign. If $f(c) < 0$, we take the $\delta$ corresponding to $\epsilon = -\frac{1}{2}f(c)$ and arrive at the same conclusion.

*Note:* If there is one-sided continuity at $c$, then there is a corresponding one-sided interval $[c, c + \delta)$ or $(c - \delta, c]$ in which $f$ has the same sign as $f(c)$.

*Proof of Bolzano's theorem.* To be specific, assume $f(a) < 0$ and $f(b) > 0$, as shown in Figure 3.6. There may be many values of $x$ between $a$ and $b$ for which $f(x) = 0$. Our problem is to find *one*. We shall do this by finding the largest $x$ for which $f(x) = 0$. For this purpose we let $S$ denote the set of all those points $x$ in the interval $[a, b]$ for which $f(x) \leq 0$. There is at least one point in $S$ because $f(a) < 0$. Therefore $S$ is a nonempty set. Also, $S$ is bounded above since all of $S$ lies within $[a, b]$, so $S$ has a supremum. Let $c = \sup S$. We shall prove that $f(c) = 0$.

There are only three possiblities: $f(c) > 0$, $f(c) < 0$, and $f(c) = 0$. If $f(c) > 0$, there is an interval $(c - \delta, c + \delta)$, or $(c - \delta, c]$ if $c = b$, in which $f$ is positive. Therefore no points of $S$ can lie to the right of $c - \delta$, and hence $c - \delta$ is an upper bound for the set $S$. But $c - \delta < c$, and $c$ is the *least* upper bound of $S$. Therefore the inequality $f(c) > 0$ is impossible. If $f(c) < 0$, there is an interval $(c - \delta, c + \delta)$, or $[c, c + \delta)$ if $c = a$, in which $f$ is negative. Hence $f(x) < 0$ for some $x > c$, contradicting the fact that $c$ is an upper bound for $S$. Therefore $f(c) < 0$ is also impossible, and the only remaining possibility is $f(c) = 0$. Also, $a < c < b$ because $f(a) < 0$ and $f(b) > 0$. This proves Bolzano's theorem.

### 3.10   The intermediate-value theorem for continuous functions

An immediate consequence of Bolzano's theorem is the *intermediate-value theorem* for continuous functions, illustrated in Figure 3.8.

THEOREM 3.8.   *Let $f$ be continuous at each point of a closed interval $[a, b]$. Choose two arbitrary points $x_1 < x_2$ in $[a, b]$ such that $f(x_1) \neq f(x_2)$. Then $f$ takes on every value between $f(x_1)$ and $f(x_2)$ somewhere in the interval $(x_1, x_2)$.*

*Proof.* Suppose $f(x_1) < f(x_2)$ and let $k$ be any value between $f(x_1)$ and $f(x_2)$. Let $g$ be the function defined on $[x_1, x_2]$ as follows:

$$g(x) = f(x) - k.$$

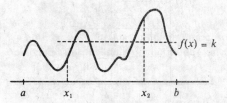

FIGURE 3.8   Illustrating the intermediate-value theorem.

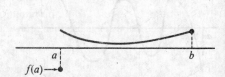

FIGURE 3.9   An example for which Bolzano's theorem is not applicable.

Then $g$ is continuous at each point of $[x_1, x_2]$, and we have

$$g(x_1) = f(x_1) - k < 0, \qquad g(x_2) = f(x_2) - k > 0.$$

Applying Bolzano's theorem to $g$, we have $g(c) = 0$ for some $c$ between $x_1$ and $x_2$. But this means $f(c) = k$, and the proof is complete.

*Note:* In both Bolzano's theorem and the intermediate-value theorem, it is assumed that $f$ is continuous at each point of $[a, b]$, including the endpoints $a$ and $b$. To understand why continuity at both endpoints is necessary, we refer to the curve in Figure 3.9. Here $f$ is continuous everywhere in $[a, b]$ except at $a$. Although $f(a)$ is negative and $f(b)$ is positive, there is no $x$ in $[a, b]$ for which $f(x) = 0$.

We conclude this section with an application of the intermediate-value theorem in which we prove that every positive real number has a positive $n$th root, a fact mentioned earlier in Section I 3.14. We state this as a formal theorem.

THEOREM 3.9. *If $n$ is a positive integer and if $a > 0$, then there is exactly one positive $b$ such that $b^n = a$.*

*Proof.* Choose $c > 1$ such that $0 < a < c$, and consider the function $f$ defined on the interval $[0, c]$ by the equation $f(x) = x^n$. This function is continuous on $[0, c]$, and at the endpoints we have $f(0) = 0$, $f(c) = c^n$. Since $0 < a < c < c^n$, the given number $a$ lies between the function values $f(0)$ and $f(c)$. Therefore, by the intermediate-value theorem, we have $f(x) = a$ for some $x$ in $(0, c)$, say for $x = b$. This proves the existence of at least one positive $b$ such that $b^n = a$. There cannot be more than one such $b$ because $f$ is strictly increasing on $[0, c]$. This completes the proof.

### 3.11 Exercises

1. Let $f$ be a polynomial of degree $n$, say $f(x) = \sum_{k=0}^{n} c_k x^k$, such that the first and last coefficients $c_0$ and $c_n$ have opposite signs. Prove that $f(x) = 0$ for at least one positive $x$.
2. A real number $x_1$, such that $f(x_1) = 0$, is said to be a real root of the equation $f(x) = 0$. We say that a real root of an equation has been *isolated* if we exhibit an interval $[a, b]$ containing this root and no others. With the aid of Bolzano's theorem, isolate the real roots of each of the following equations (each has four real roots).
   (a) $3x^4 - 2x^3 - 36x^2 + 36x - 8 = 0$.
   (b) $2x^4 - 14x^2 + 14x - 1 = 0$.
   (c) $x^4 + 4x^3 + x^2 - 6x + 2 = 0$.
3. If $n$ is an odd positive integer and $a < 0$, prove that there is exactly one negative $b$ such that $b^n = a$.
4. Let $f(x) = \tan x$. Although $f(\pi/4) = 1$ and $f(3\pi/4) = -1$, there is no $x$ in the interval $[\pi/4, 3\pi/4]$ such that $f(x) = 0$. Explain why this does not contradict Bolzano's theorem.
5. Given a real-valued function $f$ which is continuous on the closed interval $[0, 1]$. Assume that $0 \le f(x) \le 1$ for each $x$ in $[0, 1]$. Prove that there is at least one point $c$ in $[0, 1]$ for which $f(c) = c$. Such a point is called a *fixed point* of $f$. The result of this exercise is a special case of *Brouwer's fixed-point theorem*. [*Hint:* Apply Bolzano's theorem to $g(x) = f(x) - x$.]
6. Given a real-valued function $f$ which is continuous on the closed interval $[a, b]$. Assume that $f(a) \le a$ and that $f(b) \ge b$. Prove that $f$ has a fixed point in $[a, b]$. (See Exercise 5.)

## 3.12   The process of inversion

This section describes another important method that is often used to construct new functions from given ones. Before we describe the method in detail, we will illustrate it with a simple example.

Consider the function $f$ defined on the interval $[0, 2]$ by the equation $f(x) = 2x + 1$. The range of $f$ is the interval $[1, 5]$. Each point $x$ in $[0, 2]$ is carried by $f$ onto exactly one point $y$ in $[1, 5]$, namely

(3.21)                              $$y = 2x + 1.$$

Conversely, for every $y$ in $[1, 5]$, there is exactly one $x$ in $[0, 2]$ for which $y = f(x)$. To find this $x$, we solve Equation (3.21) to obtain

$$x = \tfrac{1}{2}(y - 1).$$

This equation defines $x$ as a function of $y$. If we denote this function by $g$, we have

$$g(y) = \tfrac{1}{2}(y - 1)$$

for each $y$ in $[1, 5]$. The function $g$ is called the *inverse* of $f$. Note that $g[f(x)] = x$ for each $x$ in $[0, 2]$, and that $f[g(y)] = y$ for each $y$ in $[1, 5]$.

Consider now a more general function $f$ with domain $A$ and range $B$. For each $x$ in $A$, there is exactly one $y$ in $B$ such that $y = f(x)$. For each $y$ in $B$, there is at least one $x$ in $A$ such that $f(x) = y$. Suppose that there is *exactly one* such $x$. Then we can define a new function $g$ on $B$ as follows:

$$g(y) = x \qquad \text{means} \qquad y = f(x).$$

In other words, the value of $g$ at each point $y$ in $B$ is that unique $x$ in $A$ such that $f(x) = y$. This new function $g$ is called the *inverse* of $f$. The process by which $g$ is obtained from $f$ is called *inversion*. Note that $g[f(x)] = x$ for all $x$ in $A$, and that $f[g(y)] = y$ for all $y$ in $B$.

The process of inversion can be applied to any function $f$ having the property that for each $y$ in the range of $f$, there is exactly one $x$ in the domain of $f$ such that $f(x) = y$. In particular, a function that is continuous and strictly monotonic on an interval $[a, b]$ has this property. An example is shown in Figure 3.10. Let $c = f(a)$, $d = f(b)$. The intermediate-value theorem for continuous functions tells us that in the interval $[a, b]$, $f$ takes on every value between $c$ and $d$. Moreover, $f$ cannot take on the same value twice because $f(x_1) \neq f(x_2)$ whenever $x_1 \neq x_2$. Therefore, every continuous strictly monotonic function has an inverse.

The relation between a function $f$ and its inverse $g$ can also be simply explained in the ordered-pair formulation of the function concept. In Section 1.3 we described a function $f$ as a set of ordered pairs $(x, y)$ no two of which have the same first element. The inverse function $g$ is formed by taking the pairs $(x, y)$ in $f$ and interchanging the elements $x$ and $y$. That is, $(y, x) \in g$ if and only if $(x, y) \in f$. If $f$ is strictly monotonic, then no two pairs in $f$ have the same second element, and hence no two pairs of $g$ have the same first element. Thus $g$ is, indeed, a function.

EXAMPLE. *The nth-root function.* If $n$ is a positive integer, let $f(x) = x^n$ for $x \geq 0$. Then $f$ is strictly increasing on every interval $[a, b]$ with $0 \leq a \leq b$. The inverse function $g$ is the $n$th-root function, defined for $y \geq 0$ by the equation

$$g(y) = y^{1/n}.$$

## 3.13 Properties of functions preserved by inversion

Many properties possessed by the function $f$ are transmitted to the inverse $g$. Figure 3.11 illustrates the relationship between their graphs. One can be obtained from the other merely by reflection through the line $y = x$, because a point $(u, v)$ lies on the graph of $f$ if and only if the point $(v, u)$ lies on the graph of $g$.

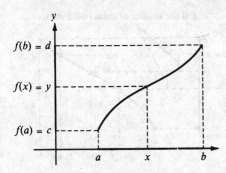

Point $(v,u)$ with $u = g(v)$

$g$

$f$

Point $(u,v)$ with $v = f(u)$

FIGURE 3.10   A continuous, strictly increasing function.

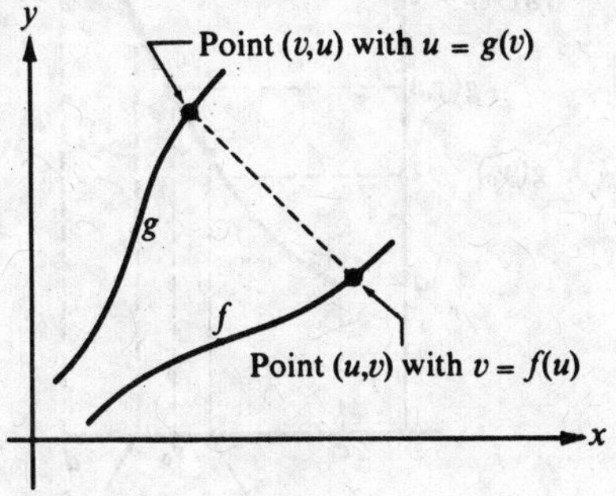

FIGURE 3.11   Illustrating the process of inversion.

The properties of monotonicity and continuity possessed by $f$ are transmitted to the inverse function $g$, as described by the following theorem.

THEOREM 3.10.   *Assume $f$ is strictly increasing and continuous on an interval $[a, b]$. Let $c = f(a)$ and $d = f(b)$ and let $g$ be the inverse of $f$. That is, for each $y$ in $[c, d]$, let $g(y)$ be that $x$ in $[a, b]$ such that $y = f(x)$. Then*
   (a) *$g$ is strictly increasing on $[c, d]$;*
   (b) *$g$ is continuous on $[c, d]$.*

*Proof.* Choose $y_1 < y_2$ in $[c, d]$ and let $x_1 = g(y_1)$, $x_2 = g(y_2)$. Then $y_1 = f(x_1)$ and $y_2 = f(x_2)$. Since $f$ is strictly increasing, the relation $y_1 < y_2$ implies $x_1 < x_2$, which, in turn, implies $g$ is strictly increasing on $[c, d]$. This proves part (a).

Now we prove (b). The proof is illustrated in Figure 3.12. Choose a point $y_0$ in the open interval $(c, d)$. To prove $g$ is continuous at $y_0$, we must show that for every $\epsilon > 0$ there is a $\delta > 0$ such that

$$(3.22) \qquad g(y_0) - \epsilon < g(y) < g(y_0) + \epsilon \qquad \text{whenever} \quad y_0 - \delta < y < y_0 + \delta.$$

Let $x_0 = g(y_0)$, so that $f(x_0) = y_0$. Suppose $\epsilon$ is given. (There is no loss in generality if we consider only those $\epsilon$ small enough so that both $x_0 - \epsilon$ and $x_0 + \epsilon$ are in $[a, b]$.) Let $\delta$

be the smaller of the two numbers

$$f(x_0) - f(x_0 - \epsilon) \quad \text{and} \quad f(x_0 + \epsilon) - f(x_0).$$

It is easy to check that this $\delta$ works in (3.22). A slight modification of the argument proves that $g$ is continuous from the right at $c$, and continuous from the left at $d$.

There is a corresponding theorem for decreasing functions. That is, the inverse of a strictly decreasing continuous function $f$ is strictly decreasing and continuous. This follows by applying Theorem 3.10 to $-f$.

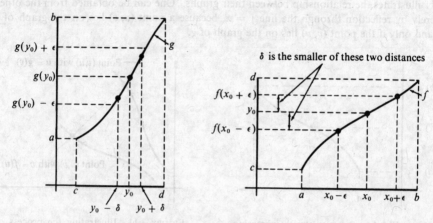

FIGURE 3.12    Proof of the continuity of the inverse function.

EXAMPLE. *Continuity of the nth-root function.* The $n$th-root function $g$, defined for $y \geq 0$ by the equation $g(y) = y^{1/n}$, is strictly increasing and continuous on every interval $[c, d]$ with $0 \leq c < d$, since it is the inverse of a strictly increasing continuous function. This gives an alternate proof of the continuity of the $n$th-root function, independent of the theory of integration. Since the product of continuous functions is continuous, we again deduce the continuity of the $r$th-power function, $h(y) = y^r$, where $r = m/n$ is a positive rational number and $y \geq 0$.

### 3.14 Inverses of piecewise monotonic functions

Suppose we try to apply the process of inversion to a function that is not monotonic on $[a, b]$. For example, suppose that $f(x) = x^2$ on an interval of the form $[-c, c]$ on the $x$-axis. Each point $x$ in this interval is carried by $f$ into exactly one point $y$ in the interval $[0, c^2]$, namely,

(3.23)                                      $$y = x^2.$$

We can solve Equation (3.23) for $x$ in terms of $y$, but there are *two* values of $x$ corresponding to each $y$ in $(0, c^2]$, namely,

$$x = \sqrt{y} \quad \text{and} \quad x = -\sqrt{y}.$$

As we have mentioned once before, there was a time when mathematicians would have said that the inverse $g$ in this case is a *double-valued function* defined by

$$g(y) = \pm\sqrt{y}.$$

But since the more modern point of view does not admit double-valuedness as a property of functions, in a case like this we say that the process of inversion gives rise to *two* new functions, say $g_1$ and $g_2$, where

(3.24)     $g_1(y) = \sqrt{y}$     and     $g_2(y) = -\sqrt{y}$     for each $y$ in $[0, c^2]$.

To fit this in with the notion of inverse as explained above, we can look upon the equation $y = x^2$ as defining not *one* function $f$ but *two* functions $f_1$ and $f_2$, say, where

$$f_1(x) = x^2 \quad \text{if} \ \ 0 \leq x \leq c \quad \text{and} \quad f_2(x) = x^2 \quad \text{if} \ \ -c \leq x \leq 0.$$

These may be considered as *distinct* functions because they have different domains. Each function is monotonic on its domain and each has an inverse, the inverse of $f_1$ being $g_1$ and the inverse of $f_2$ being $g_2$, where $g_1$ and $g_2$ are given by (3.24).

This illustrates how the process of inversion can be applied to piecewise monotonic functions. We simply consider such a function as a union of monotonic functions and invert each monotonic piece.

We shall make extensive use of the process of inversion in Chapter 6.

### 3.15 Exercises

In each of Exercises 1 through 5, show that $f$ is strictly monotonic on the whole real axis. Let $g$ denote the inverse of $f$. Describe the domain of $g$ in each case. Write $y = f(x)$ and solve for $x$ in terms of $y$; thus find a formula (or formulas) for computing $g(y)$ for each $y$ in the domain of $g$.

1. $f(x) = x + 1$.                    4. $f(x) = x^3$.
2. $f(x) = 2x + 5$.
3. $f(x) = 1 - x$.                    5. $f(x) = \begin{cases} x & \text{if} \ \ x < 1, \\ x^2 & \text{if} \ \ 1 \leq x \leq 4, \\ 8x^{1/2} & \text{if} \ \ x > 4. \end{cases}$

*Mean values.* Let $f$ be continuous and strictly monotonic on the positive real axis and let $g$ denote the inverse of $f$. If $a_1 < a_2 < \cdots < a_n$ are $n$ given positive real numbers, we define their *mean value* (or *average*) *with respect to $f$* to be the number $M_f$ defined as follows:

$$M_f = g\left(\frac{1}{n}\sum_{i=1}^{n} f(a_i)\right).$$

In particular, when $f(x) = x^p$ for $p \neq 0$, $M_f$ is called the $p$th *power mean* (See also Section I 4.10.) The exercises which follow deal with properties of mean values.

6. Show that $f(M_f) = (1/n)\sum_{i=1}^{n} f(a_i)$. In other words, the value of $f$ at the average $M_f$ is the arithmetic mean of the function values $f(a_1), \ldots, f(a_n)$.

7. Show that $a_1 < M_f < a_n$. In other words, the average of $a_1, \ldots, a_n$ lies between the largest and smallest of the $a_i$.

8. If $h(x) = af(x) + b$, where $a \neq 0$, show that $M_h = M_f$. This shows that different functions may lead to the same average. Interpret this theorem geometrically by comparing the graphs of $h$ and $f$.

### 3.16    The extreme-value theorem for continuous functions

Let $f$ be a real-valued function defined on a set $S$ of real numbers. The function $f$ is said to have an *absolute maximum* on the set $S$ if there is at least one point $c$ in $S$ such that

$$f(x) \le f(c) \qquad \text{for all } x \text{ in } S.$$

The number $f(c)$ is called the absolute maximum value of $f$ on $S$. We say that $f$ has an *absolute minimum* on $S$ if there is a point $d$ in $S$ such that

$$f(x) \ge f(d) \qquad \text{for all } x \text{ in } S.$$

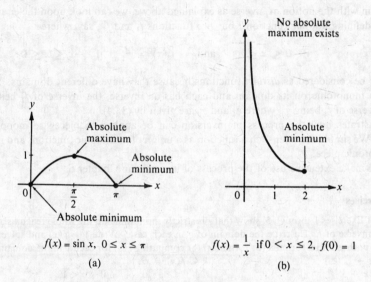

$$f(x) = \sin x, \ 0 \le x \le \pi$$

(a)

$$f(x) = \frac{1}{x} \ \text{if } 0 < x \le 2, \ f(0) = 1$$

(b)

FIGURE 3.13    Maximum and minimum values of functions.

These concepts are illustrated in Figure 3.13. In Figure 3.13(a), $S$ is the closed interval $[0, \pi]$ and $f(x) = \sin x$. The absolute minimum, which occurs at both endpoints of the interval, is 0. The absolute maximum is $f(\tfrac{1}{2}\pi) = 1$.

In Figure 3.13(b), $S$ is the closed interval $[0, 2]$ and $f(x) = 1/x$ if $x > 0, f(0) = 1$. In this example, $f$ has an absolute minimum at $x = 2$, but it has no absolute maximum. It fails to have a maximum because of a discontinuity at a point of $S$.

We wish to prove that if $S$ is a closed interval and if $f$ is continuous everywhere on $S$, then $f$ has both an absolute maximum and an absolute minimum on $S$. This result, known as the extreme-value theorem for continuous functions, will be deduced as a simple consequence of the following theorem.

THEOREM 3.11.    BOUNDEDNESS THEOREM FOR CONTINUOUS FUNCTIONS.    *Let $f$ be continuous on a closed interval $[a, b]$. Then $f$ is bounded on $[a, b]$. That is, there is a number $C \ge 0$ such that $|f(x)| \le C$ for all $x$ in $[a, b]$.*

*Proof.* We argue by contradiction, using a technique called the method of successive bisection. Assume that $f$ is *unbounded* (not bounded) on $[a, b]$. Let $c$ be the midpoint of $[a, b]$. Since $f$ is unbounded on $[a, b]$ it is unbounded on at least one of the subintervals $[a, c]$ or $[c, b]$. Let $[a_1, b_1]$ be that half of $[a, b]$ in which $f$ is unbounded. If $f$ is unbounded in both halves, let $[a_1, b_1]$ be the left half, $[a, c]$. Now continue the bisection process repeatedly, denoting by $[a_{n+1}, b_{n+1}]$ that half of $[a_n, b_n]$ in which $f$ is unbounded, with the understanding that we choose the left half if $f$ is unbounded in both halves. Since the length of each interval is half that of its predecessor, we note that the length of $[a_n, b_n]$ is $(b - a)/2^n$.

Let $A$ denote the set of leftmost endpoints $a, a_1, a_2, \ldots$, so constructed, and let $\alpha$ be the supremum of $A$. Then $\alpha$ lies in $[a, b]$. By continuity of $f$ at $\alpha$, there is an interval of the form $(\alpha - \delta, \alpha + \delta)$ in which

$$(3.25) \qquad |f(x) - f(\alpha)| < 1 .$$

If $\alpha = a$ this interval has the form $[a, a + \delta)$, and if $\alpha = b$ it has the form $(b - \delta, b]$. Inequality (3.25) implies

$$|f(x)| < 1 + |f(\alpha)| ,$$

so $f$ is bounded by $1 + |f(\alpha)|$ in this interval. However, the interval $[a_n, b_n]$ lies inside $(\alpha - \delta, \alpha + \delta)$ when $n$ is so large that $(b - a)/2^n < \delta$. Therefore $f$ is also bounded in $[a_n, b_n]$, contradicting the fact that $f$ is unbounded on $[a_n, b_n]$. This contradiction completes the proof.

If $f$ is bounded on $[a, b]$, then the set of all function values $f(x)$ is bounded above and below. Therefore, this set has a supremum and an infimum which we denote by $\sup f$ and $\inf f$, respectively. That is, we write

$$\sup f = \sup \{f(x) \mid a \le x \le b\}, \qquad \inf f = \inf \{f(x) \mid a \le x \le b\} .$$

For any bounded function we have $\inf f \le f(x) \le \sup f$ for all $x$ in $[a, b]$. Now we prove that a continuous function takes on both values $\inf f$ and $\sup f$ somewhere in $[a, b]$.

THEOREM 3.12. EXTREME-VALUE THEOREM FOR CONTINUOUS FUNCTIONS. *Assume $f$ is continuous on a closed interval $[a, b]$. Then there exist points $c$ and $d$ in $[a, b]$ such that*

$$f(c) = \sup f \qquad and \qquad f(d) = \inf f.$$

*Proof.* It suffices to prove that $f$ attains its supremum in $[a, b]$. The result for the infimum then follows as a consequence because the infimum of $f$ is the supremum of $-f$.

Let $M = \sup f$. We shall assume that there is no $x$ in $[a, b]$ for which $f(x) = M$ and obtain a contradiction. Let $g(x) = M - f(x)$. Then $g(x) > 0$ for all $x$ in $[a, b]$ so the reciprocal $1/g$ is continuous on $[a, b]$. By Theorem 3.11, $1/g$ is bounded on $[a, b]$, say $1/g(x) < C$ for all $x$ in $[a, b]$, where $C > 0$. This implies $M - f(x) > 1/C$, so that $f(x) < M - 1/C$ for all $x$ in $[a, b]$. This contradicts the fact that $M$ is the least upper bound of $f$ on $[a, b]$. Hence, $f(x) = M$ for at least one $x$ in $[a, b]$.

*Note:* This theorem shows that if $f$ is continuous on $[a, b]$, then sup $f$ is its absolute maximum, and inf $f$ its absolute minimum. Hence, by the intermediate-value theorem, the range of $f$ is the closed interval $[\inf f, \sup f]$.

## 3.17  The small-span theorem for continuous functions (uniform continuity)

Let $f$ be real-valued and continuous on a closed interval $[a, b]$ and let $M(f)$ and $m(f)$ denote, respectively, the maximum and minimum values of $f$ on $[a, b]$. We shall call the difference

$$M(f) - m(f)$$

the *span* of $f$ in the interval $[a, b]$. Some authors use the term *oscillation* instead of span. However, oscillation has the disadvantage of suggesting undulating or wavelike functions. Older texts use the word *saltus*, which is Latin for *leap*. The word "span" seems more suggestive of what is being measured here. We note that the span of $f$ in any subinterval of $[a, b]$ cannot exceed the span of $f$ in $[a, b]$.

We shall prove next that the interval $[a, b]$ can be partitioned so that the span of $f$ in each subinterval is arbitrarily small. More precisely, we have the following theorem which we call the *small-span theorem* for continuous functions. It is usually referred to in the literature as the theorem on uniform continuity.

THEOREM 3.13.   *Let $f$ be continuous on a closed interval $[a, b]$. Then, for every $\epsilon > 0$ there is a partition of $[a, b]$ into a finite number of subintervals such that the span of $f$ in every subinterval is less than $\epsilon$.*

*Proof.* We argue by contradiction, using the method of successive bisections. Assume the theorem is *false*. That is, assume that for some $\epsilon$, say for $\epsilon = \epsilon_0$, the interval $[a, b]$ cannot be partitioned into a finite number of subintervals in each of which the span of $f$ is less than $\epsilon_0$. Let $c$ be the midpoint of $[a, b]$. Then for the same $\epsilon_0$, the theorem is false in at least one of the two subintervals $[a, c]$ or $[c, b]$. (If the theorem were true in both intervals $[a, c]$ and $[c, b]$, it would also be true in the full interval $[a, b]$.) Let $[a_1, b_1]$ be that half of $[a, b]$ in which the theorem is false for $\epsilon_0$. If it is false in both halves, let $[a_1, b_1]$ be the left half, $[a, c]$. Now continue the bisection process repeatedly, denoting by $[a_{n+1}, b_{n+1}]$ that half of $[a_n, b_n]$ in which the theorem is false for $\epsilon_0$, with the understanding that we choose the left half if the theorem is false in both halves of $[a_n, b_n]$. Note that the span of $f$ in each subinterval $[a_n, b_n]$ so constructed is at least $\epsilon_0$.

Let $A$ denote the collection of leftmost endpoints $a, a_1, a_2, \ldots$, so constructed, and let $\alpha$ be the least upper bound of $A$. Then $\alpha$ lies in $[a, b]$. By continuity of $f$ at $\alpha$, there is an interval $(\alpha - \delta, \alpha + \delta)$ in which the span of $f$ is less than $\epsilon_0$. (If $\alpha = a$, this interval is $[a, a + \delta)$, and if $\alpha = b$, it is $(b - \delta, b]$.) However, the interval $[a_n, b_n]$ lies inside $(\alpha - \delta, \alpha + \delta)$ when $n$ is so large that $(b - a)/2^n < \delta$, so the span of $f$ in $[a_n, b_n]$ is also less than $\epsilon_0$, contradicting the fact that the span of $f$ is at least $\epsilon_0$ in $[a_n, b_n]$. This contradiction completes the proof of Theorem 3.13.

## 3.18  The integrability theorem for continuous functions

The small-span theorem can be used to prove that a function which is continuous on $[a, b]$ is also integrable on $[a, b]$.

THEOREM 3.14. INTEGRABILITY OF CONTINUOUS FUNCTIONS. *If a function f is continuous at each point of a closed interval $[a, b]$, then f is integrable on $[a, b]$.*

*Proof.* Theorem 3.11 shows that $f$ is bounded on $[a, b]$, so $f$ has an upper integral, $\bar{I}(f)$, and a lower integral, $\underline{I}(f)$. We shall prove that $\underline{I}(f) = \bar{I}(f)$.

Choose an integer $N \geq 1$ and let $\epsilon = 1/N$. By the small-span theorem, for this choice of $\epsilon$ there is a partition $P = \{x_0, x_1, \ldots, x_n\}$ of $[a, b]$ into $n$ subintervals such that the span of $f$ in every subinterval is less than $\epsilon$. Denote by $M_k(f)$ and $m_k(f)$, respectively, the absolute maximum and minimum values of $f$ in the $k$th subinterval $[x_{k-1}, x_k]$. Then we have

$$M_k(f) - m_k(f) < \epsilon$$

for each $k = 1, 2, \ldots, n$. Now let $s_n$ and $t_n$ be two step functions defined on $[a, b]$ as follows:

$$s_n(x) = m_k(f) \quad \text{if} \quad x_{k-1} < x \leq x_k, \quad s_n(a) = m_1(f),$$

$$t_n(x) = M_k(f) \quad \text{if} \quad x_{k-1} \leq x < x_k, \quad t_n(b) = M_n(f).$$

Then we have $s_n(x) \leq f(x) \leq t_n(x)$ for all $x$ in $[a, b]$. Also, we have

$$\int_a^b s_n = \sum_{k=1}^n m_k(f)(x_k - x_{k-1}) \quad \text{and} \quad \int_a^b t_n = \sum_{k=1}^n M_k(f)(x_k - x_{k-1}).$$

The difference of these two integrals is

$$\int_a^b t_n - \int_a^b s_n = \sum_{k=1}^n [M_k(f) - m_k(f)](x_k - x_{k-1}) < \epsilon \sum_{k=1}^n (x_k - x_{k-1}) = \epsilon(b - a).$$

Since $\epsilon = 1/N$, this inequality can be written in the form

$$(3.26) \qquad \int_a^b t_n - \int_a^b s_n < \frac{b - a}{N}.$$

On the other hand, the upper and lower integrals of $f$ satisfy the inequalities

$$\int_a^b s_n \leq \underline{I}(f) \leq \int_a^b t_n \quad \text{and} \quad \int_a^b s_n \leq \bar{I}(f) \leq \int_a^b t_n.$$

Multiplying the first set of inequalities by $(-1)$ and adding the result to the second set, we obtain

$$\bar{I}(f) - \underline{I}(f) \leq \int_a^b t_n - \int_a^b s_n.$$

Using (3.26) and the relation $\underline{I}(f)) \leq \bar{I}(f)$, we have

$$0 \leq \bar{I}(f) - \underline{I}(f) < \frac{b - a}{N}.$$

for every integer $N \geq 1$. Therefore, by Theorem I.31, we must have $\underline{I}(f) = \bar{I}(f)$. This proves that $f$ is integrable on $[a, b]$.

## 3.19 Mean-value theorems for integrals of continuous functions

In Section 2.16 we defined the average value $A(f)$ of a function $f$ over an interval $[a, b]$ to be the quotient $\int_a^b f(x)\, dx/(b - a)$. When $f$ is continuous, we can prove that this average value is equal to the value of $f$ at some point in $[a, b]$.

THEOREM 3.15.  MEAN-VALUE THEOREM FOR INTEGRALS.  *If $f$ is continuous on $[a, b]$, then for some $c$ in $[a, b]$ we have*

$$\int_a^b f(x)\, dx = f(c)(b - a)\,.$$

*Proof.* Let $m$ and $M$ denote, respectively, the minimum and maximum values of $f$ on $[a, b]$. Then $m \leq f(x) \leq M$ for all $x$ in $[a, b]$. Integrating these inequalities and dividing by $b - a$, we find $m \leq A(f) \leq M$, where $A(f) = \int_a^b f(x)\, dx/(b - a)$. But now the inter-mediate-value theorem tells us that $A(f) = f(c)$ for some $c$ in $[a, b]$. This completes the proof.

There is a corresponding result for weighted mean values.

THEOREM 3.16.  WEIGHTED MEAN-VALUE THEOREM FOR INTEGRALS.  *Assume $f$ and $g$ are continuous on $[a, b]$. If $g$ never changes sign in $[a, b]$ then, for some $c$ in $[a, b]$, we have*

$$(3.27) \qquad \int_a^b f(x)g(x)\, dx = f(c) \int_a^b g(x)\, dx\,.$$

*Proof.* Since $g$ never changes sign in $[a, b]$, $g$ is always nonnegative or always nonpositive on $[a, b]$. Let us assume that $g$ is nonnegative on $[a, b]$. Then we may argue as in the proof of Theorem 3.15, except that we integrate the inequalities $mg(x) \leq f(x)g(x) \leq Mg(x)$ to obtain

$$(3.28) \qquad m \int_a^b g(x)\, dx \leq \int_a^b f(x)g(x)\, dx \leq M \int_a^b g(x)\, dx.$$

If $\int_a^b g(x)\, dx = 0$, this inequality shows that $\int_a^b f(x)g(x)\, dx = 0$. In this case, Equation (3.27) holds trivially for any choice of $c$ since both members are zero. Otherwise, the integral of $g$ is positive, and we may divide by this integral in (3.28) and apply the intermediate-value theorem as before to complete the proof. If $g$ is nonpositive, we apply the same argument to $-g$.

The weighted mean-value theorem sometimes leads to a useful estimate for the integral of a product of two functions, especially if the integral of one of the factors is easy to compute. Examples are given in the next set of exercises.

## 3.20 Exercises

1. Use Theorem 3.16 to establish the following inequalities:

$$\frac{1}{10\sqrt{2}} \le \int_0^1 \frac{x^9}{\sqrt{1+x}}\,dx \le \frac{1}{10}.$$

2. Note that $\sqrt{1-x^2} = (1-x^2)/\sqrt{1-x^2}$ and use Theorem 3.16 to obtain the inequalities

$$\frac{11}{24} \le \int_0^{1/2} \sqrt{1-x^2}\,dx \le \frac{11}{24}\sqrt{\frac{4}{3}}.$$

3. Use the identity $1+x^6 = (1+x^2)(1-x^2+x^4)$ and Theorem 3.16 to prove that for $a > 0$, we have

$$\frac{1}{1+a^6}\left(a - \frac{a^3}{3} + \frac{a^5}{5}\right) \le \int_0^a \frac{dx}{1+x^2} \le a - \frac{a^3}{3} + \frac{a^5}{5}.$$

Take $a = 1/10$ and calculate the value of the integral rounded off to six decimal places.

4. One of the following two statements is incorrect. Explain why it is wrong.
   (a) The integral $\int_{2\pi}^{4\pi} (\sin t)/t\, dt > 0$ because $\int_{2\pi}^{3\pi} (\sin t)/t\, dt > \int_{3\pi}^{4\pi} |\sin t|/t\, dt$.
   (b) The integral $\int_{2\pi}^{4\pi} (\sin t)/t\, dt = 0$ because, by Theorem 3.16, for some $c$ between $2\pi$ and $4\pi$ we have

$$\int_{2\pi}^{4\pi} \frac{\sin t}{t}\,dt = \frac{1}{c}\int_{2\pi}^{4\pi} \sin t\, dt = \frac{\cos(2\pi) - \cos(4\pi)}{c} = 0.$$

5. If $n$ is a positive integer, use Theorem 3.16 to show that

$$\int_{\sqrt{n\pi}}^{\sqrt{(n+1)\pi}} \sin(t^2)\, dt = \frac{(-1)^n}{c}, \qquad \text{where } \sqrt{n\pi} \le c \le \sqrt{(n+1)\pi}.$$

6. Assume $f$ is continuous on $[a, b]$. If $\int_a^b f(x)\, dx = 0$, prove that $f(c) = 0$ for at least one $c$ in $[a, b]$.

7. Assume that $f$ is integrable and nonnegative on $[a, b]$. If $\int_a^b f(x)\, dx = 0$, prove that $f(x) = 0$ at each point of continuity of $f$. [*Hint:* If $f(c) > 0$ at a point of continuity $c$, there is an interval about $c$ in which $f(x) > \frac{1}{2}f(c)$.]

8. Assume $f$ is continuous on $[a, b]$. Assume also that $\int_a^b f(x)g(x)\, dx = 0$ for every function $g$ that is continuous on $[a, b]$. Prove that $f(x) = 0$ for all $x$ in $[a, b]$.

# 4

# DIFFERENTIAL CALCULUS

## 4.1  Historical introduction

Newton and Leibniz, quite independently of one another, were largely responsible for developing the ideas of integral calculus to the point where hitherto insurmountable problems could be solved by more or less routine methods. The successful accomplishments of these men were primarily due to the fact that they were able to fuse together the integral calculus with the second main branch of calculus, differential calculus.

The central idea of differential calculus is the notion of *derivative*. Like the integral, the derivative originated from a problem in geometry—the problem of finding the tangent line at a point of a curve. Unlike the integral, however, the derivative evolved very late in the history of mathematics. The concept was not formulated until early in the 17th century when the French mathematician Pierre de Fermat, attempted to determine the maxima and minima of certain special functions.

Fermat's idea, basically very simple, can be understood if we refer to the curve in Figure 4.1. It is assumed that at each of its points this curve has a definite direction that can be described by a tangent line. Some of these tangents are indicated by broken lines in the figure. Fermat noticed that at certain points where the curve has a maximum or

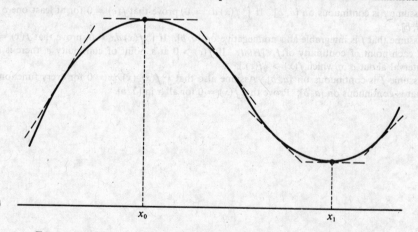

FIGURE 4.1   The curve has horizontal tangents above the points $x_0$ and $x_1$.

minimum, such as those shown in the figure with abscissae $x_0$ and $x_1$, the tangent line must be horizontal. Thus the problem of locating such extreme values is seen to depend on the solution of another problem, that of locating the horizontal tangents.

This raises the more general question of determining the direction of the tangent line at an *arbitrary point* of the curve. It was the attempt to solve this general problem that led Fermat to discover some of the rudimentary ideas underlying the notion of derivative.

At first sight there seems to be no connection whatever between the problem of finding the area of a region lying under a curve and the problem of finding the tangent line at a point of a curve. The first person to realize that these two seemingly remote ideas are, in fact, rather intimately related appears to have been Newton's teacher, Isaac Barrow (1630–1677). However, Newton and Leibniz were the first to understand the real importance of this relation and they exploited it to the fullest, thus inaugurating an unprecedented era in the development of mathematics.

Although the derivative was originally formulated to study the problem of tangents, it was soon found that it also provides a way to calculate *velocity* and, more generally, the *rate of change* of a function. In the next section we shall consider a special problem involving the calculation of a velocity. The solution of this problem contains all the essential features of the derivative concept and may help to motivate the general definition of derivative which is given in Section 4.3.

### 4.2 A problem involving velocity

Suppose a projectile is fired straight up from the ground with initial velocity of 144 feet per second. Neglect friction, and assume the projectile is influenced only by gravity so that it moves up and back along a straight line. Let $f(t)$ denote the height in feet that the projectile attains $t$ seconds after firing. If the force of gravity were not acting on it, the projectile would continue to move upward with a constant velocity, traveling a distance of 144 feet every second, and at time $t$ we would have $f(t) = 144t$. In actual practice, gravity causes the projectile to slow down until its velocity decreases to zero and then it drops back to earth. Physical experiments suggest that as long as the projectile is aloft, its height $f(t)$ is given by the formula

$$(4.1) \qquad\qquad f(t) = 144t - 16t^2.$$

The term $-16t^2$ is due to the influence of gravity. Note that $f(t) = 0$ when $t = 0$ and when $t = 9$. This means that the projectile returns to earth after 9 seconds and it is to be understood that formula (4.1) is valid only for $0 \leq t \leq 9$.

The problem we wish to consider is this: *To determine the velocity of the projectile at each instant of its motion.* Before we can understand this problem, we must decide on what is *meant* by the velocity at each instant. To do this, we introduce first the notion of *average velocity during a time interval*, say from time $t$ to time $t + h$. This is defined to be the quotient

$$\frac{\text{change in distance during time interval}}{\text{length of time interval}} = \frac{f(t + h) - f(t)}{h}.$$

This quotient, called a *difference quotient*, is a number which may be calculated whenever

*Differential calculus*

both $t$ and $t + h$ are in the interval $[0, 9]$. The number $h$ may be positive or negative, but not zero. We shall keep $t$ fixed and see what happens to the difference quotient as we take values of $h$ with smaller and smaller absolute value.

For example, consider the instant $t = 2$. The distance traveled after 2 seconds is

$$f(2) = 288 - 64 = 224.$$

At time $t = 2 + h$, the distance covered is

$$f(2 + h) = 144(2 + h) - 16(2 + h)^2 = 224 + 80h - 16h^2.$$

Therefore the average velocity in the interval from $t = 2$ to $t = 2 + h$ is

$$\frac{f(2 + h) - f(2)}{h} = \frac{80h - 16h^2}{h} = 80 - 16h.$$

As we take values of $h$ with smaller and smaller absolute value, this average velocity gets closer and closer to 80. For example, if $h = 0.1$, we get an average velocity of 78.4; when $h = 0.001$, we get 79.984; when $h = 0.00001$, we obtain the value 79.99984; and when $h = -0.00001$, we obtain 80.00016. The important thing is that we can make the average velocity as close to 80 as we please by taking $|h|$ sufficiently small. In other words, the average velocity approaches 80 as a limit when $h$ approaches zero. It seems natural to call this limiting value the *instantaneous velocity* at time $t = 2$.

The same kind of calculation can be carried out for any other instant. The average velocity for an arbitrary time interval from $t$ to $t + h$ is given by the quotient

$$\frac{f(t + h) - f(t)}{h} = \frac{[144(t + h) - 16(t + h)^2] - [144t - 16t^2]}{h} = 144 - 32t - 16h.$$

When $h$ approaches zero, the expression on the right approaches $144 - 32t$ as a limit, and this limit is defined to be the *instantaneous velocity* at time $t$. If we denote the instantaneous velocity by $v(t)$, we may write

(4.2)                                    $$v(t) = 144 - 32t.$$

The formula in (4.1) for the distance $f(t)$ defines a function $f$ which tells us how high the projectile is at each instant of its motion. We may refer to $f$ as the *position function*. Its domain is the closed interval $[0, 9]$ and its graph is shown in Figure 4.2(a). [The scale on the vertical axis is distorted in both Figures 4.2(a) and (b).] The formula in (4.2) for the velocity $v(t)$ defines a new function $v$ which tells us how fast the projectile is moving at each instant of its motion. This is called the *velocity function*, and its graph is shown in Figure 4.2(b). As $t$ increases from 0 to 9, $v(t)$ decreases steadily from $v(0) = 144$ to $v(9) = -144$. To find the time $t$ for which $v(t) = 0$, we solve the equation $144 = 32t$ to obtain $t = 9/2$. Therefore, at the midpoint of the motion the influence of gravity reduces the velocity to zero, and the projectile is momentarily at rest. The height at this instant is $f(9/2) = 324$. When $t > 9/2$, the velocity is negative, indicating that the height is decreasing.

The limit process by which $v(t)$ is obtained from the difference quotient is written symbolically as follows:

$$(4.3) \qquad v(t) = \lim_{h \to 0} \frac{f(t + h) - f(t)}{h}.$$

This equation is used to define velocity not only for this particular example but, more generally, for any particle moving along a straight line, provided the position function $f$ is such that the difference quotient tends to a definite limit as $h$ approaches zero.

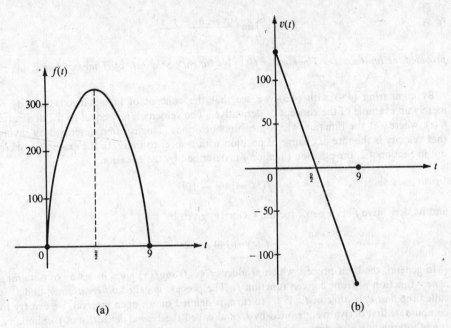

FIGURE 4.2   (a) Graph of the position function $f(t) = 144t - 16t^2$. (b) Graph of the velocity function: $v(t) = 144 - 32t$.

## 4.3   The derivative of a function

The example described in the foregoing section points the way to the introduction of the concept of derivative. We begin with a function $f$ defined at least on some open interval $(a, b)$ on the $x$-axis. Then we choose a fixed point $x$ in this interval and introduce the difference quotient

$$\frac{f(x + h) - f(x)}{h},$$

where the number $h$, which may be positive or negative (but not zero), is such that $x + h$ also lies in $(a, b)$. The numerator of this quotient measures the change in the function when $x$ changes from $x$ to $x + h$. The quotient itself is referred to as the *average rate of change* of $f$ in the interval joining $x$ to $x + h$.

Now we let $h$ approach zero and see what happens to this quotient. If the quotient approaches some definite value as a limit (which implies that the limit is the same whether $h$ approaches zero through positive values or through negative values), then this limit is called the *derivative* of $f$ at $x$ and is denoted by the symbol $f'(x)$ (read as "$f$ prime of $x$"). Thus, the formal definition of $f'(x)$ may be stated as follows:

DEFINITION OF DERIVATIVE.   *The derivative $f'(x)$ is defined by the equation*

$$(4.4) \qquad f'(x) = \lim_{h \to 0} \frac{f(x + h) - f(x)}{h},$$

*provided the limit exists. The number $f'(x)$ is also called the rate of change of $f$ at $x$.*

By comparing (4.4) with (4.3), we see that the concept of instantaneous velocity is merely an example of the concept of derivative. The velocity $v(t)$ is equal to the derivative $f'(t)$, where $f$ is the function which measures position. This is often described by saying that velocity is the rate of change of position with respect to time. In the example worked out in Section 4.2, the position function $f$ is described by the equation

$$f(t) = 144t - 16t^2,$$

and its derivative $f'$ is a new function (velocity) given by

$$f'(t) = 144 - 32t.$$

In general, the limit process which produces $f'(x)$ from $f(x)$ gives us a way of obtaining a new function $f'$ from a given function $f$. The process is called *differentiation*, and $f'$ is called the *first derivative* of $f$. If $f'$, in turn, is defined on an open interval, we can try to compute *its* first derivative, denoted by $f''$ and called the *second derivative* of $f$. Similarly, the $n$th derivative of $f$, denoted by $f^{(n)}$, is defined to be the first derivative of $f^{(n-1)}$. We make the convention that $f^{(0)} = f$, that is, the zeroth derivative is the function itself.

For rectilinear motion, the first derivative of velocity (second derivative of position) is called *acceleration*. For example, to compute the acceleration in the example of Section 4.2, we can use Equation (4.2) to form the difference quotient

$$\frac{v(t + h) - v(t)}{h} = \frac{[144 - 32(t + h)] - [144 - 32t]}{h} = \frac{-32h}{h} = -32.$$

Since this quotient has the constant value $-32$ for each $h \neq 0$, its limit as $h \to 0$ is also $-32$. Thus, the acceleration in this problem is constant and equal to $-32$. This result tells us that the velocity is decreasing at the rate of 32 feet per second every second. In 9 seconds the total decrease in velocity is $9 \cdot 32 = 288$ feet per second. This agrees with the fact that during the 9 seconds of motion the velocity changes from $v(0) = 144$ to $v(9) = -144$.

## 4.4 Examples of derivatives

EXAMPLE 1. *Derivative of a constant function.* Suppose $f$ is a constant function, say $f(x) = c$ for all $x$. The difference quotient is

$$\frac{f(x + h) - f(x)}{h} = \frac{c - c}{h} = 0 .$$

Since the quotient is 0 for all $h \neq 0$, its limit, $f'(x)$, is also 0 for every $x$. In other words, a constant function has a zero derivative everywhere.

EXAMPLE 2. *Derivative of a linear function.* Suppose $f$ is a linear function, say $f(x) = mx + b$ for all real $x$. If $h \neq 0$, we have

$$\frac{f(x + h) - f(x)}{h} = \frac{m(x + h) + b - (mx + b)}{h} = \frac{mh}{h} = m .$$

Since the difference quotient does not change when $h$ approaches 0, we conclude that

$$f'(x) = m \qquad \text{for every } x.$$

Thus, the derivative of a linear function is a constant function.

EXAMPLE 3. *Derivative of a positive integer power function.* Consider next the case $f(x) = x^n$, where $n$ is a positive integer. The difference quotient becomes

$$\frac{f(x + h) - f(x)}{h} = \frac{(x + h)^n - x^n}{h} .$$

To study this quotient as $h$ approaches 0, we can proceed in two ways, either by factoring the numerator as a difference of two $n$th powers or by using the binomial theorem to expand $(x + h)^n$. We shall carry out the details by the first method and leave the other method as an exercise for the reader. (See Exercise 39 in Section 4.6.)

From elementary algebra we have the identity†

$$a^n - b^n = (a - b) \sum_{k=0}^{n-1} a^k b^{n-1-k} .$$

If we take $a = x + h$ and $b = x$ and divide both sides by $h$, this identity becomes

$$\frac{(x + h)^n - x^n}{h} = \sum_{k=0}^{n-1} (x + h)^k x^{n-1-k} .$$

---

† This identity is an immediate consequence of the telescoping property of finite sums. In fact, if we multiply each term of the sum by $(a - b)$, we find

$$(a - b) \sum_{k=0}^{n-1} a^k b^{n-1-k} = \sum_{k=0}^{n-1} (a^{k+1} b^{n-(k+1)} - a^k b^{n-k}) = a^n - b^n.$$

There are $n$ terms in the sum. As $h$ approaches 0, $(x + h)^k$ approaches $x^k$, the $k$th term approaches $x^k x^{n-1-k} = x^{n-1}$, and therefore the sum of all $n$ terms approaches $nx^{n-1}$. From this it follows that

$$f'(x) = nx^{n-1} \qquad \text{for every } x.$$

EXAMPLE 4. *Derivative of the sine function.* Let $s(x) = \sin x$. The difference quotient in question is

$$\frac{s(x + h) - s(x)}{h} = \frac{\sin (x + h) - \sin x}{h}.$$

To transform this into a form that makes it possible to calculate the limit as $h \to 0$, we use the trigonometric identity

$$\sin y - \sin x = 2 \sin \frac{y - x}{2} \cos \frac{y + x}{2}$$

with $y = x + h$. This leads to the formula

$$\frac{\sin (x + h) - \sin x}{h} = \frac{\sin (h/2)}{h/2} \cos \left(x + \frac{h}{2}\right).$$

As $h \to 0$, the factor $\cos (x + \tfrac{1}{2}h) \to \cos x$ because of the continuity of the cosine. Also, the limit formula

$$\lim_{x \to 0} \frac{\sin x}{x} = 1,$$

established earlier in Section 3.4, shows that

(4.5) $$\frac{\sin (h/2)}{h/2} \to 1 \qquad \text{as} \quad h \to 0.$$

Therefore the difference quotient has the limit $\cos x$ as $h \to 0$. In other words, $s'(x) = \cos x$ for every $x$; the derivative of the sine function is the cosine function.

EXAMPLE 5. *The derivative of the cosine function.* Let $c(x) = \cos x$. We shall prove that $c'(x) = -\sin x$; that is, the derivative of the cosine function is minus the sine function. We start with the identity

$$\cos y - \cos x = -2 \sin \frac{y - x}{2} \sin \frac{y + x}{2}$$

and take $y = x + h$. This leads to the formula

$$\frac{\cos (x + h) - \cos x}{h} = - \frac{\sin (h/2)}{h/2} \sin \left(x + \frac{h}{2}\right).$$

Continuity of the sine shows that $\sin (x + \frac{1}{2}h) \to \sin x$ as $h \to 0$; from (4.5), we obtain $c'(x) = -\sin x$.

EXAMPLE 6. *Derivative of the nth-root function.* If $n$ is a positive integer, let $f(x) = x^{1/n}$ for $x > 0$. The difference quotient for $f$ is

$$\frac{f(x + h) - f(x)}{h} = \frac{(x + h)^{1/n} - x^{1/n}}{h}.$$

Let $u = (x + h)^{1/n}$ and let $v = x^{1/n}$. Then we have $u^n = x + h$ and $v^n = x$, so $h = u^n - v^n$, and the difference quotient becomes

$$\frac{f(x + h) - f(x)}{h} = \frac{u - v}{u^n - v^n} = \frac{1}{u^{n-1} + u^{n-2}v + \cdots + uv^{n-2} + v^{n-1}}.$$

The continuity of the $n$th-root function shows that $u \to v$ as $h \to 0$. Therefore each term in the denominator on the right has the limit $v^{n-1}$ as $h \to 0$. There are $n$ terms altogether, so the difference quotient has the limit $v^{1-n}/n$. Since $v = x^{1/n}$, this proves that

$$f'(x) = \frac{1}{n} x^{1/n-1}.$$

EXAMPLE 7. *Continuity of functions having derivatives.* If a function $f$ has a derivative at a point $x$, then it is also continuous at $x$. To prove this, we use the identity

$$f(x + h) = f(x) + h\left(\frac{f(x + h) - f(x)}{h}\right)$$

which is valid for $h \neq 0$. If we let $h \to 0$, the difference quotient on the right approaches $f'(x)$ and, since this quotient is multiplied by a factor which tends to 0, the second term on the right approaches $0 \cdot f'(x) = 0$. This shows that $f(x + h) \to f(x)$ as $h \to 0$, and hence that $f$ is continuous at $x$.

This example provides a new way of showing that functions are continuous. Every time we establish the existence of a derivative $f'(x)$, we also establish, at the same time, the continuity of $f$ at $x$. It should be noted, however, that the converse is not true. Continuity at $x$ does not necessarily mean that the derivative $f'(x)$ exists. For example, when $f(x) = |x|$, the point $x = 0$ is a point of continuity of $f$ [since $f(x) \to 0$ as $x \to 0$] but there is no derivative at 0. (See Figure 4.3.) The difference quotient $[f(0 + h) - f(0)]/h$ is

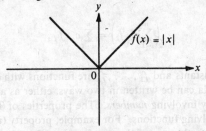

FIGURE 4.3 The function is continuous at 0 but $f'(0)$ does not exist.

equal to $|h|/h$. This has the value $+1$ if $h > 0$ and $-1$ if $h < 0$, and hence does not tend to a limit as $h \to 0$.

## 4.5  The algebra of derivatives

Just as the limit theorems of Section 3.4 tell us how to compute limits of the sum, difference, product, and quotient of two functions, so the next theorem provides us with a corresponding set of rules for computing derivatives.

THEOREM 4.1.  *Let f and g be two functions defined on a common interval. At each point where f and g have a derivative, the same is true of the sum $f + g$, the difference $f - g$, the product $f \cdot g$, and the quotient $f/g$. (For $f/g$ we need the extra proviso that g is not zero at the point in question.)  The derivatives of these functions are given by the following formulas:*

(i) $(f + g)' = f' + g'$,

(ii) $(f - g)' = f' - g'$,

(iii) $(f \cdot g)' = f \cdot g' + g \cdot f'$

(iv) $\left(\dfrac{f}{g}\right)' = \dfrac{g \cdot f' - f \cdot g'}{g^2}$     *at points x where $g(x) \neq 0$.*

We shall prove this theorem in a moment, but first we want to mention some of its consequences. A special case of (iii) occurs when one of the two functions is constant, say $g(x) = c$ for all $x$ under consideration. In this case, (iii) becomes $(c \cdot f)' = c \cdot f'$. In other words, the derivative of a constant times $f$ is the constant times the derivative of $f$. Combining this with the fact that the derivative of a sum is the sum of derivatives [property (i)], we find that for every pair of constants $c_1$ and $c_2$ we have

$$(c_1 f + c_2 g)' = c_1 f' + c_2 g'.$$

This is called the *linearity property* of the derivative, and it is analogous to the linearity property of the integral. Using mathematical induction, we can extend the linearity property to arbitrary finite sums as follows:

$$\left(\sum_{i=1}^{n} c_i \cdot f_i\right)' = \sum_{i=1}^{n} c_i \cdot f_i',$$

where $c_1, \ldots, c_n$ are constants and $f_1, \ldots, f_n$ are functions with derivatives $f_1', \ldots, f_n'$.

Every derivative formula can be written in two ways, either as an equality between two *functions* or as an equality involving *numbers*. The properties of Theorem 4.1, as written above, are equations involving functions. For example, property (i) states that the derivative of the function $f + g$ is the sum of the two functions $f'$ and $g'$. When these functions are evaluated at a point $x$, we obtain formulas involving numbers. Thus formula (i) implies

$$(f + g)'(x) = f'(x) + g'(x).$$

We proceed now to the proof of Theorem 4.1.

*Proof of* (i). Let $x$ be a point where both derivatives $f'(x)$ and $g'(x)$ exist. The difference quotient for $f + g$ is

$$\frac{[f(x + h) + g(x + h)] - [f(x) + g(x)]}{h} = \frac{f(x + h) - f(x)}{h} + \frac{g(x + h) - g(x)}{h}.$$

When $h \to 0$ the first quotient on the right approaches $f'(x)$, the second approaches $g'(x)$, and hence the sum approaches $f'(x) + g'(x)$. This proves (i), and the proof of (ii) is similar.

*Proof of* (iii). The difference quotient for the product $f \cdot g$ is

$$(4.6) \qquad \frac{f(x + h)g(x + h) - f(x)g(x)}{h}.$$

To study this quotient as $h \to 0$, we add and subtract in the numerator a term which enables us to write (4.6) as a sum of two terms involving difference quotients of $f$ and $g$. Adding and subtracting $g(x)f(x + h)$, we see that (4.6) becomes

$$\frac{f(x + h)g(x + h) - f(x)g(x)}{h} = g(x)\frac{f(x + h) - f(x)}{h} + f(x + h)\frac{g(x + h) - g(x)}{h}.$$

When $h \to 0$ the first term on the right approaches $g(x)f'(x)$. Since $f$ is continuous at $x$, we have $f(x + h) \to f(x)$, so the second term approaches $f(x)g'(x)$. This proves (iii).

*Proof of* (iv). A special case of (iv) occurs when $f(x) = 1$ for all $x$. In this case $f'(x) = 0$ for all $x$ and (iv) reduces to the formula

$$(4.7) \qquad \left(\frac{1}{g}\right)' = -\frac{g'}{g^2}$$

provided $g(x) \neq 0$. We can deduce the general formula (iv) from this special case by writing $f/g$ as a product and using (iii), since

$$\left(f \cdot \frac{1}{g}\right)' = \frac{1}{g} \cdot f' + f \cdot \left(\frac{1}{g}\right)' = \frac{f'}{g} - \frac{f \cdot g'}{g^2} = \frac{g \cdot f' - f \cdot g'}{g^2}.$$

Therefore it remains to prove (4.7). The difference quotient for $1/g$ is

$$(4.8) \qquad \frac{[1/g(x + h)] - [1/g(x)]}{h} = -\frac{g(x + h) - g(x)}{h} \cdot \frac{1}{g(x)} \cdot \frac{1}{g(x + h)}.$$

When $h \to 0$, the first quotient on the right approaches $g'(x)$ and the third factor approaches $1/g(x)$. The continuity of $g$ at $x$ is required since we are using the fact that $g(x + h) \to g(x)$ as $h \to 0$. Hence the quotient in (4.8) approaches $-g'(x)/g(x)^2$, and this proves (4.7).

*Note:* In order to write (4.8) we need to know that $g(x + h) \neq 0$ for all sufficiently small $h$. This follows from Theorem 3.7.

Theorem 4.1, when used in conjunction with the examples worked out in Section 4.4, enables us to derive new examples of differentiation formulas.

EXAMPLE 1. *Polynomials.* In Example 3 of Section 4.4 we showed that if $f(x) = x^n$, where $n$ is a positive integer, then $f'(x) = nx^{n-1}$. The reader may find it instructive to rederive this result as a consequence of the special case $n = 1$, using mathematical induction in conjunction with the formula for differentiating a product.

Using this result along with the linearity property, we can differentiate any polynomial by computing the derivative of each term and adding the derivatives. Thus, if

$$f(x) = \sum_{k=0}^{n} c_k x^k ,$$

then, by differentiating term by term, we obtain

$$f'(x) = \sum_{k=0}^{n} k c_k x^{k-1} .$$

Note that the derivative of a polynomial of degree $n$ is a new polynomial of degree $n - 1$. For example, if $f(x) = 2x^3 + 5x^2 - 7x + 8$, then $f'(x) = 6x^2 + 10x - 7$.

EXAMPLE 2. *Rational functions.* If $r$ is the quotient of two polynomials, say $r(x) = p(x)/q(x)$, then the derivative $r'(x)$ may be computed by the quotient formula (iv) in Theorem 4.1. The derivative $r'(x)$ exists at every $x$ for which the denominator $q(x) \neq 0$. Note that the function $r'$ so defined is itself a rational function. In particular, when $r(x) = 1/x^m$, where $m$ is a positive integer and $x \neq 0$, we find

$$r'(x) = \frac{x^m \cdot 0 - mx^{m-1}}{x^{2m}} = \frac{-m}{x^{m+1}} .$$

If this is written in the form $r'(x) = -mx^{-m-1}$, it provides an extension from positive exponents to negative exponents of the formula for differentiating $n$th powers.

EXAMPLE 3. *Rational powers.* Let $f(x) = x^r$ for $x > 0$, where $r$ is a rational number. We have already proved the differentiation formula

(4.9) $$f'(x) = rx^{r-1}$$

for $r = 1/n$, where $n$ is a positive integer. Now we extend it to all rational powers. The formula for differentiating a product shows that Equation (4.9) is also valid for $r = 2/n$

and, by induction, for $r = m/n$, where $m$ is any positive integer. (The induction argument refers to $m$.) Therefore Equation (4.9) is valid for all positive rational $r$. The formula for differentiating a quotient now shows that (4.9) is also valid for negative rational $r$. Thus, if $f(x) = x^{2/3}$, we have $f'(x) = \frac{2}{3}x^{-1/3}$. If $f(x) = x^{-1/2}$, then $f'(x) = -\frac{1}{2}x^{-3/2}$. In each case, we require $x > 0$.

## 4.6 Exercises

1. If $f(x) = 2 + x - x^2$, compute $f'(0), f'(\frac{1}{2}), f'(1), f'(-10)$.
2. If $f(x) = \frac{1}{3}x^3 + \frac{1}{2}x^2 - 2x$, find all $x$ for which (a) $f'(x) = 0$; (b) $f'(x) = -2$; (c) $f'(x) = 10$.

In Exercises 3 through 12, obtain a formula for $f'(x)$ if $f(x)$ is described as indicated.

3. $f(x) = x^2 + 3x + 2$.

8. $f(x) = \dfrac{x}{x-1}$, $\quad x \neq 1$.

4. $f(x) = x^4 + \sin x$.

9. $f(x) = \dfrac{1}{2 + \cos x}$.

5. $f(x) = x^4 \sin x$.

10. $f(x) = \dfrac{x^2 + 3x + 2}{x^4 + x^2 + 1}$.

6. $f(x) = \dfrac{1}{x+1}$, $\quad x \neq -1$.

11. $f(x) = \dfrac{2 - \sin x}{2 - \cos x}$.

7. $f(x) = \dfrac{1}{x^2 + 1} + x^5 \cos x$.

12. $f(x) = \dfrac{x \sin x}{1 + x^2}$.

13. Assume that the height $f(t)$ of a projectile, $t$ seconds after being fired directly upward from the ground with an initial velocity of $v_0$ ft/sec, is given by the formula

$$f(t) = v_0 t - 16t^2.$$

(a) Use the method described in Section 4.2 to show that the average velocity of the projectile during a time interval from $t$ to $t + h$ is $v_0 - 32t - 16h$ ft/sec, and that the instantaneous velocity at time $t$ is $v_0 - 32t$ ft/sec.
(b) Compute (in terms of $v_0$) the time required for the velocity to drop to zero.
(c) What is the velocity on return to earth?
(d) What must the initial velocity be for the projectile to return to earth after 1 sec? after 10 sec? after $T$ sec?
(e) Show that the projectile moves with constant acceleration.
(f) Give an example of another formula for the height which will lead to a constant acceleration of $-20$ ft/sec/sec.

14. What is the rate of change of the volume of a cube with respect to the length of each edge?
15. (a) The area of a circle of radius $r$ is $\pi r^2$ and its circumference is $2\pi r$. Show that the rate of change of the area with respect to the radius is equal to the circumference.
(b) The volume of a sphere of radius $r$ is $4\pi r^3/3$ and its surface area is $4\pi r^2$. Show that the rate of change of the volume with respect to the radius is equal to the surface area.

In Exercises 16 through 23, obtain a formula for $f'(x)$ if $f(x)$ is defined as indicated.

16. $f(x) = \sqrt{x}$, $\quad x > 0$.

18. $f(x) = x^{3/2}$, $\quad x > 0$.

17. $f(x) = \dfrac{1}{1 + \sqrt{x}}$, $\quad x > 0$.

19. $f(x) = x^{-3/2}$, $\quad x > 0$.

20. $f(x) = x^{1/2} + x^{1/3} + x^{1/4}$,    $x > 0$.    22. $f(x) = \dfrac{\sqrt{x}}{1+x}$,    $x > 0$.

21. $f(x) = x^{-1/2} + x^{-1/3} + x^{-1/4}$,    $x > 0$.    23. $f(x) = \dfrac{x}{1+\sqrt{x}}$,    $x > 0$.

24. Let $f_1, \ldots, f_n$ be $n$ functions having derivatives $f_1', \ldots, f_n'$. Develop a rule for differentiating the product $g = f_1 \cdots f_n$ and prove it by mathematical induction. Show that for those points $x$, where none of the function values $f_1(x), \ldots, f_n(x)$ are zero, we have

$$\frac{g'(x)}{g(x)} = \frac{f_1'(x)}{f_1(x)} + \cdots + \frac{f_n'(x)}{f_n(x)}.$$

25. Verify the entries in the following short table of derivatives. It is understood that the formulas hold for those $x$ for which $f(x)$ is defined.

| $f(x)$ | $f'(x)$ | $f(x)$ | $f'(x)$ |
|--------|---------|--------|---------|
| $\tan x$ | $\sec^2 x$ | $\sec x$ | $\tan x \sec x$ |
| $\cot x$ | $-\csc^2 x$ | $\csc x$ | $-\cot x \csc x$ |

In Exercises 26 through 35, compute the derivative $f'(x)$. It is understood that each formula holds for those $x$ for which $f(x)$ is defined.

26. $f(x) = \tan x \sec x$.

27. $f(x) = x \tan x$.

28. $f(x) = \dfrac{1}{x} + \dfrac{2}{x^2} + \dfrac{3}{x^3}$.

29. $f(x) = \dfrac{2x}{1-x^2}$.

30. $f(x) = \dfrac{1+x-x^2}{1-x+x^2}$.

31. $f(x) = \dfrac{\sin x}{x}$.

32. $f(x) = \dfrac{1}{x+\sin x}$.

33. $f(x) = \dfrac{ax+b}{cx+d}$.

34. $f(x) = \dfrac{\cos x}{2x^2+3}$.

35. $f(x) = \dfrac{ax^2+bx+c}{\sin x + \cos x}$.

36. If $f(x) = (ax+b)\sin x + (cx+d)\cos x$, determine values of the constants $a, b, c, d$ such that $f'(x) = x \cos x$.

37. If $g(x) = (ax^2+bx+c)\sin x + (dx^2+ex+f)\cos x$, determine values of the constants $a, b, c, d, e, f$ such that $g'(x) = x^2 \sin x$.

38. Given the formula

$$1 + x + x^2 + \cdots + x^n = \frac{x^{n+1}-1}{x-1}$$

(valid if $x \neq 1$), determine, by differentiation, formulas for the following sums:
(a) $1 + 2x + 3x^2 + \cdots + nx^{n-1}$,
(b) $1^2 x + 2^2 x^2 + 3^2 x^3 + \cdots + n^2 x^n$.

39. Let $f(x) = x^n$, where $n$ is a positive integer. Use the binomial theorem to expand $(x + h)^n$ and derive the formula

$$\frac{f(x + h) - f(x)}{h} = nx^{n-1} + \frac{n(n - 1)}{2} x^{n-2}h + \cdots + nxh^{n-2} + h^{n-1}.$$

Express the sum on the right in summation notation. Let $h \to 0$ and deduce that $f'(x) = nx^{n-1}$. State which limit theorems you are using. (This result was derived in another way in Example 3 of Section 4.4.)

## 4.7 Geometric interpretation of the derivative as a slope

The procedure used to define the derivative has a geometric interpretation which leads in a natural way to the idea of a tangent line to a curve. A portion of the graph of a function $f$ is shown in Figure 4.4. Two of its points $P$ and $Q$ are shown with respective coordinates

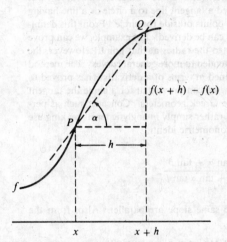

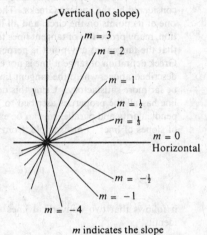

FIGURE 4.4   Geometric interpretation of the difference quotient as the tangent of an angle.

FIGURE 4.5   Lines of various slopes.

$(x, f(x))$ and $(x + h, f(x + h))$. Consider the right triangle with hypotenuse $PQ$; its altitude, $f(x + h) - f(x)$, represents the difference of the ordinates of the two points $Q$ and $P$. Therefore, the difference quotient

(4.10) $$\frac{f(x + h) - f(x)}{h}$$

represents the trigonometric tangent of the angle $\alpha$ that $PQ$ makes with the horizontal. The real number $\tan \alpha$ is called the *slope* of the line through $P$ and $Q$ and it provides a way of measuring the "steepness" of this line. For example, if $f$ is a linear function, say $f(x) = mx + b$, the difference quotient (4.10) has the value $m$, so $m$ is the slope of the line.

Some examples of lines of various slopes are shown in Figure 4.5. For a horizontal line,

$\alpha = 0$ and the slope, $\tan \alpha$, is also 0. If $\alpha$ lies between 0 and $\frac{1}{2}\pi$, the line is rising as we move from left to right and the slope is positive. If $\alpha$ lies between $\frac{1}{2}\pi$ and $\pi$, the line is falling as we move from left to right and the slope is negative. A line for which $\alpha = \frac{1}{4}\pi$ has slope 1. As $\alpha$ increases from 0 to $\frac{1}{2}\pi$, $\tan \alpha$ increases without bound, and the corresponding lines of slope $\tan \alpha$ approach a vertical position. Since $\tan \frac{1}{2}\pi$ is not defined, we say that *vertical lines have no slope.*

Suppose now that $f$ has a derivative at $x$. This means that the difference quotient approaches a certain limit $f'(x)$ as $h$ approaches 0. When this is interpreted geometrically it tells us that, as $h$ gets nearer to 0, the point $P$ remains fixed, $Q$ moves along the curve toward $P$, and the line through $PQ$ changes its direction in such a way that its slope approaches the number $f'(x)$ as a limit. For this reason it seems natural to define the *slope of the curve* at $P$ to be the number $f'(x)$. The line through $P$ having this slope is called the *tangent line* at $P$.

> *Note:* The concept of a line tangent to a circle (and to a few other special curves) was considered by the ancient Greeks. They defined a tangent line to a circle as a line having one of its points on the circle and all its other points outside the circle. From this definition, many properties of tangent lines to circles can be derived. For example, we can prove that the tangent at any point is perpendicular to the radius at that point. However, the Greek definition of tangent line is not easily extended to more general curves. The method described above, where the tangent line is defined in terms of a derivative, has proved to be far more satisfactory. Using this definition, we can prove that for a circle the tangent line has all the properties ascribed to it by the Greek geometers. Concepts such as perpendicularity and parallelism can be explained rather simply in analytic terms making use of slopes of lines. For example, from the trigonometric identity
>
> $$\tan (\alpha - \beta) = \frac{\tan \alpha - \tan \beta}{1 + \tan \alpha \tan \beta},$$
>
> it follows that two nonvertical lines with the same slope are parallel. Also, from the identity
>
> $$\cot (\alpha - \beta) = \frac{1 + \tan \alpha \tan \beta}{\tan \alpha - \tan \beta},$$
>
> we find that two nonvertical lines with slopes having product $-1$ are perpendicular.

The algebraic sign of the derivative of a function gives us useful information about the behavior of its graph. For example, if $x$ is a point in an open interval where the derivative is *positive*, then the graph is rising in the immediate vicinity of $x$ as we move from left to right. This occurs at $x_3$ in Figure 4.6. A *negative* derivative in an interval means the graph is falling, as shown at $x_1$, while a zero derivative at a point means a horizontal tangent line. At a maximum or minimum, such as those shown at $x_2$, $x_5$, and $x_6$, the slope must be zero. Fermat was the first to notice that points like $x_2$, $x_5$, and $x_6$, where $f$ has a maximum or minimum, must occur among the roots of the equation $f'(x) = 0$. It is important to realize that $f'(x)$ may also be zero at points where there is no maximum or minimum, such as above the point $x_4$. Note that this particular tangent line crosses the graph. This is an example of a situation not covered by the Greek definition of tangency.

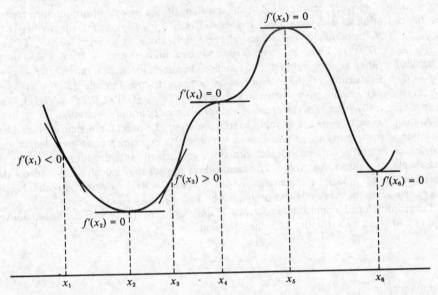

FIGURE 4.6 Geometric significance of the sign of the derivative.

The foregoing remarks concerning the significance of the algebraic sign of the derivative may seem quite obvious when we interpret them geometrically. Analytic proofs of these statements, based on general properties of derivatives, will be given in Section 4.16.

## 4.8 Other notations for derivatives

Notation has played an extremely important role in the development of mathematics. Some mathematical symbols, such as $x^n$ or $n!$, are merely abbreviations that compress long statements or formulas into a short space. Others, like the integration symbol $\int_a^b f(x)\,dx$, not only remind us of the process being represented but also help us in carrying out computations.

Sometimes several different notations are used for the same idea, preference for one or another being dependent on the circumstances that surround the use of the symbols. This is especially true in differential calculus where many different notations are used for derivatives. The derivative of a function $f$ has been denoted in our previous discussions by $f'$, a notation introduced by J. L. Lagrange (1736–1813) late in the 18th century. This emphasizes the fact that $f'$ is a new function obtained from $f$ by differentiation, its value at $x$ being denoted by $f'(x)$. Each point $(x, y)$ on the graph of $f$ has its coordinates $x$ and $y$ related by the equation $y = f(x)$, and the symbol $y'$ is also used to represent the derivative $f'(x)$. Similarly, $y'', \ldots, y^{(n)}$ represent the higher derivatives $f''(x), \ldots, f^{(n)}(x)$. For example, if $y = \sin x$, then $y' = \cos x$, $y'' = -\sin x$, etc. Lagrange's notation is not too far removed from that used by Newton who wrote $\dot{y}$ and $\ddot{y}$, instead of $y'$ and $y''$. Newton's dots are still used by some authors, especially to denote velocity and acceleration.

Another symbol was introduced in 1800 by L. Arbogast (1759–1803) who denoted the derivative of $f$ by $Df$, a symbol that has widespread use today. The symbol $D$ is called a *differentiation operator*, and it helps to suggest that $Df$ is a new function obtained from $f$ by the operation of differentiation. Higher derivatives $f''$, $f'''$, ..., $f^{(n)}$ are written $D^2f$, $D^3f$, ..., $D^nf$, respectively, the values of these derivatives at $x$ being written $D^2f(x)$, $D^3f(x)$, ..., $D^nf(x)$. Thus, we have $D \sin x = \cos x$ and $D^2 \sin x = D \cos x = -\sin x$. The rule for differentiating a sum of two functions becomes, in the $D$-notation, $D(f + g) = Df + Dg$. Evaluation of the derivatives at $x$ leads to the formula $[D(f + g)](x) = Df(x) + Dg(x)$ which is also written in the form $D[f(x) + g(x)] = Df(x) + Dg(x)$. The reader may easily formulate the product and quotient rules in the $D$-notation.

Among the early pioneers of mathematical analysis, Leibniz, more than anyone else, understood the importance of well-chosen symbols. He experimented at great length and carried on extensive correspondence with other mathematicians, debating the merits or drawbacks of various notations. The tremendous impact that calculus has had on the development of modern mathematics is due in part to its well-developed and highly suggestive symbols, many of them originated by Leibniz.

Leibniz developed a notation for derivatives quite different from those mentioned above. Using $y$ for $f(x)$, he wrote the difference quotient

$$\frac{f(x + h) - f(x)}{h}$$

in the form

$$\frac{\Delta y}{\Delta x},$$

where $\Delta x$ (read as "delta $x$") was written for $h$, and $\Delta y$ for $f(x + h) - f(x)$. The symbol $\Delta$ is called a *difference operator*. For the limit of the difference quotient, that is, for the derivative $f'(x)$, Leibniz wrote $dy/dx$. In this notation, the definition of derivative becomes

$$\frac{dy}{dx} = \lim_{\Delta x \to 0} \frac{\Delta y}{\Delta x}.$$

Not only was Leibniz's notation different, but his way of thinking about derivatives was different. He thought of the limit $dy/dx$ as a quotient of "infinitesimal" quantities $dy$ and $dx$ called "differentials," and he referred to the derivative $dy/dx$ as a "differential quotient." Leibniz imagined infinitesimals as entirely new types of numbers which, although not zero, were smaller than every positive real number.

Even though Leibniz was not able to give a satisfactory definition of infinitesimals, he and his followers used them freely in their development of calculus. Consequently, many people found calculus somewhat mysterious and began to question the validity of the methods. The work of Cauchy and others in the 19th century gradually led to the replacement of infinitesimals by the classical theory of limits. Nevertheless, many people have found it helpful to try to think as Leibniz did in terms of infinitesimals. This kind of thinking has intuitive appeal and often leads quickly to results that can be proved correct by more conventional means.

Recently Abraham Robinson has shown that the real number system can be extended to incorporate infinitesimals as envisaged by Leibniz. A discussion of this extension and its impact on many branches of mathematics is given in Robinson's book, *Non-standard Analysis*, North-Holland Publishing Company, Amsterdam, 1966.

Although some of Leibniz's ideas fell into temporary disrepute, the same cannot be said of his notations. The symbol $dy/dx$ for the derivative has the obvious advantage that it summarizes the whole process of forming the difference quotient and passing to the limit. Later we shall find the further advantage that certain formulas become easier to remember and to work with when derivatives are written in the Leibniz notation.

## 4.9 Exercises

1. Let $f(x) = \frac{1}{3}x^3 - 2x^2 + 3x + 1$ for all $x$. Find the points on the graph of $f$ at which the tangent line is horizontal.
2. Let $f(x) = \frac{2}{3}x^3 + \frac{1}{2}x^2 - x - 1$ for all $x$. Find the points on the graph of $f$ at which the slope is: (a) 0; (b) $-1$; (c) 5.
3. Let $f(x) = x + \sin x$ for all $x$. Find all points $x$ for which the graph of $f$ at $(x, f(x))$ has slope zero.
4. Let $f(x) = x^2 + ax + b$ for all $x$. Find values of $a$ and $b$ such that the line $y = 2x$ is tangent to the graph of $f$ at the point $(2, 4)$.
5. Find values of the constants $a$, $b$, and $c$ for which the graphs of the two polynomials $f(x) = x^2 + ax + b$ and $g(x) = x^3 - c$ will intersect at the point $(1, 2)$ and have the same tangent line at that point.
6. Consider the graph of the function $f$ defined by the equation $f(x) = x^2 + ax + b$, where $a$ and $b$ are constants.
   (a) Find the slope of the chord joining the points on the graph for which $x = x_1$ and $x = x_2$.
   (b) Find, in terms of $x_1$ and $x_2$, all values of $x$ for which the tangent line at $(x, f(x))$ has the same slope as the chord in part (a).
7. Show that the line $y = -x$ is tangent to the curve given by the equation $y = x^3 - 6x^2 + 8x$. Find the point of tangency. Does this tangent line intersect the curve anywhere else?
8. Make a sketch of the graph of the cubic polynomial $f(x) = x - x^3$ over the closed interval $-2 \le x \le 2$. Find constants $m$ and $b$ such that the line $y = mx + b$ will be tangent to the graph of $f$ at the point $(-1, 0)$. A second line through $(-1, 0)$ is also tangent to the graph of $f$ at a point $(a, c)$. Determine the coordinates $a$ and $c$.
9. A function $f$ is defined as follows:

$$f(x) = \begin{cases} x^2 & \text{if } x \le c, \\ ax + b & \text{if } x > c, \end{cases} \quad (a, b, c \text{ constants}).$$

   Find values of $a$ and $b$ (in terms of $c$) such that $f'(c)$ exists.
10. Solve Exercise 9 when $f$ is defined as follows:

$$f(x) = \begin{cases} \dfrac{1}{|x|} & \text{if } |x| > c, \\ a + bx^2 & \text{if } |x| \le c. \end{cases}$$

11. Solve Exercise 9 when $f$ is defined as follows:

$$f(x) = \begin{cases} \sin x & \text{if } x \le c, \\ ax + b & \text{if } x > c. \end{cases}$$

12. If $f(x) = (1 - \sqrt{x})/(1 + \sqrt{x})$ for $x > 0$, find formulas for $Df(x)$, $D^2f(x)$, and $D^3f(x)$.

13. There is a polynomial $P(x) = ax^3 + bx^2 + cx + d$ such that $P(0) = P(1) = -2$, $P'(0) = -1$, and $P''(0) = 10$. Compute $a$, $b$, $c$, $d$.

14. Two functions $f$ and $g$ have first and second derivatives at 0 and satisfy the relations

$$f(0) = 2/g(0), \quad f'(0) = 2g'(0) = 4g(0), \quad g''(0) = 5f''(0) = 6f(0) = 3 .$$

   (a) Let $h(x) = f(x)/g(x)$, and compute $h'(0)$.
   (b) Let $k(x) = f(x)g(x) \sin x$, and compute $k'(0)$.
   (c) Compute the limit of $g'(x)/f'(x)$ as $x \to 0$.

15. Given that the derivative $f'(a)$ exists. State which of the following statements are true and which are false. Give a reason for your decision in each case.

   (a) $f'(a) = \lim\limits_{h \to a} \dfrac{f(h) - f(a)}{h - a}$.

   (c) $f'(a) = \lim\limits_{t \to 0} \dfrac{f(a + 2t) - f(a)}{t}$.

   (b) $f'(a) = \lim\limits_{h \to 0} \dfrac{f(a) - f(a - h)}{h}$.

   (d) $f'(a) = \lim\limits_{t \to 0} \dfrac{f(a + 2t) - f(a + t)}{2t}$.

16. Suppose that instead of the usual definition of the derivative $Df(x)$, we define a new kind of derivative, $D^*f(x)$, by the formula

$$D^*f(x) = \lim_{h \to 0} \frac{f^2(x + h) - f^2(x)}{h} ,$$

where $f^2(x)$ means $[f(x)]^2$.
   (a) Derive formulas for computing the derivative $D^*$ of a sum, difference, product, and quotient.
   (b) Express $D^*f(x)$ in terms of $Df(x)$.
   (c) For what functions does $D^*f = Df$?

## 4.10 The chain rule for differentiating composite functions

With the differentiation formulas developed thus far, we can find derivatives of functions $f$ for which $f(x)$ is a finite sum of products or quotients of constant multiples of $\sin x$, $\cos x$, and $x^r$ ($r$ rational). As yet, however, we have not learned to deal with something like $f(x) = \sin (x^2)$ without going back to the definition of derivative. In this section we shall present a theorem, called the *chain rule*, that enables us to differentiate composite functions such as $f(x) = \sin (x^2)$. This increases substantially the number of functions that we can differentiate.

We recall that if $u$ and $v$ are functions such that the domain of $u$ includes the range of $v$, we can define the composite function $f = u \circ v$ by the equation

$$f(x) = u[v(x)] .$$

The chain rule tells us how to express the derivative of $f$ in terms of the derivatives $u'$ and $v'$.

THEOREM 4.2. CHAIN RULE. *Let $f$ be the composition of two functions $u$ and $v$, say $f = u \circ v$. Suppose that both derivatives $v'(x)$ and $u'(y)$ exist, where $y = v(x)$. Then the* derivative $f'(x)$ also exists and is given by the formula

(4.11) $$f'(x) = u'(y) \cdot v'(x) .$$

In other words, to compute the derivative of $u \circ v$ at $x$, we first compute the derivative of $u$ at the point $y$, where $y = v(x)$, and multiply this by $v'(x)$.

Before we discuss the proof of (4.11), we shall mention some alternative ways of expressing the chain rule formula. If we write (4.11) entirely in terms of $x$, we obtain the formula

$$f'(x) = u'[v(x)] \cdot v'(x) .$$

Expressed as an equation involving *functions* rather than numbers, the chain rule assumes the following form

$$(u \circ v)' = (u' \circ v) \cdot v'.$$

In the $u(v)$-notation, let us write $u(v)'$ for the derivative of the composite function $u(v)$ and $u'(v)$ for the composition $u' \circ v$. Then the last formula becomes

$$u(v)' = u'(v) \cdot v'.$$

*Proof of Theorem* 4.2. We turn now to the proof of (4.11). We assume that $v$ has a derivative at $x$ and that $u$ has a derivative at $v(x)$, and we wish to prove that $f$ has a derivative at $x$ given by the product $u'[v(x)] \cdot v'(x)$. The difference quotient for $f$ is

(4.12) $$\frac{f(x + h) - f(x)}{h} = \frac{u[v(x + h)] - u[v(x)]}{h} .$$

It is helpful at this stage to introduce some new notation. Let $y = v(x)$ and let $k = v(x + h) - v(x)$. (It is important to realize that $k$ depends on $h$.) Then we have $v(x + h) = y + k$ and (4.12) becomes

(4.13) $$\frac{f(x + h) - f(x)}{h} = \frac{u(y + k) - u(y)}{h} .$$

The right-hand side of (4.13) resembles the difference quotient whose limit defines $u'(y)$ except that $h$ appears in the denominator instead of $k$. If $k \neq 0$, it is easy to complete the proof. We simply multiply numerator and denominator by $k$, and the right-hand side of (4.13) becomes

(4.14) $$\frac{u(y + k) - u(y)}{k} \cdot \frac{k}{h} = \frac{u(y + k) - u(y)}{k} \cdot \frac{v(x + h) - v(x)}{h} .$$

When $h \to 0$, the last quotient on the right tends to $v'(x)$. Also, $k \to 0$ as $h \to 0$ because

$k = v(x + h) - v(x)$ and $v$ is continuous at $x$. Therefore the first quotient on the right of (4.14) approaches $u'(y)$ as $h \to 0$, and this leads at once to (4.11).

Although the foregoing argument seems to be the most natural way to proceed, it is not completely general. Since $k = v(x + h) - v(x)$, it may happen that $k = 0$ for infinitely many values of $h$ as $h \to 0$, in which case the passage from (4.13) to (4.14) is not valid. To overcome this difficulty, a slight modification of the proof is needed.

Let us return to Equation (4.13) and express the quotient on the right in a form that does not involve $k$ in the denominator. For this purpose we introduce the difference between the derivative $u'(y)$ and the difference quotient whose limit is $u'(y)$. That is, we define a new function $g$ as follows:

$$(4.15) \qquad g(t) = \frac{u(y + t) - u(y)}{t} - u'(y) \quad \text{if} \quad t \neq 0 .$$

This equation defines $g(t)$ only if $t \neq 0$. Multiplying by $t$ and rearranging terms, we may write (4.15) in the following form:

$$(4.16) \qquad u(y + t) - u(y) = t[g(t) + u'(y)] .$$

Although (4.16) has been derived under the hypothesis that $t \neq 0$, it also holds for $t = 0$, provided we assign some definite value to $g(0)$. Since $g(t) \to 0$ as $t \to 0$, we shall define $g(0)$ to be 0. This will ensure the continuity of $g$ at 0. If, now, we replace $t$ in (4.16) by $k$, where $k = v(x + h) - v(x)$, and substitute the right-hand side of (4.16) in (4.13), we obtain

$$(4.17) \qquad \frac{f(x + h) - f(x)}{h} = \frac{k}{h}[g(k) + u'(y)] ,$$

a formula that is valid even if $k = 0$. When $h \to 0$ the quotient $k/h \to v'(x)$ and $g(k) \to 0$ so the right-hand side of (4.17) approaches the limit $u'(y) \cdot v'(x)$. This completes the proof of the chain rule.

### 4.11 Applications of the chain rule. Related rates and implicit differentiation

The chain rule is an excellent example to illustrate the usefulness of the Leibniz notation for derivatives. In fact, if we write (4.11) in the Leibniz notation, it assumes the appearance of a trivial algebraic identity. First we introduce new symbols, say

$$y = v(x) \quad \text{and} \quad z = u(y) .$$

Then we write $dy/dx$ for the derivative $v'(x)$, and $dz/dy$ for $u'(y)$. The formation of the composite function is indicated by writing

$$z = u(y) = u[v(x)] = f(x) ,$$

and $dz/dx$ is written for the derivative $f'(x)$. The chain rule, as expressed in Equation

(4.11), now becomes

$$(4.18) \qquad \frac{dz}{dx} = \frac{dz}{dy} \frac{dy}{dx}.$$

The strong suggestive power of this formula is obvious. It is especially attractive to people who use calculus in physical problems. For example, suppose the foregoing symbol $z$ represents a physical quantity measured in terms of other physical quantities $x$ and $y$. The equation $z = f(x)$ tells us how to find $z$ if $x$ is given, and the equation $z = u(y)$ tells us how to find $z$ if $y$ is given. The relation between $x$ and $y$ is expressed by the equation $y = v(x)$. The chain rule, as expressed in (4.18), tells us that the rate of change of $z$ with respect to $x$ is equal to the product of the rate of change of $z$ with respect to $y$ and the rate of change of $y$ with respect to $x$. The following example illustrates how the chain rule may be used in a special physical problem.

EXAMPLE 1. Suppose a gas is pumped into a spherical balloon at a constant rate of 50 cubic centimeters per second. Assume that the gas pressure remains constant and that the balloon always has a spherical shape. How fast is the radius of the balloon increasing when the radius is 5 centimeters?

*Solution.* Let $r$ denote the radius and $V$ the volume of the balloon at time $t$. We are given $dV/dt$, the rate of change of volume with respect to time, and we want to determine $dr/dt$, the rate of change of the radius with respect to time, at the instant when $r = 5$. The chain rule provides the connection between the given data and the unknown. It states that

$$(4.19) \qquad \frac{dV}{dt} = \frac{dV}{dr} \frac{dr}{dt}.$$

To compute $dV/dr$, we use the formula $V = 4\pi r^3/3$ which expresses the volume of the sphere in terms of its radius. Differentiation gives us $dV/dr = 4\pi r^2$, and hence (4.19) becomes

$$\frac{dV}{dt} = 4\pi r^2 \frac{dr}{dt}.$$

Substituting $dV/dt = 50$ and $r = 5$, we obtain $dr/dt = 1/(2\pi)$. That is to say, the radius is increasing at a rate of $1/(2\pi)$ centimeters per second at the instant when $r = 5$.

The foregoing example is called a problem in *related rates*. Note that it was not necessary to express $r$ as a function of $t$ in order to determine the derivative $dr/dt$. It is this fact that makes the chain rule especially useful in related-rate problems.

The next two examples show how the chain rule may be used to obtain new differentiation formulas.

EXAMPLE 2. Given $f(x) = \sin (x^2)$, compute $f'(x)$.

*Solution.* The function $f$ is a composition, $f(x) = u[v(x)]$, where $v(x) = x^2$ and $u(x) = \sin x$. To use the chain rule, we need to determine $u'[v(x)] = u'(x^2)$. Since $u'(x) = \cos x$, we have $u'(x^2) = \cos (x^2)$, and hence (4.11) gives us

$$f'(x) = \cos (x^2) \cdot v'(x) = \cos (x^2) \cdot 2x.$$

We may also solve the problem using the Leibniz notation. If we write $y = x^2$ and $z = f(x)$, then $z = \sin y$ and $dz/dx = f'(x)$. The chain rule yields

$$\frac{dz}{dx} = \frac{dz}{dy}\frac{dy}{dx} = (\cos y)(2x) = \cos(x^2) \cdot 2x \,,$$

which agrees with the foregoing result for $f'(x)$.

EXAMPLE 3. If $f(x) = [v(x)]^n$, where $n$ is a positive integer, compute $f'(x)$ in terms of $v(x)$ and $v'(x)$.

*Solution.* The function $f$ is a composition, $f(x) = u[v(x)]$, where $u(x) = x^n$. Since $u'(x) = nx^{n-1}$, we have $u'[v(x)] = n[v(x)]^{n-1}$, and the chain rule yields

$$f'(x) = n[v(x)]^{n-1}v'(x) \,.$$

If we omit the reference to $x$ and write this as an equality involving functions, we obtain the important formula

$$(v^n)' = nv^{n-1}v'$$

which tells us how to differentiate the $n$th power of $v$ when $v'$ exists. The formula is also valid for *rational* powers if $v^n$ and $v^{n-1}$ are defined. To solve the problem in the Leibniz notation, we write $y = v(x)$ and $z = f(x)$. Then $z = y^n$, $dz/dx = f'(x)$, and the chain rule gives us

$$\frac{dz}{dx} = \frac{dz}{dy}\frac{dy}{dx} = ny^{n-1}v'(x) = n[v(x)]^{n-1}v'(x) \,,$$

which agrees with the first solution.

EXAMPLE 4. The equation $x^2 + y^2 = r^2$ represents a circle of radius $r$ and center at the origin. If we solve this equation for $y$ in terms of $x$, we obtain two solutions which serve to define two functions $f$ and $g$ given on the interval $[-r, r]$ by the formulas

$$f(x) = \sqrt{r^2 - x^2} \qquad \text{and} \qquad g(x) = -\sqrt{r^2 - x^2} \,.$$

(The graph of $f$ is the upper semicircle and the graph of $g$ the lower semicircle.) We may compute the derivatives of $f$ and $g$ by the chain rule. For $f$ we use the result of Example 3 with $v(x) = r^2 - x^2$ and $n = \frac{1}{2}$ to obtain

$$(4.20) \qquad f'(x) = \tfrac{1}{2}(r^2 - x^2)^{-1/2}(-2x) = \frac{-x}{\sqrt{r^2 - x^2}} = \frac{-x}{f(x)}$$

whenever $f(x) \neq 0$. The same method, applied to $g$, gives us

$$(4.21) \qquad g'(x) = -\frac{-x}{\sqrt{r^2 - x^2}} = \frac{-x}{g(x)}$$

whenever $g(x) \neq 0$. Notice that if we let $y$ stand for either $f(x)$ or $g(x)$, then both formulas (4.20) and (4.21) can be combined into one, namely,

$$(4.22) \qquad\qquad y' = \frac{-x}{y} \quad \text{if} \quad y \neq 0.$$

Another useful application of the chain rule has to do with a technique known as *implicit differentiation*. We shall explain the method and illustrate its advantages by rederiving the result of Example 4 in a simpler way.

EXAMPLE 5. *Implicit differentiation*. Formula (4.22) may be derived directly from the equation $x^2 + y^2 = r^2$ without the necessity of solving for $y$. We remember that $y$ is a function of $x$ [either $y = f(x)$ or $y = g(x)$]. Assuming that $y'$ exists, we differentiate both sides of the equation $x^2 + y^2 = r^2$ to obtain

$$(4.23) \qquad\qquad 2x + 2yy' = 0.$$

(The term $2yy'$ comes from differentiating $y^2$ as explained in Example 3.) When Equation (4.23) is solved for $y'$ it yields (4.22).

The equation $x^2 + y^2 = r^2$ is said to define $y$ *implicitly* as a function of $x$ (it actually defines *two* functions), and the process by which (4.23) is obtained from this equation is called *implicit differentiation*. The end result is valid for either of the two functions $f$ and $g$ so defined. Notice that at a point $(x, y)$ on the circle with $x \neq 0$ and $y \neq 0$, the tangent line has a slope $-x/y$, whereas the radius from the center to $(x, y)$ has the slope $y/x$. The product of the two slopes is $-1$ so the tangent is perpendicular to the radius.

## 4.12 Exercises

In Exercises 1 through 14, determine the derivative $f'(x)$. In each case it is understood that $x$ is restricted to those values for which the formula for $f(x)$ is meaningful.

1. $f(x) = \cos 2x - 2 \sin x$.

2. $f(x) = \sqrt{1 + x^2}$.

3. $f(x) = (2 - x^2) \cos x^2 + 2x \sin x^3$.

4. $f(x) = \sin(\cos^2 x) \cdot \cos(\sin^2 x)$.

5. $f(x) = \sin^n x \cdot \cos nx$.

6. $f(x) = \sin[\sin(\sin x)]$.

7. $f(x) = \dfrac{\sin^2 x}{\sin x^2}$.

8. $f(x) = \tan \dfrac{x}{2} - \cot \dfrac{x}{2}$.

9. $f(x) = \sec^2 x + \csc^2 x$.

10. $f(x) = x\sqrt{1 + x^2}$.

11. $f(x) = \dfrac{x}{\sqrt{4 - x^2}}$.

12. $f(x) = \left(\dfrac{1 + x^3}{1 - x^3}\right)^{1/3}$.

13. $f(x) = \dfrac{1}{\sqrt{1 + x^2}\,(x + \sqrt{1 + x^2})}$.

14. $f(x) = \sqrt{x + \sqrt{x + \sqrt{x}}}$.

15. Compute $f'(x)$ if $f(x) = (1 + x)(2 + x^2)^{1/2}(3 + x^3)^{1/3}$, $x^3 \neq -3$.

16. Let $f(x) = \dfrac{1}{1 + 1/x}$ if $x \neq 0$, and let $g(x) = \dfrac{1}{1 + 1/f(x)}$. Compute $f'(x)$ and $g'(x)$.

17. The following table of values was computed for a pair of functions $f$ and $g$ and their derivatives $f'$ and $g'$. Construct a corresponding table for the two composite functions $h$ and $k$ given by $h(x) = f[g(x)]$, $k(x) = g[f(x)]$.

| $x$ | $f(x)$ | $f'(x)$ | $g(x)$ | $g'(x)$ |
|-----|--------|---------|--------|---------|
| 0   | 1      | 5       | 2      | −5      |
| 1   | 3      | −2      | 0      | 1       |
| 2   | 0      | 2       | 3      | 1       |
| 3   | 2      | 4       | 1      | −6      |

18. A function $f$ and its first two derivatives are tabulated as shown. Let $g(x) = xf(x^2)$ and make a table of $g$ and its first two derivatives for $x = 0, 1, 2$.

| $x$ | $f(x)$ | $f'(x)$ | $f''(x)$ |
|-----|--------|---------|----------|
| 0   | 0      | 1       | 2        |
| 1   | 1      | 1       | 1        |
| 2   | 3      | 2       | 1        |
| 4   | 6      | 3       | 0        |

19. Determine the derivative $g'(x)$ in terms of $f'(x)$ if:
   (a) $g(x) = f(x^2)$;
   (b) $g(x) = f(\sin^2 x) + f(\cos^2 x)$;
   (c) $g(x) = f[f(x)]$;
   (d) $g(x) = f\{f[f(x)]\}$.

*Related rates and implicit differentiation.*

20. Each edge of a cube is expanding at the rate of 1 centimeter (cm) per second. How fast is the volume changing when the length of each edge is (a) 5 cm? (b) 10 cm? (c) $x$ cm?

21. An airplane flies in level flight at constant velocity, eight miles above the ground. (In this exercise assume the earth is flat.) The flight path passes directly over a point $P$ on the ground. The distance from the plane to $P$ is decreasing at the rate of 4 miles per minute at the instant when this distance is 10 miles. Compute the velocity of the plane in miles per hour.

22. A baseball diamond is a 90-foot square. A ball is batted along the third-base line at a constant speed of 100 feet per second. How fast is its distance from first base changing when (a) it is halfway to third base? (b) it reaches third base?

23. A boat sails parallel to a straight beach at a constant speed of 12 miles per hour, staying 4 miles offshore. How fast is it approaching a lighthouse on the shoreline at the instant it is exactly 5 miles from the lighthouse?

24. A reservoir has the shape of a right-circular cone. The altitude is 10 feet, and the radius of the base is 4 ft. Water is poured into the reservoir at a constant rate of 5 cubic feet per minute. How fast is the water level rising when the depth of the water is 5 feet if (a) the vertex of the cone is up? (b) the vertex of the cone is down?

25. A water tank has the shape of a right-circular cone with its vertex down. Its altitude is 10 feet and the radius of the base is 15 feet. Water leaks out of the bottom at a constant rate of 1 cubic foot per second. Water is poured into the tank at a constant rate of $c$ cubic feet per second. Compute $c$ so that the water level will be rising at the rate of 4 feet per second at the instant when the water is 2 feet deep.

26. Water flows into a hemispherical tank of radius 10 feet (flat side up). At any instant, let $h$ denote the depth of the water, measured from the bottom, $r$ the radius of the surface of the water, and $V$ the volume of the water in the tank. Compute $dV/dh$ at the instant when $h = 5$ feet. If the water flows in at a constant rate of $5\sqrt{3}$ cubic feet per second, compute $dr/dt$, the rate at which $r$ is changing, at the instant $t$ when $h = 5$ feet.

27. A variable right triangle $ABC$ in the $xy$-plane has its right angle at vertex $B$, a fixed vertex $A$ at the origin, and the third vertex $C$ restricted to lie on the parabola $y = 1 + \frac{7}{36} x^2$. The point $B$ starts at the point $(0, 1)$ at time $t = 0$ and moves upward along the $y$-axis at a constant velocity of 2 cm/sec. How fast is the area of the triangle increasing when $t = 7/2$ sec?

28. The radius of a right-circular cylinder increases at a constant rate. Its altitude is a linear function of the radius and increases three times as fast as the radius. When the radius is 1 foot the altitude is 6 feet. When the radius is 6 feet, the volume is increasing at a rate of 1 cubic foot per second. When the radius is 36 feet, the volume is increasing at a rate of $n$ cubic feet per second, where $n$ is an integer. Compute $n$.

29. A particle is constrained to move along a parabola whose equation is $y = x^2$. (a) At what point on the curve are the abscissa and the ordinate changing at the same rate? (b) Find this rate if the motion is such that at time $t$ we have $x = \sin t$ and $y = \sin^2 t$.

30. The equation $x^3 + y^3 = 1$ defines $y$ as one or more functions of $x$. (a) Assuming the derivative $y'$ exists, and without attempting to solve for $y$, show that $y'$ satisfies the equation $x^2 + y^2 y' = 0$. (b) Assuming the second derivative $y''$ exists, show that $y'' = -2xy^{-5}$ whenever $y \neq 0$.

31. If $0 < x < 5$, the equation $x^{1/2} + y^{1/2} = 5$ defines $y$ as a function of $x$. Without solving for $y$, show that the derivative $y'$ has a fixed sign. (You may assume the existence of $y'$.)

32. The equation $3x^2 + 4y^2 = 12$ defines $y$ implicitly as two functions of $x$ if $|x| \leq 2$. Assuming the second derivative $y''$ exists, show that it satisfies the equation $4y^3 y'' = -9$.

33. The equation $x \sin xy + 2x^2 = 0$ defines $y$ implicitly as a function of $x$. Assuming the derivative $y'$ exists, show that it satisfies the equation $y'x^2 \cos xy + xy \cos xy + \sin xy + 4x = 0$.

34. If $y = x^r$, where $r$ is a rational number, say $r = m/n$, then $y^n = x^m$. Assuming the existence of the derivative $y'$, derive the formula $y' = rx^{r-1}$ using implicit differentiation and the corresponding formula for integer exponents.

## 4.13 Applications of differentiation to extreme values of functions

Differentiation can be used to help locate maxima and minima of functions. Actually, there are two different uses of the word "maximum" in calculus, and they are distinguished by the two prefixes *absolute* and *relative*. The concept of absolute maximum was introduced in Chapter 3. We recall that a real-valued function $f$ is said to have an absolute maximum on a set $S$ if there is at least one point $c$ in $S$ such that

$$f(x) \leq f(c) \qquad \text{for all } x \text{ in } S.$$

The concept of relative maximum is defined as follows.

DEFINITION OF RELATIVE MAXIMUM. *A function f, defined on a set S, is said to have a relative maximum at a point c in S if there is some open interval I containing c such that*

$$f(x) \leq f(c) \quad \text{for all } x \text{ which lie in } I \cap S.$$

*The concept of relative minimum is similarly defined by reversing the inequality.*

In other words, a relative maximum at $c$ is an absolute maximum in some neighborhood of $c$, although this need not be an absolute maximum on the whole of $S$. Examples are shown in Figure 4.7. Of course, every absolute maximum is, in particular, a relative maximum.

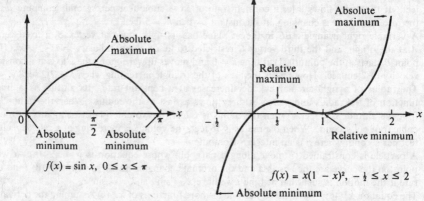

FIGURE 4.7   Extrema of functions.

DEFINITION OF EXTREMUM. *A number which is either a relative maximum or a relative minimum of a function f is called an extreme value or an extremum of f.*

The next theorem, which is illustrated in Figure 4.7, relates extrema of a function to horizontal tangents of its graph.

THEOREM 4.3.   VANISHING OF THE DERIVATIVE AT AN INTERIOR EXTREMUM. *Let f be defined on an open interval I, and assume that f has a relative maximum or a relative minimum at an interior point c of I. If the derivative f'(c) exists, then f'(c) = 0.*

*Proof.*   Define a function $Q$ on $I$ as follows:

$$Q(x) = \frac{f(x) - f(c)}{x - c} \quad \text{if} \quad x \neq c, \qquad Q(c) = f'(c).$$

Since $f'(c)$ exists, $Q(x) \to Q(c)$ as $x \to c$, so $Q$ is continuous at $c$. We wish to prove that $Q(c) = 0$. We shall do this by showing that each of the inequalities $Q(c) > 0$ and $Q(c) < 0$ leads to a contradiction.

Assume $Q(c) > 0$. By the sign-preserving property of continuous functions, there is an interval about $c$ in which $Q(x)$ is positive. Therefore the numerator of the quotient $Q(x)$ has the same sign as the denominator for all $x \neq c$ in this interval. In other words, $f(x) > f(c)$ when $x > c$, and $f(x) < f(c)$ when $x < c$. This contradicts the assumption that $f$ has an extremum at $c$. Hence, the inequality $Q(c) > 0$ is impossible. A similar argument shows that we cannot have $Q(c) < 0$. Therefore $Q(c) = 0$, as asserted. Since $Q(c) = f'(c)$, this proves the theorem.

It is important to realize that a zero derivative at $c$ does not imply an extremum at $c$. For example, let $f(x) = x^3$. The graph of $f$ is shown in Figure 4.8. Here $f'(x) = 3x^2$, so

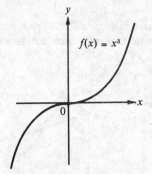

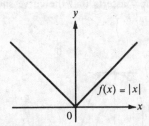

FIGURE 4.8 Here $f'(0)$ equals 0 but there is no extremum at 0.

FIGURE 4.9 There is an extremum at 0, but $f'(0)$ does not exist.

$f'(0) = 0$. However, this function is increasing in every interval containing 0 so there is no extremum at 0. This example shows that a zero derivative at $c$ is *not sufficient* for an extremum at $c$.

Another example, $f(x) = |x|$, shows that a zero derivative does not always occur at an extremum. Here there is a relative minimum at 0, as shown in Figure 4.9, but at the point 0 itself the graph has a sharp corner and there is no derivative. Theorem 4.3 assumes that the derivative $f'(c)$ *exists* at the extremum. In other words, Theorem 4.3 tells us that, *in the absence of sharp corners*, the derivative must necessarily vanish at an extremum if this extremum occurs in the interior of an interval.

In a later section we shall describe a test for extrema which is comprehensive enough to include both the examples in Figure 4.7 and also the example in Figure 4.9. This test, which is described in Theorem 4.8, tells us that an extremum always occurs at a point where the derivative changes its sign. Although this fact may seem geometrically evident, a proof is not easy to give with the materials developed thus far. We shall deduce this result as a consequence of the mean-value theorem for derivatives which we discuss next.

### 4.14 The mean-value theorem for derivatives

The mean-value theorem for derivatives holds a position of importance in calculus because many properties of functions can easily be deduced from it. Before we state the mean-value theorem, we will examine one of its special cases from which the more general theorem will be deduced. This special case was discovered in 1690 by Michel Rolle (1652–1719), a French mathematician.

THEOREM 4.4. ROLLE'S THEOREM. *Let f be a function which is continuous everywhere on a closed interval [a, b] and has a derivative at each point of the open interval (a, b). Also, assume that*

$$f(a) = f(b).$$

*Then there is at least one point c in the open interval (a, b) such that $f'(c) = 0$.*

The geometric significance of Rolle's theorem is illustrated in Figure 4.10. The theorem simply asserts that the curve shown must have a horizontal tangent somewhere between $a$ and $b$.

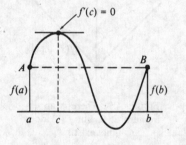 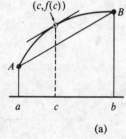 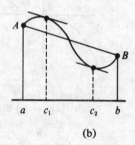

(a)                              (b)

FIGURE 4.10   Geometric interpre-   FIGURE 4.11   Geometric significance of the mean-value
tation of Rolle's theorem.          theorem.

*Proof.* We assume that $f'(x) \neq 0$ for every $x$ in the open interval $(a, b)$, and we arrive at a contradiction as follows: By the extreme-value theorem for continuous functions, $f$ must take on its absolute maximum $M$ and its absolute minimum $m$ somewhere in the closed interval $[a, b]$. Theorem 4.3 tells us that neither extreme value can be taken at any interior point (otherwise the derivative would vanish there). Hence, both extreme values are taken on at the endpoints $a$ and $b$. But since $f(a) = f(b)$, this means that $m = M$, and hence $f$ is constant on $[a, b]$. This contradicts the fact that $f'(x) \neq 0$ for all $x$ in $(a, b)$. It follows that $f'(c) = 0$ for at least one $c$ satisfying $a < c < b$, which proves the theorem.

We can use Rolle's theorem to prove the mean-value theorem. Before we state the mean-value theorem, it may be helpful to examine its geometric significance. Each of the curves shown in Figure 4.11 is the graph of a continuous function $f$ with a tangent line above each point of the open interval $(a, b)$. At the point $(c, f(c))$ shown in Figure 4.11(a), the tangent line is parallel to the chord $AB$. In Figure 4.11(b), there are two points where the tangent line is parallel to the chord $AB$. The mean-value theorem guarantees that there will be *at least one point* with this property.

To translate this geometric property into an analytic statement, we need only observe that parallelism of two lines means equality of their slopes. Since the slope of the chord

$AB$ is the quotient $[f(b) - f(a)]/(b - a)$ and since the slope of the tangent line at $c$ is the derivative $f'(c)$, the above assertion states that

$$(4.24) \qquad \frac{f(b) - f(a)}{b - a} = f'(c)$$

for *some* $c$ in the open interval $(a, b)$.

To exhibit strong intuitive evidence for the truth of (4.24), we may think of $f(t)$ as the distance traveled by a moving particle at time $t$. Then the quotient on the left of (4.24) represents the *mean* or *average* speed in the time interval $[a, b]$, and the derivative $f'(t)$ represents the instantaneous speed at time $t$. The equation asserts that there must be some moment when the instantaneous speed is equal to the average speed. For example, if the average speed during an automobile trip is 45 mph, then the speedometer must register 45 mph *at least once* during the trip.

The mean-value theorem may be stated formally as follows.

THEOREM 4.5. MEAN-VALUE THEOREM FOR DERIVATIVES. *Assume that $f$ is continuous everywhere on a closed interval $[a, b]$ and has a derivative at each point of the open interval $(a, b)$. Then there is at least one interior point $c$ of $(a, b)$ for which*

$$(4.25) \qquad f(b) - f(a) = f'(c)(b - a).$$

*Proof.* To apply Rolle's theorem we need a function which has equal values at the endpoints $a$ and $b$. To construct such a function, we modify $f$ as follows. Let

$$h(x) = f(x)(b - a) - x[f(b) - f(a)].$$

Then $h(a) = h(b) = bf(a) - af(b)$. Also, $h$ is continuous on $[a, b]$ and has a derivative in the open interval $(a, b)$. Applying Rolle's theorem to $h$, we find that $h'(c) = 0$ for some $c$ in $(a, b)$. But

$$h'(x) = f'(x)(b - a) - [f(b) - f(a)].$$

When $x = c$, this gives us Equation (4.25).

Notice that the theorem makes no assertion about the exact location of the one or more "mean values" $c$, except to say that they all lie *somewhere* between $a$ and $b$. For some functions the position of the mean values may be specified exactly, but in most cases it is very difficult to make an accurate determination of these points. Nevertheless, the real usefulness of the theorem lies in the fact that many conclusions can be drawn from the knowledge of the mere *existence* of at least one mean value.

*Note:* It is important to realize that the conclusion of the mean-value theorem may fail to hold if there is any point between $a$ and $b$ where the derivative does not exist. For example, the function $f$ defined by the equation $f(x) = |x|$ is continuous everywhere on the real axis and has a derivative everywhere except at 0. Let $A = (-1, f(-1))$ and let $B = (2, f(2))$. The slope of the chord joining $A$ and $B$ is

$$\frac{f(2) - f(-1)}{2 - (-1)} = \frac{2 - 1}{3} = \frac{1}{3}$$

but the derivative is nowhere equal to $\frac{1}{3}$.

The following extension of the mean-value theorem is often useful.

THEOREM 4.6. CAUCHY'S MEAN-VALUE FORMULA. *Let $f$ and $g$ be two functions continuous on a closed interval $[a, b]$ and having derivatives in the open interval $(a, b)$. Then, for some $c$ in $(a, b)$, we have*

$$f'(c)[g(b) - g(a)] = g'(c)[f(b) - f(a)].$$

*Proof.* The proof is similar to that of Theorem 4.5. We let

$$h(x) = f(x)[g(b) - g(a)] - g(x)[f(b) - f(a)].$$

Then $h(a) = h(b) = f(a)g(b) - g(a)f(b)$. Applying Rolle's theorem to $h$, we find that $h'(c) = 0$ for some $c$ in $(a, b)$. Computing $h'(c)$ from the formula defining $h$, we obtain Cauchy's mean-value formula. Theorem 4.5 is the special case obtained by taking $g(x) = x$.

## 4.15  Exercises

1. Show that on the graph of any quadratic polynomial the chord joining the points for which $x = a$ and $x = b$ is parallel to the tangent line at the midpoint $x = (a + b)/2$.
2. Use Rolle's theorem to prove that, regardless of the value of $b$, there is at most one point $x$ in the interval $-1 \leq x \leq 1$ for which $x^3 - 3x + b = 0$.
3. Define a function $f$ as follows:

$$f(x) = \frac{3 - x^2}{2} \quad \text{if} \quad x \leq 1, \qquad f(x) = \frac{1}{x} \quad \text{if} \quad x \geq 1.$$

   (a) Sketch the graph of $f$ for $x$ in the interval $0 \leq x \leq 2$.
   (b) Show that $f$ satisfies the conditions of the mean-value theorem over the interval $[0, 2]$ and determine all the mean values provided by the theorem.
4. Let $f(x) = 1 - x^{2/3}$. Show that $f(1) = f(-1) = 0$, but that $f'(x)$ is never zero in the interval $[-1, 1]$. Explain how this is possible, in view of Rolle's theorem.
5. Show that $x^2 = x \sin x + \cos x$ for exactly two real values of $x$.
6. Show that the mean-value formula can be expressed in the form

$$f(x + h) = f(x) + hf'(x + \theta h) \qquad \text{where} \quad 0 < \theta < 1.$$

   Determine $\theta$ in terms of $x$ and $h$ when (a) $f(x) = x^2$; (b) $f(x) = x^3$. Keep $x$ fixed, $x \neq 0$, and find the limit of $\theta$ in each case as $h \to 0$.
7. Let $f$ be a polynomial. A real number $\alpha$ is said to be a *zero* of $f$ of multiplicity $m$ if $f(x) = (x - \alpha)^m g(x)$, where $g(\alpha) \neq 0$.

(a) If $f$ has $r$ zeros in an interval $[a, b]$, prove that $f'$ has at least $r - 1$ zeros, and in general, the $k$th derivative $f^{(k)}$ has at least $r - k$ zeros in $[a, b]$. (The zeros are to be counted as often as their multiplicity indicates.)

(b) If the $k$th derivative $f^{(k)}$ has *exactly* $r$ zeros in $[a, b]$, what can you conclude about the number of zeros of $f$ in $[a, b]$?

8. Use the mean-value theorem to deduce the following inequalities:

(a) $|\sin x - \sin y| \leq |x - y|$.

(b) $ny^{n-1}(x - y) \leq x^n - y^n \leq nx^{n-1}(x - y)$     if $0 < y \leq x$, $n = 1, 2, 3, \ldots$.

9. A function $f$, continuous on $[a, b]$, has a second derivative $f''$ everywhere on the open interval $(a, b)$. The line segment joining $(a, f(a))$ and $(b, f(b))$ intersects the graph of $f$ at a third point $(c, f(c))$, where $a < c < b$. Prove that $f''(t) = 0$ for at least one point $t$ in $(a, b)$.

10. This exercise outlines a proof of the intermediate-value theorem for derivatives. *Assume $f$ has a derivative everywhere on an open interval $I$. Choose $a < b$ in $I$. Then $f'$ takes on every value between $f'(a)$ and $f'(b)$ somewhere in $(a, b)$.*

(a) Define a new function $g$ on $[a, b]$ as follows:

$$g(x) = \frac{f(x) - f(a)}{x - a} \quad \text{if} \quad x \neq a, \quad g(a) = f'(a).$$

Prove that $g$ takes on every value between $f'(a)$ and $g(b)$ in the open interval $(a, b)$. Use the mean-value theorem for derivatives to show that $f'$ takes on every value between $f'(a)$ and $g(b)$ in the open interval $(a, b)$.

(b) Define a new function $h$ on $[a, b]$ as follows:

$$h(x) = \frac{f(x) - f(b)}{x - b} \quad \text{if} \quad x \neq b, \quad h(b) = f'(b).$$

By an argument similar to that in part (a), show that $f'$ takes on every value between $f'(b)$ and $h(a)$ in $(a, b)$. Since $h(a) = g(b)$, this proves the intermediate-value theorem for derivatives.

## 4.16 Applications of the mean-value theorem to geometric properties of functions

The mean-value theorem may be used to deduce properties of a function from a knowledge of the algebraic sign of its derivative. This is illustrated by the following theorem.

THEOREM 4.7.   *Let $f$ be a function which is continuous on a closed interval $[a, b]$ and assume $f$ has a derivative at each point of the open interval $(a, b)$. Then we have:*

(a) *If $f'(x) > 0$ for every $x$ in $(a, b)$, $f$ is strictly increasing on $[a, b]$;*

(b) *If $f'(x) < 0$ for every $x$ in $(a, b)$, $f$ is strictly decreasing on $[a, b]$;*

(c) *If $f'(x) = 0$ for every $x$ in $(a, b)$, $f$ is constant throughout $[a, b]$.*

*Proof.* To prove (a) we must show that $f(x) < f(y)$ whenever $a \leq x < y \leq b$. Therefore, suppose $x < y$ and apply the mean-value theorem to the closed subinterval $[x, y]$. We obtain

(4.26)     $$f(y) - f(x) = f'(c)(y - x), \quad \text{where} \quad x < c < y.$$

Since both $f'(c)$ and $y - x$ are positive, so is $f(y) - f(x)$, and this means $f(x) < f(y)$, as asserted. This proves (a), and the proof of (b) is similar. To prove (c), we use Equation (4.26) with $x = a$. Since $f'(c) = 0$, we have $f(y) = f(a)$ for every $y$ in $[a, b]$, so $f$ is constant on $[a, b]$.

We can use Theorem 4.7 to prove that an extremum occurs whenever the derivative changes sign.

THEOREM 4.8. *Assume $f$ is continuous on a closed interval $[a, b]$ and assume that the derivative $f'$ exists everywhere in the open interval $(a, b)$, except possibly at a point $c$.*
(a) *If $f'(x)$ is positive for all $x < c$ and negative for all $x > c$, then $f$ has a relative maximum at $c$.*
(b) *If, on the other hand, $f'(x)$ is negative for all $x < c$ and positive for all $x > c$, then $f$ has a relative minimum at $c$.*

*Proof.* In case (a), Theorem 4.7(a) tells us that $f$ is strictly increasing on $[a, c]$ and strictly decreasing on $[c, b]$. Hence $f(x) < f(c)$ for all $x \neq c$ in $(a, b)$, so $f$ has a relative

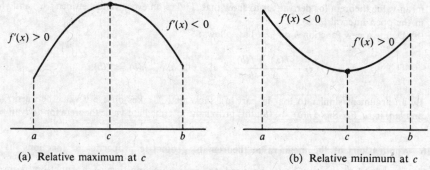

(a) Relative maximum at $c$                    (b) Relative minimum at $c$

FIGURE 4.12   An extremum occurs when the derivative changes sign.

maximum at $c$. This proves (a) and the proof of (b) is entirely analogous. The two cases are illustrated in Figure 4.12.

### 4.17   Second-derivative test for extrema

If a function $f$ is continuous on a closed interval $[a, b]$, the extreme-value theorem tells us that it has an absolute maximum and an absolute minimum somewhere in $[a, b]$. If $f$ has a derivative at each interior point, then the only places where extrema can occur are:
(1) at the endpoints $a$ and $b$;
(2) at those interior points $x$ where $f'(x) = 0$.
Points of type (2) are often called *critical points* of $f$. To decide whether there is a maximum or a minimum (or neither) at a critical point $c$, we need more information about $f$. Usually the behavior of $f$ at a critical point can be determined from the algebraic sign of the derivative near $c$. The next theorem shows that a study of the sign of the second derivative near $c$ can also be helpful.

THEOREM 4.9.   SECOND-DERIVATIVE TEST FOR AN EXTREMUM AT A CRITICAL POINT.   *Let c be a critical point of f in an open interval* $(a, b)$; *that is, assume* $a < c < b$ *and* $f'(c) = 0$. *Assume also that the second derivative* $f''$ *exists in* $(a, b)$. *Then we have the following:*

(a) *If* $f''$ *is negative in* $(a, b)$, $f$ *has a relative maximum at* $c$.
(b) *If* $f''$ *is positive in* $(a, b)$, $f$ *has a relative minimum at* $c$.

The two cases are illustrated in Figure 4.12.

*Proof.*   Consider case (a), $f'' < 0$ in $(a, b)$. By Theorem 4.7 (applied to $f'$), the function $f'$ is strictly decreasing in $(a, b)$. But $f'(c) = 0$, so $f'$ changes its sign from positive to negative at $c$, as shown in Figure 4.12(a). Hence, by Theorem 4.8, $f$ has a relative maximum at $c$. The proof in case (b) is entirely analogous.

If $f''$ is continuous at $c$, and if $f''(c) \neq 0$, there will be a neighborhood of $c$ in which $f''$ has the same sign as $f''(c)$. Therefore, if $f'(c) = 0$, the function $f$ has a relative maximum at $c$ if $f''(c)$ is negative, and a relative minimum if $f''(c)$ is positive. This test suffices for many examples that occur in practice.

The sign of the second derivative also governs the convexity or the concavity of $f$. The next theorem shows that the function is convex in intervals where $f''$ is positive, as illustrated by Figure 4.12(b). In Figure 4.12(a), $f$ is concave because $f''$ is negative. It suffices to discuss only the convex case, because if $f$ is convex, then $-f$ is concave.

THEOREM 4.10.   DERIVATIVE TEST FOR CONVEXITY.   *Assume f is continuous on* $[a, b]$ *and has a derivative in the open interval* $(a, b)$. *If* $f'$ *is increasing on* $(a, b)$, *then f is convex on* $[a, b]$. *In particular, f is convex if* $f''$ *exists and is nonnegative in* $(a, b)$.

*Proof.*   Take $x < y$ in $[a, b]$ and let $z = \alpha y + (1 - \alpha)x$, where $0 < \alpha < 1$. We wish to prove that $f(z) \leq \alpha f(y) + (1 - \alpha)f(x)$. Since $f(z) = \alpha f(z) + (1 - \alpha)f(z)$, this is the same as proving that

$$(1 - \alpha)[f(z) - f(x)] \leq \alpha[f(y) - f(z)].$$

By the mean-value theorem (applied twice), there exist points $c$ and $d$ satisfying $x < c < z$ and $z < d < y$ such that

$$f(z) - f(x) = f'(c)(z - x), \quad \text{and} \quad f(y) - f(z) = f'(d)(y - z).$$

Since $f'$ is increasing, we have $f'(c) \leq f'(d)$. Also, we have $(1 - \alpha)(z - x) = \alpha(y - z)$, so we may write

$$(1 - \alpha)[f(z) - f(x)] = (1 - \alpha)f'(c)(z - x) \leq \alpha f'(d)(y - z) = \alpha[f(y) - f(z)],$$

which proves the required inequality for convexity.

## 4.18   Curve sketching

The information gathered in the theorems of the last few sections is often useful in curve sketching. In drawing the graph of a function $f$, we should first determine the domain of $f$

[the set of $x$ for which $f(x)$ is defined] and, if it is easy to do so, we should find the range of $f$ (the set of values taken on by $f$). A knowledge of the domain and range gives us an idea of the extent of the curve $y = f(x)$, since it specifies a portion of the $xy$-plane in which the entire curve must lie. Then it is a good idea to try to locate those points (if any) where the curve crosses the coordinate axes. These are called *intercepts* of the graph. The $y$-intercept is simply the point $(0, f(0))$, assuming 0 is in the domain of $f$, and the $x$-intercepts are those points $(x, 0)$ for which $f(x) = 0$. Computing the $x$-intercepts may be extremely difficult in practice, and we may have to be content with approximate values only.

We should also try to determine intervals in which $f$ is monotonic by examining the sign of $f'$, and to determine intervals of convexity and concavity by studying the sign of $f''$. Special attention should be paid to those points where the graph has horizontal tangents.

EXAMPLE 1. *The graph of $y = f(x)$, where $f(x) = x + 1/x$ for $x \neq 0$.*

In this case, there are no intercepts on either axis. The first two derivatives are given by the formulas

$$f'(x) = 1 - 1/x^2, \qquad f''(x) = 2/x^3.$$

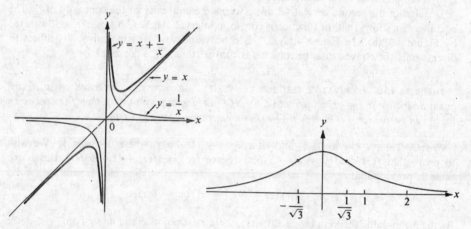

FIGURE 4.13   Graph of $f(x) = x + 1/x$.          FIGURE 4.14   Graph of $f(x) = 1/(x^2 + 1)$.

The first derivative is positive if $x^2 > 1$, negative if $x^2 < 1$, and zero if $x^2 = 1$. Hence there is a relative minimum at $x = 1$ and a relative maximum at $x = -1$. For $x > 0$, the second derivative is positive so the first derivative is strictly increasing. For $x < 0$, the second derivative is negative, and therefore the first derivative is strictly decreasing. For $x$ near 0, the term $x$ is small compared to $1/x$, and the curve behaves like the curve $y = 1/x$. (See Figure 4.13.) On the other hand, for very large $x$ (positive or negative), the term $1/x$ is small compared to $x$, and the curve behaves very much like the line $y = x$. In this example, the function is odd, $f(-x) = -f(x)$, so the graph is symmetric with respect to the origin.

In the foregoing example, the line $y = x$ is an asymptote of the curve. In general, a nonvertical line with equation $y = mx + b$ is called an *asymptote* of the graph of $y = f(x)$ if the difference $f(x) - (mx + b)$ tends to 0 as $x$ takes arbitrarily large positive values or arbitrarily large negative values. A vertical line, $x = a$, is called a *vertical asymptote* if $|f(x)|$ takes arbitrarily large values as $x \to a$ from the right or from the left. In the foregoing example, the $y$-axis is a vertical asymptote.

EXAMPLE 2. *The graph of* $y = f(x)$, *where* $f(x) = 1/(x^2 + 1)$.

This is an even function, positive for all $x$, and has the $x$-axis as a horizontal asymptote. The first derivative is given by

$$f'(x) = \frac{-2x}{(x^2 + 1)^2},$$

so $f'(x) < 0$ if $x > 0$, $f'(x) > 0$ if $x < 0$, and $f'(x) = 0$ when $x = 0$. Therefore the function increases over the negative axis, decreases over the positive axis, and has a relative maximum at $x = 0$. Differentiating once more, we find that

$$f''(x) = \frac{(x^2 + 1)^2(-2) - (-2x)2(x^2 + 1)(2x)}{(x^2 + 1)^4} = \frac{2(3x^2 - 1)}{(x^2 + 1)^3}.$$

Thus $f''(x) > 0$ if $3x^2 > 1$, and $f''(x) < 0$ if $3x^2 < 1$. Hence, the first derivative increases when $x^2 > \frac{1}{3}$ and decreases when $x^2 < \frac{1}{3}$. This information suffices to draw the curve in Figure 4.14. The two points on the graph corresponding to $x^2 = \frac{1}{3}$, where the second derivative changes its sign, are called *points of inflection*.

## 4.19 Exercises

In the following exercises, (a) find all points $x$ such that $f'(x) = 0$; (b) examine the sign of $f'$ and determine those intervals in which $f$ is monotonic; (c) examine the sign of $f''$ and determine those intervals in which $f'$ is monotonic; (d) make a sketch of the graph of $f$. In each case, the function is defined for all $x$ for which the given formula for $f(x)$ is meaningful.

1. $f(x) = x^2 - 3x + 2$.

2. $f(x) = x^3 - 4x$.
3. $f(x) = (x - 1)^2(x + 2)$.
4. $f(x) = x^3 - 6x^2 + 9x + 5$.
5. $f(x) = 2 + (x - 1)^4$.
6. $f(x) = 1/x^2$.
7. $f(x) = x + 1/x^2$.

8. $f(x) = \dfrac{1}{(x - 1)(x - 3)}$.

9. $f(x) = x/(1 + x^2)$.
10. $f(x) = (x^2 - 4)/(x^2 - 9)$.
11. $f(x) = \sin^2 x$.
12. $f(x) = x - \sin x$.
13. $f(x) = x + \cos x$.
14. $f(x) = \frac{1}{6}x^2 + \frac{1}{12}\cos 2x$.

## 4.20 Worked examples of extremum problems

Many extremum problems in both pure and applied mathematics can be attacked systematically with the use of differential calculus. As a matter of fact, the rudiments of differential calculus were first developed when Fermat tried to find general methods for determining maxima and minima. We shall solve a few examples in this section and give the reader an opportunity to solve others in the next set of exercises.

First we formulate two simple principles which can be used to solve many extremum problems.

EXAMPLE 1. *Constant-sum, maximum-product principle.* Given a positive number $S$. Prove that among all choices of positive numbers $x$ and $y$ with $x + y = S$, the product $xy$ is largest when $x = y = \frac{1}{2}S$.

*Proof.* If $x + y = S$, then $y = S - x$ and the product $xy$ is equal to $x(S - x) = xS - x^2$. Let $f(x) = xS - x^2$. This quadratic polynomial has first derivative $f'(x) = S - 2x$ which is positive for $x < \frac{1}{2}S$ and negative for $x > \frac{1}{2}S$. Hence the maximum of $xy$ occurs when $x = \frac{1}{2}S$, $y = S - x = \frac{1}{2}S$. This can also be proved without the use of calculus. We simply write $f(x) = \frac{1}{4}S^2 - (x - \frac{1}{2}S)^2$ and note that $f(x)$ is largest when $x = \frac{1}{2}S$.

EXAMPLE 2. *Constant-product, minimum-sum principle.* Given a positive number $P$. Prove that among all choices of positive numbers $x$ and $y$ with $xy = P$, the sum $x + y$ is smallest when $x = y = \sqrt{P}$.

*Proof.* We must determine the minimum of the function $f(x) = x + P/x$ for $x > 0$. The first derivative is $f'(x) = 1 - P/x^2$. This is negative for $x^2 < P$ and positive for $x^2 > P$, so $f(x)$ has its minimum at $x = \sqrt{P}$. Hence, the sum $x + y$ is smallest when $x = y = \sqrt{P}$.

EXAMPLE 3. Among all rectangles of given perimeter, the square has the largest area.

*Proof.* We use the result of Example 1. Let $x$ and $y$ denote the sides of a general rectangle. If the perimeter is fixed, then $x + y$ is constant, so the area $xy$ has its largest value when $x = y$. Hence, the maximizing rectangle is a square.

EXAMPLE 4. The geometric mean of two positive numbers does not exceed their arithmetic mean. That is, $\sqrt{ab} \leq \frac{1}{2}(a + b)$.

*Proof.* Given $a > 0$, $b > 0$, let $P = ab$. Among all positive $x$ and $y$ with $xy = P$, the sum $x + y$ is smallest when $x = y = \sqrt{P}$. In other words, if $xy = P$, then $x + y \geq \sqrt{P} + \sqrt{P} = 2\sqrt{P}$. In particular, $a + b \geq 2\sqrt{P} = 2\sqrt{ab}$, so $\sqrt{ab} \leq \frac{1}{2}(a + b)$. Equality occurs if and only if $a = b$.

EXAMPLE 5. A block of weight $W$ is to be moved along a flat table by a force inclined at an angle $\theta$ with the line of motion, where $0 \leq \theta \leq \frac{1}{2}\pi$, as shown in Figure 4.15. Assume the motion is resisted by a frictional force which is proportional to the normal force with which the block presses perpendicularly against the surface of the table. Find the angle $\theta$ for which the propelling force needed to overcome friction will be as small as possible.

*Solution.* Let $F(\theta)$ denote the propelling force. It has an upward vertical component $F(\theta) \sin \theta$, so the net normal force pressing against the table is $N = W - F(\theta) \sin \theta$. The frictional force is $\mu N$, where $\mu$ (the Greek letter *mu*) is a constant called the coefficient of friction. The horizontal component of the propelling force is $F(\theta) \cos \theta$. When this is equated to the frictional force, we get $F(\theta) \cos \theta = \mu[W - F(\theta) \sin \theta]$ from which we find

$$F(\theta) = \frac{\mu W}{\cos \theta + \mu \sin \theta}.$$

To minimize $F(\theta)$, we maximize the denominator $g(\theta) = \cos \theta + \mu \sin \theta$ in the interval $0 \leq \theta \leq \frac{1}{2}\pi$. At the endpoints, we have $g(0) = 1$ and $g(\frac{1}{2}\pi) = \mu$. In the interior of the interval, we have

$$g'(\theta) = -\sin \theta + \mu \cos \theta,$$

so $g$ has a critical point at $\theta = \alpha$, where $\sin \alpha = \mu \cos \alpha$. This gives $g(\alpha) = \cos \alpha + \mu^2 \cos \alpha = (1 + \mu^2) \cos \alpha$. We can express $\cos \alpha$ in terms of $\mu$. Since $\mu^2 \cos^2 \alpha = \sin^2 \alpha = 1 - \cos^2 \alpha$, we find $(1 + \mu^2) \cos^2 \alpha = 1$, so $\cos \alpha = 1/\sqrt{1 + \mu^2}$. Thus $g(\alpha) = \sqrt{1 + \mu^2}$.

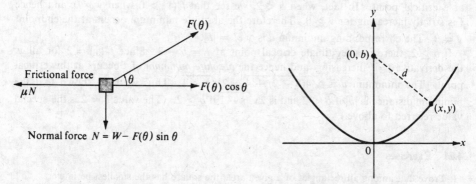

FIGURE 4.15   Example 5.                    FIGURE 4.16   Example 6.

Since $g(\alpha)$ exceeds $g(0)$ and $g(\frac{1}{2}\pi)$, the maximum of $g$ occurs at the critical point. Hence the minimum force required is

$$F(\alpha) = \frac{\mu W}{g(\alpha)} = \frac{\mu W}{\sqrt{1 + \mu^2}}.$$

EXAMPLE 6. Find the shortest distance from a given point $(0, b)$ on the $y$-axis to the parabola $x^2 = 4y$. (The number $b$ may have any real value.)

*Solution.* The parabola is shown in Figure 4.16. The quantity to be minimized is the distance $d$, where

$$d = \sqrt{x^2 + (y - b)^2},$$

subject to the restriction $x^2 = 4y$. It is clear from the figure that when $b$ is *negative* the minimum distance is $|b|$. As the point $(0, b)$ moves upward along the positive $y$-axis, the minimum is $b$ until the point reaches a certain special position, above which the minimum is $<b$. The exact location of this special position will now be determined.

First of all, we observe that the point $(x, y)$ that minimizes $d$ also minimizes $d^2$. (This observation enables us to avoid differentiation of square roots.) At this stage, we may express $d^2$ in terms of $x$ alone or else in terms of $y$ alone. We shall express $d^2$ in terms of $y$ and leave it as an exercise for the reader to carry out the calculations when $d^2$ is expressed in terms of $x$.

Therefore the function $f$ to be minimized is given by the formula

$$f(y) = d^2 = 4y + (y - b)^2 .$$

Although $f(y)$ is defined for all real $y$, the nature of the problem requires that we seek the minimum only among those $y \geq 0$. The derivative, given by $f'(y) = 4 + 2(y - b)$, is zero only when $y = b - 2$. When $b < 2$, this leads to a negative critical point $y$ which is excluded by the restriction $y \geq 0$. In other words, if $b < 2$, the minimum does not occur at a critical point. In fact, when $b < 2$, we see that $f'(y) > 0$ when $y \geq 0$, and hence $f$ is strictly increasing for $y \geq 0$. Therefore the absolute minimum occurs at the endpoint $y = 0$. The corresponding minimum $d$ is $\sqrt{b^2} = |b|$.

If $b \geq 2$, there is a legitimate critical point at $y = b - 2$. Since $f''(y) = 2$ for all $y$, the derivative $f'$ is increasing, and hence the *absolute minimum* of $f$ occurs at this critical point. The minimum $d$ is $\sqrt{4(b - 2) + 4} = 2\sqrt{b - 1}$. Thus we have shown that the minimum distance is $|b|$ if $b < 2$ and is $2\sqrt{b - 1}$ if $b \geq 2$. (The value $b = 2$ is the special value referred to above.)

## 4.21 Exercises

1. Prove that among all rectangles of a given area, the square has the smallest perimeter.
2. A farmer has $L$ feet of fencing to enclose a rectangular pasture adjacent to a long stone wall. What dimensions give the maximum area of the pasture?
3. A farmer wishes to enclose a rectangular pasture of area $A$ adjacent to a long stone wall. What dimensions require the least amount of fencing?
4. Given $S > 0$. Prove that among all positive numbers $x$ and $y$ with $x + y = S$, the sum $x^2 + y^2$ is smallest when $x = y$.
5. Given $R > 0$. Prove that among all positive numbers $x$ and $y$ with $x^2 + y^2 = R$, the sum $x + y$ is largest when $x = y$.
6. Each edge of a square has length $L$. Prove that among all squares inscribed in the given square, the one of minimum area has edges of length $\frac{1}{2}L\sqrt{2}$.
7. Each edge of a square has length $L$, Find the size of the square of largest area that can be circumscribed about the given square.
8. Prove that among all rectangles that can be inscribed in a given circle, the square has the largest area.
9. Prove that among all rectangles of a given area, the square has the smallest circumscribed circle.
10. Given a sphere of radius $R$. Find the radius $r$ and altitude $h$ of the right circular cylinder with largest lateral surface area $2\pi rh$ that can be inscribed in the sphere.
11. Among all right circular cylinders of given lateral surface area, prove that the smallest circumscribed sphere has radius $\sqrt{2}$ times that of the cylinder.

12. Given a right circular cone with radius $R$ and altitude $H$. Find the radius and altitude of the right circular cylinder of largest lateral surface area that can be inscribed in the cone.

13. Find the dimensions of the right circular cylinder of maximum volume that can be inscribed in a right circular cone of radius $R$ and altitude $H$.

14. Given a sphere of radius $R$. Compute, in terms of $R$, the radius $r$ and the altitude $h$ of the right circular cone of maximum volume that can be inscribed in this sphere.

15. Find the rectangle of largest area that can be inscribed in a semicircle, the lower base being on the diameter.

16. Find the trapezoid of largest area that can be inscribed in a semicircle, the lower base being on the diameter.

17. An open box is made from a rectangular piece of material by removing equal squares at each corner and turning up the sides. Find the dimensions of the box of largest volume that can be made in this manner if the material has sides (a) 10 and 10; (b) 12 and 18.

18. If $a$ and $b$ are the legs of a right triangle whose hypotenuse is 1, find the largest value of $2a + b$.

19. A truck is to be driven 300 miles on a freeway at a constant speed of $x$ miles per hour. Speed laws require $30 \leq x \leq 60$. Assume that fuel costs 30 cents per gallon and is consumed at the rate of $2 + x^2/600$ gallons per hour. If the driver's wages are $D$ dollars per hour and if he obeys all speed laws, find the most economical speed and the cost of the trip if (a) $D = 0$, (b) $D = 1$, (c) $D = 2$, (d) $D = 3$, (e) $D = 4$.

20. A cylinder is obtained by revolving a rectangle about the $x$-axis, the base of the rectangle lying on the $x$-axis and the entire rectangle lying in the region between the curve $y = x/(x^2 + 1)$ and the $x$-axis. Find the maximum possible volume of the cylinder.

21. The lower right-hand corner of a page is folded over so as to reach the leftmost edge. (See Figure 4.17.) If the width of the page is six inches, find the minimum length of the crease. What angle will this minimal crease make with the rightmost edge of the page? Assume the page is long enough to prevent the crease reaching the top of the page.

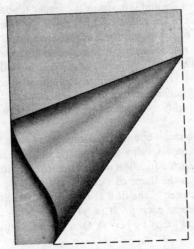

FIGURE 4.17 Exercise 21.

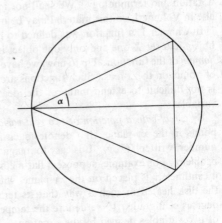

FIGURE 4.18 Exercise 22.

22. (a) An isosceles triangle is inscribed in a circle of radius $r$ as shown in Figure 4.18. If the angle $2\alpha$ at the apex is restricted to lie between 0 and $\frac{1}{2}\pi$, find the largest value and the smallest value of the perimeter of the triangle. Give full details of your reasoning.

(b) What is the radius of the smallest circular disk large enough to cover *every* isosceles triangle of a given perimeter $L$? Give full details of your reasoning.

23. A window is to be made in the form of a rectangle surmounted by a semicircle with diameter equal to the base of the rectangle. The rectangular portion is to be of clear glass, and the semicircular portion is to be of a colored glass admitting only half as much light per square foot as the clear glass. The total perimeter of the window frame is to be a fixed length $P$. Find, in terms of $P$, the dimensions of the window which will admit the most light.

24. A log 12 feet long has the shape of a frustum of a right circular cone with diameters 4 feet and $(4 + h)$ feet at its ends, where $h \geq 0$. Determine, as a function of $h$, the volume of the largest right circular cylinder that can be cut from the log, if its axis coincides with that of the log.

25. Given $n$ real numbers $a_1, \ldots, a_n$. Prove that the sum $\sum_{k=1}^{n} (x - a_k)^2$ is smallest when $x$ is the arithmetic mean of $a_1, \ldots, a_n$.

26. If $x > 0$, let $f(x) = 5x^2 + Ax^{-5}$, where $A$ is a positive constant. Find the smallest $A$ such that $f(x) \geq 24$ for all $x > 0$.

27. For each real $t$, let $f(x) = -\frac{1}{3}x^3 + t^2x$, and let $m(t)$ denote the minimum of $f(x)$ over the interval $0 \leq x \leq 1$. Determine the value of $m(t)$ for each $t$ in the interval $-1 \leq t \leq 1$. Remember that for some values of $t$ the minimum of $f(x)$ may occur at the endpoints of the interval $0 \leq x \leq 1$.

28. A number $x$ is known to lie in an interval $a \leq x \leq b$, where $a > 0$. We wish to approximate $x$ by another number $t$ in $[a, b]$ so that the relative error, $|t - x|/x$, will be as small as possible. Let $M(t)$ denote the maximum value of $|t - x|/x$ as $x$ varies from $a$ to $b$. (a) Prove that this maximum occurs at one of the endpoints $x = a$ or $x = b$. (b) Prove that $M(t)$ is smallest when $t$ is the harmonic mean of $a$ and $b$, that is, when $1/t = \frac{1}{2}(1/a + 1/b)$.

## *4.22 Partial derivatives

This section explains the concept of partial derivative and introduces the reader to some notation and terminology. We shall not make use of the results of this section anywhere else in Volume I, so this material may be omitted or postponed without loss in continuity.

In Chapter 1, a function was defined to be a correspondence which associates with each object in a set $X$ one and only one object in another set $Y$; the set $X$ is referred to as the *domain* of the function. Up to now, we have dealt with functions having a domain consisting of points on the $x$-axis. Such functions are usually called *functions of one real variable*. It is not difficult to extend many of the ideas of calculus to functions of two or more real variables.

By a *real-valued function of two real variables* we mean one whose domain $X$ is a set of points in the $xy$-plane. If $f$ denotes such a function, its value at a point $(x, y)$ is a real number, written $f(x, y)$. It is easy to imagine how such a function might arise in a physical problem. For example, suppose a flat metal plate in the shape of a circular disk of radius 4 centimeters is placed on the $xy$-plane, with the center of the disk at the origin and with the disk heated in such a way that its temperature at each point $(x, y)$ is $16 - x^2 - y^2$ degrees centigrade. If we denote the temperature at $(x, y)$ by $f(x, y)$, then $f$ is a function of two variables defined by the equation

(4.27)
$$f(x, y) = 16 - x^2 - y^2.$$

The domain of this function is the set of all points $(x, y)$ whose distance from the origin does not exceed 4. The theorem of Pythagoras tells us that all points $(x, y)$ at a distance *r* from the origin satisfy the equation

(4.28) $$x^2 + y^2 = r^2.$$

Therefore the domain in this case consists of all points $(x, y)$ which satisfy the inequality $x^2 + y^2 \leq 16$. Note that on the circle described by (4.28), the temperature is $f(x, y) = 16 - r^2$. That is, the function $f$ is constant on each circle with center at the origin. (See Figure 4.19.)

We shall describe two useful methods for obtaining a geometric picture of a function of two variables. One is by means of a *surface* in space. To construct this surface, we introduce a third coordinate axis (called the *z*-axis); it passes through the origin and is perpendicular

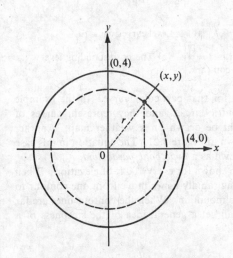

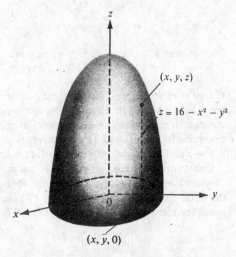

FIGURE 4.19 The temperature is constant on each circle with center at the origin.

FIGURE 4.20 The surface represented by the equation $z = 16 - x^2 - y^2$.

to the *xy*-plane. Above each point $(x, y)$ we plot the point $(x, y, z)$ whose *z*-coordinate is obtained from the equation $z = f(x, y)$.

The surface for the example described above is shown in Figure 4.20. If we placed a thermometer at a point $(x, y)$ on the plate, the top of the mercury column would just touch the surface at the point $(x, y, z)$ where $z = f(x, y)$ provided, of course, that unit distances on the *z*-axis are properly chosen.

A different kind of picture of a function of two variables can be drawn entirely in the *xy*-plane. This is the method of *contour lines* that is used by map makers to represent a three-dimensional landscape by a two-dimensional drawing. We imagine that the surface described above has been cut by various horizontal planes (parallel to the *xy*-plane). They intersect the surface at those points $(x, y, z)$ whose elevation *z* is constant. By projecting these points on the *xy*-plane, we get a family of contour lines or *level curves*. Each level curve consists of those and only those points $(x, y)$ whose coordinates satisfy the equation

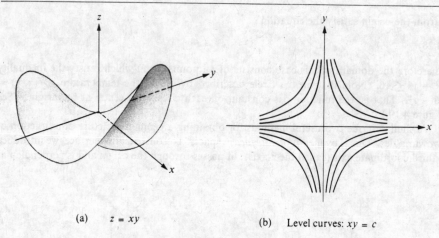

(a)    $z = xy$                                              (b)    Level curves: $xy = c$

FIGURE 4.21   (a) A surface whose equation is $z = xy$. (b) The corresponding level
curves $xy =$ constant.

$f(x, y) = c$, where $c$ is the constant elevation for that particular curve. In the example
mentioned above, the level curves are concentric circles, and they represent curves of
constant temperature, or *isothermals*, as might be drawn on a weather map. Another
example of a surface and its level curves is shown in Figure 4.21. The equation in this case
is $z = xy$. The "saddle-shaped" surface is known as a *hyperbolic paraboloid*.

Contour lines on topographic maps are often shown for every 100 ft of elevation. When
they are close together, the elevation is changing rapidly as we move from one contour to
the next; this happens in the vicinity of a steep mountain. When the contour lines are far
apart the elevation is changing slowly. We can get a general idea of the steepness of a

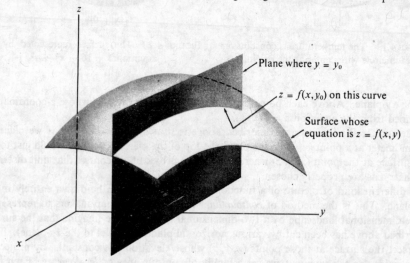

FIGURE 4.22   The curve of intersection of a surface $z = f(x, y)$ and a plane $y = y_0$.

landscape by considering the spacing of its level curves. However, to get precise information concerning the rate of change of the elevation, we must describe the surface in terms of a function to which we can apply the ideas of differential calculus.

The rate at which the elevation is changing at a point $(x_0, y_0)$ depends on the direction in which we move away from this point. For the sake of simplicity, we shall consider at this time just the two special directions parallel to the $x$- and $y$-axes. Suppose we examine a surface described by an equation of the form $z = f(x, y)$; let us cut this surface with a plane perpendicular to the $y$-axis, as shown in Figure 4.22. Such a plane consists of all points $(x, y, z)$ in space for which the $y$-coordinate is constant, say $y = y_0$. (The equation $y = y_0$ is called an equation of this plane.) The intersection of this plane with the surface is a plane curve, all points of which satisfy the equation $z = f(x, y_0)$. On this curve the elevation $f(x, y_0)$ is a function of $x$ alone.

Suppose now we move from a point $(x_0, y_0)$ to a point $(x_0 + h, y_0)$. The corresponding change in elevation is $f(x_0 + h, y_0) - f(x_0, y_0)$. This suggests that we form the difference quotient

(4.29)
$$\frac{f(x_0 + h, y_0) - f(x_0, y_0)}{h} .$$

and let $h \to 0$. If this quotient approaches a definite limit as $h \to 0$, we call this limit the *partial derivative of f with respect to x* at $(x_0, y_0)$. There are various symbols that are used to denote partial derivatives, some of the most common ones being

$$\frac{\partial f(x_0, y_0)}{\partial x} , \quad f'_x(x_0, y_0) , \quad f_x(x_0, y_0) , \quad f_1(x_0, y_0) , \quad D_1 f(x_0, y_0) .$$

The subscript 1 in the last two notations refers to the fact that only the first coordinate is allowed to change when we form the difference quotient in (4.29). Thus we have

$$f_1(x_0, y_0) = \lim_{h \to 0} \frac{f(x_0 + h, y_0) - f(x_0, y_0)}{h} .$$

Similarly, we define the *partial derivative with respect to y* at $(x_0, y_0)$ by the equation

$$f_2(x_0, y_0) = \lim_{k \to 0} \frac{f(x_0, y_0 + k) - f(x_0, y_0)}{k} ,$$

alternative notations being

$$\frac{\partial f(x_0, y_0)}{\partial y} , \quad f'_y(x_0, y_0) , \quad f_y(x_0, y_0) , \quad D_2 f(x_0, y_0) .$$

If we write $z = f(x, y)$, then $\partial z/\partial x$ and $\partial z/\partial y$ are also used to denote partial derivatives.

Partial differentiation is not a new concept. If we introduce another function $g$ of one variable, defined by the equation

$$g(x) = f(x, y_0) ,$$

then the ordinary derivative $g'(x_0)$ is exactly the same as the partial derivative $f_1(x_0, y_0)$. Geometrically, the partial derivative $f_1(x, y_0)$ represents the slope of the tangent line at a typical point of the curve shown in Figure 4.22. In the same way, when $x$ is constant, say $x = x_0$, the equation $z = f(x_0, y)$ describes the curve of intersection of the surface with the plane whose equation is $x = x_0$. The partial derivative $f_2(x_0, y)$ gives the slope of the line tangent to this curve. From these remarks we see that to compute the partial derivative of $f(x, y)$ with respect to $x$, we can treat $y$ as though it were constant and use the ordinary rules of differential calculus. Thus, for example, if $f(x, y) = 16 - x^2 - y^2$, we get $f_1(x, y) = -2x$. Similarly, if we hold $x$ fixed, we find $f_2(x, y) = -2y$.

Another example is the function given by

$$(4.30) \qquad\qquad f(x, y) = x \sin y + y^2 \cos xy .$$

Its partial derivatives are

$$f_1(x, y) = \sin y - y^3 \sin xy , \qquad f_2(x, y) = x \cos y - xy^2 \sin xy + 2y \cos xy .$$

---

Partial differentiation is a process which produces new functions $f_1 = \partial f/\partial x$ and $f_2 = \partial f/\partial y$ from a given function $f$. Since $f_1$ and $f_2$ are also functions of two variables, we can consider *their* partial derivatives. These are called *second-order* partial derivatives of $f$, denoted as follows:

$$f_{1,1} = f_{xx} = \frac{\partial^2 f}{\partial x^2} , \quad f_{1,2} = f_{xy} = \frac{\partial^2 f}{\partial y \, \partial x} , \quad f_{2,1} = f_{yx} = \frac{\partial^2 f}{\partial x \, \partial y} , \quad f_{2,2} = f_{yy} = \frac{\partial^2 f}{\partial y^2} .$$

Notice that $f_{1,2}$ means $(f_1)_2$, the partial derivative of $f_1$ with respect to $y$. In the $\partial$-notation, we indicate the order of derivatives by writing

$$\frac{\partial^2 f}{\partial y \, \partial x} = \frac{\partial}{\partial y}\left(\frac{\partial f}{\partial x}\right) .$$

This does not always yield the same result as the other mixed partial derivative,

$$\frac{\partial^2 f}{\partial x \, \partial y} = \frac{\partial}{\partial x}\left(\frac{\partial f}{\partial y}\right) .$$

However, equality of the two mixed partial derivatives does hold under certain conditions that are usually satisfied by most functions that occur in practice. We shall discuss these conditions further in Volume II.

Referring to the example in (4.27), we find that its second-order partial derivatives are given by the following formulas:

$$f_{1,1}(x, y) = -2, \quad f_{1,2}(x, y) = f_{2,1}(x, y) = 0, \quad f_{2,2}(x, y) = -2 .$$

For the example in (4.30), we obtain

$$f_{1,1}(x, y) = -y^4 \cos xy \,,$$
$$f_{1,2}(x, y) = \cos y - xy^3 \cos xy - 3y^2 \sin xy \,,$$
$$f_{2,1}(x, y) = \cos y - xy^3 \cos xy - y^2 \sin xy - 2y^2 \sin xy = f_{1,2}(x, y) \,,$$
$$f_{2,2}(x, y) = -x \sin y - x^2 y^2 \cos xy - 2xy \sin xy - 2xy \sin xy + 2 \cos xy$$
$$= -x \sin y - x^2 y^2 \cos xy - 4xy \sin xy + 2 \cos xy \,.$$

A more detailed study of partial derivatives will be undertaken in Volume II.

## *4.23 Exercises

In Exercises 1 through 8, compute all first- and second-order partial derivatives. In each case verify that the mixed partial derivatives $f_{1,2}(x, y)$ and $f_{2,1}(x, y)$ are equal.

1. $f(x, y) = x^4 + y^4 - 4x^2 y^2$.

2. $f(x, y) = x \sin (x + y)$.

3. $f(x, y) = xy + \dfrac{x}{y}$ $\quad (y \neq 0)$.

4. $f(x, y) = \sqrt{x^2 + y^2}$.

5. $f(x, y) = \sin (x^2 y^3)$.

6. $f(x, y) = \sin [\cos (2x - 3y)]$.

7. $f(x, y) = \dfrac{x + y}{x - y}$ $\quad (x \neq y)$.

8. $f(x, y) = \dfrac{x}{\sqrt{x^2 + y^2}}$ $\quad (x, y) \neq (0, 0)$.

9. Show that $x(\partial z / \partial x) + y(\partial z / \partial y) = 2z$ if (a) $z = (x - 2y)^2$, (b) $z = (x^4 + y^4)^{1/2}$.

10. If $f(x, y) = xy/(x^2 + y^2)^2$ for $(x, y) \neq (0, 0)$, show that

$$\frac{\partial^2 f}{\partial x^2} + \frac{\partial^2 f}{\partial y^2} = 0.$$

# 5

# THE RELATION BETWEEN INTEGRATION
# AND DIFFERENTIATION

## 5.1 The derivative of an indefinite integral. The first fundamental theorem of calculus

We come now to the remarkable connection that exists between integration and differentiation. The relationship between these two processes is somewhat analogous to that which holds between "squaring" and "taking the square root." If we square a positive number and then take the positive square root of the result, we get the original number back again. Similarly, if we operate on a continuous function $f$ by integration, we get a new function (an indefinite integral of $f$) which, when differentiated, leads back to the original function $f$. For example, if $f(x) = x^2$, then an indefinite integral $A$ of $f$ may be defined by the equation

$$A(x) = \int_c^x f(t)\, dt = \int_c^x t^2\, dt = \frac{x^3}{3} - \frac{c^3}{3},$$

where $c$ is a constant. Differentiating, we find $A'(x) = x^2 = f(x)$. This example illustrates a general result, called the first fundamental theorem of calculus, which may be stated as follows:

THEOREM 5.1. FIRST FUNDAMENTAL THEOREM OF CALCULUS. *Let $f$ be a function that is integrable on $[a, x]$ for each $x$ in $[a, b]$. Let $c$ be such that $a \leq c \leq b$ and define a new function $A$ as follows:*

$$A(x) = \int_c^x f(t)\, dt \qquad if \qquad a \leq x \leq b.$$

*Then the derivative $A'(x)$ exists at each point $x$ in the open interval $(a, b)$ where $f$ is continuous, and for such $x$ we have*

(5.1) $$A'(x) = f(x).$$

First we give a geometric argument which suggests why the theorem ought to be true; then we give an analytic proof.

*Geometric motivation.*   Figure 5.1 shows the graph of a function $f$ over an interval $[a, b]$. In the figure, $h$ is positive and

$$\int_{x}^{x+h} f(t)\, dt = \int_{c}^{x+h} f(t)\, dt - \int_{c}^{x} f(t)\, dt = A(x + h) - A(x).$$

The example shown is continuous throughout the interval $[x, x + h]$. Therefore, by the mean-value theorem for integrals, we have

$$A(x + h) - A(x) = hf(z), \qquad \text{where} \quad x \le z \le x + h.$$

Hence we have

(5.2)
$$\frac{A(x + h) - A(x)}{h} = f(z),$$

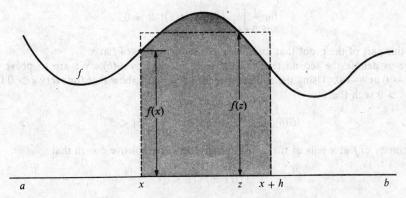

FIGURE 5.1   Geometric motivation for the first fundamental theorem of calculus.

and, since $x \le z \le x + h$, we find that $f(z) \rightarrow f(x)$ as $h \rightarrow 0$ through positive values. A similar argument is valid if $h \rightarrow 0$ through negative values. Therefore, $A'(x)$ exists and is equal to $f(x)$.

This argument assumes that the function $f$ is continuous in some *neighborhood* of the point $x$. However, the hypothesis of the theorem refers only to continuity of $f$ at a *single point* $x$. Therefore, we use a different method to prove the theorem under this weaker hypothesis.

*Analytic Proof.*   Let $x$ be a point of continuity of $f$, keep $x$ fixed, and form the quotient

$$\frac{A(x + h) - A(x)}{h}.$$

To prove the theorem we must show that this quotient approaches the limit $f(x)$ as $h \rightarrow 0$. The numerator is

$$A(x + h) - A(x) = \int_{c}^{x+h} f(t)\, dt - \int_{c}^{x} f(t)\, dt = \int_{x}^{x+h} f(t)\, dt.$$

If we write $f(t) = f(x) + [f(t) - f(x)]$ in the last integral, we obtain

$$A(x + h) - A(x) = \int_x^{x+h} f(x)\, dt + \int_x^{x+h} [f(t) - f(x)]\, dt$$

$$= hf(x) + \int_x^{x+h} [f(t) - f(x)]\, dt\, ,$$

from which we find

(5.3) $$\frac{A(x + h) - A(x)}{h} = f(x) + \frac{1}{h} \int_x^{x+h} [f(t) - f(x)]\, dt\, .$$

Therefore, to complete the proof of (5.1), all we need to do is show that

$$\lim_{h \to 0} \frac{1}{h} \int_x^{x+h} [f(t) - f(x)]\, dt = 0\, .$$

It is this part of the proof that makes use of the continuity of $f$ at $x$.

Let us denote the second term on the right of (5.3) by $G(h)$. We are to prove that $G(h) \to 0$ as $h \to 0$. Using the definition of limit, we must show that for every $\epsilon > 0$ there is a $\delta > 0$ such that

(5.4) $$|G(h)| < \epsilon \qquad \text{whenever} \quad 0 < |h| < \delta\, .$$

Continuity of $f$ at $x$ tells us that, if $\epsilon$ is given, there is a positive $\delta$ such that

(5.5) $$|f(t) - f(x)| < \tfrac{1}{2}\epsilon$$

whenever

(5.6) $$x - \delta < t < x + \delta\, .$$

If we choose $h$ so that $0 < h < \delta$, then every $t$ in the interval $[x, x + h]$ satisfies (5.6) and hence (5.5) holds for every such $t$. Using the property $|\int_x^{x+h} g(t)\, dt| \leq \int_x^{x+h} |g(t)|\, dt$ with $g(t) = f(t) - f(x)$, we see that the inequality in (5.5) leads to the relation

$$\left| \int_x^{x+h} [f(t) - f(x)]\, dt \right| \leq \int_x^{x+h} |f(t) - f(x)|\, dt \leq \int_x^{x+h} \tfrac{1}{2}\epsilon\, dt = \tfrac{1}{2}h\epsilon < h\epsilon\, .$$

If we divide by $h$, we see that (5.4) holds for $0 < h < \delta$. If $h < 0$, a similar argument proves that (5.4) holds whenever $0 < |h| < \delta$, and this completes the proof.

## 5.2 The zero-derivative theorem

If a function $f$ is constant on an open interval $(a, b)$, its derivative is zero everywhere on $(a, b)$. We proved this fact earlier as an immediate consequence of the definition of derivative. We also proved, as part (c) of Theorem 4.7, the converse of this statement which we restate here as a separate theorem.

THEOREM 5.2.   ZERO-DERIVATIVE THEOREM.   *If $f'(x) = 0$ for each x in an open interval I, then f is constant on I.*

This theorem, when used in combination with the first fundamental theorem of calculus, leads to the second fundamental theorem which is described in the next section.

## 5.3  Primitive functions and the second fundamental theorem of calculus

DEFINITION OF PRIMITIVE FUNCTION.   *A function P is called a primitive (or an antiderivative) of a function f on an open interval I if the derivative of P is f, that is, if $P'(x) = f(x)$ for all x in I.*

For example, the sine function is a primitive of the cosine on every interval because the derivative of the sine is the cosine. We speak of *a* primitive, rather than *the* primitive, because if $P$ is a primitive of $f$ then so is $P + k$ for every constant $k$. Conversely, any two primitives $P$ and $Q$ of the same function $f$ can differ only by a constant because their difference $P - Q$ has the derivative

$$P'(x) - Q'(x) = f(x) - f(x) = 0$$

for every $x$ in $I$ and hence, by Theorem 5.2, $P - Q$ is constant on $I$.

The first fundamental theorem of calculus tells us that we can always construct a primitive of a continuous function by integration. When we combine this with the fact that two primitives of the same function can differ only by a constant, we obtain the second fundamental theorem of calculus.

THEOREM 5.3.   SECOND FUNDAMENTAL THEOREM OF CALCULUS.   *Assume f is continuous on an open interval I, and let P be any primitive of f on I. Then, for each c and each x in I, we have*

$$(5.7) \qquad P(x) = P(c) + \int_c^x f(t)\, dt\,.$$

*Proof.* Let $A(x) = \int_c^x f(t)\, dt$. Since $f$ is continuous at each $x$ in $I$, the first fundamental theorem tells us that $A'(x) = f(x)$ for all $x$ in $I$. In other words, $A$ is a primitive of $f$ on $I$. Since two primitives of $f$ can differ only by a constant, we must have $A(x) - P(x) = k$ for some constant $k$. When $x = c$, this formula implies $-P(c) = k$, since $A(c) = 0$. Therefore, $A(x) - P(x) = -P(c)$, from which we obtain (5.7).

Theorem 5.3 tells us how to find every primitive $P$ of a continuous function $f$. We simply integrate $f$ from a fixed point $c$ to an arbitrary point $x$ and add the constant $P(c)$ to get $P(x)$. But the real power of the theorem becomes apparent when we write Equation (5.7) in the following form:

$$(5.8) \qquad \int_c^x f(t)\, dt = P(x) - P(c)\,.$$

In this form it tells us that we can compute the value of an integral by a mere subtraction if we know a primitive $P$. The problem of evaluating an integral is transferred to another problem—that of finding a primitive $P$ of $f$. In actual practice, the second problem is a great deal easier to deal with than the first. Every differentiation formula, when read in reverse, gives us an example of a primitive of some function $f$ and this, in turn, leads to an integration formula for this function.

From the differentiation formulas worked out thus far we can derive the following integration formulas as consequences of the second fundamental theorem.

EXAMPLE 1. *Integration of rational powers.* The integration formula

$$(5.9) \qquad \int_a^b x^n \, dx = \frac{b^{n+1} - a^{n+1}}{n+1} \qquad (n = 0, 1, 2, \ldots)$$

was proved in Section 1.23 directly from the definition of the integral. The result may be rederived and generalized to rational exponents by using the second fundamental theorem. First of all, we observe that the function $P$ defined by the equation

$$(5.10) \qquad P(x) = \frac{x^{n+1}}{n+1}$$

has the derivative $P'(x) = x^n$ if $n$ is any nonnegative integer. Since this is valid for all real $x$, we may use (5.8) to write

$$\int_a^b x^n \, dx = P(b) - P(a) = \frac{b^{n+1} - a^{n+1}}{n+1}$$

for all intervals $[a, b]$. This formula, proved for all integers $n \geq 0$, also holds for all negative integers except $n = -1$, which is excluded because $n + 1$ appears in the denominator. To prove (5.9) for negative $n$, it suffices to show that (5.10) implies $P'(x) = x^n$ when $n$ is negative and $\neq -1$, a fact which is easily verified by differentiating $P$ as a rational function. Of course, when $n$ is negative, neither $P(x)$ nor $P'(x)$ is defined for $x = 0$, and when we use (5.9) for negative $n$, it is important to exclude those intervals $[a, b]$ that contain the point $x = 0$.

The results of Example 3 in Section 4.5 enable us to extend (5.9) to all *rational* exponents (except $-1$), provided the integrand is defined everywhere on the interval $[a, b]$ under consideration. For example, if $0 < a < b$ and $n = -\frac{1}{2}$, we find

$$\int_a^b \frac{1}{\sqrt{x}} \, dx = \int_a^b x^{-1/2} dx = \frac{x^{1/2}}{\frac{1}{2}} \Big|_a^b = 2(\sqrt{b} - \sqrt{a}).$$

This result was proved earlier, using the area axioms. The present proof makes no use of these axioms.

In the next chapter we shall define a general power function $f$ such that $f(x) = x^c$ for *every real exponent c*. We shall find that this function has the derivative $f'(x) = cx^{c-1}$ and the primitive $P(x) = x^{c+1}/(c + 1)$ if $c \neq -1$. This will enable us to extend (5.9) to all real exponents except $-1$.

Note that we cannot get $P'(x) = 1/x$ by differentiation of any function of the form $P(x) = x^n$. Nevertheless, there exists a function $P$ whose derivative is $P'(x) = 1/x$. To exhibit such a function all we need to do is write a suitable indefinite integral; for example,

$$P(x) = \int_1^x \frac{1}{t}\, dt \quad \text{if} \quad x > 0 .$$

This integral exists because the integrand is monotonic. The function so defined is called the *logarithm* (more specifically, the *natural logarithm*). Its properties are developed systematically in Chapter 6.

EXAMPLE 2. *Integration of the sine and cosine.* Since the derivative of the sine is the cosine and the derivative of the cosine is minus the sine, the second fundamental theorem also gives us the following formulas:

$$\int_a^b \cos x \, dx = \sin x \,\Big|_a^b = \sin b - \sin a ,$$

$$\int_a^b \sin x \, dx = (-\cos x)\,\Big|_a^b = \cos a - \cos b .$$

These formulas were also proved in Chapter 2 directly from the definition of the integral.

Further examples of integration formulas can be obtained from Examples 1 and 2 by taking finite sums of terms of the form $Ax^n$, $B \sin x$, $C \cos x$, where $A$, $B$, $C$ are constants.

## 5.4 Properties of a function deduced from properties of its derivative

If a function $f$ has a continuous derivative $f'$ on an open interval $I$, the second fundamental theorem states that

$$(5.11) \qquad\qquad f(x) = f(c) + \int_c^x f'(t) \, dt$$

for every choice of points $x$ and $c$ in $I$. This formula, which expresses $f$ in terms of its derivative $f'$, enables us to deduce properties of a function from properties of its derivative. Although the following properties have already been discussed in Chapter 4, it may be of interest to see how they can also be deduced as simple consequences of Equation (5.11).

Suppose $f'$ is continuous and nonnegative on $I$. If $x > c$, then $\int_c^x f'(t) \, dt \geq 0$, and hence $f(x) \geq f(c)$. In other words, if the derivative is continuous and nonnegative on $I$, the function is increasing on $I$.

In Theorem 2.9 we proved that the indefinite integral of an increasing function is convex. Therefore, if $f'$ is continuous and increasing on $I$, Equation (5.11) shows that $f$ is convex on $I$. Similarly, $f$ is concave on those intervals where $f'$ is continuous and decreasing.

## 5.5 Exercises

In each of Exercises 1 through 10, find a primitive of $f$; that is, find a function $P$ such that $P'(x) = f(x)$ and use the second fundamental theorem to evaluate $\int_a^b f(x)\, dx$.

1. $f(x) = 5x^3$.

2. $f(x) = 4x^4 - 12x$.

3. $f(x) = (x + 1)(x^3 - 2)$.

4. $f(x) = \dfrac{x^4 + x - 3}{x^3}$,     $x \neq 0$.

5. $f(x) = (1 + \sqrt{x})^2$,     $x > 0$.

6. $f(x) = \sqrt{2x} + \sqrt{\frac{1}{2}x}$,     $x > 0$.

7. $f(x) = \dfrac{2x^2 - 6x + 7}{2\sqrt{x}}$,     $x > 0$.

8. $f(x) = 2x^{1/3} - x^{-1/3}$,     $x > 0$.

9. $f(x) = 3 \sin x + 2x^5$.

10. $f(x) = x^{4/3} - 5 \cos x$.

11. Prove that there is no polynomial $f$ whose derivative is given by the formula $f'(x) = 1/x$.

12. Show that $\int_0^x |t|\, dt = \frac{1}{2}x|x|$ for all real $x$.

13. Show that

$$\int_0^x (t + |t|)^2\, dt = \frac{2x^2}{3}\,(x + |x|) \qquad \text{for all real } x\,.$$

14. A function $f$ is continuous everywhere and satisfies the equation

$$\int_0^x f(t)\, dt = -\tfrac{1}{2} + x^2 + x \sin 2x + \tfrac{1}{2} \cos 2x$$

for all $x$. Compute $f(\frac{1}{4}\pi)$ and $f'(\frac{1}{4}\pi)$.

15. Find a function $f$ and a value of the constant $c$ such that

$$\int_c^x f(t)\, dt = \cos x - \tfrac{1}{2} \qquad \text{for all real } x\,.$$

16. Find a function $f$ and a value of the constant $c$ such that

$$\int_c^x tf(t)\, dt = \sin x - x \cos x - \tfrac{1}{2}x^2 \qquad \text{for all real } x\,.$$

17. There is a function $f$, defined and continuous for all real $x$, which satisfies an equation of the form

$$\int_0^x f(t)\, dt = \int_x^1 t^2 f(t)\, dt + \frac{x^{16}}{8} + \frac{x^{18}}{9} + c\,,$$

where $c$ is a constant. Find an explicit formula for $f(x)$ and find the value of the constant $c$.

18. A function $f$ is defined for all real $x$ by the formula

$$f(x) = 3 + \int_0^x \frac{1 + \sin t}{2 + t^2}\, dt\,.$$

Without attempting to evaluate this integral, find a quadratic polynomial $p(x) = a + bx + cx^2$ such that $p(0) = f(0)$, $p'(0) = f'(0)$, and $p''(0) = f''(0)$.

19. Given a function $g$, continuous everywhere, such that $g(1) = 5$ and $\int_0^1 g(t)\, dt = 2$. Let $f(x) = \frac{1}{2} \int_0^x (x - t)^2\, g(t)\, dt$. Prove that

$$f'(x) = x \int_0^x g(t)\, dt - \int_0^x t g(t)\, dt \,,$$

then compute $f''(1)$ and $f'''(1)$.

20. Without attempting to evaluate the following indefinite integrals, find the derivative $f'(x)$ in each case if $f(x)$ is equal to

   (a) $\int_0^x (1 + t^2)^{-3}\, dt \,,$  (b) $\int_0^{x^2} (1 + t^2)^{-3}\, dt \,,$  (c) $\int_{x^3}^{x^2} (1 + t^2)^{-3}\, dt \,.$

21. Without attempting to evaluate the integral, compute $f'(x)$ if $f$ is defined by the formula

$$f(x) = \int_{x^3}^{x^2} \frac{t^6}{1 + t^4}\, dt \,.$$

22. In each case, compute $f(2)$ if $f$ is continuous and satisfies the given formula for all $x \geq 0$.

   (a) $\int_0^x f(t)\, dt = x^2(1 + x) \,.$   (c) $\int_0^{f(x)} t^2\, dt = x^2(1 + x) \,.$

   (b) $\int_0^{x^2} f(t)\, dt = x^2(1 + x) \,.$   (d) $\int_0^{x^2(1+x)} f(t)\, dt = x \,.$

23. The base of a solid is the ordinate set of a nonnegative function $f$ over the interval $[0, a]$. All cross sections perpendicular to this interval are squares. The volume of the solid is

$$a^3 - 2a \cos a + (2 - a^2) \sin a$$

for every $a \geq 0$. Assume $f$ is continuous on $[0, a]$ and calculate $f(a)$.

24. A mechanism propels a particle along a straight line. It is designed so that the displacement of the particle at time $t$ from an initial point 0 on the line is given by the formula $f(t) = \frac{1}{2}t^2 + 2t \sin t$. The mechanism works perfectly until time $t = \pi$ when an unexpected malfunction occurs. From then on the particle moves with constant velocity (the velocity it acquires at time $t = \pi$). Compute the following: (a) its velocity at time $t = \pi$; (b) its acceleration at time $t = \frac{1}{2}\pi$; (c) its acceleration at time $t = \frac{3}{2}\pi$; (d) its displacement from 0 at time $t = \frac{5}{2}\pi$. (e) Find a time $t > \pi$ when the particle returns to the initial point 0, or else prove that it never returns to 0.

25. A particle moves along a straight line. Its position at time $t$ is $f(t)$. When $0 \leq t \leq 1$, the position is given by the integral

$$f(t) = \int_0^t \frac{1 + 2 \sin \pi x \cos \pi x}{1 + x^2}\, dx \,.$$

(Do not attempt to evaluate this integral.) For $t \geq 1$, the particle moves with constant acceleration (the acceleration it acquires at time $t = 1$). Compute the following: (a) its acceleration at time $t = 2$; (b) its velocity when $t = 1$; (c) its velocity when $t > 1$; (d) the difference $f(t) - f(1)$ when $t > 1$.

26. In each case, find a function $f$ with a continuous second derivative $f''$ which satisfies all the given conditions or else explain why such an example cannot exist.
   (a) $f''(x) > 0$    for every $x$,    $f'(0) = 1$,    $f'(1) = 0$.
   (b) $f''(x) > 0$    for every $x$,    $f'(0) = 1$,    $f'(1) = 3$.
   (c) $f''(x) > 0$  ,   for every $x$,    $f'(0) = 1$,    $f(x) \leq 100$    for all $x > 0$.
   (d) $f''(x) > 0$    for every $x$,    $f'(0) = 1$,    $f(x) \leq 100$    for all $x < 0$.

27. A particle moves along a straight line, its position at time $t$ being $f(t)$. It starts with an initial velocity $f'(0) = 0$ and has a continuous acceleration $f''(t) \geq 6$ for all $t$ in the interval $0 \leq t \leq 1$. Prove that the velocity $f'(t) \geq 3$ for all $t$ in some interval $[a, b]$, where $0 \leq a < b \leq 1$, with $b - a = \frac{1}{2}$.

28. Given a function $f$ such that the integral $A(x) = \int_a^x f(t)\, dt$ exists for each $x$ in an interval $[a, b]$. Let $c$ be a point in the open interval $(a, b)$. Consider the following ten statements about this $f$ and this $A$:

(a) $f$ is continuous at $c$.

(b) $f$ is discontinuous at $c$.

(c) $f$ is increasing on $(a, b)$.

(d) $f'(c)$ exists.

(e) $f'$ is continuous at $c$.

($\alpha$) $A$ is continuous at $c$.

($\beta$) $A$ is discontinuous at $c$.

($\gamma$) $A$ is convex on $(a, b)$.

($\delta$) $A'(c)$ exists.

($\epsilon$) $A'$ is continuous at $c$.

In a table like the one shown here, mark $T$ in the appropriate square if the statement labeled with a Latin letter always implies the statement labeled with a Greek letter. Leave the other squares blank. For example, if (a) implies ($\alpha$), mark $T$ in the upper left-hand corner square, etc.

|   | $\alpha$ | $\beta$ | $\gamma$ | $\delta$ | $\epsilon$ |
|---|---|---|---|---|---|
| a |   |   |   |   |   |
| b |   |   |   |   |   |
| c |   |   |   |   |   |
| d |   |   |   |   |   |
| e |   |   |   |   |   |

## 5.6  The Leibniz notation for primitives

We return now to a further study of the relationship between integration and differentiation. First we discuss some notation introduced by Leibniz.

We have defined a primitive $P$ of a function $f$ to be any function for which $P'(x) = f(x)$. If $f$ is continuous on an interval, one primitive is given by a formula of the form

$$P(x) = \int_c^x f(t)\, dt \, ,$$

and all other primitives can differ from this one only by a constant. Leibniz used the symbol $\int f(x)\, dx$ to denote a general primitive of $f$. In this notation, an equation like

(5.12)
$$\int f(x)\, dx = P(x) + C$$

is considered to be merely an alternative way of writing $P'(x) = f(x)$. For example, since the derivative of the sine is the cosine, we may write

(5.13)
$$\int \cos x\, dx = \sin x + C \, .$$

Similarly, since the derivative of $x^{n+1}/(n + 1)$ is $x^n$, we may write

(5.14)
$$\int x^n\, dx = \frac{x^{n+1}}{n + 1} + C \, ,$$

for any rational power $n \neq -1$. The symbol $C$ represents an arbitrary constant so each of Equations (5.13) and (5.14) is really a statement about a whole set of functions.

Despite similarity in appearance, the symbol $\int f(x)\,dx$ is conceptually distinct from the integration symbol $\int_a^b f(x)\,dx$. The symbols originate from two entirely different processes—differentiation and integration. Since, however, the two processes are related by the fundamental theorems of calculus, there are corresponding relationships between the two symbols.

The first fundamental theorem states that any indefinite integral of $f$ is also a primitive of $f$. Therefore we may replace $P(x)$ in Equation (5.12) by $\int_c^x f(t)\,dt$ for some lower limit $c$ and write (5.12) as follows:

$$(5.15) \qquad \int f(x)\,dx = \int_c^x f(t)\,dt + C \,.$$

This means that we can think of the symbol $\int f(x)\,dx$ as representing some indefinite integral of $f$, plus a constant.

The second fundamental theorem tells us that for any primitive $P$ of $f$ and for any constant $C$, we have

$$\int_a^b f(x)\,dx = \left[ P(x) + C \right] \Big|_a^b \,.$$

If we replace $P(x) + C$ by $\int f(x)\,dx$, this formula may be written in the form

$$(5.16) \qquad \int_a^b f(x)\,dx = \int f(x)\,dx \,\Big|_a^b \,.$$

The two formulas in (5.15) and (5.16) may be thought of as symbolic expressions of the first and second fundamental theorems of calculus.

Because of long historical usage, many calculus textbooks refer to the symbol $\int f(x)\,dx$ as an "indefinite integral" rather than as a primitive or an antiderivative. This is justified, in part, by Equation (5.15), which tells us that the symbol $\int f(x)\,dx$ is, apart from an additive constant $C$, an indefinite integral of $f$. For the same reason, many handbooks of mathematical tables contain extensive lists of formulas labeled "tables of indefinite integrals" which, in reality, are tables of primitives. To distinguish the symbol $\int f(x)\,dx$ from $\int_a^b f(x)\,dx$, the latter is called a *definite* integral. Since the second fundamental theorem reduces the problem of integration to that of finding a primitive, the term "technique of integration" is used to refer to any systematic method for finding primitives. This terminology is widely used in the mathematical literature, and it will be adopted also in this book. Thus, for example, when one is asked to "integrate" $\int f(x)\,dx$, it is to be understood that what is wanted is the most general primitive of $f$.

There are three principal techniques that are used to construct tables of indefinite integrals, and they should be learned by anyone who desires a good working knowledge of calculus. They are (1) *integration by substitution* (to be described in the next section), a method based on the chain rule; (2) *integration by parts*, a method based on the formula for differentiating a product (to be described in Section 5.9); and (3) *integration by partial fractions*, an algebraic technique which is discussed at the end of Chapter 6. These techniques not only explain how tables of indefinite integrals are constructed, but also they tell us how certain formulas are converted to the basic forms listed in the tables.

## 5.7 Integration by substitution

Let $Q$ be a composition of two functions $P$ and $g$, say $Q(x) = P[g(x)]$ for all $x$ in some interval $I$. If we know the derivative of $P$, say $P'(x) = f(x)$, the chain rule tells us that the derivative of $Q$ is given by the formula $Q'(x) = P'[g(x)]g'(x)$. Since $P' = f$, this states that $Q'(x) = f[g(x)]g'(x)$. In other words,

(5.17) $\qquad\qquad P'(x) = f(x) \qquad \text{implies} \qquad Q'(x) = f[g(x)]g'(x)$.

In Leibniz notation, this statement can be written as follows: If we have the integration formula

(5.18) $$\int f(x)\,dx = P(x) + C,$$

then we also have the more general formula

(5.19) $$\int f[g(x)]g'(x)\,dx = P[g(x)] + C.$$

For example, if $f(x) = \cos x$, then (5.18) holds with $P(x) = \sin x$, so (5.19) becomes

(5.20) $$\int \cos g(x) \cdot g'(x)\,dx = \sin g(x) + C.$$

In particular, if $g(x) = x^3$, this gives us

$$\int \cos x^3 \cdot 3x^2\,dx = \sin x^3 + C,$$

a result that is easily verified directly since the derivative of $\sin x^3$ is $3x^2 \cos x^3$.

Now we notice that the general formula in (5.19) is related to (5.18) by a simple mechanical process. Suppose we replace $g(x)$ everywhere in (5.19) by a new symbol $u$ and replace $g'(x)$ by $du/dx$, the Leibniz notation for derivatives. Then (5.19) becomes

$$\int f(u)\frac{du}{dx}\,dx = P(u) + C.$$

At this stage the temptation is strong to replace the combination $\frac{du}{dx}\,dx$ by $du$. If we do this, the last formula becomes

(5.21) $$\int f(u)\,du = P(u) + C.$$

Notice that this has exactly the same form as (5.18), except that the symbol $u$ appears everywhere instead of $x$. In other words, every integration formula such as (5.18) can be made to yield a more general integration formula if we simply substitute symbols. We replace $x$ in (5.18) by a new symbol $u$ to obtain (5.21), and then we think of $u$ as representing a new function of $x$, say $u = g(x)$. Then we replace the symbol $du$ by the combination $g'(x) \, dx$, and Equation (5.21) reduces to the general formula in (5.19).

For example, if we replace $x$ by $u$ in the formula $\int \cos x \, dx = \sin x + C$, we obtain

$$\int \cos u \, du = \sin u + C .$$

In this latter formula, $u$ may be replaced by $g(x)$ and $du$ by $g'(x) \, dx$, and a correct integration formula, (5.20), results.

When this mechanical process is used *in reverse*, it becomes the method of *integration by substitution*. The object of the method is to transform an integral with a complicated integrand, such as $\int 3x^2 \cos x^3 \, dx$, into a more familiar integral, such as $\int \cos u \, du$. The method is applicable whenever the original integral can be written in the form

$$\int f[g(x)]g'(x) \, dx ,$$

since the substitution

$$u = g(x), \qquad du = g'(x) \, dx ,$$

transforms this to $\int f(u) \, du$. If we succeed in carrying out the integration indicated by $\int f(u) \, du$, we obtain a primitive, say $P(u)$, and then the original integral may be evaluated by replacing $u$ by $g(x)$ in the formula for $P(u)$.

The reader should realize that we have attached no meanings to the symbols $dx$ and $du$ by themselves. They are used as purely formal devices to help us perform the mathematical operations in a mechanical way. Each time we use the process, we are really applying the statement (5.17).

Success in this method depends on one's ability to determine at the outset which part of the integrand should be replaced by the symbol $u$, and this ability comes from a lot of experience in working out specific examples. The following examples illustrate how the method is carried out in actual practice.

EXAMPLE 1. Integrate $\int x^3 \cos x^4 \, dx$.

*Solution.* Let us keep in mind that we are trying to write $x^3 \cos x^4$ in the form $f[g(x)]g'(x)$ with a suitable choice of $f$ and $g$. Since $\cos x^4$ is a composition, this suggests that we take $f(x) = \cos x$ and $g(x) = x^4$ so that $\cos x^4$ becomes $f[g(x)]$. This choice of $g$ gives $g'(x) = 4x^3$, and hence $f[g(x)]g'(x) = (\cos x^4)(4x^3)$. The extra factor 4 is easily taken care of by multiplying and dividing the integrand by 4. Thus we have

$$x^3 \cos x^4 = \tfrac{1}{4}(\cos x^4)(4x^3) = \tfrac{1}{4}f[g(x)]g'(x) .$$

Now, we make the substitution $u = g(x) = x^4$, $du = g'(x) \, dx = 4x^3 \, dx$, and obtain

$$\int x^3 \cos x^4 \, dx = \tfrac{1}{4} \int f(u) \, du = \tfrac{1}{4} \int \cos u \, du = \tfrac{1}{4} \sin u + C .$$

Replacing $u$ by $x^4$ in the end result, we obtain the formula

$$\int x^3 \cos x^4 \, dx = \tfrac{1}{4} \sin x^4 + C,$$

which can be verified directly by differentiation.

After a little practice one can perform some of the above steps mentally, and the entire calculation can be given more briefly as follows: Let $u = x^4$. Then $du = 4x^3 \, dx$, and we obtain

$$\int x^3 \cos x^4 \, dx = \tfrac{1}{4} \int (\cos x^4)(4x^3 \, dx) = \tfrac{1}{4} \int \cos u \, du = \tfrac{1}{4} \sin u + C = \tfrac{1}{4} \sin x^4 + C.$$

Notice that the method works in this example because the factor $x^3$ has an exponent one less than the power of $x$ which appears in $\cos x^4$.

EXAMPLE 2. Integrate $\int \cos^2 x \sin x \, dx$.

*Solution.* Let $u = \cos x$. Then $du = -\sin x \, dx$, and we get

$$\int \cos^2 x \sin x \, dx = -\int (\cos x)^2 (-\sin x \, dx) = -\int u^2 \, du = -\frac{u^3}{3} + C = -\frac{\cos^3 x}{3} + C.$$

Again, the final result is easily verified by differentiation.

EXAMPLE 3. Integrate $\displaystyle\int \frac{\sin \sqrt{x}}{\sqrt{x}} \, dx$.

*Solution.* Let $u = \sqrt{x} = x^{1/2}$. Then $du = \tfrac{1}{2} x^{-1/2} \, dx$, or $dx/\sqrt{x} = 2 \, du$. Hence

$$\int \frac{\sin \sqrt{x}}{\sqrt{x}} \, dx = 2 \int \sin u \, du = -2 \cos u + C = -2 \cos \sqrt{x} + C.$$

EXAMPLE 4. Integrate $\displaystyle\int \frac{x \, dx}{\sqrt{1 + x^2}}$.

*Solution.* Let $u = 1 + x^2$. Then $du = 2x \, dx$ so $x \, dx = \tfrac{1}{2} \, du$, and we obtain

$$\int \frac{x \, dx}{\sqrt{1 + x^2}} = \frac{1}{2} \int \frac{du}{\sqrt{u}} = \frac{1}{2} \int u^{-1/2} \, du = u^{1/2} + C = \sqrt{1 + x^2} + C.$$

The method of substitution is, of course, also applicable to definite integrals. For example, to evaluate the definite integral $\int_0^{\pi/2} \cos^2 x \sin x \, dx$, we first determine the indefinite integral, as explained in Example 2, and then we use the second fundamental theorem to write

$$\int_0^{\pi/2} \cos^2 x \sin x \, dx = -\frac{1}{3} \cos^3 x \Big|_0^{\pi/2} = -\frac{1}{3}\left(\cos^3 \frac{\pi}{2} - \cos^3 0\right) = \frac{1}{3}.$$

Sometimes it is desirable to apply the second fundamental theorem directly to the integral expressed in terms of $u$. This may be done by using new limits of integration. We shall illustrate how this is carried out in a particular example, and then we shall justify the process with a general theorem.

EXAMPLE 5. Evaluate $\displaystyle\int_2^3 \frac{(x+1)\,dx}{\sqrt{x^2 + 2x + 3}}$.

*Solution.* Let $u = x^2 + 2x + 3$. Then $du = (2x+2)\,dx$, so that

$$\frac{(x+1)\,dx}{\sqrt{x^2 + 2x + 3}} = \frac{1}{2}\frac{du}{\sqrt{u}}.$$

Now we obtain new limits of integration by noting that $u = 11$ when $x = 2$, and that $u = 18$ when $x = 3$. Then we write

$$\int_2^3 \frac{(x+1)\,dx}{\sqrt{x^2 + 2x + 3}} = \frac{1}{2}\int_{11}^{18} u^{-1/2}\,du = \sqrt{u}\,\Big|_{11}^{18} = \sqrt{18} - \sqrt{11}.$$

The same result is arrived at by expressing everything in terms of $x$. Thus we have

$$\int_2^3 \frac{(x+1)\,dx}{\sqrt{x^2 + 2x + 3}} = \sqrt{x^2 + 2x + 3}\,\Big|_2^3 = \sqrt{18} - \sqrt{11}.$$

Now we prove a general theorem which justifies the process used in Example 5.

THEOREM 5.4. SUBSTITUTION THEOREM FOR INTEGRALS. *Assume g has a continuous derivative g' on an open interval I. Let J be the set of values taken by g on I and assume that f is continuous on J. Then for each x and c in I, we have*

$$(5.22) \qquad \int_c^x f[g(t)]g'(t)\,dt = \int_{g(c)}^{g(x)} f(u)\,du.$$

*Proof.* Let $a = g(c)$ and define two new functions $P$ and $Q$ as follows:

$$P(x) = \int_a^x f(u)\,du \quad \text{if} \quad x \in J, \qquad Q(x) = \int_c^x f[g(t)]g'(t)\,dt \quad \text{if} \quad x \in I.$$

Since $P$ and $Q$ are indefinite integrals of continuous functions, they have derivatives given by the formulas

$$P'(x) = f(x), \qquad Q'(x) = f[g(x)]g'(x).$$

Now let $R$ denote the composite function, $R(x) = P[g(x)]$. Using the chain rule, we find

$$R'(x) = P'[g(x)]g'(x) = f[g(x)]g'(x) = Q'(x).$$

Applying the second fundamental theorem twice, we obtain

$$\int_{g(c)}^{g(x)} f(u) \, du = \int_{g(c)}^{g(x)} P'(u) \, du = P[g(x)] - P[g(c)] = R(x) - R(c),$$

and

$$\int_{c}^{x} f[g(t)]g'(t) \, dt = \int_{c}^{x} Q'(t) \, dt = \int_{c}^{x} R'(t) \, dt = R(x) - R(c).$$

This shows that the two integrals in (5.22) are equal.

## 5.8  Exercises

In Exercises 1 through 20, evaluate the integrals by the method of substitution.

1. $\int \sqrt{2x + 1} \, dx.$

2. $\int x\sqrt{1 + 3x} \, dx.$

3. $\int x^2 \sqrt{x + 1} \, dx.$

4. $\int_{-2/3}^{1/3} \dfrac{x \, dx}{\sqrt{2 - 3x}}.$

5. $\int \dfrac{(x + 1) \, dx}{(x^2 + 2x + 2)^3}.$

6. $\int \sin^3 x \, dx.$

7. $\int z(z - 1)^{1/3} \, dz.$

8. $\int \dfrac{\cos x \, dx}{\sin^3 x}.$

9. $\int_{0}^{\pi/4} \cos 2x \sqrt{4 - \sin 2x} \, dx.$

10. $\int \dfrac{\sin x \, dx}{(3 + \cos x)^2}.$

11. $\int \dfrac{\sin x \, dx}{\sqrt{\cos^3 x}}.$

12. $\int_{3}^{8} \dfrac{\sin \sqrt{x + 1} \, dx}{\sqrt{x + 1}}.$

13. $\int x^{n-1} \sin x^n \, dx, \qquad n \neq 0.$

14. $\int \dfrac{x^5 \, dx}{\sqrt{1 - x^6}}.$

15. $\int t(1 + t)^{1/4} \, dt.$

16. $\int (x^2 + 1)^{-3/2} \, dx.$

17. $\int x^2 (8x^3 + 27)^{2/3} \, dx.$

18. $\int \dfrac{(\sin x + \cos x) \, dx}{(\sin x - \cos x)^{1/3}}.$

19. $\int \dfrac{x \, dx}{\sqrt{1 + x^2 + \sqrt{(1 + x^2)^3}}}.$

20. $\int \dfrac{(x^2 + 1 - 2x)^{1/5} \, dx}{1 - x}.$

21. Deduce the formulas in Theorems 1.18 and 1.19 by the method of substitution.
22. Let

$$F(x, a) = \int_0^x \frac{t^p}{(t^2 + a^2)^q} \, dt,$$

where $a > 0$, and $p$ and $q$ are positive integers. Show that $F(x, a) = a^{p+1-2q}F(x/a, 1)$.
23. Show that

$$\int_x^1 \frac{dt}{1 + t^2} = \int_1^{1/x} \frac{dt}{1 + t^2} \quad \text{if} \quad x > 0.$$

24. If $m$ and $n$ are positive integers, show that

$$\int_0^1 x^m(1 - x)^n \, dx = \int_0^1 x^n(1 - x)^m \, dx.$$

25. If $m$ is a positive integer, show that

$$\int_0^{\pi/2} \cos^m x \sin^m x \, dx = 2^{-m} \int_0^{\pi/2} \cos^m x \, dx.$$

26. (a) Show that

$$\int_0^\pi x f(\sin x) \, dx = \frac{\pi}{2} \int_0^\pi f(\sin x) \, dx. \qquad [Hint: \quad u = \pi - x.]$$

  (b) Use part (a) to deduce the formula

$$\int_0^\pi \frac{x \sin x}{1 + \cos^2 x} \, dx = \pi \int_0^1 \frac{dx}{1 + x^2}.$$

27. Show that $\int_0^1 (1 - x^2)^{n-1/2} \, dx = \int_0^{\pi/2} \cos^{2n} u \, du$ if $n$ is a positive integer. [*Hint:* $x = \sin u$.] The integral on the right can be evaluated by the method of integration by parts, to be discussed in the next section.

## 5.9 Integration by parts

We proved in Chapter 4 that the derivative of a product of two functions $f$ and $g$ is given by the formula

$$h'(x) = f(x)g'(x) + f'(x)g(x),$$

where $h(x) = f(x)g(x)$. When this is translated into the Leibniz notation for primitives, it becomes $\int f(x)g'(x) \, dx + \int f'(x)g(x) \, dx = f(x)g(x) + C$, usually written as follows:

$$(5.23) \qquad \int f(x)g'(x) \, dx = f(x)g(x) - \int f'(x)g(x) \, dx + C.$$

This equation, known as the formula for *integration by parts*, provides us with a new integration technique.

To evaluate an integral, say $\int k(x)\,dx$, using (5.23), we try to find two functions $f$ and $g$ such that $k(x)$ can be written in the form $f(x)g'(x)$. If we can do this, then (5.23) tells us that we have

$$\int k(x)\,dx = f(x)g(x) - \int g(x)f'(x)\,dx + C,$$

and the difficulty has been transferred to the evaluation of $\int g(x)f'(x)\,dx$. If $f$ and $g$ are properly chosen, this last integral may be easier to evaluate than the original one. Sometimes two or more applications of (5.23) will lead to an integral that is easily evaluated or that may be found in a table. The examples worked out below have been chosen to illustrate the advantages of this method. For definite integrals, (5.23) leads to the formula

$$\int_a^b f(x)g'(x)\,dx = f(b)g(b) - f(a)g(a) - \int_a^b f'(x)g(x)\,dx.$$

If we introduce the substitutions $u = f(x)$, $v = g(x)$, $du = f'(x)\,dx$, and $dv = g'(x)\,dx$, the formula for integration by parts assumes an abbreviated form that many people find easier to remember, namely

$$(5.24) \qquad\qquad \int u\,dv = uv - \int v\,du + C.$$

EXAMPLE 1. Integrate $\int x \cos x\,dx$.

*Solution.* We choose $f(x) = x$ and $g'(x) = \cos x$. This means that we have $f'(x) = 1$ and $g(x) = \sin x$, so (5.23) becomes

$$(5.25) \qquad \int x \cos x\,dx = x \sin x - \int \sin x\,dx + C = x \sin x + \cos x + C.$$

Note that in this case the second integral is one we have already calculated.

To carry out the same calculation in the abbreviated notation of (5.24), we write

$$u = x, \qquad dv = \cos x\,dx,$$

$$du = dx, \qquad v = \int \cos x\,dx = \sin x,$$

$$\int x \cos x\,dx = uv - \int v\,du = x \sin x - \int \sin x\,dx + C = x \sin x + \cos x + C.$$

Had we chosen $u = \cos x$ and $dv = x\,dx$, we would have obtained $du = -\sin x\,dx$, $v = \frac{1}{2}x^2$, and (5.24) would have given us

$$\int x \cos x\,dx = \tfrac{1}{2}x^2 \cos x - \tfrac{1}{2}\int x^2(-\sin x)\,dx + C = \tfrac{1}{2}x^2 \cos x + \tfrac{1}{2}\int x^2 \sin x\,dx + C.$$

Since the last integral is one which we have not yet calculated, this choice of $u$ and $v$ is not as useful as the first choice. Notice, however, that we can solve this last equation for $\int x^2 \sin x \, dx$ and use (5.25) to obtain

$$\int x^2 \sin x \, dx = 2x \sin x + 2 \cos x - x^2 \cos x + C .$$

EXAMPLE 2. Integrate $\int x^2 \cos x \, dx$.

*Solution.* Let $u = x^2$ and $dv = \cos x \, dx$. Then $du = 2x \, dx$ and $v = \int \cos x \, dx = \sin x$, so we have

(5.26) $\quad \int x^2 \cos x \, dx = \int u \, dv = uv - \int v \, du + C = x^2 \sin x - 2 \int x \sin x \, dx + C .$

The last integral can be evaluated by applying integration by parts once more. Since it is similar to Example 1, we simply state the result:

$$\int x \sin x \, dx = -x \cos x + \sin x + C .$$

Substituting in (5.26) and consolidating the two arbitrary constants into one, we obtain

$$\int x^2 \cos x \, dx = x^2 \sin x + 2x \cos x - 2 \sin x + C .$$

EXAMPLE 3. The method sometimes fails because it leads back to the original integral. For example, let us try to integrate $\int x^{-1} \, dx$ by parts. If we let $u = x$ and $dv = x^{-2} \, dx$, then $\int x^{-1} \, dx = \int u \, dv$. For this choice of $u$ and $v$, we have $du = dx$ and $v = -x^{-1}$, so (5.24) gives us

(5.27) $\quad \int x^{-1} \, dx = \int u \, dv = uv - \int v \, du + C = -1 + \int x^{-1} \, dx + C ,$

and we are back where we started. Moreover, the situation does not improve if we try $u = x^n$ and $dv = x^{-n-1} \, dx$.

This example is often used to illustrate the importance of paying attention to the arbitrary constant $C$. If formula (5.27) is written without $C$, it leads to the equation $\int x^{-1} \, dx = -1 + \int x^{-1} \, dx$, which is sometimes used to give a fallacious proof that $0 = -1$.

As an application of the method of integration by parts, we obtain another version of the weighted mean-value theorem for integrals (Theorem 3.16).

THEOREM 5.5. SECOND MEAN-VALUE THEOREM FOR INTEGRALS. *Assume g is continuous on* $[a, b]$, *and assume f has a derivative which is continuous and never changes sign in* $[a, b]$. *Then, for some c in* $[a, b]$, *we have*

(5.28) $\quad \displaystyle\int_a^b f(x)g(x) \, dx = f(a) \int_a^c g(x) \, dx + f(b) \int_c^b g(x) \, dx .$

*Proof.* Let $G(x) = \int_a^x g(t)\,dt$. Since $g$ is continuous, we have $G'(x) = g(x)$. Therefore, integration by parts gives us

$$(5.29) \qquad \int_a^b f(x)g(x)\,dx = \int_a^b f(x)G'(x)\,dx = f(b)G(b) - \int_a^b f'(x)G(x)\,dx\,,$$

since $G(a) = 0$. By the weighted mean-value theorem, we have

$$\int_a^b f'(x)G(x)\,dx = G(c)\int_a^b f'(x)\,dx = G(c)[f(b) - f(a)]$$

for some $c$ in $[a, b]$. Therefore, (5.29) becomes

$$\int_a^b f(x)g(x)\,dx = f(b)G(b) - G(c)[f(b) - f(a)] = f(a)G(c) + f(b)[G(b) - G(c)]\,.$$

This proves (5.28) since $G(c) = \int_a^c g(x)\,dx$ and $G(b) - G(c) = \int_c^b g(x)\,dx$.

## 5.10   Exercises

Use integration by parts to evaluate the integrals in Exercises 1 through 6.

1. $\int x \sin x\,dx$.

2. $\int x^2 \sin x\,dx$.

3. $\int x^3 \cos x\,dx$.

4. $\int x^3 \sin x\,dx$.

5. $\int \sin x \cos x\,dx$.

6. $\int x \sin x \cos x\,dx$.

7. Use integration by parts to deduce the formula

$$\int \sin^2 x\,dx = -\sin x \cos x + \int \cos^2 x\,dx\,.$$

In the second integral, write $\cos^2 x = 1 - \sin^2 x$ and thereby deduce the formula

$$\int \sin^2 x\,dx = \tfrac{1}{2}x - \tfrac{1}{4}\sin 2x\,.$$

8. Use integration by parts to deduce the formula

$$\int \sin^n x\,dx = -\sin^{n-1} x \cos x + (n - 1)\int \sin^{n-2} x \cos^2 x\,dx\,.$$

In the second integral, write $\cos^2 x = 1 - \sin^2 x$ and thereby deduce the recursion formula

$$\int \sin^n x\,dx = -\frac{\sin^{n-1} x \cos x}{n} + \frac{n-1}{n}\int \sin^{n-2} x\,dx\,.$$

9. Use the results of Exercises 7 and 8 to show that

(a) $\displaystyle\int_0^{\pi/2} \sin^2 x\,dx = \frac{\pi}{4}$.

(b) $\displaystyle\int_0^{\pi/2} \sin^4 x \, dx = \frac{3}{4} \int_0^{\pi/2} \sin^2 x \, dx = \frac{3\pi}{16}$ .

(c) $\displaystyle\int_0^{\pi/2} \sin^6 x \, dx = \frac{5}{6} \int_0^{\pi/2} \sin^4 x \, dx = \frac{5\pi}{32}$ .

10. Use the results of Exercises 7 and 8 to derive the following formulas.

   (a) $\displaystyle\int \sin^3 x \, dx = -\frac{3}{4} \cos x + \frac{1}{12} \cos 3x$.

   (b) $\displaystyle\int \sin^4 x \, dx = \frac{3}{8} x - \frac{1}{4} \sin 2x + \frac{1}{32} \sin 4x$.

   (c) $\displaystyle\int \sin^5 x \, dx = -\frac{5}{8}x + \frac{5}{48} \cos 3x - \frac{1}{80} \cos 5x$.

11. Use integration by parts and the results of Exercises 7 and 10 to deduce the following formulas.

   (a) $\displaystyle\int x \sin^2 x \, dx = \frac{1}{4} x^2 - \frac{1}{4} x \sin 2x - \frac{1}{8} \cos 2x$.

   (b) $\displaystyle\int x \sin^3 x \, dx = \frac{3}{4} \sin x - \frac{1}{36} \sin 3x - \frac{3}{4}x \cos x + \frac{1}{12} x \cos 3x$.

   (c) $\displaystyle\int x^2 \sin^2 x \, dx = \frac{1}{6}x^3 + (\frac{1}{8} - \frac{1}{4}x^2) \sin 2x - \frac{1}{4}x \cos 2x$.

12. Use integration by parts to derive the recursion formula

$$\int \cos^n x \, dx = \frac{\cos^{n-1} x \sin x}{n} + \frac{n-1}{n} \int \cos^{n-2} x \, dx .$$

13. Use the result of Exercise 12 to obtain the following formulas.

   (a) $\displaystyle\int \cos^2 x \, dx = \frac{1}{2}x + \frac{1}{4} \sin 2x$.

   (b) $\displaystyle\int \cos^3 x \, dx = \frac{3}{4} \sin x + \frac{1}{12} \sin 3x$.

   (c) $\displaystyle\int \cos^4 x \, dx = \frac{3}{8}x + \frac{1}{4} \sin 2x + \frac{1}{32} \sin 4x$.

14. Use integration by parts to show that

$$\int \sqrt{1 - x^2} \, dx = x\sqrt{1 - x^2} + \int \frac{x^2}{\sqrt{1 - x^2}} \, dx.$$

Write $x^2 = x^2 - 1 + 1$ in the second integral and deduce the formula

$$\int \sqrt{1 - x^2} \, dx = \frac{1}{2}x\sqrt{1 - x^2} + \frac{1}{2} \int \frac{1}{\sqrt{1 - x^2}} \, dx.$$

15. (a) Use integration by parts to derive the formula

$$\int (a^2 - x^2)^n \, dx = \frac{x(a^2 - x^2)^n}{2n + 1} + \frac{2a^2 n}{2n + 1} \int (a^2 - x^2)^{n-1} \, dx + C .$$

   (b) Use part (a) to evaluate $\int_0^a (a^2 - x^2)^{5/2} \, dx$.

16. (a) If $I_n(x) = \int_0^x t^n(t^2 + a^2)^{-1/2}\, dt$, use integration by parts to show that

$$nI_n(x) = x^{n-1}\sqrt{x^2 + a^2} - (n-1)a^2 I_{n-2}(x) \qquad \text{if} \quad n \geq 2\,.$$

(b) Use part (a) to show that $\int_0^2 x^5(x^2 + 5)^{-1/2}\, dx = 168/5 - 40\sqrt{5}/3$.

17. Evaluate the integral $\int_{-1}^3 t^3(4 + t^3)^{-1/2}\, dt$, given that $\int_{-1}^3 (4 + t^3)^{1/2}\, dt = 11.35$. Leave the answer in terms of $\sqrt{3}$ and $\sqrt{31}$.

18. Use integration by parts to derive the formula

$$\int \frac{\sin^{n+1} x}{\cos^{m+1} x}\, dx = \frac{1}{m}\frac{\sin^n x}{\cos^m x} - \frac{n}{m}\int \frac{\sin^{n-1} x}{\cos^{m-1} x}\, dx\,.$$

Apply the formula to integrate $\int \tan^2 x\, dx$ and $\int \tan^4 x\, dx$.

19. Use integration by parts to derive the formula

$$\int \frac{\cos^{m+1} x}{\sin^{n+1} x}\, dx = -\frac{1}{n}\frac{\cos^m x}{\sin^n x} - \frac{m}{n}\int \frac{\cos^{m-1} x}{\sin^{n-1} x}\, dx\,.$$

Apply the formula to integrate $\int \cot^2 x\, dx$ and $\int \cot^4 x\, dx$.

20. (a) Find an integer $n$ such that $n \int_0^1 xf''(2x)\, dx = \int_0^2 tf''(t)\, dt$.
(b) Compute $\int_0^1 xf''(2x)\, dx$, given that $f(0) = 1$, $f(2) = 3$, and $f'(2) = 5$.

21. (a) If $\phi''$ is continuous and nonzero on $[a, b]$, and if there is a constant $m > 0$ such that $\phi'(t) \geq m$ for all $t$ in $[a, b]$, use Theorem 5.5 to prove that

$$\left| \int_a^b \sin \phi(t)\, dt \right| \leq \frac{4}{m}\,.$$

[*Hint:* Multiply and divide the integrand by $\phi'(t)$.]

(b) If $a > 0$, show that $\left| \int_a^x \sin(t^2)\, dt \right| \leq 2/a$ for all $x > a$.

## *5.11  Miscellaneous review exercises

1. Let $f$ be a polynomial with $f(0) = 1$ and let $g(x) = x^n f(x)$. Compute $g(0), g'(0), \ldots, g^{(n)}(0)$.
2. Find a polynomial $P$ of degree $\leq 5$ with $P(0) = 1, P(1) = 2, P'(0) = P''(0) = P'(1) = P''(1) = 0$.
3. If $f(x) = \cos x$ and $g(x) = \sin x$, prove that

$$f^{(n)}(x) = \cos\left(x + \tfrac{1}{2}n\pi\right) \qquad \text{and} \qquad g^{(n)}(x) = \sin\left(x + \tfrac{1}{2}n\pi\right).$$

4. If $h(x) = f(x)g(x)$, prove that the $n$th derivative of $h$ is given by the formula

$$h^{(n)}(x) = \sum_{k=0}^n \binom{n}{k} f^{(k)}(x) g^{(n-k)}(x)\,,$$

where $\binom{n}{k}$ denotes the binomial coefficient. This is called *Leibniz's formula*.

5. Given two functions $f$ and $g$ whose derivatives $f'$ and $g'$ satisfy the equations

$$(5.30) \qquad f'(x) = g(x)\,, \qquad g'(x) = -f(x)\,, \qquad f(0) = 0\,, \qquad g(0) = 1\,,$$

for every $x$ in some open interval $J$ containing 0. For example, these equations are satisfied when $f(x) = \sin x$ and $g(x) = \cos x$.

(a) Prove that $f^2(x) + g^2(x) = 1$ for every $x$ in $J$.

(b) Let $F$ and $G$ be another pair of functions satisfying (5.30). Prove that $F(x) = f(x)$ and $G(x) = g(x)$ for every $x$ in $J$. [*Hint:*  Consider $h(x) = [F(x) - f(x)]^2 + [G(x) - g(x)]^2$.]

(c) What more can you say about functions $f$ and $g$ satisfying (5.30)?

6. A function $f$, defined for all positive real numbers, satisfies the equation $f(x^2) = x^3$ for every $x > 0$. Determine $f'(4)$.

7. A function $g$, defined for all positive real numbers, satisfies the following two conditions: $g(1) = 1$ and $g'(x^2) = x^3$ for all $x > 0$. Compute $g(4)$.

8. Show that

$$\int_0^x \frac{\sin t}{t + 1}\, dt \geq 0 \qquad \text{for all}\ \ x \geq 0.$$

9. Let $C_1$ and $C_2$ be two curves passing through the origin as indicated in Figure 5.2. A curve $C$ is said to "bisect in area" the region between $C_1$ and $C_2$ if, for each point $P$ of $C$, the two shaded regions $A$ and $B$ shown in the figure have equal areas. Determine the upper curve $C_2$, given that the bisecting curve $C$ has the equation $y = x^2$ and that the lower curve $C_1$ has the equation $y = \frac{1}{2}x^2$.

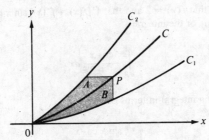

FIGURE 5.2    Exercise 9.

10. A function $f$ is defined for all $x$ as follows:

$$f(x) = \begin{cases} x^2 & \text{if}\ \ x\ \text{is rational}, \\ 0 & \text{if}\ \ x\ \text{is irrational}. \end{cases}$$

Let $Q(h) = f(h)/h$ if $h \neq 0$. (a) Prove that $Q(h) \to 0$ as $h \to 0$. (b) Prove that $f$ has a derivative at 0, and compute $f'(0)$.

In Exercises 11 through 20, evaluate the given integrals. Try to simplify the calculations by using the method of substitution and/or integration by parts whenever possible.

11. $\int (2 + 3x) \sin 5x\, dx$.

12. $\int x\sqrt{1 + x^2}\, dx$.

13. $\int_{-2}^1 x(x^2 - 1)^9\, dx$.

14. $\int_0^1 \frac{2x + 3}{(6x + 7)^3}\, dx$.

15. $\int x^4(1 + x^5)^5\, dx$.

16. $\int_0^1 x^4(1 - x)^{20}\, dx$.

17. $\int_1^2 x^{-2} \sin \frac{1}{x}\, dx$.

18. $\int \sin \sqrt[4]{x - 1}\, dx$.

19. $\int x \sin x^2 \cos x^2\, dx$.

20. $\int \sqrt{1 + 3\cos^2 x}\, \sin 2x\, dx$.

21. Show that the value of the integral $\int_0^2 375x^5(x^2 + 1)^{-4}\, dx$ is $2^n$ for some integer $n$.

22. Determine a pair of numbers $a$ and $b$ for which $\int_0^1 (ax + b)(x^2 + 3x + 2)^{-2}\, dx = 3/2$.

23. Let $I_n = \int_0^1 (1 - x^2)^n\, dx$. Show that $(2n + 1)I_n = 2n\,I_{n-1}$, then use this relation to compute $I_2, I_3, I_4,$ and $I_5$.

24. Let $F(m, n) = \int_0^x t^m(1 + t)^n\, dt$, $m > 0$, $n > 0$. Show that

$$(m + 1)F(m, n) + nF(m + 1, n - 1) = x^{m+1}(1 + x)^n.$$

Use this to evaluate $F(10, 2)$.

25. Let $f(n) = \int_0^{\pi/4} \tan^n x\, dx$ where $n \geq 1$. Show that

(a) $f(n + 1) < f(n)$.

(b) $f(n) + f(n - 2) = \dfrac{1}{n - 1}$  if  $n > 2$.

(c) $\dfrac{1}{n + 1} < 2f(n) < \dfrac{1}{n - 1}$  if  $n > 2$.

26. Compute $f(0)$, given that $f(\pi) = 2$ and that $\int_0^\pi [f(x) + f''(x)] \sin x\, dx = 5$.

27. Let $A$ denote the value of the integral

$$\int_0^\pi \frac{\cos x}{(x + 2)^2}\, dx.$$

Compute the following integral in terms of $A$:

$$\int_0^{\pi/2} \frac{\sin x \cos x}{x + 1}\, dx.$$

The formulas in Exercises 28 through 33 appear in integral tables. Verify each of these formulas by any method.

28. $\displaystyle \int \frac{\sqrt{a + bx}}{x}\, dx = 2\sqrt{a + bx} + a \int \frac{dx}{x\sqrt{a + bx}} + C.$

29. $\displaystyle \int x^n \sqrt{ax + b}\, dx = \frac{2}{a(2n + 3)}\left( x^n(ax + b)^{3/2} - nb \int x^{n-1}\sqrt{ax + b}\, dx \right) + C \quad (n \neq -\tfrac{3}{2}).$

30. $\displaystyle \int \frac{x^m}{\sqrt{a + bx}}\, dx = \frac{2}{(2m + 1)b}\left( x^m \sqrt{a + bx} - ma \int \frac{x^{m-1}}{\sqrt{a + bx}}\, dx \right) + C \quad (m \neq -\tfrac{1}{2}).$

31. $\displaystyle \int \frac{dx}{x^n \sqrt{ax + b}} = -\frac{\sqrt{ax + b}}{(n - 1)bx^{n-1}} - \frac{(2n - 3)a}{(2n - 2)b}\int \frac{dx}{x^{n-1}\sqrt{ax + b}} + C \quad (n \neq 1).$

32. $\displaystyle \int \frac{\cos^m x}{\sin^n x}\, dx = \frac{\cos^{m-1} x}{(m - n)\sin^{n-1}x} + \frac{m - 1}{m - n}\int \frac{\cos^{m-2} x}{\sin^n x}\, dx + C \quad (m \neq n).$

33. $\displaystyle \int \frac{\cos^m x}{\sin^n x}\, dx = -\frac{\cos^{m+1} x}{(n - 1)\sin^{n-1} x} - \frac{m - n + 2}{n - 1}\int \frac{\cos^m x}{\sin^{n-2} x}\, dx + C \quad (n \neq 1).$

34. (a) Find a polynomial $P(x)$ such that $P'(x) - 3P(x) = 4 - 5x + 3x^2$. Prove that there is only one solution.

(b) If $Q(x)$ is a given polynomial, prove that there is one and only one polynomial $P(x)$ such that $P'(x) - 3P(x) = Q(x)$.

35. A sequence of polynomials (called the *Bernoulli polynomials*) is defined inductively as follows:

$$P_0(x) = 1; \quad P_n'(x) = nP_{n-1}(x) \quad \text{and} \quad \int_0^1 P_n(x)\, dx = 0 \quad \text{if} \quad n \geq 1.$$

(a) Determine explicit formulas for $P_1(x), P_2(x), \ldots, P_5(x)$.

(b) Prove, by induction, that $P_n(x)$ is a polynomial in $x$ of degree $n$, the term of highest degree being $x^n$.

(c) Prove that $P_n(0) = P_n(1)$ if $n \geq 2$.

(d) Prove that $P_n(x + 1) - P_n(x) = nx^{n-1}$ if $n \geq 1$.

(e) Prove that for $n \geq 2$ we have

$$\sum_{r=1}^{k-1} r^n = \int_0^k P_n(x)\, dx = \frac{P_{n+1}(k) - P_{n+1}(0)}{n + 1}.$$

(f) Prove that $P_n(1 - x) = (-1)^n P_n(x)$ if $n \geq 1$.

(g) Prove that $P_{2n+1}(0) = 0$ and $P_{2n-1}(\frac{1}{2}) = 0$ if $n \geq 1$.

36. Assume that $|f''(x)| \leq m$ for each $x$ in the interval $[0, a]$, and assume that $f$ takes on its largest value at an interior point of this interval. Show that $|f'(0)| + |f'(a)| \leq am$. You may assume that $f''$ is continuous in $[0, a]$.

# 6

# THE LOGARITHM, THE EXPONENTIAL,
# AND THE INVERSE TRIGONOMETRIC FUNCTIONS

## 6.1 Introduction

Whenever man focuses his attention on quantitative relationships, he is either studying the properties of a known function or trying to discover the properties of an unknown function. The function concept is so broad and so general that it is not surprising to find an endless variety of functions occurring in nature. What *is* surprising is that a few rather special functions govern so many totally different kinds of natural phenomena. We shall study some of these functions in this chapter—first of all, the logarithm and its inverse (the exponential function) and secondly, the inverses of the trigonometric functions. Anyone who studies mathematics, either as an abstract discipline or as a tool for some other scientific field, will find that a good working knowledge of these functions and their properties is indispensable.

The reader probably has had occasion to work with logarithms to the base 10 in an elementary algebra or trigonometry course. The definition usually given in elementary algebra is this: If $x > 0$, the logarithm of $x$ to the base 10, denoted by $\log_{10} x$, is that real number $u$ such that $10^u = x$. If $x = 10^u$ and $y = 10^v$, the law of exponents yields $xy = 10^{u+v}$. In terms of logarithms, this becomes

$$(6.1) \qquad \log_{10}(xy) = \log_{10} x + \log_{10} y.$$

It is this fundamental property that makes logarithms particularly adaptable to computations involving multiplication. The number 10 is useful as a base because real numbers are commonly written in the decimal system, and certain important numbers like 0.01, 0.1, 1, 10, 100, 1000, ... have for their logarithms the integers $-2$, $-1$, 0, 1, 2, 3, ..., respectively.

It is not necessary to restrict ourselves to base 10. Any other positive base $b \neq 1$ would serve equally well. Thus

$$(6.2) \qquad u = \log_b x \qquad \text{means} \qquad x = b^u,$$

and the fundamental property in (6.1) becomes

$$(6.3) \qquad \log_b(xy) = \log_b x + \log_b y.$$

226

If we examine the definition in (6.2) from a critical point of view, we find that it suffers from several logical gaps. First of all, to understand (6.2) we must know what is meant by $b^u$. This is easy to define when $u$ is an *integer* or a *rational number* (the quotient of two integers), but it is not a trivial matter to define $b^u$ when $u$ is *irrational*. For example, how should we define $10^{\sqrt{2}}$? Even if we manage to obtain a satisfactory definition for $b^u$, there are further difficulties to overcome before we can use (6.2) as a good definition of logarithms. It must be shown that for every $x > 0$, there actually *exists* a number $u$ such that $x = b^u$. Also, the law of exponents, $b^u b^v = b^{u+v}$, must be established for all real exponents $u$ and $v$ in order to derive (6.3) from (6.2).

It is possible to overcome these difficulties and arrive at a satisfactory definition of logarithms by this method, but the process is long and tedious. Fortunately, however, the study of logarithms can proceed in an entirely different way which is much simpler and which illustrates the power and elegance of the methods of calculus. The idea is to introduce logarithms *first*, and then use logarithms to define $b^u$.

## 6.2 Motivation for the definition of the natural logarithm as an integral

The logarithm is an example of a mathematical concept that can be defined in many different ways. When a mathematician tries to formulate a definition of a concept, such as the logarithm, he usually has in mind a number of properties he wants this concept to have. By examining these properties, he is often led to a simple formula or process that might serve as a definition from which all the desired properties spring forth as logical deductions. We shall illustrate how this procedure may be used to arrive at the definition of the logarithm which is given in the next section.

One of the properties we want logarithms to have is that the logarithm of a product should be the sum of the logarithms of the individual factors. Let us consider this property by itself and see where it leads us. If we think of the logarithm as a function $f$, then we want this function to have the property expressed by the formula

$$(6.4) \qquad f(xy) = f(x) + f(y)$$

whenever $x$, $y$, and $xy$ are in the domain of $f$.

An equation like (6.4), which expresses a relationship between the values of a function at two or more points, is called a *functional equation*. Many mathematical problems can be reduced to solving a functional equation, a solution being any function which satisfies the equation. Ordinarily an equation of this sort has many different solutions, and it is usually very difficult to find them all. It is easier to seek only those solutions which have some additional property such as continuity or differentiability. For the most part, these are the only solutions we are interested in anyway. We shall adopt this point of view and determine all differentiable solutions of (6.4). But first let us try to deduce what information we can from (6.4) alone, without any further restrictions on $f$.

One solution of (6.4) is the function that is zero everywhere on the real axis. In fact, this is the only solution of (6.4) that is defined for all real numbers. To prove this, let $f$ be any function that satisfies (6.4). If 0 is in the domain of $f$, then we may put $y = 0$ in (6.4) to obtain $f(0) = f(x) + f(0)$, and this implies that $f(x) = 0$ for every $x$ in the domain of $f$. In other words, if 0 is in the domain of $f$, then $f$ must be identically zero. Therefore, a solution of (6.4) that is not identically zero cannot be defined at 0.

If $f$ is a solution of (6.4) and if the domain of $f$ includes 1, we may put $x = y = 1$ in (6.4) to obtain $f(1) = 2f(1)$, and this implies

$$f(1) = 0.$$

If both 1 and $-1$ are in the domain of $f$, we may take $x = -1$ and $y = -1$ to deduce that $f(1) = 2f(-1)$; hence $f(-1) = 0$. If now $x$, $-x$, 1, and $-1$ are in the domain of $f$, we may put $y = -1$ in (6.4) to deduce $f(-x) = f(-1) + f(x)$ and, since $f(-1) = 0$, we find

$$f(-x) = f(x).$$

In other words, any solution of (6.4) is necessarily an *even* function.

Suppose, now, we assume that $f$ has a derivative $f'(x)$ at each $x \neq 0$. If we hold $y$ fixed in (6.4) and differentiate with respect to $x$ (using the chain rule on the left), we find

$$yf'(xy) = f'(x).$$

When $x = 1$, this gives us $yf'(y) = f'(1)$, and hence we have

$$f'(y) = \frac{f'(1)}{y} \qquad \text{for each} \qquad y \neq 0.$$

From this equation we see that the derivative $f'$ is monotonic and hence integrable on every closed interval not containing the origin. Also, $f'$ is continuous on every such interval, and we may apply the second fundamental theorem of calculus to write

$$f(x) - f(c) = \int_c^x f'(t)\,dt = f'(1)\int_c^x \frac{1}{t}\,dt.$$

If $x > 0$, this equation holds for any positive $c$, and if $x < 0$, it holds for any negative $c$. Since $f(1) = 0$, the choice $c = 1$ gives us

$$f(x) = f'(1)\int_1^x \frac{1}{t}\,dt \qquad \text{if} \qquad x > 0.$$

If $x$ is negative then $-x$ is positive and, since $f(x) = f(-x)$, we find

$$f(x) = f'(1)\int_1^{-x} \frac{1}{t}\,dt \qquad \text{if} \qquad x < 0.$$

These two formulas for $f(x)$ may be combined into one formula that is valid for both positive and negative $x$, namely,

(6.5) $$f(x) = f'(1)\int_1^{|x|} \frac{1}{t}\,dt \qquad \text{if} \qquad x \neq 0.$$

Therefore we have shown that if there is a solution of (6.4) which has a derivative at each point $x \neq 0$, then this solution must necessarily be given by the integral formula in (6.5). If $f'(1) = 0$, then (6.5) implies that $f(x) = 0$ for all $x \neq 0$, and this solution agrees with the solution that is identically zero. Therefore, if $f$ is not identically zero, we must have $f'(1) \neq 0$, in which case we can divide both sides of (6.5) by $f'(1)$ to obtain

$$(6.6) \qquad g(x) = \int_1^{|x|} \frac{1}{t}\, dt \qquad \text{if } x \neq 0,$$

where $g(x) = f(x)/f'(1)$. The function $g$ is also a solution of (6.4), since $cf$ is a solution whenever $f$ is. This proves that if (6.4) has a solution that is not identically zero and if this solution has a derivative everywhere except at the origin, then the function $g$ given by (6.6) is also a solution, and *all* solutions may be obtained from this one by multiplying $g$ by a suitable constant.

It should be emphasized that this argument does not prove that the function $g$ in (6.6) actually *is* a solution, because we derived (6.6) on the assumption that there is at least one solution that is not identically zero. Formula (6.6) suggests a way to construct such a solution. We simply operate in reverse. That is, we use the integral in (6.6) to define a function $g$, and then we verify directly that this function actually satisfies (6.4). This suggests that we should define the logarithm to be the function $g$ given by (6.6). If we did so, this function would have the property that $g(-x) = g(x)$ or, in other words, distinct numbers would have the same logarithm. For some of the things we want to do later, it is preferable to define the logarithm in such a way that no two distinct numbers have the same logarithm. This latter property may be achieved by defining the logarithm only for positive numbers. Therefore we use the following definition.

### 6.3 The definition of the logarithm. Basic properties

DEFINITION. *If $x$ is a positive real number, we define the natural logarithm of $x$, denoted temporarily by $L(x)$, to be the integral*

$$(6.7) \qquad L(x) = \int_1^x \frac{1}{t}\, dt .$$

When $x > 1$, $L(x)$ may be interpreted geometrically as the area of the shaded region shown in Figure 6.1.

THEOREM 6.1. *The logarithm function has the following properties:*

(a) $L(1) = 0$.

(b) $L'(x) = \dfrac{1}{x}$ *for every $x > 0$.*

(c) $L(ab) = L(a) + L(b)$ *for every $a > 0, b > 0$.*

*Proof.* Part (a) follows at once from the definition. To prove (b), we simply note that $L$ is an indefinite integral of a continuous function and apply the first fundamental theorem of calculus. Property (c) follows from the additive property of the integral. We write

$$L(ab) = \int_1^{ab} \frac{dt}{t} = \int_1^a \frac{dt}{t} + \int_a^{ab} \frac{dt}{t} = L(a) + \int_a^{ab} \frac{dt}{t}.$$

In the last integral we make the substitution $u = t/a$, $du = dt/a$, and we find that the integral reduces to $L(b)$, thus proving (c).

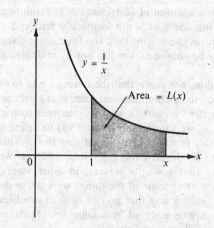

FIGURE 6.1    Interpretation of the logarithm as an area.

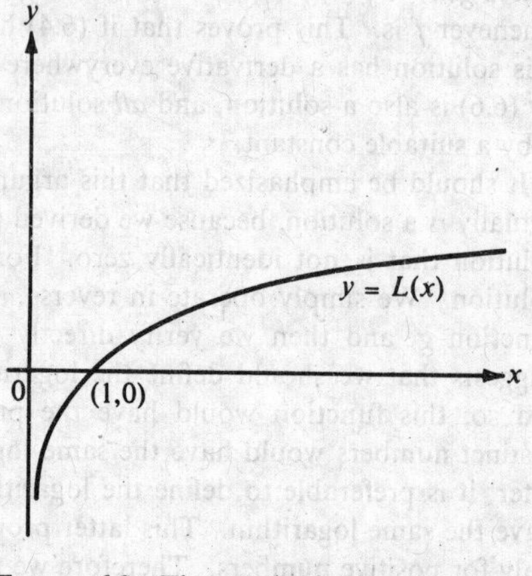

FIGURE 6.2    The graph of the natural logarithm.

## 6.4  The graph of the natural logarithm

The graph of the logarithm function has the general shape shown in Figure 6.2. Many properties of this curve can be discovered without undue calculation simply by referring to the properties in Theorem 6.1. For example, from (b) we see that $L$ has a positive derivative everywhere so it is strictly increasing on every interval. Since $L(1) = 0$, the graph lies above the $x$-axis if $x > 1$ and below the axis if $0 < x < 1$. The curve has slope 1 when $x = 1$. For $x > 1$, the slope gradually decreases toward zero as $x$ increases indefinitely. For small values of $x$, the slope is large and, moreover, it increases without bound as $x$ decreases toward zero. The second derivative is $L''(x) = -1/x^2$ which is negative for all $x$, so $L$ is a concave function.

## 6.5  Consequences of the functional equation $L(ab) = L(a) + L(b)$

Since the graph of the logarithm tends to level off as $x$ increases indefinitely, it might be suspected that the values of $L$ have an upper bound. Actually, the function is unbounded above; that is, for every positive number $M$ (no matter how large) there exist values of $x$ such that

(6.8)                    $L(x) > M.$

We can deduce this from the functional equation. When $a = b$, we get $L(a^2) = 2L(a)$. Using the functional equation once more with $b = a^2$, we obtain $L(a^3) = 3L(a)$. By induction we find the general formula

$$L(a^n) = nL(a)$$

for every integer $n \geq 1$. When $a = 2$, this becomes $L(2^n) = nL(2)$, and hence we have

(6.9)          $$L(2^n) > M \quad \text{when} \quad n > \frac{M}{L(2)}.$$

This proves the assertion in (6.8). Taking $b = 1/a$ in the functional equation, we find $L(1/a) = -L(a)$. In particular, when $a = 2^n$, where $n$ is chosen as in (6.9), we have

$$L\left(\frac{1}{2^n}\right) = -L(2^n) < -M,$$

which shows that there is also no lower bound to the function values.

Finally we observe that the graph crosses every horizontal line exactly once. That is, given an *arbitrary* real number $b$ (positive, negative, or zero), there is *one and only one* $a > 0$ such that

(6.10)          $$L(a) = b.$$

To prove this we can argue as follows: If $b > 0$, choose any integer $n > b/L(2)$. Then $L(2^n) > b$ because of (6.9). Now examine the function $L$ on the closed interval $[1, 2^n]$. Its value at the left endpoint is $L(1) = 0$, and its value at the right endpoint is $L(2^n)$. Since $0 < b < L(2^n)$, the intermediate-value theorem for continuous functions (Theorem 3.8 in Section 3.10) guarantees the existence of at least one $a$ such that $L(a) = b$. There cannot be another value $a'$ such that $L(a') = b$ because this would mean $L(a) = L(a')$ for $a \neq a'$, thus contradicting the increasing property of the logarithm. Therefore the assertion in (6.10) has been proved for $b > 0$. The proof for negative $b$ follows from this if we use the equation $L(1/a) = -L(a)$. In other words, we have proved the following.

THEOREM 6.2. *For every real number $b$ there is exactly one positive real number $a$ whose logarithm, $L(a)$, is equal to $b$.*

In particular, there is exactly one number whose natural logarithm is equal to 1. This number, like $\pi$, occurs repeatedly in so many mathematical formulas that it was inevitable that a special symbol would be adopted for it. Leonard Euler (1707–1783) seems to have been the first to recognize the importance of this number, and he modestly denoted it by $e$, a notation which soon became standard.

DEFINITION. *We denote by $e$ that number for which*

(6.11)          $$L(e) = 1.$$

In Chapter 7 we shall obtain explicit formulas that enable us to calculate the decimal expansion of $e$ to any desired degree of accuracy. Its value, correct to ten decimal places, is 2.7182818285. In Chapter 7 we also prove that $e$ is irrational.

Natural logarithms are also called *Napierian logarithms*, in honor of their inventor, John Napier (1550–1617). It is common practice to use the symbols ln $x$ or log $x$ instead of $L(x)$ to denote the logarithm of $x$.

### 6.6  Logarithms referred to any positive base $b \neq 1$

The work of Section 6.2 tells us that the most general $f$ which is differentiable on the positive real axis and which satisfies the functional equation $f(xy) = f(x) + f(y)$ is given by the formula

$$(6.12) \qquad\qquad f(x) = c \log x,$$

where $c$ is a constant. For each $c$, we could call this $f(x)$ the logarithm of $x$ associated with $c$ although, of course, its value would not be necessarily the same as the natural logarithm of $x$. When $c = 0$, $f$ is identically zero, so this case is uninteresting. If $c \neq 0$, we may indicate in another way the dependence of $f$ on $c$ by introducing the concept of a *base* for logarithms.

From (6.12) we see that when $c \neq 0$, there exists a unique real number $b > 0$ such that $f(b) = 1$. This $b$ is related to $c$ by the equation $c \log b = 1$; hence $b \neq 1$, $c = 1/\log b$, and (6.12) becomes

$$f(x) = \frac{\log x}{\log b}.$$

For this choice of $c$ we say that $f(x)$ is *the logarithm of $x$ to the base $b$* and we write $\log_b x$ for $f(x)$.

DEFINITION. *If $b > 0$, $b \neq 1$, and if $x > 0$, the logarithm of $x$ to the base $b$ is the number*

$$\log_b x = \frac{\log x}{\log b},$$

*where the logarithms on the right are natural logarithms.*

Note that $\log_b b = 1$. Also, when $b = e$, we have $\log_e x = \log x$, so natural logarithms are those with base $e$. Since logarithms to base $e$ are used so frequently in mathematics, the word logarithm almost invariably means *natural* logarithm. Later, in Section 6.15, we shall define $b^u$ in such a way that the equation $b^u = x$ will mean exactly the same as the equation $u = \log_b x$.

Since logarithms to the base $b$ are obtained from natural logarithms by multiplying by the constant $1/\log b$, the graph of the equation $y = \log_b x$ may be obtained from that of the equation $y = \log x$ by simply multiplying all ordinates by the same factor. When $b > 1$, this factor is positive, and, when $b < 1$, it is negative. Examples with $b > 1$ are

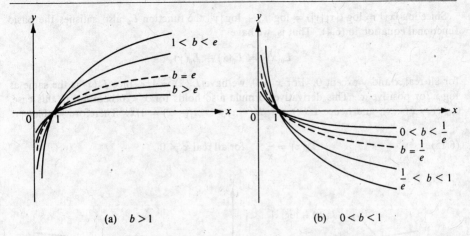

**FIGURE 6.3**   The graph of $y = \log_b x$ for various values of $b$.

shown in Figure 6.3($a$). When $b < 1$, we note that $1/b > 1$ and $\log b = -\log(1/b)$, so the graph of $y = \log_b x$ may be obtained from that of $y = \log_{1/b} x$ by reflection through the $x$-axis. Examples are shown in Figure 6.3(b).

## 6.7   Differentiation and integration formulas involving logarithms

Since the derivative of the logarithm is given by the formula $D \log x = 1/x$ for $x > 0$, we have the integration formula

$$\int \frac{1}{x} dx = \log x + C .$$

More generally, if $u = f(x)$, where $f$ has a continuous derivative, we have

(6.13)     $$\int \frac{du}{u} = \log u + C \quad \text{or} \quad \int \frac{f'(x)}{f(x)} dx = \log f(x) + C .$$

Some care must be exercised when using (6.13) because the logarithm is not defined for negative numbers. Therefore, the integration formulas in (6.13) are valid only if $u$, or $f(x)$, is positive.

Fortunately it is easy to extend the range of validity of these formulas to accommodate functions that are negative or positive (but *nonzero*). We simply introduce a new function $L_0$ defined for all real $x \neq 0$ by the equation

(6.14)     $$L_0(x) = \log |x| = \int_1^{|x|} \frac{1}{t} dt ,$$

a definition suggested by Equation (6.6) of Section 6.2. The graph of $L_0$ is symmetric about the $y$-axis, as shown in Figure 6.4. The portion to the right of the $y$-axis is exactly the same as the logarithmic curve of Figure 6.2.

Since $\log |xy| = \log (|x|\,|y|) = \log |x| + \log |y|$, the function $L_0$ also satisfies the basic functional equation in (6.4). That is, we have

$$L_0(xy) = L_0(x) + L_0(y)$$

for all real $x$ and $y$ except 0. For $x > 0$, we have $L_0'(x) = 1/x$ since $L_0(x)$ is the same as $\log x$ for positive $x$. This derivative formula also holds for $x < 0$ because, in this case, $L_0(x) = L(-x)$, and hence $L_0'(x) = -L'(-x) = -1/(-x) = 1/x$. Therefore we have

(6.15)     $$L_0'(x) = \frac{1}{x} \qquad \text{for all real } x \neq 0.$$

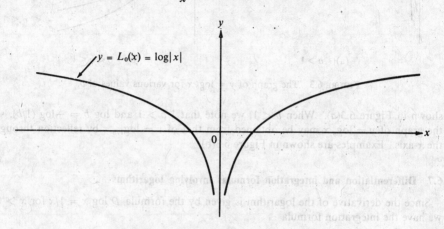

FIGURE 6.4   The graph of the function $L_0$.

Hence, if we use $L_0$ instead of $L$ in the foregoing integration formulas, we can extend their scope to include functions which assume negative values as well as positive values. For example, (6.13) can be generalized as follows:

(6.16)     $$\int \frac{du}{u} = \log |u| + C, \qquad \int \frac{f'(x)}{f(x)}\,dx = \log |f(x)| + C.$$

Of course, when we use (6.16) along with the second fundamental theorem of calculus to evaluate a definite integral, we must avoid intervals that include points where $u$ or $f(x)$ might be zero.

EXAMPLE 1.   Integrate $\int \tan x \, dx$.

*Solution.* The integral has the form $-\int du/u$, where $u = \cos x$, $du = -\sin x \, dx$. Therefore we have

$$\int \tan x \, dx = -\int \frac{du}{u} = -\log |u| + C = -\log |\cos x| + C,$$

a formula which is valid on any interval in which $\cos x \neq 0$.

The next two examples illustrate the use of integration by parts.

EXAMPLE 2. Integrate $\int \log x \, dx$.

*Solution.* Let $u = \log x$, $dv = dx$. Then $du = dx/x$, $v = x$, and we obtain

$$\int \log x \, dx = \int u \, dv = uv - \int v \, du = x \log x - \int x \frac{1}{x} \, dx = x \log x - x + C.$$

EXAMPLE 3. Integrate $\int \sin (\log x) \, dx$.

*Solution.* Let $u = \sin (\log x)$, $v = x$. Then $du = \cos (\log x)(1/x) \, dx$, and we find

$$\int \sin (\log x) \, dx = \int u \, dv = uv - \int v \, du = x \sin (\log x) - \int \cos (\log x) \, dx.$$

In the last integral we use integration by parts once more to get

$$\int \cos (\log x) \, dx = x \cos (\log x) + \int \sin (\log x) \, dx.$$

Combining this with the foregoing equation, we find that

$$\int \sin (\log x) \, dx = \tfrac{1}{2}x \sin (\log x) - \tfrac{1}{2}x \cos (\log x) + C,$$

and

$$\int \cos (\log x) \, dx = \tfrac{1}{2}x \sin (\log x) + \tfrac{1}{2}x \cos (\log x) + C.$$

## 6.8 Logarithmic differentiation

We shall describe now a technique known as *logarithmic differentiation* which is often a great help in computing derivatives. The method was developed in 1697 by Johann Bernoulli (1667–1748), and all it amounts to is a simple application of the chain rule. Suppose we form the composition of $L_0$ with any differentiable function $f$; say we let

$$g(x) = L_0[f(x)] = \log |f(x)|$$

for those $x$ such that $f(x) \neq 0$. The chain rule, used in conjunction with (6.15), yields the formula

(6.17) $$g'(x) = L_0'[f(x)] \cdot f'(x) = \frac{f'(x)}{f(x)}.$$

If the derivative $g'(x)$ can be found in some other way, then we may use (6.17) to obtain $f'(x)$ by simply multiplying $g'(x)$ by $f(x)$. The process is useful in practice because in many cases $g'(x)$ is easier to compute than $f'(x)$ itself. In particular, this is true when $f$ is a product or quotient of several simpler functions. The following example is typical.

EXAMPLE. Compute $f'(x)$ if $f(x) = x^2 \cos x (1 + x^4)^{-7}$.

*Solution.* We take the logarithm of the absolute value of $f(x)$ and then we differentiate. Let

$$g(x) = \log |f(x)| = \log x^2 + \log |\cos x| + \log (1 + x^4)^{-7}$$
$$= 2 \log |x| + \log |\cos x| - 7 \log (1 + x^4).$$

Differentiation yields

$$g'(x) = \frac{f'(x)}{f(x)} = \frac{2}{x} - \frac{\sin x}{\cos x} - \frac{28x^3}{1 + x^4}.$$

Multiplying by $f(x)$, we obtain

$$f'(x) = \frac{2x \cos x}{(1 + x^4)^7} - \frac{x^2 \sin x}{(1 + x^4)^7} - \frac{28x^5 \cos x}{(1 + x^4)^8}.$$

## 6.9   Exercises

1. (a) Find all $c$ such that $\log x = c + \int_e^x t^{-1} \, dt$ for all $x > 0$.
   (b) Let $f(x) = \log [(1 + x)/(1 - x)]$ if $x > 0$. If $a$ and $b$ are given numbers, with $ab \neq -1$, find all $x$ such that $f(x) = f(a) + f(b)$.
2. In each case, find a real $x$ satisfying the given equation.
   (a) $\log (1 + x) = \log (1 - x)$.          (c) $2 \log x = x \log 2$, $x \neq 2$.
   (b) $\log (1 + x) = 1 + \log (1 - x)$.       (d) $\log (\sqrt{x} + \sqrt{x + 1}) = 1$.
3. Let $f(x) = (\log x)/x$ if $x > 0$. Describe the intervals in which $f$ is increasing, decreasing, convex, and concave. Sketch the graph of $f$.

In Exercises 4 through 15, find the derivative $f'(x)$. In each case, the function $f$ is assumed to be defined for all real $x$ for which the given formula for $f(x)$ is meaningful.

4. $f(x) = \log (1 + x^2)$.
5. $f(x) = \log \sqrt{1 + x^2}$.
6. $f(x) = \log \sqrt{4 - x^2}$.
7. $f(x) = \log (\log x)$.
8. $f(x) = \log(x^2 \log x)$.
9. $f(x) = \frac{1}{4} \log \dfrac{x^2 - 1}{x^2 + 1}$.

10. $f(x) = (x + \sqrt{1 + x^2})^n$.
11. $f(x) = \sqrt{x + 1} - \log (1 + \sqrt{x + 1})$.
12. $f(x) = x \log (x + \sqrt{1 + x^2}) - \sqrt{1 + x^2}$.
13. $f(x) = \dfrac{1}{2\sqrt{ab}} \log \dfrac{\sqrt{a} + x\sqrt{b}}{\sqrt{a} - x\sqrt{b}}$.
14. $f(x) = x[\sin (\log x) - \cos (\log x)]$.
15. $f(x) = \log_a e$.

In Exercises 16 through 26, evaluate the integrals.

16. $\displaystyle\int \frac{dx}{2 + 3x}$.

17. $\int \log^2 x \, dx$.

18. $\int x \log x \, dx$.

19. $\int x \log^2 x \, dx$.

20. $\displaystyle\int_0^{e^3 - 1} \frac{dt}{1 + t}$.

21. $\int \cot x \, dx$.

22. $\int x^n \log (ax) \, dx$.

23. $\int x^2 \log^2 x \, dx$.

24. $\displaystyle\int \frac{dx}{x \log x}$ .

25. $\displaystyle\int_0^{1-e^{-2}} \frac{\log (1 - t)}{1 - t} \, dt.$

26. $\displaystyle\int \frac{\log |x|}{x\sqrt{1 + \log |x|}} \, dx.$

27. Derive the recursion formula

$$\int x^m \log^n x \, dx = \frac{x^{m+1} \log^n x}{m + 1} - \frac{n}{m + 1}\int x^m \log^{n-1} x \, dx$$

and use it to integrate $\int x^3 \log^3 x \, dx$.

28. (a) If $x > 0$, let $f(x) = x - 1 - \log x$, $g(x) = \log x - 1 + 1/x$. Examine the signs of $f'$ and $g'$ to prove that the inequalities

$$1 - \frac{1}{x} < \log x < x - 1$$

are valid for $x > 0$, $x \neq 1$. When $x = 1$, they become equalities.

(b) Sketch graphs of the functions $A$ and $B$ defined by the equations $A(x) = x - 1$ and $B(x) = 1 - 1/x$ for $x > 0$, and interpret geometrically the inequalities in part (a).

29. Prove the limit relation

$$\lim_{x \to 0} \frac{\log (1 + x)}{x} = 1$$

by the following two methods: (a) using the definition of the derivative $L'(1)$; (b) using the result of Exercise 28.

30. If $a > 0$, use the functional equation for the logarithm to prove that $\log (a^r) = r \log a$ for every rational number $r$.

31. Let $P = \{a_0, a_1, a_2, \ldots, a_n\}$ be any partition of the interval $[1, x]$, where $x > 1$.

(a) Integrate suitable step functions that are constant on the open subintervals of $P$ to derive the following inequalities:

$$\sum_{k=1}^{n} \left(\frac{a_k - a_{k-1}}{a_k}\right) < \log x < \sum_{k=1}^{n} \left(\frac{a_k - a_{k-1}}{a_{k-1}}\right).$$

(b) Interpret the inequalities of part (a) geometrically in terms of areas.

(c) Specialize the partition to show that for every integer $n > 1$,

$$\sum_{k=2}^{n} \frac{1}{k} < \log n < \sum_{k=1}^{n-1} \frac{1}{k}.$$

32. Prove the following formulas for changing from one logarithmic base to another:

(a) $\log_b x = \log_b a \log_a x$;

(b) $\log_b x = \dfrac{\log_a x}{\log_a b}$ .

33. Given that $\log_e 10 = 2.302585$, correct to six decimal places, compute $\log_{10} e$ using one of the formulas in Exercise 32. How many correct decimal places can you be certain of in the result of your calculation? *Note:* A table, correct to six decimal places, gives $\log_{10} e = 0.434294$.

34. A function $f$, continuous on the positive real axis, has the property that for all choices of $x > 0$ and $y > 0$, the integral

$$\int_x^{xy} f(t)\, dt$$

is independent of $x$ (and therefore depends only on $y$). If $f(2) = 2$, compute the value of the integral $A(x) = \int_1^x f(t)\, dt$ for all $x > 0$.

35. A function $f$, continuous on the positive real axis, has the property that

$$\int_1^{xy} f(t)\, dt = y \int_1^x f(t)\, dt + x \int_1^y f(t)\, dt$$

for all $x > 0$ and all $y > 0$. If $f(1) = 3$, compute $f(x)$ for each $x > 0$.

36. The base of a solid is the ordinate set of a function $f$ which is continuous over the interval $[1, a]$. All cross sections perpendicular to the interval $[1, a]$ are squares. The volume of the solid is $\frac{1}{3}a^3 \log^2 a - \frac{2}{9}a^3 \log a + \frac{2}{27}a^3 - \frac{2}{27}$ for every $a \geq 1$. Compute $f(a)$.

## 6.10 Polynomial approximations to the logarithm

In this section we will show that the logarithm function can be approximated by certain polynomials which can be used to compute logarithms to any desired degree of accuracy.

To simplify the resulting formulas, we first replace $x$ by $1 - x$ in the integral defining the logarithm to obtain

$$\log (1 - x) = \int_1^{1-x} \frac{dt}{t},$$

which is valid if $x < 1$. The change of variable $t = 1 - u$ converts this to the form

$$-\log (1 - x) = \int_0^x \frac{du}{1 - u}, \qquad \text{valid for} \quad x < 1.$$

Now we approximate the integrand $1/(1 - u)$ by polynomials which we then integrate to obtain corresponding approximations for the logarithm. To illustrate the method, we begin with a simple linear approximation to the integrand.

From the algebraic identity $1 - u^2 = (1 - u)(1 + u)$, we obtain the formula

(6.18)
$$\frac{1}{1 - u} = 1 + u + \frac{u^2}{1 - u},$$

valid for any real $u \neq 1$. Integrating this from 0 to $x$, where $x < 1$, we have

(6.19)
$$-\log (1 - x) = x + \frac{x^2}{2} + \int_0^x \frac{u^2}{1 - u}\, du.$$

The graph of the quadratic polynomial $P(x) = x + \frac{1}{2}x^2$ which appears on the right of (6.19) is shown in Figure 6.5 along with the curve $y = -\log (1 - x)$. Note that for $x$ near zero the polynomial $P(x)$ is a good approximation to $-\log (1 - x)$. In the next theorem we use a polynomial of degree $n - 1$ to approximate $1/(1 - u)$, and thereby obtain a polynomial of degree $n$ which approximates $\log (1 - x)$.

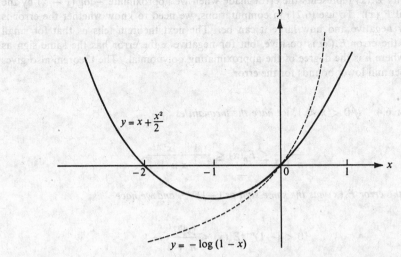

FIGURE 6.5   A quadratic polynomial approximation to the curve $y = -\log(1 - x)$.

THEOREM 6.3.    *Let $P_n$ denote the polynomial of degree $n$ given by*

$$P_n(x) = x + \frac{x^2}{2} + \frac{x^3}{3} + \cdots + \frac{x^n}{n} = \sum_{k=1}^{n} \frac{x^k}{k}.$$

*Then, for every $x < 1$ and every $n \geq 1$, we have*

(6.20)
$$-\log(1 - x) = P_n(x) + \int_0^x \frac{u^n}{1 - u} \, du.$$

*Proof.* From the algebraic identity

$$1 - u^n = (1 - u)(1 + u + u^2 + \cdots + u^{n-1}),$$

we obtain the formula

$$\frac{1}{1 - u} = 1 + u + u^2 + \cdots + u^{n-1} + \frac{u^n}{1 - u},$$

which is valid for $u \neq 1$. Integrating this from 0 to $x$, where $x < 1$, we obtain (6.20).
We can rewrite (6.20) in the form

(6.21)
$$-\log(1 - x) = P_n(x) + E_n(x),$$

where $E_n(x)$ is the integral,

$$E_n(x) = \int_0^x \frac{u^n}{1 - u} \, du.$$

The quantity $E_n(x)$ represents the error made when we approximate $-\log(1 - x)$ by the polynomial $P_n(x)$. To use (6.21) in computations, we need to know whether the error is positive or negative and how large it can be. The next theorem tells us that for small positive $x$ the error $E_n(x)$ is positive, but for negative $x$ the error has the same sign as $(-1)^{n+1}$, where $n$ is the degree of the approximating polynomial. The theorem also gives useful upper and lower bounds for the error.

THEOREM 6.4. *If $0 < x < 1$, we have the inequalities*

(6.22)
$$\frac{x^{n+1}}{n+1} \le E_n(x) \le \frac{1}{1-x}\frac{x^{n+1}}{n+1}.$$

*If $x < 0$, the error $E_n(x)$ has the same sign as $(-1)^{n+1}$, and we have*

(6.23)
$$0 < (-1)^{n+1}E_n(x) \le \frac{|x|^{n+1}}{n+1}.$$

*Proof.* Assume that $0 < x < 1$. In the integral defining $E_n(x)$ we have $0 \le u \le x$, so $1 - x \le 1 - u \le 1$, and hence the integrand satisfies the inequalities

$$u^n \le \frac{u^n}{1-u} \le \frac{u^n}{1-x}.$$

Integrating these inequalities, we obtain (6.22).

To prove (6.23), assume $x < 0$ and let $t = -x = |x|$. Then $t > 0$ and we have

$$E_n(x) = E_n(-t) = \int_0^{-t} \frac{u^n}{1-u}\, du = -\int_0^t \frac{(-v)^n}{1+v}\, dv = (-1)^{n+1} \int_0^t \frac{v^n}{1+v}\, dv.$$

This shows that $E_n(x)$ has the same sign as $(-1)^{n+1}$. Also, we have

$$(-1)^{n+1}E_n(x) = \int_0^t \frac{v^n}{1+v}\, dv \le \int_0^t v^n\, dv = \frac{t^{n+1}}{n+1} = \frac{|x|^{n+1}}{n+1},$$

which completes the proof of (6.23).

The next theorem gives a formula which is admirably suited for computations of logarithms.

THEOREM 6.5. *If $0 < x < 1$ and if $m \ge 1$, we have*

$$\log\frac{1+x}{1-x} = 2\left(x + \frac{x^3}{3} + \cdots + \frac{x^{2m-1}}{2m-1}\right) + R_m(x),$$

*where the error term, $R_m(x)$, satisfies the inequalities*

$$(6.24) \qquad \frac{x^{2m+1}}{2m + 1} < R_m(x) \le \frac{2 - x}{1 - x} \frac{x^{2m+1}}{2m + 1}.$$

*Proof.* Equation (6.21) is valid for any real $x < 1$. If we replace $x$ by $-x$ in (6.21), keeping $x > -1$, we obtain the formula

$$(6.25) \qquad -\log(1 + x) = P_n(-x) + E_n(-x).$$

If $-1 < x < 1$, both (6.21) and (6.25) are valid. Subtracting (6.25) from (6.21), we find

$$(6.26) \qquad \log \frac{1 + x}{1 - x} = P_n(x) - P_n(-x) + E_n(x) - E_n(-x).$$

In the difference $P_n(x) - P_n(-x)$, the even powers of $x$ cancel and the odd powers double up. Therefore, if $n$ is even, say $n = 2m$, we have

$$P_{2m}(x) - P_{2m}(-x) = 2\left(x + \frac{x^3}{3} + \cdots + \frac{x^{2m-1}}{2m - 1}\right),$$

and Equation (6.26) becomes

$$\log \frac{1 + x}{1 - x} = 2\left(x + \frac{x^3}{3} + \cdots + \frac{x^{2m-1}}{2m - 1}\right) + R_m(x),$$

where $R_m(x) = E_{2m}(x) - E_{2m}(-x)$. This formula is valid if $x$ lies in the open interval $-1 < x < 1$. Now we restrict $x$ to the interval $0 < x < 1$. Then the estimates of Theorem 6.4 give us

$$\frac{x^{2m+1}}{2m + 1} \le E_{2m}(x) \le \frac{1}{1 - x} \frac{x^{2m+1}}{2m + 1} \qquad \text{and} \qquad 0 < -E_{2m}(-x) \le \frac{x^{2m+1}}{2m + 1}.$$

Adding these, we obtain the inequalities in (6.24), since $1 + 1/(1 - x) = (2 - x)/(1 - x)$.

EXAMPLE. Taking $m = 2$ and $x = \frac{1}{3}$, we have $(1 + x)/(1 - x) = 2$, and we obtain the formula

$$\log 2 = 2(\tfrac{1}{3} + \tfrac{1}{81}) + R_2(\tfrac{1}{3}), \qquad \text{where} \qquad \tfrac{1}{5}(\tfrac{1}{3})^5 < R_2(\tfrac{1}{3}) \le \tfrac{1}{2}(\tfrac{1}{3})^5 = \tfrac{1}{486}.$$

This gives us the inequalities $0.6921 < \log 2 < 0.6935$ with very little calculation.

### 6.11   Exercises

1. Use Theorem 6.5 with $x = \frac{1}{3}$ and $m = 5$ to calculate approximations to log 2. Retain nine decimals in your calculations and obtain the inequalities $0.6931460 < \log 2 < 0.6931476$.
2. If $x = \frac{1}{5}$, then $(1 + x)/(1 - x) = \frac{3}{2}$. Thus, Theorem 6.5 enables us to compute log 3 in terms of log 2. Take $x = \frac{1}{5}$ and $m = 5$ in Theorem 6.5 and use the results of Exercise 1 to obtain the inequalities $1.098611 < \log 3 < 1.098617$.
     *Note:* Since $\log 2 < \log e < \log 3$, it follows that $2 < e < 3$.
3. Use Theorem 6.5 with $x = \frac{1}{9}$ to calculate log 5 in terms of log 2. Choose the degree of the approximating polynomial high enough to obtain the inequalities $1.609435 < \log 5 < 1.609438$.
4. Use Theorem 6.5 with $x = \frac{1}{8}$ to calculate log 7 in terms of log 5. Choose the degree of the approximating polynomial high enough to obtain the inequalities $1.945907 < \log 7 < 1.945911$.
5. Use the results of Exercises 1 through 4 to calculate a short table listing log $n$ for $n = 2, 3, \ldots,$ 10. Tabulate each entry with as many *correct* decimal places as you can be certain of from the inequalities in Exercises 1 through 4.

### 6.12   The exponential function

Theorem 6.2 shows that for every real $x$ there is one and only one $y$ such that $L(y) = x$. Therefore we can use the process of inversion to define $y$ as a function of $x$. The resulting inverse function is called the *exponential function*, or the *antilogarithm*, and is denoted by $E$.

DEFINITION.   *For any real $x$, we define $E(x)$ to be that number $y$ whose logarithm is $x$. That is, $y = E(x)$ means that $L(y) = x$.*

The domain of $E$ is the entire real axis; its range is the set of positive real numbers. The graph of $E$, which is shown in Figure 6.6, is obtained from the graph of the logarithm by

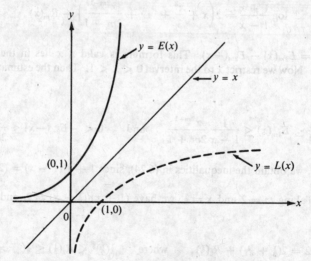

FIGURE 6.6   The graph of the exponential function is obtained from that of the logarithm by reflection through the line $y = x$.

reflection through the line $y = x$. Since $L$ and $E$ are inverses of each other, we have

$$L[E(x)] = x \quad \text{for all } x \quad \text{and} \quad E[L(y)] = y \quad \text{for all } y > 0.$$

Each property of the logarithm can be translated into a property of the exponential. For example, since the logarithm is strictly increasing and continuous on the positive real axis, it follows from Theorem 3.10 that the exponential is strictly increasing and continuous on the entire real axis. The counterpart of Theorem 6.1 is given by the following theorem.

THEOREM 6.6. *The exponential function has the following properties:*
(a) $E(0) = 1, \quad E(1) = e$.
(b) $E'(x) = E(x) \quad$ *for every x*.
(c) $E(a + b) = E(a)E(b) \quad$ *for all a and b*.

*Proof.* Part (a) follows from the equations $L(1) = 0$ and $L(e) = 1$. Next we prove (c), the functional equation for the exponential. Assume that $a$ and $b$ are given and let

$$x = E(a), \quad y = E(b), \quad c = L(xy).$$

Then we have

$$L(x) = a, \quad L(y) = b, \quad E(c) = xy.$$

But $c = L(xy) = L(x) + L(y) = a + b$. That is, $c = a + b$. Hence, $E(c) = E(a + b)$. On the other hand, $E(c) = xy = E(a)E(b)$, so $E(a + b) = E(a)E(b)$, which proves (c).

Now we use the functional equation to help us prove (b). The difference quotient for the derivative $E'(x)$ is

$$\frac{E(x + h) - E(x)}{h} = \frac{E(x)E(h) - E(x)}{h} = E(x)\frac{E(h) - 1}{h}.$$

Therefore, to prove (b) we must show that

$$(6.27) \qquad \lim_{h \to 0} \frac{E(h) - 1}{h} = 1.$$

We shall express the quotient in (6.27) in terms of the logarithm. Let $k = E(h) - 1$. Then $k + 1 = E(h)$ so $L(k + 1) = h$ and the quotient is equal to

$$(6.28) \qquad \frac{E(h) - 1}{h} = \frac{k}{L(k + 1)}.$$

Now as $h \to 0$, $E(h) \to 1$ because the exponential function is continuous at 1. Since $k = E(h) - 1$, we have $k \to 0$ as $h \to 0$. But

$$\frac{L(k + 1)}{k} = \frac{L(k + 1) - L(1)}{k} \to L'(1) = 1 \quad \text{as} \quad k \to 0.$$

In view of (6.28), this proves (6.27) which, in turn, proves (b).

### 6.13   Exponentials expressed as powers of *e*

The functional equation $E(a + b) = E(a)E(b)$ has many interesting consequences. For example, we can use it to prove that

$$(6.29) \qquad\qquad E(r) = e^r$$

for every rational number *r*.

First we take $b = -a$ in the functional equation to get

$$E(a)E(-a) = E(0) = 1 ,$$

and hence $E(-a) = 1/E(a)$ for every real *a*. Taking $b = a$, $b = 2a, \ldots, b = na$ in the functional equation we obtain, successively, $E(2a) = E(a)^2$, $E(3a) = E(a)^3$, and, in general, we have

$$(6.30) \qquad\qquad E(na) = E(a)^n$$

for every positive integer *n*. In particular, when $a = 1$, we obtain

$$E(n) = e^n ,$$

whereas for $a = 1/n$, we obtain $E(1) = E(1/n)^n$. Since $E(1/n) > 0$, this implies

$$(6.31) \qquad\qquad E\!\left(\frac{1}{n}\right) = e^{1/n} .$$

Therefore, if we put $a = 1/m$ in (6.30) and use (6.31), we find

$$E\!\left(\frac{n}{m}\right) = E\!\left(\frac{1}{m}\right)^n = e^{n/m}$$

for all positive integers *m* and *n*. In other words, we have proved (6.29) for every positive rational number *r*. Since $E(-r) = 1/E(r) = e^{-r}$, it also holds for all negative rational *r*.

### 6.14   The definition of $e^x$ for arbitrary real *x*

In the foregoing section we *proved* that $e^x = E(x)$ when *x* is any *rational* number. Now we shall *define* $e^x$ for irrational *x* by writing

$$(6.32) \qquad\qquad e^x = E(x) \qquad \text{for every real } x .$$

One justification for this definition is that we can use it to prove that the law of exponents

$$(6.33) \qquad\qquad e^a e^b = e^{a+b}$$

is valid for all real exponents *a* and *b*. When we use the definition in (6.32), the proof of (6.33) is a triviality because (6.33) is nothing but a restatement of the functional equation.

The notation $e^x$ for $E(x)$ is the one that is commonly used for the exponential. Occasionally $\exp(x)$ is written instead of $e^x$, especially when complicated formulas appear in the exponent. We shall continue to use $E(x)$ from time to time in this chapter, but later we shall switch to $e^x$.

We have defined the exponential function so that the two equations

$$y = e^x \quad \text{and} \quad x = \log y$$

mean exactly the same thing. In the next section we shall define more general powers so that the two equations $y = a^x$ and $x = \log_a y$ will be equivalent.

### 6.15   The definition of $a^x$ for $a > 0$ and $x$ real

Now that we have defined $e^x$ for arbitrary real $x$, there is absolutely no difficulty in formulating a definition of $a^x$ for every $a > 0$. One way to proceed is to let $a^x$ denote that number $y$ such that $\log_a y = x$. But this does not work for $a = 1$, since logarithms to the base 1 have not been defined. Another way is to define $a^x$ by the formula

$$(6.34) \qquad a^x = e^{x \log a}.$$

The second method is preferable because, first of all, it is meaningful for all positive $a$ (including $a = 1$) and, secondly, it makes it easy to prove the following properties of exponentials:

$$\log a^x = x \log a. \qquad (ab)^x = a^x b^x.$$

$$a^x a^y = a^{x+y}. \qquad (a^x)^y = (a^y)^x = a^{xy}.$$

*If $a \neq 1$, then $y = a^x$ if and only if $x = \log_a y$.*

The proofs of these properties are left as exercises for the reader.

Just as the graph of the exponential function was obtained from that of the logarithm by reflection through the line $y = x$, so the graph of $y = a^x$ can be obtained from that of $y = \log_a x$ by reflection through the same line; examples are shown in Figure 6.7. The curves in Figures 6.7 were obtained by reflection of those in Figures 6.3. The graph corresponding to $a = 1$ is, of course, the horizontal line $y = 1$.

### 6.16   Differentiation and integration formulas involving exponentials

One of the most remarkable properties of the exponential function is the formula

$$(6.35) \qquad E'(x) = E(x),$$

which tells us that this function is its own derivative. If we use this along with the chain rule, we can obtain differentiation formulas for exponential functions with any positive base $a$.

Suppose $f(x) = a^x$ for $x > 0$. By the definition of $a^x$, we may write

$$f(x) = e^{x \log a} = E(x \log a);$$

hence, by the chain rule, we find

(6.36) $$f'(x) = E'(x \log a) \cdot \log a = E(x \log a) \cdot \log a = a^x \log a.$$

In other words, differentiation of $a^x$ simply multiplies $a^x$ by the constant factor $\log a$, this factor being 1 when $a = e$.

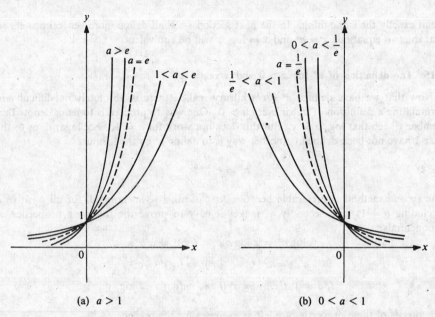

(a) $a > 1$           (b) $0 < a < 1$

FIGURE 6.7  The graph of $y = a^x$ for various values of $a$.

Of course, these differentiation formulas automatically lead to corresponding integration formulas. For example, (6.35) yields the result

(6.37) $$\int e^x \, dx = e^x + C,$$

whereas (6.36) gives us the more general formula

(6.38) $$\int a^x \, dx = \frac{a^x}{\log a} + C \qquad (a > 0, a \neq 1).$$

These may be generalized further by the method of substitution. We simply replace $x$ everywhere in (6.37) and (6.38) by $u$ to obtain

(6.39) $$\int e^u \, du = e^u + C, \qquad \int a^u \, du = \frac{a^u}{\log a} + C \qquad (a > 0, a \neq 1),$$

where $u$ now represents any function with a continuous derivative. If we write $u = f(x)$, and $du = f'(x)\, dx$, the formulas in (6.39) become

$$\int e^{f(x)} f'(x)\, dx = e^{f(x)} + C\,, \qquad \int a^{f(x)} f'(x)\, dx = \frac{a^{f(x)}}{\log a} + C\,,$$

the second of these being valid for $a > 0$, $a \neq 1$.

EXAMPLE 1. Integrate $\int x^2 e^{x^3}\, dx$.

*Solution.* Let $u = x^3$. Then $du = 3x^2\, dx$, and we obtain

$$\int x^2 e^{x^3}\, dx = \tfrac{1}{3} \int e^{x^3}(3x^2\, dx) = \tfrac{1}{3} \int e^u\, du = \tfrac{1}{3} e^u + C = \tfrac{1}{3} e^{x^3} + C\,.$$

EXAMPLE 2. Integrate $\displaystyle\int \frac{2^{\sqrt{x}}}{\sqrt{x}}\, dx$.

*Solution.* Let $u = \sqrt{x} = x^{\frac{1}{2}}$. Then $du = \tfrac{1}{2} x^{-\frac{1}{2}}\, dx = \tfrac{1}{2}\, dx/\sqrt{x}$. Hence we have

$$\int \frac{2^{\sqrt{x}}}{\sqrt{x}}\, dx = 2 \int 2^{\sqrt{x}}\left(\frac{1}{2}\frac{dx}{\sqrt{x}}\right) = 2 \int 2^u\, du = 2\frac{2^u}{\log 2} + C = \frac{2^{1+\sqrt{x}}}{\log 2} + C\,.$$

EXAMPLE 3. Integrate $\int \cos x \; e^{2 \sin x}\, dx$.

*Solution.* Let $u = 2 \sin x$. Then $du = 2 \cos x\, dx$, and hence we obtain

$$\int \cos x \; e^{2 \sin x}\, dx = \tfrac{1}{2} \int e^{2 \sin x}(2 \cos x\, dx) = \tfrac{1}{2} \int e^u\, du = \tfrac{1}{2} e^u + C = \tfrac{1}{2} e^{2 \sin x} + C\,.$$

EXAMPLE 4. Integrate $\int e^x \sin x\, dx$.

*Solution.* Let $u = e^x$, $dv = \sin x\, dx$. Then $du = e^x\, dx$, $v = -\cos x$, and we find

$$(6.40) \qquad \int e^x \sin x\, dx = \int u\, dv = uv - \int v\, du = -e^x \cos x + \int e^x \cos x\, dx + C\,.$$

The integral $\int e^x \cos x\, dx$ is treated in the same way. We let $u = e^x$, $dv = \cos x\, dx$, $du = e^x\, dx$, $v = \sin x$, and we obtain

$$(6.41) \qquad \int e^x \cos x\, dx = e^x \sin x - \int e^x \sin x\, dx + C\,.$$

Substituting this in (6.40), we may solve for $\int e^x \sin x\, dx$ and consolidate the arbitrary constants to obtain

$$\int e^x \sin x\, dx = \frac{e^x}{2}(\sin x - \cos x) + C\,.$$

Notice that we can use this in (6.41) to obtain also

$$\int e^x \cos x\, dx = \frac{e^x}{2}(\cos x + \sin x) + C\,.$$

EXAMPLE 5. Integrate $\int \dfrac{dx}{1 + e^x}$ .

*Solution.* One way to treat this example is to rewrite the integrand as follows:

$$\frac{1}{1 + e^x} = \frac{e^{-x}}{e^{-x} + 1} .$$

Now put $u = e^{-x} + 1$. Then $du = -e^{-x}\, dx$, and we get

$$\int \frac{e^{-x}}{e^{-x} + 1}\, dx = -\int \frac{-e^{-x}\, dx}{e^{-x} + 1} = -\int \frac{du}{u} = -\log |u| + C = -\log (1 + e^{-x}) + C .$$

The result can be written in other ways if we manipulate the logarithm. For instance,

$$-\log (1 + e^{-x}) = \log \frac{1}{1 + e^{-x}} = \log \frac{e^x}{e^x + 1}$$

$$= \log (e^x) - \log (e^x + 1) = x - \log (1 + e^x) .$$

Another way to treat this same example is to write

$$\frac{1}{1 + e^x} = 1 - \frac{e^x}{1 + e^x} .$$

Then we have

$$\int \frac{dx}{1 + e^x} = x - \int \frac{e^x}{1 + e^x}\, dx = x - \int \frac{du}{u} ,$$

where $u = 1 + e^x$. Thus we find

$$\int \frac{dx}{1 + e^x} = x - \log (1 + e^x) + C ,$$

which is one of the forms obtained above.

## 6.17 Exercises

In Exercises 1 through 12, find the derivative $f'(x)$. In each case the function $f$ is assumed to be defined for all real $x$ for which the given formula for $f(x)$ is meaningful.

1. $f(x) = e^{3x-1}$.
2. $f(x) = e^{4x^2}$.
3. $f(x) = e^{-x^2}$.
4. $f(x) = e^{\sqrt{x}}$.
5. $f(x) = e^{1/x}$.
6. $f(x) = 2^x$.

7. $f(x) = 2^{x^2}$ [which means $2^{(x^2)}$].
8. $f(x) = e^{\sin x}$.
9. $f(x) = e^{\cos^2 x}$.
10. $f(x) = e^{\log x}$.
11. $f(x) = e^{e^x}$ [which means $e^{(e^x)}$].
12. $f(x) = e^{e^{e^x}}$ [which means $\exp (e^{(e^x)})$].

Evaluate the indefinite integrals in Exercises 13 through 18.

13. $\int x\, e^x\, dx.$

14. $\int x\, e^{-x}\, dx.$

15. $\int x^2\, e^x\, dx.$

16. $\int x^2\, e^{-2x}\, dx.$

17. $\int e^{\sqrt{x}}\, dx.$

18. $\int x^3 e^{-x^2}\, dx.$

19. Determine all constants $a$ and $b$ such that $e^x = b + \int_a^x e^t\, dt.$

20. Let $A = \int e^{ax} \cos bx\, dx$ and $B = \int e^{ax} \sin bx\, dx$, where $a$ and $b$ are constants, not both zero. Use integration by parts to show that

$$aA - bB = e^{ax}\cos bx + C_1, \qquad aB + bA = e^{ax}\sin bx + C_2,$$

where $C_1$ and $C_2$ are arbitrary constants. Solve for $A$ and $B$ to deduce the following integration formulas:

$$\int e^{ax} \cos bx\, dx = \frac{e^{ax}(a \cos bx + b \sin bx)}{a^2 + b^2} + C,$$

$$\int e^{ax} \sin bx\, dx = \frac{e^{ax}(a \sin bx - b \cos bx)}{a^2 + b^2} + C.$$

In Exercises 21 through 34, find the derivative $f'(x)$. In each case, the function $f$ is assumed to be defined for all real $x$ for which the given formula for $f(x)$ is meaningful. Logarithmic differentiation may simplify the work in some cases.

21. $f(x) = x^x.$

22. $f(x) = (1 + x)(1 + e^{x^2}).$

23. $f(x) = \dfrac{e^x - e^{-x}}{e^x + e^{-x}}.$

24. $f(x) = x^{a^a} + a^{x^a} + a^{a^x}.$

25. $f(x) = \log\,[\log\,(\log x)].$

26. $f(x) = \log\,(e^x + \sqrt{1 + e^{2x}}).$

27. $f(x) = x^{x^x}.$

28. $f(x) = (\log x)^x.$

29. $f(x) = x^{\log x}.$

30. $f(x) = \dfrac{(\log x)^x}{x^{\log x}}.$

31. $f(x) = (\sin x)^{\cos x} + (\cos x)^{\sin x}.$

32. $f(x) = x^{1/x}.$

33. $f(x) = \dfrac{x^2(3 - x)^{1/3}}{(1 - x)(3 + x)^{2/3}}.$

34. $f(x) = \displaystyle\prod_{i=1}^n (x - a_i)^{b_i}.$

35. Let $f(x) = x^r$, where $x > 0$ and $r$ is any real number. The formula $f'(x) = rx^{r-1}$ was proved earlier for *rational* $r$.
    (a) Show that this formula also holds for arbitrary real $r$. [*Hint:* Write $x^r = e^{r \log x}$.]
    (b) Discuss under what conditions the result of part (a) applies for $x \le 0$.

36. Use the definition $a^x = e^{x \log a}$ to derive the following properties of general exponentials:
    (a) $\log a^x = x \log a.$
    (b) $(ab)^x = a^x b^x.$
    (c) $a^x a^y = a^{x+y}.$
    (d) $(a^x)^y = (a^y)^x = a^{xy}.$
    (e) If $a \ne 1$, then $y = a^x$ if and only if $x = \log_a y.$

37. Let $f(x) = \frac{1}{2}(a^x + a^{-x})$ if $a > 0$. Show that

$$f(x + y) + f(x - y) = 2f(x)f(y).$$

38. Let $f(x) = e^{cx}$, where $c$ is a constant. Show that $f'(0) = c$, and use this to deduce the following limit relation:

$$\lim_{x \to 0} \frac{e^{cx} - 1}{x} = c.$$

39. Let $f$ be a function defined everywhere on the real axis, with a derivative $f'$ which satisfies the equation

$$f'(x) = cf(x) \qquad \text{for every } x,$$

where $c$ is a constant. Prove that there is a constant $K$ such that $f(x) = Ke^{cx}$ for every $x$.
   [*Hint:* Let $g(x) = f(x)e^{-cx}$ and consider $g'(x)$.]

40. Let $f$ be a function defined everywhere on the real axis. Suppose also that $f$ satisfies the functional equation

(i) $$f(x + y) = f(x)f(y) \qquad \text{for all } x \text{ and } y.$$

   (a) Using only the functional equation, prove that $f(0)$ is either 0 or 1. Also, prove that if $f(0) \neq 0$ then $f(x) \neq 0$ for *all* $x$.
   Assume, in addition to (i), that $f'(x)$ exists for all $x$, and prove the following statements:
   (b) $f'(x)f(y) = f'(y)f(x)$ for all $x$ and $y$.
   (c) There is a constant $c$ such that $f'(x) = cf(x)$ for all $x$.
   (d) $f(x) = e^{cx}$ if $f(0) \neq 0$.   [*Hint:* See Exercise 39.]

41. (a) Let $f(x) = e^x - 1 - x$ for all $x$. Prove that $f'(x) \geq 0$ if $x \geq 0$ and $f'(x) \leq 0$ if $x \leq 0$. Use this fact to deduce the inequalities

$$e^x > 1 + x, \qquad e^{-x} > 1 - x,$$

valid for all $x > 0$. (When $x = 0$, these become equalities.)
   Integrate these inequalities to derive the following further inequalities, all valid for $x > 0$:

   (b) $$e^x > 1 + x + \frac{x^2}{2!}, \qquad e^{-x} < 1 - x + \frac{x^2}{2!}.$$

   (c) $$e^x > 1 + x + \frac{x^2}{2!} + \frac{x^3}{3!}, \qquad e^{-x} > 1 - x + \frac{x^2}{2!} - \frac{x^3}{3!}.$$

   (d) Guess the generalization suggested and prove your result.

42. If $n$ is a positive integer and if $x > 0$, show that

$$\left(1 + \frac{x}{n}\right)^n < e^x, \qquad \text{and that} \qquad e^x < \left(1 - \frac{x}{n}\right)^{-n} \qquad \text{if } x < n.$$

By choosing a suitable value of $n$, deduce that $2.5 < e < 2.99$.

43. Let $f(x, y) = x^y$ where $x > 0$. Show that

$$\frac{\partial f}{\partial x} = yx^{y-1} \qquad \text{and} \qquad \frac{\partial f}{\partial y} = x^y \log x.$$

## 6.18 The hyperbolic functions

Certain combinations of exponential functions occur quite frequently in analysis, and it is worth while to give these combinations special names and to study them as examples of new functions. These combinations, called the *hyperbolic sine* (sinh), the *hyperbolic cosine* (cosh), the *hyperbolic tangent* (tanh), etc., are defined as follows:

$$\sinh x = \frac{e^x - e^{-x}}{2}, \qquad \cosh x = \frac{e^x + e^{-x}}{2}, \qquad \tanh x = \frac{\sinh x}{\cosh x} = \frac{e^x - e^{-x}}{e^x + e^{-x}},$$

$$\operatorname{csch} x = \frac{1}{\sinh x}, \qquad \operatorname{sech} x = \frac{1}{\cosh x}, \qquad \coth x = \frac{1}{\tanh x}.$$

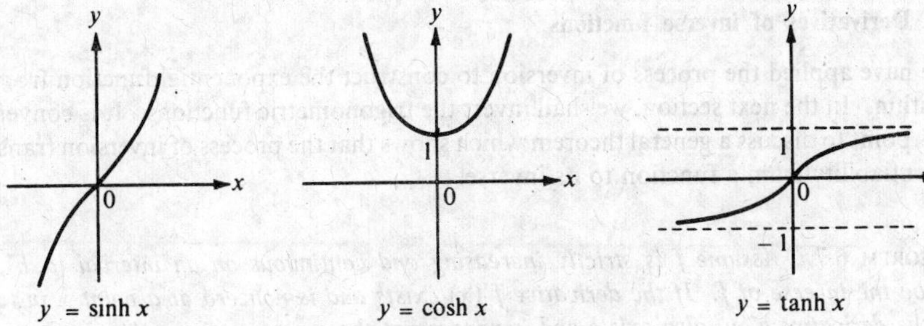

$$y = \sinh x \qquad\qquad y = \cosh x \qquad\qquad y = \tanh x$$

FIGURE 6.8 Graphs of hyperbolic functions.

The prefix "hyperbolic" is due to the fact that these functions are related geometrically to a hyperbola in much the same way as the trigonometric functions are related to a circle. This relation will be discussed in more detail in Chapter 14 when we study the hyperbola. The graphs of the sinh, cosh, and tanh are shown in Figure 6.8.

The hyperbolic functions possess many properties that resemble those of the trigonometric functions. Some of these are listed as exercises in the following section.

## 6.19 Exercises

Derive the properties of the hyperbolic functions listed in Exercises 1 through 15 and compare them, whenever possible, with the corresponding properties of the trigonometric functions.

1. $\cosh^2 x - \sinh^2 x = 1$.
2. $\sinh(-x) = -\sinh x$.
3. $\cosh(-x) = \cosh x$.
4. $\tanh(-x) = -\tanh x$.
5. $\sinh(x + y) = \sinh x \cosh y + \cosh x \sinh y$.
6. $\cosh(x + y) = \cosh x \cosh y + \sinh x \sinh y$.
7. $\sinh 2x = 2 \sinh x \cosh x$.
8. $\cosh 2x = \cosh^2 x + \sinh^2 x$.
9. $\cosh x + \sinh x = e^x$.
10. $\cosh x - \sinh x = e^{-x}$.
11. $(\cosh x + \sinh x)^n = \cosh nx + \sinh nx$ ($n$ an integer).
12. $2 \sinh^2 \frac{1}{2}x = \cosh x - 1$.

13. $2 \cosh^2 \tfrac{1}{2}x = \cosh x + 1$.

14. $\tanh^2 x + \operatorname{sech}^2 x = 1$.

15. $\coth^2 x - \operatorname{csch}^2 x = 1$.

16. Find $\cosh x$ if $\sinh x = \tfrac{4}{3}$.

17. Find $\sinh x$ if $\cosh x = \tfrac{5}{4}$ and $x > 0$.

18. Find $\sinh x$ and $\cosh x$ if $\tanh x = \tfrac{5}{13}$.

19. Find $\cosh (x + y)$ if $\sinh x = \tfrac{4}{3}$ and $\sinh y = \tfrac{3}{4}$.

20. Find $\tanh 2x$ if $\tanh x = \tfrac{3}{4}$.

In Exercises 21 through 26, prove the differentiation formulas.

21. $D \sinh x = \cosh x$.

22. $D \cosh x = \sinh x$.

23. $D \tanh x = \operatorname{sech}^2 x$.

24. $D \coth x = -\operatorname{csch}^2 x$.

25. $D \operatorname{sech} x = -\operatorname{sech} x \tanh x$.

26. $D \operatorname{csch} x = -\operatorname{csch} x \coth x$.

## 6.20  Derivatives of inverse, functions

We have applied the process of inversion to construct the exponential function from the logarithm. In the next section, we shall invert the trigonometric functions. It is convenient at this point to discuss a general theorem which shows that the process of inversion transmits differentiability from a function to its inverse.

THEOREM 6.7.  *Assume f is strictly increasing and continuous on an interval* $[a, b]$, *and let g be the inverse of f. If the derivative* $f'(x)$ *exists and is nonzero at a point x in* $(a, b)$, *then the derivative* $g'(y)$ *also exists and is nonzero at the corresponding point y, where* $y = f(x)$. *Moreover, the two derivatives are reciprocals of each other; that is, we have*

(6.42)
$$g'(y) = \frac{1}{f'(x)}.$$

*Note:* If we use the Leibniz notation and write $y$ for $f(x)$, $dy/dx$ for $f'(x)$, $x$ for $g(y)$, and $dx/dy$ for $g'(y)$, then Equation (6.42) becomes

$$\frac{dx}{dy} = \frac{1}{\left(\dfrac{dy}{dx}\right)},$$

which has the appearance of a trivial algebraic identity.

*Proof.* Assume $x$ is a point in $(a, b)$ where $f'(x)$ exists and is nonzero, and let $y = f(x)$. We shall show that the difference quotient

$$\frac{g(y + k) - g(y)}{k}$$

approaches the limit $1/f'(x)$ as $k \to 0$.

Let $h = g(y + k) - g(y)$. Since $x = g(y)$, this implies $h = g(y + k) - x$ or $x + h = g(y + k)$. Therefore $y + k = f(x + h)$, and hence $k = f(x + h) - f(x)$. Note that

$h \neq 0$ if $k \neq 0$ because $g$ is strictly increasing. Therefore, if $k \neq 0$, the difference quotient in question is

$$(6.43) \qquad \frac{g(y + k) - g(y)}{k} = \frac{h}{f(x + h) - f(x)} = \frac{1}{[f(x + h) - f(x)]/h}.$$

As $k \to 0$, the difference $g(y + k) - g(y) \to 0$ because of the continuity of $g$ at $y$ [property (b) of Theorem 3.10]. This means that $h \to 0$ as $k \to 0$. But we know that the difference quotient in the denominator on the extreme right of (6.43) approaches $f'(x)$ as $h \to 0$ [since $f'(x)$ exists]. Therefore, when $k \to 0$, the quotient on the extreme left of (6.43) approaches the limit $1/f'(x)$. This proves Theorem 6.7.

### 6.21 Inverses of the trigonometric functions

The process of inversion may be applied to the trigonometric functions. Suppose we begin with the sine function. To determine a unique inverse, we must consider the sine over some interval where it is monotonic. There are, of course, many such intervals, for

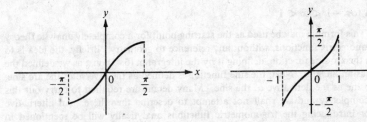

FIGURE 6.9  $y = \sin x$.          FIGURE 6.10  $y = \arcsin x$.

example $[-\frac{1}{2}\pi, \frac{1}{2}\pi]$, $[\frac{1}{2}\pi, \frac{3}{2}\pi]$, $[-\frac{3}{2}\pi, -\frac{1}{2}\pi]$, etc., and it really does not matter which one of these we choose. It is customary to select $[-\frac{1}{2}\pi, \frac{1}{2}\pi]$ and define a new function $f$ as follows:

$$f(x) = \sin x \qquad \text{if} \quad -\frac{\pi}{2} \leq x \leq \frac{\pi}{2}.$$

The function $f$ so defined is strictly increasing and it assumes every value between $-1$ and $+1$ exactly once on the interval $[-\frac{1}{2}\pi, \frac{1}{2}\pi]$. (See Figure 6.9.) Hence there is a uniquely determined function $g$ defined on $[-1, 1]$ which assigns to each number $y$ in $[-1, 1]$ that number $x$ in $[-\frac{1}{2}\pi, \frac{1}{2}\pi]$ for which $y = \sin x$. This function $g$ is called the *inverse sine* or *arc sine*, and its value at $y$ is denoted by arcsin $y$, or by $\sin^{-1} y$. Thus,

$$u = \arcsin v \qquad \text{means} \quad v = \sin u \qquad \text{and} \quad -\frac{\pi}{2} \leq u \leq \frac{\pi}{2}.$$

The graph of the arc sine is shown in Figure 6.10. Note that the arc sine is not defined outside the interval $[-1, 1]$.

The derivative of the arc sine can be obtained from formula (6.42) of Section 6.20. In this case we have $f'(x) = \cos x$ and this is nonzero in the open interval $(-\tfrac{1}{2}\pi, \tfrac{1}{2}\pi)$. Therefore formula (6.42) yields

$$g'(y) = \frac{1}{f'(x)} = \frac{1}{\cos x} = \frac{1}{\sqrt{1 - \sin^2 x}} = \frac{1}{\sqrt{1 - y^2}} \quad \text{if } -1 < y < 1.$$

With a change in notation we can write this result as follows:

(6.44) $$D \arcsin x = \frac{1}{\sqrt{1 - x^2}} \quad \text{if } -1 < x < 1.$$

Of course, this now gives us a new integration formula,

(6.45) $$\int_0^x \frac{1}{\sqrt{1 - t^2}} \, dt = \arcsin x \, ,$$

which is valid for $-1 < x < 1$.

> *Note:* This formula may be used as the starting point for a completely analytic theory of the trigonometric functions, without any reference to geometry. Briefly, the idea is to begin with the arc sine function, defining it by the integral in (6.45), just as we defined the logarithm as an integral. Next, the sine function is defined as the inverse of the arc sine, and the cosine as the derivative of the sine. Many details are required to carry out this program completely and we shall not attempt to describe them here. An alternative method for introducing the trigonometric functions analytically will be mentioned in Chapter 11.

In the Leibniz notation for indefinite integrals we may write formula (6.45) in the form

(6.46) $$\int \frac{dx}{\sqrt{1 - x^2}} = \arcsin x + C \, .$$

Integration by parts yields the following further integration formula:

$$\int \arcsin x \, dx = x \arcsin x - \int \frac{x \, dx}{\sqrt{1 - x^2}} = x \arcsin x + \sqrt{1 - x^2} + C \, .$$

The cosine and tangent are inverted in a similar fashion. For the cosine it is customary to choose the interval $[0, \pi]$ in which to perform the inversion. (See Figure 6.11.) The resulting inverse function, called the arc cosine, is defined as follows:

$$u = \arccos v \quad \text{means} \quad v = \cos u \quad \text{and} \quad 0 \le u \le \pi.$$

The graph of the arc cosine function is shown in Figure 6.12.

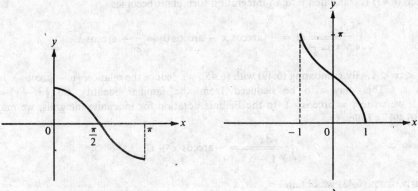

FIGURE 6.11   $y = \cos x$.          FIGURE 6.12   $y = \arccos x$.

To invert the tangent we choose the open interval $(-\tfrac{1}{2}\pi, \tfrac{1}{2}\pi)$ (see Figure 6.13) and we define the arc tangent as follows:

$$u = \arctan v \quad \text{means} \quad v = \tan u \quad \text{and} \quad -\frac{\pi}{2} < u < \frac{\pi}{2}.$$

Figure 6.14 shows a portion of the graph of the arc tangent function.

The argument used to derive (6.44) can also be applied to the arc cosine and arc tangent functions, and it yields the following differentiation formulas:

(6.47) $$D \arccos x = \frac{-1}{\sqrt{1 - x^2}},$$

valid for $-1 < x < 1$, and

(6.48) $$D \arctan x = \frac{1}{1 + x^2},$$

valid for all real $x$.

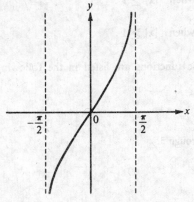

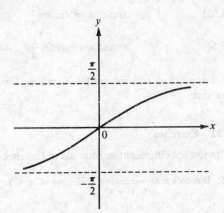

FIGURE 6.13   $y = \tan x$.          FIGURE 6.14   $y = \arctan x$.

When (6.47) is translated into an integration formula it becomes

(6.49)  $$\int_0^x \frac{1}{\sqrt{1-t^2}}\, dt = -(\arccos x - \arccos 0) = \frac{\pi}{2} - \arccos x$$

if $-1 < x < 1$. By comparing (6.49) with (6.45), we deduce the relation $\frac{1}{2}\pi - \arccos x = \arcsin x$. ( This may also be deduced from the familiar identity $\sin\left(\frac{1}{2}\pi - y\right) = \cos y$ if we write $y = \arccos x$.)  In the Leibniz notation for indefinite integrals, we may write (6.49) as follows:

(6.50)  $$\int \frac{dx}{\sqrt{1-x^2}} = -\arccos x + C \,.$$

Similarly, from (6.48) we obtain

(6.51)  $$\int_0^x \frac{dt}{1+t^2} = \arctan x \qquad \text{or} \qquad \int \frac{dx}{1+x^2} = \arctan x + C \,.$$

Using integration by parts in conjunction with (6.50) and (6.51), we can derive the following further integration formulas:

$$\int \arccos x \, dx = x \arccos x + \int \frac{x\, dx}{\sqrt{1-x^2}} = x \arccos x - \sqrt{1-x^2} + C \,,$$

$$\int \arctan x \, dx = x \arctan x - \int \frac{x\, dx}{1+x^2} = x \arctan x - \tfrac{1}{2}\log(1+x^2) + C \,.$$

The inverses of the cotangent, secant, and cosecant can be defined by means of the following formulas:

(6.52)  $$\operatorname{arccot} x = \frac{\pi}{2} - \arctan x \qquad \text{for all real } x \,,$$

(6.53)  $$\operatorname{arcsec} x = \arccos \frac{1}{x} \qquad \text{when } |x| \ge 1 \,,$$

(6.54)  $$\operatorname{arccsc} x = \arcsin \frac{1}{x} \qquad \text{when } |x| \ge 1 \,.$$

Differentiation and integration formulas for these functions are listed in the following exercises.

## 6.22   Exercises

Derive the differentiation formulas in Exercises 1 through 5.

1. $D \arccos x = \dfrac{-1}{\sqrt{1-x^2}} \quad$ if $\ -1 < x < 1$.

2. $D \arctan x = \dfrac{1}{1+x^2} \quad$ for all real $x$.

3. $D \operatorname{arccot} x = \dfrac{-1}{1 + x^2}$    for all real $x$.

4. $D \operatorname{arcsec} x = \dfrac{1}{|x|\sqrt{x^2 - 1}}$   if $|x| > 1$.

5. $D \operatorname{arccsc} x = \dfrac{-1}{|x|\sqrt{x^2 - 1}}$   if $|x| > 1$.

Derive the integration formulas in Exercises 6 through 10.

6. $\int \operatorname{arccot} x \, dx = x \operatorname{arccot} x + \frac{1}{2}\log(1 + x^2) + C.$

7. $\int \operatorname{arcsec} x \, dx = x \operatorname{arcsec} x - \dfrac{x}{|x|} \log |x + \sqrt{x^2 - 1}| + C.$

8. $\int \operatorname{arccsc} x \, dx = x \operatorname{arccsc} x + \dfrac{x}{|x|} \log |x + \sqrt{x^2 - 1}| + C.$

9. $\int (\arcsin x)^2 \, dx = x(\arcsin x)^2 - 2x + 2\sqrt{1 - x^2} \arcsin x + C.$

10. $\int \dfrac{\arcsin x}{x^2} \, dx = \log \left| \dfrac{1 - \sqrt{1 - x^2}}{x} \right| - \dfrac{\arcsin x}{x} + C.$

11. (a) Show that $D\left( \operatorname{arccot} x - \arctan \dfrac{1}{x} \right) = 0$ for all $x \neq 0$.

   (b) Prove that there is no constant $C$ such that $\operatorname{arccot} x - \arctan (1/x) = C$ for all $x \neq 0$. Explain why this does not contradict the zero-derivative theorem (Theorem 5.2).

In Exercises 12 through 25, find the derivative $f'(x)$. In each case the function $f$ is assumed to be defined for all real $x$ for which the given formula for $f(x)$ is meaningful.

12. $f(x) = \arcsin \dfrac{x}{2}.$

13. $f(x) = \arccos \dfrac{1 - x}{\sqrt{2}}.$

14. $f(x) = \arccos \dfrac{1}{x}.$

15. $f(x) = \arcsin (\sin x).$

16. $f(x) = \sqrt{x} - \arctan \sqrt{x}.$

17. $f(x) = \arctan x + \frac{1}{3} \arctan (x^3).$

18. $f(x) = \arcsin \dfrac{1 - x^2}{1 + x^2}.$

19. $f(x) = \arctan (\tan^2 x).$

20. $f(x) = \arctan (x + \sqrt{1 + x^2}).$

21. $f(x) = \arcsin (\sin x - \cos x).$

22. $f(x) = \arccos \sqrt{1 - x^2}.$

23. $f(x) = \arctan \dfrac{1 + x}{1 - x}.$

24. $f(x) = [\arccos (x^2)]^{-2}.$

25. $f(x) = \log\left( \arccos \dfrac{1}{\sqrt{x}} \right).$

26. Show that $dy/dx = (x + y)/(x - y)$ if $\arctan (y/x) = \log \sqrt{x^2 + y^2}$.

27. Compute $d^2y/dx^2$ if $y = (\arcsin x)/\sqrt{1 - x^2}$ for $|x| < 1$.

28. Let $f(x) = \arctan x - x + \frac{1}{3}x^3$. Examine the sign of $f'$ to prove that

$$x - \dfrac{x^3}{3} < \arctan x \quad \text{if} \quad x > 0.$$

In Exercises 29 through 47, evaluate the indefinite integrals.

29. $\int \dfrac{dx}{\sqrt{a^2 - x^2}}$,    $a \neq 0$.

30. $\int \dfrac{dx}{\sqrt{1 - 2x - x^2}}$.

31. $\int \dfrac{dx}{a^2 + x^2}$,    $a \neq 0$.

32. $\int \dfrac{dx}{a + bx^2}$    $(ab \neq 0)$.

33. $\int \dfrac{dx}{x^2 - x + 2}$.

34. $\int x \arctan x \, dx$.

35. $\int x^2 \arccos x \, dx$.

36. $\int x(\arctan x)^2 \, dx$.

37. $\int \arctan \sqrt{x} \, dx$.

38. $\int \dfrac{\arctan \sqrt{x}}{\sqrt{x}(1 + x)} \, dx$.

39. $\int \sqrt{1 - x^2} \, dx$.    [*Hint:*  $x = \sin u$.]

40. $\int \dfrac{x \, e^{\arctan x}}{(1 + x^2)^{3/2}} \, dx$.

41. $\int \dfrac{e^{\arctan x}}{(1 + x^2)^{3/2}} \, dx$.

42. $\int \dfrac{x^2}{(1 + x^2)^2} \, dx$.

43. $\int \dfrac{e^x}{1 + e^{2x}} \, dx$.

44. $\int \dfrac{\text{arccot } e^x}{e^x} \, dx$.

45. $\int \left( \dfrac{a + x}{a - x} \right)^{1/2} dx$,    $a > 0$.

46. $\int \sqrt{(x - a)(b - x)} \, dx$,    $b \neq a$.

47. $\int \dfrac{dx}{\sqrt{(x - a)(b - x)}}$,    $b \neq a$.    [*Hint:*  $x - a = (b - a) \sin^2 u$.]

## 6.23  Integration by partial fractions

We recall that a quotient of two polynomials is called a rational function. Differentiation of a rational function leads to a new rational function which may be obtained by the quotient rule for derivatives. On the other hand, integration of a rational function may lead to functions that are not rational. For example, we have

$$\int \frac{dx}{x} = \log |x| + C \quad \text{and} \quad \int \frac{dx}{1 + x^2} = \arctan x + C \,.$$

We shall describe a method for computing the integral of any rational function, and we shall find that the result can always be expressed in terms of polynomials, rational functions, inverse tangents, and logarithms.

The basic idea of the method is to decompose a given rational function into a sum of simpler fractions (called partial fractions) that can be integrated by the techniques discussed earlier. We shall describe the general procedure by means of a number of simple examples that illustrate all the essential features of the method.

EXAMPLE 1. In this example we begin with two simple fractions, $1/(x - 1)$ and $1/(x + 3)$, which we know how to integrate, and see what happens when we form a linear combination of these fractions. For example, if we take twice the first fraction plus three times the second, we obtain

$$\frac{2}{x - 1} + \frac{3}{x + 3} = \frac{2(x + 3) + 3(x - 1)}{(x - 1)(x + 3)} = \frac{5x + 3}{x^2 + 2x - 3} \,.$$

If, now, we read this formula from right to left, it tells us that the rational function $r$ given by $r(x) = (5x + 3)/(x^2 + 2x - 3)$ has been expressed as a linear combination of $1/(x - 1)$ and $1/(x + 3)$. Therefore, we may evaluate the integral of $r$ by writing

$$\int \frac{5x + 3}{x^2 + 2x - 3} \, dx = 2 \int \frac{dx}{x - 1} + 3 \int \frac{dx}{x + 3} = 2 \log |x - 1| + 3 \log |x + 3| + C \, .$$

EXAMPLE 2. The foregoing example suggests a procedure for dealing with integrals of the form $\int (ax + b)/(x^2 + 2x - 3) \, dx$. For example, to evaluate $\int (2x + 5)/(x^2 + 2x - 3) \, dx$, we try to express the integral as a linear combination of $1/(x - 1)$ and $1/(x + 3)$ by writing

$$(6.55) \qquad \frac{2x + 5}{x^2 + 2x - 3} = \frac{A}{x - 1} + \frac{B}{x + 3}$$

with constants $A$ and $B$ to be determined. If we can choose $A$ and $B$ so that Equation (6.55) is an identity, then the integral of the fraction on the left is equal to the sum of the integrals of the simpler fractions on the right. To find $A$ and $B$, we multiply both sides of (6.55) by $(x - 1)(x + 3)$ to remove the fractions. This gives us

$$(6.56) \qquad A(x + 3) + B(x - 1) = 2x + 5 \, .$$

At this stage there are two methods commonly used to find $A$ and $B$. One method is to equate coefficients of like powers of $x$ in (6.56). This leads to the equations $A + B = 2$ and $3A - B = 5$. Solving this pair of simultaneous equations, we obtain $A = \frac{7}{4}$ and $B = \frac{1}{4}$. The other method involves the substitution of two values of $x$ in (6.56) and leads to another pair of equations for $A$ and $B$. In this particular case, the presence of the factors $x - 1$ and $x + 3$ suggests that we use the values $x = 1$ and $x = -3$. When we put $x = 1$ in (6.56), the coefficient of $B$ vanishes, and we find $4A = 7$, or $A = \frac{7}{4}$. Similarly, we can make the coefficient of $A$ vanish by putting $x = -3$. This gives us $-4B = -1$, or $B = \frac{1}{4}$. In any event, we have found values of $A$ and $B$ to satisfy (6.55), so we have

$$\int \frac{2x + 5}{x^2 + 2x - 3} \, dx = \frac{7}{4} \int \frac{dx}{x - 1} + \frac{1}{4} \int \frac{dx}{x + 3} = \frac{7}{4} \log |x - 1| + \frac{1}{4} \log |x + 3| + C \, .$$

It is clear that the method described in Example 2 also applies to integrals of the form $\int f(x)/g(x) \, dx$ in which $f$ is a linear polynomial and $g$ is a quadratic polynomial that can be factored into distinct linear factors with real coefficients, say $g(x) = (x - x_1)(x - x_2)$. In this case the quotient $f(x)/g(x)$ can be expressed as a linear combination of $1/(x - x_1)$ and $1/(x - x_2)$, and integration of $f(x)/g(x)$ leads to a corresponding combination of the logarithmic terms $\log |x - x_1|$ and $\log |x - x_2|$.

The foregoing examples involve rational functions $f/g$ in which the degree of the numerator is less than that of the denominator. A rational function with this property is said to be a *proper* rational function. If $f/g$ is *improper*, that is, if the degree of $f$ is not less than that of $g$, then we can express $f/g$ as the sum of a polynomial and a proper rational function. In fact, we simply divide $f$ by $g$ to obtain

$$\frac{f(x)}{g(x)} = Q(x) + \frac{R(x)}{g(x)} \, ,$$

where $Q$ and $R$ are polynomials (called the *quotient* and *remainder*, respectively) such that the remainder has degree less than that of $g$. For example,

$$\frac{x^3 + 3x}{x^2 - 2x - 3} = x + 2 + \frac{10x + 6}{x^2 - 2x - 3}.$$

Therefore, in the study of integration technique, there is no loss in generality if we restrict ourselves to *proper* rational functions, and from now on we consider $\int f(x)/g(x)\,dx$, where $f$ has degree less than that of $g$.

A general theorem in algebra states that every proper rational function can be expressed as a finite sum of fractions of the forms

$$\frac{A}{(x + a)^k} \quad \text{and} \quad \frac{Bx + C}{(x^2 + bx + c)^m},$$

where $k$ and $m$ are positive integers and $A$, $B$, $C$, $a$, $b$, $c$ are constants with $b^2 - 4c < 0$. The condition $b^2 - 4c < 0$ means that the quadratic polynomial $x^2 + bx + c$ cannot be factored into linear factors with real coefficients or, what amounts to the same thing, the quadratic equation $x^2 + bx + c = 0$ has no real roots. Such a quadratic factor is said to be *irreducible*. When a rational function has been so expressed, we say that it has been decomposed into *partial fractions*. Therefore the problem of integrating this rational function reduces to that of integrating its partial fractions. These may be easily dealt with by the techniques described in the examples which follow.

We shall not bother to prove that partial-fraction decompositions always exist. Instead, we shall show (by means of examples) how to obtain the partial fractions in specific problems. In each case that arises the partial-fraction decomposition can be verified directly.

It is convenient to separate the discussion into cases depending on the way in which the denominator of the quotient $f(x)/g(x)$ can be factored.

CASE 1. *The denominator is a product of distinct linear factors.* Suppose that $g(x)$ splits into $n$ distinct linear factors, say

$$g(x) = (x - x_1)(x - x_2) \cdots (x - x_n).$$

Now notice that a linear combination of the form

$$\frac{A_1}{x - x_1} + \cdots + \frac{A_n}{x - x_n}$$

may be expressed as a single fraction with the common denominator $g(x)$, and the numerator of this fraction will be a polynomial of degree $< n$ involving the $A$'s. Therefore, if we can find $A$'s to make this numerator equal to $f(x)$, we shall have the decomposition

$$\frac{f(x)}{g(x)} = \frac{A_1}{x - x_1} + \cdots + \frac{A_n}{x - x_n},$$

and the integral of $f(x)/g(x)$ will be equal to $\sum_{i=1}^{n} A_i \log |x - x_i|$. In the next example, we work out a case with $n = 3$.

**EXAMPLE 3.** Integrate $\displaystyle\int \frac{2x^2 + 5x - 1}{x^3 + x^2 - 2x} dx$.

*Solution.* Since $x^3 + x^2 - 2x = x(x - 1)(x + 2)$, the denominator is a product of distinct linear factors, and we try to find $A_1$, $A_2$, and $A_3$ such that

$$\frac{2x^2 + 5x - 1}{x^3 + x^2 - 2x} = \frac{A_1}{x} + \frac{A_2}{x - 1} + \frac{A_3}{x + 2} \, .$$

Clearing the fractions, we obtain

$$2x^2 + 5x - 1 = A_1(x - 1)(x + 2) + A_2 x(x + 2) + A_3 x(x - 1) \, .$$

When $x = 0$, we find $-2A_1 = -1$, so $A_1 = \frac{1}{2}$. When $x = 1$, we obtain $3A_2 = 6$, $A_2 = 2$, and when $x = -2$, we find $6A_3 = -3$, or $A_3 = -\frac{1}{2}$. Therefore we have

$$\int \frac{2x^2 + 5x - 1}{x^3 + x^2 - 2x} dx = \frac{1}{2} \int \frac{dx}{x} + 2 \int \frac{dx}{x - 1} - \frac{1}{2} \int \frac{dx}{x + 2}$$

$$= \tfrac{1}{2} \log |x| + 2 \log |x - 1| - \tfrac{1}{2} \log |x + 2| + C \, .$$

*CASE 2. The denominator is a product of linear factors, some of which are repeated.* We illustrate this case with an example.

**EXAMPLE 4.** Integrate $\displaystyle\int \frac{x^2 + 2x + 3}{(x - 1)(x + 1)^2} dx$.

*Solution.* Here we try to find $A_1$, $A_2$, $A_3$ so that

(6.57) $$\frac{x^2 + 2x + 3}{(x - 1)(x + 1)^2} = \frac{A_1}{x - 1} + \frac{A_2}{x + 1} + \frac{A_3}{(x + 1)^2} \, .$$

We need both $A_2/(x + 1)$ and $A_3/(x + 1)^2$ as well as $A_1/(x - 1)$ in order to get a polynomial of degree two in the numerator and to have as many constants as equations when we try to determine the $A$'s. Clearing the fractions, we obtain

(6.58) $$x^2 + 2x + 3 = A_1(x + 1)^2 + A_2(x - 1)(x + 1) + A_3(x - 1) \, .$$

Substituting $x = 1$, we find $4A_1 = 6$, so $A_1 = \frac{3}{2}$. When $x = -1$, we obtain $-2A_3 = 2$ and $A_3 = -1$. We need one more equation to determine $A_2$. Since there are no other choices of $x$ that will make any factor vanish, we choose a convenient $x$ that will help to simplify the calculations. For example, the choice $x = 0$ leads to the equation $3 = A_1 - A_2 - A_3$ from which we find $A_2 = -\frac{1}{2}$. An alternative method is to differentiate both sides of (6.58) and then substitute a convenient $x$. Differentiation of (6.58) leads to the equation

$$2x + 2 = 2A_1(x + 1) + A_2(x - 1) + A_2(x + 1) + A_3,$$

and, if we put $x = -1$, we find $0 = -2A_2 + A_3$, so $A_2 = \frac{1}{2}A_3 = -\frac{1}{2}$, as before. Therefore we have found $A$'s to satisfy (6.57), so we have

$$\int \frac{x^2 + 2x + 3}{(x - 1)(x + 1)^2} dx = \frac{3}{2} \int \frac{dx}{x - 1} - \frac{1}{2} \int \frac{dx}{x + 1} - \int \frac{dx}{(x + 1)^2}$$

$$= \frac{3}{2} \log |x - 1| - \frac{1}{2} \log |x + 1| + \frac{1}{x + 1} + C.$$

If, on the left of (6.57), the factor $(x + 1)^3$ had appeared instead of $(x + 1)^2$, we would have added an extra term $A_4/(x + 1)^3$ on the right. More generally, if a linear factor $x + a$ appears $p$ times in the denominator, then for this factor we must allow for a sum of $p$ terms, namely

(6.59)
$$\sum_{k=1}^{p} \frac{A_k}{(x + a)^k},$$

where the $A$'s are constants. A sum of this type is to be used for each repeated linear factor.

CASE 3. *The denominator contains irreducible quadratic factors, none of which are repeated.*

EXAMPLE 5. Integrate $\displaystyle\int \frac{3x^2 + 2x - 2}{x^3 - 1} dx$.

*Solution.* The denominator can be split as the product $x^3 - 1 = (x - 1)(x^2 + x + 1)$, where $x^2 + x + 1$ is irreducible, and we try a decomposition of the form

$$\frac{3x^2 + 2x - 2}{x^3 - 1} = \frac{A}{x - 1} + \frac{Bx + C}{x^2 + x + 1}.$$

In the fraction with denominator $x^2 + x + 1$, we have used a linear polynomial $Bx + C$ in the numerator in order to have as many constants as equations when we solve for $A$, $B$, $C$. Clearing the fractions and solving for $A$, $B$, and $C$, we find $A = 1$, $B = 2$, and $C = 3$. Therefore we have

$$\int \frac{3x^2 + 2x - 2}{x^3 - 1} dx = \int \frac{dx}{x - 1} + \int \frac{2x + 3}{x^2 + x + 1} dx.$$

The first integral on the right is $\log |x - 1|$. To evaluate the second integral, we write

$$\int \frac{2x + 3}{x^2 + x + 1} dx = \int \frac{2x + 1}{x^2 + x + 1} dx + \int \frac{2}{x^2 + x + 1} dx$$

$$= \log (x^2 + x + 1) + 2 \int \frac{dx}{(x + \frac{1}{2})^2 + \frac{3}{4}}.$$

If we let $u = x + \frac{1}{2}$ and $\alpha = \sqrt{\frac{3}{4}}$, the last integral is

$$2 \int \frac{du}{u^2 + \alpha^2} = \frac{2}{\alpha} \arctan \frac{u}{\alpha} = \frac{4}{3} \sqrt{3} \arctan \frac{2x + 1}{\sqrt{3}} .$$

Therefore, we have

$$\int \frac{3x^2 + 2x - 2}{x^3 - 1} \, dx = \log |x - 1| + \log (x^2 + x + 1) + \frac{4}{3} \sqrt{3} \arctan \frac{2x + 1}{\sqrt{3}} + C .$$

*CASE 4. The denominator contains irreducible quadratic factors, some of which are repeated.* Here the situation is analogous to Case 2. In the partial-fraction decomposition of $f(x)/g(x)$ we allow, first of all, a sum of the form (6.59) for each linear factor, as already described. In addition, if an irreducible quadratic factor $x^2 + bx + c$ is repeated $m$ times, we allow a sum of $m$ terms, namely

$$\sum_{k=1}^{m} \frac{B_k x + C_k}{(x^2 + bx + c)^k} ,$$

where each numerator is linear.

EXAMPLE 6. Integrate $\displaystyle \int \frac{x^4 - x^3 + 2x^2 - x + 2}{(x - 1)(x^2 + 2)^2} \, dx$ .

*Solution.* We write

$$\frac{x^4 - x^3 + 2x^2 - x + 2}{(x - 1)(x^2 + 2)^2} = \frac{A}{x - 1} + \frac{Bx + C}{x^2 + 2} + \frac{Dx + E}{(x^2 + 2)^2} .$$

Clearing the fractions and solving for $A$, $B$, $C$, $D$, and $E$, we find that

$$A = \tfrac{1}{3}, \qquad B = \tfrac{2}{3}, \qquad C = -\tfrac{1}{3}, \qquad D = -1, \qquad E = 0 .$$

Therefore, we have

$$\int \frac{x^4 - x^3 + 2x^2 - x + 2}{(x - 1)(x^2 + 2)^2} \, dx = \frac{1}{3} \int \frac{dx}{x - 1} + \int \frac{\frac{2}{3}x - \frac{1}{3}}{x^2 + 2} \, dx - \int \frac{x \, dx}{(x^2 + 2)^2}$$

$$= \frac{1}{3} \int \frac{dx}{x - 1} + \frac{1}{3} \int \frac{2x \, dx}{x^2 + 2} - \frac{1}{3} \int \frac{dx}{x^2 + 2} - \frac{1}{2} \int \frac{2x \, dx}{(x^2 + 2)^2}$$

$$= \frac{1}{3} \log |x - 1| + \frac{1}{3} \log (x^2 + 2) - \frac{\sqrt{2}}{6} \arctan \frac{x}{\sqrt{2}}$$

$$+ \frac{1}{2} \frac{1}{x^2 + 2} + C .$$

The foregoing examples are typical of what happens in general. The problem of integrating a proper rational function reduces to that of calculating integrals of the forms

$$\int \frac{dx}{(x + a)^n}, \qquad \int \frac{x\,dx}{(x^2 + bx + c)^m}, \qquad \text{and} \qquad \int \frac{dx}{(x^2 + bx + c)^m}.$$

The first integral is $\log |x + a|$ if $n = 1$ and $(x + a)^{1-n}/(1 - n)$ if $n > 1$. To treat the other two, we express the quadratic as a sum of two squares by writing

$$x^2 + bx + c = \left(x + \frac{b}{2}\right)^2 + \left(c - \frac{b^2}{4}\right) = u^2 + \alpha^2,$$

where $u = x + b/2$ and $\alpha = \frac{1}{2}\sqrt{4c - b^2}$. (This is possible because $4c - b^2 > 0$.) The substitution $u = x + b/2$ reduces the problem to that of computing

$$(6.60) \qquad\qquad \int \frac{u\,du}{(u^2 + \alpha^2)^m} \qquad \text{and} \qquad \int \frac{du}{(u^2 + \alpha^2)^m}.$$

The first of these is $\frac{1}{2}\log (u^2 + \alpha^2)$ if $m = 1$, and $\frac{1}{2}(u^2 + \alpha^2)^{1-m}/(1 - m)$ if $m > 1$. When $m = 1$, the second integral in (6.60) is evaluated by the formula

$$\int \frac{du}{u^2 + \alpha^2} = \frac{1}{\alpha} \arctan \frac{u}{\alpha} + C.$$

The case $m > 1$ may be reduced to the case $m = 1$ by repeated application of the recursion formula

$$\int \frac{du}{(u^2 + \alpha^2)^m} = \frac{1}{2\alpha^2(m - 1)} \frac{u}{(u^2 + \alpha^2)^{m-1}} + \frac{2m - 3}{2\alpha^2(m - 1)} \int \frac{du}{(u^2 + \alpha^2)^{m-1}},$$

which is obtained by integration by parts. This discussion shows that every rational function may be integrated in terms of polynomials, rational functions, inverse tangents, and logarithms.

## 6.24  Integrals which can be transformed into integrals of rational functions

A function of two variables defined by an equation of the form

$$P(x, y) = \sum_{m=0}^{p} \sum_{n=0}^{q} a_{m,n} x^m y^n$$

is called a *polynomial in two variables*. The quotient of two such polynomials is called a *rational function of two variables*. Integrals of the form $\int R(\sin x, \cos x)\,dx$, where $R$ is a rational function of two variables, may be reduced by the substitution $u = \tan \frac{1}{2}x$ to integrals of the form $\int r(u)\,du$ where $r$ is a rational function of one variable. The latter integral may be evaluated by the techniques just described. We illustrate the method with a particular example.

EXAMPLE 1. Integrate $\displaystyle\int \frac{1}{\sin x + \cos x}\,dx$.

*Solution.* The substitution $u = \tan \frac{1}{2}x$ gives us

$$x = 2 \arctan u , \qquad dx = \frac{2}{1 + u^2} \, du ,$$

$$\sin x = 2 \sin \frac{x}{2} \cos \frac{x}{2} = \frac{2 \tan \frac{1}{2}x}{\sec^2 \frac{1}{2}x} = \frac{2u}{1 + u^2} ,$$

$$\cos x = 2 \cos^2 \frac{x}{2} - 1 = \frac{2}{\sec^2 \frac{1}{2}x} - 1 = \frac{2}{1 + u^2} - 1 = \frac{1 - u^2}{1 + u^2} ,$$

and

$$\sin x + \cos x = \frac{2u + 1 - u^2}{1 + u^2}$$

Therefore, we have

$$\int \frac{dx}{\sin x + \cos x} = -2 \int \frac{du}{u^2 - 2u - 1} = -2 \int \frac{du}{(u - a)(u - b)} ,$$

where $a = 1 + \sqrt{2}$ and $b = 1 - \sqrt{2}$. The method of partial fractions leads to

$$\int \frac{du}{(u - a)(u - b)} = \frac{1}{a - b} \int \left( \frac{1}{u - a} - \frac{1}{u - b} \right) du$$

and, since $a - b = 2\sqrt{2}$, we obtain

(6.61)     $$\int \frac{dx}{\sin x + \cos x} = \frac{\sqrt{2}}{2} \log \left| \frac{u - b}{u - a} \right| + C = \frac{\sqrt{2}}{2} \log \left| \frac{\tan \frac{1}{2}x - 1 + \sqrt{2}}{\tan \frac{1}{2}x - 1 - \sqrt{2}} \right| + C .$$

The final answer may be simplified somewhat by using suitable trigonometric identities. First we note that $\sqrt{2} - 1 = \tan \frac{1}{8}\pi$ so the numerator of the last fraction in (6.61) is $\tan \frac{1}{2}x + \tan \frac{1}{8}\pi$. In the denominator we write

$$\left| \tan \frac{x}{2} - 1 - \sqrt{2} \right| = (\sqrt{2} + 1) \left| (\sqrt{2} - 1) \tan \frac{x}{2} - 1 \right| = (\sqrt{2} + 1) \left| 1 - \tan \frac{x}{2} \tan \frac{\pi}{8} \right| .$$

Taking logarithms as indicated in (6.61), we may combine the term $-\frac{1}{2}\sqrt{2} \log (\sqrt{2} + 1)$ with the arbitrary constant and rewrite (6.61) as follows:

$$\int \frac{dx}{\sin x + \cos x} = \frac{\sqrt{2}}{2} \log \left| \tan \left( \frac{x}{2} + \frac{\pi}{8} \right) \right| + C .$$

In an earlier section we derived the integration formula

$$\int \frac{dx}{\sqrt{1 - x^2}} = \arcsin x$$

as a consequence of the formula for differentiating $\arcsin x$. The presence of $\arcsin x$ suggests that we could also evaluate this integral by the trigonometric substitution $t = \arcsin x$. We then have

$$x = \sin t, \qquad dx = \cos t \, dt, \qquad \sqrt{1 - x^2} = \sqrt{1 - \sin^2 t} = \cos t,$$

and we find that

$$\int \frac{dx}{\sqrt{1 - x^2}} = \int \frac{\cos t \, dt}{\cos t} = \int dt = t = \arcsin x .$$

This is always a good substitution to try if the integrand involves $\sqrt{1 - x^2}$. More generally, any integral of the form $\int R(x, \sqrt{a^2 - x^2}) \, dx$, where $R$ is a rational function of two variables, can be transformed by the substitution

$$x = a \sin t, \qquad dx = a \cos t \, dt ,$$

into an integral of the form $\int R(a \sin t, a \cos t) a \cos t \, dt$. This, in turn, can always be integrated by one of the methods described above.

EXAMPLE 2. Integrate $\displaystyle\int \frac{x \, dx}{4 - x^2 + \sqrt{4 - x^2}}$ .

*Solution.* We let $x = 2 \sin t$, $dx = 2 \cos t \, dt$, $\sqrt{4 - x^2} = 2 \cos t$, and we find that

$$\int \frac{x \, dx}{4 - x^2 + \sqrt{4 - x^2}} = \int \frac{4 \sin t \cos t \, dt}{4 \cos^2 t + 2 \cos t} = \int \frac{\sin t \, dt}{\cos t + \tfrac{1}{2}}$$

$$= -\log |\tfrac{1}{2} + \cos t| + C = -\log (1 + \sqrt{4 - x^2}) + C .$$

The same method works for integrals of the form

$$\int R(x, \sqrt{a^2 - (cx + d)^2}) \, dx ;$$

we use the trigonometric substitution $cx + d = a \sin t$.
We can deal similarly with integrals of the form

$$\int R(x, \sqrt{a^2 + (cx + d)^2}) \, dx$$

by the substitution $cx + d = a \tan t$, $c \, dx = a \sec^2 t \, dt$. For integrals of the form

$$\int R(x, \sqrt{(cx + d)^2 - a^2}) \, dx ,$$

we use the substitution $cx + d = a \sec t$, $c \, dx = a \sec t \tan t \, dt$. In either case, the new integrand becomes a rational function of $\sin t$ and $\cos t$.

## 6.25 Exercises

Evaluate the following integrals:

1. $\int \dfrac{2x + 3}{(x - 2)(x + 5)}\, dx.$

2. $\int \dfrac{x\, dx}{(x + 1)(x + 2)(x + 3)}.$

3. $\int \dfrac{x\, dx}{x^3 - 3x + 2}.$

4. $\int \dfrac{x^4 + 2x - 6}{x^3 + x^2 - 2x}\, dx.$

5. $\int \dfrac{8x^3 + 7}{(x + 1)(2x + 1)^3}\, dx.$

6. $\int \dfrac{4x^2 + x + 1}{x^3 - 1}\, dx.$

7. $\int \dfrac{x^4\, dx}{x^4 + 5x^2 + 4}.$

8. $\int \dfrac{x + 2}{x^2 + x}\, dx.$

9. $\int \dfrac{dx}{x(x^2 + 1)^2}.$

10. $\int \dfrac{dx}{(x + 1)(x + 2)^2(x + 3)^3}.$

11. $\int \dfrac{x\, dx}{(x + 1)^2}.$

12. $\int \dfrac{dx}{x^3 - x}.$

13. $\int \dfrac{x^2\, dx}{x^2 + x - 6}.$

14. $\int \dfrac{(x + 2)\, dx}{x^2 - 4x + 4}.$

15. $\int \dfrac{dx}{(x^2 - 4x + 4)(x^2 - 4x + 5)}.$

16. $\int \dfrac{(x - 3)\, dx}{x^3 + 3x^2 + 2x}.$

17. $\int \dfrac{dx}{(x^2 - 1)^2}.$

18. $\int \dfrac{x + 1}{x^3 - 1}\, dx.$

19. $\int \dfrac{x^4 + 1}{x(x^2 + 1)^2}\, dx.$

20. $\int \dfrac{dx}{x^4 - 2x^3}.$

21. $\int \dfrac{1 - x^3}{x(x^2 + 1)}\, dx.$

22. $\int \dfrac{dx}{x^4 - 1}.$

23. $\int \dfrac{dx}{x^4 + 1}.$

24. $\int \dfrac{x^2\, dx}{(x^2 + 2x + 2)^2}.$

25. $\int \dfrac{4x^5 - 1}{(x^5 + x + 1)^2}\, dx.$

26. $\int \dfrac{dx}{2 \sin x - \cos x + 5}.$

27. $\int \dfrac{dx}{1 + a \cos x} \qquad (0 < a < 1).$

28. $\int \dfrac{dx}{1 + a \cos x} \qquad (a > 1).$

29. $\int \dfrac{\sin^2 x}{1 + \sin^2 x}\, dx.$

30. $\int \dfrac{dx}{a^2 \sin^2 x + b^2 \cos^2 x} \qquad (ab \neq 0).$

31. $\int \dfrac{dx}{(a \sin x + b \cos x)^2} \qquad (a \neq 0).$

32. $\int_0^{\pi/2} \dfrac{\sin x\, dx}{1 + \cos x + \sin x}.$

33. $\int \sqrt{3 - x^2}\, dx.$

34. $\int \dfrac{x}{\sqrt{3 - x^2}}\, dx.$

35. $\int \dfrac{\sqrt{3 - x^2}}{x}\, dx.$

36. $\int \dfrac{\sqrt{x^2 + x}}{x}\, dx.$

37. $\int \sqrt{x^2 + 5}\, dx.$

38. $\int \dfrac{x}{\sqrt{x^2 + x + 1}}\, dx.$

39. $\displaystyle\int \frac{dx}{\sqrt{x^2 + x}}.$     40. $\displaystyle\int \frac{\sqrt{2 - x - x^2}}{x^2}\, dx.$

[*Hint:*  In Exercise 40, multiply numerator and denominator by $\sqrt{2 - x - x^2}$.]

## 6.26  Miscellaneous review exercises

1. Let $f(x) = \int_1^x (\log t)/(t + 1)\, dt$ if $x > 0$. Compute $f(x) + f(1/x)$. As a check, you should obtain $f(2) + f(\frac{1}{2}) = \frac{1}{2} \log^2 2$.
2. Find a function $f$, continuous for all $x$ (and not everywhere zero), such that

$$f^2(x) = \int_0^x f(t)\, \frac{\sin t}{2 + \cos t}\, dt.$$

3. Try to evaluate $\int e^x/x\, dx$ by using integration by parts.
4. Integrate $\int_0^{\pi/2} \log(e^{\cos x})\, dx.$
5. A function $f$ is defined by the equation

$$f(x) = \sqrt{\frac{4x + 2}{x(x + 1)(x + 2)}} \qquad \text{if} \quad x > 0.$$

(a) Find the slope of the graph of $f$ at the point for which $x = 1$.
(b) The region under the graph and above the interval $[1, 4]$ is rotated about the $x$-axis, thus generating a solid of revolution. Write an integral for the volume of this solid. Compute this integral and show that its value is $\pi \log(25/8)$.
6. A function $F$ is defined by the following indefinite integral:

$$F(x) = \int_1^x \frac{e^t}{t}\, dt \qquad \text{if} \quad x > 0.$$

(a) For what values of $x$ is it true that $\log x \le F(x)$?
(b) Prove that $\int_1^x e^t/(t + a)\, dt = e^{-a}[F(x + a) - F(1 + a)]$.
(c) In a similar way, express the following integrals in terms of $F$:

$$\int_1^x \frac{e^{at}}{t}\, dt, \qquad \int_1^x \frac{e^t}{t^2}\, dt, \qquad \int_1^x e^{1/t}\, dt .$$

7. In each case, give an example of a continuous function $f$ satisfying the conditions stated for all real $x$, or else explain why there is no such function:
(a) $\int_0^x f(t)\, dt = e^x.$
(b) $\int_0^x f(t)\, dt = 1 - 2^{x^2}.$     [$2^{x^2}$ means $2^{(x^2)}$.]
(c) $\int_0^x f(t)\, dt = f^2(x) - 1.$
8. If $f(x + y) = f(x)f(y)$ for all $x$ and $y$ and if $f(x) = 1 + xg(x)$, where $g(x) \to 1$ as $x \to 0$, prove that (a) $f'(x)$ exists for every $x$, and (b) $f(x) = e^x$.
9. Given a function $g$ which has a derivative $g'(x)$ for every real $x$ and which satisfies the following equations:

$$g'(0) = 2 \qquad \text{and} \qquad g(x + y) = e^y g(x) + e^x g(y) \qquad \text{for all } x \text{ and } y .$$

(a) Show that $g(2x) = 2e^x g(x)$ and find a similar formula for $g(3x)$.
(b) Generalize (a) by finding a formula relating $g(nx)$ to $g(x)$, valid for every positive integer $n$. Prove your result by induction.

(c) Show that $g(0) = 0$ and find the limit of $g(h)/h$ as $h \to 0$.

(d) There is a constant $C$ such that $g'(x) = g(x) + Ce^x$ for all $x$. Prove this statement and find the value of $C$. [*Hint:* Use the definition of the derivative $g'(x)$.]

10. A periodic function with period $a$ satisfies $f(x + a) = f(x)$ for all $x$ in its domain. What can you conclude about a function which has a derivative everywhere and satisfies an equation of the form

$$f(x + a) = bf(x)$$

for all $x$, where $a$ and $b$ are positive constants?

11. Use logarithmic differentiation to derive the formulas for differentiation of products and quotients from the corresponding formulas for sums and differences.

12. Let $A = \int_0^1 e^t/(t + 1) \, dt$. Express the values of the following integrals in terms of $A$:

(a) $\displaystyle\int_{a-1}^a \frac{e^{-t}}{t - a - 1} \, dt.$

(c) $\displaystyle\int_0^1 \frac{e^t}{(t + 1)^2} \, dt.$

(b) $\displaystyle\int_0^1 \frac{te^{t^2}}{t^2 + 1} \, dt.$

(d) $\displaystyle\int_0^1 e^t \log(1 + t) \, dt.$

13. Let $p(x) = c_0 + c_1 x + c_2 x^2$ and let $f(x) = e^x p(x)$.

(a) Show that $f^{(n)}(0)$, the $n$th derivative of $f$ at $0$, is $c_0 + nc_1 + n(n - 1)c_2$.

(b) Solve the problem when $p$ is a polynomial of degree 3.

(c) Generalize to a polynomial of degree $m$.

14. Let $f(x) = x \sin ax$. Show that $f^{(2n)}(x) = (-1)^n(a^{2n}x \sin ax - 2na^{2n-1} \cos ax)$.

15. Prove that

$$\sum_{k=0}^n (-1)^k \binom{n}{k} \frac{1}{k + m + 1} = \sum_{k=0}^m (-1)^k \binom{m}{k} \frac{1}{k + n + 1}.$$

[*Hint:* $1/(k + m + 1) = \int_0^1 t^{k+m} \, dt.$]

16. Let $F(x) = \int_0^x f(t) \, dt$. Determine a formula (or formulas) for computing $F(x)$ for all real $x$ if $f$ is defined as follows:

(a) $f(t) = (t + |t|)^2$.

(c) $f(t) = e^{-|t|}$.

(b) $f(t) = \begin{cases} 1 - t^2 & \text{if } |t| \le 1, \\ 1 - |t| & \text{if } |t| > 1, \end{cases}$

(d) $f(t) =$ the maximum of $1$ and $t^2$.

17. A solid of revolution is generated by rotating the graph of a continuous function $f$ around the interval $[0, a]$ on the $x$-axis. If, for every $a > 0$, the volume is $a^2 + a$, find the function $f$.

18. Let $f(x) = e^{-2x}$ for all $x$. Denote by $S(t)$ the ordinate set of $f$ over the interval $[0, t]$, where $t > 0$. Let $A(t)$ be the area of $S(t)$, $V(t)$ the volume of the solid obtained by rotating $S(t)$ about the $x$-axis, and $W(t)$ the volume of the solid obtained by rotating $S(t)$ about the $y$-axis. Compute the following: (a) $A(t)$; (b) $V(t)$; (c) $W(t)$; (d) $\lim_{t \to 0} V(t)/A(t)$.

19. Let $c$ be the number such that $\sinh c = \frac{3}{4}$. (Do not attempt to compute $c$.) In each case find all those $x$ (if any exist) satisfying the given equation. Express your answers in terms of $\log 2$ and $\log 3$.

(a) $\log(e^x + \sqrt{e^{2x} + 1}) = c$.

(b) $\log(e^x - \sqrt{e^{2x} - 1}) = c$.

20. Determine whether each of the following statements is true or false. Prove each true statement.

(a) $2^{\log 5} = 5^{\log 2}$.

(c) $\displaystyle\sum_{k=1}^n k^{-1/2} < 2\sqrt{n}$ for every $n \ge 1$.

(b) $\log_2 5 = \dfrac{\log_3 5}{\log_3 3}$.

(d) $1 + \sinh x \le \cosh x$ for every $x$.

In Exercises 21 through 24, establish each inequality by examining the sign of the derivative of an appropriate function.

21. $\dfrac{2}{\pi} x < \sin x < x$    if $0 < x < \dfrac{\pi}{2}$.

22. $\dfrac{1}{x + \frac{1}{2}} < \log\left(1 + \dfrac{1}{x}\right) < \dfrac{1}{x}$    if $x > 0$.

23. $x - \dfrac{x^3}{6} < \sin x < x$    if $x > 0$.

24. $(x^b + y^b)^{1/b} < (x^a + y^a)^{1/a}$    if $x > 0, y > 0$, and $0 < a < b$.

25. Show that

(a) $\int_0^x e^{-t} t \, dt = e^{-x}(e^x - 1 - x)$.

(b) $\displaystyle\int_0^x e^{-t} t^2 \, dt = 2! e^{-x}\left(e^x - 1 - x - \dfrac{x^2}{2!}\right)$.

(c) $\displaystyle\int_0^x e^{-t} t^3 \, dt = 3! e^{-x}\left(e^x - 1 - x - \dfrac{x^2}{2!} - \dfrac{x^3}{3!}\right)$.

(d) Guess the generalization suggested and prove it by induction.

26. If $a, b, a_1, b_1$ are given, with $ab \neq 0$, show that there exist constants $A, B, C$ such that

$$\int \frac{a_1 \sin x + b_1 \cos x}{a \sin x + b \cos x} \, dx = Ax + B \log |a \sin x + b \cos x| + C.$$

[*Hint:* Show that $A$ and $B$ exist such that

$$a_1 \sin x + b_1 \cos x = A(a \sin x + b \cos x) + B(a \cos x - b \sin x).]$$

27. In each case, find a function $f$ satisfying the given conditions.

(a) $f'(x^2) = 1/x$    for $x > 0$,    $f(1) = 1$.

(b) $f'(\sin^2 x) = \cos^2 x$    for all $x$,    $f(1) = 1$.

(c) $f'(\sin x) = \cos^2 x$    for all $x$,    $f(1) = 1$.

(d) $f'(\log x) = \begin{cases} 1 & \text{for } 0 < x \le 1, \\ x & \text{for } x > 1, \end{cases}$    $f(0) = 0$.

28. A function, called the *integral logarithm* and denoted by Li, is defined as follows:

$$\text{Li}(x) = \int_2^x \frac{dt}{\log t} \quad \text{if } x \ge 2.$$

This function occurs in analytic number theory where it is proved that $\text{Li}(x)$ is a very good approximation to the number of primes $\le x$. Derive the following properties of $\text{Li}(x)$:

(a) $\text{Li}(x) = \dfrac{x}{\log x} + \displaystyle\int_2^x \dfrac{dt}{\log^2 t} - \dfrac{2}{\log 2}$.

(b) $\text{Li}(x) = \dfrac{x}{\log x} + \displaystyle\sum_{k=1}^{n-1} \dfrac{k! \, x}{\log^{k+1} x} + n! \int_2^x \dfrac{dt}{\log^{n+1} t} + C_n$,

where $C_n$ is a constant (depending on $n$). Find this constant.

(c) Show that there is a constant $b$ such that $\int_b^{\log x} e^t/t \, dt = \text{Li}(x)$ and find the value of $b$.

(d) Express $\int_c^x e^{2t}/(t - 1) \, dt$ in terms of the integral logarithm, where $c = 1 + \frac{1}{2} \log 2$.

(e) Let $f(x) = e^4 \, \mathrm{Li}(e^{2x-4}) - e^2 \, \mathrm{Li}(e^{2x-2})$ if $x > 3$. Show that

$$f'(x) = \frac{e^{2x}}{x^2 - 3x + 2}.$$

29. Let $f(x) = \log |x|$ if $x < 0$. Show that $f$ has an inverse, and denote this inverse by $g$. What is the domain of $g$? Find a formula for computing $g(y)$ for each $y$ in the domain of $g$. Sketch the graph of $g$.

30. Let $f(x) = \int_0^x (1 + t^3)^{-1/2} \, dt$ if $x \geq 0$. (Do not attempt to evaluate this integral.)
    (a) Show that $f$ is strictly increasing on the nonnegative real axis.
    (b) Let $g$ denote the inverse of $f$. Show that the second derivative of $g$ is proportional to $g^2$ [that is, $g''(y) = cg^2(y)$ for each $y$ in the domain of $g$] and find the constant of proportionality.

# 7

# POLYNOMIAL APPROXIMATIONS TO FUNCTIONS

## 7.1 Introduction

Polynomials are among the simplest functions that occur in analysis. They are pleasant to work with in numerical computations because their values may be found by performing a finite number of multiplications and additions. In Chapter 6 we showed that the logarithm function can be approximated by polynomials that enable us to compute logarithms to any desired degree of accuracy. In this chapter we will show that many other functions, such as the exponential and trigonometric functions, can also be approximated by polynomials. If the difference between a function and its polynomial approximation is sufficiently small, then we can, for practical purposes, compute with the polynomial in place of the original function.

There are many ways to approximate a given function $f$ by polynomials, depending on what use is to be made of the approximation. In this chapter we shall be interested in obtaining a polynomial which agrees with $f$ and some of its derivatives at a given point. We begin our discussion with a simple example.

Suppose $f$ is the exponential function, $f(x) = e^x$. At the point $x = 0$, the function $f$ and all its derivatives have the value 1. The linear polynomial

$$g(x) = 1 + x$$

also has $g(0) = 1$ and $g'(0) = 1$, so it agrees with $f$ and its first derivative at 0. Geometrically, this means the graph of $g$ is the tangent line of $f$ at the point $(0, 1)$, as shown in Figure 7.1.

If we approximate $f$ by a quadratic polynomial $Q$ which agrees with $f$ and its first two derivatives at 0, we might expect a better approximation to $f$ than the linear function $g$, at least near the point $(0, 1)$. The polynomial

$$Q(x) = 1 + x + \tfrac{1}{2}x^2$$

has $Q(0) = Q'(0) = 1$ and $Q''(0) = f''(0) = 1$. Figure 7.1 shows that the graph of $Q$ approximates the curve $y = e^x$ more closely than the line $y = 1 + x$ near the point $(0, 1)$. We can improve further the accuracy of the approximation by using polynomials which agree with $f$ in the third and higher derivatives as well. It is easy to verify that the polynomial

$$(7.1) \qquad P(x) = \sum_{k=0}^{n} \frac{x^k}{k!} = 1 + x + \frac{x^2}{2!} + \cdots + \frac{x^n}{n!}$$

272

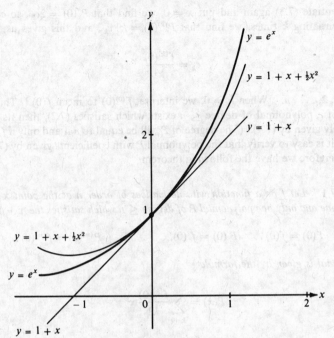

$$y = e^x$$

$$y = 1 + x + \tfrac{1}{2}x^2$$

$$y = 1 + x$$

$$y = 1 + x + \tfrac{1}{2}x^2$$

$$y = e^x$$

$$y = 1 + x$$

FIGURE 7.1   Polynomial approximations to the curve $y = e^x$ near $(0, 1)$.

agrees with the exponential function and its first $n$ derivatives at the point $x = 0$. Of course, before we can use such polynomials to compute approximate values for the exponential function, we need some information about the error made in the approximation. Rather than discuss this particular example in more detail, we turn now to the general theory.

## 7.2 The Taylor polynomials generated by a function

Suppose $f$ has derivatives up to order $n$ at the point $x = 0$, where $n \geq 1$, and let us try to find a polynomial $P$ which agrees with $f$ and its first $n$ derivatives at 0. There are $n + 1$ conditions to be satisfied, namely

$$(7.2) \qquad P(0) = f(0), \qquad P'(0) = f'(0), \qquad \ldots, \qquad P^{(n)}(0) = f^{(n)}(0),$$

so we try a polynomial of degree $n$, say

$$(7.3) \qquad P(x) = c_0 + c_1 x + c_2 x^2 + \cdots + c_n x^n,$$

with $n + 1$ coefficients to be determined. We shall use the conditions in (7.2) to determine these coefficients in succession.

First, we put $x = 0$ in (7.3) and we find $P(0) = c_0$, so $c_0 = f(0)$. Next, we differentiate both sides of (7.3) and then substitute $x = 0$ once more to find $P'(0) = c_1$; hence $c_1 = f'(0)$.

If we differentiate (7.3) again and put $x = 0$, we find that $P''(0) = 2c_2$, so $c_2 = f''(0)/2$. After differentiating $k$ times, we find that $P^{(k)}(0) = k!\, c_k$, and this gives us the formula

$$(7.4) \qquad c_k = \frac{f^{(k)}(0)}{k!}$$

for $k = 0, 1, 2, \ldots, n$. [When $k = 0$, we interpret $f^{(0)}(0)$ to mean $f(0)$.] This argument proves that if a polynomial of degree $\leq n$ exists which satisfies (7.2), then its coefficients are necessarily given by (7.4). (The degree of $P$ will be equal to $n$ if and only if $f^{(n)}(0) \neq 0$.) Conversely, it is easy to verify that the polynomial $P$ with coefficients given by (7.4) satisfies (7.2), and therefore we have the following theorem.

THEOREM 7.1. *Let $f$ be a function with derivatives of order $n$ at the point $x = 0$. Then there exists one and only one polynomial $P$ of degree $\leq n$ which satisfies the $n + 1$ conditions*

$$P(0) = f(0)\,, \qquad P'(0) = f'(0)\,, \qquad \ldots, \qquad P^{(n)}(0) = f^{(n)}(0)\,.$$

*This polynomial is given by the formula*

$$P(x) = \sum_{k=0}^{n} \frac{f^{(k)}(0)}{k!}\, x^k\,.$$

In the same way, we may show that there is one and only one polynomial of degree $\leq n$ which agrees with $f$ and its first $n$ derivatives at a point $x = a$. In fact, instead of (7.3), we may write $P$ in powers of $x - a$ and proceed as before. If we evaluate the derivatives at $a$ in place of 0, we are led to the polynomial

$$(7.5) \qquad P(x) = \sum_{k=0}^{n} \frac{f^{(k)}(a)}{k!}\, (x - a)^k\,.$$

This is the one and only polynomial of degree $\leq n$ which satisfies the conditions

$$P(a) = f(a)\,, \qquad P'(a) = f'(a)\,, \qquad \ldots, \qquad P^{(n)}(a) = f^{(n)}(a)\,,$$

and it is referred to as a *Taylor polynomial* in honor of the English mathematician Brook Taylor (1685–1731). More precisely, we say that the polynomial in (7.5) is the *Taylor polynomial of degree $n$ generated by $f$ at the point $a$*.

It is convenient to have a notation that indicates the dependence of the Taylor polynomial $P$ on $f$ and $n$. We shall indicate this dependence by writing $P = T_n f$ or $P = T_n(f)$. The symbol $T_n$ is called the *Taylor operator* of degree $n$. When this operator is applied to a function $f$, it produces a new function $T_n f$, the Taylor polynomial of degree $n$. The value of this function at $x$ is denoted by $T_n f(x)$ or by $T_n[f(x)]$. If we also wish to indicate the dependence on $a$, we write $T_n f(x; a)$ instead of $T_n f(x)$.

EXAMPLE 1. When $f$ is the exponential function, $f(x) = E(x) = e^x$, we have $E^{(k)}(x) = e^x$ for all $k$, so $E^{(k)}(0) = e^0 = 1$, and the Taylor polynomial of degree $n$ generated by $E$ at 0 is given by the formula

$$T_n E(x) = T_n(e^x) = \sum_{k=0}^{n} \frac{x^k}{k!} = 1 + x + \frac{x^2}{2!} + \cdots + \frac{x^n}{n!}.$$

If we want a polynomial which agrees with $E$ and its derivatives at the point $a = 1$, we have $E^{(k)}(1) = e$ for all $k$, so (7.5) gives us

$$T_n E(x; 1) = \sum_{k=0}^{n} \frac{e}{k!} (x - 1)^k.$$

EXAMPLE 2. When $f(x) = \sin x$, we have $f'(x) = \cos x$, $f''(x) = -\sin x$, $f'''(x) = -\cos x$, $f^{(4)}(x) = \sin x$, etc., so $f^{(2n+1)}(0) = (-1)^n$ and $f^{(2n)}(0) = 0$. Thus only odd powers of $x$ appear in the Taylor polynomials generated by the sine function at 0. The Taylor polynomial of degree $2n + 1$ has the form

$$T_{2n+1}(\sin x) = x - \frac{x^3}{3!} + \frac{x^5}{5!} - \frac{x^7}{7!} + \cdots + (-1)^n \frac{x^{2n+1}}{(2n+1)!}.$$

EXAMPLE 3. Arguing as in Example 2, we find that the Taylor polynomials generated by the cosine function at 0 contain only even powers of $x$. The polynomial of degree $2n$ is given by

$$T_{2n}(\cos x) = 1 - \frac{x^2}{2!} + \frac{x^4}{4!} - \frac{x^6}{6!} + \cdots + (-1)^n \frac{x^{2n}}{(2n)!}.$$

Note that each Taylor polynomial $T_{2n}(\cos x)$ is the derivative of the Taylor polynomial $T_{2n+1}(\sin x)$. This is due to the fact that the cosine itself is the derivative of the sine. In the next section we learn that certain relations which hold between functions are transmitted to their Taylor polynomials.

## 7.3 Calculus of Taylor polynomials

If a function $f$ has derivatives of order $n$ at a point $a$, we can always form its Taylor polynomial $T_n f$ by the formula

$$T_n f(x) = \sum_{k=0}^{n} \frac{f^{(k)}(a)}{k!} (x - a)^k.$$

Sometimes the calculation of the derivatives $f^{(k)}(a)$ may become lengthy, so it is desirable to have alternate methods for determining Taylor polynomials. The next theorem describes properties of the Taylor operator that often enable us to obtain new Taylor polynomials from given ones. In this theorem it is understood that all Taylor polynomials are generated at a common point $a$.

THEOREM 7.2.    *The Taylor operator $T_n$ has the following properties:*

(a) *Linearity property. If $c_1$ and $c_2$ are constants, then*

$$T_n(c_1 f + c_2 g) = c_1 T_n(f) + c_2 T_n(g).$$

(b) *Differentiation property. The derivative of a Taylor polynomial of $f$ is a Taylor polynomial of $f'$; in fact, we have*

$$(T_n f)' = T_{n-1}(f').$$

(c) *Integration property. An indefinite integral of a Taylor polynomial of $f$ is a Taylor polynomial of an indefinite integral of $f$. More precisely, if $g(x) = \int_a^x f(t)\, dt$, then we have*

$$T_{n+1} g(x) = \int_a^x T_n f(t)\, dt.$$

*Proof.*    Each statement (a), (b), or (c), is an equation involving two polynomials of the same degree. To prove each statement we simply observe that the polynomial which appears on the left has the same value and the same derivatives at the point $a$ as the one which appears on the right. Then we invoke the uniqueness property of Theorem 7.1. Note that differentiation of a polynomial lowers its degree, whereas integration increases its degree.

The next theorem tells us what happens when we replace $x$ by $cx$ in a Taylor polynomial.

THEOREM 7.3.    SUBSTITUTION PROPERTY.    *Let $g(x) = f(cx)$, where $c$ is a constant. Then we have*

$$T_n g(x; a) = T_n f(cx; ca).$$

*In particular, when $a = 0$, we have $T_n g(x) = T_n f(cx)$.*

*Proof.*    Since $g(x) = f(cx)$, the chain rule gives us

$$g'(x) = cf'(cx), \qquad g''(x) = c^2 f''(cx), \qquad \ldots, \qquad g^{(k)}(x) = c^k f^{(k)}(cx).$$

Hence we obtain

$$T_n g(x; a) = \sum_{k=0}^{n} \frac{g^{(k)}(a)}{k!} (x - a)^k = \sum_{k=0}^{n} \frac{f^{(k)}(ca)}{k!} (cx - ca)^k = T_n f(cx; ca).$$

EXAMPLES.    Replacing $x$ by $-x$ in the Taylor polynomial for $e^x$, we find that

$$T_n(e^{-x}) = 1 - x + \frac{x^2}{2!} - \frac{x^3}{3!} + \cdots + (-1)^n \frac{x^n}{n!}.$$

Since $\cosh x = \frac{1}{2} e^x + \frac{1}{2} e^{-x}$, we may use the linearity property to obtain

$$T_{2n}(\cosh x) = \tfrac{1}{2} T_{2n}(e^x) + \tfrac{1}{2} T_{2n}(e^{-x}) = 1 + \frac{x^2}{2!} + \frac{x^4}{4!} + \cdots + \frac{x^{2n}}{(2n)!}.$$

The differentiation property gives us

$$T_{2n-1}(\sinh x) = x + \frac{x^3}{3!} + \frac{x^5}{5!} + \cdots + \frac{x^{2n-1}}{(2n-1)!}.$$

The next theorem is also useful in simplifying calculations of Taylor polynomials.

THEOREM 7.4. *Let $P_n$ be a polynomial of degree $n \geq 1$. Let $f$ and $g$ be two functions with derivatives of order $n$ at 0 and assume that*

(7.6) $$f(x) = P_n(x) + x^n g(x),$$

*where $g(x) \to 0$ as $x \to 0$. Then $P_n$ is the Taylor polynomial generated by $f$ at 0.*

*Proof.* Let $h(x) = f(x) - P_n(x) = x^n g(x)$. By differentiating the product $x^n g(x)$ repeatedly, we see that $h$ and its first $n$ derivatives are 0 at $x = 0$. Therefore, $f$ agrees with $P_n$ and its first $n$ derivatives at 0, so $P_n = T_n f$, as asserted.

EXAMPLES. From the algebraic identity

(7.7) $$\frac{1}{1-x} = 1 + x + x^2 + \cdots + x^n + \frac{x^{n+1}}{1-x},$$

valid for all $x \neq 1$, we see that (7.6) is satisfied with $f(x) = 1/(1-x)$, $P_n(x) = 1 + x + \cdots + x^n$, and $g(x) = x/(1-x)$. Since $g(x) \to 0$ as $x \to 0$, Theorem 7.4 tells us that

$$T_n\left(\frac{1}{1-x}\right) = 1 + x + x^2 + \cdots + x^n.$$

Integration of this relation gives us the further Taylor polynomial

$$T_{n+1}[-\log(1-x)] = x + \frac{x^2}{2} + \frac{x^3}{3} + \cdots + \frac{x^{n+1}}{n+1}.$$

In (7.7) we may replace $x$ by $-x^2$ to get

$$\frac{1}{1+x^2} = 1 - x^2 + x^4 - \cdots + (-1)^n x^{2n} - (-1)^n \frac{x^{2n+1}}{1+x^2}.$$

Applying Theorem 7.4 once more, we find that

$$T_{2n}\left(\frac{1}{1+x^2}\right) = \sum_{k=0}^{n} (-1)^k x^{2k}.$$

Integration of this relation leads to the formula

$$T_{2n+1}(\arctan x) = \sum_{k=0}^{n} (-1)^k \frac{x^{2k+1}}{2k+1}.$$

## 7.4 Exercises

1. Draw graphs of the Taylor polynomials $T_3(\sin x) = x - x^3/3!$ and $T_5(\sin x) = x - x^3/3! + x^5/5!$. Pay careful attention to the points where the curves cross the $x$-axis. Compare these graphs with that of $f(x) = \sin x$.
2. Do the same as in Exercise 1 for the Taylor polynomials $T_2(\cos x), T_4(\cos x)$, and $f(x) = \cos x$.

In Exercises 3 through 10, obtain the Taylor polynomials $T_n f(x)$ as indicated. In each case, it is understood that $f(x)$ is defined for all $x$ for which $f(x)$ is meaningful. Theorems 7.2, 7.3, and 7.4 will help simplify the computations in many cases.

3. $T_n(a^x) = \displaystyle\sum_{k=0}^{n} \frac{(\log a)^k}{k!} x^k$.

6. $T_n[\log(1 + x)] = \displaystyle\sum_{k=1}^{n} \frac{(-1)^{k+1} x^k}{k}$.

4. $T_n\left(\dfrac{1}{1 + x}\right) = \displaystyle\sum_{k=0}^{n} (-1)^k x^k$.

7. $T_{2n+1}\left(\log\sqrt{\dfrac{1 + x}{1 - x}}\right) = \displaystyle\sum_{k=0}^{n} \frac{x^{2k+1}}{2k + 1}$.

5. $T_{2n+1}\left(\dfrac{x}{1 - x^2}\right) = \displaystyle\sum_{k=0}^{n} x^{2k+1}$.

8. $T_n\left(\dfrac{1}{2 - x}\right) = \displaystyle\sum_{k=0}^{n} \frac{x^k}{2^{k+1}}$.

9. $T_n[(1 + x)^\alpha] = \displaystyle\sum_{k=0}^{n} \binom{\alpha}{k} x^k$, where $\binom{\alpha}{k} = \dfrac{\alpha(\alpha - 1)\cdots(\alpha - k + 1)}{k!}$.

10. $T_{2n}(\sin^2 x) = \displaystyle\sum_{k=1}^{n} (-1)^{k+1} \frac{2^{2k-1}}{(2k)!} x^{2k}$.     [*Hint:* $\cos 2x = 1 - 2\sin^2 x$.]

## 7.5 Taylor's formula with remainder

We turn now to a discussion of the error in the approximation of a function $f$ by its Taylor polynomial $T_n f$ at a point $a$. The error is defined to be the difference $E_n(x) = f(x) - T_n f(x)$. Thus, if $f$ has a derivative of order $n$ at $a$, we may write

$$(7.8) \qquad f(x) = \sum_{k=0}^{n} \frac{f^{(k)}(a)}{k!}(x - a)^k + E_n(x).$$

This is known as *Taylor's formula with remainder* $E_n(x)$; it is useful whenever we can estimate the size of $E_n(x)$. We shall express the error as an integral and then estimate the size of the integral. To illustrate the principal ideas, we consider first the error arising from a linear approximation.

THEOREM 7.5.    *Assume $f$ has a continuous second derivative $f''$ in some neighborhood of $a$. Then, for every $x$ in this neighborhood, we have*

$$f(x) = f(a) + f'(a)(x - a) + E_1(x),$$

*where*

$$E_1(x) = \int_a^x (x - t)f''(t)\, dt.$$

*Proof.* From the definition of the error we may write

$$E_1(x) = f(x) - f(a) - f'(a)(x - a) = \int_a^x f'(t)\, dt - f'(a) \int_a^x dt = \int_a^x [f'(t) - f'(a)]\, dt\,.$$

The last integral may be written as $\int_a^x u\, dv$, where $u = f'(t) - f'(a)$, and $v = t - x$. Now $du/dt = f''(t)$ and $dv/dt = 1$, so the formula for integration by parts gives us

$$E_1(x) = \int_a^x u\, dv = uv \Big|_a^x - \int_a^x (t - x)f''(t)\, dt = \int_a^x (x - t)f''(t)\, dt\,,$$

since $u = 0$ when $t = a$, and $v = 0$ when $t = x$. This proves the theorem.

The corresponding result for a polynomial approximation of degree $n$ is given by the following.

THEOREM 7.6. *Assume $f$ has a continuous derivative of order $n + 1$ in some interval containing $a$. Then, for every $x$ in this interval, we have the Taylor formula*

$$f(x) = \sum_{k=0}^{n} \frac{f^{(k)}(a)}{k!} (x - a)^k + E_n(x)\,,$$

*where*

$$E_n(x) = \frac{1}{n!} \int_a^x (x - t)^n f^{(n+1)}(t)\, dt\,.$$

*Proof.* The theorem is proved by induction on $n$. We have already proved it for $n = 1$. Now we assume it is true for some $n$ and prove it for $n + 1$. We write Taylor's formula (7.8) with $n + 1$ and with $n$ and subtract to get

$$E_{n+1}(x) = E_n(x) - \frac{f^{(n+1)}(a)}{(n+1)!} (x - a)^{n+1}\,.$$

Now we use the integral for $E_n(x)$ and note that $(x - a)^{n+1}/(n + 1) = \int_a^x (x - t)^n\, dt$ to obtain

$$E_{n+1}(x) = \frac{1}{n!} \int_a^x (x - t)^n f^{(n+1)}(t)\, dt - \frac{f^{(n+1)}(a)}{n!} \int_a^x (x - t)^n\, dt$$

$$= \frac{1}{n!} \int_a^x (x - t)^n [f^{(n+1)}(t) - f^{(n+1)}(a)]\, dt\,.$$

The last integral may be written in the form $\int_a^x u\, dv$, where $u = f^{(n+1)}(t) - f^{(n+1)}(a)$ and $v = -(x - t)^{n+1}/(n + 1)$. Integrating by parts and noting that $u = 0$ when $t = a$, and that $v = 0$ when $t = x$, we find that

$$E_{n+1}(x) = \frac{1}{n!} \int_a^x u\, dv = -\frac{1}{n!} \int_a^x v\, du = \frac{1}{(n + 1)!} \int_a^x (x - t)^{n+1} f^{(n+2)}(t)\, dt\,.$$

This completes the inductive step from $n$ to $n + 1$, so the theorem is true for all $n \geq 1$.

## 7.6  Estimates for the error in Taylor's formula

Since the error $E_n(x)$ in Taylor's formula has been expressed as an integral involving the $(n + 1)$st derivative of $f$, we need some further information about $f^{(n+1)}$ before we can estimate the size of $E_n(x)$. If upper and lower bounds for $f^{(n+1)}$ are known, we can deduce corresponding upper and lower bounds for $E_n(x)$, as described in the next theorem.

THEOREM 7.7.    *If the $(n + 1)$st derivative of $f$ satisfies the inequalities*

$$(7.9) \qquad m \leq f^{(n+1)}(t) \leq M$$

*for all $t$ in some interval containing $a$, then for every $x$ in this interval we have the following estimates:*

$$(7.10) \qquad m \frac{(x - a)^{n+1}}{(n + 1)!} \leq E_n(x) \leq M \frac{(x - a)^{n+1}}{(n + 1)!} \qquad \text{if } x > a,$$

*and*

$$(7.11) \qquad m \frac{(a - x)^{n+1}}{(n + 1)!} \leq (-1)^{n+1} E_n(x) \leq M \frac{(a - x)^{n+1}}{(n + 1)!} \qquad \text{if } x < a.$$

*Proof.*    Assume first that $x > a$. Then the integral for $E_n(x)$ is extended over the interval $[a, x]$. For each $t$ in this interval we have $(x - t)^n \geq 0$, so the inequalities in (7.9) give us

$$m \frac{(x - t)^n}{n!} \leq \frac{(x - t)^n}{n!} f^{(n+1)}(t) \leq M \frac{(x - t)^n}{n!}.$$

Integrating from $a$ to $x$, we find that

$$(7.12) \qquad \frac{m}{n!} \int_a^x (x - t)^n \, dt \leq E_n(x) \leq \frac{M}{n!} \int_a^x (x - t)^n \, dt.$$

The substitution $u = x - t$, $du = -dt$ gives us

$$\int_a^x (x - t)^n \, dt = \int_0^{x-a} u^n \, du = \frac{(x - a)^{n+1}}{n + 1},$$

so (7.12) reduces to (7.10).

If $x < a$, the integration takes place over the interval $[x, a]$. For each $t$ in this interval we have $t \geq x$, so $(-1)^n (x - t)^n = (t - x)^n \geq 0$. Therefore, we may multiply the inequalities (7.9) by the nonnegative factor $(-1)^n (x - t)^n/n!$ and integrate from $x$ to $a$ to obtain (7.11).

EXAMPLE 1.    If $f(x) = e^x$ and $a = 0$, we have the formula

$$e^x = \sum_{k=0}^n \frac{x^k}{k!} + E_n(x).$$

Since $f^{(n+1)}(x) = e^x$, the derivative $f^{(n+1)}$ is monotonic increasing on every interval, and therefore satisfies the inequalities $e^b \leq f^{(n+1)}(t) \leq e^c$ on every interval of the form $[b, c]$. In such an interval, the inequalities for $E_n(x)$ of Theorem 7.7 are satisfied with $m = e^b$ and $M = e^c$. In particular, when $b = 0$, we have

$$\frac{x^{n+1}}{(n+1)!} \leq E_n(x) \leq e^c \frac{x^{n+1}}{(n+1)!} \qquad \text{if} \quad 0 < x \leq c.$$

We can use these estimates to calculate the Euler number $e$. We take $b = 0$, $c = 1$, $x = 1$, and use the inequality $e < 3$ to obtain

(7.13) $$e = \sum_{k=0}^{n} \frac{1}{k!} + E_n(1), \qquad \text{where} \quad \frac{1}{(n+1)!} \leq E_n(1) < \frac{3}{(n+1)!}.$$

This enables us to compute $e$ to any desired degree of accuracy. For example, if we want the value of $e$ correct to seven decimal places, we choose an $n$ so that $3/(n+1)! < \frac{1}{2}10^{-8}$. We shall see presently that $n = 12$ suffices. A table of values of $1/n!$ may be computed rather quickly because $1/n!$ may be obtained from $1/(n-1)!$ by simply dividing by $n$. The following table for $3 \leq n \leq 12$ contains these numbers rounded off to nine decimals. The "round-off error" in each case is indicated by a plus or minus sign which tells whether the correct value exceeds or is less than the recorded value. (In any case, this error is less than one-half unit in the last decimal place.)

| $n$ | $\dfrac{1}{n!}$ | $n$ | $\dfrac{1}{n!}$ |
|---|---|---|---|
| 3 | 0.166 666 667 − | 8 | 0.000 024 802 − |
| 4 | 0.041 666 667 − | 9 | 0.000 002 756 − |
| 5 | 0.008 333 333 + | 10 | 0.000 000 276 − |
| 6 | 0.001 388 889 − | 11 | 0.000 000 025 + |
| 7 | 0.000 198 413 − | 12 | 0.000 000 002 + |

The terms corresponding to $n = 0, 1, 2$ have sum $\frac{5}{2}$. Adding this to the sum of the entries in the table (for $n \leq 12$), we obtain a total of 2.718281830. If we take into account the roundoff errors, the *actual* value of this sum may be less than this by as much as $\frac{7}{2}$ of a unit in the last decimal place (due to the seven minus signs) or may exceed this by as much as $\frac{3}{2}$ of a unit in the last place (due to the three plus signs). Call the sum $s$. Then all we can assert by this calculation is the inequality $2.718281826 < s < 2.718281832$. Now the estimates for the error $E_{12}(1)$ give us $0.000000000 \leq E_{12}(1) < 0.000000001$. Since $e = s + E_{12}(1)$, this calculation leads to the following inequalities for $e$:

$$2.718281826 < e < 2.718281833.$$

This tells us that the value of $e$, *correct to seven decimals*, is $e = 2.7182818$, or that the value of $e$, *rounded off to eight decimals*, is $e = 2.71828183$.

EXAMPLE 2. *Irrationality of e.* We can use the foregoing estimates for the error $E_n(1)$ to prove that $e$ is irrational. First we rewrite the inequalities in (7.13) as follows:

$$\frac{1}{(n+1)!} \le e - \sum_{k=0}^{n} \frac{1}{k!} < \frac{3}{(n+1)!}.$$

Multiplying through by $n!$, we obtain

(7.14)
$$\frac{1}{n+1} \le n!\, e - \sum_{k=0}^{n} \frac{n!}{k!} < \frac{3}{n+1} \le \frac{3}{4}$$

if $n \ge 3$. For every $n$, the sum on $k$ is an integer. If $e$ were rational, we could choose $n$ so large that $n!\, e$ would also be an integer. But then (7.14) would tell us that the difference of these two integers is a positive number not exceeding $\frac{3}{4}$, which is impossible. Therefore $e$ cannot be rational.

Polynomial approximations often enable us to obtain approximate numerical values for integrals that cannot be evaluated directly in terms of elementary functions. A famous example is the integral

$$f(x) = \int_0^x e^{-t^2}\, dt$$

which occurs in probability theory and in many physical problems. It is known that the function $f$ so defined is not an *elementary function*. That is to say, $f$ cannot be obtained from polynomials, exponentials, logarithms, trigonometric or inverse trigonometric functions in a finite number of steps by using the operations of addition, subtraction, multiplication, division, or composition. Other examples which occur rather frequently in both theory and practice are the integrals

$$\int_0^x \frac{\sin t}{t}\, dt\,, \qquad \int_0^x \sin(t^2)\, dt\,, \qquad \int_0^x \sqrt{1 - k^2 \sin^2 t}\, dt\,.$$

(In the first of these, it is understood that the quotient $(\sin t)/t$ is to be replaced by 1 when $t = 0$. In the third integral, $k$ is a constant, $0 < k < 1$.) We conclude this section with an example which illustrates how Taylor's formula may be used to obtain an accurate estimate of the integral $\int_0^{1/2} e^{-t^2} dt$.

EXAMPLE 3. The Taylor formula for $e^x$ with $n = 4$ gives us

(7.15)
$$e^x = 1 + x + \frac{x^2}{2!} + \frac{x^3}{3!} + \frac{x^4}{4!} + E_4(x)\,.$$

Suppose now that $x \le 0$. In any interval of the form $[-c, 0]$ we have $e^{-c} \le e^x \le 1$, so we may use the inequalities (7.11) of Theorem 7.7 with $m = e^{-c}$ and $M = 1$ to write

$$0 < (-1)^5 E_4(x) \le \frac{(-x)^5}{5!} \qquad \text{if} \quad x < 0\,.$$

In other words, if $x < 0$, then $E_4(x)$ is negative and $\geq x^5/5!$. Replacing $x$ by $-t^2$ in (7.15), we have

$$(7.16) \qquad e^{-t^2} = 1 - t^2 + \frac{t^4}{2!} - \frac{t^6}{3!} + \frac{t^8}{4!} + E_4(-t^2),$$

where $-t^{10}/5! \leq E_4(-t^2) < 0$. If $0 \leq t \leq \frac{1}{2}$, we find that $t^{10}/5! \leq (\frac{1}{2})^{10}/5! < 0.000\,009$. Thus, if we integrate (7.16) from 0 to $\frac{1}{2}$, we obtain

$$\int_0^{1/2} e^{-t^2}\,dt = \frac{1}{2} - \frac{1}{3 \cdot 2^3} + \frac{1}{5 \cdot 2^5 \cdot 2!} - \frac{1}{7 \cdot 2^7 \cdot 3!} + \frac{1}{9 \cdot 2^9 \cdot 4!} - \theta,$$

where $0 < \theta \leq 0.000\,0045$. Rounding off to four decimals, we find $\int_0^{1/2} e^{-t^2}\,dt = 0.4613$.

## ★7.7  Other forms of the remainder in Taylor's formula

We have expressed the error in Taylor's formula as an integral,

$$E_n(x) = \frac{1}{n!} \int_a^x (x - t)^n f^{(n+1)}(t)\,dt.$$

It can also be expressed in many other forms. Since the factor $(x - t)^n$ in the integrand never changes sign in the interval of integration, and since $f^{(n+1)}$ is continuous on this interval, the weighted mean-value theorem for integrals (Theorem 3.16) gives us

$$\int_a^x (x - t)^n f^{(n+1)}(t)\,dt = f^{(n+1)}(c) \int_a^x (x - t)^n\,dt = f^{(n+1)}(c) \frac{(x - a)^{n+1}}{n + 1},$$

where $c$ lies in the closed interval joining $a$ and $x$. Therefore, the error can be written as

$$E_n(x) = \frac{f^{(n+1)}(c)}{(n + 1)!} (x - a)^{n+1}.$$

This is called Lagrange's form of the remainder. It resembles the earlier terms in Taylor's formula, except that the derivative $f^{(n+1)}(c)$ is evaluated at some unknown point $c$ rather than at $a$. The point $c$ depends on $x$ and on $n$, as well as on $f$.

Using a different type of argument, we can drop the continuity requirement on $f^{(n+1)}$ and derive Lagrange's formula and other forms of the remainder under a weaker hypothesis. Suppose that $f^{(n+1)}$ exists in some open interval $(h, k)$ containing the point $a$, and assume that $f^{(n)}$ is continuous in the closed interval $[h, k]$. Choose any $x \neq a$ in $[h, k]$. For simplicity, say $x > a$. Keep $x$ fixed and define a new function $F$ on the interval $[a, x]$ as follows:

$$F(t) = f(t) + \sum_{k=1}^{n} \frac{f^{(k)}(t)}{k!} (x - t)^k.$$

Note that $F(x) = f(x)$ and $F(a) = T_n f(x; a)$, so $F(x) - F(a) = E_n(x)$. The function $F$ is continuous in the closed interval $[a, x]$ and has a derivative in the open interval $(a, x)$. If we compute $F'(t)$, keeping in mind that each term of the sum defining $F(t)$ is a product, we find that all terms cancel except one, and we are left with the equation

$$F'(t) = \frac{(x - t)^n}{n!} f^{(n+1)}(t) \,.$$

Now let $G$ be any function that is continuous on $[a, x]$ and differentiable on $(a, x)$. Then we can apply Cauchy's mean-value formula (Theorem 4.6) to write

$$G'(c)[F(x) - F(a)] = F'(c)[G(x) - G(a)] \,,$$

for some $c$ in the open interval $(a, x)$. If $G'$ is nonzero in $(a, x)$, this gives the following formula for the error $E_n(x)$:

$$E_n(x) = \frac{F'(c)}{G'(c)} [G(x) - G(a)] \,.$$

We can express the error in various forms by different choices of $G$. For example, taking $G(t) = (x - t)^{n+1}$, we obtain Lagrange's form,

$$E_n(x) = \frac{f^{(n+1)}(c)}{(n + 1)!} (x - a)^{n+1} \,, \qquad \text{where} \quad a < c < x \,.$$

Taking $G(t) = x - t$, we obtain another formula, called Cauchy's form of the remainder,

$$E_n(x) = \frac{f^{(n+1)}(c)}{n!} (x - c)^n (x - a) \,, \qquad \text{where} \quad a < c < x \,.$$

If $G(t) = (x - t)^p$, where $p \geq 1$, we obtain the formula

$$E_n(x) = \frac{f^{(n+1)}(c)}{n! \, p} (x - c)^{n+1-p} (x - a)^p \,, \qquad \text{where} \quad a < c < x \,.$$

## 7.8 Exercises

Examples of Taylor's formula with remainder are given in Exercises 1, 2, and 3. In each case prove that the error satisfies the given inequalities.

1. $\sin x = \sum_{k=1}^{n} \frac{(-1)^{k-1} x^{2k-1}}{(2k - 1)!} + E_{2n}(x), \qquad |E_{2n}(x)| \leq \frac{|x|^{2n+1}}{(2n + 1)!} \,.$

2. $\cos x = \sum_{k=0}^{n} \frac{(-1)^k x^{2k}}{(2k)!} + E_{2n+1}(x), \qquad |E_{2n+1}(x)| \leq \frac{|x|^{2n+2}}{(2n + 2)!} \,.$

3. $\arctan x = \sum_{k=0}^{n-1} \frac{(-1)^k x^{2k+1}}{2k + 1} + E_{2n}(x), \qquad |E_{2n}(x)| \leq \frac{x^{2n+1}}{2n + 1} \qquad \text{if} \quad 0 \leq x \leq 1.$

4. (a) Obtain the number $r = \sqrt{15} - 3$ as an approximation to the nonzero root of the equation $x^2 = \sin x$ by using the cubic Taylor polynomial approximation to $\sin x$.

(b) Show that the approximation in part (a) satisfies the inequality

$$|\sin r - r^2| < \frac{1}{200},$$

given that $\sqrt{15} - 3 < 0.9$. Is the difference $(\sin r - r^2)$ positive or negative? Give full details of your reasoning.

5. (a) Use the cubic Taylor polynomial approximation to $\arctan x$ to obtain the number $r = (\sqrt{21} - 3)/2$ as an approximation to the nonzero root of the equation $\arctan x = x^2$.

(b) Given that $\sqrt{21} < 4.6$ and that $2^{16} = 65536$, prove that the approximation in part (a) satisfies the inequality

$$|r^2 - \arctan r| < \frac{7}{100}.$$

Is the difference $(r^2 - \arctan r)$ positive or negative? Give full details of your reasoning.

6. Prove that $\displaystyle\int_0^1 \frac{1 + x^{30}}{1 + x^{60}}\, dx = 1 + \frac{c}{31},$ where $0 < c < 1$.

7. Prove that $0.493948 < \displaystyle\int_0^{1/2} \frac{1}{1 + x^4}\, dx < 0.493958$.

8. (a) If $0 \le x \le \frac{1}{2}$, show that $\sin x = x - x^3/3! + r(x)$, where $|r(x)| \le (\frac{1}{2})^5/5!$.

(b) Use the estimate in part (a) to find an approximate value for the integral $\int_0^{\sqrt{2}/2} \sin (x^2)\, dx$. Make sure you give an estimate for the error.

9. Use the first three nonzero terms of Taylor's formula for $\sin x$ to find an approximate value for the integral $\int_0^1 (\sin x)/x\, dx$ and give an estimate for the error. [It is to be understood that the quotient $(\sin x)/x$ is equal to 1 when $x = 0$.]

10. This exercise outlines a method for computing $\pi$, using Taylor's formula for $\arctan x$ given in Exercise 3. It is based on the fact that $\pi$ is nearly 3.2, so $\frac{1}{4}\pi$ is nearly 0.8 or $\frac{4}{5}$, and this is nearly $4 \arctan \frac{1}{5}$. Let $\alpha = \arctan \frac{1}{5}$, $\beta = 4\alpha - \frac{1}{4}\pi$.

(a) Use the identity $\tan(A + B) = (\tan A + \tan B)/(1 - \tan A \tan B)$ with $A = B = \alpha$ and then again with $A = B = 2\alpha$ to get $\tan 2\alpha = \frac{5}{12}$ and $\tan 4\alpha = \frac{120}{119}$. Then use the identity once more with $A = 4\alpha$, $B = -\frac{1}{4}\pi$ to obtain $\tan \beta = \frac{1}{239}$. This yields the following remarkable identity discovered in 1706 by John Machin (1680–1751):

$$\pi = 16 \arctan \tfrac{1}{5} - 4 \arctan \tfrac{1}{239}.$$

(b) Use the Taylor polynomial $T_{11}(\arctan x)$ with $x = \frac{1}{5}$ to show that

$$3.158328934 < 16 \arctan \tfrac{1}{5} < 3.158328972.$$

(c) Use the Taylor polynomial $T_3(\arctan x)$ with $x = \frac{1}{239}$ to show that

$$-0.016736309 < -4 \arctan \tfrac{1}{239} < -0.016736300.$$

(d) Use parts (a), (b) and (c) to show that the value of $\pi$, correct to seven decimals, is 3.1415926.

## 7.9  Further remarks on the error in Taylor's formula.  The $o$-notation

If $f$ has a continuous $(n + 1)$st derivative in some interval containing a point $a$, we may write Taylor's formula in the form

(7.17)
$$f(x) = \sum_{k=0}^{n} \frac{f^{(k)}(a)}{k!} (x - a)^k + E_n(x).$$

Suppose we restrict $x$ to lie in some closed interval $[a - c, a + c]$ about $a$, in which $f^{(n+1)}$ is continuous. Then $f^{(n+1)}$ is bounded on this interval and hence satisfies an inequality of the form

$$|f^{(n+1)}(t)| \le M,$$

where $M > 0$. Hence, by Theorem 7.7, we have the error estimate

$$|E_n(x)| \le M \frac{|x - a|^{n+1}}{(n + 1)!}$$

for each $x$ in $[a - c, a + c]$. If we keep $x \ne a$ and divide this inequality by $|x - a|^n$, we find that

$$0 \le \left| \frac{E_n(x)}{(x - a)^n} \right| \le \frac{M}{(n + 1)!} |x - a|.$$

If now we let $x \to a$, we see that $E_n(x)/(x - a)^n \to 0$. We describe this by saying that the error $E_n(x)$ is of smaller order than $(x - a)^n$ as $x \to a$.

In other words, under the conditions stated, $f(x)$ may be approximated near $a$ by a polynomial in $(x - a)$ of degree $n$, and the error in this approximation is of smaller order than $(x - a)^n$ as $x \to a$.

A special notation, introduced in 1909 by E. Landau,† is particularly appropriate when used in connection with Taylor's formula. This is called the $o$-notation (the little-oh notation) and it is defined as follows.

DEFINITION.  *Assume $g(x) \ne 0$ for all $x \ne a$ in some interval containing $a$. The notation*

$$f(x) = o(g(x)) \qquad as \quad x \to a$$

*means that*

$$\lim_{x \to a} \frac{f(x)}{g(x)} = 0.$$

The symbol $f(x) = o(g(x))$ is read "$f(x)$ is little-oh of $g(x)$," or "$f(x)$ is of smaller order than $g(x)$," and it is intended to convey the idea that for $x$ near $a$, $f(x)$ is small compared with $g(x)$.

---

† Edmund Landau (1877–1938) was a famous German mathematician who made many important contributions to mathematics. He is best known for his lucid books in analysis and in the theory of numbers.

EXAMPLE 1. $f(x) = o(1)$ as $x \to a$ means that $f(x) \to 0$ as $x \to a$.

EXAMPLE 2. $f(x) = o(x)$ as $x \to 0$ means that $\dfrac{f(x)}{x} \to 0$ as $x \to 0$.

An equation of the form $f(x) = h(x) + o(g(x))$ is understood to mean that $f(x) - h(x) = o(g(x))$ or, in other words, $[f(x) - h(x)]/g(x) \to 0$ as $x \to a$.

EXAMPLE 3. We have $\sin x = x + o(x)$ because $\dfrac{\sin x - x}{x} = \dfrac{\sin x}{x} - 1 \to 0$ as $x \to 0$.

The foregoing remarks concerning the error in Taylor's formula can now be expressed in the $o$-notation. We may write

$$f(x) = \sum_{k=0}^{n} \frac{f^{(k)}(a)}{k!} (x - a)^k + o((x - a)^n) \qquad \text{as} \quad x \to a \, ,$$

whenever the derivative $f^{(n+1)}$ is continuous in some closed interval containing the point $a$. This expresses, in a brief way, the fact that the error term is small compared to $(x - a)^n$ when $x$ is near $a$. In particular, from the discussion of earlier sections, we have the following examples of Taylor's formula expressed in the $o$-notation:

$$\frac{1}{1 - x} = 1 + x + x^2 + \cdots + x^n + o(x^n) \qquad \text{as} \quad x \to 0 \, .$$

$$\log(1 + x) = x - \frac{x^2}{2} + \frac{x^3}{3} - \frac{x^4}{4} + \cdots + (-1)^{n-1} \frac{x^n}{n} + o(x^n) \qquad \text{as} \quad x \to 0 \, .$$

$$e^x = 1 + x + \frac{x^2}{2!} + \cdots + \frac{x^n}{n!} + o(x^n) \qquad \text{as} \quad x \to 0 \, .$$

$$\sin x = x - \frac{x^3}{3!} + \frac{x^5}{5!} - \frac{x^7}{7!} + \cdots + (-1)^{n-1} \frac{x^{2n-1}}{(2n - 1)!} + o(x^{2n}) \qquad \text{as} \quad x \to 0 \, .$$

$$\cos x = 1 - \frac{x^2}{2!} + \frac{x^4}{4!} - \frac{x^6}{6!} + \cdots + (-1)^n \frac{x^{2n}}{(2n)!} + o(x^{2n+1}) \qquad \text{as} \quad x \to 0 \, .$$

$$\arctan x = x - \frac{x^3}{3} + \frac{x^5}{5} - \frac{x^7}{7} + \cdots + (-1)^{n-1} \frac{x^{2n-1}}{2n - 1} + o(x^{2n}) \qquad \text{as} \quad x \to 0 \, .$$

In calculations involving Taylor approximations, it often becomes necessary to combine several terms involving the $o$-symbol. A few simple rules for manipulating $o$-symbols are discussed in the next theorem. These cover most situations that arise in practice.

THEOREM 7.8.    ALGEBRA OF *o*-SYMBOLS.    *As* $x \to a$, *we have the following:*

(a) $o(g(x)) \pm o(g(x)) = o(g(x))$.

(b) $o(cg(x)) = o(g(x))$      *if* $c \neq 0$.

(c) $f(x) \cdot o(g(x)) = o(f(x)g(x))$.

(d) $o(o(g(x))) = o(g(x))$.

(e) $\dfrac{1}{1 + g(x)} = 1 - g(x) + o(g(x))$      *if* $g(x) \to 0$     *as*  $x \to a$ .

*Proof.*  The statement in part (a) is understood to mean that if $f_1(x) = o(g(x))$ and if $f_2(x) = o(g(x))$, then $f_1(x) \pm f_2(x) = o(g(x))$.  But since we have

$$\frac{f_1(x) \pm f_2(x)}{g(x)} = \frac{f_1(x)}{g(x)} \pm \frac{f_2(x)}{g(x)},$$

each term on the right tends to 0 as $x \to a$, so part (a) is proved.  The statements in (b), (c), and (d) are proved in a similar way.

To prove (e), we use the algebraic identity

$$\frac{1}{1 + u} = 1 - u + u\,\frac{u}{1 + u}$$

with $u$ replaced by $g(x)$ and then note that $\dfrac{g(x)}{1 + g(x)} \to 0$ as $x \to a$.

EXAMPLE 1.  Prove that $\tan x = x + \frac{1}{3}x^3 + o(x^3)$ as $x \to 0$.

*Solution.*  We use the Taylor approximations for the sine and cosine.  From part (e) of Theorem 7.8, with $g(x) = -\frac{1}{2}x^2 + o(x^3)$, we have

$$\frac{1}{\cos x} = \frac{1}{1 - \frac{1}{2}x^2 + o(x^3)} = 1 + \frac{1}{2}x^2 + o(x^2)    \text{ as }  x \to 0 .$$

Therefore, we have

$$\tan x = \frac{\sin x}{\cos x} = \left(x - \frac{1}{6}x^3 + o(x^4)\right)\left(1 + \frac{1}{2}x^2 + o(x^2)\right) = x + \frac{1}{3}x^3 + o(x^3) .$$

EXAMPLE 2.  Prove that $(1 + x)^{1/x} = e \cdot \left(1 - \dfrac{x}{2} + \dfrac{11x^2}{24} + o(x^2)\right)$     as   $x \to 0$.

*Solution.*  Since $(1 + x)^{1/x} = e^{(1/x)\log(1+x)}$, we begin with a polynomial approximation to $\log(1 + x)$.  Taking a cubic approximation, we have

$$\log(1 + x) = x - \frac{x^2}{2} + \frac{x^3}{3} + o(x^3), \qquad \frac{\log(1 + x)}{x} = 1 - \frac{x}{2} + \frac{x^2}{3} + o(x^2),$$

and so we obtain

(7.18) $$(1 + x)^{1/x} = \exp(1 - x/2 + x^2/3 + o(x^2)) = e \cdot e^u,$$

where $u = -x/2 + x^2/3 + o(x^2)$. But as $u \to 0$, we have $e^u = 1 + u + \frac{1}{2}u^2 + o(u^2)$, so we obtain

$$e^u = 1 - \frac{x}{2} + \frac{x^2}{3} + o(x^2) + \frac{1}{2}\left(-\frac{x}{2} + \frac{x^2}{3} + o(x^2)\right)^2 + o(x^2) = 1 - \frac{x}{2} + \frac{11x^2}{24} + o(x^2).$$

When we use this in Equation (7.18), we obtain the desired formula.

## 7.10 Applications to indeterminate forms

We have already illustrated how polynomial approximations are used in the computation of function values. They can also be used as an aid in the calculation of limits. We illustrate with some examples.

EXAMPLE 1. If $a$ and $b$ are positive numbers, determine the limit

$$\lim_{x \to 0} \frac{a^x - b^x}{x}.$$

*Solution.* We cannot solve this problem by computing the limit of the numerator and denominator separately, because the denominator tends to 0 and the quotient theorem on limits is not applicable. The numerator in this case also tends to 0 and the quotient is said to assume the "*indeterminate form* 0/0" as $x \to 0$. Taylor's formula and the $o$-notation often enable us to calculate the limit of an indeterminate form like this one very simply. The idea is to approximate the numerator $a^x - b^x$ by a polynomial in $x$, then divide by $x$ and let $x \to 0$. We could apply Taylor's formula directly to $f(x) = a^x - b^x$ but, since $a^x = e^{x \log a}$ and $b^x = e^{x \log b}$, it is simpler in this case to use the polynomial approximations already derived for the exponential function. If we begin with the linear approximation

$$e^t = 1 + t + o(t) \qquad \text{as} \quad t \to 0$$

and replace $t$ by $x \log a$ and $x \log b$, respectively, we find

$$a^x = 1 + x \log a + o(x) \qquad \text{and} \qquad b^x = 1 + x \log b + o(x) \qquad \text{as} \quad x \to 0.$$

Here we have used the fact that $o(x \log a) = o(x)$ and $o(x \log b) = o(x)$. If now we subtract and note that $o(x) - o(x) = o(x)$, we find $a^x - b^x = x(\log a - \log b) + o(x)$. Dividing by $x$ and using the relation $o(x)/x = o(1)$, we obtain

$$\frac{a^x - b^x}{x} = \log \frac{a}{b} + o(1) \to \log \frac{a}{b} \qquad \text{as} \quad x \to 0.$$

**EXAMPLE 2.** Prove that $\lim_{x\to 0} \frac{1}{x}\left(\cot x - \frac{1}{x}\right) = -\frac{1}{3}$ .

*Solution.* We use Example 1 of Section 7.9, and Theorem 7.8(e) to write

$$\cot x = \frac{1}{\tan x} = \frac{1}{x + \frac{1}{3}x^3 + o(x^3)} = \frac{1}{x}\,\frac{1}{1 + \frac{1}{3}x^2 + o(x^2)}$$

$$= \frac{1}{x}\left(1 - \frac{1}{3}x^2 + o(x^2)\right) = \frac{1}{x} - \frac{1}{3}x + o(x) .$$

Hence, we have

$$\frac{1}{x}\left(\cot x - \frac{1}{x}\right) = -\frac{1}{3} + o(1) \to -\frac{1}{3} \quad \text{as} \quad x \to 0 .$$

**EXAMPLE 3.** Prove that $\lim_{x\to 0} \dfrac{\log(1 + ax)}{x} = a$ for every real $a$.

*Solution.* If $a = 0$, the result holds trivially. If $a \neq 0$, we use the linear approximation $\log(1 + x) = x + o(x)$. Replacing $x$ by $ax$, we obtain $\log(1 + ax) = ax + o(ax) = ax + o(x)$. Dividing by $x$ and letting $x \to 0$, we obtain the limit $a$.

**EXAMPLE 4.** Prove that for every real $a$, we have

(7.19) $$\lim_{x\to 0} (1 + ax)^{1/x} = e^a .$$

*Solution.* We simply note that $(1 + ax)^{1/x} = e^{(1/x)\log(1+ax)}$ and use the result of Example 3 along with the continuity of the exponential function.

Replacing $ax$ by $y$ in (7.19), we find another important limit relation:

$$\lim_{y\to 0} (1 + y)^{a/y} = e^a .$$

Sometimes these limit relations are taken as the starting point for the theory of the exponential function.

## 7.11  Exercises

1. Find a quadratic polynomial $P(x)$ such that $2^x = P(x) + o(x^2)$ as $x \to 0$.
2. Find a cubic polynomial $P(x)$ such that $x \cos x = P(x) + o((x - 1)^3)$ as $x \to 1$.
3. Find the polynomial $P(x)$ of smallest degree such that $\sin(x - x^2) = P(x) + o(x^6)$ as $x \to 0$.
4. Find constants $a$, $b$, $c$ such that $\log x = a + b(x - 1) + c(x - 1)^2 + o((x - 1)^2)$ as $x \to 1$.
5. Recall that $\cos x = 1 - \frac{1}{2}x^2 + o(x^3)$ as $x \to 0$. Use this to prove that $x^{-2}(1 - \cos x) \to \frac{1}{2}$ as $x \to 0$. In a similar way, find the limit of $x^{-4}(1 - \cos 2x - 2x^2)$ as $x \to 0$.

Evaluate the limits in Exercises 6 through 29.

6. $\lim\limits_{x\to 0} \dfrac{\sin ax}{\sin bx}$.

7. $\lim\limits_{x\to 0} \dfrac{\tan 2x}{\sin 3x}$.

8. $\lim\limits_{x\to 0} \dfrac{\sin x - x}{x^3}$.

9. $\lim\limits_{x\to 0} \dfrac{\log(1+x)}{e^{2x}-1}$.

10. $\lim\limits_{x\to 0} \dfrac{1-\cos^2 x}{x \tan x}$.

11. $\lim\limits_{x\to 0} \dfrac{\sin x}{\arctan x}$.

12. $\lim\limits_{x\to 0} \dfrac{a^x - 1}{b^x - 1}$, $\quad b \neq 1$.

13. $\lim\limits_{x\to 1} \dfrac{\log x}{x^2 + x - 2}$.

14. $\lim\limits_{x\to 0} \dfrac{1-\cos x^2}{x^2 \sin x^2}$.

15. $\lim\limits_{x\to 0} \dfrac{x(e^x+1)-2(e^x-1)}{x^3}$.

16. $\lim\limits_{x\to 0} \dfrac{\log(1+x)-x}{1-\cos x}$.

17. $\lim\limits_{x\to \frac{1}{2}\pi} \dfrac{\cos x}{x - \frac{1}{2}\pi}$.

18. $\lim\limits_{x\to 1} \dfrac{[\sin(\pi/2x)](\log x)}{(x^3+5)(x-1)}$.

19. $\lim\limits_{x\to 0} \dfrac{\cosh x - \cos x}{x^2}$.

20. $\lim\limits_{x\to 0} \dfrac{3 \tan 4x - 12 \tan x}{3 \sin 4x - 12 \sin x}$.

21. $\lim\limits_{x\to 0} \dfrac{a^x - a^{\sin x}}{x^3}$.

22. $\lim\limits_{x\to 0} \dfrac{\cos(\sin x) - \cos x}{x^4}$.

23. $\lim\limits_{x\to 1} x^{1/(1-x)}$.

24. $\lim\limits_{x\to 0} (x + e^{2x})^{1/x}$.

25. $\lim\limits_{x\to 0} \dfrac{(1+x)^{1/x} - e}{x}$.

26. $\lim\limits_{x\to 0} \left(\dfrac{(1+x)^{1/x}}{e}\right)^{1/x}$.

27. $\lim\limits_{x\to 0} \left(\dfrac{\arcsin x}{x}\right)^{1/x^2}$.

28. $\lim\limits_{x\to 0} \left(\dfrac{1}{x} - \dfrac{1}{e^x - 1}\right)$.

29. $\lim\limits_{x\to 1} \left(\dfrac{1}{\log x} - \dfrac{1}{x-1}\right)$.

30. For what value of the constant $a$ will $x^{-2}(e^{ax} - e^x - x)$ tend to a finite limit as $x \to 0$? What is the value of this limit?

31. Given two functions $f$ and $g$ with derivatives in some interval containing 0, where $g$ is positive. Assume also $f(x) = o(g(x))$ as $x \to 0$. Prove or disprove each of the following statements:

   (a) $\int_0^x f(t)\, dt = o\left(\int_0^x g(t)\, dt\right)$ as $x \to 0$,     (b) $f'(x) = o(g'(x))$ as $x \to 0$.

32. (a) If $g(x) = o(1)$ as $x \to 0$, prove that

$$\frac{1}{1+g(x)} = 1 - g(x) + g^2(x) + o(g^2(x)) \qquad \text{as} \quad x \to 0.$$

   (b) Use part (a) to prove that $\tan x = x + \dfrac{x^3}{3} + \dfrac{2x^5}{15} + o(x^5)$     as $x \to 0$.

33. A function $f$ has a continuous third derivative everywhere and satisfies the relation

$$\lim_{x\to 0}\left(1 + x + \frac{f(x)}{x}\right)^{1/x} = e^3.$$

Compute $f(0), f'(0), f''(0)$, and $\lim_{x \to 0} \left( 1 + \dfrac{f(x)}{x} \right)^{1/x}$ .

[*Hint:* If $\lim_{x \to 0} g(x) = A$, then $g(x) = A + o(1)$ as $x \to 0$.]

## 7.12 L'Hôpital's rule for the indeterminate form 0/0

In many examples in the foregoing sections we have calculated the limit of a quotient $f(x)/g(x)$ in which both the numerator $f(x)$ and the denominator $g(x)$ approached 0. In examples like these, the quotient $f(x)/g(x)$ is said to assume the "indeterminate form 0/0."

One way to attack problems on indeterminate forms is to obtain polynomial approximations to $f(x)$ and $g(x)$ as we did in treating the above examples. Sometimes the work can be shortened by use of a differentiation technique known as *L'Hôpital's rule*.† The basic idea of the method is to study the quotient of derivatives $f'(x)/g'(x)$ and thereby to try to deduce information about $f(x)/g(x)$.

Before stating L'Hôpital's rule, we show why the quotient of derivatives $f'(x)/g'(x)$ bears a relation to the quotient $f(x)/g(x)$. Suppose $f$ and $g$ are two functions with $f(a) = g(a) = 0$. Then, for $x \neq a$, we have

$$\frac{f(x)}{g(x)} = \frac{f(x) - f(a)}{g(x) - g(a)} = \frac{f(x) - f(a)}{x - a} \bigg/ \frac{g(x) - g(a)}{x - a} .$$

If the derivatives $f'(a)$ and $g'(a)$ exist, and if $g'(a) \neq 0$, then as $x \to a$ the quotient on the right approaches $f'(a)/g'(a)$ and hence $f(x)/g(x) \to f'(a)/g'(a)$.

EXAMPLE. Compute $\lim_{x \to 0} \dfrac{1 - e^{2x}}{x}$ .

*Solution.* Here $f(x) = 1 - e^{2x}$ and $g(x) = x$, so $f'(x) = -2e^{2x}$, $g'(x) = 1$. Hence we have $f'(0)/g'(0) = -2$, so the limit in question is $-2$.

In L'Hôpital's rule, no assumptions are made about $f$, $g$ or their derivatives *at* the point $x = a$. Instead, we assume that $f(x)$ and $g(x)$ approach 0 as $x \to a$ and that the quotient $f'(x)/g'(x)$ tends to a finite limit as $x \to a$. L'Hôpital's rule then tells us that $f(x)/g(x)$ tends to the same limit. More precisely, we have the following.

THEOREM 7.9. L'HÔPITAL'S RULE FOR 0/0. *Assume $f$ and $g$ have derivatives $f'(x)$ and $g'(x)$ at each point $x$ of an open interval $(a, b)$, and suppose that*

$$(7.20) \qquad\qquad \lim_{x \to a+} f(x) = 0 \qquad and \qquad \lim_{x \to a+} g(x) = 0 .$$

---

† In 1696, Guillaume François Antoine de L'Hôpital (1661–1704) wrote the first textbook on differential calculus. This work appeared in many editions and played a significant role in the popularization of the subject. Much of the content of the book, including the method known as "L'Hôpital's rule," was based on the earlier work of Johann Bernoulli, one of L'Hôpital's teachers.

*Assume also that $g'(x) \neq 0$ for each $x$ in $(a, b)$. If the limit*

(7.21)
$$\lim_{x \to a+} \frac{f'(x)}{g'(x)}$$

*exists and has the value L, say, then the limit*

(7.22)
$$\lim_{x \to a+} \frac{f(x)}{g(x)}$$

*also exists and has the value L.*

Note that the limits in (7.20), (7.21), and (7.22) are "right-handed." There is, of course, a similar theorem in which the hypotheses are satisfied in some open interval of the form $(b, a)$ and all the limits are "left-handed." Also, by combining the two "one-sided" theorems, there follows a "two-sided" result of the same kind in which $x \to a$ in an unrestricted fashion.

Before we discuss the proof of Theorem 7.9, we shall illustrate the use of this theorem in a number of examples.

EXAMPLE 1. We shall use L'Hôpital's rule to obtain the familiar formula

(7.23)
$$\lim_{x \to 0} \frac{\sin x}{x} = 1.$$

Here $f(x) = \sin x$ and $g(x) = x$. The quotient of derivatives is $f'(x)/g'(x) = (\cos x)/1$ and this tends to 1 as $x \to 0$. By Theorem 7.9 the limit in (7.23) also exists and equals 1.

EXAMPLE 2. To determine the limit

$$\lim_{x \to 0} \frac{x - \tan x}{x - \sin x}$$

by L'Hôpital's rule, we let $f(x) = x - \tan x$, $g(x) = x - \sin x$, and we find that

(7.24)
$$\frac{f'(x)}{g'(x)} = \frac{1 - \sec^2 x}{1 - \cos x}.$$

Although this, too, assumes the form 0/0 as $x \to 0$, we may remove the indeterminacy at this stage by algebraic means. If we write

$$1 - \sec^2 x = 1 - \frac{1}{\cos^2 x} = \frac{\cos^2 x - 1}{\cos^2 x} = -\frac{(1 + \cos x)(1 - \cos x)}{\cos^2 x},$$

the quotient in (7.24) becomes

$$\frac{f'(x)}{g'(x)} = -\frac{1 + \cos x}{\cos^2 x},$$

and this approaches $-2$ as $x \to 0$. Notice that the indeterminacy disappeared when we canceled the common factor $1 - \cos x$. Canceling common factors usually tends to simplify the work in problems of this kind.

When the quotient of derivatives $f'(x)/g'(x)$ also assumes the indeterminate form $0/0$, we may try L'Hôpital's rule again. In the next example, the indeterminacy is removed after two applications of the rule.

EXAMPLE 3. For any real number $c$, we have

$$\lim_{x \to 1} \frac{x^c - cx + c - 1}{(x - 1)^2} = \lim_{x \to 1} \frac{cx^{c-1} - c}{2(x - 1)} = \lim_{x \to 1} \frac{c(c - 1)x^{c-2}}{2} = \frac{c(c - 1)}{2}.$$

In this sequence of equations it is understood that the existence of each limit implies that of the preceding and also their equality.

The next example shows that L'Hôpital's rule is not infallible.

EXAMPLE 4. Let $f(x) = e^{-1/x}$ if $x \neq 0$, and let $g(x) = x$. The quotient $f(x)/g(x)$ assumes the indeterminate form $0/0$ as $x \to 0+$, and one application of L'Hôpital's rule leads to the quotient

$$\frac{f'(x)}{g'(x)} = \frac{(1/x^2)e^{-1/x}}{1} = \frac{e^{-1/x}}{x^2}.$$

This, too, is indeterminate as $x \to 0+$, and if we differentiate numerator and denominator we obtain $(1/x^2)e^{-1/x}/(2x) = e^{-1/x}/(2x^3)$. After $n$ steps we are led to the quotient $e^{-1/x}/(n! \, x^{n+1})$, so the indeterminacy never disappears by this method.

EXAMPLE 5. When using L'Hôpital's rule repeatedly, some care is needed to make certain that the quotient under consideration actually assumes an indeterminate form. A common type of error is illustrated by the following calculation:

$$\lim_{x \to 1} \frac{3x^2 - 2x - 1}{x^2 - x} = \lim_{x \to 1} \frac{6x - 2}{2x - 1} = \lim_{x \to 1} \frac{6}{2} = 3.$$

The first step is correct but the second is not. The quotient $(6x - 2)/(2x - 1)$ is not indeterminate as $x \to 1$. The correct limit, 4, is obtained by substituting 1 for $x$ in $(6x - 2)/(2x - 1)$.

EXAMPLE 6. Sometimes the work can be shortened by a change of variable. For example, we could apply L'Hôpital's rule directly to calculate the limit

$$\lim_{x \to 0+} \frac{\sqrt{x}}{1 - e^{2\sqrt{x}}},$$

but we may avoid differentiation of square roots by writing $t = \sqrt{x}$ and noting that

$$\lim_{x \to 0+} \frac{\sqrt{x}}{1 - e^{2\sqrt{x}}} = \lim_{t \to 0+} \frac{t}{1 - e^{2t}} = \lim_{t \to 0+} \frac{1}{-2e^{2t}} = -\frac{1}{2}.$$

We turn now to the proof of Theorem 7.9.

*Proof.* We make use of Cauchy's mean-value formula (Theorem 4.6 of Section 4.14) applied to a closed interval having $a$ as its left endpoint. Since the functions $f$ and $g$ may not be defined at $a$, we introduce two new functions that *are* defined there. Let

$$F(x) = f(x) \quad \text{if} \quad x \neq a, \qquad F(a) = 0,$$

$$G(x) = g(x) \quad \text{if} \quad x \neq a, \qquad G(a) = 0.$$

Both $F$ and $G$ are continuous at $a$. In fact, if $a < x < b$, both functions $F$ and $G$ are continuous on the *closed interval* $[a, x]$ and have derivatives everywhere in the *open interval* $(a, x)$. Therefore Cauchy's formula is applicable to the interval $[a, x]$ and we obtain

$$[F(x) - F(a)]G'(c) = [G(x) - G(a)]F'(c),$$

where $c$ is some point satisfying $a < c < x$. Since $F(a) = G(a) = 0$, this becomes

$$f(x)g'(c) = g(x)f'(c).$$

Now $g'(c) \neq 0$ [since, by hypothesis, $g'$ is never zero in $(a, b)$] and also $g(x) \neq 0$. In fact, if we had $g(x) = 0$ then we would have $G(x) = G(a) = 0$ and, by Rolle's theorem, there would be a point $x_1$ between $a$ and $x$ where $G'(x_1) = 0$, contradicting the hypothesis that $g'$ is never zero in $(a, b)$. Therefore we may divide by $g'(c)$ and $g(x)$ to obtain

$$\frac{f(x)}{g(x)} = \frac{f'(c)}{g'(c)}.$$

As $x \to a$, the point $c \to a$ (since $a < c < x$) and the quotient on the right approaches $L$ [by (7.21)]. Hence, $f(x)/g(x)$ also approaches $L$ and the theorem is proved.

## 7.13 Exercises

Evaluate the limits in Exercises 1 through 12.

1. $\lim\limits_{x \to 2} \dfrac{3x^2 + 2x - 16}{x^2 - x - 2}$.

2. $\lim\limits_{x \to 3} \dfrac{x^2 - 4x + 3}{2x^2 - 13x + 21}$.

3. $\lim\limits_{x \to 0} \dfrac{\sinh x - \sin x}{x^3}$.

4. $\lim\limits_{x \to 0} \dfrac{(2 - x)e^x - x - 2}{x^3}$.

5. $\lim\limits_{x \to 0} \dfrac{\log (\cos ax)}{\log (\cos bx)}$.

6. $\lim\limits_{x \to 0+} \dfrac{x - \sin x}{(x \sin x)^{3/2}}$.

7. $\lim\limits_{x \to a+} \dfrac{\sqrt{x} - \sqrt{a} + \sqrt{x - a}}{\sqrt{x^2 - a^2}}$.

8. $\lim\limits_{x \to 1+} \dfrac{x^x - x}{1 - x + \log x}$.

9. $\lim\limits_{x \to 0} \dfrac{\arcsin 2x - 2\arcsin x}{x^3}$.

10. $\lim\limits_{x \to 0} \dfrac{x \cot x - 1}{x^2}$.

11. $\lim\limits_{x \to 1} \dfrac{\sum_{k=1}^{n} x^k - n}{x - 1}$.

12. $\lim\limits_{x \to 0+} \dfrac{1}{x\sqrt{x}}\left( a \arctan \dfrac{\sqrt{x}}{a} - b \arctan \dfrac{\sqrt{x}}{b} \right)$.

13. Determine the limit of the quotient

$$\frac{(\sin 4x)(\sin 3x)}{x \sin 2x}$$

as $x \to 0$ and also as $x \to \frac{1}{2}\pi$.

14. For what values of the constants $a$ and $b$ is

$$\lim_{x \to 0} (x^{-3} \sin 3x + ax^{-2} + b) = 0?$$

15. Find constants $a$ and $b$ such that $\lim_{x \to 0} \dfrac{1}{bx - \sin x} \displaystyle\int_0^x \frac{t^2 \, dt}{\sqrt{a + t}} = 1$.

16. A circular arc of radius 1 subtends an angle of $x$ radians, $0 < x < \frac{1}{2}\pi$, as shown in Figure 7.2. The point $C$ is the intersection of the two tangent lines at $A$ and $B$. Let $T(x)$ be the area of

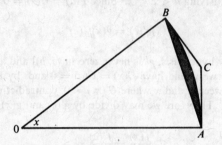

FIGURE 7.2    Exercise 16.

triangle $ABC$ and let $S(x)$ be the area of the shaded region. Compute the following: (a) $T(x)$; (b) $S(x)$; (c) the limit of $T(x)/S(x)$ as $x \to 0+$.

17. The current $I(t)$ flowing in a certain electrical circuit at time $t$ is given by

$$I(t) = \frac{E}{R}(1 - e^{-Rt/L}),$$

where $E$, $R$, and $L$ are positive numbers. Determine the limiting value of $I(t)$ as $R \to 0+$.

18. A weight hangs by a spring and is caused to vibrate by a sinusoidal force. Its displacement $f(t)$ at time $t$ is given by an equation of the form

$$f(t) = \frac{A}{c^2 - k^2}(\sin kt - \sin ct),$$

where $A$, $c$, and $k$ are positive constants, with $c \neq k$. Determine the limiting value of the displacement as $c \to k$.

## 7.14 The symbols $+\infty$ and $-\infty$. Extension of L'Hôpital's rule

L'Hôpital's rule may be extended in several ways. First of all, we may wish to consider the quotient $f(x)/g(x)$ as $x$ increases without bound. It is convenient to have a short descriptive symbolism to express the fact that we are allowing $x$ to increase indefinitely. For this purpose, mathematicians use the special symbol $+\infty$, called "plus infinity." Although we shall not attach any meaning to the symbol $+\infty$ *by itself*, we shall give precise definitions of various statements involving this symbol.

One of these statements is written as follows:

$$\lim_{x \to +\infty} f(x) = A ,$$

and is read "The limit of $f(x)$, as $x$ tends to plus infinity, is $A$." The idea we are trying to express here is that the function values $f(x)$ can be made arbitrarily close to the real number $A$ by taking $x$ large enough. To make this statement mathematically precise, we must explain what is meant by "arbitrarily close" and by "large enough." This is done by means of the following definition:

DEFINITION. *The symbolism*

$$\lim_{x \to +\infty} f(x) = A$$

*means that for every number $\epsilon > 0$, there is another number $M > 0$ (which may depend on $\epsilon$) such that*

$$|f(x) - A| < \epsilon \quad \textit{whenever} \quad x > M .$$

Calculations involving limits as $x \to +\infty$ may be reduced to a more familiar case. We simply replace $x$ by $1/t$ (that is, let $t = 1/x$) and note that $t \to 0$ through positive values as $x \to +\infty$. More precisely, we introduce a new function $F$, where

(7.25) $$F(t) = f\left(\frac{1}{t}\right) \quad \text{if} \quad t \neq 0,$$

and simply observe that the two statements

$$\lim_{x \to +\infty} f(x) = A \quad \text{and} \quad \lim_{t \to 0+} F(t) = A$$

mean exactly the same thing. The proof of this equivalence requires only the definitions of the two limit symbols and is left as an exercise.

When we are interested in the behavior of $f(x)$ for large *negative* $x$, we introduce the symbol $-\infty$ ("minus infinity") and write

$$\lim_{x \to -\infty} f(x) = A$$

to mean: For every $\epsilon > 0$, there is an $M > 0$ such that

$$|f(x) - A| < \epsilon \quad \textit{whenever} \quad x < -M .$$

If $F$ is defined by (7.25), it is easy to verify that the two statements

$$\lim_{x \to -\infty} f(x) = A \quad \text{and} \quad \lim_{t \to 0-} F(t) = A$$

are equivalent.

In view of the above remarks, it is not surprising to find that all the usual rules for calculating with limits (as stated in Theorem 3.1 of Section 3.4) also apply to limits as $x \to \pm\infty$. The same is true of L'Hôpital's rule which may be extended as follows:

THEOREM 7.10. *Assume that $f$ and $g$ have derivatives $f'(x)$ and $g'(x)$ for all $x$ greater than a certain fixed $M > 0$. Suppose that*

$$\lim_{x \to +\infty} f(x) = 0 \quad \text{and} \quad \lim_{x \to +\infty} g(x) = 0 ,$$

*and that $g'(x) \neq 0$ for $x > M$. If $f'(x)/g'(x)$ tends to a limit as $x \to +\infty$, then $f(x)/g(x)$ also tends to a limit and the two limits are equal. In other words,*

(7.26) $$\lim_{x \to +\infty} \frac{f'(x)}{g'(x)} = L \quad \text{implies} \quad \lim_{x \to +\infty} \frac{f(x)}{g(x)} = L .$$

*Proof.* Let $F(t) = f(1/t)$ and $G(t) = g(1/t)$. Then $f(x)/g(x) = F(t)/G(t)$ if $t = 1/x$, and $t \to 0+$ as $x \to +\infty$. Since $F(t)/G(t)$ assumes the indeterminate form $0/0$ as $t \to 0+$, we examine the quotient of derivatives $F'(t)/G'(t)$. By the chain rule, we have

$$F'(t) = \frac{-1}{t^2} f'\left(\frac{1}{t}\right) \quad \text{and} \quad G'(t) = \frac{-1}{t^2} g'\left(\frac{1}{t}\right) .$$

Also, $G'(t) \neq 0$ if $0 < t < 1/M$. When $x = 1/t$ and $x > M$, we have $F'(t)/G'(t) = f'(x)/g'(x)$ since the common factor $-1/t^2$ cancels. Therefore, if $f'(x)/g'(x) \to L$ as $x \to +\infty$, then $F'(t)/G'(t) \to L$ as $t \to 0+$ and hence, by Theorem 7.9, $F(t)/G(t) \to L$. Since $F(t)/G(t) = f(x)/g(x)$ this proves (7.26).

There is, of course, a result analogous to Theorem 7.10 in which we consider limits as $x \to -\infty$.

## 7.15 Infinite limits

In the foregoing section we used the notation $x \to +\infty$ to convey the idea that $x$ takes on arbitrarily large positive values. We also write

(7.27) $$\lim_{x \to a} f(x) = +\infty$$

or, alternatively,

(7.28) $$f(x) \to +\infty \quad \text{as} \quad x \to a$$

to indicate that $f(x)$ takes arbitrarily large values as $x$ approaches $a$. The precise meaning of these symbols is given in the following definition.

DEFINITION. *The symbolism in (7.27) or in (7.28) means that to every positive number M (no matter how large), there corresponds another positive number δ (which may depend on M) such that*

$$f(x) > M \quad \textit{whenever} \quad 0 < |x - a| < \delta .$$

*If $f(x) > M$ whenever $0 < x - a < \delta$, we write*

$$\lim_{x \to a+} f(x) = +\infty ,$$

*and we say that $f(x)$ tends to plus infinity as $x$ approaches $a$ from the right. If $f(x) > M$ whenever $0 < a - x < \delta$, we write*

$$\lim_{x \to a-} f(x) = +\infty ,$$

*and we say that $f(x)$ tends to plus infinity as $x$ approaches $a$ from the left.*

The symbols

$$\lim_{x \to a} f(x) = -\infty , \qquad \lim_{x \to a+} f(x) = -\infty , \qquad \text{and} \qquad \lim_{x \to a-} f(x) = -\infty$$

are similarly defined, the only difference being that we replace $f(x) > M$ by $f(x) < -M$. Examples are shown in Figure 7.3.

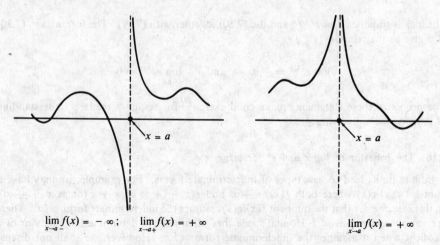

$$\lim_{x \to a-} f(x) = -\infty ; \qquad \lim_{x \to a+} f(x) = +\infty \qquad\qquad\qquad \lim_{x \to a} f(x) = +\infty$$

FIGURE 7.3 Infinite limits.

It is also convenient to extend the definitions of these symbols further to cover the cases when $x \to \pm \infty$. Thus, for example, we write

$$\lim_{x \to +\infty} f(x) = +\infty$$

if, for every positive number $M$, there exists another positive number $X$ such that $f(x) > M$ whenever $x > X$.

The reader should have no difficulty in formulating similar definitions for the symbols

$$\lim_{x \to -\infty} f(x) = +\infty, \qquad \lim_{x \to +\infty} f(x) = -\infty, \qquad \text{and} \qquad \lim_{x \to -\infty} f(x) = -\infty.$$

EXAMPLES. In Chapter 6 we proved that the logarithm function is increasing and unbounded on the positive real axis. We may express this fact briefly by writing

(7.29)                    $$\lim_{x \to +\infty} \log x = +\infty.$$

We also proved in Chapter 6 that $\log x < 0$ when $0 < x < 1$ and that the logarithm has no lower bound in the interval $(0, 1)$. Therefore, we may also write $\lim_{x \to 0+} \log x = -\infty$.

From the relation that holds between the logarithm and the exponential function it is easy to prove that

(7.30)          $$\lim_{x \to +\infty} e^x = +\infty \quad \text{and} \quad \lim_{x \to -\infty} e^x = 0 \quad (\text{or} \quad \lim_{x \to +\infty} e^{-x} = 0).$$

Using these results it is not difficult to show that for $\alpha > 0$ we have

$$\lim_{x \to +\infty} x^\alpha = +\infty \quad \text{and} \quad \lim_{x \to +\infty} \frac{1}{x^\alpha} = 0.$$

The idea is to write $x^\alpha = e^{\alpha \log x}$ and use (7.30) together with (7.29). The formulas in (7.30) also give us the relations

$$\lim_{x \to 0-} e^{-1/x} = +\infty \quad \text{and} \quad \lim_{x \to 0+} e^{-1/x} = 0.$$

The proofs of these statements make good exercises for testing a reader's understanding of limit symbols involving $\pm \infty$.

## 7.16 The behavior of $\log x$ and $e^x$ for large $x$

Infinite limits lead to new types of indeterminate forms. For example, we may have a quotient $f(x)/g(x)$ where both $f(x) \to +\infty$ and $g(x) \to +\infty$ as $x \to a$ (or as $x \to \pm \infty$). In this case, we say that the quotient $f(x)/g(x)$ assumes the indeterminate form $\infty/\infty$. There are various extensions of L'Hôpital's rule that often help to determine the behavior of a quotient when it assumes the indeterminate form $\infty/\infty$. However, we shall not discuss these extensions because most examples that occur in practice can be treated by use of the following theorem which describes the behavior of the logarithm and the exponential for large values of $x$.

THEOREM 7.11. *If $a > 0$ and $b > 0$, we have*

$$(7.31) \qquad \lim_{x \to +\infty} \frac{(\log x)^b}{x^a} = 0$$

*and*

$$(7.32) \qquad \lim_{x \to +\infty} \frac{x^b}{e^{ax}} = 0 .$$

*Proof.* We prove (7.31) first and then use it to derive (7.32). A simple proof of (7.31) may be given directly from the definition of the logarithm as an integral. If $c > 0$ and $t \geq 1$, we have $t^{-1} \leq t^{c-1}$. Hence, if $x > 1$, we may write

$$0 < \log x = \int_1^x \frac{1}{t} \, dt \leq \int_1^x t^{c-1} \, dt = \frac{x^c - 1}{c} < \frac{x^c}{c} .$$

Therefore, we have

$$0 < \frac{(\log x)^b}{x^a} < \frac{x^{bc-a}}{c^b} \qquad \text{for every } c > 0 .$$

If we choose $c = \tfrac{1}{2}a/b$, then $x^{bc-a} = x^{-a/2}$ which tends to 0 as $x \to +\infty$. This proves (7.31). To prove (7.32), we make the change of variable $t = e^x$. Then $x = \log t$, and hence $x^b/e^{ax} = (\log t)^b/t^a$. But $t \to +\infty$ as $x \to +\infty$, so (7.32) follows from (7.31).

With a natural extension of the $o$-notation, we can write the limit relations just proved in the form

$$(\log x)^b = o(x^a) \qquad \text{as} \quad x \to +\infty ,$$

and

$$x^b = o(e^{ax}) \qquad \text{as} \quad x \to +\infty .$$

In other words, no matter how large $b$ may be and no matter how small $a$ may be (as long as both are positive), $(\log x)^b$ tends to infinity more slowly than $x^a$. Also, $x^b$ tends to infinity more slowly than $e^{ax}$.

EXAMPLE 1. In Example 4 of Section 7.12 we showed that the behavior of $e^{-1/x}/x$ for $x$ near 0 could not be decided by any number of applications of L'Hôpital's rule for $0/0$. However, if we write $t = 1/x$, this quotient becomes $t/e^t$ and it assumes the indeterminate form $\infty/\infty$ as $t \to +\infty$. Theorem 7.11 tells us that

$$\lim_{t \to +\infty} \frac{t}{e^t} = 0 .$$

Therefore, $e^{-1/x}/x \to 0$ as $x \to 0+$ or, in other words, $e^{-1/x} = o(x)$ as $x \to 0+$.

There are other indeterminate forms besides $0/0$ and $\infty/\infty$. Some of these, denoted by the symbols $0 \cdot \infty$, $0^0$, and $\infty^0$, are illustrated by the examples given below. In examples like these, algebraic manipulation often enables us to reduce the problem to an indeterminate form of the type $0/0$ or $\infty/\infty$ which may be handled by L'Hôpital's rule, by polynomial approximation, or by Theorem 7.11.

EXAMPLE 2. $(0 \cdot \infty)$. Prove that $\lim_{x \to 0+} x^\alpha \log x = 0$ for each fixed $\alpha > 0$.

*Solution.* Writing $t = 1/x$, we find that $x^\alpha \log x = -(\log t)/t^\alpha$ and, by (7.31), this tends to 0 as $t \to +\infty$.

EXAMPLE 3. $(0^0)$. Show that $\lim_{x \to 0+} x^x = 1$.

*Solution.* Since $x^x = e^{x \log x}$, by continuity of the exponential function we have

$$\lim_{x \to 0+} x^x = \exp\left( \lim_{x \to 0+} x \log x \right),$$

if the last limit exists. But by Example 2 we know that $x \log x \to 0$ as $x \to 0+$, and hence $x^x \to e^0 = 1$.

EXAMPLE 4. $(\infty^0)$. Show that $\lim_{x \to +\infty} x^{1/x} = 1$.

*Solution.* Put $t = 1/x$ and use the result of Example 3.

In Section 7.10 we proved the limit relations

$$(7.33) \qquad \lim_{x \to 0} (1 + ax)^{1/x} = e^a \qquad \text{and} \qquad \lim_{x \to 0} (1 + x)^{a/x} = e^a.$$

Each of these is an indeterminate form of the type $1^\infty$. We may replace $x$ by $1/x$ in these formulas and obtain, respectively,

$$\lim_{x \to +\infty} \left(1 + \frac{a}{x}\right)^x = e^a \qquad \text{and} \qquad \lim_{x \to +\infty} \left(1 + \frac{1}{x}\right)^{ax} = e^a,$$

both of which are valid for all real $a$.

The relations (7.33) and those in Examples 2, 3, and 4 are all of the type $f(x)^{g(x)}$. These are usually dealt with by writing

$$f(x)^{g(x)} = e^{g(x) \log f(x)}$$

and then treating the exponent $g(x) \log f(x)$ by one of the methods discussed earlier.

## 7.17  Exercises

Evaluate the limits in Exercises 1 through 25.  The letters $a$ and $b$ denote positive constants.

1. $\lim\limits_{x \to 0} \dfrac{e^{-1/x^2}}{x^{1000}}$ .

2. $\lim\limits_{x \to +\infty} \dfrac{\sin{(1/x)}}{\arctan{(1/x)}}$ .

3. $\lim\limits_{x \to \frac{1}{2}\pi} \dfrac{\tan 3x}{\tan x}$ .

4. $\lim\limits_{x \to +\infty} \dfrac{\log(a + be^x)}{\sqrt{a + bx^2}}$ .

5. $\lim\limits_{x \to +\infty} x^4 \left( \cos \dfrac{1}{x} - 1 + \dfrac{1}{2x^2} \right)$ .

6. $\lim\limits_{x \to \pi} \dfrac{\log |\sin x|}{\log |\sin 2x|}$ .

7. $\lim\limits_{x \to \frac{1}{2}-} \dfrac{\log (1 - 2x)}{\tan \pi x}$ .

8. $\lim\limits_{x \to +\infty} \dfrac{\cosh (x + 1)}{e^x}$ .

9. $\lim\limits_{x \to +\infty} \dfrac{a^x}{x^b}$ ,    $a > 1$.

10. $\lim\limits_{x \to \frac{1}{2}\pi} \dfrac{\tan x - 5}{\sec x + 4}$ .

11. $\lim\limits_{x \to 0+} \dfrac{1}{\sqrt{x}} \left( \dfrac{1}{\sin x} - \dfrac{1}{x} \right)$ .

12. $\lim\limits_{x \to +\infty} x^{1/4} \sin (1/\sqrt{x})$ .

13. $\lim\limits_{x \to +\infty} (x^2 - \sqrt{x^4 - x^2 + 1})$.

14. $\lim\limits_{x \to 0+} \left[ \dfrac{\log x}{(1 + x)^2} - \log\!\left( \dfrac{x}{1 + x} \right) \right]$ .

15. $\lim\limits_{x \to 1-} (\log x) \log (1 - x)$.

16. $\lim\limits_{x \to 0+} x^{(x^x - 1)}$.

17. $\lim\limits_{x \to 0+} [x^{(x^x)} - 1]$.

18. $\lim\limits_{x \to 0-} (1 - 2^x)^{\sin x}$.

19. $\lim\limits_{x \to 0+} x^{1/\log x}$.

20. $\lim\limits_{x \to 0+} (\cot x)^{\sin x}$.

21. $\lim\limits_{x \to \frac{1}{4}\pi} (\tan x)^{\tan 2x}$.

22. $\lim\limits_{x \to 0+} \left( \log \dfrac{1}{x} \right)^x$ .

23. $\lim\limits_{x \to 0+} x^{e/(1 + \log x)}$.

24. $\lim\limits_{x \to 1} (2 - x)^{\tan(\pi x/2)}$.

25. $\lim\limits_{x \to 0} \left( \dfrac{1}{\log (x + \sqrt{1 + x^2})} - \dfrac{1}{\log 1( + x)} \right)$ .

26. Find $c$ so that

$$\lim_{x \to +\infty} \left( \frac{x + c}{x - c} \right)^x = 4.$$

27. Prove that $(1 + x)^c = 1 + cx + o(x)$ as $x \to 0$.  Use this to compute the limit of

$$\{(x^4 + x^2)^{1/2} - x^2\} \qquad \text{as } x \to +\infty.$$

28. For a certain value of $c$, the limit

$$\lim_{x \to +\infty} \{(x^5 + 7x^4 + 2)^c - x\}$$

is finite and nonzero.  Determine this $c$ and compute the value of the limit.

29. Let $g(x) = xe^{x^2}$ and let $f(x) = \int_1^x g(t)(t + 1/t)\,dt$. Compute the limit of $f''(x)/g''(x)$ as $x \to +\infty$.

30. Let $g(x) = x^c e^{2x}$ and let $f(x) = \int_0^x e^{2t}(3t^2 + 1)^{1/2}\,dt$. For a certain value of $c$, the limit of $f'(x)/g'(x)$ as $x \to +\infty$ is finite and nonzero. Determine $c$ and compute the value of the limit.

31. Let $f(x) = e^{-1/x^2}$ if $x \neq 0$, and let $f(0) = 0$.
    (a) Prove that for every $m > 0$, $f(x)/x^m \to 0$ as $x \to 0$.
    (b) Prove that for $x \neq 0$ the $n$th derivative of $f$ has the form $f^{(n)}(x) = f(x)P(1/x)$, where $P(t)$ is a polynomial in $t$.
    (c) Prove that $f^{(n)}(0) = 0$ for all $n \geq 1$. This shows that every Taylor polynomial generated by $f$ at 0 is the zero polynomial.

32. An amount of $P$ dollars is deposited in a bank which pays interest at a rate $r$ per year, compounded $m$ times a year. (For example, $r = 0.06$ when the annual rate is $6\%$.) (a) Prove that the total amount of principal plus interest at the end of $n$ years is $P(1 + r/m)^{mn}$. If $r$ and $n$ are kept fixed, this amount approaches the limit $Pe^{rn}$ as $m \to +\infty$. This motivates the following definition: We say that money grows at an annual rate $r$ when compounded continuously if the amount $f(t)$ after $t$ years is $f(0)e^{rt}$, where $t$ is any nonnegative real number. Approximately how long does it take for a bank account to double in value if it receives interest at an annual rate of $6\%$ compounded (b) continuously? (c) four times a year?

# 8

# INTRODUCTION TO DIFFERENTIAL EQUATIONS

## 8.1 Introduction

A large variety of scientific problems arise in which one tries to determine something from its rate of change. For example, we could try to compute the position of a moving particle from a knowledge of its velocity or acceleration. Or a radioactive substance may be disintegrating at a known rate and we may be required to determine the amount of material present after a given time. In examples like these, we are trying to determine an *unknown function* from prescribed information expressed in the form of an equation involving at least one of the derivatives of the unknown function. These equations are called *differential equations*, and their study forms one of the most challenging branches of mathematics.

Differential equations are classified under two main headings: *ordinary* and *partial*, depending on whether the unknown is a function of just *one* variable or of *two or more* variables. A simple example of an ordinary differential equation is the relation

$$(8.1) \qquad\qquad f'(x) = f(x)$$

which is satisfied, in particular, by the exponential function, $f(x) = e^x$. We shall see presently that every solution of (8.1) must be of the form $f(x) = Ce^x$, where $C$ may be any constant.

On the other hand, an equation like

$$\frac{\partial^2 f(x, y)}{\partial x^2} + \frac{\partial^2 f(x, y)}{\partial y^2} = 0$$

is an example of a partial differential equation. This particular one, called *Laplace's equation*, appears in the theory of electricity and magnetism, fluid mechanics, and elsewhere. It has many different kinds of solutions, among which are $f(x, y) = x + 2y$, $f(x, y) = e^x \cos y$, and $f(x, y) = \log (x^2 + y^2)$.

The study of differential equations is one part of mathematics that, perhaps more than any other, has been directly inspired by mechanics, astronomy, and mathematical physics. Its history began in the 17th century when Newton, Leibniz, and the Bernoullis solved some simple differential equations arising from problems in geometry and mechanics.

These early discoveries, beginning about 1690, gradually led to the development of a now-classic "bag of tricks" for solving certain special kinds of differential equations. Although these special tricks are applicable in relatively few cases, they do enable us to solve many differential equations that arise in mechanics and geometry, so their study is of practical importance. Some of these special methods and some of the problems which they help us solve are discussed near the end of this chapter.

Experience has shown that it is difficult to obtain mathematical theories of much generality about solutions of differential equations, except for a few types. Among these are the so-called *linear* differential equations which occur in a great variety of scientific problems. The simplest types of linear differential equations and some of their applications are also discussed in this introductory chapter. A more thorough study of linear equations is carried out in Volume II.

## 8.2 Terminology and notation

When we work with a differential equation such as (8.1), it is customary to write $y$ in place of $f(x)$ and $y'$ in place of $f'(x)$, the higher derivatives being denoted by $y''$, $y'''$, etc. Of course, other letters such as $u$, $v$, $z$, etc. are also used instead of $y$. By the *order* of an equation is meant the order of the highest derivative which appears. For example, (8.1) is a first-order equation which may be written as $y' = y$. The differential equation $y' = x^3 y + \sin(xy'')$ is one of second order.

In this chapter we shall begin our study with first-order equations which can be solved for $y'$ and written as follows:

$$(8.2) \qquad\qquad y' = f(x, y),$$

where the expression $f(x, y)$ on the right has various special forms. A differentiable function $y = Y(x)$ will be called a *solution* of (8.2) on an interval $I$ if the function $Y$ and its derivative $Y'$ satisfy the relation

$$Y'(x) = f[x, Y(x)]$$

for every $x$ in $I$. The simplest case occurs when $f(x, y)$ is independent of $y$. In this case, (8.2) becomes

$$(8.3) \qquad\qquad y' = Q(x),$$

say, where $Q$ is assumed to be a given function defined on some interval $I$. To solve the differential equation (8.3) means to find a primitive of $Q$. The second fundamental theorem of calculus tells us how to do it when $Q$ is continuous on an open interval $I$. We simply integrate $Q$ and add any constant. Thus, every solution of (8.3) is included in the formula

$$(8.4) \qquad\qquad y = \int Q(x)\, dx + C,$$

where $C$ is any constant (usually called an arbitrary constant of integration). The differential equation (8.3) has infinitely many solutions, one for each value of $C$.

If it is not possible to evaluate the integral in (8.4) in terms of familiar functions, such as polynomials, rational functions, trigonometric and inverse trigonometric functions, logarithms, and exponentials, still we consider the differential equation as having been solved if the solution can be expressed in terms of integrals of known functions. In actual practice, there are various methods for obtaining approximate evaluations of integrals which lead to useful information about the solution. Automatic high-speed computing machines are often designed with this kind of problem in mind.

EXAMPLE. *Linear motion determined from the velocity.* Suppose a particle moves along a straight line in such a way that its velocity at time $t$ is $2 \sin t$. Determine its position at time $t$.

*Solution.* If $Y(t)$ denotes the position at time $t$ measured from some starting point, then the derivative $Y'(t)$ represents the velocity at time $t$. We are given that

$$Y'(t) = 2 \sin t.$$

Integrating, we find that

$$Y(t) = 2 \int \sin t \, dt + C = -2 \cos t + C.$$

This is all we can deduce about $Y(t)$ from a knowledge of the velocity alone; some other piece of information is needed to fix the position function. We can determine $C$ if we know the value of $Y$ at some particular instant. For example, if $Y(0) = 0$, then $C = 2$ and the position function is $Y(t) = 2 - 2 \cos t$. But if $Y(0) = 2$, then $C = 4$ and the position function is $Y(t) = 4 - 2 \cos t$.

In some respects the example just solved is typical of what happens in general. Somewhere in the process of solving a first-order differential equation, an integration is required to remove the derivative $y'$ and in this step an arbitrary constant $C$ appears. The way in which the arbitrary constant $C$ enters into the solution will depend on the nature of the given differential equation. It may appear as an additive constant, as in Equation (8.4), but it is more likely to appear in some other way. For example, when we solve the equation $y' = y$ in Section 8.3, we shall find that every solution has the form $y = Ce^x$.

In many problems it is necessary to select from the collection of all solutions one having a prescribed value at some point. The prescribed value is called an *initial condition*, and the problem of determining such a solution is called an *initial-value problem*. This terminology originated in mechanics where, as in the above example, the prescribed value represents the displacement at some initial time.

We shall begin our study of differential equations with an important special case.

## 8.3 . A first-order differential equation for the exponential function

The exponential function is equal to its own derivative, and the same is true of any constant multiple of the exponential. It is easy to show that these are the only functions that satisfy this property on the whole real axis.

THEOREM 8.1. *If C is a given real number, there is one and only one function f which satisfies the differential equation*

$$f'(x) = f(x)$$

*for all real x and which also satisfies the initial condition* $f(0) = C$. *This function is given by the formula*

$$f(x) = Ce^x.$$

*Proof.* It is easy to verify that the function $f(x) = Ce^x$ satisfies both the given differential equation and the given initial condition. Now we must show that this is the *only* solution. Let $y = g(x)$ be any solution of this initial-value problem:

$$g'(x) = g(x) \qquad \text{for all } x, \qquad g(0) = C.$$

We wish to show that $g(x) = Ce^x$ or that $g(x)e^{-x} = C$. We consider the function $h(x) = g(x)e^{-x}$ and show that its derivative is always zero. The derivative of $h$ is given by

$$h'(x) = g'(x)e^{-x} - g(x)e^{-x} = e^{-x}[g'(x) - g(x)] = 0.$$

Hence, by the zero-derivative theorem, $h$ is constant. But $g(0) = C$ so $h(0) = g(0)e^0 = C$. Hence, we have $h(x) = C$ for all $x$ which means that $g(x) = Ce^x$, as required.

Theorem 8.1 is an example of an existence-uniqueness theorem. It tells us that the given initial-value problem *has* a solution (existence) and that it has *only one* solution (uniqueness). The object of much of the research in the theory of differential equations is to discover existence and uniqueness theorems for wide classes of equations.

We discuss next an important type which includes both the differential equation $y' = Q(x)$ and the equation $y' = y$ as special cases.

## 8.4 First-order linear differential equations

A differential equation of the form

(8.5) $$y' + P(x)y = Q(x),$$

where $P$ and $Q$ are given functions, is called a *first-order linear* differential equation. The terms involving the unknown function $y$ and its derivative $y'$ appear as a linear combination of $y$ and $y'$. The functions $P$ and $Q$ are assumed to be continuous on some open interval $I$. We seek all solutions $y$ defined on $I$.

First we consider the special case in which the right member, $Q(x)$, is identically zero. The equation

(8.6) $$y' + P(x)y = 0$$

is called the *homogeneous* or *reduced* equation corresponding to (8.5). We will show how to solve the homogeneous equation and then use the result to help us solve the non-homogeneous equation (8.5).

If $y$ is nonzero on $I$, Equation (8.6) is equivalent to the equation

(8.7) $$\frac{y'}{y} = -P(x).$$

That is, every nonzero $y$ which satisfies (8.6) also satisfies (8.7) and vice versa. Now suppose $y$ is a positive function satisfying (8.7). Since the quotient $y'/y$ is the derivative of $\log y$, Equation (8.7) becomes $D \log y = -P(x)$, from which we find $\log y = -\int P(x)\, dx + C$, so we have

$$(8.8) \qquad y = e^{-A(x)}, \qquad \text{where} \quad A(x) = \int P(x)\, dx - C.$$

In other words, if there is a positive solution of (8.6), it must necessarily have the form (8.8) for some $C$. But now it is easy to verify that every function in (8.8) is a solution of the homogeneous equation (8.6). In fact, we have

$$y' = -e^{-A(x)} A'(x) = -P(x)e^{-A(x)} = -P(x)y.$$

Thus, we have found all positive solutions of (8.6). But now it is easy to describe all solutions. We state the result as an existence-uniqueness theorem.

THEOREM 8.2. *Assume $P$ is continuous on an open interval $I$. Choose any point $a$ in $I$ and let $b$ be any real number. Then there is one and only one function $y = f(x)$ which satisfies the initial-value problem*

$$(8.9) \qquad y' + P(x)y = 0, \qquad \text{with} \quad f(a) = b,$$

*on the interval $I$. This function is given by the formula*

$$(8.10) \qquad f(x) = be^{-A(x)}, \qquad \text{where} \quad A(x) = \int_a^x P(t)\, dt.$$

*Proof.* Let $f$ be defined by (8.10). Then $A(a) = 0$ so $f(a) = be^0 = b$. Differentiation shows that $f$ satisfies the differential equation in (8.9), so $f$ is a solution of the initial-value problem. Now we must show that it is the only solution.

Let $g$ be an arbitrary solution. We wish to show that $g(x) = be^{-A(x)}$ or that $g(x)e^{A(x)} = b$. Therefore it is natural to introduce $h(x) = g(x)e^{A(x)}$. The derivative of $h$ is given by

$$(8.11) \qquad h'(x) = g'(x)e^{A(x)} + g(x)e^{A(x)}A'(x) = e^{A(x)}[g'(x) + P(x)g(x)].$$

Now since $g$ satisfies the differential equation in (8.9), we have $g'(x) + P(x)g(x) = 0$ everywhere on $I$, so $h'(x) = 0$ for all $x$ in $I$. This means that $h$ is constant on $I$. Hence, we have $h(x) = h(a) = g(a)e^{A(a)} = g(a) = b$. In other words, $g(x)e^{A(x)} = b$, so $g(x) = be^{-A(x)}$, which shows that $g = f$. This completes the proof.

The last part of the foregoing proof suggests a method for solving the nonhomogeneous differential equation in (8.5). Suppose that $g$ is any function satisfying (8.5), and let $h(x) = g(x)e^{A(x)}$ where, as above, $A(x) = \int_a^x P(t)\, dt$. Then Equation (8.11) is again valid, but since $g$ satisfies (8.5), the formula for $h'(x)$ gives us

$$h'(x) = e^{A(x)}Q(x).$$

Now we may invoke the second fundamental theorem to write

$$h(x) = h(a) + \int_a^x e^{A(t)}Q(t)\, dt \, .$$

Hence, since $h(a) = g(a)$, every solution $g$ of (8.5) has the form

(8.12)          $$g(x) = e^{-A(x)}h(x) = g(a)e^{-A(x)} + e^{-A(x)}\int_a^x Q(t)e^{A(t)}\, dt \, .$$

Conversely, by direct differentiation of (8.12), it is easy to verify that each such $g$ is a solution of (8.5), so we have found *all* solutions. We state the result as follows.

THEOREM 8.3.    *Assume P and Q are continuous on an open interval I. Choose any point a in I and let b be any real number. Then there is one and only one function $y = f(x)$ which satisfies the initial-value problem*

$$y' + P(x)y = Q(x), \quad \text{with} \quad f(a) = b \, ,$$

*on the interval I. This function is given by the formula*

$$f(x) = be^{-A(x)} + e^{-A(x)}\int_a^x Q(t)e^{A(t)}\, dt \, ,$$

*where $A(x) = \int_a^x P(t)\, dt$.*

Up to now the word "interval" has meant a bounded interval of the form $(a, b)$, $[a, b]$, $[a, b)$, or $(a, b]$, with $a < b$. It is convenient to consider also unbounded intervals. They are denoted by the symbols $(a, +\infty)$, $(-\infty, a)$, $[a, +\infty)$ and $(-\infty, a]$, and they are defined as follows:

$$(a, +\infty) = \{x \mid x > a\} \, , \qquad (-\infty, a) = \{x \mid x < a\} \, ,$$

$$[a, +\infty) = \{x \mid x \geq a\} \, , \qquad (-\infty, a] = \{x \mid x \leq a\} \, .$$

In addition, it is convenient to refer to the collection of *all* real numbers as the interval $(-\infty, +\infty)$. Thus, when we discuss a differential equation or its solution over an interval $I$, it will be understood that $I$ is one of the nine types just described.

EXAMPLE.    Find all solutions of the first-order differential equation $xy' + (1 - x)y = e^{2x}$ on the interval $(0, +\infty)$.

Solution.    First we transform the equation to the form $y' + P(x)y = Q(x)$ by dividing through by $x$. This gives us

$$y' + \left(\frac{1}{x} - 1\right)y = \frac{e^{2x}}{x} \, ,$$

so $P(x) = 1/x - 1$ and $Q(x) = e^{2x}/x$. Since $P$ and $Q$ are continuous on the interval $(0, +\infty)$, there is a unique solution $y = f(x)$ satisfying any given initial condition of the form $f(a) = b$. We shall express all solutions in terms of the initial value at the point $a = 1$. In other words, given any real number $b$, we will determine all solutions for which $f(1) = b$.

First we compute

$$A(x) = \int_1^x P(t)\, dt = \int_1^x \left(\frac{1}{t} - 1\right) dt = \log x - (x - 1).$$

Hence we have $e^{-A(x)} = e^{x-1-\log x} = e^{x-1}/x$, and $e^{A(t)} = te^{1-t}$, so Theorem 8.3 tells us that the solution is given by the formula

$$f(x) = b\frac{e^{x-1}}{x} + \frac{e^{x-1}}{x}\int_1^x \frac{e^{2t}}{t} te^{1-t}\, dt = b\frac{e^{x-1}}{x} + \frac{e^x}{x}\int_1^x e^t\, dt$$

$$= b\frac{e^{x-1}}{x} + \frac{e^x}{x}(e^x - e) = b\frac{e^{x-1}}{x} + \frac{e^{2x}}{x} - \frac{e^{x+1}}{x}.$$

We can also write this in the form

$$f(x) = \frac{e^{2x} + Ce^x}{x},$$

where $C = be^{-1} - e$. This gives all solutions on the interval $(0, +\infty)$.

It may be of interest to study the behavior of the solutions as $x \to 0$. If we approximate the exponential by its linear Taylor polynomial, we find that $e^{2x} = 1 + 2x + o(x)$ and $e^x = 1 + x + o(x)$ as $x \to 0$, so we have

$$f(x) = \frac{(1 + C) + (2 + C)x + o(x)}{x} = \frac{1 + C}{x} + (2 + C) + o(1).$$

Therefore, only the solution with $C = -1$ tends to a finite limit as $x \to 0$, this limit being 1.

## 8.5 Exercises

In each of Exercises 1 through 5, solve the initial-value problem on the specified interval.

1. $y' - 3y = e^{2x}$ on $(-\infty, +\infty)$, with $y = 0$ when $x = 0$.
2. $xy' - 2y = x^5$ on $(0, +\infty)$, with $y = 1$ when $x = 1$.
3. $y' + y\tan x = \sin 2x$ on $(-\frac{1}{2}\pi, \frac{1}{2}\pi)$, with $y = 2$ when $x = 0$.
4. $y' + xy = x^3$ on $(-\infty, +\infty)$, with $y = 0$ when $x = 0$.
5. $\dfrac{dx}{dt} + x = e^{2t}$ on $(-\infty, +\infty)$, with $x = 1$ when $t = 0$.
6. Find all solutions of $y'\sin x + y\cos x = 1$ on the interval $(0, \pi)$. Prove that exactly one of these solutions has a finite limit as $x \to 0$, and another has a finite limit as $x \to \pi$.
7. Find all solutions of $x(x + 1)y' + y = x(x + 1)^2 e^{-x^2}$ on the interval $(-1, 0)$. Prove that all solutions approach 0 as $x \to -1$, but that only one of them has a finite limit as $x \to 0$.
8. Find all solutions of $y' + y\cot x = 2\cos x$ on the interval $(0, \pi)$. Prove that exactly one of these is also a solution on $(-\infty, +\infty)$.

9. Find all solutions of $(x - 2)(x - 3)y' + 2y = (x - 1)(x - 2)$ on each of the following intervals: (a) $(-\infty, 2)$; (b) $(2, 3)$; (c) $(3, +\infty)$. Prove that all solutions tend to a finite limit as $x \to 2$, but that none has a finite limit as $x \to 3$.

10. Let $s(x) = (\sin x)/x$ if $x \neq 0$, and let $s(0) = 1$. Define $T(x) = \int_0^x s(t) \, dt$. Prove that the function $f(x) = xT(x)$ satisfies the differential equation $xy' - y = x \sin x$ on the interval $(-\infty, +\infty)$ and find all solutions on this interval. Prove that the differential equation has no solution satisfying the initial condition $f(0) = 1$, and explain why this does not contradict Theorem 8.3.

11. Prove that there is exactly one function $f$, continuous on the positive real axis, such that

$$f(x) = 1 + \frac{1}{x} \int_1^x f(t) \, dt$$

for all $x > 0$ and find this function.

12. The function $f$ defined by the equation

$$f(x) = xe^{(1-x^2)/2} - xe^{-x^2/2} \int_1^x t^{-2} e^{t^2/2} \, dt$$

for $x > 0$ has the properties that (i) it is continuous on the positive real axis, and (ii) it satisfies the equation

$$f(x) = 1 - x \int_1^x f(t) \, dt$$

for all $x > 0$. Find all functions with these two properties.

*The Bernoulli equation.* A differential equation of the form $y' + P(x)y = Q(x)y^n$, where $n$ is not 0 or 1, is called a Bernoulli equation. This equation is nonlinear because of the presence of $y^n$. The next exercise shows that it can always be transformed into a linear first-order equation for a new unknown function $v$, where $v = y^k$, $k = 1 - n$.

13. Let $k$ be a nonzero constant. Assume $P$ and $Q$ are continuous on an interval $I$. If $a \in I$ and if $b$ is any real number, let $v = g(x)$ be the unique solution of the initital-value problem $v' + kP(x)v = kQ(x)$ on $I$, with $g(a) = b$. If $n \neq 1$ and $k = 1 - n$, prove that a function $y = f(x)$, which is never zero on $I$, is a solution of the initial-value problem

$$y' + P(x)y = Q(x)y^n \quad \text{on} \quad I, \quad \text{with} \quad f(a)^k = b$$

if and only if the $k$th power of $f$ is equal to $g$ on $I$.

In each of Exercises 14 through 17, solve the initial-value problem on the specified interval.

14. $y' - 4y = 2e^x y^{1/2}$ on $(-\infty, +\infty)$, with $y = 2$ when $x = 0$.
15. $y' - y = -y^2(x^2 + x + 1)$ on $(-\infty, +\infty)$, with $y = 1$ when $x = 0$.
16. $xy' - 2y = 4x^3 y^{1/2}$ on $(-\infty, +\infty)$, with $y = 0$ when $x = 1$.
17. $xy' + y = y^2 x^2 \log x$ on $(0, +\infty)$, with $y = \frac{1}{2}$ when $x = 1$.
18. $2xyy' + (1 + x)y^2 = e^x$ on $(0, +\infty)$, with (a) $y = \sqrt{e}$ when $x = 1$; (b) $y = -\sqrt{e}$ when $x = 1$; (c) a finite limit as $x \to 0$.
19. An equation of the form $y' + P(x)y + Q(x)y^2 = R(x)$ is called a *Riccati equation*. (There is no known method for solving the general Riccati equation.) Prove that if $u$ is a known solution of this equation, then there are further solutions of the form $y = u + 1/v$, where $v$ satisfies a first-order linear equation.

20. The Riccati equation $y' + y + y^2 = 2$ has two constant solutions. Start with each of these and use Exercise 19 to find further solutions as follows: (a) If $-2 \leq b < 1$, find a solution on $(-\infty, +\infty)$ for which $y = b$ when $x = 0$. (b) If $b \geq 1$ or $b < -2$, find a solution on the interval $(-\infty, +\infty)$ for which $y = b$ when $x = 0$.

## 8.6 Some physical problems leading to first-order linear differential equations

In this section we will discuss various physical problems that can be formulated mathematically as differential equations. In each case, the differential equation represents an idealized simplification of the physical problem and is called a *mathematical model* of the problem. The differential equation occurs as a translation of some physical law, such as Newton's second law of motion, a "conservation" law, etc. Our purpose here is not to justify the choice of the mathematical model but rather to deduce logical consequences from it. Each model is only an approximation to reality, and its justification properly belongs to the science from which the problem emanates. If intuition or experimental evidence agrees with the results deduced mathematically, then we feel that the model is a useful one. If not, we try to find a more suitable model.

EXAMPLE 1. *Radioactive decay.* Although various radioactive elements show marked differences in their rates of decay, they all seem to share a common property—the rate at which a given substance decomposes at any instant is proportional to the amount present at that instant. If we denote by $y = f(t)$ the amount present at time $t$, the derivative $y' = f'(t)$ represents the rate of change of $y$ at time $t$, and the "law of decay" states that

$$y' = -ky ,$$

where $k$ is a positive constant (called the *decay constant*) whose actual value depends on the particular element that is decomposing. The minus sign comes in because $y$ decreases as $t$ increases, and hence $y'$ is always negative. The differential equation $y' = -ky$ is the mathematical model used for problems concerning radioactive decay. Every solution $y = f(t)$ of this differential equation has the form

$$(8.13) \qquad f(t) = f(0)e^{-kt}.$$

Therefore, to determine the amount present at time $t$, we need to know the initial amount $f(0)$ and the value of the decay constant $k$.

It is interesting to see what information can be deduced from (8.13), without knowing the exact value of $f(0)$ or of $k$. First we observe that there is no finite time $t$ at which $f(t)$ will be zero because the exponential $e^{-kt}$ never vanishes. Therefore, it is not useful to study the "total lifetime" of a radioactive substance. However, it is possible to determine the time required for any particular *fraction* of a sample to decay. The fraction $\frac{1}{2}$ is usually chosen for convenience and the time $T$ at which $f(T)/f(0) = \frac{1}{2}$ is called the *half-life* of the substance. This can be determined by solving the equation $e^{-kT} = \frac{1}{2}$ for $T$. Taking logarithms, we get $-kT = -\log 2$ or $T = (\log 2)/k$. This equation relates the half-life to the decay constant. Since we have

$$\frac{f(t + T)}{f(t)} = \frac{f(0)e^{-k(t+T)}}{f(0)e^{-kt}} = e^{-kT} = \frac{1}{2} ,$$

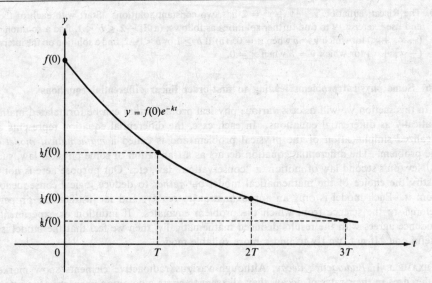

FIGURE 8.1   Radioactive decay with half-life $T$.

we see that the half-life is the same for every sample of a given material. Figure 8.1 illustrates
the general shape of a radioactive decay curve.

EXAMPLE 2. *Falling body in a resisting medium.* A body of mass $m$ is dropped from
rest from a great height in the earth's atmosphere. Assume that it falls in a straight line
and that the only forces acting on it are the earth's gravitational attraction ($mg$, where $g$ is
the acceleration due to gravity, assumed to be constant) and a resisting force (due to air
resistance) which is proportional to its velocity. It is required to discuss the resulting
motion.

Let $s = f(t)$ denote the distance the body has fallen at time $t$ and let $v = s' = f'(t)$ denote
its velocity. The assumption that it falls from rest means that $f'(0) = 0$.

There are two forces acting on the body, a downward force $mg$ (due to its weight) and
an upward force $-kv$ (due to air resistance), where $k$ is some positive constant. Newton's
second law states that the net sum of the forces acting on the body at any instant is equal
to the product of its mass $m$ and its acceleration. If we denote the acceleration at time $t$
by $a$, then $a = v' = s''$ and Newton's law gives us the equation

$$ma = mg - kv.$$

This can be considered as a second-order differential equation for the displacement $s$ or
as a first-order equation for the velocity $v$. As a first-order equation for $v$, it is linear and
can be written in the form

$$v' + \frac{k}{m}v = g.$$

This equation is the mathematical model of the problem. Since $v = 0$ when $t = 0$, the unique solution of the differential equation is given by the formula

$$(8.14) \qquad v = e^{-kt/m} \int_0^t g e^{ku/m} \, du = \frac{mg}{k} (1 - e^{-kt/m}).$$

Note that $v \to mg/k$ as $t \to +\infty$. If we differentiate Equation (8.14), we find that the acceleration at every instant is $a = ge^{-kt/m}$. Note that $a \to 0$ as $t \to +\infty$. Interpreted physically, this means that the air resistance tends to balance out the force of gravity.

Since $v = s'$, Equation (8.14) is itself a differential equation for the displacement $s$, and it may be integrated directly to give

$$s = \frac{mg}{k} t + \frac{gm^2}{k^2} e^{-kt/m} + C$$

Since $s = 0$ when $t = 0$, we find that $C = -gm^2/k^2$ and the equation of motion becomes

$$s = \frac{mg}{k} t + \frac{gm^2}{k^2} (e^{-kt/m} - 1)$$

If the initial velocity is $v_0$ when $t = 0$, formula (8.14) for the velocity at time $t$ must be replaced by

$$v = \frac{mg}{k} (1 - e^{-kt/m}) + v_0 e^{-kt/m}$$

It is interesting to note that for *every* initial velocity (positive, negative, or zero), the limiting velocity, as $t$ increases without bound, is $mg/k$, a number independent of $v_0$. The reader should convince himself, on physical grounds, that this seems reasonable.

EXAMPLE 3. *A cooling problem.* The rate at which a body changes temperature is proportional to the difference between its temperature and that of the surrounding medium. (This is called *Newton's law of cooling*.) If $y = f(t)$ is the (unknown) temperature of the body at time $t$ and if $M(t)$ denotes the (known) temperature of the surrounding medium, Newton's law leads to the differential equation

$$(8.15) \qquad y' = -k[y - M(t)] \qquad \text{or} \qquad y' + ky = kM(t),$$

where $k$ is a positive constant. This first-order linear equation is the mathematical model we use for cooling problems. The unique solution of the equation satisfying the initial condition $f(a) = b$ is given by the formula

$$(8.16) \qquad f(t) = be^{-kt} + e^{-kt} \int_a^t kM(u)e^{ku} \, du.$$

Consider now a specific problem in which a body cools from 200° to 100° in 40 minutes while immersed in a medium whose temperature is kept constant, say $M(t) = 10°$. If we measure $t$ in minutes and $f(t)$ in degrees, we have $f(0) = 200$ and Equation (8.16) gives us

(8.17) $$f(t) = 200e^{-kt} + 10ke^{-kt}\int_0^t e^{ku}\,du$$

$$= 200e^{-kt} + 10(1 - e^{-kt}) = 10 + 190e^{-kt}.$$

We can compute $k$ from the information that $f(40) = 100$. Putting $t = 40$ in (8.17), we find $90 = 190e^{-40k}$, so $-40k = \log(90/190)$, $k = \frac{1}{40}(\log 19 - \log 9)$.

Next, let us compute the time required for this same material to cool from $200°$ to $100°$ if the temperature of the medium is kept at $5°$. Then Equation (8.16) is valid with the same constant $k$ but with $M(u) = 5$. Instead of (8.17), we get the formula

$$f(t) = 5 + 195e^{-kt}.$$

To find the time $t$ for which $f(t) = 100$, we get $95 = 195e^{-kt}$, so $-kt = \log(95/195) = \log(19/39)$, and hence

$$t = \frac{1}{k}(\log 39 - \log 19) = 40\,\frac{\log 39 - \log 19}{\log 19 - \log 9}.$$

From a four-place table of natural logarithms, we find $\log 39 = 3.6636$, $\log 19 = 2.9444$, and $\log 9 = 2.1972$ so, with slide-rule accuracy, we get $t = 40(0.719)/(0.747) = 38.5$ minutes.

The differential equation in (8.15) tells us that the rate of cooling decreases considerably as the temperature of the body begins to approach the temperature of the medium. To illustrate, let us find the time required to cool the same substance from $100°$ to $10°$ with the medium kept at $5°$. The calculation leads to $\log(5/95) = -kt$, or

$$t = \frac{1}{k}\log 19 = 40\,\frac{\log 19}{\log 19 - \log 9} = \frac{40(2.944)}{0.747} = 158 \text{ minutes}.$$

Note that the temperature drop from $100°$ to $10°$ takes more than four times as long as the change from $200°$ to $100°$.

EXAMPLE 4. *A dilution problem.* A tank contains 100 gallons of brine whose concentration is 2.5 pounds of salt per gallon. Brine containing 2 pounds of salt per gallon runs into the tank at a rate of 5 gallons per minute and the mixture (kept uniform by stirring) runs out at the same rate. Find the amount of salt in the tank at every instant.

Let $y = f(t)$ denote the number of pounds of salt in the tank at time $t$ minutes after mixing begins. There are two factors which cause $y$ to change, the incoming brine which brings salt in at a rate of 10 pounds per minute and the outgoing mixture which removes salt at a rate of $5(y/100)$ pounds per minute. (The fraction $y/100$ represents the concentration at time $t$.) Hence the differential equation is

$$y' = 10 - \tfrac{1}{20}y \quad \text{or} \quad y' + \tfrac{1}{20}y = 10.$$

This linear equation is the mathematical model for our problem. Since $y = 250$ when

$t = 0$, the unique solution is given by the formula

(8.18)
$$y = 250e^{-t/20} + e^{-t/20}\int_0^t 10e^{u/20}\,du = 200 + 50e^{-t/20}.$$

This equation shows that $y > 200$ for all $t$ and that $y \to 200$ as $t$ increases without bound. Hence, the minimum salt content is 200 pounds. (This could also have been guessed from the statement of the problem.) Equation (8.18) can be solved for $t$ in terms of $y$ to yield

$$t = 20 \log\left(\frac{50}{y - 200}\right).$$

This enables us to find the time at which the salt content will be a given amount $y$, provided that $200 < y < 250$.

EXAMPLE 5. *Electric circuits.* Figure 8.2(a), page 318, shows an electric circuit which has an electromotive force, a resistor, and an inductor connected in series. The electromotive force produces a voltage which causes an electric current to flow in the circuit. If the reader is not familiar with electric circuits, he should not be concerned. For our purposes, all we need to know about the circuit is that the voltage, denoted by $V(t)$, and the current, denoted by $I(t)$, are functions of time $t$ related by a differential equation of the form

(8.19)
$$LI'(t) + RI(t) = V(t).$$

Here $L$ and $R$ are assumed to be positive constants. They are called, respectively, the *inductance* and *resistance* of the circuit. The differential equation is a mathematical formulation of a conservation law known as *Kirchhoff's voltage law*, and it serves as a mathematical model for the circuit.

Those readers unfamiliar with circuits may find it helpful to think of the current as being analogous to water flowing in a pipe. The electromotive force (usually a battery or a generator) is analogous to a pump which causes the water to flow; the resistor is analogous to friction in the pipe, which tends to oppose the flow; and the inductance is a stabilizing influence which tends to oppose sudden changes in the current due to sudden changes in the voltage.

The usual type of question concerning such circuits is this: If a given voltage $V(t)$ is impressed on the circuit, what is the resulting current $I(t)$? Since we are dealing with a first-order linear differential equation, the solution is a routine matter. If $I(0)$ denotes the initial current at time $t = 0$, the equation has the solution

$$I(t) = I(0)e^{-Rt/L} + e^{-Rt/L}\int_0^t \frac{V(x)}{L}e^{Rx/L}\,dx.$$

An important special case occurs when the impressed voltage is constant, say $V(t) = E$ for all $t$. In this case, the integration is easy to perform and we are led to the formula

$$I(t) = \frac{E}{R} + \left(I(0) - \frac{E}{R}\right)e^{-Rt/L}.$$

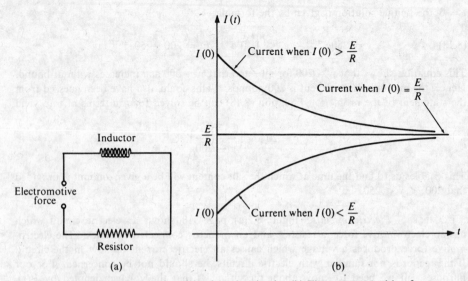

FIGURE 8.2    (a) Diagram for a simple series circuit.  (b) The current resulting from
a constant impressed voltage $E$.

This shows that the nature of the solution depends on the relation between the initial
current $I(0)$ and the quotient $E/R$. If $I(0) = E/R$, the exponential term is not present and
the current is constant, $I(t) = E/R$. If $I(0) > E/R$, the coefficient of the exponential term
is positive and the current decreases to the limiting value $E/R$ as $t \to +\infty$. If $I(0) < E/R$,
the current increases to the limiting value $E/R$. The constant $E/R$ is called the *steady-state
current*, and the exponential term $[I(0) - E/R]e^{-Rt/L}$ is called the *transient current*. Examples are illustrated in Figure 8.2(b).

The foregoing examples illustrate the unifying power and practical utility of differential
equations. They show how several different types of physical problems may lead to
exactly the same type of differential equation.

The differential equation in (8.19) is of special interest because it suggests the possibility
of attacking a wide variety of physical problems by electrical means. For example, suppose
a physical problem leads to a differential equation of the form

$$y' + ay = Q,$$

where $a$ is a positive constant and $Q$ is a known function. We can try to construct an
electric circuit with inductance $L$ and resistance $R$ in the ratio $R/L = a$ and then try to
impress a voltage $LQ$ on the circuit. We would then have an electric circuit with exactly the
same mathematical model as the physical problem. Thus, we can hope to get numerical
data about the solution of the physical problem by making measurements of current in
the electric circuit. This idea has been used in practice and has led to the development of
the *analog computer*.

## 8.7 Exercises

In the following exercises, use an appropriate first-order differential equation as a mathematical model of the problem.

1. The half-life for radium is approximately 1600 years. Find what percentage of a given quantity of radium disintegrates in 100 years.
2. If a strain of bacteria grows at a rate proportional to the amount present and if the population doubles in one hour, by how much will it increase at the end of two hours?
3. Denote by $y = f(t)$ the amount of a substance present at time $t$. Assume it disintegrates at a rate proportional to the amount present. If $n$ is a positive integer, the number $T$ for which $f(T) = f(0)/n$ is called the $1/n$th life of the substance.
   (a) Prove that the $1/n$th life is the same for every sample of a given material, and compute $T$ in terms of $n$ and the decay constant $k$.
   (b) If $a$ and $b$ are given, prove that $f$ can be expressed in the form

$$f(t) = f(a)^{w(t)} f(b)^{1-w(t)}$$

and determine $w(t)$. This shows that the amount present at time $t$ is a weighted geometric mean of the amounts present at two instants $t = a$ and $t = b$.

4. A man wearing a parachute jumps from a great height. The combined weight of man and parachute is 192 pounds. Let $v(t)$ denote his speed (in feet per second) at time $t$ seconds after falling. During the first 10 seconds, before the parachute opens, assume the air resistance is $\frac{3}{4}v(t)$ pounds. Thereafter, while the parachute is open, assume the resistance is $12v(t)$ pounds. Assume the acceleration of gravity is 32 ft/sec² and find explicit formulas for the speed $v(t)$ at time $t$. (You may use the approximation $e^{-5/4} = 37/128$ in your calculations.)
5. Refer to Example 2 of Section 8.6. Use the chain rule to write

$$\frac{dv}{dt} = \frac{ds}{dt}\frac{dv}{ds} = v\frac{dv}{ds}$$

and thus show that the differential equation in the example can be expressed as follows:

$$\frac{ds}{dv} = \frac{bv}{c - v},$$

where $b = m/k$ and $c = gm/k$. Integrate this equation to express $s$ in terms of $v$. Check your result with the formulas for $v$ and $s$ derived in the example.

6. Modify Example 2 of Section 8.6 by assuming the air resistance is proportional to $v^2$. Show that the differential equation can be put in each of the following forms:

$$\frac{ds}{dv} = \frac{m}{k}\frac{v}{c^2 - v^2}; \qquad \frac{dt}{dv} = \frac{m}{k}\frac{1}{c^2 - v^2},$$

where $c = \sqrt{mg/k}$. Integrate each of these and obtain the following formulas for $v$:

$$v^2 = \frac{mg}{k}(1 - e^{-2ks/m}); \qquad v = c\frac{e^{bt} - e^{-bt}}{e^{bt} + e^{-bt}} = c\tanh bt,$$

where $b = \sqrt{kg/m}$. Determine the limiting value of $v$ as $t \to +\infty$.

7. A body in a room at 60° cools from 200° to 120° in half an hour.
   (a) Show that its temperature after $t$ minutes is $60 + 140e^{-kt}$, where $k = (\log 7 - \log 3)/30$.
   (b) Show that the time $t$ required to reach a temperature of $T$ degrees is given by the formula $t = [\log 140 - \log (T - 60)]/k$, where $60 < T \le 200$.
   (c) Find the time at which the temperature is 90°.
   (d) Find a formula for the temperature of the body at time $t$ if the room temperature is not kept constant but falls at a rate of 1° each ten minutes. Assume the room temperature is 60° when the body temperature is 200°.

8. A thermometer has been stored in a room whose temperature is 75°. Five minutes after being taken outdoors it reads 65°. After another five minutes, it reads 60°. Compute the outdoor temperature.

9. In a tank are 100 gallons of brine containing 50 pounds of dissolved salt. Water runs into the tank at the rate of 3 gallons per minute, and the concentration is kept uniform by stirring. How much salt is in the tank at the end of one hour if the mixture runs out at a rate of 2 gallons per minute?

10. Refer to Exercise 9. Suppose the bottom of the tank is covered with a mixture of salt and insoluble material. Assume that the salt dissolves at a rate proportional to the difference between the concentration of the solution and that of a saturated solution (3 pounds of salt per gallon), and that if the water were fresh 1 pound of salt would dissolve per minute. How much salt will be in solution at the end of one hour?

11. Consider an electric circuit like that in Example 5 of Section 8.6. Assume the electromotive force is an alternating current generator which produces a voltage $V(t) = E \sin \omega t$, where $E$ and $\omega$ are positive constants ($\omega$ is the Greek letter *omega*). If $I(0) = 0$, prove that the current has the form
$$I(t) = \frac{E}{\sqrt{R^2 + \omega^2 L^2}} \sin (\omega t - \alpha) + \frac{E \omega L}{R^2 + \omega^2 L^2} e^{-Rt/L},$$
where $\alpha$ depends only on $\omega$, $L$, and $R$. Show that $\alpha = 0$ when $L = 0$.

12. Refer to Example 5 of Section 8.6. Assume the impressed voltage is a step function defined as follows: $E(t) = E$ if $a \le t \le b$, where $a > 0$; $E(t) = 0$ for all other $t$. If $I(0) = 0$ prove that the current is given by the following formulas: $I(t) = 0$ if $t \le a$;
$$I(t) = \frac{E}{R} (1 - e^{-R(t-a)/L}) \quad \text{if} \quad a \le t \le b; \qquad I(t) = \frac{E}{R} e^{-Rt/L} (e^{Rb/L} - e^{Ra/L}) \quad \text{if} \quad t \ge b.$$

Make a sketch indicating the nature of the graph of $I$.

*Population growth.* In a study of the growth of a population (whether human, animal, or bacterial), the function which counts the number $x$ of individuals present at time $t$ is necessarily a *step function* taking on only integer values. Therefore the true *rate of growth* $dx/dt$ is zero (when $t$ lies in an open interval where $x$ is constant), or else the derivative $dx/dt$ does not exist (when $x$ jumps from one integer to another). Nevertheless, useful information can often be obtained if we assume that the population $x$ is a continuous function of $t$ with a continuous derivative $dx/dt$ at each instant. We then postulate various "laws of growth" for the population, depending on the factors in the environment which may stimulate or hinder growth.

For example, if environment has little or no effect, it seems reasonable to assume that the rate of growth is proportional to the amount present. The simplest kind of growth law takes the form

(8.20)
$$\frac{dx}{dt} = kx,$$

where $k$ is a constant that depends on the particular kind of population. Conditions may develop which cause the factor $k$ to change with time, and the growth law (8.20) can be generalized as follows:

$$(8.21) \qquad \frac{dx}{dt} = k(t)x.$$

If, for some reason, the population cannot exceed a certain maximum $M$ (for example, because the food supply may be exhausted), we may reasonably suppose that the rate of growth is jointly proportional to both $x$ and $M - x$. Thus we have a second type of growth law:

$$(8.22) \qquad \frac{dx}{dt} = kx(M - x),$$

where, as in (8.21), $k$ may be constant or, more generally, $k$ may change with time. Technological improvements may tend to increase or decrease the value of $M$ slowly, and hence we can generalize (8.22) even further by allowing $M$ to change with time.

13. Express $x$ as a function of $t$ for each of the "growth laws" in (8.20) and (8.22) (with $k$ and $M$ both constant). Show that the result for (8.22) can be expressed as follows:

$$(8.23) \qquad x = \frac{M}{1 + e^{-\alpha(t-t_1)}},$$

where $\alpha$ is a constant and $t_1$ is the time at which $x = M/2$.

14. Assume the growth law in formula (8.23) of Exercise 13, and suppose a census is taken at three equally spaced times $t_1$, $t_2$, $t_3$, the resulting numbers being $x_1$, $x_2$, $x_3$. Show that this suffices to determine $M$ and that, in fact, we have

$$(8.24) \qquad M = x_2 \frac{x_3(x_2 - x_1) - x_1(x_3 - x_2)}{x_2^2 - x_1 x_3}.$$

15. Derive a formula that generalizes (8.23) of Exercise 13 for the growth law (8.22) when $k$ is not necessarily constant. Express the result in terms of the time $t_0$ for which $x = M/2$.

16. The Census Bureau reported the following population figures (in millions) for the United States at ten-year intervals from 1790 to 1950: 3.9, 5.3, 7.2, 9.6, 12.9, 17, 23, 31, 39, 50, 63, 76, 92, 108, 122, 135, 150.

 (a) Use Equation (8.24) to determine a value of $M$ on the basis of the census figures for 1790, 1850, and 1910.

 (b) Same as (a) for the years 1910, 1930, 1950.

 (c) On the basis of your calculations in (a) and (b), would you be inclined to accept or reject the growth law (8.23) for the population of the United States?

17. (a) Plot a graph of $\log x$ as a function of $t$, where $x$ denotes the population figures quoted in Exercise 16. Use this graph to show that the growth law (8.20) was very nearly satisfied from 1790 to 1910. Determine a reasonable average value of $k$ for this period.

 (b) Determine a reasonable average value of $k$ for the period from 1920 to 1950, assume that the growth law (8.20) will hold for this $k$, and predict the United States population for the years 2000 and 2050.

18. The presence of toxins in a certain medium destroys a strain of bacteria at a rate jointly proportional to the number of bacteria present and to the amount of toxin. If there were no

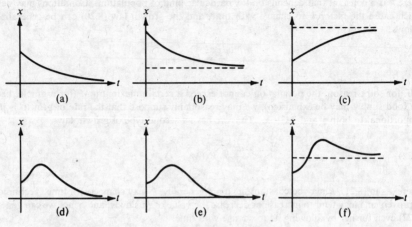

FIGURE 8.3   Exercise 18.

toxins present, the bacteria would grow at a rate proportional to the amount present. Let $x$ denote the number of living bacteria present at time $t$. Assume that the amount of toxin is increasing at a constant rate and that the production of toxin begins at time $t = 0$. Set up a differential equation for $x$. Solve the differential equation. One of the curves shown in Figure 8.3 best represents the general behavior of $x$ as a function of $t$. State your choice and explain your reasoning.

## 8.8   Linear equations of second order with constant coefficients

A differential equation of the form

$$y'' + P_1(x)y' + P_2(x)y = R(x)$$

is said to be a *linear equation of second order*. The functions $P_1$ and $P_2$ which multiply the unknown function $y$ and its derivative $y'$ are called the *coefficients* of the equation.

For first-order linear equations, we proved an existence-uniqueness theorem and determined all solutions by an explicit formula. Although there is a corresponding existence-uniqueness theorem for the general second-order linear equation, there is no explicit formula which gives all solutions, except in some special cases. A study of the general linear equation of second order is undertaken in Volume II. Here we treat only the case in which the coefficients $P_1$ and $P_2$ are constants. When the right-hand member $R(x)$ is identically zero, the equation is said to be *homogeneous*.

The homogeneous linear equation with constant coefficients was the first differential equation of a general type to be completely solved. A solution was first published by Euler in 1743. Apart from its historical interest, this equation arises in a great variety of applied problems, so its study is of practical importance. Moreover, we can give explicit formulas for all the solutions.

Consider a homogeneous linear equation with constant coefficients which we write as follows:

$$y'' + ay' + by = 0.$$

We seek solutions on the entire real axis $(-\infty, +\infty)$. One solution is the constant function $y = 0$. This is called the *trivial* solution. We are interested in finding nontrivial solutions, and we begin our study with some special cases for which nontrivial solutions can be found by inspection. In all these cases, the coefficient of $y'$ is zero, and the equation has the form $y'' + by = 0$. We shall find that solving this special equation is tantamount to solving the general case.

## 8.9 Existence of solutions of the equation $y'' + by = 0$

EXAMPLE 1. *The equation* $y'' = 0$. Here both coefficients $a$ and $b$ are zero, and we can easily determine all solutions. Assume $y$ is any function satisfying $y'' = 0$ on $(-\infty, +\infty)$. Then its derivative $y'$ is constant, say $y' = c_1$. Integrating this relation, we find that $y$ necessarily has the form

$$y = c_1 x + c_2 ,$$

where $c_1$ and $c_2$ are constants. Conversely, for any choice of constants $c_1$ and $c_2$, the linear polynomial $y = c_1 x + c_2$ satisfies $y'' = 0$, so we have found all solutions in this case.

Next we assume that $b \neq 0$ and treat separately the cases $b < 0$ and $b > 0$.

EXAMPLE 2. *The equation* $y'' + by = 0$, *where* $b < 0$. Since $b < 0$, we can write $b = -k^2$, where $k > 0$, and the differential equation takes the form

$$y'' = k^2 y .$$

One obvious solution is $y = e^{kx}$, and another is $y = e^{-kx}$. From these we can obtain further solutions by constructing linear combinations of the form

$$y = c_1 e^{kx} + c_2 e^{-kx},$$

where $c_1$ and $c_2$ are arbitrary constants. It will be shown presently, in Theorem 8.6, that *all* solutions are included in this formula.

EXAMPLE 3. *The equation* $y'' + by = 0$, *where* $b > 0$. Here we can write $b = k^2$, where $k > 0$, and the differential equation takes the form

$$y'' = -k^2 y .$$

Again we obtain some solutions by inspection. One solution is $y = \cos kx$, and another is $y = \sin kx$. From these we get further solutions by forming linear combinations,

$$y = c_1 \cos kx + c_2 \sin kx ,$$

where $c_1$ and $c_2$ are arbitrary constants. Theorem 8.6 will show that this formula includes all solutions.

## 8.10 Reduction of the general equation to the special case $y'' + by = 0$

The problem of solving a second-order linear equation with constant coefficients can be reduced to that of solving the special cases just discussed. There is a method for doing this that also applies to more general equations. The idea is to consider three functions $y$, $u$, and $v$ such that $y = uv$. Differentiation gives us $y' = uv' + u'v$, and $y'' = uv'' + 2u'v' + u''v$. Now we express the combination $y'' + ay' + by$ in terms of $u$ and $v$. We have

$$(8.25) \qquad y'' + ay' + by = uv'' + 2u'v' + u''v + a(uv' + u'v) + buv$$
$$= (v'' + av' + bv)u + (2v' + av)u' + vu''.$$

Next we choose $v$ to make the coefficient of $u'$ zero. This requires that $v' = -av/2$, so we may choose $v = e^{-ax/2}$. For this $v$ we have $v'' = -av'/2 = a^2v/4$, and the coefficient of $u$ in (8.25) becomes

$$v'' + av' + bv = \frac{a^2v}{4} - \frac{a^2v}{2} + bv = \frac{4b - a^2}{4} v .$$

Thus, Equation (8.25) reduces to

$$y'' + ay' + by = \left( u'' + \frac{4b - a^2}{4} u \right) v .$$

Since $v = e^{-ax/2}$, the function $v$ is never zero, so $y$ satisfies the differential equation $y'' + ay' + by = 0$ if and only if $u$ satisfies $u'' + \frac{1}{4}(4b - a^2)u = 0$. Thus, we have proved the following theorem.

THEOREM 8.4. *Let $y$ and $u$ be two functions such that $y = ue^{-ax/2}$. Then, on the interval $(-\infty, +\infty)$, $y$ satisfies the differential equation $y'' + ay' + by = 0$ if and only if $u$ satisfies the differential equation*

$$u'' + \frac{4b - a^2}{4} u = 0 .$$

This theorem reduces the study of the equation $y'' + ay' + by = 0$ to the special case $y'' + by = 0$. We have exhibited nontrivial solutions of this equation but, except for the case $b = 0$, we have not yet shown that we have found *all* solutions.

## 8.11 Uniqueness theorem for the equation $y'' + by = 0$

The problem of determining all solutions of the equation $y'' + by = 0$ can be solved with the help of the following *uniqueness theorem*.

THEOREM 8.5. *Assume two functions $f$ and $g$ satisfy the differential equation $y'' + by = 0$ on $(-\infty, +\infty)$. Assume also that $f$ and $g$ satisfy the initial conditions*

$$f(0) = g(0) , \qquad f'(0) = g'(0) .$$

*Then $f(x) = g(x)$ for all $x$.*

*Proof.* Let $h(x) = f(x) - g(x)$. We wish to prove that $h(x) = 0$ for all $x$. We shall do this by expressing $h$ in terms of its Taylor polynomial approximations.

First we note that $h$ is also a solution of the differential equation $y'' + by = 0$ and satisfies the initial conditions $h(0) = 0$, $h'(0) = 0$. Now every function $y$ satisfying the differential equation has derivatives of every order on $(-\infty, +\infty)$ and they can be computed by repeated differentiation of the differential equation. For example, since $y'' = -by$, we have $y''' = -by'$, and $y^{(4)} = -by'' = b^2 y$. By induction we find that the derivatives of even order are given by

$$y^{(2n)} = (-1)^n b^n y \, ,$$

while those of odd order are $y^{(2n-1)} = (-1)^{n-1} b^{n-1} y'$. Since $h(0)$ and $h'(0)$ are both 0, it follows that all derivatives $h^{(n)}(0)$ are zero. Therefore, each Taylor polynomial generated by $h$ at 0 has all its coefficients zero.

Now we apply Taylor's formula with remainder (Theorem 7.6), using a polynomial approximation of odd degree $2n - 1$, and we find that

$$h(x) = E_{2n-1}(x) \, ,$$

where $E_{2n-1}(x)$ is the error term in Taylor's formula. To complete the proof, we show that the error can be made arbitrarily small by taking $n$ large enough.

We use Theorem 7.7 to estimate the size of the error term. For this we need estimates for the size of the derivative $h^{(2n)}$. Consider any finite closed interval $[-c, c]$, where $c > 0$. Since $h$ is continuous on this interval, it is bounded there, say $|h(x)| \leq M$ on $[-c, c]$. Since $h^{(2n)}(x) = (-1)^n b^n h(x)$, we have the estimate $|h^{(2n)}(x)| \leq M |b|^n$ on $[-c, c]$. Theorem 7.7 gives us $|E_{2n-1}(x)| \leq M |b|^n x^{2n}/(2n)!$ so, on the interval $[-c, c]$, we have the estimate

$$(8.26) \qquad 0 \leq |h(x)| \leq \frac{M |b|^n x^{2n}}{(2n)!} \leq \frac{M |b|^n c^{2n}}{(2n)!} = \frac{M A^{2n}}{(2n)!} \, ,$$

where $A = |b|^{1/2} c$. Now we show that $A^m/m!$ tends to 0 as $m \to +\infty$. This is obvious if $0 \leq A \leq 1$. If $A > 1$, we may write

$$\frac{A^m}{m!} = \frac{A}{1} \cdot \frac{A}{2} \cdots \frac{A}{k} \cdot \frac{A}{k+1} \cdots \frac{A}{m} \leq \frac{A^k}{k!} \left( \frac{A}{k+1} \right)^{m-k} ,$$

where $k < m$. If we choose $k$ to be the greatest integer $\leq A$, then $A < k + 1$ and the last factor tends to 0 as $m \to +\infty$. Hence $A^m/m!$ tends to 0 as $m \to \infty$, so inequality (8.26) shows that $h(x) = 0$ for every $x$ in $[-c, c]$. But, since $c$ is arbitrary, it follows that $h(x) = 0$ for all real $x$. This completes the proof.

*Note:* Theorem 8.5 tells us that two solutions of the differential equation $y'' + by = 0$ which have the same value and the same derivative at 0 must agree everywhere. The choice of the point 0 is not essential. The same argument shows that the theorem is also true if 0 is replaced by an arbitrary point $c$. In the foregoing proof, we simply use Taylor polynomial approximations at $c$ instead of at 0.

## 8.12 Complete solution of the equation $y'' + by = 0$

The uniqueness theorem enables us to characterize all solutions of the differential equation $y'' + by = 0$.

THEOREM 8.6. *Given a real number b, define two functions $u_1$ and $u_2$ on $(-\infty, +\infty)$ as follows:*

(a) *If $b = 0$, let $u_1(x) = 1$, $u_2(x) = x$.*
(b) *If $b < 0$, write $b = -k^2$ and define $u_1(x) = e^{kx}$, $u_2(x) = e^{-kx}$.*
(c) *If $b > 0$, write $b = k^2$ and define $u_1(x) = \cos kx$, $u_2(x) = \sin kx$.*
*Then every solution of the differential equation $y'' + by = 0$ on $(-\infty, +\infty)$ has the form*

$$(8.27) \qquad y = c_1 u_1(x) + c_2 u_2(x),$$

*where $c_1$ and $c_2$ are constants.*

*Proof.* We proved in Section 8.9 that for each choice of constants $c_1$ and $c_2$ the function $y$ given in (8.27) is a solution of the equation $y'' + by = 0$. Now we show that all solutions have this form. The case $b = 0$ was settled in Section 8.9, so we may assume that $b \neq 0$.

The idea of the proof is this: Let $y = f(x)$ be any solution of $y'' + by = 0$. If we can show that constants $c_1$ and $c_2$ exist satisfying the pair of equations

$$(8.28) \qquad c_1 u_1(0) + c_2 u_2(0) = f(0), \qquad c_1 u_1'(0) + c_2 u_2'(0) = f'(0),$$

then both $f$ and $c_1 u_1 + c_2 u_2$ are solutions of the differential equation $y'' + by = 0$ having the same value and the same derivative at 0. By the uniqueness theorem, it follows that $f = c_1 u_1 + c_2 u_2$.

In case (b), we have $u_1(x) = e^{kx}$, $u_2(x) = e^{-kx}$, so $u_1(0) = u_2(0) = 1$ and $u_1'(0) = k$, $u_2'(0) = -k$. Thus the equations in (8.28) become $c_1 + c_2 = f(0)$, and $c_1 - c_2 = f'(0)/k$. They have the solution $c_1 = \frac{1}{2}f(0) + \frac{1}{2}f'(0)/k$, $c_2 = \frac{1}{2}f(0) - \frac{1}{2}f'(0)/k$.

In case (c), we have $u_1(x) = \cos kx$, $u_2(x) = \sin kx$, so $u_1(0) = 1$, $u_2(0) = 0$, $u_1'(0) = 0$, $u_2'(0) = k$, and the solutions are $c_1 = f(0)$, and $c_2 = f'(0)/k$. Since $c_1$ and $c_2$ always exist to satisfy (8.28), the proof is complete.

## 8.13 Complete solution of the equation $y'' + ay' + by = 0$

Theorem 8.4 tells us that $y$ satisfies the differential equation $y'' + ay' + by = 0$ if and only if $u$ satisfies $u'' + \frac{1}{4}(4b - a^2)u = 0$, where $y = e^{-ax/2}u$. From Theorem 8.6 we know that the nature of each solution $u$ depends on the algebraic sign of the coefficient of $u$, that is, on the algebraic sign of $4b - a^2$ or, alternatively, of $a^2 - 4b$. We call the number $a^2 - 4b$ the *discriminant* of the differential equation $y'' + ay' + by = 0$ and denote it by $d$. When we combine the results of Theorem 8.4 and 8.6 we obtain the following.

THEOREM 8.7. *Let $d = a^2 - 4b$ be the discriminant of the linear differential equation $y'' + ay' + by = 0$. Then every solution of this equation on $(-\infty, +\infty)$ has the form*

$$(8.29) \qquad y = e^{-ax/2}[c_1 u_1(x) + c_2 u_2(x)],$$

where $c_1$ and $c_2$ are constants, and the functions $u_1$ and $u_2$ are determined according to the algebraic sign of the discriminant as follows:

(a) *If* $d = 0$, *then* $u_1(x) = 1$ *and* $u_2(x) = x$.

(b) *If* $d > 0$, *then* $u_1(x) = e^{kx}$ *and* $u_2(x) = e^{-kx}$, *where* $k = \frac{1}{2}\sqrt{d}$.

(c) *If* $d < 0$, *then* $u_1(x) = \cos kx$ *and* $u_2(x) = \sin kx$, *where* $k = \frac{1}{2}\sqrt{-d}$.

*Note:* In case (b), where the discriminant $d$ is positive, the solution $y$ in (8.29) is a linear combination of two exponential functions,

$$y = e^{-ax/2}(c_1 e^{kx} + c_2 e^{-kx}) = c_1 e^{r_1 x} + c_2 e^{r_2 x},$$

where

$$r_1 = -\frac{a}{2} + k = \frac{-a + \sqrt{d}}{2}, \qquad r_2 = -\frac{a}{2} - k = \frac{-a - \sqrt{d}}{2}.$$

The two numbers $r_1$ and $r_2$ have sum $r_1 + r_2 = -a$ and product $r_1 r_2 = \frac{1}{4}(a^2 - d) = b$. Therefore, they are the roots of the quadratic equation

$$r^2 + ar + b = 0.$$

This is called the *characteristic equation* associated with the differential equation

$$y'' + ay' + by = 0.$$

The number $d = a^2 - 4b$ is also called the discriminant of this quadratic equation; its algebraic sign determines the nature of the roots. If $d \geq 0$, the quadratic equation has real roots given by $(-a \pm \sqrt{d})/2$. If $d < 0$, the quadratic equation has no real roots but it does have *complex* roots $r_1$ and $r_2$. The definition of the exponential function can be extended so that $e^{r_1 x}$ and $e^{r_2 x}$ are meaningful when $r_1$ and $r_2$ are complex numbers. This extension, described in Chapter 9, is made in such a way that the linear combination in (8.29) can also be written as a linear combination of $e^{r_1 x}$ and $e^{r_2 x}$, when $r_1$ and $r_2$ are complex.

We conclude this section with some miscellaneous remarks. Since all the solutions of the differential equation $y'' + ay' + by = 0$ are contained in formula (8.29), the linear combination on the right is often called the *general solution* of the differential equation. Any solution obtained by specializing the constants $c_1$ and $c_2$ is called a *particular solution*. For example, taking $c_1 = 1$, $c_2 = 0$, and then $c_1 = 0$, $c_2 = 1$, we obtain the two particular solutions

$$v_1 = e^{-ax/2}u_1(x), \qquad v_2 = e^{-ax/2}u_2(x).$$

These two solutions are of special importance because linear combinations of them give us all solutions. Any pair of solutions with this property is called a *basis* for the set of all solutions.

A differential equation always has more than one basis. For example, the equation $y'' = 9y$ has the basis $v_1 = e^{3x}$, $v_2 = e^{-3x}$. But it also has the basis $w_1 = \cosh 3x$, $w_2 = \sinh 3x$. In fact, since $e^{3x} = w_1 + w_2$ and $e^{-3x} = w_1 - w_2$, every linear combination of $e^{3x}$ and $e^{-3x}$ is also a linear combination of $w_1$ and $w_2$. Hence, the pair $w_1$, $w_2$ is another basis.

It can be shown that any pair of solutions $v_1$ and $v_2$ of a differential equation $y'' + ay' + by = 0$ will be a basis if the ratio $v_2/v_1$ is not constant. Although we shall not need this fact, we mention it here because it is important in the theory of second-order linear equations with nonconstant coefficients. A proof is outlined in Exercise 23 of Section 8.14.

## 8.14 Exercises

Find all solutions of the following differential equations on $(-\infty, +\infty)$.

1. $y'' - 4y = 0$.
2. $y'' + 4y = 0$.
3. $y'' - 4y' = 0$.
4. $y'' + 4y' = 0$.
5. $y'' - 2y' + 3y = 0$.
6. $y'' + 2y' - 3y = 0$.
7. $y'' - 2y' + 2y = 0$.
8. $y'' - 2y' + 5y = 0$.
9. $y'' + 2y' + y = 0$.
10. $y'' - 2y' + y = 0$.

In Exercises 11 through 14, find the particular solution satisfying the given initial conditions.

11. $2y'' + 3y' = 0$, with $y = 1$ and $y' = 1$ when $x = 0$.
12. $y'' + 25y = 0$, with $y = -1$ and $y' = 0$ when $x = 3$.
13. $y'' - 4y' - y = 0$, with $y = 2$ and $y' = -1$ when $x = 1$.
14. $y'' + 4y' + 5y = 0$, with $y = 2$ and $y' = y''$ when $x = 0$.
15. The graph of a solution $u$ of the differential equation $y'' - 4y' + 29y = 0$ intersects the graph of a solution $v$ of the equation $y'' + 4y' + 13y = 0$ at the origin. The two curves have equal slopes at the origin. Determine $u$ and $v$ if $u'(\frac{1}{2}\pi) = 1$.
16. The graph of a solution $u$ of the differential equation $y'' - 3y' - 4y = 0$ intersects the graph of a solution $v$ of the equation $y'' + 4y' - 5y = 0$ at the origin. Determine $u$ and $v$ if the two curves have equal slopes at the origin and if

$$\lim_{x \to +\infty} \frac{v(x)^4}{u(x)} = \frac{5}{6}.$$

17. Find all values of the constant $k$ such that the differential equation $y'' + ky = 0$ has a non-trivial solution $y = f_k(x)$ for which $f_k(0) = f_k(1) = 0$. For each permissible value of $k$, determine the corresponding solution $y = f_k(x)$. Consider both positive and negative values of $k$.
18. If $(a, b)$ is a given point in the plane and if $m$ is a given real number, prove that the differential equation $y'' + k^2 y = 0$ has exactly one solution whose graph passes through $(a, b)$ and has the slope $m$ there. Discuss also the case $k = 0$.
19. (a) Let $(a_1, b_1)$ and $(a_2, b_2)$ be two points in the plane such that $a_1 - a_2 \neq n\pi$, where $n$ is an integer. Prove that there is exactly one solution of the differential equation $y'' + y = 0$ whose graph passes through these two points.
    (b) Is the statement in part (a) ever true if $a_1 - a_2$ is a multiple of $\pi$?
    (c) Generalize the result in part (a) for the equation $y'' + k^2 y = 0$. Discuss also the case $k = 0$.
20. In each case, find a linear differential equation of second order satisfied by $u_1$ and $u_2$.
    (a) $u_1(x) = e^x$, $u_2(x) = e^{-x}$.
    (b) $u_1(x) = e^{2x}$, $u_2(x) = xe^{2x}$.
    (c) $u_1(x) = e^{-x/2} \cos x$, $u_2(x) = e^{-x/2} \sin x$.
    (d) $u_1(x) = \sin(2x + 1)$, $u_2(x) = \sin(2x + 2)$.
    (e) $u_1(x) = \cosh x$, $u_2(x) = \sinh x$.

*The Wronskian.* Given two functions $u_1$ and $u_2$, the function $W$ defined by $W(x) = u_1(x)u_2'(x) - u_2(x)u_1'(x)$ is called their *Wronskian*, after J. M. H. Wronski (1778–1853). The following exercises are concerned with properties of the Wronskian.

21. (a) If the Wronskian $W(x)$ of $u_1$ and $u_2$ is zero for all $x$ in an open interval $I$, prove that the quotient $u_2/u_1$ is constant on $I$. In other words, if $u_2/u_1$ is not constant on $I$, then $W(c) \neq 0$ for at least one $c$ in $I$.
    (b) Prove that the derivative of the Wronskian is $W' = u_1 u_2'' - u_2 u_1''$.

22. Let $W$ be the Wronskian of two solutions $u_1$, $u_2$ of the differential equation $y'' + ay' + by = 0$, where $a$ and $b$ are constants.
    (a) Prove that $W$ satisfies the first-order equation $W' + aW = 0$ and hence $W(x) = W(0)e^{-ax}$. This formula shows that if $W(0) \neq 0$, then $W(x) \neq 0$ for all $x$.
    (b) Assume $u_1$ is not identically zero. Prove that $W(0) = 0$ if and only if $u_2/u_1$ is constant.
23. Let $v_1$ and $v_2$ be any two solutions of the differential equation $y'' + ay' + by = 0$ such that $v_2/v_1$ is not constant.
    (a) Let $y = f(x)$ be any solution of the differential equation. Use properties of the Wronskian to prove that constants $c_1$ and $c_2$ exist such that

$$c_1 v_1(0) + c_2 v_2(0) = f(0), \qquad c_1 v_1'(0) + c_2 v_2'(0) = f'(0).$$

(b) Prove that every solution has the form $y = c_1 v_1 + c_2 v_2$. In other words, $v_1$ and $v_2$ form a basis for the set of all solutions.

## 8.15 Nonhomogeneous linear equations of second order with constant coefficients

We turn now to a discussion of nonhomogeneous equations of the form

(8.30)
$$y'' + ay' + by = R,$$

where the coefficients $a$ and $b$ are constants but the right-hand member $R$ is any function continuous on $(-\infty, +\infty)$. The discussion may be simplified by the use of operator notation. For any function $f$ with derivatives $f'$ and $f''$, we may define an operator $L$ which transforms $f$ into another function $L(f)$ defined by the equation

$$L(f) = f'' + af' + bf.$$

In operator notation, the differential equation (8.30) is written in the simpler form

$$L(y) = R.$$

It is easy to verify that $L(y_1 + y_2) = L(y_1) + L(y_2)$, and that $L(cy) = cL(y)$ for every constant $c$. Therefore, for every pair of constants $c_1$ and $c_2$, we have

$$L(c_1 y_1 + c_2 y_2) = c_1 L(y_1) + c_2 L(y_2).$$

This is called the *linearity property* of the operator $L$.

Now suppose $y_1$ and $y_2$ are any two solutions of the equation $L(y) = R$. Since $L(y_1) = L(y_2) = R$, linearity gives us

$$L(y_2 - y_1) = L(y_2) - L(y_1) = R - R = 0,$$

so $y_2 - y_1$ is a solution of the homogeneous equation $L(y) = 0$. Therefore, we must have $y_2 - y_1 = c_1 v_1 + c_2 v_2$, where $c_1 v_1 + c_2 v_2$ is the general solution of the homogeneous equation, or

$$y_2 = c_1 v_1 + c_2 v_2 + y_1.$$

This equation must be satisfied by *every* pair of solutions $y_1$ and $y_2$ of the nonhomogeneous equation $L(y) = R$. Therefore, if we can determine *one particular solution* $y_1$ of the nonhomogeneous equation, *all* solutions are contained in the formula

$$(8.31) \qquad y = c_1 v_1 + c_2 v_2 + y_1,$$

where $c_1$ and $c_2$ are arbitrary constants. Each such $y$ is clearly a solution of $L(y) = R$ because $L(c_1 v_1 + c_2 v_2 + y_1) = L(c_1 v_1 + c_2 v_2) + L(y_1) = 0 + R = R$. Since all solutions of $L(y) = R$ are found in (8.31), the linear combination $c_1 v_1 + c_2 v_2 + y_1$ is called the *general solution* of (8.30). Thus, we have proved the following theorem.

THEOREM 8.8. *If $y_1$ is a particular solution of the nonhomogeneous equation $L(y) = R$, the general solution is obtained by adding to $y_1$ the general solution of the corresponding homogeneous equation $L(y) = 0$.*

Theorem 8.7 tells us how to find the general solution of the homogeneous equation $L(y) = 0$. It has the form $y = c_1 v_1 + c_2 v_2$, where

$$(8.32) \qquad v_1(x) = e^{-ax/2} u_1(x), \qquad v_2(x) = e^{-ax/2} u_2(x),$$

the functions $u_1$ and $u_2$ being determined by the discriminant of the equation, as described in Theorem 8.7. Now we show that $v_1$ and $v_2$ can be used to construct a particular solution $y_1$ of the nonhomogeneous equation $L(y) = R$.

The construction involves a function $W$ defined by the equation

$$W(x) = v_1(x)v_2'(x) - v_2(x)v_1'(x).$$

This is called the *Wronskian* of $v_1$ and $v_2$; some of its properties are described in Exercises 21 and 22 of Section 8.14. We shall need the property that $W(x)$ is never zero. This can be proved by the methods outlined in the exercises or it can be verified directly for the particular functions $v_1$ and $v_2$ given in (8.32).

THEOREM 8.9. *Let $v_1$ and $v_2$ be the solutions of the equation $L(y) = 0$ given by (8.32), where $L(y) = y'' + ay' + by$. Let $W$ denote the Wronskian of $v_1$ and $v_2$. Then the nonhomogeneous equation $L(y) = R$ has a particular solution $y_1$ given by the formula*

$$y_1(x) = t_1(x)v_1(x) + t_2(x)v_2(x),$$

*where*

$$(8.33) \qquad t_1(x) = -\int v_2(x) \frac{R(x)}{W(x)} \, dx, \qquad t_2(x) = \int v_1(x) \frac{R(x)}{W(x)} \, dx.$$

*Proof.* Let us try to find functions $t_1$ and $t_2$ such that the combination $y_1 = t_1 v_1 + t_2 v_2$ will satisfy the equation $L(y_1) = R$. We have

$$y' = t_1 v_1' + t_2 v_2' + (t_1' v_1 + t_2' v_2),$$

$$y_1'' = t_1 v_1'' + t_2 v_2'' + (t_1' v_1' + t_2' v_2') + (t_1' v_1 + t_2' v_2)'.$$

When we form the linear combination $L(y_1) = y_1'' + ay_1' + by_1$, the terms involving $t_1$ and $t_2$ drop out because of the relations $L(v_1) = L(v_2) = 0$. The remaining terms give us the relation

$$L(y_1) = (t_1'v_1' + t_2'v_2') + (t_1'v_1 + t_2'v_2)' + a(t_1'v_1 + t_2'v_2).$$

We want to choose $t_1$ and $t_2$ so that $L(y_1) = R$. We can satisfy this equation if we choose $t_1$ and $t_2$ so that

$$t_1'v_1 + t_2'v_2 = 0 \quad \text{and} \quad t_1'v_1' + t_2'v_2' = R.$$

This is a pair of algebraic equations for $t_1'$ and $t_2'$. The determinant of the system is the Wronskian of $v_1$ and $v_2$. Since this is never zero, the system has a solution given by

$$t_1' = -v_2R/W \quad \text{and} \quad t_2' = v_1R/W.$$

Integrating these relations, we obtain Equation (8.33), thus completing the proof.

The method by which we obtained the solution $y_1$ is sometimes called *variation of parameters*. It was first used by Johann Bernoulli in 1697 to solve linear equations of first order, and then by Lagrange in 1774 to solve linear equations of second order.

*Note:* Since the functions $t_1$ and $t_2$ in Theorem 8.9 are expressed as indefinite integrals, each of them is determined only to within an additive constant. If we add a constant $c_1$ to $t_1$ and a constant $c_2$ to $t_2$ we change the function $y_1$ to a new function $y_2 = y_1 + c_1v_1 + c_2v_2$. By linearity, we have

$$L(y_2) = L(y_1) + L(c_1v_2 + c_2v_2) = L(y_1),$$

so the new function $y_2$ is also a particular solution of the nonhomogeneous equation.

EXAMPLE 1. Find the general solution of the equation $y'' + y = \tan x$ on $(-\pi/2, \pi/2)$.

*Solution.* The functions $v_1$ and $v_2$ of Equation (8.32) are given by

$$v_1(x) = \cos x, \qquad v_2(x) = \sin x.$$

Their Wronskian is $W(x) = v_1(x)v_2'(x) - v_2(x)v_1'(x) = \cos^2 x + \sin^2 x = 1$. Therefore Equation (8.33) gives us

$$t_1(x) = -\int \sin x \tan x \, dx = \sin x - \log|\sec x + \tan x|,$$

and

$$t_2(x) = \int \cos x \tan x \, dx = \int \sin x \, dx = -\cos x.$$

Thus, a particular solution of the nonhomogeneous equation is

$$y_1 = t_1(x)v_1(x) + t_2(x)v_2(x) = \sin x \cos x - \cos x \log|\sec x + \tan x| - \sin x \cos x$$
$$= -\cos x \log|\sec x + \tan x|.$$

By Theorem 8.8, its general solution is

$$y = c_1 \cos x + c_2 \sin x - \cos x \log |\sec x + \tan x| \,.$$

Although Theorem 8.9 provides a general method for determining a particular solution of $L(y) = R$, special methods are available that are often easier to apply when the function $R$ has certain special forms. In the next section we describe a method that works when $R$ is a polynomial or a polynomial times an exponential.

## 8.16 Special methods for determining a particular solution of the nonhomogeneous equation $y'' + ay' + by = R$

*CASE 1. The right-hand member R is a polynomial of degree n.* If $b \neq 0$, we can always find a polynomial of degree $n$ that satisfies the equation. We try a polynomial of the form

$$y_1(x) = \sum_{k=0}^{n} a_k x^k$$

with undetermined coefficients. Substituting in the differential equation $L(y) = R$ and equating coefficients of like powers of $x$, we may determine $a_n, a_{n-1}, \ldots, a_1, a_0$ in succession. The method is illustrated by the following example.

EXAMPLE 1. Find the general solution of the equation $y'' + y = x^3$.

*Solution.* The general solution of the homogeneous equation $y'' + y = 0$ is given by $y = c_1 \cos x + c_2 \sin x$. To this we must add one particular solution of the nonhomogeneous equation. Since the right member is a cubic polynomial and since the coefficient of $y$ is nonzero, we try to find a particular solution of the form $y_1(x) = Ax^3 + Bx^2 + Cx + D$. Differentiating twice, we find that $y''(x) = 6Ax + 2B$. The differential equation leads to the relation

$$(6Ax + 2B) + (Ax^3 + Bx^2 + Cx + D) = x^3 \,.$$

Equating coefficients of like powers of $x$, we obtain $A = 1$, $B = 0$, $C = -6$, and $D = 0$, so a particular solution is $y_1(x) = x^3 - 6x$. Thus, the general solution is

$$y = c_1 \cos x + c_2 \sin x + x^3 - 6x \,.$$

It may be of interest to compare this method with variation of parameters. Equation (8.33) gives us

$$t_1(x) = -\int x^3 \sin x \, dx = -(3x^3 - 6) \sin x + (x^3 - 6x) \cos x$$

and

$$t_2(x) = \int x^3 \cos x \, dx = (3x^2 - 6) \cos x + (x^3 - 6x) \sin x \,.$$

When we form the combination $t_1 v_1 + t_2 v_2$, we find the particular solution $y_1(x) = x^3 - 6x$, as before. In this case, the use of variation of parameters required the evaluation of the integrals $\int x^3 \sin x \, dx$ and $\int x^3 \cos x \, dx$. With the method of undetermined coefficients, no integration is required.

If the coefficient $b$ is zero, the equation $y'' + ay' = R$ cannot be satisfied by a polynomial of degree $n$, but it can be satisfied by a polynomial of degree $n + 1$ if $a \neq 0$. If both $a$ and $b$ are zero, the equation becomes $y'' = R$; its general solution is a polynomial of degree $n + 2$ obtained by two successive integrations.

CASE 2. *The right-hand member has the form* $R(x) = p(x)e^{mx}$, *where $p$ is a polynomial of degree $n$, and $m$ is constant.*

In this case the change of variable $y = u(x)e^{mx}$ transforms the differential equation $y'' + ay' + by = R$ to a new equation,

$$u'' + (2m + a)u' + (m^2 + am + b)u = p \, .$$

This is the type discussed in Case 1 so it always has a polynomial solution $u_1$. Hence, the original equation has a particular solution of the form $y_1 = u_1(x)e^{mx}$, where $u_1$ is a polynomial. If $m^2 + am + b \neq 0$, the degree of $u_1$ is the same as the degree of $p$. If $m^2 + am + b = 0$ but $2m + a \neq 0$, the degree of $u_1$ is one greater than that of $p$. If both $m^2 + am + b = 0$ and $2m + a = 0$, the degree of $u_1$ is two greater than the degree of $p$.

EXAMPLE 2. Find a particular solution of the equation $y'' + y = xe^{3x}$.

*Solution.* The change of variable $y = ue^{3x}$ leads to the new equation $u'' + 6u' + 10u = x$. Trying $u_1(x) = Ax + B$, we find the particular solution $u_1(x) = (5x - 3)/50$, so a particular solution of the original equation is $y_1 = e^{3x}(5x - 3)/50$.

The method of undetermined coefficients can also be used if $R$ has the form $R(x) = p(x)e^{mx} \cos \alpha x$, or $R(x) = p(x)e^{mx} \sin \alpha x$, where $p$ is a polynomial and $m$ and $\alpha$ are constants. In either case, there is always a particular solution of the form $y_1(x) = e^{mx}[q(x) \cos \alpha x + r(x) \sin \alpha x]$, where $q$ and $r$ are polynomials.

## 8.17 Exercises

Find the general solution of each of the differential equations in Exercises 1 through 17. If the solution is not valid over the entire real axis, describe an interval over which it is valid.

1. $y'' - y = x$.
2. $y'' - y' = x^2$.
3. $y'' + y' = x^2 + 2x$.
4. $y'' - 2y' + 3y = x^3$.
5. $y'' - 5y' + 4y = x^2 - 2x + 1$.
6. $y'' + y' - 6y = 2x^3 + 5x^2 - 7x + 2$.
7. $y'' - 4y = e^{2x}$.
8. $y'' + 4y = e^{-2x}$.
9. $y'' + y' - 2y = e^x$.
10. $y'' + y' - 2y = e^{2x}$.
11. $y'' + y' - 2y = e^x + e^{2x}$.
12. $y'' - 2y' + y = x + 2x \, e^x$.
13. $y'' + 2y' + y = e^{-x}/x^2$.
14. $y'' + y = \cot^2 x$.
15. $y'' - y = 2/(1 + e^x)$.
16. $y'' + y' - 2y = e^x/(1 + e^x)$.
17. $y'' + 6y' + 9y = f(x)$, where $f(x) = 1$ for $1 \leq x \leq 2$, and $f(x) = 0$ for all other $x$.
18. If $k$ is a nonzero constant, prove that the equation $y'' - k^2y = R(x)$ has a particular solution $y_1$ given by

$$y_1 = \frac{1}{k} \int_0^x R(t) \sinh k(x - t) \, dt \, .$$

Find the general solution of the equation $y'' - 9y = e^{3x}$.

19. If $k$ is a nonzero constant, prove that the equation $y'' + k^2 y = R(x)$ has a particular solution $y_1$ given by

$$y_1 = \frac{1}{k} \int_0^x R(t) \sin k(x - t)\, dt\,.$$

Find the general solution of the equation $y'' + 9y = \sin 3x$.

In each of Exercises 20 through 25, determine the general solution.

20. $y'' + y = \sin x$.
21. $y'' + y = \cos x$.
22. $y'' + 4y = 3x \cos x$.
23. $y'' + 4y = 3x \sin x$.
24. $y'' - 3y' = 2e^{2x} \sin x$.
25. $y'' + y = e^{2x} \cos 3x$.

## 8.18 Examples of physical problems leading to linear second-order equations with constant coefficients

EXAMPLE 1. *Simple harmonic motion.* Suppose a particle is constrained to move in a straight line with its acceleration directed toward a fixed point of the line and proportional to the displacement from that point. If we take the origin as the fixed point and let $y$ be the displacement at time $x$, then the acceleration $y''$ must be negative when $y$ is positive, and positive when $y$ is negative. Therefore we can write $y'' = -k^2 y$, or

$$y'' + k^2 y = 0\,,$$

where $k^2$ is a positive constant. This is called the differential equation of *simple harmonic motion*. It is often used as the mathematical model for the motion of a point on a vibrating mechanism such as a plucked string or a vibrating tuning fork. The same equation arises in electric circuit theory where it is called the equation of the harmonic oscillator.

Theorem 8.6 tells us that all solutions have the form

(8.34) $$y = A \sin kx + B \cos kx\,,$$

where $A$ and $B$ are arbitrary constants. We can express the solutions in terms of the sine or cosine alone. For example, we can introduce new constants $C$ and $\alpha$, where

$$C = \sqrt{A^2 + B^2} \quad \text{and} \quad \alpha = \arctan \frac{B}{A}$$

then we have (see Figure 8.4) $A = C \cos \alpha$, $B = C \sin \alpha$, and Equation (8.34) becomes

$$y = C \cos \alpha \sin kx + C \sin \alpha \cos kx = C \sin (kx + \alpha)\,.$$

When the solution is written in this way, the constants $C$ and $\alpha$ have a simple geometric interpretation (see Figure 8.5). The extreme values of $y$, which occur when $\sin(kx + \alpha) = \pm 1$, are $\pm C$. When $x = 0$, the initial displacement is $C \sin \alpha$. As $x$ increases, the particle oscillates between the extreme values $+C$ and $-C$ with period $2\pi/k$. The angle $kx + \alpha$ is called the *phase angle* and $\alpha$ itself is called the initial value of the phase angle.

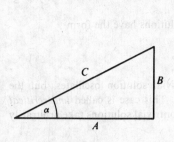

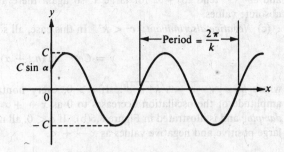

FIGURE 8.4

FIGURE 8.5  Simple harmonic motion.

EXAMPLE 2. *Damped vibrations.* If a particle undergoing simple harmonic motion is suddenly subjected to an external force proportional to its velocity, the new motion satisfies a differential equation of the form

$$y'' + 2cy' + k^2 y = 0,$$

where $c$ and $k^2$ are constants, $c \neq 0$, $k > 0$. If $c > 0$, we will show that all solutions tend to zero as $x \to +\infty$. In this case, the differential equation is said to be *stable*. The external force causes *damping* of the motion. If $c < 0$, we will show that some solutions have arbitrarily large absolute values as $x \to +\infty$. In this case, the equation is said to be *unstable*.

Since the discriminant of the equation is $d = (2c)^2 - 4k^2 = 4(c^2 - k^2)$, the nature of the solutions is determined by the relative sizes of $c^2$ and $k^2$. The three cases $d = 0$, $d > 0$, and $d < 0$ may be analyzed as follows:

(a) *Zero discriminant:* $c^2 = k^2$. In this case, all solutions have the form

$$y = e^{-cx}(A + Bx).$$

If $c > 0$, all solutions tend to 0 as $x \to +\infty$. This case is referred to as *critical damping*. If $B \neq 0$, each solution will change sign exactly once because of the linear factor $A + Bx$. An example is shown in Figure 8.6(a). If $c < 0$, each nontrivial solution tends to $+\infty$ or to $-\infty$ as $x \to +\infty$.

(b) *Positive discriminant:* $c^2 > k^2$. By Theorem 8.7 all solutions have the form

$$y = e^{-cx}(Ae^{hx} + Be^{-hx}) = Ae^{(h-c)x} + Be^{-(h+c)x},$$

where $h = \frac{1}{2}\sqrt{d} = \sqrt{c^2 - k^2}$. Since $h^2 = c^2 - k^2$, we have $h^2 - c^2 < 0$ so $(h - c)(h + c) < 0$. Therefore, the numbers $h - c$ and $h + c$ have opposite signs. If $c > 0$, then $h + c$ is positive so $h - c$ is negative, and hence both exponentials $e^{(h-c)x}$ and $e^{-(h+c)x}$ tend to zero as $x \to +\infty$. In this case, referred to as *overcritical damping*, all solutions tend to 0 for large $x$. An example is shown in Figure 8.6(a). Each solution can change sign at most once.

If $c < 0$, then $h - c$ is positive but $h + c$ is negative. Thus, both exponentials $e^{(h-c)x}$

and $e^{-(h+c)x}$ tend to $+\infty$ for large $x$, so again there are solutions with arbitrarily large absolute values.

(c) *Negative discriminant:* $c^2 < k^2$. In this case, all solutions have the form

$$y = Ce^{-cx} \sin (hx + \alpha) ,$$

where $h = \frac{1}{2}\sqrt{-d} = \sqrt{k^2 - c^2}$. If $c > 0$, every nontrivial solution oscillates, but the amplitude of the oscillation decreases to 0 as $x \to +\infty$. This case is called *undercritical damping* and is illustrated in Figure 8.6(b). If $c < 0$, all nontrivial solutions take arbitrarily large positive and negative values as $x \to +\infty$.

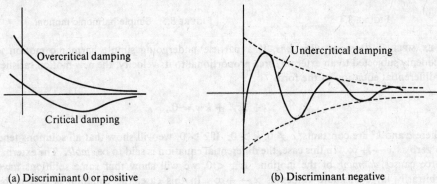

(a) Discriminant 0 or positive        (b) Discriminant negative

FIGURE 8.6    Damped vibrations occurring as solutions of $y'' + 2cy' + k^2 y = 0$, with $c > 0$, and discriminant $4(c^2 - k^2)$.

EXAMPLE 3. *Electric circuits.* If we insert a capacitor in the electric circuit of Example 5 in Section 8.6, the differential equation which serves as a model for this circuit is given by

$$LI'(t) + RI(t) + \frac{1}{C} \int I(t) \, dt = V(t) ,$$

where $C$ is a positive constant called the *capacitance*. Differentiation of this equation gives a second-order linear equation of the form

$$LI''(t) + RI'(t) + \frac{1}{C} I(t) = V'(t) .$$

If the impressed voltage $V(t)$ is constant, the right member is zero and the equation takes the form

$$I''(t) + \frac{R}{L} I'(t) + \frac{1}{LC} I(t) = 0 .$$

This is the same type of equation analyzed in Example 2 except that $2c$ is replaced by $R/L$, and $k^2$ is replaced by $1/(LC)$. In this case, the coefficient $c$ is positive so the equation is always stable. In other words, the current $I(t)$ always tends to 0 as $t \to +\infty$. The terminology of Example 2 is also used here. The current is said to be critically damped when the discriminant is zero ($CR^2 = 4L$), overcritically damped when the discriminant is positive ($CR^2 > 4L$), and undercritically damped when the discriminant is negative ($CR^2 < 4L$).

EXAMPLE 4. *Motion of a rocket with variable mass.* A rocket is propelled by burning fuel in a combustion chamber, allowing the products of combustion to be expelled backward. Assume the rocket starts from rest and moves vertically upward along a straight line. Designate the altitude of the rocket at time $t$ by $r(t)$, the mass of the rocket (including fuel) by $m(t)$, and the velocity of the exhaust matter, relative to the rocket, by $c(t)$. In the absence of external forces, the equation

$$(8.35) \qquad m(t)r''(t) = m'(t)c(t)$$

is used as a mathematical model for discussing the motion. The left member, $m(t)r''(t)$, is the product of the mass of the rocket and its acceleration. The right member, $m'(t)c(t)$, is the accelerating force on the rocket caused by the thrust developed by the rocket engine. In the examples to be considered here, $m(t)$ and $c(t)$ are known or can be prescribed in terms of $r(t)$ or its derivative $r'(t)$ (the velocity of the rocket). Equation (8.35) then becomes a second-order differential equation for the position function $r$.

If external forces are also present, such as gravitational attraction, then, instead of (8.35), we use the equation

$$(8.36) \qquad m(t)r''(t) = m'(t)c(t) + F(t) ,$$

where $F(t)$ represents the sum of all external forces acting on the rocket at time $t$.

Before we consider a specific example, we will give an argument which may serve to motivate the Equation (8.35). For this purpose we consider first a rocket that fires its exhaust matter intermittently, like bullets from a gun. Specifically, we consider a time interval $[t, t + h]$, where $h$ is a small positive number; we assume that some exhaust matter is expelled at time $t$, and that no further exhaust matter is expelled in the half-open interval $(t, t + h]$. On the basis of this assumption, we obtain a formula whose limit, as $h \to 0$, is Equation (8.35).

Just before the exhaust material is expelled at time $t$, the rocket has mass $m(t)$ and velocity $v(t)$. At the end of the time interval $[t, t + h]$, the rocket has mass $m(t + h)$ and velocity $v(t + h)$. The mass of the expelled matter is $m(t) - m(t + h)$, and its velocity during the interval is $v(t) + c(t)$, since $c(t)$ is the velocity of the exhaust relative to the rocket. Just before the exhaust material is expelled at time $t$, the rocket is a system with momentum $m(t)v(t)$. At time $t + h$, this system consists of two parts, a rocket with momentum $m(t + h)v(t + h)$ and exhaust matter with momentum $[m(t) - m(t + h)][v(t) + c(t)]$. The law of conservation of momentum states that the momentum of the new system must be equal to that of the old. Therefore, we have

$$m(t)v(t) = m(t + h)v(t + h) + [m(t) - m(t + h)][v(t) + c(t)] ,$$

from which we obtain

$$m(t + h)[v(t + h) - v(t)] = [m(t + h) - m(t)]c(t) .$$

Dividing by $h$ and letting $h \to 0$, we find that

$$m(t)v'(t) = m'(t)c(t),$$

which is equivalent to Equation (8.35).

Consider a special case in which the rocket starts from rest with an initial weight of $w$ pounds (including $b$ pounds of fuel) and moves vertically upward along a straight line. Assume the fuel is consumed at a constant rate of $k$ pounds per second and that the products of combustion are discharged directly backward with a constant speed of $c$ feet per second relative to the rocket. Assume the only external force acting on the rocket is the earth's gravitational attraction. We want to know how high the rocket will travel before all its fuel is consumed.

Since all the fuel is consumed when $kt = b$, we restrict $t$ to the interval $0 \le t \le b/k$. The only external force acting on the rocket is $-m(t)g$, the velocity $c(t) = -c$, so Equation (8.36) becomes

$$m(t)r''(t) = -m'(t)c - m(t)g.$$

The weight of the rocket at time $t$ is $w - kt$, and its mass $m(t)$ is $(w - kt)/g$; hence we have $m'(t) = -k/g$ and the foregoing equation becomes

$$r''(t) = -\frac{m'(t)}{m(t)} c - g = \frac{kc}{w - kt} - g.$$

Integrating, and using the initial condition $r'(0) = 0$, we find

$$r'(t) = -c \log \frac{w - kt}{w} - gt.$$

Integrating again and using the initial condition $r(0) = 0$, we obtain the relation

$$r(t) = \frac{c(w - kt)}{k} \log \frac{w - kt}{w} - \frac{1}{2} gt^2 + ct.$$

All the fuel is consumed when $t = b/k$. At that instant the altitude is

$$(8.37) \qquad r\left(\frac{b}{k}\right) = \frac{c(w - b)}{k} \log \frac{w - b}{w} - \frac{1}{2} \frac{gb^2}{k^2} + \frac{cb}{k}.$$

This formula is valid if $b < w$. For some rockets, the weight of the carrier is negligible compared to the weight of the fuel, and it is of interest to consider the limiting case $b = w$. We cannot put $b = w$ in (8.37) because of the presence of the term $\log (w - b)/w$. However, if we let $b \to w$, the first term in (8.37) is an indeterminate form with limit 0. Therefore, when $b \to w$, the limiting value of the right member of (8.37) is

$$\lim_{b \to w} r\left(\frac{b}{k}\right) = -\frac{1}{2} \frac{gw^2}{k^2} + \frac{cw}{k} = -\frac{1}{2} gT^2 + cT,$$

where $T = w/k$ is the time required for the entire weight $w$ to be consumed.

## 8.19   Exercises

In Exercises 1 through 5, a particle is assumed to be moving in simple harmonic motion, according to the equation $y = C \sin(kx + \alpha)$. The *velocity* of the particle is defined to be the derivative $y'$. The *frequency* of the motion is the reciprocal of the period. (Period $= 2\pi/k$; frequency $= k/2\pi$.) The frequency represents the number of cycles completed in unit time, provided $k > 0$.

1.  Find the amplitude $C$ if the frequency is $1/\pi$ and if the initial values of $y$ and $y'$ (when $x = 0$) are 2 and 4, respectively.
2.  Find the velocity when $y$ is zero, given that the amplitude is 7 and the frequency is 10.
3.  Show that the equation of motion can also be written as follows:

$$y = A \cos(mx + \beta).$$

Find equations that relate the constants $A$, $m$, $\beta$, and $C$, $k$, $\alpha$.

4.  Find the equation of motion given that $y = 3$ and $y' = 0$ when $x = 0$ and that the period is $\frac{1}{2}$.
5.  Find the amplitude of the motion if the period is $2\pi$ and the velocity is $\pm v_0$ when $y = y_0$.
6.  A particle undergoes simple harmonic motion. Initially its displacement is 1, its velocity is 2 and its acceleration is $-12$. Compute its displacement and acceleration when the velocity is $\sqrt{8}$.
7.  For a certain positive number $k$, the differential equation of simple harmonic motion $y'' + k^2 y = 0$ has solutions of the form $y = f(x)$ with $f(0) = f(3) = 0$ and $f(x) < 0$ for all $x$ in the open interval $0 < x < 3$. Compute $k$ and find all solutions.
8.  The current $I(t)$ at time $t$ flowing in an electric circuit obeys the differential equation $I''(t) + I(t) = G(t)$, where $G$ is a step function given by $G(t) = 1$ if $0 \leq t \leq 2\pi$, $G(t) = 0$ for all other $t$. Determine the solution which satisfies the initial conditions $I(0) = 0$, $I'(0) = 1$.
9.  The current $I(t)$ at time $t$ flowing in an electric circuit obeys the differential equation

$$I''(t) + RI'(t) + I(t) = \sin \omega t,$$

where $R$ and $\omega$ are positive constants. The solution can be expressed in the form $I(t) = F(t) + A \sin(\omega t + \alpha)$, where $F(t) \to 0$ as $t \to +\infty$, and $A$ and $\alpha$ are constants depending on $R$ and $\omega$, with $A > 0$. If there is a value of $\omega$ which makes $A$ as large as possible, then $\omega/(2\pi)$ is called a *resonance frequency* of the circuit.
    (a)  Find all resonance frequencies when $R = 1$.
    (b)  Find those values of $R$ for which the circuit will have a resonance frequency.
10. A spaceship is returning to earth. Assume that the only external force acting on it is the action of gravity, and that it falls along a straight line toward the center of the earth. The effect of gravity is partly overcome by firing a rocket directly downward. The rocket fuel is consumed at a constant rate of $k$ pounds per second and the exhaust material has a constant speed of $c$ feet per second relative to the rocket. Find a formula for the distance the spaceship falls in time $t$ if it starts from rest at time $t = 0$ with an initial weight of $w$ pounds.
11. A rocket of initial weight $w$ pounds starts from rest in free space (no external forces) and moves along a straight line. The fuel is consumed at a constant rate of $k$ pounds per second and the products of combustion are discharged directly backward at a constant speed of $c$ feet per second relative to the rocket. Find the distance traveled at time $t$.
12. Solve Exercise 11 if the initial speed of the rocket is $v_0$ and if the products of combustion are fired at such a speed that the discharged material remains at rest in space.

## 8.20   Remarks concerning nonlinear differential equations

Since second-order linear differential equations with constant coefficients occur in such a wide variety of scientific problems, it is indeed fortunate that we have systematic methods for solving these equations. Many nonlinear equations also arise naturally from both physical and geometrical problems, but there is no comprehensive theory comparable to that for linear equations. In the introduction to this chapter we mentioned a classic "bag of tricks" that has been developed for treating many special cases of nonlinear equations. We conclude this chapter with a discussion of some of these tricks and some of the problems they help to solve. We shall consider only first-order equations which can be solved for the derivative $y'$ and expressed in the form

$$(8.38) \qquad\qquad y' = f(x, y) .$$

We recall that a solution of (8.38) on an interval $I$ is any function, say $y = Y(x)$, which is differentiable on $I$ and satisfies the relation $Y'(x) = f[x, Y(x)]$ for all $x$ in $I$. In the linear case, we proved an existence-uniqueness theorem which tells us that one and only one solution exists satisfying a prescribed initial condition. Moreover, we have an explicit formula for determining this solution.

This is not typical of the general case. A nonlinear equation may have *no* solution satisfying a given initial condition, or it may have *more than one*. For example, the equation $(y')^2 - xy' + y + 1 = 0$ has no solution with $y = 0$ when $x = 0$, since this would require that $(y')^2 = -1$ when $x = 0$. On the other hand, the equation $y' = 3y^{2/3}$ has two distinct solutions, $Y_1(x) = 0$ and $Y_2(x) = x^3$, satisfying the initial condition $y = 0$ when $x = 0$.

Thus, the study of nonlinear equations is more difficult because of the possible non-existence or nonuniqueness of solutions. Also, even when solutions exist, it may not be possible to determine them explicitly in terms of familiar functions. Sometimes we can eliminate the derivative $y'$ from the differential equation and arrive at a relation of the form

$$F(x, y) = 0$$

satisfied by some, or perhaps all, solutions. If this equation can be solved for $y$ in terms of $x$, we get an explicit formula for the solution. More often than not, however, the equation is too complicated to solve for $y$. For example, in a later section we shall study the differential equation

$$y' = \frac{y - x}{y + x} ,$$

and we shall find that every solution necessarily satisfies the relation

$$(8.39) \qquad\qquad \frac{1}{2} \log (x^2 + y^2) + \arctan \frac{y}{x} + C = 0$$

for some constant $C$. It would be hopeless to try to solve this equation for $y$ in terms of $x$. In a case like this, we say that the relation (8.39) is an *implicit formula* for the solutions. It is common practice to say that the differential equation has been "solved" or "integrated" when we arrive at an implicit formula such as $F(x, y) = 0$ in which no derivatives of the unknown function appear. Sometimes this formula reveals useful information about the solutions. On the other hand, the reader should realize that such an implicit relation may be less helpful than the differential equation itself for studying properties of the solutions.

In the next section we show how qualitative information about the solutions can often be obtained directly from the differential equation without a knowledge of explicit or implicit formulas for the solutions.

## 8.21 Integral curves and direction fields

Consider a differential equation of first order, say $y' = f(x, y)$, and suppose some of the solutions satisfy an implicit relation of the form

(8.40) $$F(x, y, C) = 0,$$

where $C$ denotes a constant. If we introduce a rectangular coordinate system and plot all the points $(x, y)$ whose coordinates satisfy (8.40) for a particular $C$, we obtain a curve called an *integral curve* of the differential equation. Different values of $C$ usually give different integral curves, but all of them share a common geometric property. The differential equation $y' = f(x, y)$ relates the slope $y'$ at each point $(x, y)$ of the curve to the coordinates $x$ and $y$. As $C$ takes on all its values, the collection of integral curves obtained is called a *one-parameter family* of curves.

For example, when the differential equation is $y' = 3$, integration gives us $y = 3x + C$, and the integral curves form a family of straight lines, all having slope 3. The arbitrary constant $C$ represents the $y$-intercept of these lines.

If the differential equation is $y' = x$, integration yields $y = \frac{1}{2}x^2 + C$, and the integral curves form a family of parabolas as shown in Figure 8.7. Again, the constant $C$ tells us where the various curves cross the $y$-axis. Figure 8.8 illustrates the family of exponential

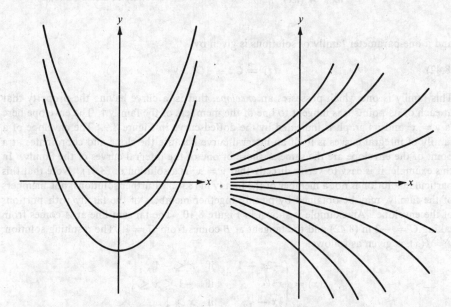

FIGURE 8.7   Integral curves of the differential equation $y' = x$.

FIGURE 8.8   Integral curves of the differential
equation $y' = y$.

curves, $y = Ce^x$, which are integral curves of the differential equation $y' = y$. Once more, $C$ represents the $y$-intercept. In this case, $C$ is also equal to the slope of the curve at the point where it crosses the $y$-axis.

A family of nonparallel straight lines is shown in Figure 8.9. These are integral curves of the differential equation

(8.41)
$$ y = x \frac{dy}{dx} - \frac{1}{4}\left(\frac{dy}{dx}\right)^2 $$

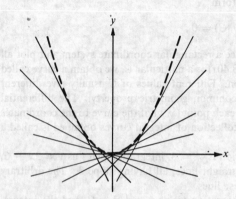

FIGURE 8.9  Integral curves of the differential equation $y = x \dfrac{dy}{dx} - \dfrac{1}{4}\left(\dfrac{dy}{dx}\right)^2$.

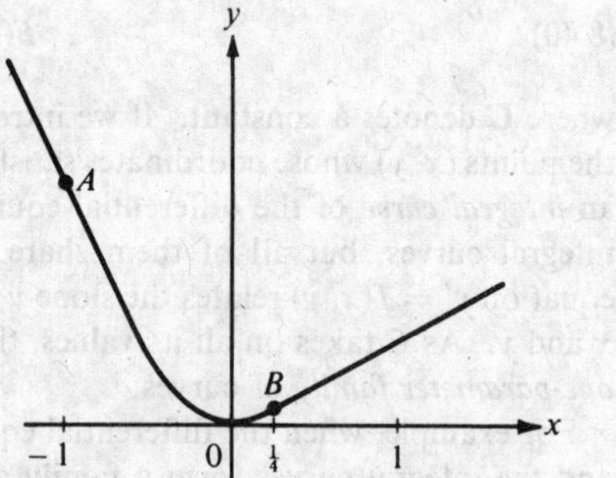

FIGURE 8.10  A solution of Equation (8.41) that is not a member of the family in Equation (8.42).

and a one-parameter family of solutions is given by

(8.42)
$$ y = Cx - \tfrac{1}{4}C^2 . $$

This family is one which possesses an *envelope*, that is, a curve having the property that at each of its points it is tangent to one of the members of the family.† The envelope here is $y = x^2$ and its graph is indicated by the dotted curve in Figure 8.9. The envelope of a family of integral curves is itself an integral curve because the slope and coordinates at a point of the envelope are the same as those of one of the integral curves of the family. In this example, it is easy to verify directly that $y = x^2$ is a solution of (8.41). Note that this particular solution is not a member of the family in (8.42). Further solutions, not members of the family, may be obtained by piecing together members of the family with portions of the envelope. An example is shown in Figure 8.10. The tangent line at $A$ comes from taking $C = -2$ in (8.42) and the tangent at $B$ comes from $C = \frac{1}{2}$. The resulting solution, $y = f(x)$, is given as follows:

$$ f(x) = \begin{cases} -2x - 1 & \text{if } x \le -1 , \\ x^2 & \text{if } -1 \le x \le \frac{1}{4} , \\ \frac{1}{2}x - \frac{1}{16} & \text{if } x \ge \frac{1}{4} . \end{cases} $$

---

† And conversely, each member of the family is tangent to the envelope.

This function has a derivative and satisfies the differential equation in (8.41) for every real $x$. It is clear that an infinite number of similar examples could be constructed in the same way. This example shows that it may not be easy to exhibit all possible solutions of a differential equation.

Sometimes it is possible to find a first-order differential equation satisfied by all members of a one-parameter family of curves. We illustrate with two examples.

EXAMPLE 1. Find a first-order differential equation satisfied by all circles with center at the origin.

*Solution.* A circle with center at the origin and radius $C$ satisfies the equation $x^2 + y^2 = C^2$. As $C$ varies over all positive numbers, we obtain every circle with center at the origin. To find a first-order differential equation having these circles as integral curves, we simply differentiate the Cartesian equation to obtain $2x + 2yy' = 0$. Thus, each circle satisfies the differential equation $y' = -x/y$.

EXAMPLE 2. Find a first-order differential equation for the family of all circles passing through the origin and having their centers on the $x$-axis.

*Solution.* If the center of a circle is at $(C, 0)$ and if it passes through the origin, the theorem of Pythagoras tells us that each point $(x, y)$ on the circle satisfies the Cartesian equation $(x - C)^2 + y^2 = C^2$, which can be written as

$$(8.43) \qquad\qquad x^2 + y^2 - 2Cx = 0 .$$

To find a differential equation having these circles as integral curves, we differentiate (8.43) to obtain $2x + 2yy' - 2C = 0$, or

$$(8.44) \qquad\qquad x + yy' = C .$$

Since this equation contains $C$, it is satisfied only by that circle in (8.43) corresponding to the same $C$. To obtain one differential equation satisfied by all the curves in (8.43), we must eliminate $C$. We could differentiate (8.44) to obtain $1 + yy'' + (y')^2 = 0$. This is a second-order differential equation satisfied by all the curves in (8.43). We can obtain a first-order equation by eliminating $C$ algebraically from (8.43) and (8.44). Substituting $x + yy'$ for $C$ in (8.43), we obtain $x^2 + y^2 - 2x(x + yy')$, a first-order equation which can be solved for $y'$ and written as $y' = (y^2 - x^2)/(2xy)$.

Figure 8.11 illustrates what is called a *direction field* of a differential equation. This is simply a collection of short line segments drawn tangent to the various integral curves. The particular example shown in Figure 8.11 is a direction field of the equation $y' = y$.

A direction field can be constructed without solving the differential equation. Choose a point, say $(a, b)$, and compute the number $f(a, b)$ obtained by substituting in the righthand side of the differential equation $y' = f(x, y)$. If there is an integral curve through this point, its slope there must be equal to $f(a, b)$. Therefore, if we draw a short line segment through $(a, b)$ having this slope, it will be part of a direction field of the differential equation. By drawing several of these line segments, we can get a fair idea of the general behavior of the

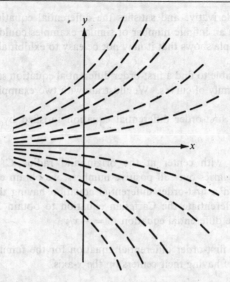

FIGURE 8.11  A direction field for the differential equation $y' = y$.

integral curves. Sometimes such qualitative information about the solution may be all
that is needed. Notice that different points $(0, b)$ on the $y$-axis yield different integral
curves. This gives us a geometric reason for expecting an arbitrary constant to appear
when we integrate a first-order equation.

## 8.22 Exercises

In Exercises 1 through 12, find a first-order differential equation having the given family of
curves as integral curves.

1. $2x + 3y = C$.
2. $y = Ce^{-2x}$.
3. $x^2 - y^2 = C$.
4. $xy = C$.
5. $y^2 = Cx$.
6. $x^2 + y^2 + 2Cy = 1$.
7. $y = C(x - 1)e^x$.
8. $y^4(x + 2) = C(x - 2)$.
9. $y = C \cos x$.
10. $\arctan y + \arcsin x = C$.
11. All circles through the points $(1, 0)$ and $(-1, 0)$.
12. All circles through the points $(1, 1)$ and $(-1, -1)$.

In the construction of a direction field of a differential equation, sometimes the work may be
speeded considerably if we first locate those points at which the slope $y'$ has a constant value $C$.
For each $C$, these points lie on a curve called an *isocline*.

13. Plot the isoclines corresponding to the constant slopes $\frac{1}{2}$, 1, $\frac{3}{2}$, and 2 for the differential equation
$y' = x^2 + y^2$. With the aid of the isoclines, construct a direction field for the equation and try
to determine the shape of the integral curve passing through the origin.

14. Show that the isoclines of the differential equation $y' = x + y$ form a one-parameter family
of straight lines. Plot the isoclines corresponding to the constant slopes 0, $\pm\frac{1}{2}$, $\pm 1$, $\pm\frac{3}{2}$, $\pm 2$.
With the aid of the isoclines, construct a direction field and sketch the integral curve passing
through the origin. One of the integral curves is also an isocline; find this curve.

15. Plot a number of isoclines and construct a direction field for the equation

$$y = x\frac{dy}{dx} + \left(\frac{dy}{dx}\right)^2$$

If you draw the direction field carefully, you should be able to determine a one-parameter family of solutions of this equation from the appearance of the direction field.

## 8.23 First-order separable equations

A first-order differential equation of the form $y' = f(x, y)$ in which the right member $f(x, y)$ splits into a product of two factors, one depending on $x$ alone and the other depending on $y$ alone, is said to be a *separable equation*. Examples are $y' = x^3$, $y' = y$, $y' = \sin y \log x$, $y' = x/\tan y$, etc. Thus each separable equation can be expressed in the form

$$y' = Q(x)R(y),$$

where $Q$ and $R$ are given functions. When $R(y) \neq 0$, we can divide by $R(y)$ and rewrite this differential equation in the form

$$A(y)y' = Q(x),$$

where $A(y) = 1/R(y)$. The next theorem tells us how to find an implicit formula satisfied by every solution of such an equation.

THEOREM 8.10. *Let $y = Y(x)$ be any solution of the separable differential equation*

(8.45) $$A(y)y' = Q(x)$$

*such that $Y'$ is continuous on an open interval $I$. Assume that both $Q$ and the composite function $A \circ Y$ are continuous on $I$. Let $G$ be any primitive of $A$, that is, any function such that $G' = A$. Then the solution $Y$ satisfies the implicit formula*

(8.46) $$G(y) = \int Q(x)\, dx + C$$

*for some constant $C$. Conversely, if $y$ satisfies* (8.46) *then $y$ is a solution of* (8.45).

*Proof.* Since $Y$ is a solution of (8.45), we must have

(8.47) $$A[Y(x)]Y'(x) = Q(x)$$

for each $x$ in $I$. Since $G' = A$, this equation becomes

$$G'[Y(x)]Y'(x) = Q(x).$$

But, by the chain rule, the left member is the derivative of the composite function $G \circ Y$.

Therefore $G \circ Y$ is a primitive of $Q$, which means that

$$(8.48) \qquad\qquad G[Y(x)] = \int Q(x)\, dx + C$$

for some constant $C$. This is the relation (8.46). Conversely, if $y = Y(x)$ satisfies (8.46), differentiation gives us (8.47), which shows that $Y$ is a solution of the differential equation (8.45).

> *Note:*  The implicit formula (8.46) can also be expressed in terms of $A$. From (8.47) we have
>
> $$\int A[Y(x)] Y'(x)\, dx = \int Q(x)\, dx + C\,.$$
>
> If we make the substitution $y = Y(x)$, $dy = Y'(x)\, dx$ in the integral on the left, the equation becomes
>
> $$(8.49) \qquad\qquad \int A(y)\, dy = \int Q(x)\, dx + C\,.$$

Since the indefinite integral $\int A(y)\, dy$ represents any primitive of $A$, Equation (8.49) is an alternative way of writing (8.46).

In practice, formula (8.49) is obtained directly from (8.45) by a mechanical process. In the differential equation (8.45) we write $dy/dx$ for the derivative $y'$ and then treat $dy/dx$ as a fraction to obtain the relation $A(y)\, dy = Q(x)\, dx$. Now we simply attach integral signs to both sides of this equation and add the constant $C$ to obtain (8.49). The justification for this mechanical process is provided by Theorem 8.10. This process is another example illustrating the effectiveness of the Leibniz notation.

EXAMPLE.  The nonlinear equation $xy' + y = y^2$ is separable since it can be written in the form

$$(8.50) \qquad\qquad \frac{y'}{y(y-1)} = \frac{1}{x}\,,$$

provided that $y(y-1) \neq 0$ and $x \neq 0$. Now the two constant functions $y = 0$ and $y = 1$ are clearly solutions of $xy' + y = y^2$. The remaining solutions, if any exist, satisfy (8.50) and, hence, by Theorem 8.10 they also satisfy

$$\int \frac{dy}{y(y-1)} = \int \frac{dx}{x} + K$$

for some constant $K$. Since the integrand on the left is $1/(y-1) - 1/y$, when we integrate, we find that

$$\log|y-1| - \log|y| = \log|x| + K\,.$$

This gives us $|(y-1)/y| = |x|\, e^K$ or $(y-1)/y = Cx$ for some constant $C$. Solving for $y$, we obtain the explicit formula

$$(8.51) \qquad\qquad y = \frac{1}{1 - Cx}\,.$$

Theorem 8.10 tells us that for any choice of $C$ this $y$ is a solution; therefore, in this example we have determined all solutions: the constant functions $y = 0$ and $y = 1$ and all the functions defined by (8.51). Note that the choice $C = 0$ gives the constant solution $y = 1$.

## 8.24 Exercises

In Exercises 1 through 12, assume solutions exist and find an implicit formula satisfied by the solutions.

1. $y' = x^3/y^2$.
2. $\tan x \cos y = -y' \tan y$.
3. $(x + 1)y' + y^2 = 0$.
4. $y' = (y - 1)(y - 2)$.
5. $y\sqrt{1 - x^2}\, y' = x$.
6. $(x - 1)y' = xy$.

7. $(1 - x^2)^{1/2}y' + 1 + y^2 = 0$.
8. $xy(1 + x^2)y' - (1 + y^2) = 0$.
9. $(x^2 - 4)y' = y$.
10. $xyy' = 1 + x^2 + y^2 + x^2y^2$.
11. $yy' = e^{x+2y} \sin x$.
12. $x\,dx + y\,dy = xy(x\,dy - y\,dx)$.

In Exercises 13 through 16, find functions $f$, continuous on the whole real axis, which satisfy the conditions given. When it is easy to enumerate all of them, do so; in any case, find as many as you can.

13. $f(x) = 2 + \int_1^x f(t)\, dt$.
14. $f(x)f'(x) = 5x$, $\quad f(0) = 1$.
15. $f'(x) + 2xe^{f(x)} = 0$, $\quad f(0) = 0$.
16. $f^2(x) + [f'(x)]^2 = 1$. $\quad$ *Note:* $f(x) = -1$ is one solution.
17. A nonnegative function $f$, continuous on the whole real axis, has the property that its ordinate set over an arbitrary interval has an area proportional to the length of the interval. Find $f$.
18. Solve Exercise 17 if the area is proportional to the difference of the function values at the endpoints of the interval.
19. Solve Exercise 18 when "difference" is replaced by "sum."
20. Solve Exercise 18 when "difference" is replaced by "product."

## 8.25 Homogeneous first-order equations

We consider now a special kind of first-order equation,

$$(8.52) \qquad\qquad y' = f(x, y),$$

in which the right-hand side has a special property known as *homogeneity*. This means that

$$(8.53) \qquad\qquad f(tx, ty) = f(x, y)$$

for all $x$, $y$, and all $t \neq 0$. In other words, replacement of $x$ by $tx$ and $y$ by $ty$ has no effect on the value of $f(x, y)$. Equations of the form (8.52) which have this property are called *homogeneous* (sometimes called *homogeneous of degree zero*). Examples are the following:

$$y' = \frac{y - x}{y + x}, \qquad y' = \left(\frac{x^2 + y^2}{xy}\right)^3, \qquad y' = \frac{x}{y}\sin\frac{x^2 + y^2}{x^2 - y^2}, \qquad y' = \log x - \log y.$$

If we use (8.53) with $t = 1/x$, the differential equation in (8.52) becomes

$$(8.54) \qquad\qquad y' = f\left(1, \frac{y}{x}\right).$$

The appearance of the quotient $y/x$ on the right suggests that we introduce a new unknown function $v$ where $v = y/x$. Then $y = vx$, $y' = v'x + v$, and this substitution transforms (8.54) into

$$v'x + v = f(1, v) \quad \text{or} \quad x\frac{dv}{dx} = f(1, v) - v \,.$$

This last equation is a first-order separable equation for $v$. We may use Theorem 8.10 to obtain an implicit formula for $v$ and then replace $v$ by $y/x$ to obtain an implicit formula for $y$.

EXAMPLE. Solve the differential equation $y' = (y - x)/(y + x)$.

*Solution.* We rewrite the equation as follows:

$$y' = \frac{y/x - 1}{y/x + 1} \,.$$

The substitution $v = y/x$ transforms this into

$$x\frac{dv}{dx} = \frac{v - 1}{v + 1} - v = -\frac{1 + v^2}{v + 1} \,.$$

Applying Theorem 8.10, we get

$$\int \frac{v}{1 + v^2}\, dv + \int \frac{1}{1 + v^2}\, dv = -\int \frac{dx}{x} + C \,.$$

Integration yields

$$\tfrac{1}{2} \log(1 + v^2) + \arctan v = -\log |x| + C \,.$$

Replacing $v$ by $y/x$, we have

$$\tfrac{1}{2} \log(x^2 + y^2) - \tfrac{1}{2} \log x^2 + \arctan \frac{y}{x} = -\log |x| + C \,,$$

and since $\log x^2 = 2 \log |x|$, this simplifies to

$$\tfrac{1}{2} \log(x^2 + y^2) + \arctan \frac{y}{x} = C \,.$$

There are some interesting geometric properties possessed by the solutions of a homogeneous equation $y' = f(x, y)$. First of all, it is easy to show that straight lines through the origin are isoclines of the equation. We recall that an isocline of $y' = f(x, y)$ is a curve along which the slope $y'$ is constant. This property is illustrated in Figure 8.12 which shows a direction field of the differential equation $y' = -2y/x$. The isocline corresponding to slope $c$ has the equation $-2y/x = c$, or $y = -\frac{1}{2}cx$ and is therefore a line of slope $-\frac{1}{2}c$ through the origin. To prove the property in general, consider a line of slope $m$ through the origin. Then $y = mx$ for all $(x, y)$ on this line; in particular, the point $(1, m)$ is on the line. Suppose now, for the sake of simplicity, that there is an integral curve through each point of the line $y = mx$. The slope of the integral curve through a point $(a, b)$ on this line is $f(a, b) = f(a, ma)$. If $a \neq 0$, we may use the homogeneity property in (8.53) to

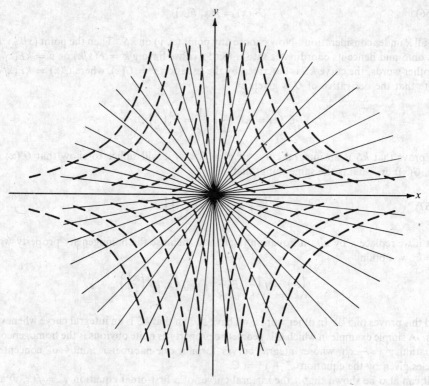

FIGURE 8.12 A direction field for the differential equation $y' = -2y/x$. The isoclines are straight lines through the origin.

write $f(a, ma) = f(1, m)$. In other words, if $(a, b) \neq (0, 0)$, the integral curve through $(a, b)$ has the same slope as the integral curve through $(1, m)$. Therefore the line $y = mx$ is an isocline, as asserted. (It can also be shown that these are the only isoclines of a homogeneous equation.)

This property of the isoclines suggests a property of the integral curves known as *invariance under similarity transformations*. We recall that a similarity transformation carries a set $S$ into a new set $kS$ obtained by multiplying the coordinates of each point of $S$ by a constant factor $k > 0$. Every line through the origin remains fixed under a similarity transformation. Therefore, the isoclines of a homogeneous equation do not change under a similarity transformation; hence the appearance of the direction field does not change either. This suggests that similarity transformations carry integral curves into integral curves. To prove this analytically, let us assume that $S$ is an integral curve described by an explicit formula of the form

$$(8.55) \qquad\qquad y = F(x).$$

To say that $S$ is an integral curve of $y' = f(x, y)$ means that we have

$$(8.56) \qquad\qquad F'(x) = f(x, F(x))$$

for all $x$ under consideration. Now choose any point $(x, y)$ on $kS$. Then the point $(x/k, y/k)$ lies on $S$ and hence its coordinates satisfy (8.55), so we have $y/k = F(x/k)$ or $y = kF(x/k)$. In other words, the curve $kS$ is described by the equation $y = G(x)$, where $G(x) = kF(x/k)$. Note that the derivative of $G$ is given by

$$G'(x) = kF'\left(\frac{x}{k}\right) \cdot \frac{1}{k} = F'\left(\frac{x}{k}\right).$$

To prove that $kS$ is an integral curve of $y' = f(x, y)$ it will suffice to show that $G'(x) = f(x, G(x))$ or, what is the same thing, that

$$(8.57) \qquad\qquad F'\left(\frac{x}{k}\right) = f\left(x, kF\left(\frac{x}{k}\right)\right).$$

But if we replace $x$ by $x/k$ in Equation (8.56) and then use the homogeneity property with $t = k$, we obtain

$$F'\left(\frac{x}{k}\right) = f\left(\frac{x}{k}, F\left(\frac{x}{k}\right)\right) = f\left(x, kF\left(\frac{x}{k}\right)\right),$$

and this proves (8.57). In other words, we have shown that $kS$ is an integral curve whenever $S$ is. A simple example in which this geometric property is quite obvious is the homogeneous equation $y' = -x/y$ whose integral curves form a one-parameter family of concentric circles given by the equation $x^2 + y^2 = C$.

It can also be shown that if the integral curves of a first-order equation $y' = f(x, y)$ are invariant under similarity transformations, then the differential equation is necessarily homogeneous.

## 8.26 Exercises

1. Show that the substitution $y = x/v$ transforms a homogeneous equation $y' = f(x, y)$ into a first-order equation for $v$ which is separable. Sometimes this substitution leads to integrals that are easier to evaluate than those obtained by the substitution $y = xv$ discussed in the text.

Integrate the differential equations in Exercises 2 through 11.

2. $y' = \dfrac{-x}{y}$.

3. $y' = 1 + \dfrac{y}{x}$.

4. $y' = \dfrac{x^2 + 2y^2}{xy}$.

5. $(2y^2 - x^2)y' + 3xy = 0$.

6. $xy' = y - \sqrt{x^2 + y^2}$.

9. $y' = \dfrac{y(x^2 + xy + y^2)}{x(x^2 + 3xy + y^2)}$.

7. $x^2 y' + xy + 2y^2 = 0$.

10. $y' = \dfrac{y}{x} + \sin\dfrac{y}{x}$.

8. $y^2 + (x^2 - xy + y^2)y' = 0$.

11. $x(y + 4x)y' + y(x + 4y) = 0$.

## 8.27 Some geometrical and physical problems leading to first-order equations

We discuss next some examples of geometrical and physical problems that lead to first-order differential equations that are either separable or homogeneous.

*Orthogonal trajectories.* Two curves are said to intersect *orthogonally* at a point if their tangent lines are perpendicular at that point. A curve which intersects every member of a family of curves orthogonally is called an orthogonal trajectory for the family. Figure 8.13 shows some examples. Problems involving orthogonal trajectories are of importance in both pure and applied mathematics. For example, in the theory of fluid flow, two orthogonal families of curves are called the *equipotential lines* and the *stream lines*, respectively. In the theory of heat, they are known as *isothermal lines* and *lines of flow*.

Suppose a given family of curves satisfies a first-order differential equation, say

$$(8.58) \qquad y' = f(x, y) .$$

The number $f(x, y)$ is the slope of an integral curve passing through $(x, y)$. The slope of each orthogonal trajectory through this point is the negative reciprocal $-1/f(x, y)$, so the orthogonal trajectories satisfy the differential equation

$$(8.59) \qquad y' = - \frac{1}{f(x, y)} .$$

If (8.58) is separable, then (8.59) is also separable. If (8.58) is homogeneous, then (8.59) is also homogeneous.

EXAMPLE 1. Find the orthogonal trajectories of the family of all circles through the origin with their centers on the $x$-axis.

*Solution.* In Example 2 of Section 8.21 we found that this family is given by the Cartesian equation $x^2 + y^2 - 2Cx = 0$ and that it satisfies the differential equation $y' = (y^2 - x^2)/(2xy)$. Replacing the right member by its negative reciprocal, we find that the orthogonal trajectories satisfy the differential equation

$$y' = \frac{2xy}{x^2 - y^2} .$$

This homogeneous equation may be integrated by the substitution $y = vx$, and it leads to the family of integral curves

$$x^2 + y^2 - 2Cy = 0 .$$

This is a family of circles passing through the origin and having their centers on the $y$-axis. Examples are shown in Figure 8.13.

*Pursuit problems.* A point $Q$ is constrained to move along a prescribed plane curve $C_1$. Another point $P$ in the same plane "pursues" the point $Q$. That is, $P$ moves in such a manner that its direction of motion is always toward $Q$. The point $P$ thereby traces out another curve $C_2$ called a *curve of pursuit*. An example is shown in Figure 8.14 where $C_1$ is

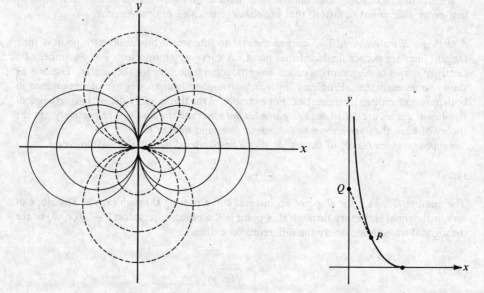

FIGURE 8.13   Orthogonal circles.

FIGURE 8.14   The tractrix as a curve of pursuit. The distance from $P$ to $Q$ is constant.

the $y$-axis. In a typical problem of pursuit we seek to determine the curve $C_2$ when the curve $C_1$ is known and some additional piece of information is given concerning $P$ and $Q$, for example, a relation between their positions or their velocities.

When we say that the direction of motion of $P$ is always toward $Q$, we mean that the tangent line of $C_2$ through $P$ passes through $Q$. Therefore, if we denote by $(x, y)$ the rectangular coordinates of $P$ at a given instant, and by $(X, Y)$ those of $Q$ at the same instant, we must have

(8.60)
$$y' = \frac{Y - y}{X - x}.$$

The additional piece of information usually enables us to consider $X$ and $Y$ as known functions of $x$ and $y$, in which case Equation (8.60) becomes a first-order differential equation for $y$. Now we consider a specific example in which this equation is separable.

EXAMPLE 2. A point $Q$ moves on a straight line $C_1$, and a point $P$ pursues $Q$ in such a way that the distance from $P$ to $Q$ has a constant value $k > 0$. If $P$ is initially not on $C_1$, find the curve of pursuit.

*Solution.* We take $C_1$ to be the $y$-axis and place $P$ initially at the point $(k, 0)$. Since the distance from $P$ to $Q$ is $k$, we must have $(X - x)^2 + (Y - y)^2 = k^2$. But $X = 0$ on $C_1$, so we have $Y - y = \sqrt{k^2 - x^2}$, and the differential equation (8.60) becomes

$$y' = \frac{\sqrt{k^2 - x^2}}{-x}.$$

Integrating this equation with the help of the substitution $x = k \cos t$ and using the fact that $y = 0$ when $x = k$, we obtain the relation

$$y = k \log \frac{k + \sqrt{k^2 - x^2}}{x} - \sqrt{k^2 - x^2}.$$

The curve of pursuit in this example is called a *tractrix;* it is shown in Figure 8.14.

*Flow of fluid through an orifice.* Suppose we are given a tank (not necessarily cylindrical) containing a fluid. The fluid flows from the tank through a sharp-edged orifice. If there were no friction (and hence no loss of energy) the speed of the jet would be equal to $\sqrt{2gy}$ feet per second, where $y$ denotes the height (in feet) of the surface above the orifice.† (See Figure 8.15.) If $A_0$ denotes the area (in square feet) of the orifice, then $A_0\sqrt{2gy}$ represents the number of cubic feet per second of fluid flowing from the orifice. Because of friction, the jet stream contracts somewhat and the actual rate of discharge is more nearly $cA_0\sqrt{2gy}$, where $c$ is an experimentally determined number called the *discharge coefficient.* For ordinary sharp-edged orifices, the approximate value of $c$ is 0.60. Using this and taking $g = 32$, we find that the speed of the jet is $4.8\sqrt{y}$ feet per second, and therefore the rate of discharge of volume is $4.8A_0\sqrt{y}$ cubic feet per second.

Let $V(y)$ denote the volume of the fluid in the tank when the height of the fluid is $y$. If the cross-sectional area of the tank at the height $u$ is $A(u)$, then we have $V(y) = \int_0^y A(u)\, du$, from which we obtain $dV/dy = A(y)$. The argument in the foregoing paragraph tells us that the rate of change of volume with respect to time is $dV/dt = -4.8A_0\sqrt{y}$ cubic feet per second, the minus sign coming in because the volume is decreasing. By the chain rule we have

$$\frac{dV}{dt} = \frac{dV}{dy}\frac{dy}{dt} = A(y)\frac{dy}{dt}.$$

Combining this with the equation $dV/dt = -4.8A_0\sqrt{y}$, we obtain the differential equation

$$A(y)\frac{dy}{dt} = -4.8A_0\sqrt{y}.$$

---

† If a particle of mass $m$ falls freely through a distance $y$ and reaches a speed $v$, its kinetic energy $\frac{1}{2}mv^2$ must be equal to the potential energy $mgy$ (the work done in lifting it up a distance $y$). Solving for $v$, we get $v = \sqrt{2gy}$.

This separable differential equation is used as the mathematical model for problems concerning fluid flow through an orifice. The height $y$ of the surface is related to the time $t$ by an equation of the form

(8.61)
$$\int \frac{A(y)}{\sqrt{y}}\, dy = -4.8 A_0 \int dt + C\,.$$

Area = $A(y)$

$y$

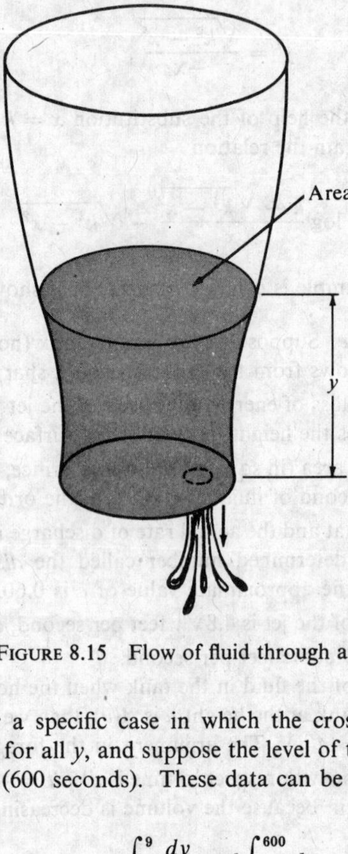

FIGURE 8.15   Flow of fluid through an orifice.

EXAMPLE 3. Consider a specific case in which the cross-sectional area of the tank is constant, say $A(y) = A$ for all $y$, and suppose the level of the fluid is lowered from 10 feet to 9 feet in 10 minutes (600 seconds). These data can be combined with Equation (8.61) to give us

$$-\int_{10}^{9} \frac{dy}{\sqrt{y}} = k \int_{0}^{600} dt\,,$$

where $k = 4.8 A_0 / A$. Using this, we can determine $k$ and we find that

$$\frac{\sqrt{10} - \sqrt{9}}{\frac{1}{2}} = 600k \qquad \text{or} \qquad k = \frac{\sqrt{10} - 3}{300}\,.$$

Now we can compute the time required for the level to fall from one given value to any other. For example, if at time $t_1$ the level is 7 feet and at time $t_2$ it is 1 foot ($t_1$, $t_2$ measured in minutes, say), then we must have

$$-\int_7^1 \frac{dy}{\sqrt{y}} = k\int_{60t_1}^{60t_2} dt \, ,$$

which yields

$$t_2 - t_1 = \frac{2(\sqrt{7} - 1)}{60k} = 10 \, \frac{\sqrt{7} - 1}{\sqrt{10} - 3} = \frac{10(\sqrt{7} - 1)(\sqrt{10} + 3)}{10 - 9} = (10)(1.645)(6.162)$$

$$= 101.3 \text{ min.}$$

## 8.28 Miscellaneous review exercises

In each of Exercises 1 through 10 find the orthogonal trajectories of the given family of curves.

1. $2x + 3y = C$.
2. $xy = C$.
3. $x^2 + y^2 + 2Cy = 1$.
4. $y^2 = Cx$.
5. $x^2y = C$.
6. $y = Ce^{-2x}$.
7. $x^2 - y^2 = C$.
8. $y = C \cos x$.
9. All circles through the points $(1, 0)$ and $(-1, 0)$.
10. All circles through the points $(1, 1)$ and $(-1, -1)$.
11. A point $Q$ moves upward along the positive $y$-axis. A point $P$, initially at $(1, 0)$, pursues $Q$ in such a way that its distance from the $y$-axis is $\frac{1}{2}$ the distance of $Q$ from the origin. Find a Cartesian equation for the path of pursuit.
12. Solve Exercise 11 when the fraction $\frac{1}{2}$ is replaced by an arbitrary positive number $k$.
13. A curve with Cartesian equation $y = f(x)$ passes through the origin. Lines drawn parallel to the coordinate axes through an arbitrary point of the curve form a rectangle with two sides on the axes. The curve divides every such rectangle into two regions $A$ and $B$, one of which has an area equal to $n$ times the other. Find the function $f$.
14. Solve Exercise 13 if the two regions $A$ and $B$ have the property that, when rotated about the $x$-axis, they sweep out solids one of which has a volume $n$ times that of the other.
15. The graph of a nonnegative differentiable function $f$ passes through the origin and through the point $(1, 2/\pi)$. If, for every $x > 0$, the ordinate set of $f$ above the interval $[0, x]$ sweeps out a solid of volume $x^2f(x)$ when rotated about the $x$-axis, find the function $f$.
16. A nonnegative differentiable function $f$ is defined on the closed interval $[0, 1]$ with $f(1) = 0$. For each $a$, $0 < a < 1$, the line $x = a$ cuts the ordinate set of $f$ into two regions having areas $A$ and $B$, respectively, $A$ being the area of the leftmost region. If $A - B = 2f(a) + 3a + b$, where $b$ is a constant independent of $a$, find the function $f$ and the constant $b$.
17. The graph of a function $f$ passes through the two points $P_0 = (0, 1)$ and $P_1 = (1, 0)$. For every point $P = (x, y)$ on the graph, the curve lies above the chord $P_0P$, and the area $A(x)$ of the region between the curve and the chord $PP_0$ is equal to $x^3$. Determine the function $f$.
18. A tank with vertical sides has a square cross-section of area 4 square feet. Water is leaving the tank through an orifice of area 5/3 square inches. If the water level is initially 2 feet above the orifice, find the time required for the level to drop 1 foot.
19. Refer to the preceding problem. If water also flows into the tank at the rate of 100 cubic inches per second, show that the water level approaches the value $(25/24)^2$ feet above the orifice, regardless of the initial water level.
20. A tank has the shape of a right circular cone with its vertex up. Find the time required to empty a liquid from the tank through an orifice in its base. Express your result in terms of the dimensions of the cone and the area $A_0$ of the orifice.

21. The equation $xy'' - y' + (1 - x)y = 0$ possesses a solution of the form $y = e^{mx}$, where $m$ is constant. Determine this solution explicitly.

22. Solve the differential equation $(x + y^3) + 6xy^2y' = 0$ by making a suitable change of variable which converts it into a linear equation.

23. Solve the differential equation $(1 + y^2e^{2x})y' + y = 0$ by introducing a change of variable of the form $y = ue^{mx}$, where $m$ is constant and $u$ is a new unknown function.

24. (a) Given a function $f$ which satisfies the relations

$$2f'(x) = f\left(\frac{1}{x}\right) \quad \text{if} \quad x > 0, \quad f(1) = 2,$$

let $y = f(x)$ and show that $y$ satisfies a differential equation of the form

$$x^2y'' + axy' + by = 0,$$

where $a$ and $b$ are constants. Determine $a$ and $b$.
(b) Find a solution of the form $f(x) = Cx^n$.

25. (a) Let $u$ be a nonzero solution of the second-order equation

$$y'' + P(x)y' + Q(x)y = 0.$$

Show that the substitution $y = uv$ converts the equation

$$y'' + P(x)y' + Q(x)y = R(x)$$

into a first-order linear equation for $v'$.
(b) Obtain a nonzero solution of the equation $y'' - 4y' + x^2(y' - 4y) = 0$ by inspection and use the method of part (a) to find a solution of

$$y'' - 4y' + x^2(y' - 4y) = 2xe^{-x^3/3}$$

such that $y = 0$ and $y' = 4$ when $x = 0$.

26. Scientists at the Ajax Atomics Works isolated one gram of a new radioactive element called Deteriorum. It was found to decay at a rate proportional to the *square* of the amount present. After one year, $\frac{1}{2}$ gram remained.
(a) Set up and solve the differential equation for the mass of Deteriorum remaining at time $t$.
(b) Evaluate the decay constant in units of $gm^{-1} yr^{-1}$.

27. In the preceding problem, suppose the word *square* were replaced by *square root*, the other data remaining the same. Show that in this case the substance would decay entirely within a finite time, and find this time.

28. At the beginning of the Gold Rush, the population of Coyote Gulch, Arizona was 365. From then on, the population would have grown by a factor of $e$ each year, except for the high rate of "accidental" death, amounting to one victim per day among every 100 citizens. By solving an appropriate differential equation determine, as functions of time, (a) the actual population of Coyote Gulch $t$ years from the day the Gold Rush began, and (b) the cumulative number of fatalities.

29. With what speed should a rocket be fired upward so that it never returns to earth? (Neglect all forces except the earth's gravitational attraction.)

30. Let $y = f(x)$ be that solution of the differential equation

$$y' = \frac{2y^2 + x}{3y^2 + 5}$$

which satisfies the initial condition $f(0) = 0$. (Do not attempt to solve this differential equation.)
(a) The differential equation shows that $f'(0) = 0$. Discuss whether $f$ has a relative maximum or minimum or neither at 0.
(b) Notice that $f'(x) \geq 0$ for each $x \geq 0$ and that $f'(x) \geq \frac{2}{3}$ for each $x \geq \frac{10}{3}$. Exhibit two positive numbers $a$ and $b$ such that $f(x) > ax - b$ for each $x \geq \frac{10}{3}$.
(c) Show that $x/y^2 \to 0$ as $x \to +\infty$. Give full details of your reasoning.
(d) Show that $y/x$ tends to a finite limit as $x \to +\infty$ and determine this limit.

31. Given a function $f$ which satisfies the differential equation

$$xf''(x) + 3x[f'(x)]^2 = 1 - e^{-x}$$

for all real $x$. (Do not attempt to solve this differential equation.)
(a) If $f$ has an extremum at a point $c \neq 0$, show that this extremum is a minimum.
(b) If $f$ has an extremum at 0, is it a maximum or a minimum? Justify your conclusion.
(c) If $f(0) = f'(0) = 0$, find the *smallest* constant $A$ such that $f(x) \leq Ax^2$ for all $x \geq 0$.

# 9

# COMPLEX NUMBERS

## 9.1 Historical introduction

The quadratic equation $x^2 + 1 = 0$ has no solution in the real-number system because there is no real number whose square is $-1$. New types of numbers, called *complex numbers*, have been introduced to provide solutions to such equations. In this brief chapter we discuss complex numbers and show that they are important in solving algebraic equations and that they have an impact on differential and integral calculus.

As early as the 16th century, a symbol $\sqrt{-1}$ was introduced to provide solutions of the quadratic equation $x^2 + 1 = 0$. This symbol, later denoted by the letter $i$, was regarded as a fictitious or imaginary number which could be manipulated algebraically like an ordinary real number, except that its square was $-1$. Thus, for example, the quadratic polynomial $x^2 + 1$ was factored by writing $x^2 + 1 = x^2 - i^2 = (x - i)(x + i)$, and the solutions of the equation $x^2 + 1 = 0$ were exhibited as $x = \pm i$, without any concern regarding the meaning or validity of such formulas. Expressions such as $2 + 3i$ were called complex numbers, and they were used in a purely formal way for nearly 300 years before they were described in a manner that would be considered satisfactory by present-day standards.

Early in the 19th century, Karl Friedrich Gauss (1777–1855) and William Rowan Hamilton (1805–1865) independently and almost simultaneously proposed the idea of defining complex numbers as ordered pairs $(a, b)$ of real numbers endowed with certain special properties. This idea is widely accepted today and is described in the next section.

## 9.2 Definitions and field properties

DEFINITION. *If $a$ and $b$ are real numbers, the pair $(a, b)$ is called a complex number, provided that equality, addition, and multiplication of pairs is defined as follows:*
(a) *Equality:* $(a, b) = (c, d)$ *means* $a = c$ *and* $b = d$.
(b) *Sum:* $(a, b) + (c, d) = (a + c, b + d)$.
(c) *Product:* $(a, b)(c, d) = (ac - bd, ad + bc)$.

The definition of equality tells us that the pair $(a, b)$ is to be regarded as an *ordered* pair. Thus, the complex number $(2, 3)$ is not equal to the complex number $(3, 2)$. The numbers *a* and *b* are called *components* of $(a, b)$. The first component, *a*, is also called the *real part* of the complex number; the second component, *b*, is called the *imaginary part*.

Note that the symbol $i = \sqrt{-1}$ does not appear anywhere in this definition. Presently we shall introduce *i* as a particular complex number which has all the algebraic properties ascribed to the fictitious symbol $\sqrt{-1}$ by the early mathematicians. However, before we do this, we will discuss the basic properties of the operations just defined.

THEOREM 9.1. *The operations of addition and multiplication of complex numbers satisfy the commutative, associative and distributive laws. That is, if x, y, and z are arbitrary complex numbers, we have the following.*

*Commutative laws:* $x + y = y + x$, $\quad xy = yx$.

*Associative laws:* $x + (y + z) = (x + y) + z$, $\quad x(yz) = (xy)z$.

*Distributive law:* $x(y + z) = xy + xz$.

*Proof.* All these laws are easily verified directly from the definition of sum and product. For example, to prove the associative law for multiplication, we write $x = (x_1, x_2)$, $y = (y_1, y_2)$, $z = (z_1, z_2)$ and note that

$$x(yz) = (x_1, x_2)(y_1z_1 - y_2z_2, y_1z_2 + y_2z_1)$$
$$= (x_1(y_1z_1 - y_2z_2) - x_2(y_1z_2 + y_2z_1), x_1(y_1z_2 + y_2z_1) + x_2(y_1z_1 - y_2z_2))$$
$$= ((x_1y_1 - x_2y_2)z_1 - (x_1y_2 + x_2y_1)z_2, (x_1y_2 + x_2y_1)z_1 + (x_1y_1 - x_2y_2)z_2)$$
$$= (x_1y_1 - x_2y_2, x_1y_2 + x_2y_1)(z_1, z_2) = (xy)z.$$

The commutative and distributive laws may be similarly proved.

Theorem 9.1 shows that the set of all complex numbers satisfies the first three field axioms for the real number system, as given in Section I 3.2. Now we will show that Axioms 4, 5, and 6 are also satisfied.

Since $(0, 0) + (a, b) = (a, b)$ for all complex numbers $(a, b)$, the complex number $(0, 0)$ is an identity element for addition. It is called the zero complex number. Similarly, the complex number $(1, 0)$ is an identity for multiplication because

$$(a, b)(1, 0) = (a, b)$$

for all $(a, b)$. Thus, Axiom 4 is satisfied with $(0, 0)$ as the identity for addition and $(1, 0)$ as the identity for multiplication.

To verify Axiom 5, we simply note that $(-a, -b) + (a, b) = (0, 0)$, so $(-a, -b)$ is the negative of $(a, b)$. We write $-(a, b)$ for $(-a, -b)$.

Finally, we show that each nonzero complex number has a reciprocal relative to the identity element $(1, 0)$. That is, if $(a, b) \neq (0, 0)$, there is a complex number $(c, d)$ such that

$$(a, b)(c, d) = (1, 0).$$

In fact, this equation is equivalent to the pair of equations

$$ac - bd = 1, \quad ad + bc = 0,$$

which has the unique solution

$$(9.1) \qquad c = \frac{a}{a^2 + b^2}, \qquad d = \frac{-b}{a^2 + b^2}.$$

The condition $(a, b) \neq (0, 0)$ ensures that $a^2 + b^2 \neq 0$, so the reciprocal is well defined. We write $(a, b)^{-1}$ or $1/(a, b)$ for the reciprocal of $(a, b)$. Thus, we have

$$(9.2) \qquad \frac{1}{(a, b)} = \left( \frac{a}{a^2 + b^2}, \frac{-b}{a^2 + b^2} \right) \qquad \text{if} \quad (a, b) \neq (0, 0).$$

The foregoing discussion shows that the set of all complex numbers satisfies the six field axioms for the real-number system. Therefore, all the laws of algebra deducible from the field axioms also hold for complex numbers. In particular, Theorems I.1 through I.15 of Section I 3.2 are all valid for complex numbers as well as for real numbers. Theorem I.8 tells us that quotients of complex numbers exist. That is, if $(a, b)$ and $(c, d)$ are two complex numbers with $(a, b) \neq (0, 0)$, then there is exactly one complex number $(x, y)$ such that $(a, b)(x, y) = (c, d)$. In fact, we have $(x, y) = (c, d)(a, b)^{-1}$.

### 9.3 The complex numbers as an extension of the real numbers

Let $C$ denote the set of all complex numbers. Consider the subset $C_0$ of $C$ consisting of all complex numbers of the form $(a, 0)$, that is, all complex numbers with zero imaginary part. The sum or product of two members of $C_0$ is again in $C_0$. In fact, we have

$$(9.3) \qquad (a, 0) + (b, 0) = (a + b, 0) \qquad \text{and} \qquad (a, 0)(b, 0) = (ab, 0).$$

This shows that we can add or multiply two numbers in $C_0$ by adding or multiplying the real parts alone. Or, in other words, with respect to addition and multiplication, the numbers in $C_0$ act exactly as though they were real numbers. The same is true for subtraction and division, since $-(a, 0) = (-a, 0)$ and $(b, 0)^{-1} = (b^{-1}, 0)$ if $b \neq 0$. For this reason, we ordinarily make no distinction between the real number $x$ and the complex number $(x, 0)$ whose real part is $x$; we agree to identify $x$ and $(x, 0)$, and we write $x = (x, 0)$. In particular, we write $0 = (0, 0)$, $1 = (1, 0)$, $-1 = (-1, 0)$, and so on. Thus, we can think of the complex number system as an extension of the real number system.

The relation between $C_0$ and the real-number system can be described in a slightly different way. Let $R$ denote the set of all real numbers, and let $f$ denote the function which maps each real number $x$ onto the complex number $(x, 0)$. That is, if $x \in R$, let

$$f(x) = (x, 0).$$

The function $f$ so defined has domain $R$ and range $C_0$, and it maps distinct elements of $R$ onto distinct elements of $C_0$. Because of these properties, $f$ is said to establish a *one-to-one correspondence* between $R$ and $C_0$. The operations of addition and multiplication are preserved under this correspondence. That is, we have

$$f(a + b) = f(a) + f(b) \qquad \text{and} \qquad f(ab) = f(a)f(b),$$

these equations being merely a restatement of (9.3). Since $R$ satisfies the six field axioms, the same is true of $\mathbf{C}_0$. The two fields $\mathbf{R}$ and $\mathbf{C}_0$ are said to be *isomorphic*; the function $f$ which relates them as described above is called an *isomorphism*. As far as the algebraic operations of addition and multiplication are concerned, we make no distinction between isomorphic fields. That is why we identify the real number $x$ with the complex number $(x, 0)$. The complex-number system $\mathbf{C}$ is called an *extension* of the real-number system $\mathbf{R}$ because it contains a subset $\mathbf{C}_0$ which is isomorphic to $\mathbf{R}$.

The field $\mathbf{C}_0$ can also be *ordered* in such a way that the three order axioms of Section I 3.4 are satisfied. In fact, we simply define $(x, 0)$ to be positive if and only if $x > 0$. It is trivial to verify that Axioms 7, 8, and 9 are satisfied, so $\mathbf{C}_0$ is an *ordered* field. The isomorphism $f$ described above also preserves order since it maps the positive elements of $\mathbf{R}$ onto the positive elements of $\mathbf{C}_0$.

## 9.4 The imaginary unit $i$

Complex numbers have some algebraic properties not possessed by real numbers. For example, the quadratic equation $x^2 + 1 = 0$, which has no solution among the real numbers, can now be solved with the use of complex numbers. In fact, the complex number $(0, 1)$ is a solution, since we have

$$(0, 1)^2 = (0, 1)(0, 1) = (0 \cdot 0 - 1 \cdot 1, 0 \cdot 1 + 1 \cdot 0) = (-1, 0) = -1 .$$

The complex number $(0, 1)$ is denoted by $i$ and is called the *imaginary unit*. It has the property that its square is $-1$, $i^2 = -1$. The reader can easily verify that $(-i)^2 = -1$, so $x = -i$ is another solution of the equation $x^2 + 1 = 0$.

Now we can relate the ordered-pair idea with the notation used by the early mathematicians. First we note that the definition of multiplication of complex numbers gives us $(b, 0)(0, 1) = (0, b)$, and hence we have

$$(a, b) = (a, 0) + (0, b) = (a, 0) + (b, 0)(0, 1) .$$

Therefore, if we write $a = (a, 0)$, $b = (b, 0)$, and $i = (0, 1)$, we get $(a, b) = a + bi$. In other words, we have proved the following.

THEOREM 9.2. *Every complex number $(a, b)$ can be expressed in the form $(a, b) = a + bi$.*

The advantage of this notation is that it aids us in algebraic manipulations of formulas involving addition and multiplication. For example, if we multiply $a + bi$ by $c + di$, using the distributive and associative laws, and replace $i^2$ by $-1$, we find that

$$(a + bi)(c + di) = ac - bd + (ad + bc)i ,$$

which, of course, is in agreement with the definition of multiplication. Similarly, to compute the reciprocal of a nonzero complex number $a + bi$, we may write

$$\frac{1}{a + bi} = \frac{a - bi}{(a + bi)(a - bi)} = \frac{a - bi}{a^2 + b^2} = \frac{a}{a^2 + b^2} - \frac{bi}{a^2 + b^2} .$$

This formula is in agreement with that given in (9.2).

By the introduction of complex numbers, we have gained much more than the ability to solve the simple quadratic equation $x^2 + 1 = 0$. Consider, for example, the quadratic equation $ax^2 + bx + c = 0$, where $a$, $b$, $c$ are real and $a \neq 0$. By completing the square, we may write this equation in the form

$$\left(x + \frac{b}{2a}\right)^2 + \frac{4ac - b^2}{4a^2} = 0.$$

If $4ac - b^2 \leq 0$, the equation has the real roots $(-b \pm \sqrt{b^2 - 4ac})/(2a)$. If $4ac - b^2 > 0$, the left member is positive for every real $x$ and the equation has no real roots. In this case, however, there are two complex roots, given by the formulas

$$(9.4) \qquad r_1 = -\frac{b}{2a} + i\frac{\sqrt{4ac - b^2}}{2a} \qquad \text{and} \qquad r_2 = -\frac{b}{2a} - i\frac{\sqrt{4ac - b^2}}{2a}.$$

In 1799, Gauss proved that every polynomial equation of the form

$$a_0 + a_1 x + a_2 x^2 + \cdots + a_n x^n = 0,$$

where $a_0, a_1, \ldots, a_n$ are arbitrary real numbers, with $a_n \neq 0$, has a solution among the complex numbers if $n \geq 1$. Moreover, even if the coefficients $a_0, a_1, \ldots, a_n$ are complex, a solution exists in the complex-number system. This fact is known as the *fundamental theorem of algebra*.† It shows that there is no need to construct numbers more general than complex numbers to solve polynomial equations with complex coefficients.

## 9.5 Geometric interpretation. Modulus and argument

Since a complex number $(x, y)$ is an ordered pair of real numbers, it may be represented geometrically by a point in the plane, or by an arrow or geometric vector from the origin to the point $(x, y)$, as shown in Figure 9.1. In this context, the $xy$-plane is often referred to as the complex plane. The $x$-axis is called the real axis; the $y$-axis is the imaginary axis. It is customary to use the words *complex number* and *point* interchangeably. Thus, we refer to the point $z$ rather than the point corresponding to the complex number $z$.

The operations of addition and subtraction of complex numbers have a simple geometric interpretation. If two complex numbers $z_1$ and $z_2$ are represented by arrows from the origin to $z_1$ and $z_2$, respectively, then the sum $z_1 + z_2$ is determined by the *parallelogram law*. The arrow from the origin to $z_1 + z_2$ is a diagonal of the parallelogram determined by $0$, $z_1$, and $z_2$, as illustrated by the example in Figure 9.2. The other diagonal is related to the difference of $z_1$ and $z_2$. The arrow from $z_1$ to $z_2$ is parallel to and equal in length to the arrow from $0$ to $z_2 - z_1$; the arrow in the opposite direction, from $z_2$ to $z_1$, is related in the same way to $z_1 - z_2$.

---

† A proof of the fundamental theorem of algebra can be found in almost any book on the theory of functions of a complex variable. For example, see K. Knopp, *Theory of Functions*, Dover Publications, New York, 1945, or E. Hille, *Analytic Function Theory*, Vol. I, Blaisdell Publishing Co., 1959. A more elementary proof is given in O. Schreier and E. Sperner, *Introduction to Modern Algebra and Matrix Theory*, Chelsea Publishing Company, New York, 1951.

If $(x, y) \neq (0, 0)$, we can express $x$ and $y$ in polar coordinates,

$$x = r \cos \theta, \qquad y = r \sin \theta,$$

and we obtain

(9.5) $$x + iy = r (\cos \theta + i \sin \theta).$$

The positive number $r$, which represents the distance of $(x, y)$ from the origin, is called the *modulus* or *absolute value* of $x + iy$ and is denoted by $|x + iy|$. Thus, we have

$$|x + iy| = \sqrt{x^2 + y^2}.$$

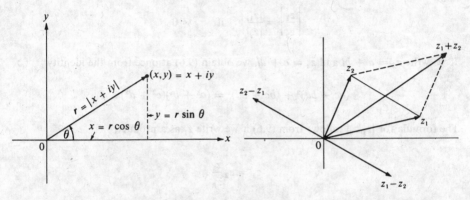

FIGURE 9.1   Geometric representation of the complex number $x + iy$.

FIGURE 9.2   Addition and subtraction of complex numbers represented geometrically by the parallelogram law.

The polar angle $\theta$ is called an *argument* of $x + iy$. We say *an* argument rather than *the* argument because for a given point $(x, y)$ the angle $\theta$ is determined only up to multiples of $2\pi$. Sometimes it is desirable to assign a unique argument to a complex number. This may be done by restricting $\theta$ to lie in a half-open interval of length $2\pi$. The intervals $[0, 2\pi)$ and $(-\pi, \pi]$ are commonly used for this purpose. We shall use the interval $(-\pi, \pi]$ and refer to the corresponding $\theta$ as the *principal argument* of $x + iy$; we denote this $\theta$ by $\arg (x + iy)$. Thus, if $x + iy \neq 0$ and $r = |x + iy|$, we define $\arg (x + iy)$ to be the unique real $\theta$ satisfying the conditions

$$x = r \cos \theta, \qquad y = r \sin \theta, \qquad -\pi < \theta \leq \pi.$$

For the zero complex number, we assign the modulus 0 and agree that any real $\theta$ may be used as an argument.

Since the absolute value of a complex number $z$ is simply the length of a line segment, it is not surprising to find that it has the usual properties of absolute values of real numbers. For example, we have

$$|z| > 0 \quad \text{if} \quad z \neq 0, \quad \text{and} \quad |z_1 - z_2| = |z_2 - z_1|.$$

Geometrically, the absolute value $|z_1 - z_2|$ represents the distance between the points $z_1$ and $z_2$ in the complex plane. The triangle inequality

$$|z_1 + z_2| \le |z_1| + |z_2|$$

is also valid. In addition, we have the following formulas for absolute values of products and quotients of complex numbers:

(9.6)                                      $$|z_1 z_2| = |z_1| \, |z_2|$$

and

$$\left| \frac{z_1}{z_2} \right| = \frac{|z_1|}{|z_2|} \quad \text{if} \quad z_2 \ne 0 \,.$$

If we write $z_1 = a + bi$ and $z_2 = c + di$, we obtain (9.6) at once from the identity

$$(ac - bd)^2 + (bc + ad)^2 = (a^2 + b^2)(c^2 + d^2) \,.$$

The formula for $|z_1/z_2|$ follows from (9.6) if we write $z_1$ as a product,

$$z_1 = z_2 \frac{z_1}{z_2} \,.$$

If $z = x + iy$, the *complex conjugate* of $z$ is the complex number $\bar{z} = x - iy$. Geometrically, $\bar{z}$ represents the reflection of $z$ through the real axis. The definition of conjugate implies that

$$\overline{z_1 + z_2} = \bar{z}_1 + \bar{z}_2 \,, \qquad \overline{z_1 z_2} = \bar{z}_1 \bar{z}_2 \,, \qquad \overline{z_1/z_2} = \bar{z}_1/\bar{z}_2 \,, \qquad z\bar{z} = |z|^2 \,.$$

The verification of these properties is left as an exercise for the reader.

If a quadratic equation with real coefficients has no real roots, its complex roots, given by (9.4), are conjugates. Conversely, if $r_1$ and $r_2$ are complex conjugates, say $r_1 = \alpha + i\beta$ and $r_2 = \alpha - i\beta$, where $\alpha$ and $\beta$ are real, then $r_1$ and $r_2$ are roots of a quadratic equation with real coefficients. In fact, we have

$$r_1 + r_2 = 2\alpha \quad \text{and} \quad r_1 r_2 = \alpha^2 + \beta^2 \,,$$

so

$$(x - r_1)(x - r_2) = x^2 - (r_1 + r_2)x + r_1 r_2 \,,$$

and the quadratic equation in question is

$$x^2 - 2\alpha x + \alpha^2 + \beta^2 = 0 \,.$$

## 9.6  Exercises

1. Express the following complex numbers in the form $a + bi$.
   (a) $(1 + i)^2$.
   (b) $1/i$.
   (c) $1/(1 + i)$.
   (d) $(2 + 3i)(3 - 4i)$.
   (e) $(1 + i)/(1 - 2i)$.
   (f) $i^5 + i^{16}$.
   (g) $1 + i + i^2 + i^3$.
   (h) $\frac{1}{2}(1 + i)(1 + i^{-8})$.

2. Compute the absolute values of the following complex numbers.
   (a) $1 + i$.
   (b) $3 + 4i$.
   (c) $(1 + i)/(1 - i)$.
   (d) $1 + i + i^2$.
   (e) $i^7 + i^{10}$.
   (f) $2(1 - i) + 3(2 + i)$.

3. Compute the modulus and principal argument of each of the following complex numbers.
   (a) $2i$.
   (b) $-3i$.
   (c) $-1$.
   (d) $1$.
   (e) $-3 + \sqrt{3}\, i$.
   (f) $(1 + i)/\sqrt{2}$.
   (g) $(-1 + i)^3$.
   (h) $(-1 - i)^3$.
   (i) $1/(1 + i)$.
   (j) $1/(1 + i)^2$.

4. In each case, determine all real numbers $x$ and $y$ which satisfy the given relation.
   (a) $x + iy = x - iy$.
   (b) $x + iy = |x + iy|$.
   (c) $|x + iy| = |x - iy|$.
   (d) $(x + iy)^2 = (x - iy)^2$.
   (e) $\dfrac{x + iy}{x - iy} = x - iy$.
   (f) $\displaystyle\sum_{k=0}^{100} i^k = x + iy$.

5. Make a sketch showing the set of all $z$ in the complex plane which satisfy each of the following conditions.
   (a) $|z| < 1$.
   (b) $z + \bar{z} = 1$.
   (c) $z - \bar{z} = i$.
   (d) $|z - 1| = |z + 1|$.
   (e) $|z - i| = |z + i|$.
   (f) $z + \bar{z} = |z|^2$.

6. Let $f$ be a polynomial with real coefficients.
   (a) Show that $\overline{f(z)} = f(\bar{z})$ for every complex $z$.
   (b) Use part (a) to deduce that the nonreal zeros of $f$ (if any exist) must occur in pairs of conjugate complex numbers.

7. Prove that an ordering relation cannot be introduced in the complex number system so that all three order axioms of Section I3.4 are satisfied.

   [*Hint:* Assume that such an ordering can be introduced and try to decide whether the imaginary unit $i$ is positive or negative.]

8. Define the following "pseudo-ordering" among the complex numbers. If $z = x + iy$, we say that $z$ is positive if and only if $x > 0$. Which of the order axioms of Section I3.4 are satisfied with this definition of positive?

9. Solve Exercise 8 if the pseudo-ordering is defined as follows: We say that $z$ is positive if and only if $|z| > 0$.

10. Solve Exercise 8 if the pseudo-ordering is defined as follows: If $z = x + iy$, we say that $z$ is positive if and only if $x > y$.

11. Make a sketch showing the set of all complex $z$ which satisfy each of the following conditions.
    (a) $|2z + 3| < 1$.
    (b) $|z + 1| < |z - 1|$.
    (c) $|z - i| \le |z + i|$.
    (d) $|z| \le |2z + 1|$.

12. Let $w = (az + b)/(cz + d)$, where $a$, $b$, $c$, and $d$ are real. Prove that

$$w - \bar{w} = (ad - bc)(z - \bar{z})/|cz + d|^2.$$

If $ad - bc > 0$, prove that the imaginary parts of $z$ and $w$ have the same sign.

### 9.7  Complex exponentials

We wish now to extend the definition of $e^x$ so that it becomes meaningful when $x$ is replaced by any complex number $z$. We wish this extension to be such that the law of exponents, $e^a e^b = e^{a+b}$, will be valid for all complex $a$ and $b$. And, of course, we want $e^z$ to agree with the usual exponential when $z$ is real. There are several equivalent ways to carry out this extension. Before we state the definition of $e^z$ that we have chosen, we shall give a heuristic discussion which will serve as motivation for this definition.

If we write $z = x + iy$, then, if the law of exponents is to be valid for complex numbers, we must have

$$e^z = e^{x+iy} = e^x e^{iy}.$$

Since $e^x$ has already been defined when $x$ is real, our task is to arrive at a reasonable definition for $e^{iy}$ when $y$ is real. Now, if $e^{iy}$ is to be a complex number, we may write

$$(9.7) \qquad\qquad e^{iy} = A(y) + iB(y),$$

where $A$ and $B$ are real-valued functions to be determined. Let us differentiate both sides of Equation (9.7), assuming $A$ and $B$ are differentiable, and treating the complex number $i$ as though it were a real number. Then we get

$$(9.8) \qquad\qquad ie^{iy} = A'(y) + iB'(y).$$

Differentiating once more, we find that

$$-e^{iy} = A''(y) + iB''(y).$$

Comparison of this equation with (9.7) shows that $A$ and $B$ must satisfy the equations

$$A''(y) = -A(y) \quad \text{and} \quad B''(y) = -B(y).$$

In other words, each of the functions $A$ and $B$ is a solution of the differential equation $f'' + f = 0$. From the work of Chapter 8, we know that this equation has exactly one solution with specified initial values $f(0)$ and $f'(0)$. If we put $y = 0$ in (9.7) and (9.8) and use the fact that $e^0 = 1$, we find that $A$ and $B$ have the initial values

$$A(0) = 1, \qquad A'(0) = 0, \quad \text{and} \quad B(0) = 0, \qquad B'(0) = 1.$$

By the uniqueness theorem for second-order differential equations with constant coefficients, we must have

$$A(y) = \cos y \quad \text{and} \quad B(y) = \sin y.$$

In other words, if $e^{iy}$ is to be a complex number with the properties just described, then we must have $e^{iy} = \cos y + i \sin y$. This discussion serves to motivate the following definition.

DEFINITION. *If $z = x + iy$, we define $e^z$ to be the complex number given by the equation*

(9.9) $$e^z = e^x(\cos y + i \sin y).$$

Note that $e^z = e^x$ when $y = 0$; hence this exponential agrees with the usual exponential when $z$ is real. Now we shall use this definition to deduce the law of exponents.

THEOREM 9.3. *If $a$ and $b$ are complex numbers, we have*

(9.10) $$e^a e^b = e^{a+b}.$$

*Proof.* Writing $a = x + iy$ and $b = u + iv$, we have

$$e^a = e^x(\cos y + i \sin y), \qquad e^b = e^u(\cos v + i \sin v),$$

so

$$e^a e^b = e^x e^u[\cos y \cos v - \sin y \sin v + i(\cos y \sin v + \sin y \cos v)].$$

Now we use the addition formulas for $\cos(y + v)$ and $\sin(y + v)$ and the law of exponents for real exponentials, and we see that the foregoing equation becomes

(9.11) $$e^a e^b = e^{x+u}[\cos(y + v) + i \sin(y + v)].$$

Since $a + b = (x + u) + i(y + v)$, the right member of (9.11) is $e^{a+b}$. This proves (9.10).

THEOREM 9.4. *Every complex number $z \neq 0$ can be expressed in the form*

(9.12) $$z = re^{i\theta},$$

*where $r = |z|$ and $\theta = \arg(z) + 2n\pi$, $n$ being any integer. This representation is called the polar form of $z$.*

*Proof.* If $z = x + iy$, the polar-coordinate representation (9.5) gives us

$$z = r(\cos \theta + i \sin \theta),$$

where $r = |z|$ and $\theta = \arg(z) + 2n\pi$, $n$ being any integer. But if we take $x = 0$ and $y = \theta$ in (9.9), we obtain the formula

$$e^{i\theta} = \cos \theta + i \sin \theta,$$

which proves (9.12).

The representation of complex numbers in the polar form (9.12) is especially useful in connection with multiplication and division of complex numbers. For example, if $z_1 = r_1 e^{i\theta}$ and $z_2 = r_2 e^{i\phi}$, we have

(9.13) $$z_1 z_2 = r_1 e^{i\theta} r_2 e^{i\phi} = r_1 r_2 e^{i(\theta+\phi)}.$$

Therefore the product of the moduli, $r_1 r_2$, is the modulus of the product $z_1 z_2$, in agreement with Equation (9.6), and the sum of the arguments, $\theta + \phi$, is an admissible argument for the product $z_1 z_2$.

When $z = re^{i\theta}$, repeated application of (9.13) gives us the formula

$$z^n = r^n e^{in\theta} = r^n(\cos n\theta + i \sin n\theta),$$

valid for any nonnegative integer $n$. This formula is also valid for negative integers $n$ if we define $z^{-m}$ to be $(z^{-1})^m$ when $m$ is a positive integer.

Similarly, we have

$$\frac{z_1}{z_2} = \frac{r_1 e^{i\theta}}{r_2 e^{i\phi}} = \frac{r_1}{r_2} e^{i(\theta-\phi)},$$

so the modulus of $z_1/z_2$ is $r_1/r_2$ and the difference $\theta - \phi$ is an admissible argument for $z_1/z_2$.

## 9.8 Complex-valued functions

A function $f$ whose values are complex numbers is called a complex-valued function. If the domain of $f$ is a set of real numbers, $f$ is called a complex-valued function of a real variable. If the domain is a set of complex numbers, $f$ is called a complex-valued function of a complex variable, or more simply, a function of a complex variable. An example is the exponential function, defined by the equation

$$f(z) = e^z$$

for all complex $z$. Most of the familiar elementary functions of calculus, such as the exponential, the logarithm, and the trigonometric functions, can be extended to become functions of a complex variable. (See Exercises 9 and 10 in Section 9.10.) In this more general framework many new properties and interrelationships are often revealed. For example, the complex exponential function is periodic. In fact, if $z = x + iy$ and if $n$ is any integer, we have

$$e^{z+2n\pi i} = e^x[\cos (y + 2n\pi) + i \sin (y + 2n\pi)] = e^x(\cos y + i \sin y) = e^z.$$

Thus we see that $f(z + 2n\pi i) = f(z)$, so $f$ has the period $2\pi i$. This property of the exponential function is revealed only when we study the exponential as a function of a complex variable.

The first systematic treatment of the differential and integral calculus of functions of a complex variable was given by Cauchy early in the 19th century. Since then the theory has developed into one of the most important and interesting branches of mathematics. It has become an indispensable tool for physicists and engineers and has connections in nearly every branch of pure mathematics. A discussion of this theory will not be given here. We shall discuss only the rudiments of the calculus of complex-valued functions of a real variable.

Suppose $f$ is a complex-valued function defined on some interval $I$ of real numbers. For each $x$ in $I$, the function value $f(x)$ is a complex number, so we can write

$$f(x) = u(x) + iv(x),$$

where $u(x)$ and $v(x)$ are real. This equation determines two real-valued functions $u$ and $v$ called, respectively, the real and imaginary parts of $f$; we write the equation more briefly as $f = u + iv$. Concepts such as continuity, differentiation, and integration of $f$ may be defined in terms of the corresponding concepts for $u$ and $v$, as described in the following definition.

DEFINITION. *If $f = u + iv$, we say $f$ is continuous at a point if both $u$ and $v$ are continuous at that point. The derivative of $f$ is defined by the equation*

$$f'(x) = u'(x) + iv'(x)$$

*whenever both derivatives $u'(x)$ and $v'(x)$ exist. Similarly, we define the integral of $f$ by the equation*

$$\int_a^b f(x)\, dx = \int_a^b u(x)\, dx + i \int_a^b v(x)\, dx$$

*whenever both integrals on the right exist.*

In view of this definition, it is not surprising to find that many of the theorems of differential and integral calculus are also valid for complex-valued functions. For example, the rules for differentiating sums, products, and quotients (Theorem 4.1) are valid for complex functions. The first and second fundamental theorems of calculus (Theorems 5.1 and 5.3) as well as the zero-derivative theorem (Theorem 5.2) also hold for complex functions. To illustrate the ease with which these theorems can be proved, we consider the zero-derivative theorem:

*If $f'(x) = 0$ for all $x$ on an open interval $I$, then $f$ is constant on $I$.*

*Proof.* Write $f = u + iv$. Since $f' = u' + iv'$, the statement $f' = 0$ on $I$ means that both $u'$ and $v'$ are zero on $I$. Hence, by Theorem 5.2, both $u$ and $v$ are constant on $I$. Therefore $f$ is constant on $I$.

## 9.9 Examples of differentiation and integration formulas

In this section we discuss an important example of a complex-valued function of a real variable, namely the function $f$ defined for all real $x$ by the equation

$$f(x) = e^{tx},$$

where $t$ is a fixed complex number. When $t$ is real, the derivative of this function is given by the formula $f'(x) = te^{tx}$. Now we prove that this formula is also valid for complex $t$.

THEOREM 9.5.    *If $f(x) = e^{tx}$ for all real $x$ and a fixed complex $t$, then $f'(x) = te^{tx}$.*

*Proof.* Write $t = \alpha + i\beta$, where $\alpha$ and $\beta$ are real. From the definition of the complex exponential, we have

$$f(x) = e^{tx} = e^{\alpha x + i\beta x} = e^{\alpha x} \cos \beta x + i e^{\alpha x} \sin \beta x\,.$$

Therefore, the real and imaginary parts of $f$ are given by

(9.14)                     $u(x) = e^{\alpha x} \cos \beta x$     and     $v(x) = e^{\alpha x} \sin \beta x\,.$

These functions are differentiable for all $x$ and their derivatives are given by the formulas

$$u'(x) = \alpha e^{\alpha x} \cos \beta x - \beta e^{\alpha x} \sin \beta x\,, \qquad v'(x) = \alpha e^{\alpha x} \sin \beta x + \beta e^{\alpha x} \cos \beta x\,.$$

Since $f'(x) = u'(x) + iv'(x)$, we have

$$f'(x) = \alpha e^{\alpha x}(\cos \beta x + i \sin \beta x) + i\beta e^{\alpha x}(\cos \beta x + i \sin \beta x)$$
$$= (\alpha + i\beta)e^{(\alpha + i\beta)x} = te^{tx}\,.$$

This completes the proof.

Theorem 9.5 has some interesting consequences. For example, if we adopt the Leibniz notation for indefinite integrals, we can restate Theorem 9.5 in the form

(9.15)                                     $$\int e^{tx}\, dx = \frac{e^{tx}}{t}$$

when $t \neq 0$. If we let $t = \alpha + i\beta$ and equate the real and imaginary parts of Equation (9.15), we obtain the integration formulas

$$\int e^{\alpha x} \cos \beta x\, dx = \frac{e^{\alpha x}(\alpha \cos \beta x + \beta \sin \beta x)}{\alpha^2 + \beta^2}$$

and

$$\int e^{\alpha x} \sin \beta x\, dx = \frac{e^{\alpha x}(\alpha \sin \beta x - \beta \cos \beta x)}{\alpha^2 + \beta^2}\,,$$

which are valid if $\alpha$ and $\beta$ are not both zero.

Another consequence of Theorem 9.5 is the connection between complex exponentials and second-order linear differential equations with constant coefficients.

THEOREM 9.6.    *Consider the differential equation*

(9.16)                                 $$y'' + ay' + by = 0\,,$$

*where $a$ and $b$ are real constants. The real and imaginary parts of the function $f$ defined on*

$(-\infty, +\infty)$ *by the equation* $f(x) = e^{tx}$ *are solutions of the differential equation* (9.16) *if and only if t is a root of the characteristic equation*

$$t^2 + at + b = 0.$$

*Proof.* Let $L(y) = y'' + ay' + by$. Since $f'(x) = te^{tx}$, we also have $f''(x) = t^2e^{tx}$, so $L(f) = e^{tx}(t^2 + at + b)$. But $e^{tx}$ is never zero since $e^{tx}e^{-tx} = e^0 = 1$. Hence, $L(f) = 0$ if and only if $t^2 + at + b = 0$. But if we write $f = u + iv$, we find $L(f) = L(u) + iL(v)$, and hence $L(f) = 0$ if and only if both $L(u) = 0$ and $L(v) = 0$. This completes the proof.

*Note:* If $t = \alpha + i\beta$, the real and imaginary parts of $f$ are given by (9.14). If the characteristic equation has two distinct roots, real or complex, the linear combination

$$y = c_1u(x) + c_2v(x)$$

is the general solution of the differential equation. This agrees with the results proved in Theorem 8.7.

Further examples of complex functions are discussed in the next set of exercises.

## 9.10 Exercises

1. Express each of the following complex numbers in the form $a + bi$.
   (a) $e^{\pi i/2}$.
   (b) $2e^{-\pi i/2}$.
   (c) $3e^{\pi i}$.
   (d) $-e^{-\pi i}$.
   (e) $i + e^{2\pi i}$.
   (f) $e^{\pi i/4}$.
   (g) $e^{\pi i/4} - e^{-\pi i/4}$.
   (h) $\dfrac{1 - e^{\pi i/2}}{1 + e^{\pi i/2}}$.

2. In each case, find all real $x$ and $y$ that satisfy the given relation.
   (a) $x + iy = xe^{iy}$.
   (b) $x + iy = ye^{ix}$.
   (c) $e^{x+iy} = -1$.
   (d) $\dfrac{1 + i}{1 - i} = xe^{iy}$.

3. (a) Prove that $e^z \neq 0$ for all complex $z$.
   (b) Find all complex $z$ for which $e^z = 1$.

4. (a) If $\theta$ is real, show that

$$\cos \theta = \frac{e^{i\theta} + e^{-i\theta}}{2} \quad \text{and} \quad \sin \theta = \frac{e^{i\theta} - e^{-i\theta}}{2i}.$$

   (b) Use the formulas in (a) to deduce the identities

$$\cos^2 \theta = \tfrac{1}{2}(1 + \cos 2\theta), \qquad \sin^2 \theta = \tfrac{1}{2}(1 - \cos 2\theta).$$

5. (a) Prove *DeMoivre's theorem*,

$$(\cos \theta + i \sin \theta)^n = \cos n\theta + i \sin n\theta,$$

   valid for every real $\theta$ and every positive integer $n$.
   (b) Take $n = 3$ in part (a) and deduce the trigonometric identities

$$\sin 3\theta = 3 \cos^2 \theta \sin \theta - \sin^3 \theta, \qquad \cos 3\theta = \cos^3 \theta - 3 \cos \theta \sin^2 \theta.$$

6. Prove that every trigonometric sum of the form

$$S_n(x) = \tfrac{1}{2}a_0 + \sum_{k=1}^{n} (a_k \cos kx + b_k \sin kx)$$

can be expressed as a sum of complex exponentials,

$$S_n(x) = \sum_{k=-n}^{n} c_k e^{ikx},$$

where $c_k = \tfrac{1}{2}(a_k - ib_k)$ for $k = 1, 2, \ldots, n$. Determine corresponding formulas for $c_{-k}$.

7. (a) If $m$ and $n$ are integers, prove that

$$\int_0^{2\pi} e^{inx} e^{-imx}\, dx = \begin{cases} 0 & \text{if } m \neq n, \\ 2\pi & \text{if } m = n. \end{cases}$$

(b) Use part (a) to deduce the orthogonality relations for the sine and cosine ($m$ and $n$ are integers, $m^2 \neq n^2$):

$$\int_0^{2\pi} \sin nx \cos mx\, dx = \int_0^{2\pi} \sin nx \sin mx\, dx = \int_0^{2\pi} \cos nx \cos mx\, dx = 0,$$

$$\int_0^{2\pi} \sin^2 nx\, dx = \int_0^{2\pi} \cos^2 nx\, dx = \pi \qquad \text{if } n \neq 0.$$

8. Given a complex number $z \neq 0$. Write $z = re^{i\theta}$, where $\theta = \arg(z)$. Let $z_1 = Re^{i\alpha}$, where $R = r^{1/n}$ and $\alpha = \theta/n$, and let $\epsilon = e^{2\pi i/n}$, where $n$ is a positive integer.
   (a) Show that $z_1^n = z$; that is, $z_1$ is an $n$th root of $z$.
   (b) Show that $z$ has exactly $n$ distinct $n$th roots,

$$z_1,\, \epsilon z_1,\, \epsilon^2 z_1,\, \ldots,\, \epsilon^{n-1} z_1,$$

and that they are equally spaced on a circle of radius $R$.
   (c) Determine the three cube roots of $i$.
   (d) Determine the four fourth roots of $i$.
   (e) Determine the four fourth roots of $-i$.

9. The definitions of the sine and cosine functions can be extended to the complex plane as follows:

$$\cos z = \frac{e^{iz} + e^{-iz}}{2}, \qquad \sin z = \frac{e^{iz} - e^{-iz}}{2i}.$$

When $z$ is real, these formulas agree with the ordinary sine and cosine functions. (See Exercise 4.) Use these formulas to deduce the following properties of complex sines and cosines. Here $u$, $v$, and $z$ denote complex numbers, with $z = x + iy$.
   (a) $\sin (u + v) = \sin u \cos v + \cos u \sin v$.
   (b) $\cos (u + v) = \cos u \cos v - \sin u \sin v$.
   (c) $\sin^2 z + \cos^2 z = 1$.
   (d) $\cos (iy) = \cosh y, \qquad \sin (iy) = i \sinh y$.
   (e) $\cos z = \cos x \cosh y - i \sin x \sinh y$.
   (f) $\sin z = \sin x \cosh y + i \cos x \sinh y$.

10. If $z$ is a nonzero complex number, we define Log $z$, the complex logarithm of $z$, by the equation

$$\text{Log } z = \log |z| + i \arg(z) .$$

When $z$ is real and positive, this formula agrees with the ordinary logarithm. Use this formula to deduce the following properties of complex logarithms.
   (a) $\text{Log}(-1) = \pi i, \quad \text{Log}(i) = \pi i/2$.
   (b) $\text{Log}(z_1 z_2) = \text{Log } z_1 + \text{Log } z_2 + 2n\pi i$, \quad where $n$ is an integer.
   (c) $\text{Log}(z_1/z_2) = \text{Log } z_1 - \text{Log } z_2 + 2n\pi i$, \quad where $n$ is an integer.
   (d) $e^{\text{Log } z} = z$.

11. If $w$ and $z$ are complex numbers, $z \neq 0$, we define $z^w$ by the equation

$$z^w = e^{w \, \text{Log } z} ,$$

where Log $z$ is defined as in Exercise 10.
   (a) Compute $1^i$, $i^i$, and $(-1)^i$.
   (b) Prove that $z^a z^b = z^{a+b}$ if $a$, $b$, and $z$ are complex, $z \neq 0$.
   (c) Note that the equation

(9.17) $$(z_1 z_2)^w = z_1^w z_2^w$$

is violated when $z_1 = z_2 = -1$ and $w = i$. What conditions on $z_1$ and $z_2$ are necessary for Equation (9.17) to hold for all complex $w$?

In Exercises 12 through 15, $L$ denotes the linear operator defined by $L(y) = y'' + ay' + by$, where $a$ and $b$ are real constants.

12. Prove that if $R$ is a complex-valued function, say $R(x) = P(x) + iQ(x)$, then a complex-valued function $f(x) = u(x) + iv(x)$ satisfies the differential equation $L(y) = R(x)$ on an interval $I$ if and only if $u$ and $v$ satisfy the equations $L(u) = P(x)$ and $L(v) = Q(x)$ on $I$.

13. If $A$ is complex and $\omega$ is real, prove that the differential equation $L(y) = Ae^{i\omega x}$ has a complex-valued solution of the form $y = Be^{i\omega x}$, provided that either $b \neq \omega^2$ or $a\omega \neq 0$. Express the complex number $B$ in terms of $a$, $b$, $A$, and $\omega$.

14. Assume $c$ is real and $b \neq \omega^2$. Use the results of Exercise 13 to prove that the differential equation $L(y) = c \cos \omega x$ has a particular solution of the form $y = A \cos(\omega x - \alpha)$, where

$$A = \frac{c}{\sqrt{(b - \omega^2)^2 + a^2 \omega^2}} \quad \text{and} \quad \tan \alpha = \frac{a\omega}{b - \omega^2} .$$

15. Assume $c$ is real and $b \neq \omega^2$. Prove that the differential equation $L(y) = c \sin \omega x$ has a particular solution of the form $y = A \sin(\omega x + \alpha)$ and express $A$ and $\alpha$ in terms of $a$, $b$, $c$, and $\omega$.

# 10

# SEQUENCES, INFINITE SERIES,
# IMPROPER INTEGRALS

## 10.1 Zeno's paradox

The principal subject matter of this chapter had its beginning nearly 2400 years ago when the Greek philosopher Zeno of Elea (495–435 B.C.) precipitated a crisis in ancient mathematics by setting forth a number of ingenious paradoxes. One of these, often called the *racecourse paradox*, may be described as follows:

A runner can never reach the end of a racecourse because he must cover half of any distance before he covers the whole. That is to say, having covered the first half he still has the second half before him. When half of this is covered, one-fourth yet remains. When half of this one-fourth is covered, there remains one-eighth, and so on, *ad infinitum*.

Zeno was referring, of course, to an idealized situation in which the runner is to be thought of as a particle or point moving from one end of a line segment to the other. We can formulate the paradox in another way. Assume that the runner starts at the point marked 1 in Figure 10.1 and runs toward the goal marked 0. The positions labeled $\frac{1}{2}$, $\frac{1}{4}$, $\frac{1}{8}$, etc., indicate the fraction of the course yet to be covered when these points are reached. These fractions, each of which is half the previous one, subdivide the whole course into an endless number of smaller portions. A positive amount of time is required to cover each portion separately, and the time required for the whole course is the sum total of all these amounts. To say that the runner can never reach the goal is to say that he never arrives there in a finite length of time; or, in other words, that the sum of an endless number of positive time intervals cannot possibly be finite.

This assertion was rejected 2000 years after Zeno's time when the theory of infinite series was created. In the 17th and 18th centuries, mathematicians began to realize that it *is* possible to extend the ideas of ordinary addition from *finite* collections of numbers to *infinite* collections so that sometimes infinitely many positive numbers have a finite "sum." To see how this extension might come about and to get an idea of some of the difficulties that might be encountered in making the extension, let us analyze Zeno's paradox in more detail.

Suppose the aforementioned runner travels at a *constant speed* and suppose it takes him $T$ minutes to cover the first half of the course. The next quarter of the course will take

$T/2$ minutes, the next eighth will take $T/4$ minutes, and, in general, the portion from $1/2^n$ to $1/2^{n+1}$ will take $T/2^n$ minutes. The "sum" of all these time intervals may be indicated symbolically by writing the following expression:

$$(10.1) \qquad T + \frac{T}{2} + \frac{T}{4} + \cdots + \frac{T}{2^n} + \cdots .$$

This is an example of what is known as an *infinite series*, and the problem here is to decide whether there is some reasonable way to assign a number which may be called the *sum* of this series.

Our physical experience tells us that a runner who travels at a constant speed should reach his goal in twice the time it takes for him to reach the halfway point. Since it takes

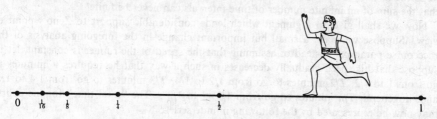

FIGURE 10.1   The racecourse paradox.

$T$ minutes to cover half the course, it should require $2T$ minutes for the whole course. This line of reasoning strongly suggests that we should assign the "sum" $2T$ to the series in (10.1), and it leads us to expect that the equation

$$(10.2) \qquad T + \frac{T}{2} + \frac{T}{4} + \cdots + \frac{T}{2^n} + \cdots = 2T$$

should be "true" in some sense.

The theory of infinite series tells us exactly how to interpret this equation. The idea is this: First we add a *finite number* of the terms, say the first $n$, and denote their sum by $s_n$. Thus we have

$$(10.3) \qquad s_n = T + \frac{T}{2} + \frac{T}{4} + \cdots + \frac{T}{2^{n-1}} .$$

This is called the *n*th *partial sum* of the series. Now we study the behavior of $s_n$ as $n$ takes larger and larger values. In particular, we try to determine whether the partial sums $s_n$ approach a finite limit as $n$ increases without bound.

In this example it is easy to see that $2T$ is the limiting value of the partial sums. In fact, if we calculate a few of these partial sums, we find that

$$s_1 = T, \qquad s_2 = T + \frac{T}{2} = \frac{3}{2}T, \qquad s_3 = T + \frac{T}{2} + \frac{T}{4} = \frac{7}{4}T,$$

$$s_4 = T + \frac{T}{2} + \frac{T}{4} + \frac{T}{8} = \frac{15}{8}T .$$

Now, observe that these results may be expressed as follows:

$$s_1 = (2 - 1)T, \qquad s_2 = (2 - \tfrac{1}{2})T, \qquad s_3 = (2 - \tfrac{1}{4})T, \qquad s_4 = (2 - \tfrac{1}{8})T.$$

This leads us to conjecture the following general formula:

$$(10.4) \qquad s_n = \left(2 - \frac{1}{2^{n-1}}\right)T \qquad \text{for all positive integers } n.$$

Formula (10.4) is easily verified by induction. Since $1/2^{n-1} \to 0$ as $n$ increases indefinitely, this shows that $s_n \to 2T$. Therefore, Equation (10.2) is "true" if we interpret it to mean that $2T$ is the *limit* of the partial sums $s_n$. This limit process seems to invalidate the assertion that the sum of an infinite number of time intervals can never be finite.

Now we shall give an argument which lends considerable support to Zeno's point of view. Suppose we make a small but important change in the foregoing analysis of the racecourse paradox. Instead of assuming that the speed of the runner is constant, let us suppose that his speed gradually decreases in such a way that he requires $T$ minutes to go from 1 to 1/2, $T/2$ minutes to go from 1/2 to 1/4, $T/3$ minutes to go from 1/4 to 1/8, and, in general, $T/n$ minutes to go from $1/2^{n-1}$ to $1/2^n$. The "total time" for the course may now be represented by the following infinite series:

$$(10.5) \qquad T + \frac{T}{2} + \frac{T}{3} + \cdots + \frac{T}{n} + \cdots.$$

In this case, our physical experience does not suggest any natural or obvious "sum" to assign to this series, and hence we must rely entirely on mathematical analysis to deal with this example.

Let us proceed as before and introduce the partial sums $s_n$. That is, let

$$(10.6) \qquad s_n = T + \frac{T}{2} + \frac{T}{3} + \cdots + \frac{T}{n}.$$

Our object is to decide what happens to $s_n$ for larger and larger values of $n$. These partial sums are not as easy to study as those in (10.3) because there is no simple formula analogous to (10.4) for simplifying the expression on the right of (10.6). Nevertheless, it is easy to obtain an *estimate* for the size of $s_n$ if we compare the partial sum with an appropriate integral.

Figure 10.2 shows the graph of the function $f(x) = 1/x$ for $x > 0$. (The scale is distorted along the $y$-axis.) The rectangles shown there have a total area equal to the sum

$$(10.7) \qquad 1 + \frac{1}{2} + \frac{1}{3} + \cdots + \frac{1}{n}.$$

The area of the shaded region is $\int_1^{n+1} x^{-1}\,dx = \log(n + 1)$. Since this area cannot exceed the sum of the areas of the rectangles, we have the inequality

$$(10.8) \qquad 1 + \frac{1}{2} + \frac{1}{3} + \cdots + \frac{1}{n} \geq \log(n + 1).$$

Multiplying both sides by $T$, we obtain $s_n \geq T \log (n + 1)$. In other words, if the runner's speed decreases in the manner described above, the time required to reach the point $1/2^n$ is at least $T \log (n + 1)$ minutes. Since $\log (n + 1)$ increases without bound as $n$ increases, we must agree with Zeno and conclude that the runner cannot reach his goal in any finite time.

The general theory of infinite series makes a distinction between series like (10.1) whose partial sums tend to a finite limit, and those like (10.5) whose partial sums have no finite

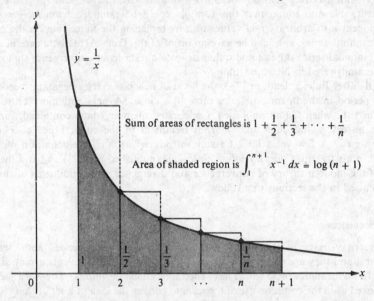

FIGURE 10.2 Geometric meaning of the inequality $1 + 1/2 + \cdots + 1/n \geq \log (n + 1)$.

limit. The former are called *convergent*, the latter *divergent*. Early investigators in the field paid little or no attention to questions of convergence or divergence. They treated infinite series as though they were ordinary finite sums, subject to the usual laws of algebra, not realizing that these laws cannot be universally extended to infinite series. Therefore, it is not surprising that some of the results they obtained were later shown to be incorrect. Fortunately, many of the early pioneers possessed unusual intuition and skill which prevented them from arriving at too many false conclusions, even though they could not justify all their methods. Foremost among these men was Leonard Euler who discovered one beautiful formula after another and at the same time used infinite series as a unifying idea to bring together many branches of mathematics, hitherto unrelated. The great quantity of Euler's work that has survived the test of history is a tribute to his remarkable instinct for what is mathematically correct.

The widespread use of infinite series began late in the 17th century, nearly fifty years before Euler was born, and coincided with the early development of the integral calculus. Nicholas Mercator (1620–1687) and William Brouncker (1620–1684) discovered an infinite series for the logarithm in 1668 while attempting to calculate the area of a hyperbolic segment. Shortly thereafter, Newton discovered the *binomial series*. This discovery proved to be a landmark in the history of mathematics. A special case of the binomial series is the now-familiar *binomial theorem* which states that

$$(1 + x)^n = \sum_{k=0}^{n} \binom{n}{k} x^k,$$

where $x$ is an arbitrary real number, $n$ is a nonnegative integer, and $\binom{n}{k}$ is the binomial coefficient. Newton found that this formula could be extended from *integer* values of the exponent $n$ to arbitrary *real* values of $n$ by replacing the finite sum on the right by a suitable infinite series, although he gave no proof of this fact. Actually, a careful treatment of the binomial series raises some rather delicate questions of convergence that could not have been answered in Newton's time.

Shortly after Euler's death in 1783, the flood of new discoveries began to recede and the formal period in the history of series came to a close. A new and more critical period began in 1812 when Gauss published a celebrated memoir which contained, for the first time in history, a thorough and rigorous treatment of the convergence of a particular infinite series. A few years later Cauchy introduced an analytic definition of the limit concept in his treatise *Cours d'analyse algébrique* (published in 1821) and laid the foundations of the modern theory of convergence and divergence. The rudiments of that theory are discussed in the sections that follow.

## 10.2  Sequences

In everyday usage of the English language, the words "sequence" and "series" are synonyms, and they are used to suggest a succession of things or events arranged in some order. In mathematics these words have special technical meanings. The word "sequence" is employed as in the common use of the term to convey the idea of a set of things arranged in order, but the word "series" is used in a somewhat different sense. The concept of a sequence will be discussed in this section, and series will be defined in Section 10.5.

If for every positive integer $n$ there is associated a real or complex number $a_n$, then the ordered set

$$a_1, a_2, a_3, \ldots, a_n, \ldots$$

is said to define an infinite sequence. The important thing here is that each member of the set has been labeled with an integer so that we may speak of the *first term* $a_1$, the *second term* $a_2$, and, in general, the *nth term* $a_n$. Each term $a_n$ has a successor $a_{n+1}$ and hence there is no "last" term.

The most common examples of sequences can be constructed if we give some rule or formula for describing the $n$th term. Thus, for example, the formula $a_n = 1/n$ defines a sequence whose first five terms are

$$1, \tfrac{1}{2}, \tfrac{1}{3}, \tfrac{1}{4}, \tfrac{1}{5}.$$

Sometimes two or more formulas may be employed as, for example,

$$a_{2n-1} = 1, \qquad a_{2n} = 2n^2,$$

the first few terms in this case being

$$1, 2, 1, 8, 1, 18, 1, 32, 1 .$$

Another common way to define a sequence is by a set of instructions which explains how to carry on after a given start. Thus we may have

$$a_1 = a_2 = 1, \qquad a_{n+1} = a_n + a_{n-1} \qquad \text{for } n \geq 2 .$$

This particular rule is known as a *recursion* formula, and it defines a famous sequence whose terms are called the *Fibonacci†* numbers. The first few terms are

$$1, 1, 2, 3, 5, 8, 13, 21, 34 .$$

In any sequence the essential thing is that there be some function $f$ defined on the positive integers such that $f(n)$ is the $n$th term of the sequence for each $n = 1, 2, 3, \ldots$ . In fact, this is probably the most convenient way to state a technical definition of sequence.

DEFINITION. *A function $f$ whose domain is the set of all positive integers $1, 2, 3, \ldots$ is called an infinite sequence. The function value $f(n)$ is called the nth term of the sequence.*

The *range* of the function (that is, the set of function values) is usually displayed by writing the terms in order, thus:

$$f(1), f(2), f(3), \ldots, f(n), \ldots .$$

For brevity, the notation $\{f(n)\}$ is used to denote the sequence whose $n$th term is $f(n)$. Very often the dependence on $n$ is denoted by using subscripts, and we write $a_n$, $s_n$, $x_n$, $u_n$, or something similar instead of $f(n)$. Unless otherwise specified, all sequences in this chapter are assumed to have real or complex terms.

The main question we are concerned with here is to decide whether or not the terms $f(n)$ tend to a finite limit as $n$ increases indefinitely. To treat this problem, we must extend the limit concept to sequences. This is done as follows.

DEFINITION. *A sequence $\{f(n)\}$ is said to have a limit $L$ if, for every positive number $\epsilon$, there is another positive number $N$ (which may depend on $\epsilon$) such that*

$$|f(n) - L| < \epsilon \qquad \text{for all } n \geq N .$$

*In this case, we say the sequence $\{f(n)\}$ converges to $L$ and we write*

$$\lim_{n \to \infty} f(n) = L, \qquad \text{or} \qquad f(n) \to L \qquad \text{as } n \to \infty .$$

*A sequence which does not converge is called divergent.*

In this definition the function values $f(n)$ and the limit $L$ may be real or complex numbers. If $f$ and $L$ are complex, we may decompose them into their real and imaginary parts, say $f = u + iv$ and $L = a + ib$. Then we have $f(n) - L = u(n) - a + i[v(n) - b]$. The

---

† Fibonacci, also known as Leonardo of Pisa (*circa* 1175–1250), encountered this sequence in a problem concerning the offspring of rabbits.

inequalities

$$|u(n) - a| \leq |f(n) - L| \quad \text{and} \quad |v(n) - b| \leq |f(n) - L|$$

show that the relation $f(n) \to L$ implies $u(n) \to a$ and $v(n) \to b$ as $n \to \infty$. Conversely, the inequality

$$|f(n) - L| \leq |u(n) - a| + |v(n) - b|$$

shows that the two relations $u(n) \to a$ and $v(n) \to b$ imply $f(n) \to L$ as $n \to \infty$. In other words, a complex-valued sequence $f$ converges if and only if both the real part $u$ and the imaginary part $v$ converge separately, in which case we have

$$\lim_{n \to \infty} f(n) = \lim_{n \to \infty} u(n) + i \lim_{n \to \infty} v(n) .$$

It is clear that any function defined for all positive real $x$ may be used to construct a sequence by restricting $x$ to take only *integer* values. This explains the strong analogy between the definition just given and the one in Section 7.14 for more general functions. The analogy carries over to *infinite limits* as well, and we leave it for the reader to define the symbols

$$\lim_{n \to \infty} f(n) = +\infty \quad \text{and} \quad \lim_{n \to \infty} f(n) = -\infty$$

as was done in Section 7.15 when $f$ is real-valued. If $f$ is complex, we write $f(n) \to \infty$ as $n \to \infty$ if $|f(n)| \to +\infty$.

The phrase "convergent sequence" is used only for a sequence whose limit is *finite*. A sequence with an infinite limit is said to diverge. There are, of course, divergent sequences that do not have infinite limits. Examples are defined by the following formulas:

$$f(n) = (-1)^n, \quad f(n) = \sin \frac{n\pi}{2}, \quad f(n) = (-1)^n \left(1 + \frac{1}{n}\right), \quad f(n) = e^{\pi i n/2} .$$

The basic rules for dealing with limits of sums, products, etc., also hold for limits of convergent sequences. The reader should have no difficulty in formulating these theorems for himself. Their proofs are somewhat similar to those given in Section 3.5.

The convergence or divergence of many sequences may be determined by using properties of familiar functions that are defined for all positive $x$. We mention a few important examples of real-valued sequences whose limits may be found directly or by using some of the results derived in Chapter 7.

(10.9)
$$\lim_{n \to \infty} \frac{1}{n^\alpha} = 0 \quad \text{if} \quad \alpha > 0 .$$

(10.10)
$$\lim_{n \to \infty} x^n = 0 \quad \text{if} \quad |x| < 1 .$$

(10.11)
$$\lim_{n \to \infty} \frac{(\log n)^a}{n^b} = 0 \quad \text{for all } a > 0, b > 0 .$$

(10.12)
$$\lim_{n \to \infty} n^{1/n} = 1 .$$

(10.13)
$$\lim_{n \to \infty} \left(1 + \frac{a}{n}\right)^n = e^a \quad \text{for all real } a .$$

## 10.3 Monotonic sequences of real numbers

A sequence $\{f(n)\}$ is said to be *increasing* if

$$f(n) \leq f(n + 1) \qquad \text{for all } n \geq 1 .$$

We indicate this briefly by writing $f(n) \nearrow$ . If, on the other hand, we have

$$f(n) \geq f(n + 1) \qquad \text{for all } n \geq 1 ,$$

we call the sequence *decreasing* and write $f(n) \searrow$. A sequence is called *monotonic* if it is increasing or if it is decreasing.

Monotonic sequences are pleasant to work with because their convergence or divergence is particularly easy to determine. In fact, we have the following simple criterion.

THEOREM 10.1. *A monotonic sequence converges if and only if it is bounded.*

*Note:* A sequence $\{f(n)\}$ is called *bounded* if there exists a positive number $M$ such that $|f(n)| \leq M$ for all $n$. A sequence that is not bounded is called *unbounded*.

*Proof.* It is clear that an unbounded sequence cannot converge. Therefore, all we need to prove is that a bounded monotonic sequence must converge.

Assume $f(n) \nearrow$ and let $L$ denote the least upper bound of the set of function values. (Since the sequence is bounded, it has a least upper bound by Axiom 10 of the real-number

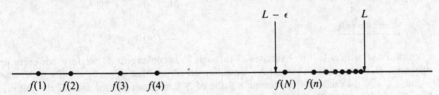

FIGURE 10.3 A bounded increasing sequence converges to its least upper bound.

system.) Then $f(n) \leq L$ for all $n$, and we shall prove that the sequence converges to $L$.

Choose any positive number $\epsilon$. Since $L - \epsilon$ cannot be an upper bound for *all* numbers $f(n)$, we must have $L - \epsilon < f(N)$ for some $N$. (This $N$ may depend on $\epsilon$.) If $n \geq N$, we have $f(N) \leq f(n)$ since $f(n) \nearrow$ . Hence, we have $L - \epsilon < f(n) \leq L$ for all $n \geq N$, as illustrated in Figure 10.3. From these inequalities we find that

$$0 \leq L - f(n) < \epsilon \qquad \text{for all } n \geq N$$

and this means that the sequence converges to $L$, as asserted.

If $f(n) \searrow$ , the proof is similar, the limit in this case being the greatest lower bound of the set of function values.

## 10.4   Exercises

In Exercises 1 through 22, a sequence $\{f(n)\}$ is defined by the formula given. In each case, (a) determine whether the sequence converges or diverges, and (b) find the limit of each convergent sequence. In some cases it may be helpful to replace the integer $n$ by an arbitrary positive real $x$ and to study the resulting function of $x$ by the methods of Chapter 7. You may use formulas (10.9) through (10.13) listed at the end of Section 10.2.

1. $f(n) = \dfrac{n}{n+1} - \dfrac{n+1}{n}$.

2. $f(n) = \dfrac{n^2}{n+1} - \dfrac{n^2+1}{n}$.

3. $f(n) = \cos \dfrac{n\pi}{2}$.

4. $f(n) = \dfrac{n^2 + 3n - 2}{5n^2}$.

5. $f(n) = \dfrac{n}{2^n}$.

6. $f(n) = 1 + (-1)^n$.

7. $f(n) = \dfrac{1 + (-1)^n}{n}$.

8. $f(n) = \dfrac{(-1)^n}{n} + \dfrac{1 + (-1)^n}{2}$.

9. $f(n) = 2^{1/n}$.

10. $f(n) = n^{(-1)^n}$.

11. $f(n) = \dfrac{n^{2/3} \sin (n!)}{n+1}$.

12. $f(n) = \dfrac{3^n + (-2)^n}{3^{n+1} + (-2)^{n+1}}$.

13. $f(n) = \sqrt{n+1} - \sqrt{n}$.

14. $f(n) = na^n$,    where   $|a| < 1$.

15. $f(n) = \dfrac{\log_a n}{n}$,    $a > 1$.

16. $f(n) = \dfrac{100,000n}{1 + n^2}$.

17. $f(n) = \left(1 + \dfrac{2}{n}\right)^n$.

18. $f(n) = 1 + \dfrac{n}{n+1} \cos \dfrac{n\pi}{2}$.

19. $f(n) = \left(1 + \dfrac{i}{2}\right)^{-n}$.

20. $f(n) = e^{-\pi in/2}$.

21. $f(n) = \dfrac{1}{n} e^{-\pi in/2}$.

22. $f(n) = ne^{-\pi in/2}$.

Each of the sequences $\{a_n\}$ in Exercises 23 through 28 is convergent. Therefore, for every pre-assigned $\epsilon > 0$, there exists an integer $N$ (depending on $\epsilon$) such that $|a_n - L| < \epsilon$ if $n \geq N$, where $L = \lim_{n \to \infty} a_n$. In each case, determine a value of $N$ that is suitable for each of the following values of $\epsilon$: $\epsilon = 1, 0.1, 0.01, 0.001, 0.0001$.

23. $a_n = \dfrac{1}{n}$.

24. $a_n = \dfrac{n}{n+1}$.

25. $a_n = \dfrac{(-1)^{n+1}}{n}$.

26. $a_n = \dfrac{1}{n!}$.

27. $a_n = \dfrac{2n}{n^3 + 1}$.

28. $a_n = (-1)^n \left(\dfrac{9}{10}\right)^n$.

29. Prove that a sequence cannot converge to two different limits.

30. Assume $\lim_{n \to \infty} a_n = 0$. Use the definition of limit to prove that $\lim_{n \to \infty} a_n^2 = 0$.

31. If $\lim_{n \to \infty} a_n = A$ and $\lim_{n \to \infty} b_n = B$, use the definition of limit to prove that we have $\lim_{n \to \infty} (a_n + b_n) = A + B$, and $\lim_{n \to \infty} (ca_n) = cA$, where $c$ is a constant.

32. From the results of Exercises 30 and 31, prove that if $\lim_{n \to \infty} a_n = A$ then $\lim_{n \to \infty} a_n^2 = A^2$. Then use the identity $2a_n b_n = (a_n + b_n)^2 - a_n^2 - b_n^2$ to prove that $\lim_{n \to \infty} (a_n b_n) = AB$ if $\lim_{n \to \infty} a_n = A$ and $\lim_{n \to \infty} b_n = B$.

33. If $\alpha$ is a real number and $n$ a nonnegative integer, the binomial coefficient $\binom{\alpha}{n}$ is defined by the equation

$$\binom{\alpha}{n} = \frac{\alpha(\alpha - 1)(\alpha - 2) \cdots (\alpha - n + 1)}{n!}.$$

(a) When $\alpha = -\frac{1}{2}$, show that

$$\binom{\alpha}{1} = -\frac{1}{2}, \quad \binom{\alpha}{2} = \frac{3}{8}, \quad \binom{\alpha}{3} = -\frac{5}{16}, \quad \binom{\alpha}{4} = \frac{35}{128}, \quad \binom{\alpha}{5} = -\frac{63}{256}.$$

(b) Let $a_n = (-1)^n \binom{-1/2}{n}$. Prove that $a_n > 0$ and that $a_{n+1} < a_n$.

34. Let $f$ be a real-valued function that is monotonic increasing and bounded on the interval $[0, 1]$. Define two sequences $\{s_n\}$ and $\{t_n\}$ as follows:

$$s_n = \frac{1}{n} \sum_{k=0}^{n-1} f\left(\frac{k}{n}\right), \qquad t_n = \frac{1}{n} \sum_{k=1}^{n} f\left(\frac{k}{n}\right).$$

(a) Prove that $s_n \leq \int_0^1 f(x)\, dx \leq t_n$ and that $0 \leq \int_0^1 f(x)\, dx - s_n \leq \dfrac{f(1) - f(0)}{n}$.

(b) Prove that both sequences $\{s_n\}$ and $\{t_n\}$ converge to the limit $\int_0^1 f(x)\, dx$.

(c) State and prove a corresponding result for the interval $[a, b]$.

35. Use Exercise 34 to establish the following limit relations:

(a) $\displaystyle \lim_{n \to \infty} \frac{1}{n} \sum_{k=1}^{n} \left(\frac{k}{n}\right)^2 = \frac{1}{3}.$

(b) $\displaystyle \lim_{n \to \infty} \sum_{k=1}^{n} \frac{1}{n + k} = \log 2.$

(c) $\displaystyle \lim_{n \to \infty} \sum_{k=1}^{n} \frac{n}{n^2 + k^2} = \frac{\pi}{4}.$

(d) $\displaystyle \lim_{n \to \infty} \sum_{k=1}^{n} \frac{1}{\sqrt{n^2 + k^2}} = \log(1 + \sqrt{2}).$

(e) $\displaystyle \lim_{n \to \infty} \sum_{k=1}^{n} \frac{1}{n} \sin \frac{k\pi}{n} = \frac{2}{\pi}.$

(f) $\displaystyle \lim_{n \to \infty} \sum_{k=1}^{n} \frac{1}{n} \sin^2 \frac{k\pi}{n} = \frac{1}{2}.$

## 10.5 Infinite series

From a given sequence of real or complex numbers, we can always generate a *new* sequence by adding together successive terms. Thus, if the given sequence has the terms

$$a_1, a_2, \ldots, a_n, \ldots,$$

we may form, in succession, the "partial sums"

$$s_1 = a_1, \qquad s_2 = a_1 + a_2, \qquad s_3 = a_1 + a_2 + a_3,$$

and so on, the partial sum $s_n$ of the first $n$ terms being defined as follows:

$$(10.14) \qquad s_n = a_1 + a_2 + \cdots + a_n = \sum_{k=1}^{n} a_k.$$

The sequence $\{s_n\}$ of partial sums is called an *infinite series*, or simply a *series*, and is also denoted by the following symbols:

(10.15)    $$a_1 + a_2 + a_3 + \cdots, \qquad a_1 + a_2 + \cdots + a_n + \cdots, \qquad \sum_{k=1}^{\infty} a_k.$$

For example, the series $\sum_{k=1}^{\infty} 1/k$ represents the sequence $\{s_n\}$ for which

$$s_n = \sum_{k=1}^{n} \frac{1}{k}.$$

The symbols in (10.15) are intended to remind us that the sequence of partial sums $\{s_n\}$ is obtained from the sequence $\{a_n\}$ by addition of successive terms.

If there is a real or complex number $S$ such that

$$\lim_{n \to \infty} s_n = S,$$

we say that the series $\sum_{k=1}^{\infty} a_k$ is *convergent* and has the *sum S*, in which case we write

$$\sum_{k=1}^{\infty} a_k = S.$$

If $\{s_n\}$ diverges, we say that the series $\sum_{k=1}^{\infty} a_k$ *diverges* and has no sum.

EXAMPLE 1. THE HARMONIC SERIES. In the discussion of Zeno's paradox, we showed that the partial sums $s_n$ of the series $\sum_{k=1}^{\infty} 1/k$ satisfy the inequality

$$s_n = \sum_{k=1}^{n} \frac{1}{k} \geq \log(n+1).$$

Since $\log(n+1) \to \infty$ as $n \to \infty$, the same is true of $s_n$, and hence the series $\sum_{k=1}^{\infty} 1/k$ diverges. This series is called the *harmonic series*.

EXAMPLE 2. In the discussion of Zeno's paradox, we also encountered the partial sums of the series $1 + \frac{1}{2} + \frac{1}{4} + \cdots$, given by the formula

$$\sum_{k=1}^{n} \frac{1}{2^{k-1}} = 2 - \frac{1}{2^{n-1}},$$

which is easily proved by induction. As $n \to \infty$, these partial sums approach the limit 2, and hence the series converges and has sum 2. We may indicate this by writing

(10.16)    $$1 + \tfrac{1}{2} + \tfrac{1}{4} + \cdots = 2.$$

The reader should realize that the word "sum" is used here in a very special sense. The sum of a convergent series is not obtained by ordinary addition but rather as the *limit of the sequence of partial sums.* Also, the reader should note that for a convergent series, the symbol $\sum_{k=1}^{\infty} a_k$ is used to denote both the *series* and its *sum*, even though the two are conceptually distinct. The sum represents a *number* and it is not capable of being convergent or divergent. Once the distinction between a series and its sum has been realized, the use of one symbol to represent both should cause no confusion.

As in the case of finite summation notation, the letter $k$ used in the symbol $\sum_{k=1}^{\infty} a_k$ is a "dummy index" and may be replaced by any other convenient symbol. The letters $n$, $m$, and $r$ are commonly used for this purpose. Sometimes it is desirable to start the summation from $k = 0$ or from $k = 2$ or from some other value of $k$. Thus, for example, the series in (10.16) could be written as $\sum_{k=0}^{\infty} 1/2^k$. In general, if $p \geq 0$, we define the symbol $\sum_{k=p}^{\infty} a_k$ to mean the same as $\sum_{k=1}^{\infty} b_k$, where $b_k = a_{p+k-1}$. Thus $b_1 = a_p$, $b_2 = a_{p+1}$, etc. When there is no danger of confusion or when the starting point is unimportant, we write $\sum a_k$ instead of $\sum_{k=p}^{\infty} a_k$.

It is easy to prove that the two series $\sum_{k=1}^{\infty} a_k$ and $\sum_{k=p}^{\infty} a_k$ both converge or both diverge. Suppose we let $s_n = a_1 + \cdots + a_n$ and $t_n = a_p + a_{p+1} + \cdots + a_{p+n-1}$. If $p = 0$, we have $t_{n+1} = a_0 + s_n$, so if $s_n \to S$ as $n \to \infty$, then $t_n \to a_0 + S$ and, conversely, if $t_n \to T$ as $n \to \infty$, then $s_n \to T - a_0$. Therefore, both series converge or both diverge when $p = 0$. The same holds true if $p \geq 1$. For $p = 1$, we have $s_n = t_n$, and for $p > 1$, we have $t_n = s_{n+p-1} - s_{p-1}$, and again it follows that the sequences $\{s_n\}$ and $\{t_n\}$ both converge or both diverge. This is often described by saying that a finite number of terms may be omitted or added at the beginning of a series without affecting its convergence or divergence.

## 10.6 The linearity property of convergent series

Ordinary finite sums have the following important properties:

$$(10.17) \qquad \sum_{k=1}^{n} (a_k + b_k) = \sum_{k=1}^{n} a_k + \sum_{k=1}^{n} b_k \qquad \text{(additive property)}$$

and

$$(10.18) \qquad \sum_{k=1}^{n} (ca_k) = c \sum_{k=1}^{n} a_k \qquad \text{(homogeneous property)}.$$

The next theorem provides a natural extension of these properties to convergent infinite series and thereby justifies many algebraic manipulations in which convergent series are treated as though they were finite sums. Both additivity and homogeneity may be combined into one property called *linearity* which may be described as follows:

THEOREM 10.2. *Let $\sum a_n$ and $\sum b_n$ be convergent infinite series of complex terms and let $\alpha$ and $\beta$ be complex constants. Then the series $\sum (\alpha a_n + \beta b_n)$ also converges, and its sum is given by the equation*

$$(10.19) \qquad \sum_{n=1}^{\infty} (\alpha a_n + \beta b_n) = \alpha \sum_{n=1}^{\infty} a_n + \beta \sum_{n=1}^{\infty} b_n .$$

*Proof.* Using (10.17) and (10.18), we may write

$$\text{(10.20)} \qquad \sum_{k=1}^{n} (\alpha a_k + \beta b_k) = \alpha \sum_{k=1}^{n} a_k + \beta \sum_{k=1}^{n} b_k .$$

When $n \to \infty$, the first term on the right of (10.20) tends to $\alpha \sum_{k=1}^{\infty} a_k$ and the second term tends to $\beta \sum_{k=1}^{\infty} b_k$. Therefore the left-hand side tends to their sum, and this proves that the series $\sum (\alpha a_k + \beta b_k)$ converges to the sum indicated by (10.19).

Theorem 10.2 has an interesting corollary which is often used to establish the divergence of a series.

THEOREM 10.3. *If $\sum a_n$ converges and if $\sum b_n$ diverges, then $\sum (a_n + b_n)$ diverges.*

*Proof.* Since $b_n = (a_n + b_n) - a_n$, and since $\sum a_n$ converges, Theorem 10.2 tells us that convergence of $\sum (a_n + b_n)$ implies convergence of $\sum b_n$. Therefore, $\sum (a_n + b_n)$ cannot converge if $\sum b_n$ diverges.

EXAMPLE. The series $\sum (1/k + 1/2^k)$ diverges because $\sum 1/k$ diverges and $\sum 1/2^k$ converges.

If $\sum a_n$ and $\sum b_n$ are *both* divergent, the series $\sum (a_n + b_n)$ may or may not converge. For example, when $a_n = b_n = 1$ for all $n$, then $\sum (a_n + b_n)$ diverges. But when $a_n = 1$ and $b_n = -1$ for all $n$, then $\sum (a_n + b_n)$ converges.

## 10.7 Telescoping series

Another important property of finite sums is the telescoping property which states that

$$\text{(10.21)} \qquad \sum_{k=1}^{n} (b_k - b_{k+1}) = b_1 - b_{n+1} .$$

When we try to extend this property to infinite series we are led to consider those series $\sum a_n$ for which each term $a_n$ may be expressed as a difference of the form

$$\text{(10.22)} \qquad a_n = b_n - b_{n+1} .$$

These series are known as *telescoping series* and their behavior is characterized by the following theorem.

THEOREM 10.4. *Let $\{a_n\}$ and $\{b_n\}$ be two sequences of complex numbers such that*

$$\text{(10.23)} \qquad a_n = b_n - b_{n+1} \qquad for \qquad n = 1, 2, 3, \ldots .$$

*Then the series $\sum a_n$ converges if and only if the sequence $\{b_n\}$ converges, in which case we have*

$$\text{(10.24)} \qquad \sum_{n=1}^{\infty} a_n = b_1 - L , \qquad where \quad L = \lim_{n \to \infty} b_n .$$

*Proof.* Let $s_n$ denote the $n$th partial sum of $\sum a_n$. Then we have

$$s_n = \sum_{k=1}^n a_k = \sum_{k=1}^n (b_k - b_{k+1}) = b_1 - b_{n+1},$$

because of (10.21). Therefore, both sequences $\{s_n\}$ and $\{b_n\}$ converge or both diverge. Moreover, if $b_n \to L$ as $n \to \infty$, then $s_n \to b_1 - L$, and this proves (10.24).

*Note:* Every series is telescoping because we can always satisfy (10.22) if we first choose $b_1$ to be arbitrary and then choose $b_{n+1} = b_1 - s_n$ for $n \geq 1$, where $s_n = a_1 + \cdots + a_n$.

EXAMPLE 1. Let $a_n = 1/(n^2 + n)$. Then we have

$$a_n = \frac{1}{n(n+1)} = \frac{1}{n} - \frac{1}{n+1},$$

and hence (10.23) holds with $b_n = 1/n$. Since $b_1 = 1$ and $L = 0$, we obtain

$$\sum_{n=1}^\infty \frac{1}{n(n+1)} = 1.$$

EXAMPLE 2. If $x$ is not a negative integer, we have the decomposition

$$\frac{1}{(n+x)(n+x+1)(n+x+2)} = \frac{1}{2}\left(\frac{1}{(n+x)(n+x+1)} - \frac{1}{(n+x+1)(n+x+2)}\right)$$

for each integer $n \geq 1$. Therefore, by the telescoping property, the following series converges and has the sum indicated:

$$\sum_{n=1}^\infty \frac{1}{(n+x)(n+x+1)(n+x+2)} = \frac{1}{2(x+1)(x+2)}.$$

EXAMPLE 3. Since $\log[n/(n+1)] = \log n - \log(n+1)$, and since $\log n \to \infty$ as $n \to \infty$, the series $\sum \log[n/(n+1)]$ diverges.

*Note:* Telescoping series illustrate an important difference between finite sums and infinite series. If we write (10.21) in extended form, it becomes

$$(b_1 - b_2) + (b_2 - b_3) + \cdots + (b_n - b_{n+1}) = b_1 - b_{n+1}$$

which can be verified by merely removing parentheses and canceling. Suppose now we perform the same operations on the infinite series

$$(b_1 - b_2) + (b_2 - b_3) + (b_3 - b_4) + \cdots.$$

We leave $b_1$, cancel $b_2$, cancel $b_3$, and so on. For each $n > 1$, at some stage we cancel $b_n$. Thus every $b_n$ cancels with the exception of $b_1$. This leads us to the conclusion that the sum of the series is $b_1$. Because of Theorem 10.4, this conclusion is false unless $\lim_{n\to\infty} b_n = 0$. This shows that parentheses cannot always be removed in an infinite series as they can in a finite sum. (See also Exercise 24 in Section 10.9.)

## 10.8  The geometric series

The telescoping property of finite sums may be used to study a very important example known as the *geometric series*. This series is generated by successive addition of the terms in a geometric progression and has the form $\sum x^n$, where the $n$th term $x^n$ is the $n$th power of a fixed real or complex number $x$. It is convenient to start this series with $n = 0$, with the understanding that the initial term, $x^0$, is equal to 1.

Let $s_n$ denote the $n$th partial sum of this series, so that

$$s_n = 1 + x + x^2 + \cdots + x^{n-1}.$$

If $x = 1$, each term on the right is 1 and $s_n = n$. In this case, the series diverges since $s_n \to \infty$ as $n \to \infty$. If $x \neq 1$, we may simplify the sum for $s_n$ by writing

$$(1 - x)s_n = (1 - x)\sum_{k=0}^{n-1} x^k = \sum_{k=0}^{n-1}(x^k - x^{k+1}) = 1 - x^n,$$

since the last sum telescopes. Dividing by $1 - x$, we obtain the formula

$$s_n = \frac{1 - x^n}{1 - x} = \frac{1}{1 - x} - \frac{x^n}{1 - x} \qquad \text{if} \quad x \neq 1.$$

This shows that the behavior of $s_n$ for large $n$ depends entirely on the behavior of $x^n$. When $|x| < 1$, then $x^n \to 0$ as $n \to \infty$, and the series converges to the sum $1/(1 - x)$.

Since $s_{n+1} - s_n = x^n$, convergence of $\{s_n\}$ implies $x^n \to 0$ as $n \to \infty$. Therefore, if $|x| \geq 1$ the sequence $\{s_n\}$ diverges since $x^n$ does not tend to 0 in this case. Thus we have proved the following theorem.

THEOREM 10.5.  *If $x$ is complex, with $|x| < 1$, the geometric series $\sum_{n=0}^{\infty} x^n$ converges and has sum $1/(1 - x)$. That is to say, we have*

(10.25)         $$1 + x + x^2 + \cdots + x^n + \cdots = \frac{1}{1 - x} \qquad \text{if} \quad |x| < 1.$$

*If $|x| \geq 1$, the series diverges.*

The geometric series, with $|x| < 1$, is one of those rare examples whose sum we are able to determine by finding first a simple formula for its partial sums. (A special case with $x = \frac{1}{2}$ was encountered in Section 10.1 in connection with Zeno's paradox.) The real importance of this series lies in the fact that it may be used as a starting point for determining the sums of a large number of other interesting series. For example, if we assume $|x| < 1$ and replace $x$ by $x^2$ in (10.25), we obtain the formula

(10.26)         $$1 + x^2 + x^4 + \cdots + x^{2n} + \cdots = \frac{1}{1 - x^2} \qquad \text{if} \quad |x| < 1.$$

Notice that this series contains those terms of (10.25) with *even* exponents. To find the sum of the odd powers alone, we need only multiply both sides of (10.26) by $x$ to obtain

$$(10.27) \qquad x + x^3 + x^5 + \cdots + x^{2n+1} + \cdots = \frac{x}{1 - x^2} \qquad \text{if } |x| < 1.$$

If we replace $x$ by $-x$ in (10.25), we find that

$$(10.28) \qquad 1 - x + x^2 - x^3 + \cdots + (-1)^n x^n + \cdots = \frac{1}{1 + x} \qquad \text{if } |x| < 1.$$

Replacing $x$ by $x^2$ in (10.28), we find that

$$(10.29) \qquad 1 - x^2 + x^4 - x^6 + \cdots + (-1)^n x^{2n} + \cdots = \frac{1}{1 + x^2} \qquad \text{if } |x| < 1.$$

Multiplying both sides of (10.29) by $x$, we obtain

$$(10.30) \qquad x - x^3 + x^5 - x^7 + \cdots + (-1)^n x^{2n+1} + \cdots = \frac{x}{1 + x^2} \qquad \text{if } |x| < 1.$$

If we replace $x$ by $2x$ in (10.26), we find that

$$1 + 4x^2 + 16x^4 + \cdots + 4^n x^{2n} + \cdots = \frac{1}{1 - 4x^2},$$

which is valid if $|2x| < 1$ or, what is the same thing, if $|x| < \frac{1}{2}$. It is clear that many other examples may be constructed by similar means.

All these series have the special form

$$\sum_{n=0}^{\infty} a_n x^n$$

and are known as *power series*. The numbers $a_0, a_1, a_2, \ldots$, which may be real or complex, are called *coefficients* of the power series. The geometric series is an example with all coefficients equal to 1. If $x$ and all the coefficients are real, the series is called a *real* power series. We shall find later, when we discuss the general theory of real power series, that it is permissible to differentiate and to integrate both sides of each of the Equations (10.25) through (10.30), treating the left-hand members as though they were ordinary finite sums. These operations lead to many remarkable new formulas. For example, differentiation of (10.25) gives us

$$(10.31) \qquad 1 + 2x + 3x^2 + \cdots + nx^{n-1} + \cdots = \frac{1}{(1 - x)^2} \qquad \text{if } |x| < 1,$$

whereas integration of (10.28) yields the interesting formula

$$(10.32) \qquad x - \frac{x^2}{2} + \frac{x^3}{3} - \frac{x^4}{4} + \cdots + \frac{(-1)^n x^{n+1}}{n+1} + \cdots = \log(1+x)$$

which expresses the logarithm as a power series. This is the discovery of Mercator and Brouncker (1668) that we mentioned earlier. Although each of the Equations (10.25) through (10.31) is valid for $x$ in the open interval $-1 < x < +1$, it turns out that the logarithmic series in (10.32) is valid at the endpoint $x = +1$ as well.

Another important example, which may be obtained by integration of (10.29), is the following power-series expansion for the inverse tangent, discovered in 1671 by James Gregory (1638–1675):

$$(10.33) \qquad x - \frac{x^3}{3} + \frac{x^5}{5} - \frac{x^7}{7} + \cdots + \frac{(-1)^n x^{2n+1}}{2n+1} + \cdots = \arctan x \,.$$

Gregory's series converges for each complex $x$ with $|x| < 1$ and also for $x = \pm 1$. When $x$ is real, the series agrees with the inverse tangent function introduced in Chapter 6. The series can be used to extend the definition of the arctangent function from real values of $x$ to complex $x$ with $|x| < 1$.

Many of the other elementary functions of calculus, such as the sine, cosine, and exponential, may also be represented by power series. This is not too surprising, in view of Taylor's formula which tells us that any function may be approximated by a Taylor polynomial in $x$ of degree $\leq n$ if it has derivatives of order $n + 1$ in some neighborhood of the origin. In the examples given above, the partial sums of the power series are precisely the Taylor polynomials. When a function $f$ has derivatives of every order in a neighborhood of the origin, then for every positive integer $n$ Taylor's formula leads to an equation of the form

$$(10.34) \qquad f(x) = \sum_{k=0}^{n} a_k x^k + E_n(x) \,,$$

where the finite sum $\sum_{k=0}^{n} a_k x^k$ is a Taylor polynomial of degree $\leq n$ and $E_n(x)$ is the error for this approximation. If, now, we keep $x$ fixed and let $n$ increase without bound in (10.34) the Taylor polynomials give rise to a power series, namely $\sum_{k=0}^{\infty} a_k x^k$, where each coefficient $a_k$ is determined as follows:

$$a_k = \frac{f^{(k)}(0)}{k!} \,.$$

If, for some $x$, the error $E_n(x)$ tends to 0 as $n \to \infty$, then for this $x$ we may let $n \to \infty$ in (10.34) to obtain

$$f(x) = \lim_{n \to \infty} \sum_{k=0}^{n} a_k x^k + \lim_{n \to \infty} E_n(x) = \sum_{k=0}^{\infty} a_k x^k \,.$$

In other words, the power series in question converges to $f(x)$. If $x$ is a point for which $E_n(x)$ does not tend to 0 as $n \to \infty$, then the partial sums will not approach $f(x)$. Conditions on $f$ for guaranteeing that $E_n(x) \to 0$ will be discussed later in Section 11.10.

To lay a better foundation for the general theory of power series, we turn next to certain general questions related to the convergence and divergence of arbitrary series. We shall return to the subject of power series in Chapter 11.

## 10.9 Exercises

Each of the series in Exercises 1 through 10 is a telescoping series, or a geometric series, or some related series whose partial sums may be simplified. In each case, prove that the series converges and has the sum indicated.

1. $\displaystyle\sum_{n=1}^{\infty} \frac{1}{(2n-1)(2n+1)} = \frac{1}{2}$.

2. $\displaystyle\sum_{n=1}^{\infty} \frac{2}{3^{n-1}} = 3$.

3. $\displaystyle\sum_{n=2}^{\infty} \frac{1}{n^2-1} = \frac{3}{4}$.

4. $\displaystyle\sum_{n=1}^{\infty} \frac{2^n + 3^n}{6^n} = \frac{3}{2}$.

5. $\displaystyle\sum_{n=1}^{\infty} \frac{\sqrt{n+1} - \sqrt{n}}{\sqrt{n^2+n}} = 1$.

6. $\displaystyle\sum_{n=1}^{\infty} \frac{n}{(n+1)(n+2)(n+3)} = \frac{1}{4}$.

7. $\displaystyle\sum_{n=1}^{\infty} \frac{2n+1}{n^2(n+1)^2} = 1$.

8. $\displaystyle\sum_{n=1}^{\infty} \frac{2^n + n^2 + n}{2^{n+1}n(n+1)} = 1$.

9. $\displaystyle\sum_{n=1}^{\infty} \frac{(-1)^{n-1}(2n+1)}{n(n+1)} = 1$.

10. $\displaystyle\sum_{n=2}^{\infty} \frac{\log\left[(1 + 1/n)^n(1+n)\right]}{(\log n^n)[\log (n+1)^{n+1}]} = \log_2 \sqrt{e}$.

Power series for $\log (1 + x)$ and $\arctan x$ were obtained in Section 10.8 by performing various operations on the geometric series. In a similar manner, without attempting to justify the steps, obtain the formulas in Exercises 11 through 19. They are all valid at least for $|x| < 1$. (The theoretical justification is provided in Section 11.8.)

11. $\displaystyle\sum_{n=1}^{\infty} nx^n = \frac{x}{(1-x)^2}$.

12. $\displaystyle\sum_{n=1}^{\infty} n^2x^n = \frac{x^2 + x}{(1-x)^3}$.

13. $\displaystyle\sum_{n=1}^{\infty} n^3x^n = \frac{x^3 + 4x^2 + x}{(1-x)^4}$.

14. $\displaystyle\sum_{n=1}^{\infty} n^4x^n = \frac{x^4 + 11x^3 + 11x^2 + x}{(1-x)^5}$.

15. $\displaystyle\sum_{n=1}^{\infty} \frac{x^n}{n} = \log\frac{1}{1-x}$.

16. $\displaystyle\sum_{n=1}^{\infty} \frac{x^{2n-1}}{2n-1} = \frac{1}{2}\log\frac{1+x}{1-x}$.

17. $\displaystyle\sum_{n=0}^{\infty} (n+1)x^n = \frac{1}{(1-x)^2}$.

18. $\displaystyle\sum_{n=0}^{\infty} \frac{(n+1)(n+2)}{2!} x^n = \frac{1}{(1-x)^3}$.

19. $\displaystyle\sum_{n=0}^{\infty} \frac{(n+1)(n+2)(n+3)}{3!} x^n = \frac{1}{(1-x)^4}$.

20. The results of Exercises 11 through 14 suggest that there exists a general formula of the form

$$\sum_{n=1}^{\infty} n^k x^n = \frac{P_k(x)}{(1-x)^{k+1}},$$

where $P_k(x)$ is a polynomial of degree $k$, the term of lowest degree being $x$ and that of highest degree being $x^k$. Prove this by induction, without attempting to justify the formal manipulations with the series.

21. The results of Exercises 17 through 19 suggest the more general formula

$$\sum_{n=0}^{\infty} \binom{n+k}{k} x^n = \frac{1}{(1-x)^{k+1}}, \quad \text{where} \quad \binom{n+k}{k} = \frac{(n+1)(n+2)\cdots(n+k)}{k!}.$$

Prove this by induction, without attempting to justify the formal manipulations with the series.

22. Given that $\sum_{n=0}^{\infty} x^n/n! = e^x$ for all $x$, find the sums of the following series, assuming it is permissible to operate on infinite series as though they were finite sums.

(a) $\displaystyle\sum_{n=2}^{\infty} \frac{n-1}{n!}$.

(b) $\displaystyle\sum_{n=2}^{\infty} \frac{n+1}{n!}$.

(c) $\displaystyle\sum_{n=2}^{\infty} \frac{(n-1)(n+1)}{n!}$.

23. (a) Given that $\sum_{n=0}^{\infty} x^n/n! = e^x$ for all $x$, show that

$$\sum_{n=1}^{\infty} \frac{n^2 x^n}{n!} = (x^2 + x)e^x,$$

assuming it is permissible to operate on these series as though they were finite sums.

(b) The sum of the series $\sum_{n=1}^{\infty} {}_1 n^3/n!$ is $ke$, where $k$ is a positive integer. Find the value of $k$. Do not attempt to justify formal manipulations.

24. Two series $\sum_{n=1}^{\infty} a_n$ and $\sum_{n=1}^{\infty} b_n$ are called *identical* if $a_n = b_n$ for each $n \geq 1$. For example, the series

$$0 + 0 + 0 + \cdots \quad \text{and} \quad (1-1) + (1-1) + (1-1) + \cdots$$

are identical, but the series

$$1 + 1 + 1 + \cdots \quad \text{and} \quad 1 + 0 + 1 + 0 + 1 + 0 + \cdots$$

are not identical. Determine whether or not the series are identical in each of the following pairs:

(a) $1 - 1 + 1 - 1 + \cdots$    and    $(2-1) - (3-2) + (4-3) - (5-4) + \cdots$.

(b) $1 - 1 + 1 - 1 + \cdots$    and    $(1-1) + (1-1) + (1-1) + \cdots$.

(c) $1 - 1 + 1 - 1 + \cdots$    and    $1 + (-1+1) + (-1+1) + (-1+1) + \cdots$.

(d) $1 + \frac{1}{2} + \frac{1}{4} + \frac{1}{8} + \cdots$,    and    $1 + (1 - \frac{1}{2}) + (\frac{1}{2} - \frac{1}{4}) + (\frac{1}{4} - \frac{1}{8}) + \cdots$.

25. (a) Use (10.26) to prove that

$$1 + 0 + x^2 + 0 + x^4 + \cdots = \frac{1}{1-x^2}, \quad \text{if} \quad |x| < 1.$$

Note that, according to the definition given in Exercise 24, this series is not identical to the one in (10.26) if $x \neq 0$.

(b) Apply Theorem 10.2 to the result in part (a) and to (10.25) to deduce (10.27).

(c) Show that Theorem 10.2 when applied directly to (10.25) and (10.26) does not yield (10.27). Instead, it yields the formula $\sum_{n=1}^{\infty} (x^n - x^{2n}) = x/(1-x^2)$, valid for $|x| < 1$.

## *10.10    Exercises on decimal expansions

Decimal representations of real numbers were introduced in Section I3.15. It was shown there that every positive real $x$ has a decimal representation of the form

$$x = a_0 . a_1 a_2 a_3 \ldots,$$

where $0 \le a_k \le 9$ for each $k \ge 1$. The number $x$ is related to the digits $a_0, a_1, a_2, \ldots$ by the inequalities

(10.35)    $$a_0 + \frac{a_1}{10} + \cdots + \frac{a_n}{10^n} \le x < a_0 + \frac{a_1}{10} + \cdots + \frac{a_{n-1}}{10^{n-1}} + \frac{a_n + 1}{10^n}.$$

If we let $s_n = \sum_{k=0}^{n} a_k/10^k$, and if we subtract $s_n$ from each member of (10.35), we obtain

$$0 \le x - s_n < 10^{-n}.$$

This shows that $s_n \to x$ as $n \to \infty$, and hence $x$ is given by the convergent series

(10.36)    $$x = \sum_{k=0}^{\infty} \frac{a_k}{10^k}.$$

Each of the infinite decimal expansions in Exercises 1 through 5 is understood to be repeated indefinitely as suggested. In each case, express the decimal as an infinite series, find the sum of the series, and thereby express $x$ as a quotient of two integers.

1. $x = 0.4444 \ldots$
2. $x = 0.51515151 \ldots$
3. $x = 2.02020202 \ldots$
4. $x = 0.123123123123 \ldots$
5. $x = 0.142857142857142857142857 \ldots$
6. Prove that every repeating decimal represents a rational number.
7. If a number has a decimal expansion which ends in zeros, such as $\frac{1}{8} = 0.1250000 \ldots$, then this number can also be written as a decimal which ends in nines if we decrease the last nonzero digit by one unit. For example, $\frac{1}{8} = 0.1249999 \ldots$. Use infinite series to prove this statement.

The decimal representation in (10.36) may be generalized by replacing the integer 10 by any other integer $b > 1$. If $x > 0$, let $a_0$ denote the greatest integer in $x$; assuming that $a_0, a_1, \ldots, a_{n-1}$ have been defined, let $a_n$ denote the largest integer such that

$$\sum_{k=0}^{n} \frac{a_k}{b^k} \le x.$$

The following exercises refer to the sequence of integers $a_0, a_1, a_2, \ldots$ so obtained.

8. Show that $0 \le a_k \le b - 1$ for each $k \ge 1$.
9. Describe a geometric method for obtaining the numbers $a_0, a_1, a_2, \ldots$.
10. Show that the series $\sum_{k=0}^{\infty} a_k/b^k$ converges and has sum $x$. This provides a decimal expansion of $x$ in the scale of $b$. Important special cases, other than $b = 10$, are the *binary scale*, $b = 2$, and the *duodecimal scale*, $b = 12$.

## 10.11 Tests for convergence

In theory, the convergence or divergence of a particular series $\sum a_n$ is decided by examining its partial sums $s_n$ to see whether or not they tend to a finite limit as $n \to \infty$. In some special cases, such as the geometric series, the sums defining $s_n$ may be simplified to the point where it becomes a simple matter to determine their behavior for large $n$. However, in the majority of cases there is no nice formula for simplifying $s_n$ and the convergence or divergence may be rather difficult to establish in a straightforward manner. Early investigators in the subject, notably Cauchy and his contemporaries, realized this difficulty and they developed a number of "convergence tests" that by-passed the need for an explicit knowledge of the partial sums. A few of the simplest and most useful of these tests will be discussed in this chapter, but first we want to make some general remarks about the nature of these tests.

Convergence tests may be broadly classified into three categories: (i) *sufficient* conditions; (ii) *necessary* conditions; (iii) *necessary and sufficient* conditions. A test of type (i) may be expressed symbolically as follows:

"If $C$ is satisfied, then $\sum a_n$ converges,"

where $C$ stands for the condition in question. Tests of type (ii) have the form

"If $\sum a_n$ converges, then $C$ is satisfied,"

whereas those of type (iii) may be written thus:

"$\sum a_n$ converges if and only if $C$ is satisfied."

We shall see presently that there are tests of type (ii) that are not of type (i) (and vice versa). Beginners often use such tests incorrectly by failing to realize the difference between a *necessary* condition and a *sufficient* condition. Therefore the reader should make an effort to keep this distinction in mind when using a particular test in practice.

The simplest of all convergence tests gives a *necessary* condition for convergence and may be stated as follows.

THEOREM 10.6. *If the series $\sum a_n$ converges, then its nth term tends to $0$; that is,*

$$(10.37) \qquad \lim_{n \to \infty} a_n = 0.$$

*Proof.* Let $s_n = a_1 + a_2 + \cdots + a_n$. Then $a_n = s_n - s_{n-1}$. As $n \to \infty$, both $s_n$ and $s_{n-1}$ tend to the same limit and hence $a_n \to 0$. This proves the theorem.

This is an example of a test of type (ii) which is not of type (i). Condition (10.37) is *not* sufficient for convergence. For example, when $a_n = 1/n$, the condition $a_n \to 0$ is satisfied but the series $\sum 1/n$ diverges. The real usefulness of this test is that it gives us a *sufficient* condition for *divergence*. That is, if the terms $a_n$ of a series $\sum a_n$ do *not* tend to zero, then the series must diverge. This statement is logically equivalent to Theorem 10.6.

## 10.12 Comparison tests for series of nonnegative terms

In this section we shall be concerned with series having *nonnegative terms*, that is, series of the form $\sum a_n$, where each $a_n \geq 0$. Since the partial sums of such series are monotonic increasing, we may use Theorem 10.1 to obtain the following *necessary and sufficient condition* for convergence.

THEOREM 10.7. *Assume that* $a_n \geq 0$ *for each* $n \geq 1$. *Then the series* $\sum a_n$ *converges if and only if the sequence of its partial sums is bounded above.*

If the partial sums are bounded above by a number $M$, say, then the sum of the series cannot exceed $M$.

EXAMPLE 1. Theorem 10.7 may be used to establish the convergence of the series $\sum_{n=1}^{\infty} 1/n!$. We estimate the partial sums from above by using the inequality

$$\frac{1}{k!} \leq \frac{1}{2^{k-1}},$$

which is obviously true for all $k \geq 1$ since $k!$ consists of $k - 1$ factors, each $\geq 2$. Therefore we have

$$\sum_{k=1}^{n} \frac{1}{k!} \leq \sum_{k=1}^{n} \frac{1}{2^{k-1}} = \sum_{k=0}^{n-1} \left(\frac{1}{2}\right)^k \leq \sum_{k=0}^{\infty} \left(\frac{1}{2}\right)^k = 2,$$

the last series being a geometric series. The series $\sum_{n=1}^{\infty} 1/n!$ is therefore convergent and has a sum $\leq 2$. We shall see later that the sum of this series is $e - 1$, where $e$ is the Euler number.

The convergence of the foregoing example was established by comparing the terms of the given series with those of a series known to converge. This idea may be pursued further to yield a number of tests known as *comparison tests*.

THEOREM 10.8. COMPARISON TEST. *Assume* $a_n \geq 0$ *and* $b_n \geq 0$ *for all* $n \geq 1$. *If there exists a positive constant* $c$ *such that*

(10.38) $$a_n \leq cb_n$$

*for all n, then convergence of* $\sum b_n$ *implies convergence of* $\sum a_n$.

*Note:* The conclusion may also be formulated as follows: "Divergence of $\sum a_n$ implies divergence of $\sum b_n$." This statement is logically equivalent to Theorem 10.8. When the inequality (10.38) is satisfied, we say that the series $\sum b_n$ *dominates* the series $\sum a_n$.

*Proof.* Let $s_n = a_1 + \cdots + a_n$, $t_n = b_1 + \cdots + b_n$. Then (10.38) implies $s_n \leq ct_n$. If $\sum b_n$ converges, its partial sums are bounded, say by $M$. Then $s_n \leq cM$, and hence $\sum a_n$ is also convergent since its partial sums are bounded by $cM$. This completes the proof.

Omitting a finite number of terms at the beginning of a series does not affect its convergence or divergence. Therefore Theorem 10.8 still holds true if the inequality (10.38) is valid only for all $n \geq N$ for some $N$.

THEOREM 10.9. LIMIT COMPARISON TEST. *Assume that* $a_n > 0$ *and* $b_n > 0$ *for all* $n \geq 1$, *and suppose that*

$$(10.39) \qquad \lim_{n \to \infty} \frac{a_n}{b_n} = 1 .$$

*Then* $\sum a_n$ *converges if and only if* $\sum b_n$ *converges.*

*Proof.* There exists an $N$ such that $n \geq N$ implies $\frac{1}{2} < a_n/b_n < \frac{3}{2}$. Therefore $b_n < 2a_n$ and $a_n < \frac{3}{2}b_n$ for all $n \geq N$, and the theorem follows by applying Theorem 10.8 twice.

Note that Theorem 10.9 also holds if $\lim_{n \to \infty} a_n/b_n = c$, provided that $c > 0$, because we then have $\lim_{n \to \infty} a_n/(cb_n) = 1$ and we may compare $\sum a_n$ with $\sum (cb_n)$. However, if $\lim_{n \to \infty} a_n/b_n = 0$, we conclude only that convergence of $\sum b_n$ implies convergence of $\sum a_n$ .

DEFINITION. *Two sequences* $\{a_n\}$ *and* $\{b_n\}$ *of complex numbers are said to be asymptotically equal if*

$$\lim_{n \to \infty} \frac{a_n}{b_n} = 1 .$$

This relation is often indicated symbolically by writing

$$(10.40) \qquad a_n \sim b_n \qquad \text{as} \quad n \to \infty .$$

The notation $a_n \sim b_n$ is read "$a_n$ is asymptotically equal to $b_n$," and it is intended to suggest that $a_n$ and $b_n$ behave in essentially the same way for large $n$. Using this terminology, we may state the limit comparison test in the following manner.

THEOREM 10.10. *Two series* $\sum a_n$ *and* $\sum b_n$ *with terms that are positive and asymptotically equal converge together or they diverge together.*

EXAMPLE 2. THE RIEMANN ZETA-FUNCTION. In Example 1 of Section 10.7, we proved that $\sum 1/(n^2 + n)$ is a convergent telescoping series. If we use this as a comparison series, it follows that $\sum 1/n^2$ is convergent, since $1/n^2 \sim 1/(n^2 + n)$ as $n \to \infty$. Also, $\sum 1/n^2$ dominates $\sum 1/n^s$ for $s \geq 2$, and therefore $\sum 1/n^s$ converges for every real $s \geq 2$. We shall prove in the next section that this series also converges for every $s > 1$. Its sum, denoted by $\zeta(s)$ ($\zeta$ is the Greek letter zeta), defines an important function in analysis known as the *Riemann zeta-function*:

$$\zeta(s) = \sum_{n=1}^{\infty} \frac{1}{n^s} \qquad \text{if} \quad s > 1 .$$

Euler discovered many beautiful formulas involving $\zeta(s)$. In particular, he found that $\zeta(2) = \pi^2/6$, a result which is not easy to derive at this stage.

EXAMPLE 3. Since $\sum 1/n$ diverges, every series having positive terms asymptotically equal to $1/n$ must also diverge. For example, this is true of the two series

$$\sum_{n=1}^{\infty} \frac{1}{\sqrt{n(n+10)}} \quad \text{and} \quad \sum_{n=1}^{\infty} \sin \frac{1}{n}.$$

The relation $\sin 1/n \sim 1/n$ follows from the fact that $(\sin x)/x \to 1$ as $x \to 0$.

## 10.13 The integral test

To use comparison tests effectively, we must have at our disposal some examples of series of known behavior. The geometric series and the zeta-function are useful for this purpose. New examples can be obtained very simply by applying the *integral test*, first proved by Cauchy in 1837.

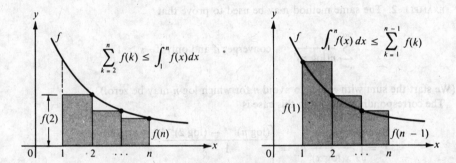

FIGURE 10.4   Proof of the integral test.

THEOREM 10.11.   INTEGRAL TEST. *Let $f$ be a positive decreasing function, defined for all real $x \geq 1$. For each $n \geq 1$, let*

$$s_n = \sum_{k=1}^{n} f(k) \quad \text{and} \quad t_n = \int_{1}^{n} f(x)\, dx.$$

*Then both sequences $\{s_n\}$ and $\{t_n\}$ converge or both diverge.*

*Proof.* By comparing $f$ with appropriate step functions as suggested in Figure 10.4, we obtain the inequalities

$$\sum_{k=2}^{n} f(k) \leq \int_{1}^{n} f(x)\, dx \leq \sum_{k=1}^{n-1} f(k)$$

or $s_n - f(1) \leq t_n \leq s_{n-1}$. Since both sequences $\{s_n\}$ and $\{t_n\}$ are monotonic increasing, these inequalities show that both are bounded above or both are unbounded. Therefore, both sequences converge or both diverge, as asserted.

EXAMPLE 1. The integral test enables us to prove that

$$\sum_{n=1}^{\infty} \frac{1}{n^s} \quad \text{converges if and only if} \quad s > 1.$$

Taking $f(x) = x^{-s}$, we have

$$t_n = \int_1^n \frac{1}{x^s}\,dx = \begin{cases} \dfrac{n^{1-s} - 1}{1 - s} & \text{if } s \neq 1, \\ \log n & \text{if } s = 1. \end{cases}$$

When $s > 1$ the term $n^{1-s} \to 0$ as $n \to \infty$ and hence $\{t_n\}$ converges. By the integral test, this implies convergence of the series for $s > 1$.

When $s \leq 1$, then $t_n \to \infty$ and the series diverges. The special case $s = 1$ (the *harmonic series*) was discussed earlier in Section 10.5. Its divergence was known to Leibniz.

EXAMPLE 2. The same method may be used to prove that

$$\sum_{n=2}^{\infty} \frac{1}{n(\log n)^s} \quad \text{converges if and only if} \quad s > 1.$$

(We start the sum with $n = 2$ to avoid $n$ for which $\log n$ may be zero.)

The corresponding integral in this case is

$$t_n = \int_2^n \frac{1}{x(\log x)^s}\,dx = \begin{cases} \dfrac{(\log n)^{1-s} - (\log 2)^{1-s}}{1 - s} & \text{if } s \neq 1, \\ \log(\log n) - \log(\log 2) & \text{if } s = 1. \end{cases}$$

Thus $\{t_n\}$ converges if and only if $s > 1$, and hence, by the integral test, the same holds true for the series in question.

## 10.14 Exercises

Test the following series for convergence or divergence. In each case, give a reason for your decision.

1. $\displaystyle\sum_{n=1}^{\infty} \frac{n}{(4n - 3)(4n - 1)}.$

2. $\displaystyle\sum_{n=1}^{\infty} \frac{\sqrt{2n - 1}\,\log(4n + 1)}{n(n + 1)}.$

3. $\displaystyle\sum_{n=1}^{\infty} \frac{n + 1}{2^n}.$

4. $\displaystyle\sum_{n=1}^{\infty} \frac{n^2}{2^n}.$

5. $\displaystyle\sum_{n=1}^{\infty} \frac{|\sin nx|}{n^2}.$

6. $\displaystyle\sum_{n=1}^{\infty} \frac{2 + (-1)^n}{2^n}.$

7. $\displaystyle\sum_{n=1}^{\infty} \frac{n!}{(n + 2)!}.$

8. $\displaystyle\sum_{n=2}^{\infty} \frac{\log n}{n\sqrt{n + 1}}.$

9. $\displaystyle\sum_{n=1}^{\infty} \frac{1}{\sqrt{n(n+1)}}$.

10. $\displaystyle\sum_{n=1}^{\infty} \frac{1+\sqrt{n}}{(n+1)^3 - 1}$.

11. $\displaystyle\sum_{n=2}^{\infty} \frac{1}{(\log n)^s}$.

12. $\displaystyle\sum_{n=1}^{\infty} \frac{|a_n|}{10^n}$, $|a_n| < 10$.

13. $\displaystyle\sum_{n=1}^{\infty} \frac{1}{1000n+1}$.

14. $\displaystyle\sum_{n=1}^{\infty} \frac{n \cos^2 (n\pi/3)}{2^n}$.

15. $\displaystyle\sum_{n=3}^{\infty} \frac{1}{n \log n (\log\log n)^s}$.

16. $\displaystyle\sum_{n=1}^{\infty} n e^{-n^2}$.

17. $\displaystyle\sum_{n=1}^{\infty} \int_0^{1/n} \frac{\sqrt{x}}{1+x^2}\, dx$.

18. $\displaystyle\sum_{n=1}^{\infty} \int_n^{n+1} e^{-\sqrt{x}}\, dx$.

19. Assume $f$ is a nonnegative increasing function defined for all $x \geq 1$. Use the method suggested by the proof of the integral test to show that

$$\sum_{k=1}^{n-1} f(k) \leq \int_1^n f(x)\, dx \leq \sum_{k=2}^{n} f(k).$$

Take $f(x) = \log x$ and deduce the inequalities

(10.41) $\qquad\qquad e\, n^n e^{-n} < n! < e\, n^{n+1} e^{-n}$.

These give a rough estimate of the order of magnitude of $n!$. From (10.41), we may write

$$\frac{e^{1/n}}{e} < \frac{(n!)^{1/n}}{n} < \frac{e^{1/n}\, n^{1/n}}{e}.$$

Letting $n \to \infty$, we find that

$$\frac{(n!)^{1/n}}{n} \to \frac{1}{e} \qquad \text{or} \qquad (n!)^{1/n} \sim \frac{n}{e} \qquad \text{as} \quad n \to \infty.$$

## 10.15 The root test and the ratio test for series of nonnegative terms

Using the geometric series $\sum x^n$ as a comparison series, Cauchy developed two useful tests known as the *root test* and the *ratio test*.

If $\sum a_n$ is a series whose terms (from some point on) satisfy an inequality of the form

(10.42) $\qquad\qquad 0 \leq a_n \leq x^n, \quad \text{where} \quad 0 < x < 1,$

a direct application of the comparison test (Theorem 10.8) tells us that $\sum a_n$ converges. The inequalities in (10.42) are equivalent to

(10.43) $\qquad\qquad 0 \leq a_n^{1/n} \leq x;$

hence the name *root test*.

If the sequence $\{a_n^{1/n}\}$ is convergent, the test may be restated in a somewhat more useful form that makes no reference to the number $x$.

THEOREM 10.12. ROOT TEST. *Let $\sum a_n$ be a series of nonnegative terms such that*

$$a_n^{1/n} \to R \qquad as \quad n \to \infty .$$

(a) *If $R < 1$, the series converges.*
(b) *If $R > 1$, the series diverges.*
(c) *If $R = 1$, the test is inconclusive.*

*Proof.* Assume $R < 1$ and choose $x$ so that $R < x < 1$. Then (10.43) must be satisfied for all $n \geq N$ for some $N$. Hence, $\sum a_n$ converges by the comparison test. This proves (a).

To prove (b), we observe that $R > 1$ implies $a_n > 1$ for infinitely many values of $n$ and hence $a_n$ cannot tend to 0. Therefore, by Theorem 10.6, $\sum a_n$ diverges. This proves (b).

To prove (c), consider the two examples in which $a_n = 1/n$ and $a_n = 1/n^2$. In both cases $R = 1$ since $n^{1/n} \to 1$ as $n \to \infty$ [see Equation (10.12) of Section 10.2], but $\sum 1/n$ diverges whereas $\sum 1/n^2$ converges.

EXAMPLE 1. The root test makes it easy to determine the convergence of the series $\sum_{n=3}^{\infty} (\log n)^{-n}$ since

$$a_n^{1/n} = \frac{1}{\log n} \to 0 \qquad as \quad n \to \infty .$$

EXAMPLE 2. Applying the root test to $\sum [n/(n + 1)]^{n^2}$, we find that

$$a_n^{1/n} = \left( \frac{n}{n + 1} \right)^n = \frac{1}{(1 + 1/n)^n} \to \frac{1}{e} \qquad as \qquad n \to \infty,$$

by Equation (10.13) of Section 10.2. Since $1/e < 1$, the series converges.

A slightly different use of the comparison test yields the ratio test.

THEOREM 10.13. RATIO TEST. *Let $\sum a_n$ be a series of positive terms such that*

$$\frac{a_{n+1}}{a_n} \to L \qquad as \quad n \to \infty .$$

(a) *If $L < 1$, the series converges.*
(b) *If $L > 1$, the series diverges.*
(c) *If $L = 1$, the test is inconclusive.*

*Proof.* Assume $L < 1$ and choose $x$ so that $L < x < 1$. Then there must be an $N$ such that $a_{n+1}/a_n < x$ for all $n \geq N$. This implies

$$\frac{a_{n+1}}{x^{n+1}} < \frac{a_n}{x^n} \qquad \text{for all } n \geq N .$$

In other words, the sequence $\{a_n/x^n\}$ is decreasing for $n \geq N$. In particular, when $n \geq N$, we must have $a_n/x^n \leq a_N/x^N$, or, in other words,

$$a_n \leq cx^n, \qquad \text{where} \quad c = \frac{a_N}{x^N}.$$

Therefore $\sum a_n$ is dominated by the convergent series $\sum x^n$. This proves (a).

To prove (b), we simply observe that $L > 1$ implies $a_{n+1} > a_n$ for all $n \geq N$ for some $N$, and hence $a_n$ cannot approach 0.

Finally, (c) is proved by using the same examples as in Theorem 10.12.

*Warning.* If the test ratio $a_{n+1}/a_n$ is always less than 1, it does not necessarily follow that the *limit* $L$ will be less than 1. For example, the harmonic series, which diverges, has test ratio $n/(n + 1)$ which is always less than 1 but the limit $L$ equals 1. On the other hand, for divergence it is sufficient that the test ratio be greater than 1 for all sufficiently large $n$ because for such $n$ we have $a_{n+1} > a_n$ and $a_n$ cannot approach 0.

EXAMPLE 3. We may establish the convergence of the series $\sum n!/n^n$ by the ratio test. The ratio of consecutive terms is

$$\frac{a_{n+1}}{a_n} = \frac{(n + 1)!}{(n + 1)^{n+1}} \cdot \frac{n^n}{n!} = \left(\frac{n}{n + 1}\right)^n = \frac{1}{(1 + 1/n)^n} \to \frac{1}{e} \qquad \text{as} \quad n \to \infty,$$

by formula (10.13) of Section 10.2. Since $1/e < 1$, the series converges. In particular, this implies that the general term of the series tends to 0; that is,

$$(10.44) \qquad \frac{n!}{n^n} \to 0 \qquad \text{as} \quad n \to \infty.$$

This is often described by saying that $n^n$ "grows faster" than $n!$ for large $n$. Also, with a natural extension of the $o$-notation, we can write (10.44) as follows: $n! = o(n^n)$ as $n \to \infty$.

*Note:* The relation (10.44) may also be proved directly by writing

$$\frac{n!}{n^n} = \frac{1}{n} \cdot \frac{2}{n} \cdots \frac{k}{n} \cdot \frac{k + 1}{n} \cdots \frac{n}{n},$$

where $k = n/2$ if $n$ is even, and $k = (n - 1)/2$ if $n$ is odd. If $n \geq 2$, the product of the first $k$ factors on the right does not exceed $(\tfrac{1}{2})^k$, and each of the remaining factors does not exceed 1. Since $(\tfrac{1}{2})^k \to 0$ as $n \to \infty$, this proves (10.44). Relation (10.44) also follows from (10.41).

The reader should realize that both the root test and the ratio test are, in reality, special cases of the comparison test. In both tests when we have case (a), convergence is deduced from the fact that the series in question can be dominated by a suitable geometric series $\sum x^n$. The usefulness of these tests in practice is that a knowledge of a particular comparison series $\sum x^n$ is not explicitly required. Further convergence tests may be deduced by using the comparison test in other ways. Two important examples known as *Raabe's test* and *Gauss' test* are described in Exercises 16 and 17 of Section 10.16. These are often helpful when the ratio test fails.

## 10.16   Exercises

Test the following series for convergence or divergence and give a reason for your decision in each case.

1. $\displaystyle\sum_{n=1}^{\infty} \frac{(n!)^2}{(2n)!}$.

2. $\displaystyle\sum_{n=1}^{\infty} \frac{(n!)^2}{2^{n^2}}$.

3. $\displaystyle\sum_{n=1}^{\infty} \frac{2^n n!}{n^n}$.

4. $\displaystyle\sum_{n=1}^{\infty} \frac{3^n n!}{n^n}$.

5. $\displaystyle\sum_{n=1}^{\infty} \frac{n!}{3^n}$.

6. $\displaystyle\sum_{n=1}^{\infty} \frac{n!}{2^{2n}}$.

7. $\displaystyle\sum_{n=2}^{\infty} \frac{1}{(\log n)^{1/n}}$.

8. $\displaystyle\sum_{n=1}^{\infty} (n^{1/n} - 1)^n$.

9. $\displaystyle\sum_{n=1}^{\infty} e^{-n^2}$.

10. $\displaystyle\sum_{n=1}^{\infty} \left( \frac{1}{n} - e^{-n^2} \right)$.

11. $\displaystyle\sum_{n=1}^{\infty} \frac{(1000)^n}{n!}$.

12. $\displaystyle\sum_{n=1}^{\infty} \frac{n^{n+1/n}}{(n+1/n)^n}$.

13. $\displaystyle\sum_{n=1}^{\infty} \frac{n^3[\sqrt{2} + (-1)^n]^n}{3^n}$.

14. $\displaystyle\sum_{n=1}^{\infty} r^n |\sin nx|$,     $r > 0$.

15. Let $\{a_n\}$ and $\{b_n\}$ be two sequences with $a_n > 0$ and $b_n > 0$ for all $n \geq N$, and let $c_n = b_n - b_{n+1}a_{n+1}/a_n$. Prove that:

   (a) If there is a positive constant $r$ such that $c_n \geq r > 0$ for all $n \geq N$, then $\sum a_n$ converges.

   [*Hint:*  Show that $\sum_{k=N}^{n} a_k \leq a_N b_N/r$.]

   (b) If $c_n \leq 0$ for $n \geq N$ and if $\sum 1/b_n$ diverges, then $\sum a_n$ diverges.

   [*Hint:*  Show that $\sum a_n$ dominates $\sum 1/b_n$ .]

16. Let $\sum a_n$ be a series of positive terms. Prove *Raabe's test*: If there is an $r > 0$ and an $N \geq 1$ such that

$$\frac{a_{n+1}}{a_n} \leq 1 - \frac{1}{n} - \frac{r}{n} \quad \text{for all } n \geq N,$$

then $\sum a_n$ converges.  The series $\sum a_n$ diverges if

$$\frac{a_{n+1}}{a_n} \geq 1 - \frac{1}{n} \quad \text{for all } n \geq N.$$

   [*Hint:*   Use Exercise 15 with $b_{n+1} = n$.]

17. Let $\sum a_n$ be a series of positive terms. Prove *Gauss' test*: If there is an $N \geq 1$, an $s > 1$, and an $M > 0$ such that

$$\frac{a_{n+1}}{a_n} = 1 - \frac{A}{n} + \frac{f(n)}{n^s} \quad \text{for } n \geq N,$$

   where $|f(n)| \leq M$ for all $n$, then $\sum a_n$ converges if $A > 1$ and diverges if $A \leq 1$.

   [*Hint:*  If $A \neq 1$, use Exercise 16.  If $A = 1$, use Exercise 15 with $b_{n+1} = n \log n$.]

18. Use Gauss' test (in Exercise 17) to prove that the series

$$\sum_{n=1}^{\infty}\left(\frac{1 \cdot 3 \cdot 5 \cdots (2n - 1)}{2 \cdot 4 \cdot 6 \cdots (2n)}\right)^k$$

converges if $k > 2$ and diverges if $k \leq 2$. For this example the ratio test fails.

## 10.17 Alternating series

Up to now we have been concerned largely with series of nonnegative terms. We wish to turn our attention next to series whose terms may be positive or negative. The simplest examples occur when the terms alternate in sign. These are called *alternating series* and they have the form

$$(10.45) \qquad \sum_{n=1}^{\infty}(-1)^{n-1}a_n = a_1 - a_2 + a_3 - a_4 + \cdots + (-1)^{n-1}a_n + \cdots ,$$

where each $a_n > 0$.

Examples of alternating series were known to many early investigators. We have already mentioned the logarithmic series

$$\log(1 + x) = x - \frac{x^2}{2} + \frac{x^3}{3} - \frac{x^4}{4} + \cdots + (-1)^{n-1}\frac{x^n}{n} + \cdots .$$

As we shall prove later on, this series converges and has the sum $\log(1 + x)$ whenever $-1 < x \leq 1$. For positive $x$, it is an alternating series. In particular, when $x = 1$ we obtain the formula

$$(10.46) \qquad \log 2 = 1 - \frac{1}{2} + \frac{1}{3} - \frac{1}{4} + \cdots + \frac{(-1)^{n-1}}{n} + \cdots ,$$

which tells us that the alternating harmonic series has the sum $\log 2$. This result is of special interest in view of the fact that the harmonic series $\sum 1/n$ diverges.

Closely related to (10.46) is the interesting formula

$$(10.47) \qquad \frac{\pi}{4} = 1 - \frac{1}{3} + \frac{1}{5} - \frac{1}{7} + \cdots + \frac{(-1)^{n-1}}{2n - 1} + \cdots$$

discovered by James Gregory in 1671. Leibniz rediscovered this result in 1673 while computing the area of a unit circular disk.

Both series in (10.46) and in (10.47) are alternating series of the form (10.45) in which the sequence $\{a_n\}$ decreases monotonically to zero. Leibniz noticed, in 1705, that this simple property of the $a_n$ implies the convergence of *any* alternating series.

THEOREM 10.14.    LEIBNIZ'S RULE.    *If $\{a_n\}$ is a monotonic decreasing sequence with limit 0, then the alternating series $\sum_{n=1}^{\infty} (-1)^{n-1} a_n$ converges. If $S$ denotes its sum and $s_n$ its nth partial sum, we also have the inequalities*

(10.48)                      $$0 < (-1)^n (S - s_n) < a_{n+1} \quad \text{for each } n \geq 1 .$$

The inequalities in (10.48) provide a useful way to estimate the error in approximating the sum $S$ by any partial sum $s_n$. The first inequality tells us that the error, $S - s_n$, has the sign $(-1)^n$, which is the same as the sign of the first neglected term, $(-1)^n a_{n+1}$. The second inequality states that the absolute value of this error is less than that of the first neglected term.

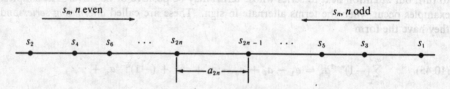

FIGURE 10.5    Proof of Leibniz's rule for alternating series.

*Proof.* The idea of the proof of Leibniz's rule is quite simple and is illustrated in Figure 10.5. The partial sums $s_{2n}$ (consisting of an even number of terms) form an increasing sequence because $s_{2n+2} - s_{2n} = a_{2n+1} - a_{2n+2} > 0$. Similarly, the partial sums $s_{2n-1}$ form a decreasing sequence. Both sequences are bounded below by $s_2$ and above by $s_1$. Therefore, each sequence $\{s_{2n}\}$ and $\{s_{2n-1}\}$, being monotonic and bounded, converges to a limit, say $s_{2n} \to S'$, and $s_{2n-1} \to S''$. But $S' = S''$ because

$$S' - S'' = \lim_{n \to \infty} s_{2n} - \lim_{n \to \infty} s_{2n-1} = \lim_{n \to \infty} (s_{2n} - s_{2n-1}) = \lim_{n \to \infty} (-a_{2n}) = 0 .$$

If we denote this common limit by $S$, it is clear that the series converges and has sum $S$. To derive the inequalities in (10.48) we argue as follows: Since $s_{2n} \nearrow$ and $s_{2n-1} \searrow$, we have

$$s_{2n} < s_{2n+2} \leq S \quad \text{and} \quad S \leq s_{2n+1} < s_{2n-1} \quad \text{for all } n \geq 1 .$$

Therefore we have the inequalities

$$0 < S - s_{2n} \leq s_{2n+1} - s_{2n} = a_{2n+1} \quad \text{and} \quad 0 < s_{2n-1} - S \leq s_{2n-1} - s_{2n} = a_{2n} ,$$

which, taken together, yield (10.48). This completes the proof.

EXAMPLE 1.    Since $1/n \searrow$ and $1/n \to 0$ as $n \to \infty$, the convergence of the alternating harmonic series $1 - \frac{1}{2} + \frac{1}{3} - \frac{1}{4} + \cdots$ is an immediate consequence of Leibniz's rule. The sum of this series is computed below in Example 4.

EXAMPLE 2.    The alternating series $\sum (-1)^n (\log n)/n$ converges. To prove this using Leibniz's rule, we must show that $(\log n)/n \to 0$ as $n \to \infty$ and that $(\log n)/n \searrow$. The first statement follows from Equation (10.11) of Section 10.2. To prove the second statement, we note that the function $f$ for which

$$f(x) = \frac{\log x}{x} \quad \text{when} \quad x > 0$$

has the derivative $f'(x) = (1 - \log x)/x^2$. When $x > e$, this is negative and $f$ is monotonic decreasing. In particular, $f(n + 1) < f(n)$ for $n \geq 3$.

EXAMPLE 3. An important limit relation may be derived as a consequence of Leibniz's rule. Let

$$a_1 = 1, \quad a_2 = \int_1^2 \frac{dx}{x}, \quad a_3 = \tfrac{1}{2}, \quad a_4 = \int_2^3 \frac{dx}{x}, \quad \ldots,$$

where, in general,

$$a_{2n-1} = \frac{1}{n} \quad \text{and} \quad a_{2n} = \int_n^{n+1} \frac{dx}{x} \quad \text{for} \quad n = 1, 2, 3, \ldots.$$

It is easy to verify that $a_n \to 0$ as $n \to \infty$ and that $a_n \searrow$. Hence the series $\sum (-1)^{n-1} a_n$ converges. Denote its sum by $C$ and its $n$th partial sum by $s_n$. The $(2n - 1)$st partial sum may be expressed as follows:

$$s_{2n-1} = 1 - \int_1^2 \frac{dx}{x} + \frac{1}{2} - \int_2^3 \frac{dx}{x} + \cdots + \frac{1}{n-1} - \int_{n-1}^n \frac{dx}{x} + \frac{1}{n}$$

$$= 1 + \frac{1}{2} + \cdots + \frac{1}{n} - \int_1^n \frac{dx}{x} = 1 + \frac{1}{2} + \cdots + \frac{1}{n} - \log n.$$

Since $s_{2n-1} \to C$ as $n \to \infty$, we obtain the following limit formula:

$$(10.49) \qquad \lim_{n \to \infty} \left(1 + \frac{1}{2} + \cdots + \frac{1}{n} - \log n\right) = C.$$

The number $C$ defined by this limit is called *Euler's constant* (sometimes denoted by $\gamma$). Like $\pi$ and $e$, this number appears in many analytic formulas. Its value, correct to ten decimals, is 0.5772156649. An interesting problem, unsolved to this time, is to decide whether Euler's constant is rational or irrational.

Relation (10.49) can also be expressed as follows:

$$(10.50) \qquad \sum_{k=1}^n \frac{1}{k} = \log n + C + o(1) \qquad \text{as} \quad n \to \infty.$$

From this it follows that the ratio $(1 + \tfrac{1}{2} + \cdots + 1/n)/\log n \to 1$ as $n \to \infty$, so the partial sums of the harmonic series are asymptotically equal to $\log n$. That is, we have

$$\sum_{k=1}^n \frac{1}{k} \sim \log n \qquad \text{as} \quad n \to \infty.$$

The relation (10.50) not only explains why the harmonic series diverges, but it also gives us some concrete idea of the rate of growth of its partial sums. In the next example we use this relation to prove that the alternating harmonic series has the sum log 2.

EXAMPLE 4. Let $s_m = \sum_{k=1}^{m} (-1)^{k-1}/k$. We know that $s_m$ tends to a limit as $m \to \infty$, and we shall prove now that this limit is log 2. When $m$ is even, say $m = 2n$, we may separate the positive and negative terms to obtain

$$s_{2n} = \sum_{k=1}^{n} \frac{1}{2k-1} - \sum_{k=1}^{n} \frac{1}{2k} = \left( \sum_{k=1}^{2n} \frac{1}{k} - \sum_{k=1}^{n} \frac{1}{2k} \right) - \sum_{k=1}^{n} \frac{1}{2k} = \sum_{k=1}^{2n} \frac{1}{k} - \sum_{k=1}^{n} \frac{1}{k}.$$

Applying (10.50) to each sum on the extreme right, we obtain

$$s_{2n} = (\log 2n + C + o(1)) - (\log n + C + o(1)) = \log 2 + o(1),$$

so $s_{2n} \to \log 2$ as $n \to \infty$. This proves that the sum of the alternating harmonic series is log 2.

## 10.18 Conditional and absolute convergence

Although the alternating harmonic series $\sum (-1)^{n-1}/n$ is convergent, the series obtained by replacing each term by its absolute value is divergent. This shows that, in general, convergence of $\sum a_n$ does not imply convergence of $\sum |a_n|$. In the other direction, we have the following theorem.

THEOREM 10.15.    *Assume $\sum |a_n|$ converges. Then $\sum a_n$ also converges, and we have*

$$(10.51) \qquad\qquad \left| \sum_{n=1}^{\infty} a_n \right| \le \sum_{n=1}^{\infty} |a_n|.$$

*Proof.* Assume first that the terms $a_n$ are real. Let $b_n = a_n + |a_n|$. We shall prove that $\sum b_n$ converges. It then follows (by Theorem 10.2) that $\sum a_n$ converges because $a_n = b_n - |a_n|$.

Since $b_n$ is either 0 or $2|a_n|$, we have $0 \le b_n \le 2|a_n|$, and hence $\sum |a_n|$ dominates $\sum b_n$. Therefore $\sum b_n$ converges and, as already mentioned, this implies convergence of $\sum a_n$.

Now suppose the terms $a_n$ are complex, say $a_n = u_n + iv_n$, where $u_n$ and $v_n$ are real. Since $|u_n| \le |a_n|$, convergence of $\sum |a_n|$ implies convergence of $\sum |u_n|$ and this, in turn, implies convergence of $\sum u_n$, since the $u_n$ are real. Similarly, $\sum v_n$ converges. By linearity, the series $\sum (u_n + iv_n)$ converges.

To prove (10.51), we note that $|\sum_{k=1}^{n} a_k| \le \sum_{k=1}^{n} |a_k|$, and then we let $n \to \infty$.

DEFINITION. *A series $\sum a_n$ is called absolutely convergent if $\sum |a_n|$ converges. It is called conditionally convergent if $\sum a_n$ converges but $\sum |a_n|$ diverges.*

If $\sum a_n$ and $\sum b_n$ are absolutely convergent, then so is the series $\sum (\alpha a_n + \beta b_n)$ for every choice of $\alpha$ and $\beta$. This follows at once from the inequalities

$$\sum_{n=1}^{M} |\alpha a_n + \beta b_n| \leq |\alpha| \sum_{n=1}^{M} |a_n| + |\beta| \sum_{n=1}^{M} |b_n| \leq |\alpha| \sum_{n=1}^{\infty} |a_n| + |\beta| \sum_{n=1}^{\infty} |b_n|,$$

which show that the partial sums of $\sum |\alpha a_n + \beta b_n|$ are bounded.

## 10.19  The convergence tests of Dirichlet and Abel

The convergence tests of the earlier sections that were developed for series of nonnegative terms may also be used to test *absolute* convergence of a series with arbitrary complex terms. In this section we discuss two tests that are often useful for determining convergence when the series might not converge absolutely. Both tests make use of an algebraic identity known as the *Abel partial summation formula*, named in honor of the Norwegian mathematician Niels Henrik Abel (1802–1829). Abel's formula is analogous to the formula for integration by parts and may be described as follows.

THEOREM 10.16.  ABEL'S PARTIAL SUMMATION FORMULA.  *Let* $\{a_n\}$ *and* $\{b_n\}$ *be two sequences of complex numbers, and let*

$$A_n = \sum_{k=1}^{n} a_k.$$

*Then we have the identity*

(10.52)
$$\sum_{k=1}^{n} a_k b_k = A_n b_{n+1} + \sum_{k=1}^{n} A_k (b_k - b_{k+1}).$$

*Proof.*  If we define $A_0 = 0$, then $a_k = A_k - A_{k-1}$ for each $k = 1, 2, \ldots, n$, so we have

$$\sum_{k=1}^{n} a_k b_k = \sum_{k=1}^{n} (A_k - A_{k-1}) b_k = \sum_{k=1}^{n} A_k b_k - \sum_{k=1}^{n} A_k b_{k+1} + A_n b_{n+1},$$

which gives us (10.52).

If we let $n \to \infty$ in (10.52), we see that the series $\sum a_k b_k$ converges if both the series $\sum A_k(b_k - b_{k+1})$ and the sequence $\{A_n b_{n+1}\}$ converge. The next two tests give sufficient conditions for these to converge.

THEOREM 10.17.  DIRICHLET'S TEST.  *Let* $\sum a_n$ *be a series of complex terms whose partial sums form a bounded sequence. Let* $\{b_n\}$ *be a decreasing sequence which converges to* 0. *Then the series* $\sum a_n b_n$ *converges.*

*Proof.*  Using the notation of Theorem 10.16, there is an $M > 0$ such that $|A_n| \leq M$ for all $n$. Therefore $A_n b_{n+1} \to 0$ as $n \to \infty$. To establish convergence of $\sum a_n b_n$, we need only show that the series $\sum A_k(b_k - b_{k+1})$ is convergent. Since $b_n \searrow$, we have the inequality

$$|A_k(b_k - b_{k+1})| \leq M(b_k - b_{k+1}).$$

But the series $\sum (b_k - b_{k+1})$ is a convergent telescoping series which dominates

$$\sum A_k(b_k - b_{k+1}) .$$

This implies absolute convergence and hence convergence of $\sum A_k(b_k - b_{k+1})$.

THEOREM 10.18.   ABEL'S TEST.   *Let $\sum a_n$ be a convergent series of complex terms and let $\{b_n\}$ be a monotonic convergent sequence of real terms. Then the series $\sum a_n b_n$ converges.*

*Proof.*   Again we use the notation of Theorem 10.16. Convergence of $\sum a_n$ implies convergence of the sequence $\{A_n\}$ and hence of the sequence $\{A_n b_{n+1}\}$. Also, $\{A_n\}$ is a bounded sequence. The rest of the proof is similar to that of Dirichlet's test.

To use Dirichlet's test effectively, we need some examples of series having bounded partial sums. Of course, every *convergent* series has this property. An important example of a divergent series with bounded partial sums is the geometric series $\sum x^n$, where $x$ is a complex number with $|x| = 1$ but $x \neq 1$. The next theorem gives an upper bound for the partial sums of this series. When $|x| = 1$, we may write $x = e^{2i\theta}$, where $\theta$ is real, and we have the following.

THEOREM 10.19.   *For every real $\theta$ not an integer multiple of $\pi$, we have the identity*

$$(10.53) \qquad \sum_{k=1}^{n} e^{2ik\theta} = \frac{\sin n\theta}{\sin \theta} e^{i(n+1)\theta},$$

*from which we obtain the estimate*

$$(10.54) \qquad \left| \sum_{k=1}^{n} e^{2ik\theta} \right| \leq \frac{1}{|\sin \theta|} .$$

*Proof.*   If $x \neq 1$, the partial sums of the geometric series are given by

$$\sum_{k=1}^{n} x^k = x \frac{x^n - 1}{x - 1} .$$

Writing $x = e^{2i\theta}$ in this formula, where $\theta$ is real but not an integer multiple of $\pi$, we find

$$\sum_{k=1}^{n} e^{2ik\theta} = e^{2i\theta} \frac{e^{2in\theta} - 1}{e^{2i\theta} - 1} = \frac{e^{in\theta} - e^{-in\theta}}{e^{i\theta} - e^{-i\theta}} e^{i(n+1)\theta} = \frac{\sin n\theta}{\sin \theta} e^{i(n+1)\theta} .$$

This proves (10.53). To deduce (10.54), we simply note that $|\sin n\theta| \leq 1$ and $|e^{i(n+1)\theta}| = 1$.

EXAMPLES. Assume $\{b_n\}$ is any decreasing sequence of real numbers with limit 0. Taking $a_n = x^n$ in Dirichlet's test, where $x$ is complex, $|x| = 1$, $x \neq 1$, we find that the series

$$(10.55) \qquad \sum_{n=1}^{\infty} b_n x^n ,$$

converges. Note that Leibniz's rule for alternating series is merely the special case in which $x = -1$. If we write $x = e^{i\theta}$, where $\theta$ is real but not an integer multiple of $2\pi$, and consider the real and imaginary parts of (10.55), we deduce that the two trigonometric series

$$\sum_{n=1}^{\infty} b_n \cos n\theta \qquad \text{and} \qquad \sum_{n=1}^{\infty} b_n \sin n\theta$$

converge. In particular, when $b_n = n^{-\alpha}$, where $\alpha > 0$, we find the following series converge:

$$\sum_{n=1}^{\infty} \frac{e^{in\theta}}{n^\alpha}, \qquad \sum_{n=1}^{\infty} \frac{\cos n\theta}{n^\alpha}, \qquad \sum_{n=1}^{\infty} \frac{\sin n\theta}{n^\alpha} .$$

When $\alpha > 1$, they converge absolutely since they are dominated by $\sum n^{-\alpha}$.

## 10.20 Exercises

In Exercises 1 through 32, determine convergence or divergence of the given series. In case of convergence, determine whether the series converges absolutely or conditionally.

1. $\displaystyle\sum_{n=1}^{\infty} \frac{(-1)^{n+1}}{\sqrt{n}}$.

2. $\displaystyle\sum_{n=1}^{\infty} (-1)^n \frac{\sqrt{n}}{n + 100}$.

3. $\displaystyle\sum_{n=1}^{\infty} \frac{(-1)^{n-1}}{n^8}$.

4. $\displaystyle\sum_{n=1}^{\infty} (-1)^n \left( \frac{1 \cdot 3 \cdot 5 \cdots (2n - 1)}{2 \cdot 4 \cdot 6 \cdots (2n)} \right)^3$.

5. $\displaystyle\sum_{n=1}^{\infty} \frac{(-1)^{n(n-1)/2}}{2^n}$.

6. $\displaystyle\sum_{n=1}^{\infty} (-1)^n \left( \frac{2n + 100}{3n + 1} \right)^n$.

7. $\displaystyle\sum_{n=2}^{\infty} \frac{(-1)^n}{\sqrt{n} + (-1)^n}$.

8. $\displaystyle\sum_{n=1}^{\infty} \frac{(-1)^n}{\sqrt[n]{n}}$.

9. $\displaystyle\sum_{n=1}^{\infty} (-1)^n \frac{n^2}{1 + n^2}$.

10. $\displaystyle\sum_{n=1}^{\infty} \frac{(-1)^n}{\log (e^n + e^{-n})}$.

11. $\displaystyle\sum_{n=1}^{\infty} \frac{(-1)^n}{n \log^2 (n + 1)}$.

12. $\displaystyle\sum_{n=1}^{\infty} \frac{(-1)^n}{\log (1 + 1/n)}$.

13. $\displaystyle\sum_{n=1}^{\infty} \frac{(-1)^n n^{37}}{(n + 1)!}$.

14. $\displaystyle\sum_{n=1}^{\infty} (-1)^n \int_n^{n+1} \frac{e^{-x}}{x} \, dx$.

15. $\displaystyle\sum_{n=1}^{\infty} \sin (\log n)$.

16. $\displaystyle\sum_{n=1}^{\infty} \log \left( n \sin \frac{1}{n} \right)$.

17. $\displaystyle\sum_{n=1}^{\infty} (-1)^n \left(1 - n \sin\frac{1}{n}\right)$ .

18. $\displaystyle\sum_{n=1}^{\infty} (-1)^n \left(1 - \cos\frac{1}{n}\right)$ .

19. $\displaystyle\sum_{n=1}^{\infty} (-1)^n \arctan\frac{1}{2n+1}$ .

20. $\displaystyle\sum_{n=1}^{\infty} (-1)^n \left(\frac{\pi}{2} - \arctan(\log n)\right)$ .

21. $\displaystyle\sum_{n=1}^{\infty} \log\left(1 + \frac{1}{|\sin n|}\right)$ .

22. $\displaystyle\sum_{n=2}^{\infty} \sin\left(n\pi + \frac{1}{\log n}\right)$ .

23. $\displaystyle\sum_{n=1}^{\infty} \frac{1}{n(1 + 1/2 + \cdots + 1/n)}$ .

24. $\displaystyle\sum_{n=1}^{\infty} (-1)^n \left[e - \left(1 + \frac{1}{n}\right)^n\right]$ .

25. $\displaystyle\sum_{n=2}^{\infty} \frac{(-1)^n}{(n + (-1)^n)^s}$ .

26. $\displaystyle\sum_{n=1}^{\infty} (-1)^{n(n-1)/2} \left(\frac{n^{100}}{2^n}\right)$ .

27. $\displaystyle\sum_{n=1}^{\infty} a_n$ ,    where    $a_n = \begin{cases} 1/n & \text{if } n \text{ is a square,} \\ 1/n^2 & \text{otherwise.} \end{cases}$

28. $\displaystyle\sum_{n=1}^{\infty} a_n$ ,    where    $a_n = \begin{cases} 1/n^2 & \text{if } n \text{ is odd,} \\ -1/n & \text{if } n \text{ is even.} \end{cases}$

29. $\displaystyle\sum_{n=1}^{\infty} \left(\sin\frac{1}{n}\right)^{3/2}$ .

30. $\displaystyle\sum_{n=1}^{\infty} \frac{\sin(1/n)}{n}$ .

31. $\displaystyle\sum_{n=1}^{\infty} \left(1 - n\sin\frac{1}{n}\right)$ .

32. $\displaystyle\sum_{n=1}^{\infty} \frac{1 - n\sin(1/n)}{n}$ .

In Exercises 33 through 46, describe the set of all complex $z$ for which the series converges.

33. $\displaystyle\sum_{n=1}^{\infty} n^n z^n$ .

34. $\displaystyle\sum_{n=1}^{\infty} \frac{(-1)^n z^{3n}}{n!}$ .

35. $\displaystyle\sum_{n=0}^{\infty} \frac{z^n}{3^n}$ .

36. $\displaystyle\sum_{n=1}^{\infty} \frac{z^n}{n^n}$ .

37. $\displaystyle\sum_{n=1}^{\infty} \frac{(-1)^n}{z+n}$ .

38. $\displaystyle\sum_{n=1}^{\infty} \frac{z^n}{\sqrt{n}} \log\frac{2n+1}{n}$ .

39. $\displaystyle\sum_{n=1}^{\infty} \left(1 + \frac{1}{5n+1}\right)^{n^2} |z|^{17n}$ .

40. $\displaystyle\sum_{n=0}^{\infty} \frac{(z-1)^n}{(n+2)!}$ .

41. $\displaystyle\sum_{n=1}^{\infty} \frac{(-1)^n (z-1)^n}{n}$ .

42. $\displaystyle\sum_{n=1}^{\infty} \frac{(2z+3)^n}{n \log(n+1)}$ .

43. $\displaystyle\sum_{n=1}^{\infty} \frac{(-1)^n}{2n-1} \left(\frac{1-z}{1+z}\right)^n$ .

44. $\displaystyle\sum_{n=1}^{\infty} \left(\frac{z}{2z+1}\right)^n$ .

45. $\displaystyle\sum_{n=1}^{\infty} \frac{n}{n+1} \left(\frac{z}{2z+1}\right)^n$ .

46. $\displaystyle\sum_{n=1}^{\infty} \frac{1}{(1 + |z|^2)^n}$ .

In Exercises 47 and 48, determine the set of real $x$ for which the given series converges.

47. $\displaystyle\sum_{n=1}^{\infty} (-1)^n \frac{2^n \sin^{2n} x}{n}$ .

48. $\displaystyle\sum_{n=1}^{\infty} \frac{2^n \sin^n x}{n^2}$ .

In Exercises 49 through 52, the series are assumed to have real terms.

49. If $a_n > 0$ and $\sum a_n$ converges, prove that $\sum 1/a_n$ diverges.

50. If $\sum |a_n|$ converges, prove that $\sum a_n^2$ converges. Give a counterexample in which $\sum a_n^2$ converges but $\sum |a_n|$ diverges.

51. Given a convergent series $\sum a_n$, where each $a_n \geq 0$. Prove that $\sum \sqrt{a_n}\, n^{-p}$ converges if $p > \frac{1}{2}$. Give a counterexample for $p = \frac{1}{2}$.

52. Prove or disprove the following statements:
    (a) If $\sum a_n$ converges absolutely, then so does $\sum a_n^2/(1 + a_n^2)$.
    (b) If $\sum a_n$ converges absolutely, and if no $a_n = -1$, then $\sum a_n/(1 + a_n)$ converges absolutely.

## *10.21  Rearrangements of series

The order of the terms in a finite sum can be rearranged without affecting the value of the sum. In 1833 Cauchy made the surprising discovery that this is not always true for infinite series. For example, consider the alternating harmonic series

$$(10.56) \qquad 1 - \tfrac{1}{2} + \tfrac{1}{3} - \tfrac{1}{4} + \tfrac{1}{5} - \tfrac{1}{6} + - \cdots = \log 2 .$$

The convergence of this series to the sum $\log 2$ was shown in Section 10.17. If we rearrange the terms of this series, taking alternately two positive terms followed by one negative term, we get a new series which can be designated as follows:

$$(10.57) \qquad 1 + \tfrac{1}{3} - \tfrac{1}{2} + \tfrac{1}{5} + \tfrac{1}{7} - \tfrac{1}{4} + \tfrac{1}{9} + \tfrac{1}{11} - \tfrac{1}{6} + + - \cdots .$$

Each term which occurs in the alternating harmonic series occurs exactly once in this rearrangement, and vice versa. But we can easily prove that this new series has a sum greater than $\log 2$. We proceed as follows:

Let $t_n$ denote the $n$th partial sum of (10.57). If $n$ is a multiple of 3, say $n = 3m$, the partial sum $t_{3m}$ contains $2m$ positive terms and $m$ negative terms and is given by

$$t_{3m} = \sum_{k=1}^{2m} \frac{1}{2k-1} - \sum_{k=1}^{m} \frac{1}{2k} = \left( \sum_{k=1}^{4m} \frac{1}{k} - \sum_{k=1}^{2m} \frac{1}{2k} \right) - \frac{1}{2} \sum_{k=1}^{m} \frac{1}{k} = \sum_{k=1}^{4m} \frac{1}{k} - \frac{1}{2} \sum_{k=1}^{2m} \frac{1}{k} - \frac{1}{2} \sum_{k=1}^{m} \frac{1}{k} .$$

In each of the last three sums, we use the asymptotic relation

$$\sum_{k=1}^{n} \frac{1}{k} = \log n + C + o(1) \qquad \text{as} \quad n \to \infty ,$$

to obtain

$$t_{3m} = (\log 4m + C + o(1)) - \tfrac{1}{2}(\log 2m + C + o(1)) - \tfrac{1}{2}(\log m + C + o(1))$$

$$= \tfrac{3}{2} \log 2 + o(1) .$$

Thus $t_{3m} \to \frac{3}{2} \log 2$ as $m \to \infty$. But $t_{3m+1} = t_{3m} + 1/(4m + 1)$ and $t_{3m-1} = t_{3m} - 1/(2m)$, so $t_{3m+1}$ and $t_{3m-1}$ have the same limit as $t_{3m}$ when $m \to \infty$. Therefore, every partial sum $t_n$ has the limit $\frac{3}{2} \log 2$ as $n \to \infty$, so the sum of the series in (10.57) is $\frac{3}{2} \log 2$.

The foregoing example shows that rearrangement of the terms of a convergent series may alter its sum. We shall prove next that this can happen only if the given series is *conditionally* convergent. That is, rearrangement of an absolutely convergent series does not alter its sum. Before we prove this, we will explain more precisely what is meant by a rearrangement.

DEFINITION. *Let* $\mathbf{P} = \{1, 2, 3, \ldots\}$ *denote the set of positive integers. Let $f$ be a function whose domain is* $\mathbf{P}$ *and whose range is* $\mathbf{P}$, *and assume $f$ has the following property:*

$$m \neq n \quad \text{implies} \quad f(m) \neq f(n) .$$

*Such a function $f$ is called a permutation of* $\mathbf{P}$, *or a one-to-one mapping of* $\mathbf{P}$ *onto itself. If* $\sum a_n$ *and* $\sum b_n$ *are two series such that for every* $n \geq 1$ *we have*

$$b_n = a_{f(n)}$$

*for some permutation $f$, then the series* $\sum b_n$ *is said to be a rearrangement of* $\sum a_n$ .

EXAMPLE. If $\sum a_n$ denotes the alternating harmonic series in (10.56) and if $\sum b_n$ denotes the series in (10.57), we have $b_n = a_{f(n)}$, where $f$ is the permutation defined by the formulas

$$f(3n + 1) = 4n + 1 , \quad f(3n + 2) = 4n + 3 , \quad f(3n + 3) = 2n + 2 .$$

THEOREM 10.20. *Let* $\sum a_n$ *be an absolutely convergent series having sum $S$. Then every rearrangement of* $\sum a_n$ *also converges absolutely and has sum $S$.*

*Proof.* Let $\sum b_n$ be a rearrangement, say $b_n = a_{f(n)}$. First we note that $\sum b_n$ converges absolutely because $\sum |b_n|$ is a series of nonnegative terms whose partial sums are bounded above by $\sum |a_n|$.

To prove that $\sum b_n$ also has sum $S$, we introduce

$$B_n = \sum_{k=1}^{n} b_k , \quad A_n = \sum_{k=1}^{n} a_k , \quad A_n^* = \sum_{k=1}^{n} |a_k| , \quad \text{and} \quad S^* = \sum_{k=1}^{\infty} |a_k| .$$

Now $A_n \to S$ and $A_n^* \to S^*$ as $n \to \infty$. Therefore, given any $\epsilon > 0$, there is an $N$ such that

$$|A_N - S| < \frac{\epsilon}{2} \quad \text{and} \quad |A_N^* - S^*| < \frac{\epsilon}{2} .$$

For this $N$ we can choose $M$ so that

$$\{1, 2, \ldots, N\} \subseteq \{f(1), f(2), \ldots, f(M)\} .$$

This is possible because the range of $f$ includes all the positive integers. If $n \geq M$, we have

$$(10.58) \quad |B_n - S| = |B_n - A_N + A_N - S| \leq |B_n - A_N| + |A_N - S| \leq |B_n - A_N| + \frac{\epsilon}{2}.$$

But we also have

$$|B_n - A_N| = \left| \sum_{k=1}^{n} b_k - \sum_{k=1}^{N} a_k \right| = \left| \sum_{k=1}^{n} a_{f(k)} - \sum_{k=1}^{N} a_k \right|.$$

The terms $a_1, \ldots, a_N$ cancel in the subtraction, so we have

$$|B_n - A_N| \leq |a_{N+1}| + |a_{N+2}| + \cdots = |A_N^* - S^*| < \frac{\epsilon}{2}.$$

Combining this with (10.58), we see that $|B_n - S| < \epsilon$ for all $n \geq M$, which means that $B_n \to S$ as $n \to \infty$. This proves that the rearranged series $\sum b_n$ has sum $S$.

The hypothesis of absolute convergence in Theorem 10.20 is essential. Riemann discovered that a conditionally convergent series of real terms can always be rearranged to give a series which converges to any preassigned sum. Riemann's argument is based on a special property of conditionally convergent series of real terms. Such a series $\sum a_n$ has infinitely many positive terms and infinitely many negative terms. Consider the two new series $\sum a_n^+$ and $\sum a_n^-$ obtained by taking the positive terms alone and the negative terms alone. More specifically, define $a_n^+$ and $a_n^-$ as follows:

$$(10.59) \quad a_n^+ = \frac{a_n + |a_n|}{2}, \qquad a_n^- = \frac{a_n - |a_n|}{2}.$$

If $a_n$ is positive, then $a_n^+ = a_n$ and $a_n^- = 0$; if $a_n$ is negative, then $a_n^- = a_n$ and $a_n^+ = 0$. The two new series $\sum a_n^+$ and $\sum a_n^-$ are related to the given series $\sum a_n$ as follows.

THEOREM 10.21. *Given a series $\sum a_n$ of real terms, define $a_n^+$ and $a_n^-$ by (10.59).*
(a) *If $\sum a_n$ is conditionally convergent, both $\sum a_n^+$ and $\sum a_n^-$ diverge.*
(b) *If $\sum a_n$ is absolutely convergent, both $\sum a_n^+$ and $\sum a_n^-$ converge, and we have*

$$(10.60) \quad \sum_{n=1}^{\infty} a_n = \sum_{n=1}^{\infty} a_n^+ + \sum_{n=1}^{\infty} a_n^-.$$

*Proof.* To prove part (a), we note that $\sum \frac{1}{2}a_n$ converges and $\sum \frac{1}{2}|a_n|$ diverges. Therefore, by the linearity property (Theorem 10.3) $\sum a_n^+$ diverges and $\sum a_n^-$ diverges. To prove part (b), we note that both $\sum \frac{1}{2}a_n$ and $\sum \frac{1}{2}|a_n|$ converge, so by the linearity property (Theorem 10.2) both $\sum a_n^+$ and $\sum a_n^-$ converge. Since $a_n = a_n^+ + a_n^-$, we also obtain (10.60).

Now we can easily prove Riemann's rearrangement theorem.

THEOREM 10.22. *Let $\sum a_n$ be a conditionally convergent series of real terms, and let $S$ be a given real number. Then there is a rearrangement $\sum b_n$ of $\sum a_n$ which converges to the sum $S$.*

*Proof.* Define $a_n^+$ and $a_n^-$ as indicated in (10.59). Both series $\sum a_n^+$ and $\sum a_n^-$ diverge since $\sum a_n$ is conditionally convergent. We rearrange $\sum a_n$ as follows:

Take, in order, just enough positive terms $a_n^+$ so that their sum exceeds $S$. If $p_1$ positive terms are required, we have

$$\sum_{n=1}^{p_1} a_n > S \quad \text{but} \quad \sum_{n=1}^{q} a_n \leq S \quad \text{if} \quad q < p_1.$$

This is always possible since the partial sums of $\sum a_n^+$ tend to $+\infty$. To this sum we add just enough negative terms $a_n^-$, say $n_1$ negative terms, so that the resulting sum is less than $S$. This is possible since the partial sums of $a_n^-$ tend to $-\infty$. Thus, we have

$$\sum_{n=1}^{p_1} a_n^+ + \sum_{n=1}^{n_1} a_n^- < S \quad \text{but} \quad \sum_{n=1}^{p_1} a_n^+ + \sum_{n=1}^{m} a_n^- \geq S \quad \text{if} \quad m < n_1.$$

Now we repeat the process, adding just enough new positive terms to make the sum exceed $S$, and then just enough new negative terms to make the sum less than $S$. Continuing in this way, we obtain a rearrangement $\sum b_n$. Each partial sum of $\sum b_n$ differs from $S$ by at most one term $a_n^+$ or $a_n^-$. But $a_n \to 0$ as $n \to \infty$ since $\sum a_n$ converges, so the partial sums of $\sum b_n$ tend to $S$. This proves that the rearranged series $\sum b_n$ converges and has sum $S$, as asserted.

## 10.22  Miscellaneous review exercises

1. (a) Let $a_n = \sqrt{n+1} - \sqrt{n}$. Compute $\lim_{n \to \infty} a_n$.
   (b) Let $a_n = (n+1)^c - n^c$, where $c$ is real. Determine those $c$ for which the sequence $\{a_n\}$ converges and those for which it diverges. In case of convergence, compute the limit of the sequence. Remember that $c$ can be positive, negative, or zero.
2. (a) If $0 < x < 1$, prove that $(1 + x^n)^{1/n}$ approaches a limit as $n \to \infty$ and compute this limit.
   (b) Given $a > 0$, $b > 0$, compute $\lim_{n \to \infty} (a^n + b^n)^{1/n}$.
3. A sequence $\{a_n\}$ is defined recursively in terms of $a_1$ and $a_2$ by the formula

$$a_{n+1} = \frac{a_n + a_{n-1}}{2} \quad \text{for} \quad n \geq 2.$$

   (a) Assuming that $\{a_n\}$ converges, compute the limit of the sequence in terms of $a_1$ and $a_2$. The result is a weighted arithmetic mean of $a_1$ and $a_2$.
   (b) Prove that for every choice of $a_1$ and $a_2$ the sequence $\{a_n\}$ converges. You may assume that $a_1 < a_2$. [*Hint:* Consider $\{a_{2n}\}$ and $\{a_{2n+1}\}$ separately.]
4. A sequence $\{x_n\}$ is defined by the following recursion formula:

$$x_1 = 1, \quad x_{n+1} = \sqrt{1 + x_n}.$$

Prove that the sequence converges and find its limit.
5. A sequence $\{x_n\}$ is defined by the following recursion formula:

$$x_0 = 1, \quad x_1 = 1, \quad \frac{1}{x_{n+2}} = \frac{1}{x_{n+1}} + \frac{1}{x_n}.$$

Prove that the sequence converges and find its limit.

6. Let $\{a_n\}$ and $\{b_n\}$ be two sequences such that for each $n$ we have

$$e^{a_n} = a_n + e^{b_n}$$

(a) Show that $a_n > 0$ implies $b_n > 0$.
(b) If $a_n > 0$ for all $n$ and if $\sum a_n$ converges, show that $\sum (b_n/a_n)$ converges.

In Exercises 7 through 11, test the given series for convergence.

7. $\sum_{n=1}^{\infty} (\sqrt{1 + n^2} - n)$.

9. $\sum_{n=2}^{\infty} \dfrac{1}{(\log n)^{\log n}}$.

8. $\sum_{n=1}^{\infty} n^s(\sqrt{n + 1} - 2\sqrt{n} + \sqrt{n - 1})$.

10. $\sum_{n=1}^{\infty} \dfrac{1}{n^{1 + 1/n}}$.

11. $\sum_{n=1}^{\infty} a_n$, where $a_n = 1/n$ if $n$ is odd, $a_n = 1/n^2$ if $n$ is even.
12. Show that the infinite series

$$\sum_{n=0}^{\infty} (\sqrt{n^a + 1} - \sqrt{n^a})$$

converges for $a > 2$ and diverges for $a = 2$.
13. Given $a_n > 0$ for each $n$. For each of the following statements, give a proof or exhibit a counterexample.
   (a) If $\sum_{n=1}^{\infty} a_n$ diverges, then $\sum_{n=1}^{\infty} a_n^2$ diverges.
   (b) If $\sum_{n=1}^{\infty} a_n^2$ converges, then $\sum_{n=1}^{\infty} a_n/n$ converges.
14. Find all real $c$ for which the series $\sum_{n=1}^{\infty} (n!)^c/(3n)!$ converges.
15. Find all integers $a \geq 1$ for which the series $\sum_{n=1}^{\infty} (n!)^3/(an)!$ converges.
16. Let $n_1 < n_2 < n_3 < \cdots$ denote those positive integers that do not involve the digit 0 in their decimal representations. Thus $n_1 = 1, n_2 = 2, \ldots, n_9 = 9, n_{10} = 11, \ldots, n_{18} = 19, n_{19} = 21$, etc. Show that the series of reciprocals $\sum_{k=1}^{\infty} 1/n_k$ converges and has a sum less than 90.

   [*Hint:* Dominate the series by $9 \sum_{n=0}^{\infty} (9/10)^n$.]

17. If $a$ is an arbitrary real number, let $s_n(a) = 1^a + 2^a + \cdots + n^a$. Determine the following limit:

$$\lim_{n \to \infty} \frac{s_n(a + 1)}{ns_n(a)}.$$

(Consider both positive and negative $a$, as well as $a = 0$.)
18. (a) If $p$ and $q$ are fixed integers, $p \geq q \geq 1$, show that

$$\lim_{n \to \infty} \sum_{k=qn}^{pn} \frac{1}{k} = \log \frac{p}{q}.$$

(b) The following series is a rearrangement of the alternating harmonic series in which there appear, alternately, three positive terms followed by two negative terms:

$$1 + \tfrac{1}{3} + \tfrac{1}{5} - \tfrac{1}{2} - \tfrac{1}{4} + \tfrac{1}{7} + \tfrac{1}{9} + \tfrac{1}{11} - \tfrac{1}{6} - \tfrac{1}{8} + + + - - \cdots.$$

Show that the series converges and has sum $\log 2 + \tfrac{1}{2} \log \tfrac{3}{2}$.

[*Hint:* Consider the partial sum $s_{5n}$ and use part (a).]

(c) Rearrange the alternating harmonic series, writing alternately $p$ positive terms followed by $q$ negative terms. Then use part (a) to show that this rearranged series converges and has sum $\log 2 + \frac{1}{2} \log (p/q)$.

## 10.23 Improper integrals

The concept of an integral $\int_a^b f(x) \, dx$ was introduced in Chapter 1 under the restriction that the function $f$ is *defined and bounded* on a *finite interval* $[a, b]$. The scope of integration theory may be extended by relaxing these restrictions.

To begin with, we may study the behavior of $\int_a^b f(x) \, dx$ as $b \to +\infty$. This leads to the notion of an *infinite integral* (also called an *improper integral of the first kind*) denoted by the symbol $\int_a^\infty f(x) \, dx$. Another extension is obtained if we keep the interval $[a, b]$ finite and allow $f$ to become unbounded at one or more points. The new integrals so obtained (by a suitable limit process) are called *improper integrals of the second kind*. To distinguish the integrals of Chapter 1 from improper integrals, the former are often called "proper" integrals.

Many important functions in analysis appear as improper integrals of one kind or another, and a detailed study of such functions is ordinarily undertaken in courses in advanced calculus. We shall be concerned here only with the most elementary aspects of the theory. In fact, we shall merely state some definitions and theorems and give some examples.

It will be evident presently that the definitions pertaining to improper integrals bear a strong resemblance to those for infinite series. Therefore it is not surprising that many of the elementary theorems on series have direct analogs for improper integrals.

If the proper integral $\int_a^b f(x) \, dx$ exists for every $b \geq a$, we may define a new function $I$ as follows:

$$I(b) = \int_a^b f(x) \, dx \qquad \text{for each } b \geq a \, .$$

The function $I$ defined in this way is called an *infinite integral*, or an *improper integral of the first kind*, and it is denoted by the symbol $\int_a^\infty f(x) \, dx$. The integral is said to *converge* if the limit

(10.61) $$\lim_{b \to +\infty} I(b) = \lim_{b \to +\infty} \int_a^b f(x) \, dx$$

exists and is finite. Otherwise, the integral $\int_a^\infty f(x) \, dx$ is said to *diverge*. If the limit in (10.61) exists and equals $A$, the number $A$ is called the *value* of the integral, and we write

$$\int_a^\infty f(x) \, dx = A \, .$$

These definitions are similar to those given for infinite series. The function values $I(b)$ play the role of the "partial sums" and may be referred to as "partial integrals." Note that the symbol $\int_a^\infty f(x) \, dx$ is used both for the integral and for the value of the integral when the integral converges. (Compare with the remarks near the end of Section 10.5.)

EXAMPLE 1. The improper integral $\int_1^\infty x^{-s}\,dx$ converges if $s > 1$ and diverges if $s \leq 1$. To prove this, we note that

$$I(b) = \int_1^b x^{-s}\,dx = \begin{cases} \dfrac{b^{1-s} - 1}{1 - s} & \text{if } s \neq 1, \\[2mm] \log b & \text{if } s = 1. \end{cases}$$

Therefore $I(b)$ tends to a finite limit if and only if $s > 1$, in which case the limit is

$$\int_1^\infty x^{-s}\,dx = \frac{1}{s-1}.$$

The behavior of this integral is analogous to that of the series for the zeta-function, $\zeta(s) = \sum_{n=1}^\infty n^{-s}$.

EXAMPLE 2. The integral $\int_0^\infty \sin x\,dx$ diverges because

$$I(b) = \int_0^b \sin x\,dx = 1 - \cos b,$$

and this does not tend to a limit as $b \to +\infty$.

Infinite integrals of the form $\int_{-\infty}^b f(x)\,dx$ are similarly defined. Also, if $\int_{-\infty}^c f(x)\,dx$ and $\int_c^\infty f(x)\,dx$ are *both convergent* for some $c$, we say that the integral $\int_{-\infty}^\infty f(x)\,dx$ is convergent, and its value is defined to be the sum

(10.62)
$$\int_{-\infty}^\infty f(x)\,dx = \int_{-\infty}^c f(x)\,dx + \int_c^\infty f(x)\,dx.$$

(It is easy to show that the choice of $c$ is unimportant.) The integral $\int_{-\infty}^\infty f(x)\,dx$ is said to diverge if at least one of the integrals on the right of (10.62) is divergent.

EXAMPLE 3. The integral $\int_{-\infty}^\infty e^{-a|x|}\,dx$ converges if $a > 0$, for if $b > 0$, we have

$$\int_0^b e^{-a|x|}\,dx = \int_0^b e^{-ax}\,dx = \frac{e^{-ab} - 1}{-a} \to \frac{1}{a} \qquad \text{as } b \to \infty.$$

Hence $\int_0^\infty e^{-a|x|}\,dx$ converges and has the value $1/a$. Also, if $b > 0$, we have

$$\int_{-b}^0 e^{-a|x|}\,dx = \int_{-b}^0 e^{ax}\,dx = -\int_b^0 e^{-at}\,dt = \int_0^b e^{-at}\,dt.$$

Therefore $\int_{-\infty}^0 e^{-a|x|}\,dx$ also converges and has the value $1/a$. Hence we have $\int_{-\infty}^\infty e^{-a|x|}\,dx = 2/a$. Note, however, that the integral $\int_{-\infty}^\infty e^{-ax}\,dx$ *diverges* because $\int_{-\infty}^0 e^{-ax}\,dx$ diverges.

As in the case of series, we have various convergence tests for improper integrals. The simplest of these refers to a positive integrand.

THEOREM 10.23. *Assume that the proper integral $\int_a^b f(x)\, dx$ exists for each $b \geq a$ and suppose that $f(x) \geq 0$ for all $x \geq a$. Then $\int_a^\infty f(x)\, dx$ converges if and only if there is a constant $M > 0$ such that*

$$\int_a^b f(x)\, dx \leq M \qquad \text{for every } b \geq a\,.$$

This theorem forms the basis for the following comparison tests.

THEOREM 10.24. *Assume the proper integral $\int_a^b f(x)\, dx$ exists for each $b \geq a$ and suppose that $0 \leq f(x) \leq g(x)$ for all $x \geq a$, where $\int_a^\infty g(x)\, dx$ converges. Then $\int_a^\infty f(x)\, dx$ also converges and*

$$\int_a^\infty f(x)\, dx \leq \int_a^\infty g(x)\, dx\,.$$

*Note:* The integral $\int_a^\infty {}'g(x)\, dx$ is said to *dominate* the integral $\int_a^\infty f(x)\, dx$.

THEOREM 10.25. LIMIT COMPARISON TEST. *Assume both proper integrals $\int_a^b f(x)\, dx$ and $\int_a^b g(x)\, dx$ exist for each $b \geq a$, where $f(x) \geq 0$ and $g(x) > 0$ for all $x \geq a$. If*

$$(10.63) \qquad \lim_{x \to +\infty} \frac{f(x)}{g(x)} = c\,, \qquad \text{where } c \neq 0\,,$$

*then both integrals $\int_a^\infty f(x)\, dx$ and $\int_a^\infty g(x)\, dx$ converge or both diverge.*

*Note:* If the limit in (10.63) is 0, we can conclude only that convergence of $\int_a^\infty g(x)\, dx$ implies convergence of $\int_a^\infty f(x)\, dx$.

The proofs of Theorem 10.23 through 10.25 are similar to the corresponding results for series and are left as exercises.

EXAMPLE 4. For each real $s$, the integral $\int_1^\infty e^{-x} x^s\, dx$ converges. This is seen by comparison with $\int_1^\infty x^{-2}\, dx$ since $e^{-x} x^s / x^{-2} \to 0$ as $x \to +\infty$.

Improper integrals of the second kind may be introduced as follows: Suppose $f$ is defined on the half-open interval $(a, b]$, and assume that the integral $\int_x^b f(t)\, dt$ exists for each $x$ satisfying $a < x \leq b$. Define a new function $I$ as follows:

$$I(x) = \int_x^b f(t)\, dt \qquad \text{if } a < x \leq b\,.$$

The function $I$ so defined is called an *improper integral of the second kind* and is denoted by the symbol $\int_{a+}^b f(t)\, dt$. The integral is said to *converge* if the limit

$$(10.64) \qquad \lim_{x \to a+} I(x) = \lim_{x \to a+} \int_x^b f(t)\, dt$$

exists and is finite. Otherwise, the integral $\int_{a+}^b f(t)\, dt$ is said to *diverge*. If the limit in (10.64) exists and equals $A$, the number $A$ is called the *value* of the integral, and we write

$$\int_{a+}^b f(t)\, dt = A\,.$$

EXAMPLE 5. Let $f(t) = t^{-s}$ if $t > 0$. If $b > 0$ and $x > 0$, we have

$$I(x) = \int_x^b t^{-s}\, dt = \begin{cases} \dfrac{b^{1-s} - x^{1-s}}{1 - s} & \text{if } s \neq 1, \\[2mm] \log b - \log x & \text{if } s = 1. \end{cases}$$

When $x \to 0+$, $I(x)$ tends to a finite limit if and only if $s < 1$. Hence the integral $\int_{0+}^b t^{-s}\, dt$ converges if $s < 1$ and diverges if $s \geq 1$.

This example may be dealt with in another way. If we introduce the substitution $t = 1/u$, $dt = -u^{-2}\, du$, we obtain

$$\int_x^b t^{-s}\, dt = \int_{1/b}^{1/x} u^{s-2}\, du\,.$$

When $x \to 0+$, $1/x \to +\infty$ and hence $\int_{0+}^b t^{-s}\, dt = \int_{1/b}^\infty u^{s-2}\, du$, provided the last integral converges. By Example 1, this converges if and only if $s - 2 < -1$, which means $s < 1$.

The foregoing example illustrates a remarkable geometric fact. Consider the function $f$ defined by the equation $f(x) = x^{-3/4}$ if $0 < x \leq 1$. The integral $\int_{0+}^1 f(x)\, dx$ converges, but the integral $\int_{0+}^1 \pi f^2(x)\, dx$ diverges. Geometrically, this means that the ordinate set of $f$ has a finite area, but the solid obtained by rotating this ordinate set about the $x$-axis has an infinite volume.

Improper integrals of the form $\int_a^{b-} f(t)\, dt$ are defined in a similar fashion. If the two integrals $\int_{a+}^c f(t)\, dt$ and $\int_c^{b-} f(t)\, dt$ *both converge*, we write

$$\int_{a+}^{b-} f(t)\, dt = \int_{a+}^c f(t)\, dt + \int_c^{b-} f(t)\, dt\,.$$

*Note:* Some authors write $\int_a^b$ where we have written $\int_{a+}^{b-}$.

The definition can be extended (in an obvious way) to cover the case of any finite number of summands. For example, if $f$ is undefined at two points $c < d$ interior to an interval $[a, b]$, we say the improper integral $\int_a^b f(t)\, dt$ converges and has the value $\int_a^{c-} f(t)\, dt +$ $\int_{c+}^{d-} f(t)\, dt + \int_{d+}^b f(t)\, dt$, provided that each of these integrals converges. Furthermore, we can consider "mixed" combinations such as $\int_{a+}^b f(t)\, dt + \int_b^\infty f(t)\, dt$ which we write as $\int_{a+}^\infty f(t)\, dt$, or mixed combinations of the form $\int_a^{b-} f(t)\, dt + \int_{b+}^c f(t)\, dt + \int_c^\infty f(t)\, dt$ which we write simply as $\int_a^\infty f(t)\, dt$.

EXAMPLE 6. *The gamma function.* If $s > 0$ the integral $\int_{0+}^\infty e^{-t} t^{s-1}\, dt$ converges. This must be interpreted as a sum, say

$$(10.65) \qquad \int_{0+}^1 e^{-t} t^{s-1}\, dt + \int_1^\infty e^{-t} t^{s-1}\, dt\,.$$

The second integral converges for all real $s$, by Example 4. To test the first integral we put $t = 1/u$ and note that

$$\int_x^1 e^{-t} t^{s-1}\, dt = \int_1^{1/x} e^{-1/u} u^{-s-1}\, du\,.$$

But $\int_1^\infty e^{-1/u}u^{-s-1}\,du$ converges for $s > 0$ by comparison with $\int_1^\infty u^{-s-1}\,du$. Therefore the integral $\int_{0+}^1 e^{-t}t^{s-1}\,dt$ converges for $s > 0$. When $s > 0$, the sum in (10.65) is denoted by $\Gamma(s)$. The function $\Gamma$ so defined is called the *gamma function*, first introduced by Euler in 1729. It has the interesting property that $\Gamma(n + 1) = n!$ when $n$ is any integer $\geq 0$. (See Exercise 19 of Section 10.24 for an outline of the proof.)

The convergence tests given in Theorems 10.23 through 10.25 have straightforward analogs for improper integrals of the second kind. The reader should have no difficulty in formulating these tests for himself.

## 10.24 Exercises

In each of Exercises 1 through 10, test the improper integral for convergence.

1. $\displaystyle\int_0^\infty \frac{x}{\sqrt{x^4 + 1}}\,dx.$

6. $\displaystyle\int_{0+}^1 \frac{\log x}{\sqrt{x}}\,dx.$

2. $\displaystyle\int_{-\infty}^\infty e^{-x^2}\,dx.$

7. $\displaystyle\int_{0+}^{1-} \frac{\log x}{1 - x}\,dx.$

3. $\displaystyle\int_0^\infty \frac{1}{\sqrt{x^3 + 1}}\,dx.$

8. $\displaystyle\int_{-\infty}^\infty \frac{x}{\cosh x}\,dx.$

4. $\displaystyle\int_0^\infty \frac{1}{\sqrt{e^x}}\,dx.$

9. $\displaystyle\int_{0+}^{1-} \frac{dx}{\sqrt{x}\log x}.$

5. $\displaystyle\int_{0+}^\infty \frac{e^{-\sqrt{x}}}{\sqrt{x}}\,dx.$

10. $\displaystyle\int_2^\infty \frac{dx}{x(\log x)^s}.$

11. For a certain real $C$ the integral

$$\int_2^\infty \left( \frac{Cx}{x^2 + 1} - \frac{1}{2x + 1} \right) dx$$

converges. Determine $C$ and evaluate the integral.

12. For a certain real $C$, the integral

$$\int_1^\infty \left( \frac{x}{2x^2 + 2C} - \frac{C}{x + 1} \right) dx$$

converges. Determine $C$ and evaluate the integral.

13. For a certain real $C$, the integral

$$\int_0^\infty \left( \frac{1}{\sqrt{1 + 2x^2}} - \frac{C}{x + 1} \right) dx$$

converges. Determine $C$ and evaluate the integral.

14. Find the values of $a$ and $b$ such that

$$\int_1^\infty \left( \frac{2x^2 + bx + a}{x(2x + a)} - 1 \right) dx = 1.$$

15. For what values of the constants $a$ and $b$ will the following limit exist and be equal to 1?

$$\lim_{p \to +\infty} \int_{-p}^{p} \frac{x^3 + ax^2 + bx}{x^2 + x + 1} \, dx.$$

16. (a) Prove that

$$\lim_{h \to 0+} \left( \int_{-1}^{-h} \frac{dx}{x} + \int_{h}^{1} \frac{dx}{x} \right) = 0 \quad \text{and that} \quad \lim_{h \to +\infty} \int_{-h}^{h} \sin x \, dx = 0.$$

(b) Do the following improper integrals converge or diverge?

$$\int_{-1}^{1} \frac{dx}{x} \; ; \quad \int_{-\infty}^{\infty} \sin x \, dx.$$

17. (a) Prove that the integral $\int_{0+}^{1} (\sin x)/x \, dx$ converges.
(b) Prove that $\lim_{x \to 0+} x \int_{x}^{1} (\cos t)/t^2 \, dt = 1$.
(c) Does the integral $\int_{0+}^{1} (\cos t)/t^2 \, dt$ converge or diverge?
18. (a) If $f$ is monotonic decreasing for all $x \geq 1$ and if $f(x) \to 0$ as $x \to +\infty$, prove that the integral $\int_{1}^{\infty} f(x) \, dx$ and the series $\sum f(n)$ both converge or both diverge.

[*Hint:* Recall the proof of the integral test.]

(b) Give an example of a nonmonotonic $f$ for which the series $\sum f(n)$ converges and the integral $\int_{1}^{\infty} f(x) \, dx$ diverges.
19. Let $\Gamma(s) = \int_{0}^{\infty} t^{s-1} e^{-t} \, dt$, if $s > 0$. (The gamma function.) Use integration by parts to show $\Gamma(s + 1) = s\Gamma(s)$. Then use induction to prove that $\Gamma(n + 1) = n!$ if $n$ is a positive integer.

Each of Exercises 20 through 25 contains a statement, not necessarily true, about a function $f$ defined for all $x \geq 1$. In each of these exercises, $n$ denotes a positive integer, and $I_n$ denotes the integral $\int_{1}^{n} f(x) \, dx$, which is always assumed to exist. For each statement either give a proof or provide a counterexample.
20. If $f$ is monotonic decreasing and if $\lim_{n \to \infty} I_n$ exists, then the integral $\int_{1}^{\infty} f(x) \, dx$ converges.
21. If $\lim_{x \to \infty} f(x) = 0$ and $\lim_{n \to \infty} I_n = A$, then $\int_{1}^{\infty} f(x) \, dx$ converges and has the value $A$.
22. If the sequence $\{I_n\}$ converges, then the integral $\int_{1}^{\infty} f(x) \, dx$ converges.
23. If $f$ is positive and if $\lim_{n \to \infty} I_n = A$, then $\int_{1}^{\infty} f(x) \, dx$ converges and has the value $A$.
24. Assume $f'(x)$ exists for each $x \geq 1$ and suppose there is a constant $M > 0$ such that $|f'(x)| \leq M$ for all $x \geq 1$. If $\lim_{n \to \infty} I_n = A$, then the integral $\int_{1}^{\infty} f(x) \, dx$ converges and has the value $A$.
25. If $\int_{1}^{\infty} f(x) \, dx$ converges, then $\lim_{x \to \infty} f(x) = 0$.

# 11

# SEQUENCES AND SERIES OF FUNCTIONS

## 11.1 Pointwise convergence of sequences of functions

In Chapter 10 we discussed sequences whose terms were real or complex numbers. Now we wish to consider sequences $\{f_n\}$ whose terms are real- or complex-valued *functions* having a common domain on the real line or in the complex plane. For each $x$ in the domain, we can form another sequence $\{f_n(x)\}$ of numbers whose terms are the corresponding function values. Let $S$ denote the set of points $x$ for which this sequence converges. The function $f$ defined on $S$ by the equation

$$f(x) = \lim_{n \to \infty} f_n(x) \qquad \text{if} \quad x \in S,$$

is called the *limit function* of the sequence $\{f_n\}$, and we say that the sequence $\{f_n\}$ *converges pointwise* to $f$ on the set $S$.

The study of such sequences is concerned primarily with the following type of question: If each term of a sequence $\{f_n\}$ has a certain property, such as continuity, differentiability, or integrability, to what extent is this property transferred to the limit function? For example, if each function $f_n$ is continuous at a point $x$, is the limit function $f$ also continuous at $x$? The following example shows that, in general, it is not.

EXAMPLE 1. *A sequence of continuous functions with a discontinuous limit function.* Let $f_n(x) = x^n$ if $0 \le x \le 1$. The graphs of a few terms are shown in Figure 11.1. The sequence $\{f_n\}$ converges pointwise on the closed interval $[0, 1]$, and its limit function $f$ is given by the formula

$$f(x) = \lim_{n \to \infty} x^n = \begin{cases} 0 & \text{if} \quad 0 \le x < 1, \\ 1 & \text{if} \quad x = 1. \end{cases}$$

Note that the limit function $f$ is discontinuous at 1, although each term of the sequence is continuous in the entire interval $[0, 1]$.

EXAMPLE 2. *A sequence for which* $\lim_{n \to \infty} \int_a^b f_n(x)\,dx \ne \int_a^b \lim_{n \to \infty} f_n(x)\,dx$. Let $f_n(x) = nx(1 - x^2)^n$ for $0 \le x \le 1$. In this example, the sequence $\{f_n\}$ converges pointwise to a limit function $f$ which is 0 everywhere in the closed interval $[0, 1]$. A few terms of the sequence are shown in Figure 11.2. The integral of $f_n$ over the interval [0, 1] is given by

$$\int_0^1 f_n(x)\,dx = n \int_0^1 x(1-x^2)^n\,dx = -\frac{n}{2}\frac{(1-x^2)^{n+1}}{n+1}\bigg|_0^1 = \frac{n}{2(n+1)}.$$

Therefore we have $\lim_{n\to\infty}\int_0^1 f_n(x)\,dx = \frac{1}{2}$, but $\int_0^1 \lim_{n\to\infty} f_n(x)\,dx = 0$. In other words, the limit of the integrals is not equal to the integral of the limit. This example shows that

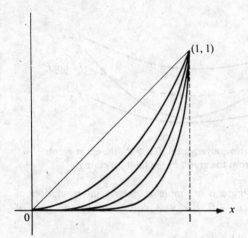

FIGURE 11.1   A sequence of continuous functions with a discontinuous limit function.

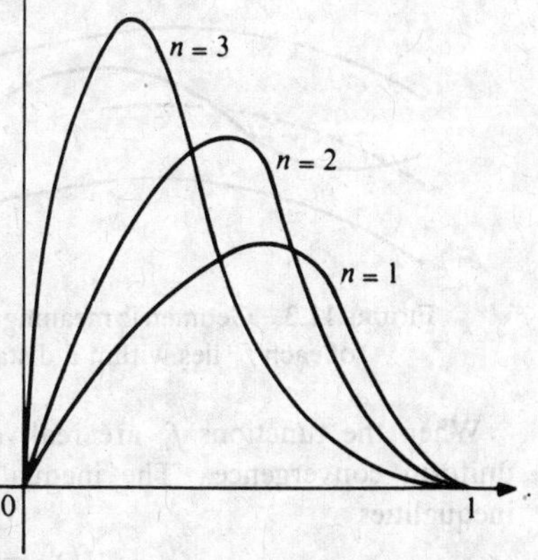

FIGURE 11.2   A sequence of functions for which $f_n \to 0$ on the interval [0, 1] but $\int_0^1 f_n \to \frac{1}{2}$ as $n \to \infty$.

the two operations of "limit" and "integration" cannot always be interchanged. (See also Exercises 17 and 18 in Section 11.7.)

George G. Stokes (1819–1903), Phillip L. v. Seidel (1821–1896), and Karl Weierstrass were the first to realize that some extra condition is needed to justify interchanging these operations. In 1848, Stokes and Seidel (independently and almost simultaneously) introduced a concept now known as *uniform convergence* and showed that for a uniformly convergent sequence the operations of limit and integration could be interchanged. Weierstrass later showed that the concept is of great importance in advanced analysis. We shall introduce the concept in the next section and show its relation to continuity and to integration.

## 11.2   Uniform convergence of sequences of functions

Let $\{f_n\}$ be a sequence which converges pointwise on a set $S$ to a limit function $f$. By the definition of limit, this means that for each $x$ in $S$ and for each $\epsilon > 0$ there is an integer $N$, which depends on both $x$ and $\epsilon$, such that $|f_n(x) - f(x)| < \epsilon$ whenever $n \geq N$. If the same $N$ serves equally well for *all* points $x$ in $S$, then the convergence is said to be *uniform* on $S$. That is, we have the following.

DEFINITION. *A sequence of functions* $\{f_n\}$ *is said to converge uniformly to* $f$ *on a set* $S$ *if for every* $\epsilon > 0$ *there is an* $N$ *(depending only on* $\epsilon$*) such that* $n \geq N$ *implies*

$$|f_n(x) - f(x)| < \epsilon \qquad \text{for all } x \text{ in } S .$$

*We denote this symbolically by writing*

$$f_n \to f \quad \text{uniformly on } S .$$

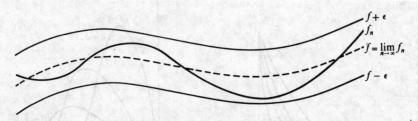

FIGURE 11.3   Geometric meaning of uniform convergence. If $n \geq N$, the entire graph
of each $f_n$ lies within a distance $\epsilon$ from the graph of the limit function $f$.

When the functions $f_n$ are real-valued, there is a simple geometric interpretation of uniform convergence. The inequality $|f_n(x) - f(x)| < \epsilon$ is equivalent to the pair of inequalities

$$f(x) - \epsilon < f_n(x) < f(x) + \epsilon .$$

If these hold for all $n \geq N$ and every $x$ in $S$, then the entire graph of $f_n$ above $S$ lies within a band of height $2\epsilon$ situated symmetrically about the graph of $f$, as indicated in Figure 11.3.

## 11.3   Uniform convergence and continuity

Now we prove that uniform convergence transmits continuity from the individual terms of the sequence $\{f_n\}$ to the limit function $f$.

THEOREM 11.1   *Assume* $f_n \to f$ *uniformly on an interval* $S$. *If each function* $f_n$ *is continuous at a point* $p$ *in* $S$, *then the limit function* $f$ *is also continuous at* $p$.

*Proof.* We will show that for every $\epsilon > 0$ there is a neighborhood $N(p)$ such that $|f(x) - f(p)| < \epsilon$ whenever $x \in N(p) \cap S$. If $\epsilon > 0$ is given, there is an integer $N$ such that $n \geq N$ implies

$$|f_n(x) - f(x)| < \frac{\epsilon}{3} \qquad \text{for all } x \text{ in } S .$$

Since $f_N$ is continuous at $p$, there is a neighborhood $N(p)$ such that

$$|f_N(x) - f_N(p)| < \frac{\epsilon}{3} \qquad \text{for all } x \text{ in } N(p) \cap S .$$

Therefore, for all $x$ in $N(p) \cap S$, we have

$$|f(x) - f(p)| = |f(x) - f_N(x) + f_N(x) - f_N(p) + f_N(p) - f(p)|$$
$$\leq |f(x) - f_N(x)| + |f_N(x) - f_N(p)| + |f_N(p) - f(p)|.$$

Since each term on the right is $< \epsilon/3$, we find $|f(x) - f(p)| < \epsilon$, which completes the proof.

The foregoing theorem has an important application to infinite series of functions. If the function values $f_n(x)$ are partial sums of other functions, say

$$f_n(x) = \sum_{k=1}^{n} u_k(x),$$

and if $f_n \to f$ pointwise on $S$, then we have

$$f(x) = \lim_{n \to \infty} f_n(x) = \sum_{k=1}^{\infty} u_k(x)$$

for each $x$ in $S$. In this case, the series $\sum u_k$ is said to converge pointwise to the sum function $f$. If $f_n \to f$ uniformly on $S$, we say the series $\sum u_k$ converges uniformly to $f$. If each term $u_k$ is continuous at a point $p$ in $S$, then each partial sum $f_n$ is also continuous at $p$ so, from Theorem 11.1, we obtain the following corollary.

**THEOREM 11.2.** *If a series of functions $\sum u_k$ converges uniformly to a sum function $f$ on a set $S$, and if each term $u_k$ is continuous at a point $p$ in $S$, then the sum $f$ is also continuous at $p$.*

*Note:* We can also express this result symbolically by writing

$$\lim_{x \to p} \sum_{k=1}^{\infty} u_k(x) = \sum_{k=1}^{\infty} \lim_{x \to p} u_k(x).$$

We describe this by saying that for a uniformly convergent series we may interchange the limit symbol with the summation symbol, or that we can pass to the limit term by term.

## 11.4 Uniform convergence and integration

The next theorem shows that uniform convergence allows us to interchange the integration symbol with the limit symbol.

**THEOREM 11.3.** *Assume $f_n \to f$ uniformly on an interval $[a, b]$, and assume that each function $f_n$ is continuous on $[a, b]$. Define a new sequence $\{g_n\}$ by the equation*

$$g_n(x) = \int_a^x f_n(t)\, dt \qquad if \quad x \in [a, b],$$

*and let*

$$g(x) = \int_a^x f(t) \, dt \, .$$

*Then* $g_n \to g$ *uniformly on* $[a, b]$. *In symbols, we have*

$$\lim_{n \to \infty} \int_a^x f_n(t) \, dt = \int_a^x \lim_{n \to \infty} f_n(t) \, dt \, .$$

*Proof.* The proof is very simple. Given $\epsilon > 0$, there is an integer $N$ such that $n \geq N$ implies

$$|f_n(t) - f(t)| < \frac{\epsilon}{b - a} \qquad \text{for all } t \text{ in } [a, b] \, .$$

Hence, if $x \in [a, b]$ and if $n \geq N$, we have

$$|g_n(x) - g(x)| = \left| \int_a^x (f_n(t) - f(t)) \, dt \right| \leq \int_a^b |f_n(t) - f(t)| \, dt < \int_a^b \frac{\epsilon}{b - a} \, dt = \epsilon \, ,$$

so $g_n \to g$ uniformly on $[a, b]$.

Again, as a corollary, we have a corresponding result for infinite series.

THEOREM 11.4. *Assume that a series of functions* $\sum u_k$ *converges uniformly to a sum function* $f$ *on an interval* $[a, b]$, *where each* $u_k$ *is continuous on* $[a, b]$. *If* $x \in [a, b]$, *define*

$$g_n(x) = \sum_{k=1}^n \int_a^x u_k(t) \, dt \qquad \text{and} \qquad g(x) = \int_a^x f(t) \, dt \, .$$

*Then* $g_n \to g$ *uniformly on* $[a, b]$. *In other words, we have*

$$\lim_{n \to \infty} \sum_{k=1}^n \int_a^x u_k(t) \, dt = \int_a^x \lim_{n \to \infty} \sum_{k=1}^n u_k(t) \, dt$$

*or*

$$\sum_{k=1}^\infty \int_a^x u_k(t) \, dt = \int_a^x \sum_{k=1}^\infty u_k(t) \, dt \, .$$

*Proof.* Apply Theorem 11.3 to the sequence of partial sums $\{f_n\}$ given by

$$f_n(t) = \sum_{k=1}^n u_k(t) \, ,$$

and note that $\int_a^x f_n(t) \, dt = \sum_{k=1}^n \int_a^x u_k(t) \, dt$.

Theorem 11.4 is often described by saying that a uniformly convergent series may be integrated term by term.

## 11.5 A sufficient condition for uniform convergence

Weierstrass developed a useful test for showing that certain series are uniformly convergent. The test is applicable whenever the given series can be dominated by a convergent series of positive constants.

THEOREM 11.5. THE WEIERSTRASS M-TEST. *Given a series of functions* $\sum u_n$ *which converges pointwise to a function f on a set S. If there is a convergent series of positive constants* $\sum M_n$ *such that*

$$0 \le |u_n(x)| \le M_n \quad \text{for every } n \ge 1 \text{ and every } x \text{ in } S,$$

*then the series* $\sum u_n$ *converges uniformly on S.*

*Proof.* The comparison test shows that the series $\sum u_n(x)$ converges absolutely for each $x$ in $S$. For each $x$ in $S$, we have

$$\left| f(x) - \sum_{k=1}^{n} u_k(x) \right| = \left| \sum_{k=n+1}^{\infty} u_k(x) \right| \le \sum_{k=n+1}^{\infty} |u_k(x)| \le \sum_{k=n+1}^{\infty} M_k .$$

Since the series $\sum M_k$ converges, for every $\epsilon > 0$ there is an integer $N$ such that $n \ge N$ implies

$$\sum_{k=n+1}^{\infty} M_k < \epsilon .$$

This shows that

$$\left| f(x) - \sum_{k=1}^{n} u_k(x) \right| < \epsilon$$

for all $n \ge N$ and every $x$ in $S$. Therefore, the series $\sum u_n$ converges uniformly to $f$ on $S$.

Term-by-term differentiation of an arbitrary series of functions is even less promising than term-by-term integration. For example, the series $\sum_{n=1}^{\infty} (\sin nx)/n^2$ converges for all real $x$ because it is dominated by $\sum 1/n^2$. Moreover, the convergence is uniform on the whole real axis. However, the series obtained by differentiating term by term is $\sum (\cos nx)/n$, and this *diverges* when $x = 0$. This example shows that term-by-term differentiation may destroy convergence, even though the original series is uniformly convergent. Therefore, the problem of justifying the interchange of the operations of differentiation and summation is, in general, more serious than in the case of integration. We mention this example so the reader may realize that familiar manipulations with finite sums do not always carry over to infinite series, even if the series involved are uniformly convergent. We turn next to special series of functions, known as power series, which can be manipulated in many respects as though they were finite sums.

## 11.6   Power series.   Circle of convergence

An infinite series of the form

$$\sum_{n=0}^{\infty} a_n(z - a)^n = a_0 + a_1(z - a) + \cdots + a_n(z - a)^n + \cdots$$

is called a power series in $z - a$. The numbers $z$, $a$, and the coefficients $a_n$ are complex. With each power series there is associated a circle, called the *circle of convergence*, such that the series converges absolutely for every $z$ interior to this circle, and diverges for every $z$ outside this circle. The center of the circle is at $a$ and its radius $r$ is called the *radius of*

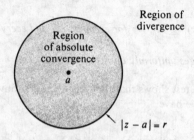

FIGURE 11.4   The circle of convergence of a power series.

*convergence.* (See Figure 11.4.) In extreme cases, the circle may shrink to the single point $a$, in which case $r = 0$, or it may consist of the entire complex plane, in which case we say that $r = +\infty$. The existence of the circle of convergence is shown in Theorem 11.7.

The behavior of the series at the boundary points of the circle cannot be predicted in advance. Examples show that there may be convergence at none, some, or all the boundary points.

For many power series that occur in practice, the radius of convergence can be determined by using either the ratio test or the root test, as in the following examples.

EXAMPLE 1.   To find the radius of convergence of the power series $\sum z^n/n!$, we apply the ratio test.   If $z \neq 0$, the ratio of consecutive terms has absolute value

$$\left| \frac{z^{n+1}}{(n + 1)!} \frac{n!}{z^n} \right| = \frac{|z|}{n + 1}.$$

Since this ratio tends to 0 as $n \to \infty$, we conclude that the series converges absolutely for all complex $z \neq 0$. It also converges for $z = 0$, so the radius of convergence is $+\infty$.

Since the general term of a convergent series must tend to 0, the result of the foregoing example proves that

$$\lim_{n \to \infty} \frac{z^n}{n!} = 0.$$

for every complex $z$. That is, $n!$ "grows faster" than the $n$th power of any fixed complex number $z$ as $n \to \infty$.

EXAMPLE 2. To test the series $\sum n^2 3^n z^n$, we use the root test. We have

$$(n^2 3^n |z|^n)^{1/n} = 3 |z| n^{2/n} \to 3 |z| \quad \text{as} \quad n \to \infty,$$

since $n^{2/n} = (n^{1/n})^2$ and $n^{1/n} \to 1$ as $n \to \infty$. Therefore, the series converges absolutely if $|z| < \frac{1}{3}$ and diverges if $|z| > \frac{1}{3}$. The radius of convergence is $\frac{1}{3}$. This particular power series diverges at every boundary point because, if $|z| = \frac{1}{3}$, the general term has absolute value $n^2$.

EXAMPLE 3. For each of the series $\sum z^n/n$ and $\sum z^n/n^2$, the ratio test tells us that the radius of convergence is 1. The first series diverges at the boundary point $z = 1$ but converges at all other boundary points (see Section 10.19). The second series converges at every boundary point since it is dominated by $\sum 1/n^2$.

We conclude this section with a proof that every power series has a circle of convergence. The proof is based on the following theorem.

THEOREM 11.6. *Assume the power series $\sum a_n z^n$ converges for a particular $z \neq 0$, say for $z = z_1$. Then we have:*
   (a) *The series converges absolutely for every $z$ with $|z| < |z_1|$.*
   (b) *The series converges uniformly on every circular disk with center at 0 and radius $R < |z_1|$.*

*Proof.* Since $\sum a_n z_1^n$ converges, its general term tends to 0 as $n \to \infty$. In particular, $|a_n z_1^n| < 1$ from some point on, say for $n \geq N$. Let $S$ be a circular disk of radius $R$, where $0 < R < |z_1|$. If $z \in S$ and $n \geq N$, we have $|z| \leq R$ and

$$|a_n z^n| = |a_n z_1^n| \left| \frac{z}{z_1} \right|^n < \left| \frac{z}{z_1} \right|^n \leq \left| \frac{R}{z_1} \right|^n = t^n, \quad \text{where} \quad t = \left| \frac{R}{z_1} \right|.$$

Since $0 < t < 1$, the series $\sum a_n z^n$ is dominated by the convergent geometric series $\sum t^n$. By Weierstrass' $M$-test, the series $\sum a_n z^n$ converges uniformly on $S$. This proves (b). The argument also shows that the series $\sum a_n z^n$ converges absolutely for each $z$ in $S$. But since each $z$ with $|z| < |z_1|$ lies in some circular disk $S$ with radius $R < |z_1|$, this also proves part (a).

THEOREM 11.7. EXISTENCE OF A CIRCLE OF CONVERGENCE. *Assume that the power series $\sum a_n z^n$ converges for at least one $z \neq 0$, say for $z = z_1$, and that it diverges for at least one $z$, say for $z = z_2$. Then there exists a positive real number $r$ such that the series converges absolutely if $|z| < r$ and diverges if $|z| > r$.*

*Proof.* Let $A$ denote the set of all positive numbers $|z|$ for which the power series $\sum a_n z^n$ converges. The set $A$ is not empty since, by hypothesis, it contains $|z_1|$. Also, no number in $A$ can exceed $|z_2|$ (because of Theorem 11.6). Hence, $|z_2|$ is an upper bound for $A$. Since $A$ is a nonempty set of positive numbers that is bounded above, it has a least upper bound which we denote by $r$. It is clear that $r > 0$ since $r \geq |z_1|$. By the definition of $r$, no number in $A$ can exceed $r$. Therefore, the series diverges if $|z| > r$. But it is easy to prove that the series converges *absolutely* if $|z| < r$. If $|z| < r$, there is a positive number $x$ in $A$ such that $|z| < x < r$. By Theorem 11.6, the series $\sum a_n z^n$ converges absolutely. This completes the proof.

There is, of course, a corresponding theorem for power series in $z - a$ which may be deduced from the case just treated by introducing the change of variable $Z = z - a$. The circle of convergence has its center at $a$, as shown in Figure 11.4.

## 11.7 Exercises

In Exercises 1 through 16, determine the radius of convergence $r$ of the given power series. In Exercises 1 through 10, test for convergence at the boundary points if $r$ is finite.

1. $\displaystyle\sum_{n=0}^{\infty} \frac{z^n}{2^n}$.

2. $\displaystyle\sum_{n=0}^{\infty} \frac{z^n}{(n+1)2^n}$.

3. $\displaystyle\sum_{n=0}^{\infty} \frac{(z+3)^n}{(n+1)2^n}$.

4. $\displaystyle\sum_{n=1}^{\infty} \frac{(-1)^n 2^{2n} z^{2n}}{2n}$.

5. $\displaystyle\sum_{n=1}^{\infty} [1 - (-2)^n] z^n$.

6. $\displaystyle\sum_{n=1}^{\infty} \frac{n! z^n}{n^n}$.

7. $\displaystyle\sum_{n=0}^{\infty} \frac{(-1)^n (z+1)^n}{n^2 + 1}$.

8. $\displaystyle\sum_{n=0}^{\infty} a^{n^2} z^n$,    $0 < a < 1$.

9. $\displaystyle\sum_{n=1}^{\infty} \frac{(n!)^2}{(2n)!} z^n$.

10. $\displaystyle\sum_{n=1}^{\infty} \frac{3^{\sqrt{n}} z^n}{n}$.

11. $\displaystyle\sum_{n=1}^{\infty} \left( \frac{1 \cdot 3 \cdot 5 \cdots (2n-1)}{2 \cdot 4 \cdot 6 \cdots (2n)} \right)^3 z^n$.

12. $\displaystyle\sum_{n=1}^{\infty} \left( 1 + \frac{1}{n} \right)^{n^2} z^n$.

13. $\displaystyle\sum_{n=0}^{\infty} (\sin an) z^n$,    $a > 0$.

14. $\displaystyle\sum_{n=0}^{\infty} (\sinh an) z^n$,    $a > 0$.

15. $\displaystyle\sum_{n=1}^{\infty} \frac{z^n}{a^n + b^n}$,    $a > 0, b > 0$.

16. $\displaystyle\sum_{n=1}^{\infty} \left( \frac{a^n}{n} + \frac{b^n}{n^2} \right) z^n$,    $a > 0, b > 0$.

17. If $f_n(x) = nxe^{-nx^2}$ for $n = 1, 2, \ldots$ and $x$ real, show that

$$\lim_{n \to \infty} \int_0^1 f_n(x)\, dx \neq \int_0^1 \lim_{n \to \infty} f_n(x)\, dx .$$

This example shows that the operations of integration and limit cannot always be interchanged.

18. Let $f_n(x) = (\sin nx)/n$, and for each fixed real $x$ let $f(x) = \lim_{n \to \infty} f_n(x)$. Show that

$$\lim_{n \to \infty} f_n'(0) \neq f'(0) .$$

This example shows that the operations of differentiation and limit cannot always be interchanged.

19. Show that the series $\sum_{n=1}^{\infty} (\sin nx)/n^2$ converges for every real $x$, and denote its sum by $f(x)$. Prove that $f$ is continuous on $[0, \pi]$, and use Theorem 11.4 to prove that

$$\int_0^\pi f(x)\,dx = 2 \sum_{n=1}^{\infty} \frac{1}{(2n-1)^3}.$$

20. It is known that

$$\sum_{n=1}^{\infty} \frac{\cos nx}{n^2} = \frac{x^2}{4} - \frac{\pi x}{2} + \frac{\pi^2}{6} \quad \text{if} \quad 0 \le x \le 2\pi.$$

Use this formula and Theorem 11.4 to deduce the following formulas:

(a) $\displaystyle\sum_{n=1}^{\infty} \frac{1}{n^2} = \frac{\pi^2}{6}$ ;

(b) $\displaystyle\sum_{n=1}^{\infty} \frac{(-1)^{n+1}}{(2n-1)^3} = \frac{\pi^3}{32}$.

## 11.8 Properties of functions represented by real power series

In this section we restrict ourselves to *real* power series, that is series of the form $\sum a_n(z-a)^n$ in which $z$, $a$, and the coefficients $a_n$ are all real numbers. We also write $x$ in place of $z$. The interior of the circle of convergence intersects the real axis along an interval $(a-r, a+r)$ symmetrically located about $a$; we refer to this as the *interval of convergence* of the real power series $\sum a_n(x-a)^n$. The number $r$ is called the radius of convergence. (See Figure 11.5.)

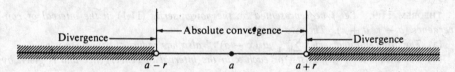

$$\text{Divergence} \quad\longleftarrow \text{Absolute convergence} \longrightarrow\quad \text{Divergence}$$

$$a - r \qquad\qquad a \qquad\qquad a + r$$

FIGURE 11.5 The interval of convergence of a real power series.

Each real power series defines a sum function whose value at each $x$ in the interval of convergence is given by

$$f(x) = \sum_{n=0}^{\infty} a_n(x-a)^n.$$

The series is said to *represent the function f* in the interval of convergence, and it is called the *power-series expansion* of $f$ about $a$.

There are two basic problems about power-series expansions that concern us here:

(1) Given the series, to find properties of the sum function $f$.

(2) Given a function $f$, to find whether or not it may be represented by a power series. It turns out that only rather special functions possess power-series expansions. Nevertheless, the class of such functions includes most examples that arise in practice, and hence their study is of great importance. We turn now to a discussion of question (1).

Theorem 11.6 tells us that the power series converges absolutely for each $x$ in the open interval $(a - r, a + r)$, and that it converges uniformly on every closed subinterval $[a - R, a + R]$, where $0 < R < r$. Since each term of the power series is continuous on the whole real axis, it follows from Theorem 11.2 that the sum function $f$ is continuous on every closed subinterval $[a - R, a + R]$, and hence on the open interval $(a - r, a + r)$. Also, Theorem 11.4 tells us that we can integrate the power series term by term on every closed subinterval $[a - R, a + R]$. These properties of functions represented by power series are stated formally in the following theorem.

THEOREM 11.8.   *Assume a function f is represented by the power series*

(11.1) $$f(x) = \sum_{n=0}^{\infty} a_n(x - a)^n$$

*in an open interval $(a - r, a + r)$. Then f is continuous on this interval, and its integral over any closed subinterval may be computed by integrating the series term by term. In particular, for every $x$ in $(a - r, a + r)$, we have*

$$\int_a^x f(t)\, dt = \sum_{n=0}^{\infty} a_n \int_a^x (t - a)^n\, dt = \sum_{n=0}^{\infty} \frac{a_n}{n + 1}(x - a)^{n+1}$$

Theorem 11.8 also shows that the radius of convergence of the integrated series is at least as large as that of the original series. We will prove presently that both series have exactly the same radius of convergence. First we show that a power series may be differentiated term by term within its interval of convergence.

THEOREM 11.9.   *Let f be represented by the power series (11.1) in the interval of convergence $(a - r, a + r)$. Then we have:*
(a) *The differentiated series $\sum_{n=1}^{\infty} na_n(x - a)^{n-1}$ also has radius of convergence r.*
(b) *The derivative $f'(x)$ exists for each $x$ in the interval of convergence and is given by*

$$f'(x) = \sum_{n=1}^{\infty} na_n(x - a)^{n-1}.$$

*Proof.* For simplicity, in the proof we assume that $a = 0$. First we prove that the differentiated series converges absolutely in the interval $(-r, r)$. Choose any positive $x$ such that $0 < x < r$, and let $h$ be a small positive number such that $0 < x < x + h < r$. Then the series for $f(x)$ and for $f(x + h)$ are each absolutely convergent. Hence, we may write

(11.2) $$\frac{f(x + h) - f(x)}{h} = \sum_{n=0}^{\infty} a_n \frac{(x + h)^n - x^n}{h}.$$

The series on the right is absolutely convergent since it is a linear combination of absolutely convergent series. Now we apply the mean-value theorem to write

$$(x + h)^n - x^n = hnc_n^{n-1},$$

where $x < c_n < x + h$. Hence, the series in (11.2) is identical to the series

(11.3)
$$\sum_{n=1}^{\infty} na_n c_n^{n-1}$$

which must be absolutely convergent, since that in Equation (11.2) is. The series (11.3) is no longer a power series, but it dominates the power series $\sum na_n x^{n-1}$, so this latter series must be absolutely convergent for this $x$. This proves that the radius of convergence of the differentiated series $\sum na_n x^{n-1}$ is at least as large as $r$. On the other hand, the radius of convergence of the differentiated series cannot exceed $r$ because the differentiated series dominates the original series $\sum a_n x^n$. This proves part (a).

To prove part (b), let $g$ be the sum function of the differentiated series,

$$g(x) = \sum_{n=1}^{\infty} na_n x^{n-1}.$$

Applying Theorem 11.8 to $g$, we may integrate term by term in the interval of convergence to obtain

$$\int_0^x g(t)\, dt = \sum_{n=1}^{\infty} a_n x^n = f(x) - a_0.$$

Since $g$ is continuous, the first fundamental theorem of calculus tells us that $f'(x)$ exists and equals $g(x)$ for each $x$ in the interval of convergence. This proves (b).

*Note:* Since every power series $\sum a_n(x - a)^n$ can be obtained by differentiating its integrated series, $\sum a_n(x - a)^{n+1}/(n + 1)$, Theorem 11.9 tells us that both these series have the same radius of convergence.

Theorems 11.8 and 11.9 justify the formal manipulations of Section 10.8 where we obtained various power-series expansions using term-by-term differentiation and integration of the geometric series. In particular, these theorems establish the validity of the expansions

$$\log(1 + x) = \sum_{n=0}^{\infty} \frac{(-1)^n x^{n+1}}{n + 1} \quad \text{and} \quad \arctan x = \sum_{n=0}^{\infty} \frac{(-1)^n x^{2n+1}}{2n + 1},$$

whenever $x$ is in the open interval $-1 < x < 1$.

As a further consequence of Theorem 11.9, we conclude that the sum function of a power series has derivatives of *every* order and they may be obtained by repeated term-by-term differentiation of the power series. If $f(x) = \sum a_n(x - a)^n$ and if we differentiate this formula $k$ times and then put $x = a$ in the result, we find that $f^{(k)}(a) = k!a_k$, so the $k$th coefficient $a_k$ is given by the formula

$$a_k = \frac{f^{(k)}(a)}{k!} \quad \text{for} \quad k = 1, 2, 3, \ldots.$$

This formula also holds for $k = 0$ if we interpret $f^{(0)}(a)$ to mean $f(a)$. Thus, the power-series expansion of $f$ has the form

$$(11.4) \qquad f(x) = \sum_{k=0}^{\infty} \frac{f^{(k)}(a)}{k!} (x - a)^k .$$

This property can be formulated as a *uniqueness theorem* for power-series expansions.

THEOREM 11.10. *If two power series $\sum a_n(x - a)^n$ and $\sum b_n(x - a)^n$ have the same sum function $f$ in some neighborhood of the point $a$, then the two series are equal term by term; in fact, we have $a_n = b_n = f^{(n)}(a)/n!$ for each $n \geq 0$.*

Equation (11.4) also shows that the partial sums of a power series are simply the Taylor polynomials of the sum function at $a$. In other words, if a function $f$ is representable by a power series in an interval $(a - r, a + r)$, then the sequence of Taylor polynomials $\{T_n f(x; a)\}$ generated by $f$ at $a$ converges pointwise in this interval to the sum function $f$. Moreover, the convergence is uniform in every closed subinterval of the interval of convergence.

## 11.9 The Taylor's series generated by a function

We turn now to the second problem raised at the beginning of the foregoing section. That is, given a function $f$, to find whether or not it has a power series expansion in some open interval about a point $a$.

We know from what was just proved that such a function must necessarily have derivatives of every order in some open interval about $a$ and that the coefficients of its power-series expansion are given by Equation (11.4). Suppose, then, that we start with a function $f$ having derivatives of every order in an open interval about $a$. We call such a function *infinitely differentiable* in this interval. Then we can certainly *form* the power series

$$(11.5) \qquad \sum_{k=0}^{\infty} \frac{f^{(k)}(a)}{k!} (x - a)^k .$$

This is called the *Taylor's series generated by $f$ at $a$*. We now ask two questions: Does this series converge for any $x$ other than $x = a$? If so, is its sum equal to $f(x)$? Surprisingly enough, the answer to both questions is, in general, "no." The series may or may not converge for $x \neq a$ and, if it does converge, its sum may or may not be $f(x)$. An example where the series converges to a sum different from $f(x)$ is given in Exercise 24 in Section 11.13.

A necessary and sufficient condition for answering both questions in the affirmative can be given by using Taylor's formula with remainder, which provides a *finite* expansion of the form

$$(11.6) \qquad f(x) = \sum_{k=0}^{n} \frac{f^{(k)}(a)}{k!} (x - a)^k + E_n(x) .$$

The finite sum is the Taylor polynomial of degree $n$ generated by $f$ at $a$, and $E_n(x)$ is the error made in approximating $f$ by its Taylor polynomial. If we let $n \to \infty$ in (11.6), we see that the power series (11.5) will converge to $f(x)$ if and only if the error term tends to 0. In the next section we discuss a useful *sufficient condition* for the error term to tend to 0.

## 11.10 A sufficient condition for convergence of a Taylor's series

In Theorem 7.6 we proved that the error term in Taylor's formula could be expressed as an integral,

$$(11.7) \qquad E_n(x) = \frac{1}{n!} \int_a^x (x - t)^n f^{(n+1)}(t) \, dt$$

in any interval about $a$ in which $f^{(n+1)}$ is continuous. Therefore, if $f$ is infinitely differentiable, we always have this representation of the error so the Taylor's series converges to $f(x)$ if and only if this integral tends to 0 as $n \to \infty$.

The integral can be put into a slightly more useful form by a change of variable. We write

$$t = x + (a - x)u, \qquad dt = -(x - a) \, du,$$

and note that $u$ varies from 1 to 0 as $t$ varies from $a$ to $x$. Therefore, the integral in (11.7) becomes

$$(11.8) \qquad E_n(x) = \frac{(x - a)^{n+1}}{n!} \int_0^1 u^n f^{(n+1)}[x + (a - x)u] \, du \, .$$

This form of the error enables us to give the following sufficient condition for convergence of a Taylor's series.

THEOREM 11.11. *Assume $f$ is infinitely differentiable in an open interval $I = (a - r, a + r)$, and assume that there is a positive constant $A$ such that*

$$(11.9) \qquad |f^{(n)}(x)| \leq A^n \quad \text{for} \quad n = 1, 2, 3, \ldots,$$

*and every $x$ in $I$. Then the Taylor's series generated by $f$ at $a$ converges to $f(x)$ for each $x$ in $I$.*

*Proof.* Using the inequality (11.9) in the integral formula (11.8), we obtain the estimate

$$0 \leq |E_n(x)| \leq \frac{|x - a|^{n+1}}{n!} A^{n+1} \int_0^1 u^n \, du = \frac{|x - a|^{n+1} A^{n+1}}{(n + 1)!} = \frac{B^{n+1}}{(n + 1)!},$$

where $B = A |x - a|$. But for every $B$, $B^n/n!$ tends to 0 as $n \to \infty$, so $E_n(x) \to 0$ for each $x$ in $I$.

## 11.11 Power-series expansions for the exponential and trigonometric functions

The sine and cosine functions and all their derivatives are bounded by 1 over the entire real axis. Therefore, inequality (11.9) holds with $A = 1$ if $f(x) = \sin x$ or if $f(x) = \cos x$, and we have the power-series expansions

$$\sin x = x - \frac{x^3}{3!} + \frac{x^5}{5!} - \frac{x^7}{7!} + \cdots + (-1)^{n-1}\frac{x^{2n-1}}{(2n-1)!} + \cdots,$$

$$\cos x = 1 - \frac{x^2}{2!} + \frac{x^4}{4!} - \frac{x^6}{6!} + \cdots + (-1)^n\frac{x^{2n}}{(2n)!} + \cdots,$$

valid for every real $x$. For the exponential function, $f(x) = e^x$, we have $f^{(n)}(x) = e^x$ for all $x$, so in any finite interval $(-r, r)$ we have $e^x \le e^r$. Therefore, (11.9) is satisfied with $A = e^r$. Since $r$ is arbitrary, this shows that the following power-series expansion is valid for all real $x$:

$$e^x = 1 + x + \frac{x^2}{2!} + \cdots + \frac{x^n}{n!} + \cdots.$$

The foregoing power-series expansions for the sine and cosine can be used as the starting point for a completely analytic treatment of the trigonometric functions. If we use these series as *definitions* of the sine and cosine, it is possible to derive all the familiar algebraic and analytic properties of the trigonometric functions from these series alone. For example, the series immediately give us the formulas

$$\sin 0 = 0, \qquad \cos 0 = 1, \qquad \sin (-x) = -\sin x, \qquad \cos (-x) = \cos x,$$

$$D \sin x = \cos x, \qquad D \cos x = -\sin x.$$

The addition formulas may be derived by the following simple device: Let $u$ and $v$ be new functions defined by the equations

$$u(x) = \sin (x + a) - \sin x \cos a - \cos x \sin a,$$

$$v(x) = \cos (x + a) - \cos x \cos a + \sin x \sin a,$$

where $a$ is a fixed real number, and let $f(x) = [u(x)]^2 + [v(x)]^2$. Then it is easy to verify that $u'(x) = v(x)$ and $v'(x) = -u(x)$, and so $f'(x) = 0$ for all $x$. Therefore, $f$ is a constant and, since $f(0) = 0$, we must have $f(x) = 0$ for all $x$. This implies $u(x) = v(x) = 0$ for all $x$ or, in other words,

$$\sin (x + a) = \sin x \cos a + \cos x \sin a,$$

$$\cos (x + a) = \cos x \cos a - \sin x \sin a.$$

The number $\pi$ may be introduced as the smallest positive $x$ such that $\sin x = 0$ (such an $x$ can be shown to exist) and then it can be shown that the sine and cosine are periodic with period $2\pi$, that $\sin (\frac{1}{2}\pi) = 1$, and that $\cos (\frac{1}{2}\pi) = 0$. The details, which we shall not present here, may be found in the book *Theory and Application of Infinite Series* by K. Knopp (New York: Hafner, 1951).

## *11.12 Bernstein's theorem

Theorem 11.11 shows that the Taylor's series of a function $f$ converges if the $n$th derivative $f^{(n)}$ grows no faster than the $n$th power of some positive number. Another sufficient condition for convergence was formulated by the Russian mathematician Sergei N. Bernstein (1880– ).

THEOREM 11.12. BERNSTEIN'S THEOREM. *Assume $f$ and all its derivatives are nonnegative on a closed interval $[0, r]$. That is, assume that*

$$f(x) \geq 0 \quad and \quad f^{(n)}(x) \geq 0$$

*for each $x$ in $[0, r]$ and each $n = 1, 2, 3, \ldots$. Then, if $0 \leq x < r$, the Taylor's series*

$$\sum_{k=0}^{\infty} \frac{f^{(k)}(0)}{k!} x^k$$

*converges to $f(x)$.*

*Proof.* The result holds trivially for $x = 0$, so we assume that $0 < x < r$. We use Taylor's formula with remainder to write

$$(11.10) \qquad f(x) = \sum_{k=0}^{n} \frac{f^{(k)}(0)}{k!} x^k + E_n(x) .$$

We will prove that the error term satisfies the inequalities

$$(11.11) \qquad 0 \leq E_n(x) \leq \left(\frac{x}{r}\right)^{n+1} f(r) .$$

This, in turn, shows that $E_n(x) \to 0$ as $n \to \infty$ since the quotient $(x/r)^{n+1} \to 0$ when $0 < x < r$.

To prove (11.11), we use the integral form of the error as given in Equation (11.8) with $a = 0$:

$$E_n(x) = \frac{x^{n+1}}{n!} \int_0^1 u^n f^{(n+1)}(x - xu) \, du .$$

This formula is valid for each $x$ in the closed interval $[0, r]$. If $x \neq 0$, let

$$F_n(x) = \frac{E_n(x)}{x^{n+1}} = \frac{1}{n!} \int_0^1 u^n f^{(n+1)}(x - xu) \, du .$$

The function $f^{(n+1)}$ is monotonic increasing in the interval $[0, r]$ since its derivative is nonnegative. Therefore, we have

$$f^{(n+1)}(x - xu) = f^{(n+1)}[x(1 - u)] \leq f^{(n+1)}[r(1 - u)]$$

if $0 \leq u \leq 1$, which implies that $F_n(x) \leq F_n(r)$ if $0 < x \leq r$. In other words, we have $E_n(x)/x^{n+1} \leq E_n(r)/r^{n+1}$ or

$$(11.12) \qquad\qquad E_n(x) \leq \left(\frac{x}{r}\right)^{n+1} E_n(r).$$

Setting $x = r$ in Equation (11.10), we see that $E_n(r) \leq f(r)$ because each term in the sum is nonnegative. Using this in (11.12), we obtain (11.11) which, in turn, completes the proof.

## 11.13  Exercises

For each of the power series in Exercises 1 through 10 determine the set of all real $x$ for which the series converges and compute the sum of the series. The power-series expansions given earlier in the text may be used whenever it is convenient to do so.

1. $\displaystyle\sum_{n=0}^{\infty} (-1)^n x^{2n}$.

2. $\displaystyle\sum_{n=0}^{\infty} \frac{x^n}{3^{n+1}}$.

3. $\displaystyle\sum_{n=0}^{\infty} nx^n$.

4. $\displaystyle\sum_{n=0}^{\infty} (-1)^n nx^n$.

5. $\displaystyle\sum_{n=0}^{\infty} (-2)^n \frac{n+2}{n+1} x^n$.

6. $\displaystyle\sum_{n=1}^{\infty} \frac{2^n x^n}{n}$.

7. $\displaystyle\sum_{n=0}^{\infty} \frac{(-1)^n}{2n+1} \left(\frac{x}{2}\right)^{2n}$.

8. $\displaystyle\sum_{n=0}^{\infty} \frac{(-1)^n x^{3n}}{n!}$.

9. $\displaystyle\sum_{n=0}^{\infty} \frac{x^n}{(n+3)!}$.

10. $\displaystyle\sum_{n=0}^{\infty} \frac{(x-1)^n}{(n+2)!}$.

Each of the functions in Exercises 11 through 21 has a power-series representation in powers of $x$. Assume the existence of the expansion, verify that the coefficients have the form given, and show that the series converges for the values of $x$ indicated. The expansions given earlier in the text may be used whenever it is convenient to do so.

11. $a^x = \displaystyle\sum_{n=0}^{\infty} \frac{(\log a)^n}{n!} x^n$,     $a > 0$     (all $x$).     [*Hint:*  $a^x = e^{x \log a}$.]

12. $\sinh x = \displaystyle\sum_{n=0}^{\infty} \frac{x^{2n+1}}{(2n+1)!}$     (all $x$).

13. $\sin^2 x = \displaystyle\sum_{n=1}^{\infty} (-1)^{n+1} \frac{2^{2n-1}}{(2n)!} x^{2n}$     (all $x$).     [*Hint:*  $\cos 2x = 1 - 2\sin^2 x$.]

14. $\dfrac{1}{2-x} = \displaystyle\sum_{n=0}^{\infty} \frac{x^n}{2^{n+1}}$     ($|x| < 2$).

15. $e^{-x^2} = \displaystyle\sum_{n=0}^{\infty} \frac{(-1)^n x^{2n}}{n!}$     (all $x$).

16. $\sin^3 x = \dfrac{3}{4} \displaystyle\sum_{n=1}^{\infty} (-1)^{n+1} \frac{3^{2n}-1}{(2n+1)!} x^{2n+1}$     (all $x$).

17. $\log \sqrt{\dfrac{1+x}{1-x}} = \displaystyle\sum_{n=0}^{\infty} \dfrac{x^{2n+1}}{2n+1}$   $(|x| < 1)$.

18. $\dfrac{x}{1+x-2x^2} = \dfrac{1}{3} \displaystyle\sum_{n=1}^{\infty} [1 - (-2)^n] x^n$   $(|x| < \frac{1}{2})$.

[*Hint*: $3x/(1 + x - 2x^2) = 1/(1 - x) - 1/(1 + 2x)$.]

19. $\dfrac{12 - 5x}{6 - 5x - x^2} = \displaystyle\sum_{n=0}^{\infty} \left(1 + \dfrac{(-1)^n}{6^n}\right) x^n$   $(|x| < 1)$.

20. $\dfrac{1}{x^2 + x + 1} = \dfrac{2}{\sqrt{3}} \displaystyle\sum_{n=0}^{\infty} \sin \dfrac{2\pi(n+1)}{3} x^n$   $(|x| < 1)$.

[*Hint*: $x^3 - 1 = (x - 1)(x^2 + x + 1)$.]

21. $\dfrac{x}{(1 - x)(1 - x^2)} = \dfrac{1}{2} \displaystyle\sum_{n=1}^{\infty} \left(n + \dfrac{1 - (-1)^n}{2}\right) x^n$   $(|x| < 1)$.

22. Determine the coefficient $a_{98}$ in the power-series expansion $\sin(2x + \frac{1}{4}\pi) = \sum_{n=0}^{\infty} a_n x^n$.

23. Let $f(x) = (2 + x^2)^{5/2}$. Determine the coefficients $a_0, a_1, \ldots, a_4$ in the Taylor's series generated by $f$ at 0.

24. Let $f(x) = e^{-1/x^2}$ if $x \neq 0$, and let $f(0) = 0$.
(a) Show that $f$ has derivatives of every order everywhere on the real axis.
(b) Show that $f^{(n)}(0) = 0$ for all $n \geq 1$. This example shows that the Taylor's series generated by $f$ about the point 0 converges everywhere on the real axis, but that it represents $f$ *only* at the origin.

## 11.14 Power series and differential equations

Power series sometimes enable us to obtain solutions of differential equations when other methods fail. A systematic discussion of the use of power series in the theory of linear second-order differential equations is given in Volume II. Here we illustrate with an example some of the ideas and techniques involved.

Consider the second-order differential equation

(11.13) $$(1 - x^2)y'' = -2y.$$

Assume there exists a solution, say $y = f(x)$, which may be represented by a power-series expansion in some neighborhood of the origin, say

(11.14) $$y = \sum_{n=0}^{\infty} a_n x^n.$$

The first thing we do is determine the coefficients $a_0, a_1, a_2, \ldots$ .
One way to proceed is this: Differentiating (11.14) twice, we obtain

$$y'' = \sum_{n=2}^{\infty} n(n - 1)a_n x^{n-2}.$$

Multiplying by $1 - x^2$, we find that

$$(11.15) \qquad (1 - x^2)y'' = \sum_{n=2}^{\infty} n(n-1)a_n x^{n-2} - \sum_{n=2}^{\infty} n(n-1)a_n x^n$$

$$= \sum_{n=0}^{\infty} (n+2)(n+1)a_{n+2} x^n - \sum_{n=0}^{\infty} n(n-1)a_n x^n$$

$$= \sum_{n=0}^{\infty} [(n+2)(n+1)a_{n+2} - n(n-1)a_n]x^n .$$

Substituting each of the series (11.14) and (11.15) in the differential equation, we obtain an equation involving two power series, valid in some neighborhood of the origin. By the uniqueness theorem, these power series must be equal term by term. Therefore we may equate coefficients of $x^n$ and obtain the relation

$$(n+2)(n+1)a_{n+2} - n(n-1)a_n = -2a_n$$

or, what amounts to the same thing,

$$a_{n+2} = \frac{n^2 - n - 2}{(n+2)(n+1)} a_n = \frac{n-2}{n+2} a_n .$$

This relation enables us to determine $a_2, a_4, a_6, \ldots$ successively in terms of $a_0$. Similarly, we can compute $a_3, a_5, a_7, \ldots$ in terms of $a_1$. For the coefficients with even subscripts, we find that

$$a_2 = -a_0, \qquad a_4 = 0 \cdot a_2 = 0, \qquad a_6 = a_8 = a_{10} = \cdots = 0.$$

The odd coefficients are

$$a_3 = \frac{1-2}{1+2} a_1 = \frac{-1}{3} a_1 , \qquad a_5 = \frac{3-2}{3+2} a_2 = \frac{1}{5} \cdot \frac{(-1)}{3} a_1 ,$$

$$a_7 = \frac{5-2}{5+2} a_5 = \frac{3}{7} \cdot \frac{1}{5} \cdot \frac{(-1)}{3} a_1 = \frac{-1}{7 \cdot 5} a_1$$

and, in general,

$$a_{2n+1} = \frac{2n-3}{2n+1} a_{2n-1} = \frac{2n-3}{2n+1} \cdot \frac{2n-5}{2n-1} \cdot \frac{2n-7}{2n-3} \cdot \ldots \cdot \frac{3}{7} \cdot \frac{1}{5} \cdot \frac{(-1)}{3} a_1 .$$

When the common factors are canceled, this simplifies to

$$a_{2n+1} = \frac{-1}{(2n+1)(2n-1)} a_1 .$$

Therefore, the series for $y$ can be written as follows:

$$y = a_0(1 - x^2) - a_1 \sum_{n=0}^{\infty} \frac{1}{(2n+1)(2n-1)} x^{2n+1} .$$

The ratio test may be used to verify the convergence of this series for $|x| < 1$. The work just carried out shows that the series actually satisfies the differential equation in (11.13), where $a_0$ and $a_1$ may be thought of as arbitrary constants. The reader should note that in this particular example the polynomial which multiplies $a_0$ is itself a solution of (11.13), and the series which multiplies $a_1$ is another solution.

The procedure just described is called the *method of undetermined coefficients*. Another way to find these coefficients is to use the formula

$$a_n = \frac{f^{(n)}(0)}{n!} \quad \text{if} \quad y = f(x).$$

Sometimes the higher derivatives of $y$ at the origin can be computed directly from the differential equation. For example, setting $x = 0$ in (11.13), we immediately obtain

$$f''(0) = -2f(0) = -2a_0,$$

and hence we have

$$a_2 = \frac{f''(0)}{2!} = -a_0.$$

To find the higher derivatives, we differentiate the differential equation to obtain

(11.16) $$(1 - x^2)y''' - 2xy'' = -2y'.$$

Putting $x = 0$, we see that $f'''(0) = -2f'(0) = -2a_1$, and hence $a_3 = f'''(0)/3! = -a_1/3$. Differentiation of (11.16) leads to the equation

$$(1 - x^2)y^{(4)} - 4xy''' = 0.$$

When $x = 0$, this yields $f^{(4)}(0) = 0$, and hence $a_4 = 0$. Repeating the process once more, we find

$$(1 - x^2)y^{(5)} - 6xy^{(4)} - 4y''' = 0,$$

$$f^{(5)}(0) = 4f'''(0) = -8a_1, \qquad a_5 = \frac{f^{(5)}(0)}{5!} = -\frac{a_1}{15}.$$

It is clear that the process may be continued as long as desired.

## 11.15 The binomial series

We can also use our knowledge of differential equations to determine the sums of certain power series. For example, we shall use the existence-uniqueness theorem for first-order linear differential equations to prove that the binomial series expansion

(11.17) $$(1 + x)^\alpha = \sum_{n=0}^{\infty} \binom{\alpha}{n} x^n$$

is valid in the interval $|x| < 1$. Here the exponent $\alpha$ is an arbitrary real number and $\binom{\alpha}{n}$ denotes the binomial coefficient defined by

$$(11.18) \qquad \binom{\alpha}{n} = \frac{\alpha(\alpha - 1) \cdots (\alpha - n + 1)}{n!}.$$

When $\alpha$ is a nonnegative integer, all but a finite number of the coefficients $\binom{\alpha}{n}$ are zero, and the series reduces to a polynomial of degree $\alpha$, giving us the familiar binomial theorem. To prove (11.17) for an arbitrary real $\alpha$, we first use the ratio test to find that the series converges absolutely in the open interval $-1 < x < 1$. Then we define a function $f$ by means of the equation

$$(11.19) \qquad f(x) = \sum_{n=0}^{\infty} \binom{\alpha}{n} x^n, \quad \text{if } |x| < 1.$$

We then show that $f$ is a solution of the linear differential equation

$$(11.20) \qquad y' - \frac{\alpha}{x + 1} y = 0$$

and satisfies the initial condition $f(0) = 1$. Theorem 8.3 tells us that in any interval not containing the point $x = -1$ there is only one solution of this differential equation with $y = 1$ when $x = 0$. Since $y = (1 + x)^{\alpha}$ is such a solution, it follows that $f(x) = (1 + x)^{\alpha}$ if $-1 < x < 1$.

Therefore, to prove (11.17) we need only show that $f$ satisfies the differential equation (11.20). For this purpose, we require the following property of the binomial coefficients:

$$(n + 1)\binom{\alpha}{n + 1} = (\alpha - n)\binom{\alpha}{n}.$$

This property, which is an immediate consequence of the definition in (11.18), holds for every real $\alpha$ and every integer $n \geq 0$. It can also be expressed in the form

$$(11.21) \qquad (n + 1)\binom{\alpha}{n + 1} + n\binom{\alpha}{n} = \alpha\binom{\alpha}{n}.$$

Differentiation of (11.19) gives us

$$f'(x) = \sum_{n=1}^{\infty} n\binom{\alpha}{n} x^{n-1} = \sum_{n=0}^{\infty} (n + 1)\binom{\alpha}{n + 1} x^n,$$

from which we find that

$$(1 + x)f'(x) = \sum_{n=0}^{\infty} \left\{(n + 1)\binom{\alpha}{n + 1} + n\binom{\alpha}{n}\right\} x^n = \alpha \sum_{n=0}^{\infty} \binom{\alpha}{n} x^n = \alpha f(x),$$

because of (11.21). This shows that $f$ satisfies the differential equation (11.20) and this, in turn, proves (11.17).

## 11.16 Exercises

1. The differential equation $(1 - x^2)y'' - 2xy' + 6y = 0$ has a power-series solution $f(x) = \sum_{n=0}^{\infty} a_n x^n$ with $f(0) = 1$ and $f'(0) = 0$. Use the method of undetermined coefficients to obtain a recursion formula relating $a_{n+2}$ to $a_n$. Determine $a_n$ explicitly for each $n$ and find the sum of the series.

2. Do the same as in Exercise 1 for the differential equation $(1 - x^2)y'' - 2xy' + 12y = 0$ and the initial conditions $f(0) = 0, f'(0) = 2$.

In each of Exercises 3 through 9, the power series is used to define the function $f$. Determine the interval of convergence in each case and show that $f$ satisfies the differential equation indicated, where $y = f(x)$. In Exercises 6 through 9, solve the differential equation and thereby obtain the sum of the series.

3. $f(x) = \displaystyle\sum_{n=0}^{\infty} \frac{x^{4n}}{(4n)!}$ ; $\quad \dfrac{d^4 y}{dx^4} = y$.

4. $f(x) = \displaystyle\sum_{n=0}^{\infty} \frac{x^n}{(n!)^2}$ ; $\quad xy'' + y' - y = 0$.

5. $f(x) = 1 + \displaystyle\sum_{n=1}^{\infty} \frac{1 \cdot 4 \cdot 7 \cdots (3n - 2)}{(3n)!} x^{3n}$; $\quad y'' = x^a y + b$. $\quad$ (Find $a$ and $b$.)

6. $f(x) = \displaystyle\sum_{n=0}^{\infty} \frac{x^{2n}}{n!}$ ; $\quad y' = 2xy$.

8. $f(x) = \displaystyle\sum_{n=0}^{\infty} \frac{(-1)^n 2^{2n} x^{2n}}{(2n)!}$ ; $\quad y'' + 4y = 0$.

7. $f(x) = \displaystyle\sum_{n=2}^{\infty} \frac{x^n}{n!}$; $\quad y' = x + y$.

9. $f(x) = x + \displaystyle\sum_{n=0}^{\infty} \frac{(3x)^{2n+1}}{(2n + 1)!}$ ; $\quad y'' = 9(y - x)$.

10. The functions $J_0$ and $J_1$ defined by the series

$$J_0(x) = \sum_{n=0}^{\infty} (-1)^n \frac{x^{2n}}{(n!)^2 2^{2n}}, \qquad J_1(x) = \sum_{n=0}^{\infty} (-1)^n \frac{x^{2n+1}}{n!(n + 1)! 2^{2n+1}}$$

are called *Bessel functions of the first kind* of orders zero and one, respectively. These functions arise in many problems in pure and applied mathematics. Show (a) both series converge for all real $x$; (b) $J_0'(x) = -J_1(x)$; (c) $j_0'(x) = j_1'(x)$, where $j_0(x) = xJ_0(x)$ and $j_1(x) = xJ_1(x)$.

11. The differential equation

$$x^2 y'' + xy' + (x^2 - n^2)y = 0$$

is called *Bessel's equation*. Show that $J_0$ and $J_1$ (as defined in Exercise 10) are solutions when $n = 0$ and 1, respectively.

In each of Exercises 12, 13, and 14, assume the given differential equation has a power-series solution and find the first four nonzero terms.

12. $y' = x^2 + y^2$, with $y = 1$ when $x = 0$.
13. $y' = 1 + xy^2$, with $y = 0$ when $x = 0$.
14. $y' = x + y^2$, with $y = 0$ when $x = 0$.

In Exercises 15, 16, and 17, assume the given differential equation has a power-series solution of the form $y = \sum a_n x^n$, and determine the $n$th coefficient $a_n$.

15. $y' = \alpha y$.  16. $y'' = xy$.  17. $y'' + xy' + y = 0$.

18. Let $f(x) = \sum_{n=0}^{\infty} a_n x^n$, where $a_0 = 1$ and the remaining coefficients are determined by the identity

$$e^{-2x} = \sum_{n=0}^{\infty} \{2a_n + (n+1)a_{n+1}\}x^n.$$

Compute $a_1$, $a_2$, $a_3$, and find the sum of the series for $f(x)$.

19. Let $f(x) = \sum_{n=0}^{\infty} a_n x^n$, where the coefficients $a_n$ are determined by the relation

$$\cos x = \sum_{n=0}^{\infty} a_n(n+2)x^n.$$

Compute $a_5$, $a_6$, and $f(\pi)$.

20. (a) Show that the first six terms of the binomial series for $(1 - x)^{-1/2}$ are:

$$1 + \frac{1}{2}x + \frac{3}{8}x^2 + \frac{5}{16}x^3 + \frac{35}{128}x^4 + \frac{63}{256}x^5.$$

(b) Let $a_n$ denote the $n$th term of this series when $x = 1/50$, and let $r_n$ denote the remainder after $n$ terms; that is, for $n \geq 0$ let

$$r_n = a_{n+1} + a_{n+2} + a_{n+3} + \cdots.$$

Show that $0 < r_n < a_n/49$.

[*Hint:* Show that $a_{n+1} < a_n/50$, and dominate $r_n$ by a suitable geometric series.]

(c) Verify the identity

$$\sqrt{2} = \frac{7}{5}\left(1 - \frac{1}{50}\right)^{-1/2}$$

and use it to compute the first ten correct decimals of $\sqrt{2}$.

[*Hint:* Use parts (a) and (b), retain twelve decimals during the calculations, and take into account round-off errors.]

21. (a) Show that

$$\sqrt{3} = \frac{1732}{1000}\left(1 - \frac{176}{3,000,000}\right)^{-1/2}$$

(b) Proceed as suggested in Exercise 20 and compute the first fifteen correct decimals of $\sqrt{3}$.

22. Integrate the binomial series for $(1 - x^2)^{-1/2}$ and thereby obtain the power-series expansion

$$\arcsin x = x + \sum_{n=1}^{\infty} \frac{1 \cdot 3 \cdot 5 \cdots (2n - 1)}{2 \cdot 4 \cdot 6 \cdots (2n)} \frac{x^{2n+1}}{2n + 1} \qquad (|x| < 1).$$

# 12

# VECTOR ALGEBRA

## 12.1 Historical introduction

In the foregoing chapters we have presented many of the basic concepts of calculus and have illustrated their use in solving a few relatively simple geometrical and physical problems. Further applications of the calculus require a deeper knowledge of analytic geometry than has been presented so far, and therefore we turn our attention to a more detailed investigation of some fundamental geometric ideas.

As we have pointed out earlier in this book, calculus and analytic geometry were intimately related throughout their historical development. Every new discovery in one subject led to an improvement in the other. The problem of drawing tangents to curves resulted in the discovery of the derivative; that of area led to the integral; and partial derivatives were introduced to investigate curved surfaces in space. Along with these accomplishments came other parallel developments in mechanics and mathematical physics. In 1788 Lagrange published his masterpiece *Mécanique analytique* (Analytical Mechanics) which showed the great flexibility and tremendous power attained by using analytical methods in the study of mechanics. Later on, in the 19th century, the Irish mathematician William Rowan Hamilton (1805–1865) introduced his *Theory of Quaternions*, a new method and a new point of view that contributed much to the understanding of both algebra and physics. The best features of quaternion analysis and Cartesian geometry were later united, largely through the efforts of J. W. Gibbs (1839–1903) and O. Heaviside (1850–1925), and a new subject called *vector algebra* sprang into being. It was soon realized that vectors are the ideal tools for the exposition and simplification of many important ideas in geometry and physics. In this chapter we propose to discuss the elements of vector algebra. Applications to analytic geometry are given in Chapter 13. In Chapter 14 vector algebra is combined with the methods of calculus, and applications are given to both geometry and mechanics.

There are essentially three different ways to introduce vector algebra: *geometrically*, *analytically*, and *axiomatically*. In the geometric approach, vectors are represented by directed line segments, or arrows. Algebraic operations on vectors, such as addition, subtraction, and multiplication by real numbers, are defined and studied by geometric methods.

In the analytic approach, vectors and vector operations are described entirely in terms of *numbers*, called *components*. Properties of the vector operations are then deduced from

445

corresponding properties of numbers. The analytic description of vectors arises naturally from the geometric description as soon as a coordinate system is introduced.

In the axiomatic approach, no attempt is made to describe the nature of a vector or of the algebraic operations on vectors. Instead, vectors and vector operations are thought of as *undefined concepts* of which we know nothing except that they satisfy a certain set of axioms. Such an algebraic system, with appropriate axioms, is called a *linear space* or a *linear vector space*. Examples of linear spaces occur in all branches of mathematics, and we will study many of them in Chapter 15. The algebra of directed line segments and the algebra of vectors described by components are merely two examples of linear spaces.

The study of vector algebra from the axiomatic point of view is perhaps the most mathematically satisfactory approach to use since it furnishes a description of vectors that is free of coordinate systems and free of any particular geometric representation. This study is carried out in detail in Chapter 15. In this chapter we base our treatment on the analytic approach, and we also use directed line segments to interpret many of the results geometrically. When possible, we give proofs by coordinate-free methods. Thus, this chapter serves to provide familiarity with important concrete examples of vector spaces, and it also motivates the more abstract approach in Chapter 15.

## 12.2 The vector space of *n*-tuples of real numbers

The idea of using a number to locate a point on a line was known to the ancient Greeks. In 1637 Descartes extended this idea, using a *pair* of numbers $(a_1, a_2)$ to locate a point in the plane, and a *triple* of numbers $(a_1, a_2, a_3)$ to locate a point in space. The 19th century mathematicians A. Cayley (1821–1895) and H. G. Grassmann (1809–1877) realized that there is no need to stop with three numbers. One can just as well consider a *quadruple* of numbers $(a_1, a_2, a_3, a_4)$ or, more generally, an *n-tuple* of real numbers

$$(a_1, a_2, \ldots, a_n)$$

for any integer $n \geq 1$. Such an *n*-tuple is called an *n-dimensional point* or an *n-dimensional vector*, the individual numbers $a_1, a_2, \ldots, a_n$ being referred to as *coordinates* or *components* of the vector. The collection of all *n*-dimensional vectors is called *the vector space of n-tuples*, or simply *n-space*. We denote this space by $V_n$.

The reader may well ask at this stage why we are interested in spaces of dimension greater than three. One answer is that many problems which involve a large number of simultaneous equations are more easily analyzed by introducing vectors in a suitable *n*-space and replacing all these equations by a single vector equation. Another advantage is that we are able to deal in one stroke with many properties common to 1-space, 2-space, 3-space, etc., that is, properties independent of the dimensionality of the space. This is in keeping with the spirit of modern mathematics which favors the development of comprehensive methods for attacking problems on a wide front.

Unfortunately, the geometric pictures which are a great help in motivating and illustrating vector concepts when $n = 1, 2,$ and 3 are not available when $n > 3$; therefore, the study of vector algebra in higher-dimensional spaces must proceed entirely by analytic means.

In this chapter we shall usually denote vectors by capital letters $A, B, C, \ldots$, and components by the corresponding small letters $a, b, c, \ldots$. Thus, we write

$$A = (a_1, a_2, \ldots, a_n).$$

To convert $V_n$ into an algebraic system, we introduce *equality* of vectors and two vector operations called *addition* and *multiplication by scalars*. The word "scalar" is used here as a synonym for "real number."

DEFINITION. *Two vectors A and B in $V_n$ are called equal whenever they agree in their respective components. That is, if $A = (a_1, a_2, \ldots, a_n)$ and $B = (b_1, b_2, \ldots, b_n)$, the vector equation $A = B$ means exactly the same as the n scalar equations*

$$a_1 = b_1, \quad a_2 = b_2, \quad \ldots, \quad a_n = b_n.$$

*The sum $A + B$ is defined to be the vector obtained by adding corresponding components:*

$$A + B = (a_1 + b_1, a_2 + b_2, \ldots, a_n + b_n).$$

*If c is a scalar, we define cA or Ac to be the vector obtained by multiplying each component of A by c:*

$$cA = (ca_1, ca_2, \ldots, ca_n).$$

From this definition it is easy to verify the following properties of these operations.

THEOREM 12.1. *Vector addition is commutative,*

$$A + B = B + A,$$

*and associative,*

$$A + (B + C) = (A + B) + C.$$

*Multiplication by scalars is associative,*

$$c(dA) = (cd)A$$

*and satisfies the two distributive laws*

$$c(A + B) = cA + cB, \quad and \quad (c + d)A = cA + dA.$$

Proofs of these properties follow quickly from the definition and are left as exercises for the reader.

The vector with all components 0 is called the *zero vector* and is denoted by $O$. It has the property that $A + O = A$ for every vector $A$; in other words, $O$ is an identity element for vector addition. The vector $(-1)A$ is also denoted by $-A$ and is called the *negative* of $A$. We also write $A - B$ for $A + (-B)$ and call this the *difference* of $A$ and $B$. The equation $(A + B) - B = A$ shows that subtraction is the inverse of addition. Note that $0A = O$ and that $1A = A$.

The reader may have noticed the similarity between vectors in 2-space and complex numbers. Both are defined as ordered pairs of real numbers and both are added in exactly the same way. Thus, as far as addition is concerned, complex numbers and two-dimensional vectors are algebraically indistinguishable. They differ only when we introduce multiplication.

Multiplication of complex numbers gives the complex-number system the field properties also possessed by the real numbers. It can be shown (although the proof is difficult) that except for $n = 1$ and 2, it is not possible to introduce multiplication in $V_n$ so as to satisfy all the field properties. However, special products can be introduced in $V_n$ which do not satisfy *all* the field properties. For example, in Section 12.5 we shall discuss the *dot product* of two vectors in $V_n$. The result of this multiplication is a scalar, not a vector. Another product, called the *cross product*, is discussed in Section 13.9. This multiplication is applicable only in the space $V_3$. The result is always a vector, but the cross product is not commutative.

## 12.3 Geometric interpretation for $n \leq 3$

Although the foregoing definitions are completely divorced from geometry, vectors and vector operations have an interesting geometric interpretation for spaces of dimension three or less. We shall draw pictures in 2-space to illustrate these concepts and ask the reader to produce the corresponding visualizations for himself in 3-space and in 1-space.

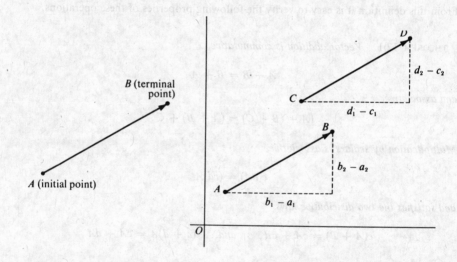

FIGURE 12.1   The geometric vector $\overrightarrow{AB}$ from $A$ to $B$.

FIGURE 12.2   $\overrightarrow{AB}$ and $\overrightarrow{CD}$ are equivalent because $B - A = D - C$.

A pair of points $A$ and $B$ is called a *geometric vector* if one of the points, say $A$, is called the *initial point* and the other, $B$, the *terminal point*, or *tip*. We visualize a geometric vector as an arrow from $A$ to $B$, as shown in Figure 12.1, and denote it by the symbol $\overrightarrow{AB}$.

Geometric vectors are especially convenient for representing certain physical quantities such as force, displacement, velocity, and acceleration, which possess both magnitude and direction. The length of the arrow is a measure of the magnitude and the arrowhead indicates the required direction.

Suppose we introduce a coordinate system with origin $O$. Figure 12.2 shows two geometric vectors $\overrightarrow{AB}$ and $\overrightarrow{CD}$ with $B - A = D - C$. In terms of components, this means that we have

$$b_1 - a_1 = d_1 - c_1 \quad \text{and} \quad b_2 - a_2 = d_2 - c_2.$$

By comparison of the congruent triangles in Figure 12.2, we see that the two arrows representing $\overrightarrow{AB}$ and $\overrightarrow{CD}$ have equal lengths, are parallel, and point in the same direction. We call such geometric vectors *equivalent*. That is, we say $\overrightarrow{AB}$ is equivalent to $\overrightarrow{CD}$ whenever

(12.1) $$B - A = D - C.$$

Note that the four points $A$, $B$, $C$, $D$ are vertices of a parallelogram. (See Figure 12.3.) Equation (12.1) can also be written in the form $A + D = B + C$ which tells us that *opposite vertices of the parallelogram have the same sum*. In particular, if one of the vertices, say $A$, is the origin $O$, as in Figure 12.4, the geometric vector from $O$ to the opposite vertex $D$ corresponds to the vector sum $D = B + C$. This is described by saying that vector addition corresponds geometrically to addition of geometric vectors by the *parallelogram law*. The importance of vectors in physics stems from the remarkable fact that many physical quantities (such as force, velocity, and acceleration) combine by the parallelogram law.

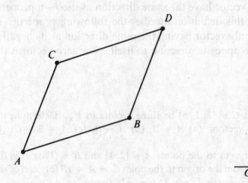

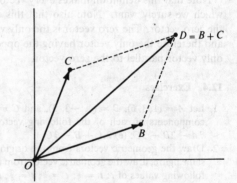

FIGURE 12.3  Opposite vertices of a parallelogram have the same sum: $A + D = B + C$.

FIGURE 12.4  Vector addition interpreted geometrically by the parallelogram law.

For simplicity in notation, we shall use the same symbol to denote a point in $V_n$ (when $n \leq 3$) and the geometric vector from the origin to this point. Thus, we write $A$ instead of $\overrightarrow{OA}$, $B$ instead of $\overrightarrow{OB}$, and so on. Sometimes we also write $A$ in place of any geometric vector equivalent to $\overrightarrow{OA}$. For example, Figure 12.5 illustrates the geometric meaning of vector subtraction. Two geometric vectors are labeled as $B - A$, but these geometric vectors are equivalent. They have the same length and the same direction.

Figure 12.6 illustrates the geometric meaning of multiplication by scalars. If $B = cA$, the geometric vector $B$ has length $|c|$ times the length of $A$; it points in the same direction as $A$ if $c$ is positive, and in the opposite direction if $c$ is negative.

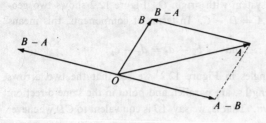

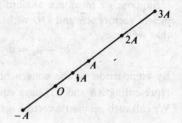

FIGURE 12.5 Geometric meaning of subtraction of vectors.

FIGURE 12.6 Multiplication of vectors by scalars.

The geometric interpretation of vectors in $V_n$ for $n \le 3$ suggests a way to define parallelism in a general $n$-space.

DEFINITION. *Two vectors $A$ and $B$ in $V_n$ are said to have the same direction if $B = cA$ for some positive scalar $c$, and the opposite direction if $B = cA$ for some negative $c$. They are called parallel if $B = cA$ for some nonzero $c$.*

Note that this definition makes every vector have the same direction as itself—a property which we surely want. Note also that this definition ascribes the following properties to the zero vector: The zero vector is the only vector having the same direction as its negative and therefore the only vector having the opposite direction to itself. The zero vector is the only vector parallel to the zero vector.

## 12.4 Exercises

1. Let $A = (1, 3, 6)$, $B = (4, -3, 3)$, and $C = (2, 1, 5)$ be three vectors in $V_3$. Determine the components of each of the following vectors: (a) $A + B$; (b) $A - B$; (c) $A + B - C$; (d) $7A - 2B - 3C$; (e) $2A + B - 3C$.

2. Draw the geometric vectors from the origin to the points $A = (2, 1)$ and $B = (1, 3)$. On the same figure, draw the geometric vector from the origin to the point $C = A + tB$ for each of the following values of $t$: $t = \frac{1}{3}$; $t = \frac{1}{2}$; $t = \frac{3}{4}$; $t = 1$; $t = 2$; $t = -1$; $t = -2$.

3. Solve Exercise 2 if $C = tA + B$.

4. Let $A = (2, 1)$, $B = (1, 3)$, and $C = xA + yB$, where $x$ and $y$ are scalars.
   (a) Draw the geometric vector from the origin to $C$ for each of the following pairs of values of $x$ and $y$: $x = y = \frac{1}{2}$; $x = \frac{1}{4}$, $y = \frac{3}{4}$; $x = \frac{1}{3}$, $y = \frac{2}{3}$; $x = 2$, $y = -1$; $x = 3$, $y = -2$; $x = -\frac{1}{2}$, $y = \frac{3}{2}$; $x = -1$, $y = 2$.
   (b) What do you think is the set of points $C$ obtained as $x$ and $y$ run through all real numbers such that $x + y = 1$? (Just make a guess and show the locus on the figure. No proof is required.)
   (c) Make a guess for the set of all points $C$ obtained as $x$ and $y$ range independently over the intervals $0 \le x \le 1$, $0 \le y \le 1$, and make a sketch of this set.
   (d) What do you think is the set of all $C$ obtained if $x$ ranges through the interval $0 \le x \le 1$ and $y$ ranges through all real numbers?
   (e) What do you think is the set if $x$ and $y$ both range over all real numbers?

5. Let $A = (2, 1)$ and $B = (1, 3)$. Show that every vector $C = (c_1, c_2)$ in $V_2$ can be expressed in the form $C = xA + yB$. Express $x$ and $y$ in terms of $c_1$ and $c_2$.

6. Let $A = (1, 1, 1)$, $B = (0, 1, 1)$, and $C = (1, 1, 0)$ be three vectors in $V_3$ and let $D = xA + yB + zC$, where $x$, $y$, $z$ are scalars.
   (a) Determine the components of $D$.
   (b) If $D = O$, prove that $x = y = z = 0$.
   (c) Find $x$, $y$, $z$ such that $D = (1, 2, 3)$.
7. Let $A = (1, 1, 1)$, $B = (0, 1, 1)$ and $C = (2, 1, 1)$ be three vectors in $V_3$, and let $D = xA + yB + zC$, where $x$, $y$, and $z$ are scalars.
   (a) Determine the components of $D$.
   (b) Find $x$, $y$, and $z$, not all zero, such that $D = O$.
   (c) Prove that no choice of $x$, $y$, $z$ makes $D = (1, 2, 3)$.
8. Let $A = (1, 1, 1, 0)$, $B = (0, 1, 1, 1)$, $C = (1, 1, 0, 0)$ be three vectors in $V_4$, and let $D = xA + yB + zC$, where $x$, $y$, and $z$ are scalars.
   (a) Determine the components of $D$.
   (b) If $D = O$, prove that $x = y = z = 0$.
   (c) Find $x$, $y$, and $z$ such that $D = (1, 5, 3, 4)$.
   (d) Prove that no choice of $x$, $y$, $z$ makes $D = (1, 2, 3, 4)$.
9. In $V_n$, prove that two vectors parallel to the same vector are parallel to each other.
10. Given four nonzero vectors $A$, $B$, $C$, $D$ in $V_n$ such that $C = A + B$ and $A$ is parallel to $D$. Prove that $C$ is parallel to $D$ if and only if $B$ is parallel to $D$.
11. (a) Prove, for vectors in $V_n$, the properties of addition and multiplication by scalars given in Theorem 12.1.
    (b) By drawing geometric vectors in the plane, illustrate the geometric meaning of the two distributive laws $(c + d)A = cA + dA$ and $c(A + B) = cA + cB$.
12. If a quadrilateral $OABC$ in $V_2$ is a parallelogram having $A$ and $C$ as opposite vertices, prove that $A + \frac{1}{2}(C - A) = \frac{1}{2}B$. What geometrical theorem about parallelograms can you deduce from this equation?

## 12.5 The dot product

We introduce now a new kind of multiplication called the dot product or scalar product of two vectors in $V_n$.

DEFINITION. *If $A = (a_1, \ldots, a_n)$ and $B = (b_1, \ldots, b_n)$ are two vectors in $V_n$, their dot product is denoted by $A \cdot B$ and is defined by the equation*

$$A \cdot B = \sum_{k=1}^{n} a_k b_k .$$

Thus, to compute $A \cdot B$ we multiply corresponding components of $A$ and $B$ and then add all the products. This multiplication has the following algebraic properties.

THEOREM 12.2. *For all vectors $A$, $B$, $C$ in $V_n$ and all scalars $c$, we have the following properties:*

(a) $A \cdot B = B \cdot A$        (*commutative law*),
(b) $A \cdot (B + C) = A \cdot B + A \cdot C$        (*distributive law*),
(c) $c(A \cdot B) = (cA) \cdot B = A \cdot (cB)$        (*homogeneity*),
(d) $A \cdot A > 0$     if   $A \neq O$        (*positivity*),
(e) $A \cdot A = 0$     if   $A = O$.

*Proof.* The first three properties are easy consequences of the definition and are left as exercises. To prove the last two, we use the relation $A \cdot A = \sum a_k^2$. Since each term is nonnegative, the sum is nonnegative. Moreover, the sum is zero if and only if each term in the sum is zero and this can happen only if $A = O$.

The dot product has an interesting geometric interpretation which will be described in Section 12.9. Before we discuss this, however, we mention an important inequality concerning dot products that is fundamental in vector algebra.

THEOREM 12.3. THE CAUCHY–SCHWARZ INEQUALITY. *If A and B are vectors in $V_n$, we have*

(12.2)
$$(A \cdot B)^2 \leq (A \cdot A)(B \cdot B).$$

*Moreover, the equality sign holds if and only if one of the vectors is a scalar multiple of the other.*

*Proof.* Expressing each member of (12.2) in terms of components, we obtain

$$\left( \sum_{k=1}^{n} a_k b_k \right)^2 \leq \left( \sum_{k=1}^{n} a_k^2 \right) \left( \sum_{k=1}^{n} b_k^2 \right).$$

which is the inequality proved earlier in Theorem I.41.

We shall present another proof of (12.2) that makes no use of components. Such a proof is of interest because it shows that the Cauchy–Schwarz inequality is a consequence of the five properties of the dot product listed in Theorem 12.2 and does not depend on the particular definition that was used to deduce these properties.

To carry out this proof, we notice first that (12.2) holds trivially if either $A$ or $B$ is the zero vector. Therefore, we may assume that both $A$ and $B$ are nonzero. Let $C$ be the vector

$$C = xA - yB, \quad \text{where} \quad x = B \cdot B \quad \text{and} \quad y = A \cdot B.$$

Properties (d) and (e) imply that $C \cdot C \geq 0$. When we translate this in terms of $x$ and $y$, it will yield (12.2). To express $C \cdot C$ in terms of $x$ and $y$, we use properties (a), (b) and (c) to obtain

$$C \cdot C = (xA - yB) \cdot (xA - yB) = x^2(A \cdot A) - 2xy(A \cdot B) + y^2(B \cdot B).$$

Using the definitions of $x$ and $y$ and the inequality $C \cdot C \geq 0$, we get

$$(B \cdot B)^2(A \cdot A) - 2(A \cdot B)^2(B \cdot B) + (A \cdot B)^2(B \cdot B) \geq 0.$$

Property (d) implies $B \cdot B > 0$ since $B \neq O$, so we may divide by $(B \cdot B)$ to obtain

$$(B \cdot B)(A \cdot A) - (A \cdot B)^2 \geq 0,$$

which is (12.2). This proof also shows that the equality sign holds in (12.2) if and only if $C = O$. But $C = O$ if and only if $xA = yB$. This equation holds, in turn, if and only if one of the vectors is a scalar multiple of the other.

The Cauchy–Schwarz inequality has important applications to the properties of the *length* or *norm* of a vector, a concept which we discuss next.

## 12.6  Length or norm of a vector

Figure 12.7 shows the geometric vector from the origin to a point $A = (a_1, a_2)$ in the plane. From the theorem of Pythagoras, we find that the length of $A$ is given by the formula

$$\text{length of } A = \sqrt{a_1^2 + a_2^2}.$$

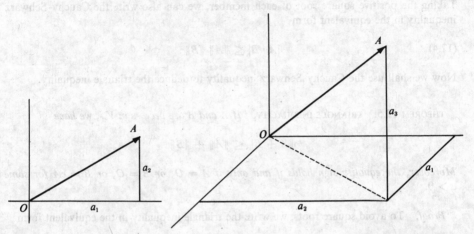

FIGURE 12.7   In $V_2$, the length of $A$ is $\sqrt{a_1^2 + a_2^2}$.

FIGURE 12.8   In $V_3$, the length of $A$ is $\sqrt{a_1^2 + a_2^2 + a_3^2}$.

A corresponding picture in 3-space is shown in Figure 12.8. Applying the theorem of Pythagoras twice, we find that the length of a geometric vector $A$ in 3-space is given by

$$\text{length of } A = \sqrt{a_1^2 + a_2^2 + a_3^2}.$$

Note that in either case the length of $A$ is given by $(A \cdot A)^{1/2}$, the square root of the dot product of $A$ with itself. This formula suggests a way to introduce the concept of length in *n*-space.

DEFINITION.   *If $A$ is a vector in $V_n$, its length or norm is denoted by $\|A\|$ and is defined by the equation*

$$\|A\| = (A \cdot A)^{1/2}.$$

The fundamental properties of the dot product lead to corresponding properties of norms.

THEOREM 12.4.   *If $A$ is a vector in $V_n$ and if $c$ is a scalar, we have the following properties:*
  (a) $\|A\| > 0$    *if*   $A \neq O$    *(positivity)*,
  (b) $\|A\| = 0$    *if*   $A = O$,
  (c) $\|cA\| = |c| \, \|A\|$    *(homogeneity)*.

*Proof.* Properties (a) and (b) follow at once from properties (d) and (e) of Theorem 12.2. To prove (c), we use the homogeneity property of dot products to obtain

$$\|cA\| = (cA \cdot cA)^{1/2} = (c^2 A \cdot A)^{1/2} = (c^2)^{1/2}(A \cdot A)^{1/2} = |c|\, \|A\| \,.$$

The Cauchy–Schwarz inequality can also be expressed in terms of norms. It states that

(12.3)                                  $(A \cdot B)^2 \leq \|A\|^2 \|B\|^2 \,.$

Taking the positive square root of each member, we can also write the Cauchy–Schwarz inequality in the equivalent form

(12.4)                                  $|A \cdot B| \leq \|A\|\, \|B\| \,.$

Now we shall use the Cauchy–Schwarz inequality to deduce the triangle inequality.

THEOREM 12.5.   TRIANGLE INEQUALITY.   *If A and B are vectors in $V_n$, we have*

$$\|A + B\| \leq \|A\| + \|B\| \,.$$

*Moreover, the equality sign holds if and only if $A = O$, or $B = O$, or $B = cA$ for some $c > 0$.*

*Proof.* To avoid square roots, we write the triangle inequality in the equivalent form

(12.5)                                  $\|A + B\|^2 \leq (\|A\| + \|B\|)^2 \,.$

The left member of (12.5) is

$$\|A + B\|^2 = (A + B) \cdot (A + B) = A \cdot A + 2A \cdot B + B \cdot B = \|A\|^2 + 2A \cdot B + \|B\|^2 \,,$$

whereas the right member is

$$(\|A\| + \|B\|)^2 = \|A\|^2 + 2\|A\|\, \|B\| + \|B\|^2 \,.$$

Comparing these two formulas, we see that (12.5) holds if and only if we have

(12.6)                                  $A \cdot B \leq \|A\|\, \|B\| \,.$

But $A \cdot B \leq |A \cdot B|$ so (12.6) follows from the Cauchy–Schwarz inequality, as expressed in (12.4). This proves that the triangle inequality is a consequence of the Cauchy–Schwarz inequality.

The converse statement is also true. That is, if the triangle inequality holds then (12.6) also holds for $A$ and for $-A$, from which we obtain (12.3). If equality holds in (12.5), then $A \cdot B = \|A\|\, \|B\|$, so $B = cA$ for some scalar $c$. Hence $A \cdot B = c\|A\|^2$ and $\|A\|\, \|B\| = |c|\, \|A\|^2$. If $A \neq O$ this implies $c = |c| \geq 0$. If $B \neq O$ then $B = cA$ with $c > 0$.

The triangle inequality is illustrated geometrically in Figure 12.9. It states that the length of one side of a triangle does not exceed the sum of the lengths of the other two sides.

## 12.7 Orthogonality of vectors

In the course of the proof of the triangle inequality (Theorem 12.5), we obtained the formula

(12.7) $$\|A + B\|^2 = \|A\|^2 + \|B\|^2 + 2A \cdot B$$

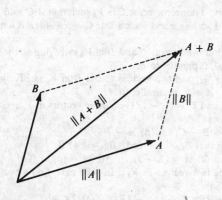

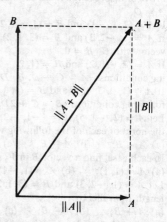

FIGURE 12.9 Geometric meaning of the triangle inequality:

$$\|A + B\| \le \|A\| + \|B\|.$$

FIGURE 12.10 Two perpendicular vectors satisfy the Pythagorean identity:

$$\|A + B\|^2 = \|A\|^2 + \|B\|^2.$$

which is valid for any two vectors $A$ and $B$ in $V_n$. Figure 12.10 shows two perpendicular geometric vectors in the plane. They determine a right triangle whose legs have lengths $\|A\|$ and $\|B\|$ and whose hypotenuse has length $\|A + B\|$. The theorem of Pythagoras states that

$$\|A + B\|^2 = \|A\|^2 + \|B\|^2.$$

Comparing this with (12.7), we see that $A \cdot B = 0$. In other words, the dot product of two perpendicular vectors in the plane is zero. This property motivates the definition of perpendicularity of vectors in $V_n$.

DEFINITION. *Two vectors $A$ and $B$ in $V_n$ are called perpendicular or orthogonal if $A \cdot B = 0$.*

Equation (12.7) shows that two vectors $A$ and $B$ in $V_n$ are orthogonal if and only if $\|A + B\|^2 = \|A\|^2 + \|B\|^2$. This is called the Pythagorean identity in $V_n$.

## 12.8 Exercises

1. Let $A = (1, 2, 3, 4)$, $B = (-1, 2, -3, 0)$, and $C = (0, 1, 0, 1)$ be three vectors in $V_4$. Compute each of the following dot products:
   (a) $A \cdot B$;   (b) $B \cdot C$;   (c) $A \cdot C$;   (d) $A \cdot (B + C)$;   (e) $(A - B) \cdot C$.

2. Given three vectors $A = (2, 4, -7)$, $B = (2, 6, 3)$, and $C = (3, 4, -5)$. In each of the following there is only one way to insert parentheses to obtain a meaningful expression. Insert parentheses and perform the indicated operations.
   (a) $A \cdot BC$;   (b) $A \cdot B + C$;   (c) $A + B \cdot C$;   (d) $AB \cdot C$;   (e) $A/B \cdot C$.

3. Prove or disprove the following statement about vectors in $V_n$: If $A \cdot B = A \cdot C$ and $A \neq O$, then $B = C$.

4. Prove or disprove the following statement about vectors in $V_n$: If $A \cdot B = 0$ for every $B$, then $A = O$.

5. If $A = (2, 1, -1)$ and $B = (1, -1, 2)$, find a nonzero vector $C$ in $V_3$ such that $A \cdot C = B \cdot C = 0$.

6. If $A = (1, -2, 3)$ and $B = (3, 1, 2)$, find scalars $x$ and $y$ such that $C = xA + yB$ is a nonzero vector with $C \cdot B = 0$.

7. If $A = (2, -1, 2)$ and $B = (1, 2, -2)$, find two vectors $C$ and $D$ in $V_3$ satisfying all the following conditions: $A = C + D$, $B \cdot D = 0$, $C$ parallel to $B$.

8. If $A = (1, 2, 3, 4, 5)$ and $B = (1, \frac{1}{2}, \frac{1}{3}, \frac{1}{4}, \frac{1}{5})$, find two vectors $C$ and $D$ in $V_5$ satisfying all the following conditions: $B = C + 2D$, $D \cdot A = 0$, $C$ parallel to $A$.

9. Let $A = (2, -1, 5)$, $B = (-1, -2, 3)$, and $C = (1, -1, 1)$ be three vectors in $V_3$. Calculate the norm of each of the following vectors:
   (a) $A + B$;   (b) $A - B$;   (c) $A + B - C$;   (d) $A - B + C$.

10. In each case, find a vector $B$ in $V_2$ such that $B \cdot A = 0$ and $\|B\| = \|A\|$ if:
    (a) $A = (1, 1)$;   (b) $A = (1, -1)$;   (c) $A = (2, -3)$;   (d) $A = (a, b)$.

11. Let $A = (1, -2, 3)$ and $B = (3, 1, 2)$ be two vectors in $V_3$. In each case, find a vector $C$ of length 1 parallel to:
    (a) $A + B$;   (b) $A - B$;   (c) $A + 2B$;   (d) $A - 2B$;   (e) $2A - B$.

12. Let $A = (4, 1, -3)$, $B = (1, 2, 2)$, $C = (1, 2, -2)$, $D = (2, 1, 2)$, and $E = (2, -2, -1)$ be vectors in $V_3$. Determine all orthogonal pairs.

13. Find all vectors in $V_2$ that are orthogonal to $A$ and have the same length as $A$ if:
    (a) $A = (1, 2)$;   (b) $A = (1, -2)$;   (c) $A = (2, -1)$;   (d) $A = (-2, 1)$.

14. If $A = (2, -1, 1)$ and $B = (3, -4, -4)$, find a point $C$ in 3-space such that $A, B$, and $C$ are the vertices of a right triangle.

15. If $A = (1, -1, 2)$ and $B = (2, 1, -1)$, find a nonzero vector $C$ in $V_3$ orthogonal to $A$ and $B$.

16. Let $A = (1, 2)$ and $B = (3, 4)$ be two vectors in $V_2$. Find vectors $P$ and $Q$ in $V_2$ such that $A = P + Q$, $P$ is parallel to $B$, and $Q$ is orthogonal to $B$.

17. Solve Exercise 16 if the vectors are in $V_4$, with $A = (1, 2, 3, 4)$ and $B = (1, 1, 1, 1)$.

18. Given vectors $A = (2, -1, 1)$, $B = (1, 2, -1)$, and $C = (1, 1, -2)$ in $V_3$. Find every vector $D$ of the form $xB + yC$ which is orthogonal to $A$ and has length 1.

19. Prove that for two vectors $A$ and $B$ in $V_n$ we have the identity

$$\|A + B\|^2 - \|A - B\|^2 = 4A \cdot B,$$

and hence $A \cdot B = 0$ if and only if $\|A + B\| = \|A - B\|$. When this is interpreted geometrically in $V_2$, it states that the diagonals of a parallelogram are of equal length if and only if the parallelogram is a rectangle.

20. Prove that for any two vectors $A$ and $B$ in $V_n$ we have

$$\|A + B\|^2 + \|A - B\|^2 = 2\|A\|^2 + 2\|B\|^2.$$

What geometric theorem about the sides and diagonals of a parallelogram can you deduce from this identity?

21. The following theorem in geometry suggests a vector identity involving three vectors $A$, $B$, and $C$. Guess the identity and prove that it holds for vectors in $V_n$. This provides a proof of the theorem by vector methods.

   "The sum of the squares of the sides of any quadrilateral exceeds the sum of the squares of the diagonals by four times the square of the length of the line segment which connects the midpoints of the diagonals."

22. A vector $A$ in $V_n$ has length 6. A vector $B$ in $V_n$ has the property that for every pair of scalars $x$ and $y$ the vectors $xA + yB$ and $4yA - 9xB$ are orthogonal. Compute the length of $B$ and the length of $2A + 3B$.

23. Given two vectors $A = (1, 2, 3, 4, 5)$ and $B = (1, \frac{1}{2}, \frac{1}{3}, \frac{1}{4}, \frac{1}{5})$ in $V_5$. Find two vectors $C$ and $D$ satisfying the following three conditions: $C$ is parallel to $A$, $D$ is orthogonal to $A$, and $B = C + D$.

24. Given two nonperpendicular vectors $A$ and $B$ in $V_n$, prove that there exist vectors $C$ and $D$ in $V_n$ satisfying the three conditions in Exercise 23 and express $C$ and $D$ in terms of $A$ and $B$.

25. Prove or disprove each of the following statements concerning vectors in $V_n$:

   (a) If $A$ is orthogonal to $B$, then $\|A + xB\| \geq \|A\|$ for all real $x$.

   (b) If $\|A + xB\| \geq \|A\|$ for all real $x$, then $A$ is orthogonal to $B$.

## 12.9 Projections. Angle between vectors in $n$-space

The dot product of two vectors in $V_2$ has an interesting geometric interpretation. Figure 12.11(a) shows two nonzero geometric vectors $A$ and $B$ making an angle $\theta$ with each other. In this example, we have $0 < \theta < \frac{1}{2}\pi$. Figure 12.11(b) shows the same vector $A$ and two perpendicular vectors whose sum is $A$. One of these, $tB$, is a scalar multiple of $B$ which we call the *projection of A along B*. In this example, $t$ is positive since $0 < \theta < \frac{1}{2}\pi$.

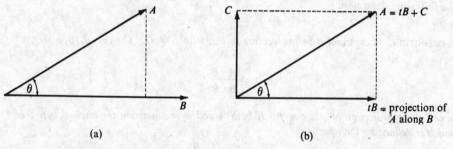

         (a)                                 (b)

FIGURE 12.11   The vector $tB$ is the projection of $A$ along $B$.

We can use dot products to express $t$ in terms of $A$ and $B$. First we write $tB + C = A$ and then take the dot product of each member with $B$ to obtain

$$tB \cdot B + C \cdot B = A \cdot B.$$

But $C \cdot B = 0$, because $C$ was drawn perpendicular to $B$. Therefore $tB \cdot B = A \cdot B$, so we have

(12.8) $$t = \frac{A \cdot B}{B \cdot B} = \frac{A \cdot B}{\|B\|^2}.$$

On the other hand, the scalar $t$ bears a simple relation to the angle $\theta$. From Figure 12.11(b), we see that

$$\cos \theta = \frac{\|tB\|}{\|A\|} = \frac{t\,\|B\|}{\|A\|}\,.$$

Using (12.8) in this formula, we find that

(12.9)                                $$\cos \theta = \frac{A \cdot B}{\|A\|\,\|B\|}$$

or

$$A \cdot B = \|A\|\,\|B\|\,\cos \theta\,.$$

In other words, the dot product of two nonzero vectors $A$ and $B$ in $V_2$ is equal to the product of three numbers: the length of $A$, the length of $B$, and the cosine of the angle between $A$ and $B$.

Equation (12.9) suggests a way to define the concept of angle in $V_n$. The Cauchy–Schwarz inequality, as expressed in (12.4), shows that the quotient on the right of (12.9) has absolute value $\leq 1$ for any two nonzero vectors in $V_n$. In other words, we have

$$-1 \leq \frac{A \cdot B}{\|A\|\,\|B\|} \leq 1\,.$$

Therefore, there is exactly one real $\theta$ in the interval $0 \leq \theta \leq \pi$ such that (12.9) holds. We define the angle between $A$ and $B$ to be this $\theta$. The foregoing discussion is summarized in the following definition.

DEFINITION. *Let $A$ and $B$ be two vectors in $V_n$, with $B \neq O$. The vector $tB$, where*

$$t = \frac{A \cdot B}{B \cdot B}\,,$$

*is called the projection of $A$ along $B$. If both $A$ and $B$ are nonzero, the angle $\theta$ between $A$ and $B$ is defined by the equation*

$$\theta = \arccos \frac{A \cdot B}{\|A\|\,\|B\|}\,.$$

*Note:* The arc cosine function restricts $\theta$ to the interval $0 \leq \theta \leq \pi$. Note also that $\theta = \frac{1}{2}\pi$ when $A \cdot B = 0$.

## 12.10  The unit coordinate vectors

In Chapter 9 we learned that every complex number $(a, b)$ can be expressed in the form $a + bi$, where $i$ denotes the complex number $(0, 1)$. Similarly, every vector $(a, b)$ in $V_2$ can be expressed in the form

$$(a, b) = a(1, 0) + b(0, 1)\,.$$

The two vectors $(1, 0)$ and $(0, 1)$ which multiply the components $a$ and $b$ are called *unit coordinate vectors*. We now introduce the corresponding concept in $V_n$.

DEFINITION. *In $V_n$, the n vectors $E_1 = (1, 0, \ldots, 0)$, $E_2 = (0, 1, 0, \ldots, 0)$, $\ldots$, $E_n = (0, 0, \ldots, 0, 1)$ are called the unit coordinate vectors. It is understood that the kth component of $E_k$ is 1 and all other components are 0.*

The name "unit vector" comes from the fact that each vector $E_k$ has length 1. Note that these vectors are mutually orthogonal, that is, the dot product of any two distinct vectors is zero,

$$E_k \cdot E_j = 0 \quad \text{if} \quad k \neq j.$$

THEOREM 12.6. *Every vector $X = (x_1, \ldots, x_n)$ in $V_n$ can be expressed in the form*

$$X = x_1 E_1 + \cdots + x_n E_n = \sum_{k=1}^{n} x_k E_k.$$

*Moreover, this representation is unique. That is, if*

$$X = \sum_{k=1}^{n} x_k E_k \quad \text{and} \quad X = \sum_{k=1}^{n} y_k E_k,$$

*then $x_k = y_k$ for each $k = 1, 2, \ldots, n$.*

*Proof.* The first statement follows immediately from the definition of addition and multiplication by scalars. The uniqueness property follows from the definition of vector equality.

A sum of the type $\sum c_i A_i$ is called a *linear combination* of the vectors $A_1, \ldots, A_n$. Theorem 12.6 tells us that every vector in $V_n$ can be expressed as a linear combination of the unit coordinate vectors. We describe this by saying that the unit coordinate vectors $E_1, \ldots, E_n$ *span* the space $V_n$. We also say they span $V_n$ *uniquely* because each representation of a vector as a linear combination of $E_1, \ldots, E_n$ is unique. Some collections of vectors other than $E_1, \ldots, E_n$ also span $V_n$ uniquely, and in Section 12.12 we turn to the study of such collections.

In $V_2$ the unit coordinate vectors $E_1$ and $E_2$ are often denoted, respectively, by the symbols $i$ and $j$ in bold-face italic type. In $V_3$ the symbols $i, j$, and $k$ are also used in place of $E_1, E_2, E_3$. Sometimes a bar or arrow is placed over the symbol, for example, $\bar{i}$ or $\vec{i}$. The geometric meaning of Theorem 12.6 is illustrated in Figure 12.12 for $n = 3$.

When vectors are expressed as linear combinations of the unit coordinate vectors, algebraic manipulations involving vectors can be performed by treating the sums $\sum x_k E_k$ according to the usual rules of algebra. The various components can be recognized at any stage in the calculation by collecting the coefficients of the unit coordinate vectors. For example, to add two vectors, say $A = (a_1, \ldots, a_n)$ and $B = (b_1, \ldots, b_n)$, we write

$$A = \sum_{k=1}^{n} a_k E_k, \quad B = \sum_{k=1}^{n} b_k E_k,$$

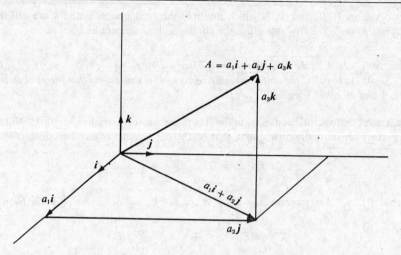

FIGURE 12.12   A vector $A$ in $V_3$ expressed as a linear combination of $i, j, k$.

and apply the linearity property of finite sums to obtain

$$A + B = \sum_{k=1}^{n} a_k E_k + \sum_{k=1}^{n} b_k E_k = \sum_{k=1}^{n} (a_k + b_k)E_k \,.$$

The coefficient of $E_k$ on the right is the $k$th component of the sum $A + B$.

## 12.11   Exercises

1. Determine the projection of $A$ along $B$ if $A = (1, 2, 3)$ and $B = (1, 2, 2)$.
2. Determine the projection of $A$ along $B$ if $A = (4, 3, 2, 1)$ and $B = (1, 1, 1, 1)$.
3. (a) Let $A = (6, 3, -2)$, and let $a, b, c$ denote the angles between $A$ and the unit coordinate vectors $i, j, k$, respectively. Compute $\cos a$, $\cos b$, and $\cos c$. These are called the direction cosines of $A$.
   (b) Find all vectors in $V_3$ of length 1 parallel to $A$.
4. Prove that the angle between the two vectors $A = (1, 2, 1)$ and $B = (2, 1, -1)$ is twice that between $C = (1, 4, 1)$ and $D = (2, 5, 5)$.
5. Use vector methods to determine the cosines of the angles of the triangle in 3-space whose vertices are at the points $(2, -1, 1)$, $(1, -3, -5)$, and $(3, -4, -4)$.
6. Three vectors $A, B, C$ in $V_3$ satisfy all the following properties:

$$\|A\| = \|C\| = 5, \qquad \|B\| = 1, \qquad \|A - B + C\| = \|A + B + C\|.$$

   If the angle between $A$ and $B$ is $\pi/8$, find the angle between $B$ and $C$.
7. Given three nonzero vectors $A, B, C$ in $V_n$. Assume that the angle between $A$ and $C$ is equal to the angle between $B$ and $C$. Prove that $C$ is orthogonal to the vector $\|B\| A - \|A\| B$.
8. Let $\theta$ denote the angle between the following two vectors in $V_n$ : $A = (1, 1, \ldots, 1)$ and $B = (1, 2, \ldots, n)$. Find the limiting value of $\theta$ as $n \to \infty$.
9. Solve Exercise 8 if $A = (2, 4, 6, \ldots, 2n)$ and $B = (1, 3, 5, \ldots, 2n - 1)$.

10. Given vectors $A = (\cos \theta, -\sin \theta)$ and $B = (\sin \theta, \cos \theta)$ in $V_2$.

    (a) Prove that $A$ and $B$ are orthogonal vectors of length 1. Make a sketch showing $A$ and $B$ when $\theta = \pi/6$.

    (b) Find all vectors $(x, y)$ in $V_2$ such that $(x, y) = xA + yB$. Be sure to consider all possible values of $\theta$.

11. Use vector methods to prove that the diagonals of a rhombus are perpendicular.

12. By forming the dot product of the two vectors $(\cos a, \sin a)$ and $(\cos b, \sin b)$, deduce the trigonometric identity $\cos(a - b) = \cos a \cos b + \sin a \sin b$.

13. If $\theta$ is the angle between two nonzero vectors $A$ and $B$ in $V_n$, prove that

$$\|A - B\|^2 = \|A\|^2 + \|B\|^2 - 2\,\|A\|\,\|B\|\cos\theta.$$

    When interpreted geometrically in $V_2$, this is the law of cosines of trigonometry.

14. Suppose that instead of defining the dot product of two vectors $A = (a_1, \ldots, a_n)$ and $B = (b_1, \ldots, b_n)$ by the formula $A \cdot B = \sum_{k=1}^{n} a_k b_k$, we used the following definition:

$$A \cdot B = \sum_{k=1}^{n} |a_k b_k|.$$

    Which of the properties of Theorem 12.2 are valid with this definition? Is the Cauchy–Schwarz inequality valid with this definition?

15. Suppose that in $V_2$ we define the dot product of two vectors $A = (a_1, a_2)$ and $B = (b_1, b_2)$ by the formula
$$A \cdot B = 2a_1 b_1 + a_2 b_2 + a_1 b_2 + a_2 b_1.$$

    Prove that all the properties of Theorem 12.2 are valid with this definition of dot product. Is the Cauchy–Schwarz inequality still valid?

16. Solve Exercise 15 if the dot product of two vectors $A = (a_1, a_2, a_3)$ and $B = (b_1, b_2, b_3)$ in $V_3$ is defined by the formula $A \cdot B = 2a_1 b_1 + a_2 b_2 + a_3 b_3 + a_1 b_3 + a_3 b_1$.

17. Suppose that instead of defining the norm of a vector $A = (a_1, \ldots, a_n)$ by the formula $(A \cdot A)^{1/2}$, we used the following definition:

$$\|A\| = \sum_{k=1}^{n} |a_k|.$$

    (a) Prove that this definition of norm satisfies all the properties in Theorems 12.4 and 12.5.

    (b) Use this definition in $V_2$ and describe on a figure the set of all points $(x, y)$ of norm 1.

    (c) Which of the properties of Theorems 12.4 and 12.5 would hold if we used the definition

$$\|A\| = \left| \sum_{k=1}^{n} a_k \right|?$$

18. Suppose that the norm of a vector $A = (a_1, \ldots, a_n)$ were defined by the formula

$$\|A\| = \max_{1 \le k \le n} |a_k|,$$

    where the symbol on the right means the maximum of the $n$ numbers $|a_1|, |a_2|, \ldots, |a_n|$.

    (a) Which of the properties of Theorems 12.4 and 12.5 are valid with this definition?

    (b) Use this definition of norm in $V_2$ and describe on a figure the set of all points $(x, y)$ of norm 1.

19. If $A = (a_1, \ldots, a_n)$ is a vector in $V_n$, define two norms as follows:

$$\|A\|_1 = \sum_{k=1}^{n} |a_k| \qquad \text{and} \qquad \|A\|_2 = \max_{1 \le k \le n} |a_k|.$$

Prove that $\|A\|_2 \le \|A\| \le \|A\|_1$. Interpret this inequality geometrically in the plane.

20. If $A$ and $B$ are two points in $n$-space, the distance from $A$ to $B$ is denoted by $d(A, B)$ and is defined by the equation $d(A, B) = \|A - B\|$. Prove that distance has the following properties:

(a) $d(A, B) = d(B, A)$.     (b) $d(A, B) = 0$     if and only if $A = B$.

(c) $d(A, B) \le d(A, C) + d(C, B)$.

## 12.12  The linear span of a finite set of vectors

Let $S = \{A_1, \ldots, A_k\}$ be a nonempty set consisting of $k$ vectors in $V_n$, where $k$, the number of vectors, may be less than, equal to, or greater than $n$, the dimension of the space. If a vector $X$ in $V_n$ can be represented as a linear combination of $A_1, \ldots, A_k$, say

$$X = \sum_{i=1}^{k} c_i A_i,$$

then the set $S$ is said to *span* the vector $X$.

DEFINITION. *The set of all vectors spanned by $S$ is called the linear span of $S$ and is denoted by $L(S)$.*

In other words, the linear span of $S$ is simply the set of all possible linear combinations of vectors in $S$. Note that linear combinations of vectors in $L(S)$ are again in $L(S)$. We say that $S$ *spans the whole space* $V_n$ if $L(S) = V_n$.

EXAMPLE 1. Let $S = \{A_1\}$. Then $L(S)$ consists of all scalar multiples of $A_1$.

EXAMPLE 2. Every set $S = \{A_1, \ldots, A_k\}$ spans the zero vector since $O = 0A_1 + \cdots + 0A_k$. This representation, in which all the coefficients $c_1, \ldots, c_k$ are zero, is called the *trivial representation* of the zero vector. However, there may be nontrivial linear combinations that represent $O$. For example, suppose one of the vectors in $S$ is a scalar multiple of another, say $A_2 = 2A_1$. Then we have many nontrivial representations of $O$, for example

$$O = 2tA_1 - tA_2 + 0A_3 + \cdots + 0A_k,$$

where $t$ is any nonzero scalar.

We are especially interested in sets $S$ that span vectors in exactly one way.

DEFINITION. *A set $S = \{A_1, \ldots, A_k\}$ of vectors in $V_n$ is said to span $X$ uniquely if $S$ spans $X$ and if*

$$(12.10) \qquad X = \sum_{i=1}^{k} c_i A_i \qquad \text{and} \qquad X = \sum_{i=1}^{k} d_i A_i \qquad \text{implies} \quad c_i = d_i \quad \text{for all } i.$$

In the two sums appearing in (12.10), it is understood that the vectors $A_1, \ldots, A_k$ are written in the same order. It is also understood that the implication (12.10) is to hold for a fixed but arbitrary ordering of the vectors $A_1, \ldots, A_k$.

THEOREM 12.7. *A set S spans every vector in L(S) uniquely if and only if S spans the zero vector uniquely.*

*Proof.* If $S$ spans every vector in $L(S)$ uniquely, then it certainly spans $O$ uniquely. To prove the converse, assume $S$ spans $O$ uniquely and choose any vector $X$ in $L(S)$. Suppose $S$ spans $X$ in two ways, say

$$X = \sum_{i=1}^{k} c_i A_i \quad \text{and} \quad X = \sum_{i=1}^{k} d_i A_i.$$

By subtraction, we find that $O = \sum_{i=1}^{k} (c_i - d_i)A_i$. But since $S$ spans $O$ uniquely, we must have $c_i - d_i = 0$ for all $i$, so $S$ spans $X$ uniquely.

## 12.13 Linear independence

Theorem 12.7 demonstrates the importance of sets that span the zero vector uniquely. Such sets are distinguished with a special name.

DEFINITION. *A set $S = \{A_1, \ldots, A_k\}$ which spans the zero vector uniquely is said to be a linearly independent set of vectors. Otherwise, S is called linearly dependent.*

In other words, *independence* means that $S$ spans $O$ with only the trivial representation:

$$\sum_{i=1}^{k} c_i A_i = O \quad \text{implies all } c_i = 0.$$

*Dependence* means that $S$ spans $O$ in some nontrivial way. That is, for some choice of scalars $c_1, \ldots, c_k$, we have

$$\sum_{i=1}^{k} c_i A_i = O \quad \text{but not all } c_i \text{ are zero}.$$

Although dependence and independence are properties of *sets* of vectors, it is common practice to also apply these terms to the vectors themselves. For example, the vectors in a linearly independent set are often called linearly independent vectors. We also agree to call the empty set linearly independent.

The following examples may serve to give further insight into the meaning of dependence and independence.

EXAMPLE 1. If a subset $T$ of a set $S$ is dependent, then $S$ itself is dependent, because if $T$ spans $O$ nontrivially, then so does $S$. This is logically equivalent to the statement that every subset of an independent set is independent.

EXAMPLE 2. The $n$ unit coordinate vectors $E_1, \ldots, E_n$ in $V_n$ span $O$ uniquely so they are linearly independent.

EXAMPLE 3. Any set containing the zero vector is dependent. For example, if $A_1 = O$, we have the nontrivial representation $O = 1A_1 + 0A_2 + \cdots + 0A_k$.

EXAMPLE 4. The set $S = \{i, j, i + j\}$ of vectors in $V_2$ is linearly dependent because we have the nontrivial representation of the zero vector

$$O = i + j + (-1)(i + j).$$

In this example the subset $T = \{i, j\}$ is linearly independent. The third vector, $i + j$, is in the linear span of $T$. The next theorem shows that if we adjoin to $i$ and $j$ any vector in the linear span of $T$, we get a dependent set.

THEOREM 12.8. *Let* $S = \{A_1, \ldots, A_k\}$ *be a linearly independent set of $k$ vectors in $V_n$, and let $L(S)$ be the linear span of $S$. Then, every set of $k + 1$ vectors in $L(S)$ is linearly dependent.*

*Proof.* The proof is by induction on $k$, the number of vectors in $S$. First suppose $k = 1$. Then, by hypothesis, $S$ consists of one vector, say $A_1$, where $A_1 \neq O$ since $S$ is independent. Now take any two distinct vectors $B_1$ and $B_2$ in $L(S)$. Then each is a scalar multiple of $A_1$, say $B_1 = c_1 A_1$ and $B_2 = c_2 A_1$, where $c_1$ and $c_2$ are not both zero. Multiplying $B_1$ by $c_2$ and $B_2$ by $c_1$ and subtracting, we find that

$$c_2 B_1 - c_1 B_2 = O.$$

This is a nontrivial representation of $O$ so $B_1$ and $B_2$ are dependent. This proves the theorem when $k = 1$.

Now we assume that the theorem is true for $k - 1$ and prove that it is also true for $k$. Take any set of $k + 1$ vectors in $L(S)$, say $T = \{B_1, B_2, \ldots, B_{k+1}\}$. We wish to prove that $T$ is linearly dependent. Since each $B_i$ is in $L(S)$, we may write

$$(12.11) \qquad\qquad B_i = \sum_{j=1}^{k} a_{ij} A_j$$

for each $i = 1, 2, \ldots, k + 1$. We examine all the scalars $a_{i1}$ that multiply $A_1$ and split the proof into two cases according to whether all these scalars are 0 or not.

CASE 1. $a_{i1} = 0$ *for every* $i = 1, 2, \ldots, k + 1$. In this case the sum in (12.11) does not involve $A_1$ so each $B_i$ in $T$ is in the linear span of the set $S' = \{A_2, \ldots, A_k\}$. But $S'$ is linearly independent and consists of $k - 1$ vectors. By the induction hypothesis, the theorem is true for $k - 1$ so the set $T$ is dependent. This proves the theorem in Case 1.

CASE 2. *Not all the scalars $a_{i1}$ are zero.* Let us assume that $a_{11} \neq 0$. (If necessary, we can renumber the $B$'s to achieve this.) Taking $i = 1$ in Equation (12.11) and multiplying both members by $c_i$, where $c_i = a_{i1}/a_{11}$, we get

$$c_i B_1 = a_{i1} A_1 + \sum_{j=2}^{k} c_i a_{1j} A_j .$$

From this we subtract Equation (12.11) to get

$$c_i B_1 - B_i = \sum_{j=2}^{k} (c_i a_{1j} - a_{ij}) A_j ,$$

for $i = 2, \ldots, k + 1$. This equation expresses each of the $k$ vectors $c_i B_1 - B_i$ as a linear combination of $k - 1$ linearly independent vectors $A_2, \ldots, A_k$. By the induction hypothesis, the $k$ vectors $c_i B_1 - B_i$ must be dependent. Hence, for some choice of scalars $t_2, \ldots, t_{k+1}$, not all zero, we have

$$\sum_{i=2}^{k+1} t_i (c_i B_1 - B_i) = O ,$$

from which we find

$$\left( \sum_{i=2}^{k+1} t_i c_i \right) B_1 - \sum_{i=2}^{k+1} t_i B_i = O .$$

But this is a nontrivial linear combination of $B_1, \ldots, B_{k+1}$ which represents the zero vector, so the vectors $B_1, \ldots, B_{k+1}$ must be dependent. This completes the proof.

We show next that the concept of orthogonality is intimately related to linear independence.

DEFINITION. *A set* $S = \{A_1, \ldots, A_k\}$ *of vectors in* $V_n$ *is called an orthogonal set if* $A_i \cdot A_j = 0$ *whenever* $i \neq j$. *In other words, any two distinct vectors in an orthogonal set are perpendicular.*

THEOREM 12.9. *Any orthogonal set* $S = \{A_1, \ldots, A_k\}$ *of nonzero vectors in* $V_n$ *is linearly independent. Moreover, if* $S$ *spans a vector* $X$, *say*

$$(12.12) \qquad\qquad X = \sum_{i=1}^{k} c_i A_i ,$$

*then the scalar multipliers* $c_1, \ldots, c_k$ *are given by the formulas*

$$(12.13) \qquad\qquad c_j = \frac{X \cdot A_j}{A_j \cdot A_j} \qquad for \quad j = 1, 2, \ldots, k .$$

*Proof.* First we prove that $S$ is linearly independent. Assume that $\sum_{i=1}^{k} c_i A_i = O$. Taking the dot product of each member with $A_1$ and using the fact that $A_1 \cdot A_i = 0$ for each $i \neq 1$, we find $c_1(A_1 \cdot A_1) = 0$. But $(A_1 \cdot A_1) \neq 0$ since $A_1 \neq O$, so $c_1 = 0$. Repeating this argument with $A_1$ replaced by $A_j$, we find that each $c_j = 0$. Therefore $S$ spans $O$ uniquely so $S$ is linearly independent.

Now suppose that $S$ spans $X$ as in Equation (12.12). Taking the dot product of $X$ with $A_j$ as above, we find that $c_j(A_j \cdot A_j) = X \cdot A_j$ from which we obtain (12.13).

If all the vectors $A_1, \ldots, A_k$ in Theorem 12.9 have norm 1, the formula for the multipliers simplifies to

$$c_j = X \cdot A_j .$$

An orthogonal set of vectors $\{A_1, \ldots, A_k\}$, each of which has norm 1, is called an *orthonormal* set. The unit coordinate vectors $E_1, \ldots, E_n$ are an example of an orthonormal set.

## 12.14 Bases

It is natural to study sets of vectors that span every vector in $V_n$ uniquely. Such sets are called *bases* for $V_n$.

DEFINITION.  *A set $S = \{A_1, \ldots, A_k\}$ of vectors in $V_n$ is called a basis for $V_n$ if $S$ spans every vector in $V_n$ uniquely. If, in addition, $S$ is orthogonal, then $S$ is called an orthogonal basis.*

Thus, a basis is a linearly independent set which spans the whole space $V_n$. The set of unit coordinate vectors is an example of a basis. This particular basis is also an orthogonal basis. Now we prove that every basis contains the same number of elements.

THEOREM 12.10.  *In a given vector space $V_n$, bases have the following properties:*
(a) *Every basis contains exactly n vectors.*
(b) *Any set of linearly independent vectors is a subset of some basis.*
(c) *Any set of n linearly independent vectors is a basis.*

*Proof.* The unit coordinate vectors $E_1, \ldots, E_n$ form one basis for $V_n$. If we prove that any two bases contain the same number of vectors we obtain (a).

Let $S$ and $T$ be two bases, where $S$ has $k$ vectors and $T$ has $r$ vectors. If $r > k$, then $T$ contains at least $k + 1$ vectors in $L(S)$, since $L(S) = V_n$. Therefore, because of Theorem 12.8, $T$ must be linearly dependent, contradicting the assumption that $T$ is a basis. This means we cannot have $r > k$, so we must have $r \leq k$. Applying the same argument with $S$ and $T$ interchanged, we find that $k \leq r$. Hence, $k = r$ so part (a) is proved.

To prove (b), let $S = \{A_1, \ldots, A_k\}$ be any linearly independent set of vectors in $V_n$. If $L(S) = V_n$, then $S$ is a basis. If not, then there is some vector $X$ in $V_n$ which is not in $L(S)$. Adjoin this vector to $S$ and consider the new set $S' = \{A_1, \ldots, A_k, X\}$. If this set were dependent, there would be scalars $c_1, \ldots, c_{k+1}$, not all zero, such that

$$\sum_{i=1}^{k} c_i A_i + c_{k+1} X = O .$$

But $c_{k+1} \neq 0$ since $A_1, \ldots, A_k$ are independent. Hence, we could solve this equation for

$X$ and find that $X \in L(S)$, contradicting the fact that $X$ is not in $L(S)$. Therefore, the set $S'$ is linearly independent but contains $k + 1$ vectors. If $L(S') = V_n$, then $S'$ is a basis and, since $S$ is a subset of $S'$, part (b) is proved. If $S'$ is not a basis, we may argue with $S'$ as we did with $S$, getting a new set $S''$ which contains $k + 2$ vectors and is linearly independent. If $S''$ is a basis, then part (b) is proved. If not, we repeat the process. We must arrive at a basis in a finite number of steps, otherwise we would eventually obtain an independent set with $n + 1$ vectors, contradicting Theorem 12.8. Therefore part (b) is proved.

Finally, we use (a) and (b) to prove (c). Let $S$ be any linearly independent set consisting of $n$ vectors. By part (b), $S$ is a subset of some basis, say $B$. But by (a) the basis $B$ has exactly $n$ elements, so $S = B$.

## 12.15 Exercises

1. Let $i$ and $j$ denote the unit coordinate vectors in $V_2$. In each case find scalars $x$ and $y$ such that $x(i - j) + y(i + j)$ is equal to
    (a) $i$;  (b) $j$;  (c) $3i - 5j$;  (d) $7i + 5j$.
2. If $A = (1, 2)$, $B = (2, -4)$, and $C = (2, -3)$ are three vectors in $V_2$, find scalars $x$ and $y$ such that $C = xA + yB$. How many such pairs $x, y$ are there?
3. If $A = (2, -1, 1)$, $B = (1, 2, -1)$, and $C = (2, -11, 7)$ are three vectors in $V_3$, find scalars $x$ and $y$ such that $C = xA + yB$.
4. Prove that Exercise 3 has no solution if $C$ is replaced by the vector $(2, 11, 7)$.
5. Let $A$ and $B$ be two nonzero vectors in $V_n$.
    (a) If $A$ and $B$ are parallel, prove that $A$ and $B$ are linearly dependent.
    (b) If $A$ and $B$ are not parallel, prove that $A$ and $B$ are linearly independent.
6. If $(a, b)$ and $(c, d)$ are two vectors in $V_2$, prove that they are linearly independent if and only if $ad - bc \neq 0$.
7. Find all real $t$ for which the two vectors $(1 + t, 1 - t)$ and $(1 - t, 1 + t)$ in $V_2$ are linearly independent.
8. Let $i, j, k$ be the unit coordinate vectors in $V_3$. Prove that the four vectors $i, j, k, i + j + k$ are linearly dependent, but that any three of them are linearly independent.
9. Let $i$ and $j$ be the unit coordinate vectors in $V_2$ and let $S = \{i, i + j\}$.
    (a) Prove that $S$ is linearly independent.
    (b) Prove that $j$ is in the linear span of $S$.
    (c) Express $3i - 4j$ as a linear combination of $i$ and $i + j$.
    (d) Prove that $L(S) = V_2$.
10. Consider the three vectors $A = i$, $B = i + j$, and $C = i + j + 3k$ in $V_3$.
    (a) Prove that the set $\{A, B, C\}$ is linearly independent.
    (b) Express each of $j$ and $k$ as a linear combination of $A$, $B$, and $C$.
    (c) Express $2i - 3j + 5k$ as a linear combination of $A$, $B$, and $C$.
    (d) Prove that $\{A, B, C\}$ is a basis for $V_3$.
11. Let $A = (1, 2)$, $B = (2, -4)$, $C = (2, -3)$, and $D = (1, -2)$ be four vectors in $V_2$. Display all nonempty subsets of $\{A, B, C, D\}$ which are linearly independent.
12. Let $A = (1, 1, 1, 0)$, $B = (0, 1, 1, 1)$ and $C = (1, 1, 0, 0)$ be three vectors in $V_4$.
    (a) Determine whether $A$, $B$, $C$ are linearly dependent or independent.
    (b) Exhibit a nonzero vector $D$ such that $A$, $B$, $C$, $D$ are dependent.
    (c) Exhibit a vector $E$ such that $A$, $B$, $C$, $E$ are independent.
    (d) Having chosen $E$ in part (c), express the vector $X = (1, 2, 3, 4)$ as a linear combination of $A$, $B$, $C$, $E$.
13. (a) Prove that the following three vectors in $V_3$ are linearly independent: $(\sqrt{3}, 1, 0), (1, \sqrt{3}, 1)$, $(0, 1, \sqrt{3})$.

(b) Prove that the following three are dependent: $(\sqrt{2}, 1, 0), (1, \sqrt{2}, 1), (0, 1, \sqrt{2})$.

(c) Find all real $t$ for which the following three vectors in $V_3$ are dependent: $(t, 1, 0), (1, t, 1),$ $(0, 1, t)$.

14. Consider the following sets of vectors in $V_4$. In each case, find a linearly independent subset containing as many vectors as possible.

    (a) $\{(1, 0, 1, 0), \ (1, 1, 1, 1), \ (0, 1, 0, 1), \ (2, 0, -1, 0)\}$.

    (b) $\{(1, 1, 1, 1), \ (1, -1, 1, 1), \ (1, -1, -1, 1), \ (1, -1, -1, -1)\}$.

    (c) $\{(1, 1, 1, 1), \ (0, 1, 1, 1), \ (0, 0, 1, 1), \ (0, 0, 0, 1)\}$.

15. Given three linearly independent vectors $A, B, C$ in $V_n$. Prove or disprove each of the following statements.

    (a) $A + B, B + C, A + C$ are linearly independent.

    (b) $A - B, B + C, A + C$ are linearly independent.

16. (a) Prove that a set $S$ of three vectors in $V_3$ is a basis for $V_3$ if and only if its linear span $L(S)$ contains the three unit coordinate vectors $i, j,$ and $k$.

    (b) State and prove a generalization of part (a) for $V_n$.

17. Find two bases for $V_3$ containing the two vectors $(0, 1, 1)$ and $(1, 1, 1)$.

18. Find two bases for $V_4$ having only the two vectors $(0, 1, 1, 1)$ and $(1, 1, 1, 1)$ in common.

19. Consider the following sets of vectors in $V_3$:

$$S = \{(1, 1, 1), (0, 1, 2), (1, 0, -1)\}, \qquad T = \{(2, 1, 0), (2, 0, -2)\}, \qquad U = \{(1, 2, 3), (1, 3, 5)\}.$$

    (a) Prove that $L(T) \subseteq L(S)$.

    (b) Determine all inclusion relations that hold among the sets $L(S), L(T),$ and $L(U)$.

20. Let $A$ and $B$ denote two finite subsets of vectors in a vector space $V_n$, and let $L(A)$ and $L(B)$ denote their linear spans. Prove each of the following statements.

    (a) If $A \subseteq B$, then $L(A) \subseteq L(B)$.

    (b) $L(A \cap B) \subseteq L(A) \cap L(B)$.

    (c) Give an example in which $L(A \cap B) \neq L(A) \cap L(B)$.

## 12.16 The vector space $V_n(\mathbf{C})$ of $n$-tuples of complex numbers

In Section 12.2 the vector space $V_n$ was defined to be the collection of all $n$-tuples of real numbers. Equality, vector addition, and multiplication by scalars were defined in terms of the components as follows: If $A = (a_1, \ldots, a_n)$ and $B = (b_1, \ldots, b_n)$, then

$$A = B \qquad \text{means} \qquad a_i = b_i \qquad \text{for each } i = 1, 2, \ldots, n,$$

$$A + B = (a_1 + b_1, \ldots, a_n + b_n), \qquad cA = (ca_1, \ldots, ca_n).$$

If all the scalars $a_i$, $b_i$ and $c$ in these relations are replaced by *complex* numbers, the new algebraic system so obtained is called *complex vector space* and is denoted by $V_n(\mathbf{C})$. Here $\mathbf{C}$ is used to remind us that the scalars are complex.

Since complex numbers satisfy the same field properties as real numbers, all theorems about real vector space $V_n$ that use only the field properties of the real numbers are also valid for $V_n(\mathbf{C})$, provided all the scalars are allowed to be complex. In particular, those theorems in this chapter that involve only vector addition and multiplication by scalars are also valid for $V_n(\mathbf{C})$.

This extension is not made simply for the sake of generalization. Complex vector spaces arise naturally in the theory of linear differential equations and in modern quantum mechanics, so their study is of considerable importance. Fortunately, many of the theorems about real vector space $V_n$ carry over without change to $V_n(\mathbf{C})$. Some small changes have to be made, however, in those theorems that involve dot products. In proving that the dot product $A \cdot A$ of a nonzero vector with itself is positive, we used the fact that a sum of squares of real numbers is positive. Since a sum of squares of complex numbers can be negative, we must modify the definition of $A \cdot B$ if we wish to retain the positivity property. For $V_n(\mathbf{C})$, we use the following definition of dot product.

DEFINITION. *If $A = (a_1, \ldots, a_n)$ and $B = (b_1, \ldots, b_n)$ are two vectors in $V_n(\mathbf{C})$, we define their dot product $A \cdot B$ by the formula*

$$A \cdot B = \sum_{k=1}^{n} a_k \bar{b}_k ,$$

*where $\bar{b}_k$ is the complex conjugate of $b_k$.*

Note that this definition agrees with the one given earlier for $V_n$ because $\bar{b}_k = b_k$ when $b_k$ is real. The fundamental properties of the dot product, corresponding to those in Theorem 12.2, now take the following form.

THEOREM 12.11. *For all vectors $A$, $B$, $C$ in $V_n(\mathbf{C})$ and all complex scalars $c$, we have*
  (a) $A \cdot B = \overline{B \cdot A}$,
  (b) $A \cdot (B + C) = A \cdot B + A \cdot C$,
  (c) $c(A \cdot B) = (cA) \cdot B = A \cdot (\bar{c}B)$,
  (d) $A \cdot A > 0$    if   $A \neq O$,
  (e) $A \cdot A = 0$    if   $A = O$.

All these properties are easy consequences of the definition and their proofs are left as exercises. The reader should note that conjugation takes place in property (a) when the order of the factors is reversed. Also, conjugation of the scalar multiplier occurs in property (c) when the scalar $c$ is moved from one side of the dot to the other.

The Cauchy–Schwarz inequality now takes the form

(12.14) $$|A \cdot B|^2 \leq (A \cdot A)(B \cdot B) .$$

The proof is similar to that given for Theorem 12.3. We consider the vector $C = xA - yB$, where $x = B \cdot B$ and $y = A \cdot B$, and compute $C \cdot C$. The inequality $C \cdot C \geq 0$ leads to (12.14). Details are left as an exercise for the reader.

Since the dot product of a vector with itself is nonnegative, we can introduce the norm of a vector in $V_n(\mathbf{C})$ by the usual formula,

$$\|A\| = (A \cdot A)^{1/2} .$$

The fundamental properties of norms, as stated in Theorem 12.4, are also valid without change for $V_n(\mathbf{C})$. The triangle inequality, $\|A + B\| \leq \|A\| + \|B\|$, also holds in $V_n(\mathbf{C})$.

Orthogonality of vectors in $V_n(\mathbf{C})$ is defined by the relation $A \cdot B = 0$. As in the real case, two vectors $A$ and $B$ in $V_n(\mathbf{C})$ are orthogonal whenever they satisfy the Pythagorean identity, $\|A + B\|^2 = \|A\|^2 + \|B\|^2$.

The concepts of linear span, linear independence, linear dependence, and basis, are defined for $V_n(\mathbf{C})$ exactly as in the real case. Theorems 12.7 through 12.10 and their proofs are all valid without change for $V_n(\mathbf{C})$.

## 12.17 Exercises

1. Let $A = (1, i)$, $B = (i, -i)$, and $C = (2i, 1)$ be three vectors in $V_2(\mathbf{C})$. Compute each of the following dot products:
   (a) $A \cdot B$;   (b) $B \cdot A$;   (c) $(iA) \cdot B$;   (d) $A \cdot (iB)$;   (e) $(iA) \cdot (iB)$;
   (f) $B \cdot C$;   (g) $A \cdot C$;   (h) $(B + C) \cdot A$;   (i) $(A - C) \cdot B$;
   (j) $(A - iB) \cdot (A + iB)$.
2. If $A = (2, 1, -i)$ and $B = (i, -1, 2i)$, find a nonzero vector $C$ in $V_3(\mathbf{C})$ orthogonal to both $A$ and $B$.
3. Prove that for any two vectors $A$ and $B$ in $V_n(\mathbf{C})$, we have the identity

$$\|A + B\|^2 = \|A\|^2 + \|B\|^2 + A \cdot B + \overline{A \cdot B}.$$

4. Prove that for any two vectors $A$ and $B$ in $V_n(\mathbf{C})$, we have the identity

$$\|A + B\|^2 - \|A - B\|^2 = 2(A \cdot B + \overline{A \cdot B}).$$

5. Prove that for any two vectors $A$ and $B$ in $V_n(\mathbf{C})$, we have the identity

$$\|A + B\|^2 + \|A - B\|^2 = 2\|A\|^2 + 2\|B\|^2.$$

6. (a) Prove that for any two vectors $A$ and $B$ in $V_n(\mathbf{C})$, the sum $\overline{A \cdot B} + A \cdot B$ is real.
   (b) If $A$ and $B$ are nonzero vectors in $V_n(\mathbf{C})$, prove that

$$-2 \leq \frac{A \cdot B + \overline{A \cdot B}}{\|A\| \, \|B\|} \leq 2.$$

7. We define the angle $\theta$ between two nonzero vectors $A$ and $B$ in $V_n(\mathbf{C})$ by the equation

$$\theta = \arccos \frac{\frac{1}{2}(A \cdot B + \overline{A \cdot B})}{\|A\| \, \|B\|}.$$

The inequality in Exercise 6 shows that there is always a unique angle $\theta$ in the closed interval $0 \leq \theta \leq \pi$ satisfying this equation. Prove that we have

$$\|A - B\|^2 = \|A\|^2 + \|B\|^2 - 2\|A\| \, \|B\| \cos \theta.$$

8. Use the definition in Exercise 7 to compute the angle between the following two vectors in $V_5(\mathbf{C})$: $A = (1, 0, i, i, i)$, and $B = (i, i, i, 0, i)$.
9. (a) Prove that the following three vectors form a basis for $V_3(\mathbf{C})$: $A = (1, 0, 0)$, $B = (0, i, 0)$, $C = (1, 1, i)$.
   (b) Express the vector $(5, 2 - i, 2i)$ as a linear combination of $A, B, C$.
10. Prove that the basis of unit coordinate vectors $E_1, \ldots, E_n$ in $V_n$ is also a basis for $V_n(\mathbf{C})$.

# 13

# APPLICATIONS OF VECTOR ALGEBRA
# TO ANALYTIC GEOMETRY

## 13.1 Introduction

This chapter discusses applications of vector algebra to the study of lines, planes, and conic sections. In Chapter 14 vector algebra is combined with the methods of calculus, and further applications are given to the study of curves and to some problems in mechanics.

The study of geometry as a deductive system, as conceived by Euclid around 300 B.C., begins with a set of axioms or postulates which describe properties of points and lines. The concepts "point" and "line" are taken as primitive notions and remain undefined. Other concepts are defined in terms of points and lines, and theorems are systematically deduced from the axioms. Euclid listed ten axioms from which he attempted to deduce all his theorems. It has since been shown that these axioms are not adequate for the theory. For example, in the proof of his very first theorem Euclid made a tacit assumption concerning the intersection of two circles that is not covered by his axioms. Since then other lists of axioms have been formulated that do give all of Euclid's theorems. The most famous of these is a list given by the German mathematician David Hilbert (1862–1943) in his now classic *Grundlagen der Geometrie*, published in 1899. (An English translation exists: *The Foundations of Geometry*, Open Court Publishing Co., 1947.) This work, which went through seven German editions in Hilbert's lifetime, is said to have inaugurated the abstract mathematics of the twentieth century.

Hilbert starts his treatment of plane geometry with five undefined concepts: *point*, *line*, *on* (a relation holding between a point and a line), *between* (a relation between a point and a pair of points), and *congruence* (a relation between pairs of points). He then gives fifteen axioms from which he develops all of plane Euclidean geometry. His treatment of solid geometry is based on twenty-one axioms involving six undefined concepts.

The approach in analytic geometry is somewhat different. We define concepts such as point, line, on, between, etc., but we do so in terms of real numbers, which are left undefined. The resulting mathematical structure is called an *analytic model* of Euclidean geometry. In this model, properties of real numbers are used to deduce Hilbert's axioms. We shall not attempt to describe all of Hilbert's axioms. Instead, we shall merely indicate how the primitive concepts may be defined in terms of numbers and give a few proofs to illustrate the methods of analytic geometry.

## 13.2 Lines in $n$-space

In this section we use real numbers to define the concepts of *point*, *line*, and *on*. The definitions are formulated to fit our intuitive ideas about three-dimensional Euclidean geometry, but they are meaningful in $n$-space for any $n \geq 1$.

A point is simply a vector in $V_n$, that is, an ordered $n$-tuple of real numbers; we shall use the words "point" and "vector" interchangeably. The vector space $V_n$ is called an analytic model of $n$-dimensional Euclidean space or simply *Euclidean n-space*. To define "line," we employ the algebraic operations of addition and multiplication by scalars in $V_n$.

DEFINITION. *Let P be a given point and A a given nonzero vector. The set of all points of the form $P + tA$, where t runs through all real numbers, is called a line through P parallel to A. We denote this line by L(P; A) and write*

$$L(P; A) = \{P + tA \mid t \text{ real}\} \quad \text{or, more briefly,} \quad L(P; A) = \{P + tA\}.$$

*A point Q is said to be on the line L(P; A) if $Q \in L(P; A)$.*

In the symbol $L(P; A)$, the point $P$ which is written first is on the line since it corresponds to $t = 0$. The second point, $A$, is called a *direction vector* for the line. The line $L(O; A)$ through the origin $O$ is the linear span of $A$; it consists of all scalar multiples of $A$. The line through $P$ parallel to $A$ is obtained by adding $P$ to each vector in the linear span of $A$.

Figure 13.1 shows the geometric interpretation of this definition in $V_3$. Each point $P + tA$ can be visualized as the tip of a geometric vector drawn from the origin. As $t$ varies over all the real numbers, the corresponding point $P + tA$ traces out a line through $P$ parallel to the vector $A$. Figure 13.1 shows points corresponding to a few values of $t$ on both lines $L(P; A)$ and $L(O; A)$.

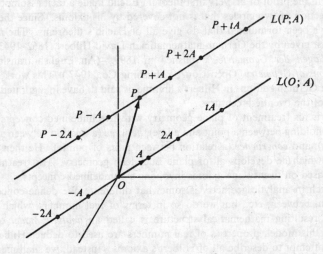

FIGURE 13.1 The line $L(P; A)$ through $P$ parallel to $A$ and its geometric relation to the line $L(O; A)$ through $O$ parallel to $A$.

## 13.3 Some simple properties of straight lines

First we show that the direction vector $A$ which occurs in the definition of $L(P; A)$ can be replaced by any vector parallel to $A$. (We recall that two vectors $A$ and $B$ are called parallel if $A = cB$ for some nonzero scalar $c$.)

THEOREM 13.1. *Two lines $L(P; A)$ and $L(P; B)$ through the same point $P$ are equal if and only if the direction vectors $A$ and $B$ are parallel.*

*Proof.* Assume first that $L(P; A) = L(P; B)$. Take a point on $L(P; A)$ other than $P$, for example, $P + A$. This point is also on $L(P; B)$ so $P + A = P + cB$ for some scalar $c$. Hence, we have $A = cB$ and $c \neq 0$ since $A \neq O$. Therefore, $A$ and $B$ are parallel.

Now we prove the converse. Assume $A$ and $B$ are parallel, say $A = cB$ for some $c \neq 0$. If $Q$ is on $L(P; A)$, then we have $Q = P + tA = P + t(cB) = P + (ct)B$, so $Q$ is on $L(P; B)$. Therefore $L(P; A) \subseteq L(P; B)$. Similarly, $L(P; B) \subseteq L(P; A)$, so $L(P; A) = L(P; B)$.

Next we show that the point $P$ which occurs in the definition of $L(P; A)$ can be replaced by any other point $Q$ on the same line.

THEOREM 13.2. *Two lines $L(P; A)$ and $L(Q; A)$ with the same direction vector $A$ are equal if and only if $Q$ is on $L(P; A)$.*

*Proof.* Assume $L(P; A) = L(Q; A)$. Since $Q$ is on $L(Q; A)$, $Q$ is also on $L(P; A)$. To prove the converse, assume that $Q$ is on $L(P; A)$, say $Q = P + cA$. We wish to prove that $L(P; A) = L(Q; A)$. If $X \in L(P; A)$, then $X = P + tA$ for some $t$. But $P = Q - cA$, so $X = Q - cA + tA = Q + (t - c)A$, and hence $X$ is also on $L(Q; A)$. Therefore $L(P; A) \subseteq L(Q; A)$. Similarly, we find $L(Q; A) \subseteq L(P; A)$, so the two lines are equal.

One of Euclid's famous postulates is the *parallel postulate* which is logically equivalent to the statement that "through a given point there exists one and only one line parallel to a given line." We shall deduce this property as an easy consequence of Theorem 13.1. First we need to define parallelism of lines.

DEFINITION. *Two lines $L(P; A)$ and $L(Q; B)$ are called parallel if their direction vectors $A$ and $B$ are parallel.*

THEOREM 13.3. *Given a line $L$ and a point $Q$ not on $L$, then there is one and only one line $L'$ containing $Q$ and parallel to $L$.*

*Proof.* Suppose the given line has direction vector $A$. Consider the line $L' = L(Q; A)$. This line contains $Q$ and is parallel to $L$. Theorem 13.1 tells us that this is the only line with these two properties.

*Note:* For a long time mathematicians suspected that the parallel postulate could be deduced from the other Euclidean postulates, but all attempts to prove this resulted in failure. Then in the early 19th century the mathematicians Karl F. Gauss (1777–1855),

J. Bolyai (1802–1860), and N. I. Lobatchevski (1793–1856) became convinced that the parallel postulate could not be derived from the others and proceeded to develop non-Euclidean geometries, that is to say, geometries in which the parallel postulate does not hold. The work of these men inspired other mathematicians and scientists to enlarge their points of view about "accepted truths" and to challenge other axioms that had been considered sacred for centuries.

It is also easy to deduce the following property of lines which Euclid stated as an axiom.

THEOREM 13.4. *Two distinct points determine a line. That is, if $P \neq Q$, there is one and only one line containing both $P$ and $Q$. It can be described as the set $\{P + t(Q - P)\}$.*

*Proof.* Let $L$ be the line through $P$ parallel to $Q - P$, that is, let

$$L = L(P; Q - P) = \{P + t(Q - P)\}.$$

This line contains both $P$ and $Q$ (take $t = 0$ to get $P$ and $t = 1$ to get $Q$). Now let $L'$ be any line containing both $P$ and $Q$. We shall prove that $L' = L$. Since $L'$ contains $P$, we have $L' = L(P; A)$ for some $A \neq O$. But $L'$ also contains $Q$ so $P + cA = Q$ for some $c$. Hence we have $Q - P = cA$, where $c \neq 0$ since $Q \neq P$. Therefore $Q - P$ is parallel to $A$ so, by Theorem 13.2, we have $L' = L(P; A) = L(P; Q - P) = L$.

EXAMPLE. Theorem 13.4 gives us an easy way to test if a point $Q$ is on a given line $L(P; A)$. It tells us that $Q$ is on $L(P; A)$ if and only if $Q - P$ is parallel to $A$. For example, consider the line $L(P; A)$, where $P = (1, 2, 3)$ and $A = (2, -1, 5)$. To test if the point $Q = (1, 1, 4)$ is on this line, we examine $Q - P = (0, -1, 1)$. Since $Q - P$ is not a scalar multiple of $A$, the point $(1, 1, 4)$ is not on this line. On the other hand, if $Q = (5, 0, 13)$, we find that $Q - P = (4, -2, 10) = 2A$, so this $Q$ is on the line.

Linear dependence of two vectors in $V_n$ can be expressed in geometric language.

THEOREM 13.5. *Two vectors $A$ and $B$ in $V_n$ are linearly dependent if and only if they lie on the same line through the origin.*

*Proof.* If either $A$ or $B$ is zero, the result holds trivially. If both are nonzero, then $A$ and $B$ are dependent if and only if $B = tA$ for some scalar $t$. But $B = tA$ if and only if $B$ lies on the line through the origin parallel to $A$.

## 13.4  Lines and vector-valued functions

The concept of a line can be related to the function concept. The correspondence which associates to each real $t$ the vector $P + tA$ on the line $L(P; A)$ is an example of a function whose domain is the set of real numbers and whose range is the line $L(P; A)$. If we denote the function by the symbol $X$, then the function value $X(t)$ at $t$ is given by the equation

(13.1)                         $X(t) = P + tA$.

We call this a vector-valued function of a real variable.

The function point of view is important because, as we shall see in Chapter 14, it provides a natural method for describing more general space curves as well.

The scalar $t$ in Equation (13.1) is often called a *parameter*, and Equation (13.1) is called a *vector parametric equation* or, simply a *vector equation* of the line. Occasionally it is convenient to think of the line as the track of a moving particle, in which case the parameter $t$ is referred to as *time* and the vector $X(t)$ is called the *position vector*.

Note that two points $X(a)$ and $X(b)$ on a given line $L(P; A)$ are equal if and only if we have $P + aA = P + bA$, or $(a - b)A = O$. Since $A \neq O$, this last relation holds if and only if $a = b$. Thus, distinct values of the parameter $t$ lead to distinct points on the line.

Now consider three distinct points on a given line, say $X(a)$, $X(b)$, and $X(c)$, where $a > b$. We say that $X(c)$ is *between* $X(a)$ and $X(b)$ if $c$ is between $a$ and $b$, that is, if $a < c < b$.

Congruence can be defined in terms of norms. A pair of points $P$, $Q$ is called *congruent* to another pair $P'$, $Q'$ if $\|P - Q\| = \|P' - Q'\|$. The norm $\|P - Q\|$ is also called the distance between $P$ and $Q$.

This completes the definitions of the concepts of *point, line, on, between*, and *congruence* in our analytic model of Euclidean $n$-space. We conclude this section with some further remarks concerning parametric equations for lines in 3-space.

If a line passes through two distinct points $P$ and $Q$, we can use $Q - P$ for the direction vector $A$ in Equation (13.1); the vector equation of the line then becomes

$$X(t) = P + t(Q - P) \qquad \text{or} \qquad X(t) = tQ + (1 - t)P.$$

Vector equations can also be expressed in terms of components. For example, if we write $P = (p, q, r)$, $A = (a, b, c)$, and $X(t) = (x, y, z)$, Equation (13.1) is equivalent to the three scalar equations

$$(13.2) \qquad x = p + ta, \qquad y = q + tb, \qquad z = r + tc.$$

These are called *scalar parametric equations* or simply *parametric equations* for the line; they are useful in computations involving components. The vector equation is simpler and more natural for studying general properties of lines.

If all the vectors are in 2-space, only the first two parametric equations in (13.2) are needed. In this case, we can eliminate $t$ from the two parametric equations to obtain the relation

$$(13.3) \qquad b(x - p) - a(y - q) = 0,$$

which is called a *Cartesian equation* for the line. If $a \neq 0$, this can be written in the *point-slope form*

$$y - q = \frac{b}{a}(x - p).$$

The point $(p, q)$ is on the line; the number $b/a$ is the slope of the line.

The Cartesian equation (13.3) can also be written in terms of dot products. If we let $N = (b, -a)$, $X = (x, y)$, and $P = (p, q)$, Equation (13.3) becomes

$$(X - P) \cdot N = 0 \qquad \text{or} \qquad X \cdot N = P \cdot N.$$

The vector $N$ is perpendicular to the direction vector $A$ since $N \cdot A = ba - ab = 0$; the vector $N$ is called a *normal vector* to the line. The line consists of all points $X$ satisfying the relation $(X - P) \cdot N = 0$.

The geometric meaning of this relation is shown in Figure 13.2. The points $P$ and $X$ are on the line and the normal vector $N$ is orthogonal to $X - P$. The figure suggests that among all points $X$ on the line, the smallest length $\|X\|$ occurs when $X$ is the projection of $P$ along $N$. We now give an algebraic proof of this fact.

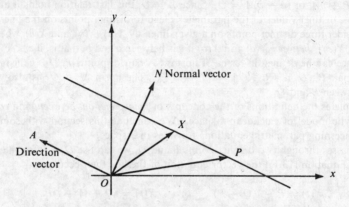

FIGURE 13.2   A line in the $xy$-plane through $P$ with normal vector $N$.   Each point $X$ on the line satisfies $(X - P) \cdot N = 0$.

THEOREM 13.6.   *Let $L$ be the line in $V_2$ consisting of all points $X$ satisfying*

$$X \cdot N = P \cdot N,$$

*where $P$ is on the line and $N$ is a nonzero vector normal to the line.   Let*

$$d = \frac{|P \cdot N|}{\|N\|}.$$

*Then every $X$ on $L$ has length $\|X\| \geq d$.   Moreover, $\|X\| = d$ if and only if $X$ is the projection of $P$ along $N$:*

$$X = tN, \qquad where \quad t = \frac{P \cdot N}{N \cdot N}.$$

*Proof.*   If $X \in L$, we have $X \cdot N = P \cdot N$.   By the Cauchy–Schwarz inequality, we have

$$|P \cdot N| = |X \cdot N| \leq \|X\| \, \|N\|,$$

which implies $\|X\| \geq |P \cdot N|/\|N\| = d$.   The equality sign holds if and only if $X = tN$ for some scalar $t$, in which case $P \cdot N = X \cdot N = tN \cdot N$, so $t = P \cdot N/N \cdot N$.   This completes the proof.

In the same way we can prove that if $Q$ is a given point in $V_2$ not on the line $L$, then for all $X$ on $L$ the smallest value of $\|X - Q\|$ is $|(P - Q) \cdot N|/\|N\|$, and this occurs when $X - Q$ is the projection of $P - Q$ along the normal vector $N$. The number

$$\frac{|(P - Q) \cdot N|}{\|N\|}$$

is called the *distance from the point $Q$ to the line $L$*. The reader should illustrate these concepts on a figure similar to that in Figure 13.2.

## 13.5 Exercises

1. A line $L$ in $V_2$ contains the two points $P = (-3, 1)$ and $Q = (1, 1)$. Determine which of the following points are on $L$. (a) $(0, 0)$; (b) $(0, 1)$; (c) $(1, 2)$; (d) $(2, 1)$; (e) $(-2, 1)$.

2. Solve Exercise 1 if $P = (2, -1)$ and $Q = (-4, 2)$.

3. A line $L$ in $V_3$ contains the point $P = (-3, 1, 1)$ and is parallel to the vector $(1, -2, 3)$. Determine which of the following points are on $L$. (a) $(0, 0, 0)$; (b) $(2, -1, 4)$; (c) $(-2, -1, 4)$; (d) $(-4, 3, -2)$; (e) $(2, -9, 16)$.

4. A line $L$ contains the two points $P = (-3, 1, 1)$ and $Q = (1, 2, 7)$. Determine which of the following points are on $L$. (a) $(-7, 0, 5)$; (b) $(-7, 0, -5)$; (c) $(-11, 1, 11)$; (d) $(-11, -1, 11)$; (e) $(-1, \frac{3}{2}, 4)$; (f) $(-\frac{5}{3}, \frac{4}{3}, 3)$; (g) $(-1, \frac{3}{2}, -4)$.

5. In each case, determine if all three points $P$, $Q$, $R$ lie on a line.
   (a) $P = (2, 1, 1)$, $Q = (4, 1, -1)$, $R = (3, -1, 1)$.
   (b) $P = (2, 2, 3)$, $Q = (-2, 3, 1)$, $R = (-6, 4, 1)$.
   (c) $P = (2, 1, 1)$, $Q = (-2, 3, 1)$, $R = (5, -1, 1)$.

6. Among the following eight points, the three points $A$, $B$, and $C$ lie on a line. Determine all subsets of three or more points which lie on a line: $A = (2, 1, 1)$, $B = (6, -1, 1)$, $C = (-6, 5, 1)$, $D = (-2, 3, 1)$, $E = (1, 1, 1)$, $F = (-4, 4, 1)$, $G = (-13, 9, 1)$, $H = (14, -6, 1)$.

7. A line through the point $P = (1, 1, 1)$ is parallel to the vector $A = (1, 2, 3)$. Another line through $Q = (2, 1, 0)$ is parallel to the vector $B = (3, 8, 13)$. Prove that the two lines intersect and determine the point of intersection.

8. (a) Prove that two lines $L(P; A)$ and $L(Q; B)$ in $V_n$ intersect if and only if $P - Q$ is in the linear span of $A$ and $B$.
   (b) Determine whether or not the following two lines in $V_3$ intersect:

$$L = \{(1, 1, -1) + t(-2, 1, 3)\}, \qquad L' = \{(3, -4, 1) + t(-1, 5, 2)\}.$$

9. Let $X(t) = P + tA$ be an arbitrary point on the line $L(P; A)$, where $P = (1, 2, 3)$ and $A = (1, -2, 2)$, and let $Q = (3, 3, 1)$.
   (a) Compute $\|Q - X(t)\|^2$, the square of the distance between $Q$ and $X(t)$.
   (b) Prove that there is exactly one point $X(t_0)$ for which the distance $\|Q - X(t)\|$ is a minimum, and compute this minimum distance.
   (c) Prove that $Q - X(t_0)$ is orthogonal to $A$.

10. Let $Q$ be a point not on the line $L(P; A)$ in $V_n$.
    (a) Let $f(t) = \|Q - X(t)\|^2$, where $X(t) = P + tA$. Prove that $f(t)$ is a quadratic polynomial in $t$ and that this polynomial takes on its minimum value at exactly one $t$, say at $t = t_0$.
    (b) Prove that $Q - X(t_0)$ is orthogonal to $A$.

11. Given two parallel lines $L(P; A)$ and $L(Q; A)$ in $V_n$. Prove that either $L(P; A) = L(Q; A)$ or the intersection $L(P; A) \cap L(Q; A)$ is empty.

12. Given two lines $L(P; A)$ and $L(Q; B)$ in $V_n$ which are not parallel. Prove that the intersection is either empty or consists of exactly one point.

## 13.6 Planes in Euclidean *n*-space

A line in *n*-space was defined to be a set of the form $\{P + tA\}$ obtained by adding to a given point $P$ all vectors in the linear span of a nonzero vector $A$. A plane is defined in a similar fashion except that we add to $P$ all vectors in the linear span of two linearly independent vectors $A$ and $B$. To make certain that $V_n$ contains two linearly independent vectors, we assume at the outset that $n \geq 2$. Most of our applications will be concerned with the case $n = 3$.

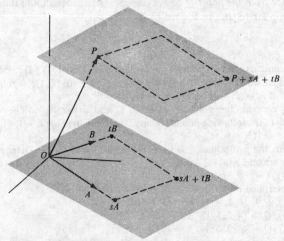

FIGURE 13.3 The plane through $P$ spanned by $A$ and $B$, and its geometric relation to the plane through $O$ spanned by $A$ and $B$.

DEFINITION. *A set M of points in $V_n$ is called a plane if there is a point P and two linearly independent vectors A and B such that*

$$M = \{P + sA + tB \mid s, t \ real\}.$$

We shall denote the set more briefly by writing $M = \{P + sA + tB\}$. Each point of $M$ is said to be *on* the plane. In particular, taking $s = t = 0$, we see that $P$ is on the plane. The set $\{P + sA + tB\}$ is also called the plane through $P$ spanned by $A$ and $B$. When $P$ is the origin, the plane is simply the linear span of $A$ and $B$. Figure 13.3 shows a plane in $V_3$ through the origin spanned by $A$ and $B$ and also a plane through a nonzero point $P$ spanned by the same two vectors.

Now we shall deduce some properties of planes analogous to the properties of lines given in Theorems 13.1 through 13.4. The first of these shows that the vectors $A$ and $B$ in the definition of the plane $\{P + sA + tB\}$ can be replaced by any other pair which has the same linear span.

THEOREM 13.7. *Two planes $M = \{P + sA + tB\}$ and $M' = \{P + sC + tD\}$ through the same point P are equal if and only if the linear span of A and B is equal to the linear span of C and D.*

*Proof.* If the linear span of $A$ and $B$ is equal to that of $C$ and $D$, then it is clear that $M = M'$. Conversely, assume that $M = M'$. Plane $M$ contains both $P + A$ and $P + B$. Since both these points are also on $M'$, each of $A$ and $B$ must be in the linear span of $C$ and $D$. Similarly, each of $C$ and $D$ is in the linear span of $A$ and $B$. Therefore the linear span of $A$ and $B$ is equal to that of $C$ and $D$.

The next theorem shows that the point $P$ which occurs in the definition of the plane $\{P + sA + tB\}$ can be replaced by any other point $Q$ on the same plane.

THEOREM 13.8.    *Two planes $M = \{P + sA + tB\}$ and $M' = \{Q + sA + tB\}$ spanned by the same vectors $A$ and $B$ are equal if and only if $Q$ is on $M$.*

*Proof.* If $M = M'$, then $Q$ is certainly on $M$. To prove the converse, assume $Q$ is on $M$, say $Q = P + aA + bB$. Take any point $X$ in $M$. Then $X = P + sA + tB$ for some scalars $s$ and $t$. But $P = Q - aA - bB$, so $X = Q + (s - a)A + (t - b)B$. Therefore $X$ is in $M'$, so $M \subseteq M'$. Similarly, we find that $M' \subseteq M$, so the two planes are equal.

Euclid's parallel postulate (Theorem 13.3) has an analog for planes. Before we state this theorem we need to define parallelism of two planes. The definition is suggested by the geometric representation in Figure 13.3.

DEFINITION.    *Two planes $M = \{P + sA + tB\}$ and $M' = \{Q + sC + tD\}$ are said to be parallel if the linear span of $A$ and $B$ is equal to the linear span of $C$ and $D$. We also say that a vector $X$ is parallel to the plane $M$ if $X$ is in the linear span of $A$ and $B$.*

THEOREM 13.9.    *Given a plane $M$ and a point $Q$ not on $M$, there is one and only one plane $M'$ which contains $Q$ and is parallel to $M$.*

*Proof.* Let $M = \{P + sA + tB\}$ and consider the plane $M' = \{Q + sA + tB\}$. This plane contains $Q$ and is spanned by the same vectors $A$ and $B$ which span $M$. Therefore $M'$ is parallel to $M$. If $M''$ is another plane through $Q$ parallel to $M$, then

$$M'' = \{Q + sC + tD\}$$

where the linear span of $C$ and $D$ is equal to that of $A$ and $B$. By Theorem 13.7, we must have $M'' = M'$. Therefore $M'$ is the only plane through $Q$ which is parallel to $M$.

Theorem 13.4 tells us that two distinct points determine a line. The next theorem shows that three distinct points determine a plane, provided that the three points are not collinear.

THEOREM 13.10.    *If $P$, $Q$, and $R$ are three points not on the same line, then there is one and only one plane $M$ containing these three points. It can be described as the set*

(13.4) $$M = \{P + s(Q - P) + t(R - P)\}.$$

*Proof.* We assume first that one of the points, say $P$, is the origin. Then $Q$ and $R$ are not on the same line through the origin so they are linearly independent. Therefore, they span a plane through the origin, say the plane

$$M' = \{sQ + tR\}.$$

This plane contains all three points $O$, $Q$, and $R$.

Now we prove that $M'$ is the only plane which contains all three points $O$, $Q$, and $R$. Any other plane through the origin has the form

$$M'' = \{sA + tB\},$$

where $A$ and $B$ are linearly independent. If $M''$ contains $Q$ and $R$, we have

(13.5) $$Q = aA + bB, \qquad R = cA + dB,$$

for some scalars $a$, $b$, $c$, $d$. Hence, every linear combination of $Q$ and $R$ is also a linear combination of $A$ and $B$, so $M' \subseteq M''$.

To prove that $M'' \subseteq M'$, it suffices to prove that each of $A$ and $B$ is a linear combination of $Q$ and $R$. Multiplying the first equation in (13.5) by $d$ and the second by $b$ and subtracting, we eliminate $B$ and get

$$(ad - bc)A = dQ - bR.$$

Now $ad - bc$ cannot be zero, otherwise $Q$ and $R$ would be dependent. Therefore we can divide by $ad - bc$ and express $A$ as a linear combination of $Q$ and $R$. Similarly, we can express $B$ as a linear combination of $Q$ and $R$, so we have $M'' \subseteq M'$. This proves the theorem when one of the three points $P$, $Q$, $R$ is the origin.

To prove the theorem in the general case, let $M$ be the set in (13.4), and let $C = Q - P$, $D = R - P$. First we show that $C$ and $D$ are linearly independent. If not we would have $D = tC$ for some scalar $t$, giving us $R - P = t(Q - P)$, or $R = P + t(Q - P)$, contradicting the fact that $P$, $Q$, $R$ are not on the same line. Therefore the set $M$ is a plane through $P$ spanned by the linearly independent pair $C$ and $D$. This plane contains all three points $P$, $Q$, and $R$ (take $s = 1$, $t = 0$ to get $Q$, and $s = 0$, $t = 1$ to get $R$). Now we must prove that this is the only plane containing $P$, $Q$, and $R$.

Let $M'$ be any plane containing $P$, $Q$, and $R$. Since $M'$ is a plane containing $P$, we have

$$M' = \{P + sA + tB\}$$

for some linearly independent pair $A$ and $B$. Let $M'_0 = \{sA + tB\}$ be the plane through the origin spanned by the same pair $A$ and $B$. Clearly, $M'$ contains a vector $X$ if and only if $M'_0$ contains $X - P$. Since $M'$ contains $Q$ and $R$, the plane $M'_0$ contains $C = Q - P$ and $D = R - P$. But we have just shown that there is one and only one plane containing $O$, $C$, and $D$ since $C$ and $D$ are linearly independent. Therefore $M'_0 = \{sC + tD\}$, so $M' = \{P + sC + tD\} = M$. This completes the proof.

In Theorem 13.5 we proved that two vectors in $V_n$ are linearly dependent if and only if they lie on a line through the origin. The next theorem is the corresponding result for three vectors.

THEOREM 13.11. *Three vectors $A$, $B$, $C$ in $V_n$ are linearly dependent if and only if they lie on the same plane through the origin.*

*Proof.* Assume $A$, $B$, $C$ are dependent. Then we can express one of the vectors as a linear combination of the other two, say $C = sA + tB$. If $A$ and $B$ are independent, they span a plane through the origin and $C$ is on this plane. If $A$ and $B$ are dependent, then $A$, $B$, and $C$ lie on a line through the origin, and hence they lie on any plane through the origin which contains all three points $A$, $B$, and $C$.

To prove the converse, assume that $A$, $B$, $C$ lie on the same plane through the origin, say the plane $M$. If $A$ and $B$ are dependent, then $A$, $B$, and $C$ are dependent, and there is nothing more to prove. If $A$ and $B$ are independent, they span a plane $M'$ through the origin. By Theorem 13.10, there is one and only one plane through $O$ containing $A$ and $B$. Therefore $M' = M$. Since $C$ is on this plane, we must have $C = sA + tB$, so $A$, $B$, and $C$ are dependent.

## 13.7 Planes and vector-valued functions

The correspondence which associates to each pair of real numbers $s$ and $t$ the vector $P + sA + tB$ on the plane $M = \{P + sA + tB\}$ is another example of a vector-valued function. In this case, the domain of the function is the set of all pairs of real numbers $(s, t)$ and its range is the plane $M$. If we denote the function by $X$ and the function values by $X(s, t)$, then for each pair $(s, t)$ we have

$$(13.6) \qquad X(s, t) = P + sA + tB.$$

We call $X$ a vector-valued function of two real variables. The scalars $s$ and $t$ are called parameters, and the equation (13.6) is called a parametric or vector equation of the plane. This is analogous to the representation of a line by a vector-valued function of one real variable. The presence of two parameters in Equation (13.6) gives the plane a two-dimensional quality. When each vector is in $V_3$ and is expressed in terms of its components, say

$$P = (p_1, p_2, p_3), \qquad A = (a_1, a_2, a_3), \qquad B = (b_1, b_2, b_3), \qquad \text{and} \qquad X(s, t) = (x, y, z),$$

the vector equation (13.6) can be replaced by three scalar equations,

$$x = p_1 + sa_1 + tb_1, \qquad y = p_2 + sa_2 + tb_2, \qquad z = p_3 + sa_3 + tb_3.$$

The parameters $s$ and $t$ can always be eliminated from these three equations to give one linear equation of the form $ax + by + cz = d$, called a Cartesian equation of the plane. We illustrate with an example.

EXAMPLE. Let $M = \{P + sA + tB\}$, where $P = (1, 2, 3)$, $A = (1, 2, 1)$, and $B = (1, -4, -1)$. The corresponding vector equation is

$$X(s, t) = (1, 2, 3) + s(1, 2, 1) + t(1, -4, -1) .$$

From this we obtain the three scalar parametric equations

$$x = 1 + s + t , \qquad y = 2 + 2s - 4t , \qquad z = 3 + s - t .$$

To obtain a Cartesian equation, we rewrite the first and third equations in the form $x - 1 = s + t$, $z - 3 = s - t$. Adding and then subtracting these equations, we find that $2s = x + z - 4$, $2t = x - z + 2$. Substituting in the equation for $y$, we are led to the Cartesian equation $x + y - 3z = -6$. We shall return to a further study of linear Cartesian equations in Section 13.16.

## 13.8 Exercises

1. Let $M = \{P + sA + tB\}$, where $P = (1, 2, -3)$, $A = (3, 2, 1)$, and $B = (1, 0, 4)$. Determine which of the following points are on $M$.
   (a) $(1, 2, 0)$; (b) $(1, 2, 1)$; (c) $(6, 4, 6)$; (d) $(6, 6, 6)$; (e) $(6, 6, -5)$.
2. The three points $P = (1, 1, -1)$, $Q = (3, 3, 2)$, and $R = (3, -1, -2)$ determine a plane $M$. Determine which of the following points are on $M$.
   (a) $(2, 2, \frac{1}{2})$; (b) $(4, 0, -\frac{1}{2})$; (c) $(-3, 1, -3)$; (d) $(3, 1, 3)$; (e) $(0, 0, 0)$.
3. Determine scalar parametric equations for each of the following planes.
   (a) The plane through $(1, 2, 1)$ spanned by the vectors $(0, 1, 0)$ and $(1, 1, 4)$.
   (b) The plane through $(1, 2, 1)$, $(0, 1, 0)$, and $(1, 1, 4)$.
4. A plane $M$ has scalar parametric equations

   $$x = 1 + s - 2t , \qquad y = 2 + s + 4t , \qquad z = 2s + t .$$

   (a) Determine which of the following points are on $M$: $(0, 0, 0)$, $(1, 2, 0)$, $(2, -3, -3)$.
   (b) Find vectors $P$, $A$, and $B$ such that $M = \{P + sA + tB\}$.
5. Let $M$ be the plane determined by three points $P$, $Q$, $R$ not on the same line.
   (a) If $p$, $q$, $r$ are three scalars such that $p + q + r = 1$, prove that $pP + qQ + rR$ is on $M$.
   (b) Prove that every point on $M$ has the form $pP + qQ + rR$, where $p + q + r = 1$.
6. Determine a linear Cartesian equation of the form $ax + by + cz = d$ for each of the following planes.
   (a) The plane through $(2, 3, 1)$ spanned by $(3, 2, 1)$ and $(-1, -2, -3)$.
   (b) The plane through $(2, 3, 1)$, $(-2, -1, -3)$, and $(4, 3, -1)$.
   (c) The plane through $(2, 3, 1)$ parallel to the plane through the origin spanned by $(2, 0, -2)$ and $(1, 1, 1)$.
7. A plane $M$ has the Cartesian equation $3x - 5y + z = 9$.
   (a) Determine which of the following points are on $M$: $(0, -2, -1)$, $(-1, -2, 2)$, $(3, 1, -5)$.
   (b) Find vectors $P$, $A$, and $B$ such that $M = \{P + sA + tB\}$.
8. Consider the two planes $M = \{P + sA + tB\}$ and $M' = \{Q + sC + tD\}$, where $P = (1, 1, 1)$, $A = (2, -1, 3)$, $B = (-1, 0, 2)$, $Q = (2, 3, 1)$, $C = (1, 2, 3)$, and $D = (3, 2, 1)$. Find two distinct points on the intersection $M \cap M'$.
9. Given a plane $M = \{P + sA + tB\}$, where $P = (2, 3, 1)$, $A = (1, 2, 3)$, and $B = (3, 2, 1)$, and another plane $M'$ with Cartesian equation $x - 2y + z = 0$.
   (a) Determine whether $M$ and $M'$ are parallel.

(b) Find two points on the intersection $M' \cap M''$ if $M''$ has the Cartesian equation

$$x + 2y + z = 0.$$

10. Let $L$ be the line through $(1, 1, 1)$ parallel to the vector $(2, -1, 3)$, and let $M$ be the plane through $(1, 1, -2)$ spanned by the vectors $(2, 1, 3)$ and $(0, 1, 1)$. Prove that there is one and only one point on the intersection $L \cap M$ and determine this point.

11. A line with direction vector $X$ is said to be parallel to a plane $M$ if $X$ is parallel to $M$. Let $L$ be the line through $(1, 1, 1)$ parallel to the vector $(2, -1, 3)$. Determine whether $L$ is parallel to each of the following planes.
    (a) The plane through $(1, 1, -2)$ spanned by $(2, 1, 3)$ and $(\frac{3}{4}, 1, 1)$.
    (b) The plane through $(1, 1, -2)$, $(3, 5, 2)$, and $(2, 4, -1)$.
    (c) The plane with Cartesian equation $x + 2y + 3z = -3$.

12. Two distinct points $P$ and $Q$ lie on a plane $M$. Prove that every point on the line through $P$ and $Q$ also lies on $M$.

13. Given the line $L$ through $(1, 2, 3)$ parallel to the vector $(1, 1, 1)$, and given a point $(2, 3, 5)$ which is not on $L$. Find a Cartesian equation for the plane $M$ through $(2, 3, 5)$ which contains every point on $L$.

14. Given a line $L$ and a point $P$ not on $L$. Prove that there is one and only one plane through $P$ which contains every point on $L$.

## 13.9 The cross product

In many applications of vector algebra to problems in geometry and mechanics it is helpful to have an easy method for constructing a vector perpendicular to each of two given vectors $A$ and $B$. This is accomplished by means of the cross product $A \times B$ (read "$A$ cross $B$") which is defined as follows:

DEFINITION. *Let* $A = (a_1, a_2, a_3)$ *and* $B = (b_1, b_2, b_3)$ *be two vectors in* $V_3$. *Their cross product* $A \times B$ *(in that order) is defined to be the vector*

$$A \times B = (a_2 b_3 - a_3 b_2, \, a_3 b_1 - a_1 b_3, \, a_1 b_2 - a_2 b_1).$$

The following properties are easily deduced from this definition.

THEOREM 13.12. *For all vectors $A$, $B$, $C$ in $V_3$ and for all real $c$ we have:*
(a) $A \times B = -(B \times A)$          *(skew symmetry)*,
(b) $A \times (B + C) = (A \times B) + (A \times C)$    *(distributive law)*,
(c) $c(A \times B) = (cA) \times B$,
(d) $A \cdot (A \times B) = 0$            *(orthogonality to $A$)*,
(e) $B \cdot (A \times B) = 0$            *(orthogonality to $B$)*,
(f) $\|A \times B\|^2 = \|A\|^2 \|B\|^2 - (A \cdot B)^2$    *(Lagrange's identity)*,
(g) $A \times B = O$    *if and only if $A$ and $B$ are linearly dependent.*

*Proof.* Parts (a), (b), and (c) follow quickly from the definition and are left as exercises for the reader. To prove (d), we note that

$$A \cdot (A \times B) = a_1(a_2 b_3 - a_3 b_2) + a_2(a_3 b_1 - a_1 b_3) + a_3(a_1 b_2 - a_2 b_1) = 0.$$

Part (e) follows in the same way, or it can be deduced from (a) and (d). To prove (f), we write

$$\|A \times B\|^2 = (a_2b_3 - a_3b_2)^2 + (a_3b_1 - a_1b_3)^2 + (a_1b_2 - a_2b_1)^2$$

and

$$\|A\|^2\|B\|^2 - (A \cdot B)^2 = (a_1^2 + a_2^2 + a_3^2)(b_1^2 + b_2^2 + b_3^2) - (a_1b_1 + a_2b_2 + a_3b_3)^2$$

and then verify by brute force that the two right-hand members are identical.

Property (f) shows that $A \times B = O$ if and only if $(A \cdot B)^2 = \|A\|^2\|B\|^2$. By the Cauchy-Schwarz inequality (Theorem 12.3), this happens if and only if one of the vectors is a scalar multiple of the other. In other words, $A \times B = O$ if and only if $A$ and $B$ are linearly dependent, which proves (g).

EXAMPLES. Both (a) and (g) show that $A \times A = O$. From the definition of cross product we find that

$$i \times j = k, \quad j \times k = i, \quad k \times i = j.$$

The cross product is *not* associative. For example, we have

$$i \times (i \times j) = i \times k = -j \quad \text{but} \quad (i \times i) \times j = O \times j = O.$$

The next theorem describes two more fundamental properties of the cross product.

THEOREM 13.13.     *Let $A$ and $B$ be linearly independent vectors in $V_3$. Then we have the following:*
   (a) *The vectors $A$, $B$, $A \times B$ are linearly independent.*
   (b) *Every vector $N$ in $V_3$ orthogonal to both $A$ and $B$ is a scalar multiple of $A \times B$.*

*Proof.* Let $C = A \times B$. Then $C \neq O$ since $A$ and $B$ are linearly independent. Given scalars $a, b, c$ such that $aA + bB + cC = O$, we take the dot product of each member with $C$ and use the relations $A \cdot C = B \cdot C = 0$ to find $c = 0$. This gives $aA + bB = O$, so $a = b = 0$ since $A$ and $B$ are independent. This proves (a).

Let $N$ be any vector orthogonal to both $A$ and $B$, and let $C = A \times B$. We shall prove that

$$(N \cdot C)^2 = (N \cdot N)(C \cdot C).$$

Then from the Cauchy–Schwarz inequality (Theorem 12.3) it follows that $N$ is a scalar multiple of $C$.

Since $A$, $B$, and $C$ are linearly independent, we know, by Theorem 12.10(c), that they span $V_3$. In particular, they span $N$, so we can write

$$N = aA + bB + cC$$

for some scalars $a, b, c$. This gives us

$$N \cdot N = N \cdot (aA + bB + cC) = c N \cdot C$$

since $N \cdot A = N \cdot B = 0$. Also, since $C \cdot A = C \cdot B = 0$, we have

$$C \cdot N = C \cdot (aA + bB + cC) = cC \cdot C.$$

Therefore, $(N \cdot N)(C \cdot C) = (cN \cdot C)(C \cdot C) = (N \cdot C)(cC \cdot C) = (N \cdot C)^2$, which completes the proof.

Theorem 13.12 helps us visualize the cross product geometrically. From properties (d) and (e), we know that $A \times B$ is perpendicular to both $A$ and $B$. When the vector $A \times B$ is represented geometrically by an arrow, the direction of the arrow depends on the relative

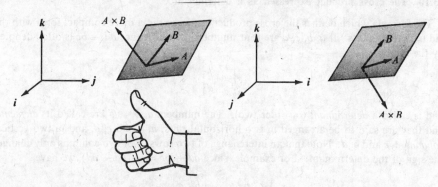

(a) A right-handed coordinate system          (b) A left-handed coordinate system

FIGURE 13.4   Illustrating the relative positions of $A$, $B$, and $A \times B$.

positions of the three unit coordinate vectors. If $i$, $j$, and $k$ are arranged as shown in Figure 13.4(a), they are said to form a *right-handed coordinate system*. In this case, the direction of $A \times B$ is determined by the "right-hand rule." That is to say, when $A$ is rotated into $B$ in such a way that the fingers of the right hand point in the direction of rotation, then the thumb indicates the direction of $A \times B$ (assuming, for the sake of the discussion, that the thumb is perpendicular to the other fingers). In a left-handed coordinate system, as shown in Figure 13.4(b), the direction of $A \times B$ is reversed and may be determined by a corresponding left-hand rule.

The length of $A \times B$ has an interesting geometric interpretation. If $A$ and $B$ are nonzero vectors making an angle $\theta$ with each other, where $0 \leq \theta \leq \pi$, we may write $A \cdot B = \|A\| \|B\| \cos \theta$ in property (f) of Theorem 13.12 to obtain

$$\|A \times B\|^2 = \|A\|^2 \|B\|^2 (1 - \cos^2 \theta) = \|A\|^2 \|B\|^2 \sin^2 \theta,$$

from which we find

$$\|A \times B\| = \|A\| \|B\| \sin \theta.$$

Since $\|B\| \sin \theta$ is the altitude of the parallelogram determined by $A$ and $B$ (see Figure 13.5), we see that *the length of $A \times B$ is equal to the area of this parallelogram*.

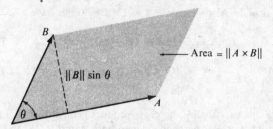

FIGURE 13.5   The length of $A \times B$ is the area of the parallelogram determined by $A$ and $B$.

## 13.10   The cross product expressed as a determinant

The formula which defines the cross product can be put in a more compact form with the aid of determinants. If $a$, $b$, $c$, $d$ are four numbers, the difference $ad - bc$ is often denoted by the symbol

$$\begin{vmatrix} a & b \\ c & d \end{vmatrix}$$

and is called a *determinant* (of order two). The numbers $a$, $b$, $c$, $d$ are called its *elements*, and they are said to be arranged in two horizontal *rows*, $a$, $b$ and $c$, $d$, and in two vertical *columns*, $a$, $c$ and $b$, $d$. Note that an interchange of two rows or of two columns only changes the sign of the determinant. For example, since $ad - bc = -(bc - ad)$, we have

$$\begin{vmatrix} a & b \\ c & d \end{vmatrix} = - \begin{vmatrix} b & a \\ d & c \end{vmatrix}.$$

If we express each of the components of the cross product as a determinant of order two, the formula defining $A \times B$ becomes

$$A \times B = \left( \begin{vmatrix} a_2 & a_3 \\ b_2 & b_3 \end{vmatrix}, \begin{vmatrix} a_3 & a_1 \\ b_3 & b_1 \end{vmatrix}, \begin{vmatrix} a_1 & a_2 \\ b_1 & b_2 \end{vmatrix} \right).$$

This can also be expressed in terms of the unit coordinate vectors $i$, $j$, $k$ as follows:

$$(13.7) \qquad A \times B = \begin{vmatrix} a_2 & a_3 \\ b_2 & b_3 \end{vmatrix} i + \begin{vmatrix} a_3 & a_1 \\ b_3 & b_1 \end{vmatrix} j + \begin{vmatrix} a_1 & a_2 \\ b_1 & b_2 \end{vmatrix} k.$$

Determinants of order three are written with three rows and three columns and they may be defined in terms of second-order determinants by the formula

$$(13.8) \qquad \begin{vmatrix} a_1 & a_2 & a_3 \\ b_1 & b_2 & b_3 \\ c_1 & c_2 & c_3 \end{vmatrix} = a_1 \begin{vmatrix} b_2 & b_3 \\ c_2 & c_3 \end{vmatrix} - a_2 \begin{vmatrix} b_1 & b_3 \\ c_1 & c_3 \end{vmatrix} + a_3 \begin{vmatrix} b_1 & b_2 \\ c_1 & c_2 \end{vmatrix}$$

This is said to be an "expansion" of the determinant along its first row. Note that the determinant on the right that multiplies $a_1$ may be obtained from that on the left by deleting the row and column in which $a_1$ appears. The other two determinants on the right are obtained similarly.

Determinants of order greater than three are discussed in Volume II. Our only purpose in introducing determinants of order two and three at this stage is to have a useful device for writing certain formulas in a compact form that makes them easier to remember.

Determinants are meaningful if the elements in the first row are vectors. For example, if we write the determinant

$$\begin{vmatrix} i & j & k \\ a_1 & a_2 & a_3 \\ b_1 & b_2 & b_3 \end{vmatrix}$$

and "expand" this according to the rule prescribed in (13.8), we find that the result is equal to the right member of (13.7). In other words, we may write the definition of the cross product $A \times B$ in the following compact form:

$$A \times B = \begin{vmatrix} i & j & k \\ a_1 & a_2 & a_3 \\ b_1 & b_2 & b_3 \end{vmatrix}.$$

For example, to compute the cross product of $A = 2i - 8j + 3k$ and $B = 4j + 3k$, we write

$$A \times B = \begin{vmatrix} i & j & k \\ 2 & -8 & 3 \\ 0 & 4 & 3 \end{vmatrix} = \begin{vmatrix} -8 & 3 \\ 4 & 3 \end{vmatrix} i - \begin{vmatrix} 2 & 3 \\ 0 & 3 \end{vmatrix} j + \begin{vmatrix} 2 & -8 \\ 0 & 4 \end{vmatrix} k = -36i - 6j + 8k$$

## 13.11 Exercises

1. Let $A = -i + 2k$, $B = 2i + j - k$, $C = i + 2j + 2k$. Compute each of the following vectors in terms of $i, j, k$:
   (a) $A \times B$;
   (b) $B \times C$;
   (c) $C \times A$;
   (d) $A \times (C \times A)$;
   (e) $(A \times B) \times C$;
   (f) $A \times (B \times C)$;
   (g) $(A \times C) \times B$;
   (h) $(A + B) \times (A - C)$;
   (i) $(A \times B) \times (A \times C)$.

2. In each case find a vector of length 1 in $V_3$ orthogonal to both $A$ and $B$:
   (a) $A = i + j + k$,    $B = 2i + 3j - k$;
   (b) $A = 2i - 3j + 4k$,    $B = -i + 5j + 7k$;
   (c) $A = i - 2j + 3k$,    $B = -3i + 2j - k$.

3. In each case use the cross product to compute the area of the triangle with vertices $A, B, C$:
   (a) $A = (0, 2, 2)$,    $B = (2, 0, -1)$,    $C = (3, 4, 0)$;
   (b) $A = (-2, 3, 1)$,    $B = (1, -3, 4)$,    $C = (1, 2, 1)$;
   (c) $A = (0, 0, 0)$,    $B = (0, 1, 1)$,    $C = (1, 0, 1)$.

4. If $A = 2i + 5j + 3k$, $B = 2i + 7j + 4k$, and $C = 3i + 3j + 6k$, express the cross product $(A - C) \times (B - A)$ in terms of $i, j, k$.

5. Prove that $\|A \times B\| = \|A\| \|B\|$ if and only if $A$ and $B$ are orthogonal.

6. Given two linearly independent vectors $A$ and $B$ in $V_3$. Let $C = (B \times A) - B$.
   (a) Prove that $A$ is orthogonal to $B + C$.

(b) Prove that the angle $\theta$ between $B$ and $C$ satisfies $\frac{1}{2}\pi < \theta < \pi$.

(c) If $\|B\| = 1$ and $\|B \times A\| = 2$, compute the length of $C$.

7. Let $A$ and $B$ be two orthogonal vectors in $V_3$, each having length 1.

(a) Prove that $A, B, A \times B$ is an orthonormal basis for $V_3$.

(b) Let $C = (A \times B) \times A$. Prove that $\|C\| = 1$.

(c) Draw a figure showing the geometric relation between $A$, $B$, and $A \times B$, and use this figure to obtain the relations

$$(A \times B) \times A = B, \qquad (A \times B) \times B = -A.$$

(d) Prove the relations in part (c) algebraically.

8. (a) If $A \times B = O$ and $A \cdot B = 0$, then at least one of $A$ or $B$ is zero. Prove this statement and give its geometric interpretation.

(b) Given $A \neq O$. If $A \times B = A \times C$ and $A \cdot B = A \cdot C$, prove that $B = C$.

9. Let $A = 2i - j + 2k$ and $C = 3i + 4j - k$.

(a) Find a vector $B$ such that $A \times B = C$. Is there more than one solution?

(b) Find a vector $B$ such that $A \times B = C$ and $A \cdot B = 1$. Is there more than one solution?

10. Given a nonzero vector $A$ and a vector $C$ orthogonal to $A$, both vectors in $V_3$. Prove that there is exactly one vector $B$ such that $A \times B = C$ and $A \cdot B = 1$.

11. Three vertices of a parallelogram are at the points $A = (1, 0, 1)$, $B = (-1, 1, 1)$, $C = (2, -1, 2)$.

(a) Find all possible points $D$ which can be the fourth vertex of the parallelogram.

(b) Compute the area of triangle $ABC$.

12. Given two nonparallel vectors $A$ and $B$ in $V_3$ with $A \cdot B = 2$, $\|A\| = 1$, $\|B\| = 4$. Let $C = 2(A \times B) - 3B$. Compute $A \cdot (B + C)$, $\|C\|$, and the cosine of the angle $\theta$ between $B$ and $C$.

13. Given two linearly independent vectors $A$ and $B$ in $V_3$. Determine whether each of the following statements is true or false.

(a) $A + B, A - B, A \times B$ are linearly independent.

(b) $A + B, A + (A \times B), B + (A \times B)$ are linearly independent.

(c) $A, B, (A + B) \times (A - B)$ are linearly independent.

14. (a) Prove that three vectors $A, B, C$ in $V_3$ lie on a line if and only if $(B - A) \times (C - A) = O$.

(b) If $A \neq B$, prove that the line through $A$ and $B$ consists of the set of all vectors $P$ such that $(P - A) \times (P - B) = O$.

15. Given two orthogonal vectors $A, B$ in $V_3$, each of length 1. Let $P$ be a vector satisfying the equation $P \times B = A - P$. Prove each of the following statements.

(a) $P$ is orthogonal to $B$ and has length $\frac{1}{2}\sqrt{2}$.

(b) $P, B, P \times B$ form a basis for $V_3$.

(c) $(P \times B) \times B = -P$.

(d) $P = \frac{1}{2}A - \frac{1}{2}(A \times B)$.

## 13.12 The scalar triple product

The dot and cross products can be combined to form the *scalar triple product* $A \cdot B \times C$, which can only mean $A \cdot (B \times C)$. Since this is a dot product of two vectors, its value is a scalar. We can compute this scalar by means of determinants. Write $A = (a_1, a_2, a_3)$, $B = (b_1, b_2, b_3)$, $C = (c_1, c_2, c_3)$ and express $B \times C$ according to Equation (13.7). Forming the dot product with $A$, we obtain

$$A \cdot B \times C = a_1 \begin{vmatrix} b_2 & b_3 \\ c_2 & c_3 \end{vmatrix} + a_2 \begin{vmatrix} b_3 & b_1 \\ c_3 & c_1 \end{vmatrix} + a_3 \begin{vmatrix} b_1 & b_2 \\ c_1 & c_2 \end{vmatrix} = \begin{vmatrix} a_1 & a_2 & a_3 \\ b_1 & b_2 & b_3 \\ c_1 & c_2 & c_3 \end{vmatrix}.$$

Thus, $A \cdot B \times C$ is equal to the determinant whose rows are the components of the factors $A$, $B$, and $C$.

In Theorem 13.12 we found that two vectors $A$ and $B$ are linearly dependent if and only if their cross product $A \times B$ is the zero vector. The next theorem gives a corresponding criterion for linear dependence of three vectors.

THEOREM 13.14. *Three vectors $A$, $B$, $C$ in $V_3$ are linearly dependent if and only if*

$$A \cdot B \times C = 0.$$

*Proof.* Assume first that $A$, $B$, and $C$ are dependent. If $B$ and $C$ are dependent, then $B \times C = O$, and hence $A \cdot B \times C = 0$. Suppose, then, that $B$ and $C$ are independent. Since all three are dependent, there exist scalars $a$, $b$, $c$, not all zero, such that $aA + bB + cC = O$. We must have $a \neq 0$ in this relation, otherwise $B$ and $C$ would be dependent. Therefore, we can divide by $a$ and express $A$ as a linear combination of $B$ and $C$, say $A = tB + sC$. Taking the dot product of each member with $B \times C$, we find

$$A \cdot (B \times C) = tB \cdot B \times C + sC \cdot B \times C = 0,$$

since each of $B$ and $C$ is orthogonal to $B \times C$. Therefore dependence of $A$, $B$, and $C$ implies $A \cdot B \times C = 0$.

To prove the converse, assume that $A \cdot B \times C = 0$. If $B$ and $C$ are dependent, then so are $A$, $B$, and $C$, and there is nothing more to prove. Assume then, that $B$ and $C$ are linearly independent. Then, by Theorem 13.13, the three vectors $B$, $C$, and $B \times C$ are linearly independent. Hence, they span $A$ so we can write

$$A = aB + bC + c(B \times C)$$

for some scalars $a$, $b$, $c$. Taking the dot product of each member with $B \times C$ and using the fact that $A \cdot (B \times C) = 0$, we find $c = 0$, so $A = aB + bC$. This proves that $A$, $B$, and $C$ are linearly dependent.

EXAMPLE. To determine whether the three vectors $(2, 3, -1)$, $(3, -7, 5)$, and $(1, -5, 2)$ are dependent, we form their scalar triple product, expressing it as the determinant

$$\begin{vmatrix} 2 & 3 & -1 \\ 3 & -7 & 5 \\ 1 & -5 & 2 \end{vmatrix} = 2(-14 + 25) - 3(6 - 5) - 1(-15 + 7) = 27$$

Since the scalar triple product is nonzero, the vectors are linearly independent.

The scalar triple product has an interesting geometric interpretation. Figure 13.6 shows a parallelepiped determined by three geometric vectors $A$, $B$, $C$ not in the same plane. Its altitude is $\|C\| \cos \phi$, where $\phi$ is the angle between $A \times B$ and $C$. In this figure, $\cos \phi$ is positive because $0 \leq \phi < \frac{1}{2}\pi$. The area of the parallelogram which forms the base is $\|A \times B\|$, and this is also the area of each cross section parallel to the base. Integrating the cross-sectional area from 0 to $\|C\| \cos \phi$, we find that the volume of the parallelepiped is $\|A \times B\| \, (\|C\| \cos \phi)$, the area of the base times the altitude. But we have

$$\|A \times B\| \, (\|C\| \cos \phi) = (A \times B) \cdot C .$$

In other words, the scalar triple product $A \times B \cdot C$ is equal to the volume of the parallelepiped determined by $A$, $B$, $C$. When $\frac{1}{2}\pi < \phi \le \pi$, $\cos \phi$ is negative and the product $A \times B \cdot C$ is the negative of the volume. If $A$, $B$, $C$ are on a plane through the origin, they are linearly dependent and their scalar triple product is zero. In this case, the parallelepiped degenerates and has zero volume.

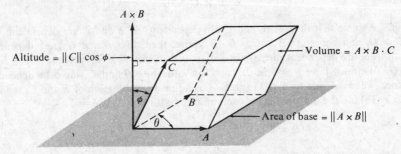

FIGURE 13.6   Geometric interpretation of the scalar triple product as the volume of a parallelepiped.

This geometric interpretation of the scalar triple product suggests certain algebraic properties of this product. For example, a cyclic permutation of the vectors $A$, $B$, $C$ leaves the scalar triple product unchanged. By this we mean that

(13.9)    $$A \times B \cdot C = B \times C \cdot A = C \times A \cdot B .$$

An algebraic proof of this property is outlined in Exercise 7 of Section 13.14. This property implies that the dot and cross are interchangeable in a scalar triple product. In fact, the commutativity of the dot product implies $(B \times C) \cdot A = A \cdot (B \times C)$ and when this is combined with the first equation in (13.9), we find that

(13.10)    $$A \times B \cdot C = A \cdot B \times C .$$

The scalar triple product $A \cdot B \times C$ is often denoted by the symbol $[ABC]$ without indicating the dot or cross. Because of Equation (13.10), there is no ambiguity in this notation—the product depends only on the order of the factors $A$, $B$, $C$ and not on the positions of the dot and cross.

### 13.13   Cramer's rule for solving a system of three linear equations

The scalar triple product may be used to solve a system of three simultaneous linear equations in three unknowns $x$, $y$, $z$. Suppose the system is written in the form

$$a_1 x + b_1 y + c_1 z = d_1 ,$$

(13.11)    $$a_2 x + b_2 y + c_2 z = d_2 ,$$

$$a_3 x + b_3 y + c_3 z = d_3 .$$

Let $A$ be the vector with components $a_1$, $a_2$, $a_3$ and define $B$, $C$, and $D$ similarly. Then the three equations in (13.11) are equivalent to the single vector equation

(13.12) $$xA + yB + zC = D.$$

If we dot multiply both sides of this equation with $B \times C$, writing $[ABC]$ for $A \cdot B \times C$, we find that

$$x[ABC] + y[BBC] + z[CBC] = [DBC].$$

Since $[BBC] = [CBC] = 0$, the coefficients of $y$ and $z$ drop out and we obtain

(13.13) $$x = \frac{[DBC]}{[ABC]} \quad \text{if} \quad [ABC] \neq 0.$$

A similar argument yields analogous formulas for $y$ and $z$. Thus we have

(13.14) $$y = \frac{[ADC]}{[ABC]} \quad \text{and} \quad z = \frac{[ABD]}{[ABC]} \quad \text{if} \quad [ABC] \neq 0.$$

The condition $[ABC] \neq 0$ means that the three vectors $A$, $B$, $C$ are linearly independent. In this case, (13.12) shows that every vector $D$ in 3-space is spanned by $A$, $B$, $C$ and the multipliers $x$, $y$, $z$ are uniquely determined by the formulas in (13.13) and (13.14). When the scalar triple products that occur in these formulas are written as determinants, the result is known as *Cramer's rule* for solving the system (13.11):

$$x = \frac{\begin{vmatrix} d_1 & b_1 & c_1 \\ d_2 & b_2 & c_2 \\ d_3 & b_3 & c_3 \end{vmatrix}}{\begin{vmatrix} a_1 & b_1 & c_1 \\ a_2 & b_2 & c_2 \\ a_3 & b_3 & c_3 \end{vmatrix}}, \quad y = \frac{\begin{vmatrix} a_1 & d_1 & c_1 \\ a_2 & d_2 & c_2 \\ a_3 & d_3 & c_3 \end{vmatrix}}{\begin{vmatrix} a_1 & b_1 & c_1 \\ a_2 & b_2 & c_2 \\ a_3 & b_3 & c_3 \end{vmatrix}}, \quad z = \frac{\begin{vmatrix} a_1 & b_1 & d_1 \\ a_2 & b_2 & d_2 \\ a_3 & b_3 & d_3 \end{vmatrix}}{\begin{vmatrix} a_1 & b_1 & c_1 \\ a_2 & b_2 & c_2 \\ a_3 & b_3 & c_3 \end{vmatrix}}.$$

If $[ABC] = 0$, then $A$, $B$, $C$ lie on a plane through the origin and the system has no solution unless $D$ lies in the same plane. In this latter case, it is easy to show that there are infinitely many solutions of the system. In fact, the vectors $A$, $B$, $C$ are linearly dependent so there exist scalars $u$, $v$, $w$ not all zero such that $uA + vB + wC = O$. If the triple $(x, y, z)$ satisfies (13.12), then so does the triple $(x + tu, y + tv, z + tw)$ for all real $t$, since we have

$$(x + tu)A + (y + tv)B + (z + tw)C$$
$$= xA + yB + zC + t(uA + vB + wC) = xA + yB + zC.$$

## 13.14 Exercises

1. Compute the scalar triple product $A \cdot B \times C$ in each case.
   (a) $A = (3, 0, 0)$,      $B = (0, 4, 0)$,      $C = (0, 0, 8)$.
   (b) $A = (2, 3, -1)$,      $B = (3, -7, 5)$,      $C = (1, -5, 2)$.
   (c) $A = (2, 1, 3)$,      $B = (-3, 0, 6)$,      $C = (4, 5, -1)$.

2. Find all real $t$ for which the three vectors $(1, t, 1)$, $(t, 1, 0)$, $(0, 1, t)$ are linearly dependent.
3. Compute the volume of the parallelepiped determined by the vectors $i + j, j + k, k + i$.
4. Prove that $A \times B = A \cdot (B \times i)i + A \cdot (B \times j)j + A \cdot (B \times k)k$.
5. Prove that $i \times (A \times i) + j \times (A \times j) + k \times (A \times k) = 2A$.
6. (a) Find all vectors $ai + bj + ck$ which satisfy the relation

$$(ai + bj + ck) \cdot k \times (6i + 3j + 4k) = 3 .$$

   (b) Find that vector $ai + bj + ck$ of shortest length which satisfies the relation in (a).
7. Use algebraic properties of the dot and cross products to derive the following properties of the scalar triple product.
   (a) $(A + B) \cdot (A + B) \times C = 0$.
   (b) $A \cdot B \times C = -B \cdot A \times C$. This shows that switching the first two vectors reverses the sign. [*Hint:* Use part (a) and distributive laws.]
   (c) $A \cdot B \times C = -A \cdot C \times B$. This shows that switching the second and third vectors reverses the sign. [*Hint:* Use skew-symmetry.]
   (d) $A \cdot B \times C = -C \cdot B \times A$. This shows that switching the first and third vectors reverses the sign. [*Hint:* Use (b) and (c).]
   Equating the right members of (b), (c), and (d), we find that

$$A \cdot B \times C = B \cdot C \times A = C \cdot A \times B ,$$

   which shows that a cyclic permutation of $A$, $B$, $C$ leaves their scalar triple product unchanged.
9. This exercise outlines a proof of the vector identity

(13.15)                     $A \times (B \times C) = (C \cdot A)B - (B \cdot A)C ,$

   sometimes referred to as the "cab minus bac" formula. Let $B = (b_1, b_2, b_3)$, $C = (c_1, c_2, c_3)$ and prove that

$$i \times (B \times C) = c_1 B - b_1 C .$$

   This proves (13.15) in the special case $A = i$. Prove corresponding formulas for $A = j$ and $A = k$, and then combine them to obtain (13.15).
10. Use the "cab minus bac" formula of Exercise 9 to derive the following vector identities.
    (a) $(A \times B) \times (C \times D) = (A \times B \cdot D)C - (A \times B \cdot C)D$.
    (b) $A \times (B \times C) + B \times (C \times A) + C \times (A \times B) = O$.
    (c) $A \times (B \times C) = (A \times B) \times C$ if and only if $B \times (C \times A) = O$.
    (d) $(A \times B) \cdot (C \times D) = (B \cdot D)(A \cdot C) - (B \cdot C)(A \cdot D)$.
11. Four vectors $A$, $B$, $C$, $D$ in $V_3$ satisfy the relations $A \times C \cdot B = 5$, $A \times D \cdot B = 3$, $C + D = i + 2j + k$, $C - D = i - k$. Compute $(A \times B) \times (C \times D)$ in terms of $i, j, k$.
12. Prove that $(A \times B) \cdot (B \times C) \times (C \times A) = (A \cdot B \times C)^2$.
13. Prove or disprove the formula $A \times [A \times (A \times B)] \cdot C = -\|A\|^2 A \cdot B \times C$.
14. (a) Prove that the volume of the tetrahedron whose vertices are $A$, $B$, $C$, $D$ is

$$\tfrac{1}{6} |(B - A) \cdot (C - A) \times (D - A)|$$

   (b) Compute this volume when $A = (1, 1, 1)$, $B = (0, 0, 2)$, $C = (0, 3, 0)$, and $D = (4, 0, 0)$.
15. (a) If $B \neq C$, prove that the perpendicular distance from $A$ to the line through $B$ and $C$ is

$$\|(A - B) \times (C - B)\|/\|B - C\| .$$

   (b) Compute this distance when $A = (1, -2, -5)$, $B = (-1, 1, 1)$, and $C = (4, 5, 1)$.

16. Heron's formula for computing the area $S$ of a triangle whose sides have lengths $a$, $b$, $c$ states that $S = \sqrt{s(s - a)(s - b)(s - c)}$, where $s = (a + b + c)/2$. This exercise outlines a vectorial proof of this formula.

Assume the triangle has vertices at $O$, $A$, and $B$, with $\|A\| = a$, $\|B\| = b$, $\|B - A\| = c$.

(a) Combine the two identities

$$\|A \times B\|^2 = \|A\|^2\|B\|^2 - (A \cdot B)^2, \qquad -2A \cdot B = \|A - B\|^2 - \|A\|^2 - \|B\|^2$$

to obtain the formula

$$4S^2 = a^2b^2 - \tfrac{1}{4}(c^2 - a^2 - b^2)^2 = \tfrac{1}{4}(2ab - c^2 + a^2 + b^2)(2ab + c^2 - a^2 - b^2).$$

(b) Rewrite the formula in part (a) to obtain

$$S^2 = \tfrac{1}{16}(a + b + c)(a + b - c)(c - a + b)(c + a - b),$$

and thereby deduce Heron's formula.

Use Cramer's rule to solve the system of equations in each of Exercises 17, 18, and 19.

17. $x + 2y + 3z = 5$, $\quad 2x - y + 4z = 11$, $\quad -y + z = 3$.
18. $x + y + 2z = 4$, $\quad 3x - y - z = 2$, $\quad 2x + 5y + 3z = 3$.
19. $x + y = 5$, $\quad x + z = 2$, $\quad y + z = 5$.
20. If $P = (1, 1, 1)$ and $A = (2, 1, -1)$, prove that each point $(x, y, z)$ on the line $\{P + tA\}$ satisfies the system of linear equations $x - y + z = 1$, $x + y + 3z = 5$, $3x + y + 7z = 11$.

## 13.15 Normal vectors to planes

A plane was defined in Section 13.6 as a set of the form $\{P + sA + tB\}$, where $A$ and $B$ are linearly independent vectors. Now we show that planes in $V_3$ can be described in an entirely different way, using the concept of a normal vector.

DEFINITION. *Let $M = \{P + sA + tB\}$ be the plane through $P$ spanned by $A$ and $B$. A vector $N$ in $V_3$ is said to be perpendicular to $M$ if $N$ is perpendicular to both $A$ and $B$. If, in addition, $N$ is nonzero, then $N$ is called a normal vector to the plane.*

*Note:* If $N \cdot A = N \cdot B = 0$, then $N \cdot (sA + tB) = 0$, so a vector perpendicular to both $A$ and $B$ is perpendicular to every vector in the linear span of $A$ and $B$. Also, if $N$ is normal to a plane, so is $tN$ for every real $t \neq 0$.

THEOREM 13.15. *Given a plane $M = \{P + sA + tB\}$ through $P$ spanned by $A$ and $B$. Let $N = A \times B$. Then we have the following:*

(a) *$N$ is a normal vector to $M$.*
(b) *$M$ is the set of all $X$ in $V_3$ satisfying the equation*

(13.16) $$(X - P) \cdot N = 0.$$

*Proof.* Since $M$ is a plane, $A$ and $B$ are linearly independent, so $A \times B \neq O$. This proves (a) since $A \times B$ is orthogonal to both $A$ and $B$.

To prove (b), let $M'$ be the set of all $X$ in $V_3$ satisfying Equation (13.16). If $X \in M$, then $X - P$ is in the linear span of $A$ and $B$, so $X - P$ is orthogonal to $N$. Therefore $X \in M'$ which proves that $M \subseteq M'$. Conversely, suppose $X \in M'$. Then $X$ satisfies (13.16). Since $A$, $B$, $N$ are linearly independent (Theorem 13.13), they span every vector in $V_3$ so, in particular, we have

$$X - P = sA + tB + uN$$

for some scalars $s, t, u$. Taking the dot product of each member with $N$, we find $u = 0$, so $X - P = sA + tB$. This shows that $X \in M$. Hence, $M' \subseteq M$, which completes the proof of (b).

The geometric meaning of Theorem 13.15 is shown in Figure 13.7. The points $P$ and $X$ are on the plane and the normal vector $N$ is orthogonal to $X - P$. This figure suggests the following theorem.

THEOREM 13.16.   *Given a plane $M$ through a point $P$, and given a nonzero vector $N$ normal to $M$, let*

$$(13.17) \qquad d = \frac{|P \cdot N|}{\|N\|} .$$

*Then every $X$ on $M$ has length $\|X\| \geq d$. Moreover, we have $\|X\| = d$ if and only if $X$ is the projection of $P$ along $N$:*

$$X = tN, \quad \text{where} \quad t = \frac{P \cdot N}{N \cdot N} .$$

*Proof.* The proof follows from the Cauchy-Schwarz inequality in exactly the same way as we proved Theorem 13.6, the corresponding result for lines in $V_2$.

By the same argument we find that if $Q$ is a point not on $M$, then among all points $X$ on $M$ the smallest length $\|X - Q\|$ occurs when $X - Q$ is the projection of $P - Q$ along $N$. This minimum length is $|(P - Q) \cdot N|/\|N\|$ and is called the *distance from $Q$ to the plane*. The number $d$ in (13.17) is the distance from the origin to the plane.

## 13.16   Linear Cartesian equations for planes

The results of Theorems 13.15 and 13.16 can also be expressed in terms of components. If we write $N = (a, b, c)$, $P = (x_1, y_1, z_1)$, and $X = (x, y, z)$, Equation (13.16) becomes

$$(13.18) \qquad a(x - x_1) + b(y - y_1) + c(z - z_1) = 0 .$$

This is called a Cartesian equation for the plane, and it is satisfied by those and only those points $(x, y, z)$ which lie on the plane. The set of points satisfying (13.18) is not altered if we multiply each of $a, b, c$ by a nonzero scalar $t$. This simply amounts to a different choice of normal vector in (13.16).

We may transpose the terms not involving $x$, $y$, and $z$, and write (13.18) in the form

$$(13.19) \qquad ax + by + cz = d_1 ,$$

where $d_1 = ax_1 + by_1 + cz_1$. An equation of this type is said to be *linear* in $x$, $y$, and $z$. We have just shown that every point $(x, y, z)$ on a plane satisfies a linear Cartesian equation (13.19) in which not all three of $a$, $b$, $c$ are zero. Conversely, every linear equation with this property represents a plane. (The reader may verify this as an exercise.)

The number $d_1$ in Equation (13.19) bears a simple relation to the distance $d$ of the plane from the origin. Since $d_1 = P \cdot N$, we have $|d_1| = |P \cdot N| = d\|N\|$. In particular $|d_1| = d$ if the normal $N$ has length 1. The plane passes through the origin if and only if $d_1 = 0$.

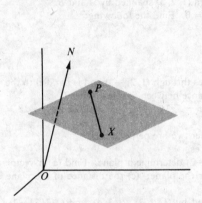

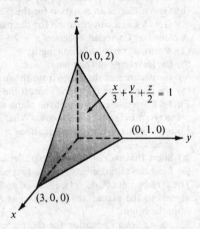

FIGURE 13.7  A plane through $P$ and
$X$ with normal vector $N$.

FIGURE 13.8  A plane with intercepts
3, 1, 2.

EXAMPLE. The Cartesian equation $2x + 6y + 3z = 6$ represents a plane with normal vector $N = 2i + 6j + 3k$. We rewrite the Cartesian equation in the form

$$\frac{x}{3} + \frac{y}{1} + \frac{z}{2} = 1$$

from which it is apparent that the plane intersects the coordinate axes at the points $(3, 0, 0)$, $(0, 1, 0)$, and $(0, 0, 2)$. The numbers 3, 1, 2 are called, respectively, the $x$-, $y$-, and $z$-*intercepts* of the plane. A knowledge of the intercepts makes it possible to sketch the plane quickly. A portion of the plane is shown in Figure 13.8. Its distance $d$ from the origin is $d = 6/\|N\| = 6/7$.

Two parallel planes will have a common normal $N$. If $N = (a, b, c)$, the Cartesian equations of two parallel planes can be written as follows:

$$ax + by + cz = d_1, \qquad ax + by + cz = d_2,$$

the only difference being in the right-hand members. The number $|d_1 - d_2|/\|N\|$ is called **the perpendicular distance between the two planes**, a definition suggested by Theorem 13.16.

Two planes are called perpendicular if a normal of one is perpendicular to a normal of the other. More generally, if the normals of two planes make an angle $\theta$ with each other, then we say that $\theta$ is an angle between the two planes.

## 13.17 Exercises

1. Given vectors $A = 2i + 3j - 4k$ and $B = j + k$.
   (a) Find a nonzero vector $N$ perpendicular to both $A$ and $B$.
   (b) Give a Cartesian equation for the plane through the origin spanned by $A$ and $B$.
   (c) Give a Cartesian equation for the plane through $(1, 2, 3)$ spanned by $A$ and $B$.

2. A plane has Cartesian equation $x + 2y - 2z + 7 = 0$. Find the following:
   (a) a normal vector of unit length;
   (b) the intercepts of the plane;
   (c) the distance of the plane from the origin;
   (d) the point $Q$ on the plane nearest the origin.

3. Find a Cartesian equation of the plane which passes through $(1, 2, -3)$ and is parallel to the plane given by $3x - y + 2z = 4$. What is the distance between the two planes?

4. Four planes have Cartesian equations $x + 2y - 2z = 5$, $3x - 6y + 3z = 2$, $2x + y + 2z = -1$, and $x - 2y + z = 7$.
   (a) Show that two of them are parallel and the other two are perpendicular.
   (b) Find the distance between the two parallel planes.

5. The three points $(1, 1, -1)$, $(3, 3, 2)$, and $(3, -1, -2)$ determine a plane. Find (a) a vector normal to the plane; (b) a Cartesian equation for the plane; (c) the distance of the plane from the origin.

6. Find a Cartesian equation for the plane determined by $(1, 2, 3)$, $(2, 3, 4)$, and $(-1, 7, -2)$.

7. Determine an angle between the planes with Cartesian equations $x + y = 1$ and $y + z = 2$.

8. A line parallel to a nonzero vector $N$ is said to be perpendicular to a plane $M$ if $N$ is normal to $M$. Find a Cartesian equation for the plane through $(2, 3, -7)$, given that the line through $(1, 2, 3)$ and $(2, 4, 12)$ is perpendicular to this plane.

9. Find a vector parametric equation for the line which contains the point $(2, 1, -3)$ and is perpendicular to the plane given by $4x - 3y + z = 5$.

10. A point moves in space in such a way that at time $t$ its position is given by the vector $X(t) = (1 - t)i + (2 - 3t)j + (2t - 1)k$.
    (a) Prove that the point moves along a line. (Call it $L$.)
    (b) Find a vector $N$ parallel to $L$.
    (c) At what time does the point strike the plane given by $2x + 3y + 2z + 1 = 0$?
    (d) Find a Cartesian equation for that plane parallel to the one in part (c) which contains the point $X(3)$.
    (e) Find a Cartesian equation for that plane perpendicular to $L$ which contains the point $X(2)$.

11. Find a Cartesian equation for the plane through $(1, 1, 1)$ if a normal vector $N$ makes angles $\frac{1}{3}\pi$, $\frac{1}{4}\pi$, $\frac{1}{3}\pi$, with $i, j, k$, respectively.

12. Compute the volume of the tetrahedron whose vertices are at the origin and at the points where the coordinate axes intersect the plane given by $x + 2y + 3z = 6$.

13. Find a vector $A$ of length 1 perpendicular to $i + 2j - 3k$ and parallel to the plane with Cartesian equation $x - y + 5z = 1$.

14. Find a Cartesian equation of the plane which is parallel to both vectors $i + j$ and $j + k$ and intersects the x-axis at $(2, 0, 0)$.

15. Find all points which lie on the intersection of the three planes given by $3x + y + z = 5$, $3x + y + 5z = 7$, $x - y + 3z = 3$.

16. Prove that three planes whose normals are linearly independent intersect in one and only one point.

17. A line with direction vector $A$ is said to be parallel to a plane $M$ if $A$ is parallel to $M$. A line containing $(1, 2, 3)$ is parallel to each of the planes given by $x + 2y + 3z = 4$, $2x + 3y + 4z = 5$. Find a vector parametric equation for this line.

18. Given a line $L$ not parallel to a plane $M$, prove that the intersection $L \cap M$ contains exactly one point.

19. (a) Prove that the distance from the point $(x_0, y_0, z_0)$ to the plane with Cartesian equation $ax + by + cz + d = 0$ is

$$\frac{|ax_0 + by_0 + cz_0 + d|}{(a^2 + b^2 + c^2)^{1/2}}.$$

(b) Find the point $P$ on the plane given by $5x - 14y + 2z + 9 = 0$ which is nearest to the point $Q = (-2, 15, -7)$.

20. Find a Cartesian equation for the plane parallel to the plane given by $2x - y + 2z + 4 = 0$ if the point $(3, 2, -1)$ is equidistant from both planes.

21. (a) If three points $A$, $B$, $C$ determine a plane, prove that the distance from a point $Q$ to this plane is $|(Q - A) \cdot (B - A) \times (C - A)| / \|(B - A) \times (C - A)\|$.

(b) Compute this distance if $Q = (1, 0, 0)$, $A = (0, 1, 1)$, $B = (1, -1, 1)$, and $C = (2, 3, 4)$.

22. Prove that if two planes $M$ and $M'$ are not parallel, their intersection $M \cap M'$ is a line.

23. Find a Cartesian equation for the plane which is parallel to $j$ and which passes through the intersection of the planes described by the equations $x + 2y + 3z = 4$, and $2x + y + z = 2$.

24. Find a Cartesian equation for the plane parallel to the vector $3i - j + 2k$ if it contains every point on the line of intersection of the planes with equations $x + y = 3$ and $2y + 3z = 4$.

## 13.18 The conic sections

A moving line $G$ which intersects a fixed line $A$ at a given point $P$, making a constant angle $\theta$ with $A$, where $0 < \theta < \frac{1}{2}\pi$, generates a surface in 3-space called a *right circular cone*. The line $G$ is called a *generator* of the cone, $A$ is its *axis*, and $P$ its *vertex*. Each of the cones shown in Figure 13.9 has a vertical axis. The upper and lower portions of the cone meeting at the vertex are called *nappes* of the cone. The curves obtained by slicing the cone with a plane not passing through the vertex are called *conic sections*, or simply *conics*. If the cutting plane is parallel to a line of the cone through the vertex, the conic is called a

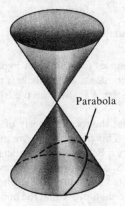
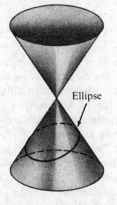
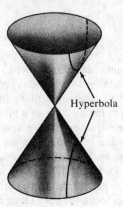

Parabola      Ellipse      Hyperbola

FIGURE 13.9 The conic sections.

*parabola*. Otherwise the intersection is called an *ellipse* or a *hyperbola*, according as the plane cuts just one or both nappes. (See Figure 13.9.) The hyperbola consists of two "branches," one on each nappe.

Many important discoveries in both pure and applied mathematics have been related to the conic sections. Appolonius' treatment of conics as early as the 3rd century B.C. was one of the most profound achievements of classical Greek geometry. Nearly 2000 years later, Galileo discovered that a projectile fired horizontally from the top of a tower falls to earth along a parabolic path (if air resistance is neglected and if the motion takes place above a part of the earth that can be regarded as a flat plane). One of the turning points in the history of astronomy occurred around 1600 when Kepler suggested that all planets move in elliptical orbits. Some 80 years later, Newton was able to demonstrate that an elliptical planetary path implies an inverse-square law of gravitational attraction. This led Newton to formulate his famous theory of universal gravitation which has often been referred to as the greatest scientific discovery ever made. Conic sections appear not only as orbits of planets and satellites but also as trajectories of elementary atomic particles. They are used in the design of lenses and mirrors, and in architecture. These examples and many others show that the importance of the conic sections can hardly be overestimated.

There are other equivalent definitions of the conic sections. One of these refers to special points known as *foci* (singular: *focus*). An ellipse may be defined as the set of all points in a plane the sum of whose distances $d_1$ and $d_2$ from two fixed points $F_1$ and $F_2$ (the foci) is

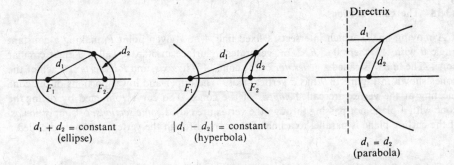

$d_1 + d_2 = $ constant  
(ellipse)

$|d_1 - d_2| = $ constant  
(hyperbola)

$d_1 = d_2$  
(parabola)

FIGURE 13.10   Focal definitions of the conic sections.

constant. (See Figure 13.10.) If the foci coincide, the ellipse reduces to a circle. A hyperbola is the set of all points for which the difference $|d_1 - d_2|$ is constant. A parabola is the set of all points in a plane for which the distance to a fixed point $F$ (called the focus) is equal to the distance to a given line (called the directrix).

There is a very simple and elegant argument which shows that the focal property of an ellipse is a consequence of its definition as a section of a cone. This proof, which we may refer to as the "ice-cream-cone proof," was discovered in 1822 by a Belgian mathematician, G. P. Dandelin (1794–1847), and makes use of the two spheres $S_1$ and $S_2$ which are drawn so as to be tangent to the cutting plane and the cone, as illustrated in Figure 13.11. These spheres touch the cone along two parallel circles $C_1$ and $C_2$. We shall prove that the points $F_1$ and $F_2$, where the spheres contact the plane, can serve as foci of the ellipse.

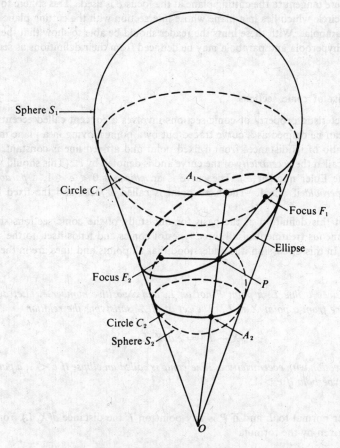

FIGURE 13.11   The ice-cream-cone proof.

Let $P$ be an arbitrary point of the ellipse. The problem is to prove that $\|\overrightarrow{PF_1}\| + \|\overrightarrow{PF_2}\|$ is constant, that is, independent of the choice of $P$. For this purpose, draw that line on the cone from the vertex $O$ to $P$ and let $A_1$ and $A_2$ be its intersections with the circles $C_1$ and $C_2$, respectively. Then $\overrightarrow{PF_1}$ and $\overrightarrow{PA_1}$ are two tangents to $S_1$ from $P$, and hence $\|\overrightarrow{PF_1}\| = \|\overrightarrow{PA_1}\|$. Similarly $\|\overrightarrow{PF_2}\| = \|\overrightarrow{PA_2}\|$, and therefore we have

$$\|\overrightarrow{PF_1}\| + \|\overrightarrow{PF_2}\| = \|\overrightarrow{PA_1}\| + \|\overrightarrow{PA_2}\| .$$

But $\|\overrightarrow{PA_1}\| + \|\overrightarrow{PA_2}\| = \|\overrightarrow{A_1A_2}\|$, which is the distance between the parallel circles $C_1$ and $C_2$ measured along the surface of the cone. This proves that $F_1$ and $F_2$ can serve as foci of the ellipse, as asserted.

Modifications of this proof work also for the hyperbola and the parabola. In the case of the hyperbola, the proof employs one sphere in each portion of the cone. For the parabola one sphere tangent to the cutting plane at the focus $F$ is used. This sphere touches the cone along a circle which lies in a plane whose intersection with the cutting plane is the directrix of the parabola. With these hints the reader should be able to show that the focal properties of the hyperbola and parabola may be deduced from their definitions as sections of a cone.

## 13.19 Eccentricity of conic sections

Another characteristic property of conic sections involves a concept called eccentricity. A conic section can be defined as a curve traced out by a point moving in a plane in such a way that the ratio of its distances from a fixed point and a fixed line is constant. This constant ratio is called the *eccentricity* of the curve and is denoted by $e$. (This should not be confused with the Euler number $e$.) The curve is an *ellipse* if $0 < e < 1$, a *parabola* if $e = 1$, and a *hyperbola* if $e > 1$. The fixed point is called a *focus* and the fixed line a *directrix*.

We shall adopt this definition as the basis for our study of the conic sections since it permits a simultaneous treatment of all three types of conics and lends itself to the use of vector methods. In this discussion it is understood that all points and lines are in the same plane.

DEFINITION. *Given a line $L$, a point $F$ not on $L$, and a positive number $e$. Let $d(X, L)$ denote the distance from a point $X$ to $L$. The set of all $X$ satisfying the relation*

$$(13.20) \qquad \|X - F\| = e\, d(X, L)$$

*is called a conic section with eccentricity $e$. The conic is called an ellipse if $e < 1$, a parabola if $e = 1$, and a hyperbola if $e > 1$.*

If $N$ is a vector normal to $L$ and if $P$ is any point on $L$ the distance $d(X, L)$ from any point $X$ to $L$ is given by the formula

$$d(X, L) = \frac{|(X - P) \cdot N|}{\|N\|} .$$

When $N$ has length 1, this simplifies to $d(X, L) = |(X - P) \cdot N|$, and the basic equation (13.20) for the conic sections becomes

$$(13.21) \qquad \|X - F\| = e\,|(X - P) \cdot N| .$$

The line $L$ separates the plane into two parts which we shall arbitrarily label as "positive" and "negative" according to the choice of $N$. If $(X - P) \cdot N > 0$, we say that $X$ is in the positive half-plane, and if $(X - P) \cdot N < 0$, we say that $X$ is in the negative half-plane. On the line $L$ itself we have $(X - P) \cdot N = 0$. In Figure 13.12 the choice of the normal vector $N$ dictates that points to the right of $L$ are in the positive half-plane and those to the left are in the negative half-plane.

Now we place the focus $F$ in the negative half-plane, as indicated in Figure 13.12, and choose $P$ to be that point on $L$ nearest to $F$. Then $P - F = dN$, where $|d| = \|P - F\|$ is

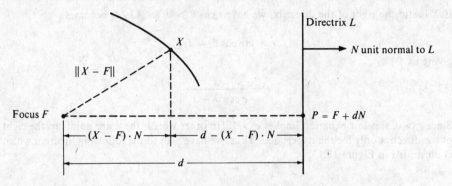

FIGURE 13.12  A conic section with eccentricity $e$ is the set of all $X$ satisfying
$$\|X - F\| = e\,|(X - F)\cdot N - d|.$$

the distance from the focus to the directrix. Since $F$ is in the negative half-plane, we have $(F - P)\cdot N = -d < 0$, so $d$ is positive. Replacing $P$ by $F + dN$ in (13.21), we obtain the following theorem, which is illustrated in Figure 13.12.

THEOREM 13.17. *Let $C$ be a conic section with eccentricity $e$, focus $F$, and directrix $L$ at a distance $d$ from $F$. If $N$ is a unit normal to $L$ and if $F$ is in the negative half-plane determined by $N$, then $C$ consists of all points $X$ satisfying the equation*

$$(13.22)\qquad\qquad \|X - F\| = e\,|(X - F)\cdot N - d|.$$

## 13.20 Polar equations for conic sections

The equation in Theorem 13.17 can be simplified if we place the focus in a special position. For example, if the focus is at the origin the equation becomes

$$(13.23)\qquad\qquad \|X\| = e\,|X\cdot N - d|.$$

This form is especially useful if we wish to express $X$ in terms of polar coordinates. Take the directrix $L$ to be vertical, as shown in Figure 13.13, and let $N = i$. If $X$ has polar coordinates $r$ and $\theta$, we have $\|X\| = r$, $X\cdot N = r\cos\theta$, and Equation (13.23) becomes

$$(13.24)\qquad\qquad r = e\,|r\cos\theta - d|.$$

If $X$ lies to the left of the directrix, we have $r\cos\theta < d$, so $|r\cos\theta - d| = d - r\cos\theta$ and (13.24) becomes $r = e(d - r\cos\theta)$, or, solving for $r$, we obtain

$$(13.25)\qquad\qquad r = \frac{ed}{e\cos\theta + 1}.$$

If $X$ lies to the right of the directrix, we have $r \cos \theta > d$, so (13.24) becomes

$$r = e(r \cos \theta - d),$$

giving us

(13.26)
$$r = \frac{ed}{e \cos \theta - 1}.$$

Since $r > 0$, this last equation implies $e > 1$. In other words, there are points to the right of the directrix only for the hyperbola. Thus, we have proved the following theorem which is illustrated in Figure 13.13.

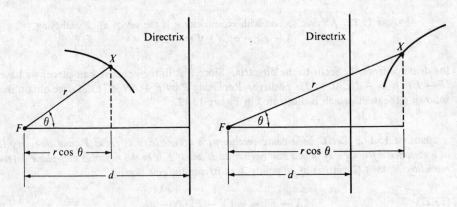

(a) $r \cos \theta < d$ on the ellipse, parabola, and left branch of the hyperbola

(b) $r \cos \theta > d$ on the right branch of the hyperbola

FIGURE 13.13   Conic sections with polar equation $r = e \,|r \cos \theta - d|$. The focus $F$ is at the origin and lies to the left of the directrix.

THEOREM 13.18.   *Let C be a conic section with eccentricity e, with a focus F at the origin, and with a vertical directrix L at a distance d to the right of F. If $0 < e \le 1$, the conic C is an ellipse or a parabola; every point on C lies to the left of L and satisfies the polar equation*

(13.27)
$$r = \frac{ed}{e \cos \theta + 1}.$$

*If $e > 1$, the curve is a hyperbola with a branch on each side of L. Points on the left branch satisfy (13.27) and points on the right branch satisfy*

(13.28)
$$r = -\frac{ed}{e \cos \theta - 1}.$$

Polar equations corresponding to other positions of the directrix are discussed in the next set of exercises.

## 13.21 Exercises

1. Prove that Equation (13.22) in Theorem 13.17 must be replaced by

$$\|X - F\| = e \,|(X - F) \cdot N + d|$$

if $F$ is in the positive half-plane determined by $N$.

2. Let $C$ be a conic section with eccentricity $e$, with a focus at the origin, and with a vertical directrix $L$ at a distance $d$ to the left of $F$.

(a) Prove that if $C$ is an ellipse or parabola, every point of $C$ lies to the right of $L$ and satisfies the polar equation

$$r = \frac{ed}{1 - e \cos \theta}.$$

(b) Prove that if $C$ is a hyperbola, points on the right branch satisfy the equation in part (a) and points on the left branch satisfy $r = -ed/(1 + e \cos \theta)$. Note that $1 + e \cos \theta$ is always negative in this case.

3. If a conic section has a horizontal directrix at a distance $d$ above a focus at the origin, prove that its points satisfy the polar equations obtained from those in Theorem 13.18 by replacing $\cos \theta$ by $\sin \theta$. What are the corresponding polar equations if the directrix is horizontal and lies below the focus?

Each of Exercises 4 through 9 gives a polar equation for a conic section with a focus $F$ at the origin and a vertical directrix lying to the right of $F$. In each case, determine the eccentricity $e$ and the distance $d$ from the focus to the directrix. Make a sketch showing the relation of the curve to its focus and directrix.

4. $r = \dfrac{2}{1 + \cos \theta}.$

5. $r = \dfrac{3}{1 + \frac{1}{2} \cos \theta}.$

6. $r = \dfrac{6}{3 + \cos \theta}.$

7. $r = \dfrac{1}{-\frac{1}{2} + \cos \theta}.$

8. $r = \dfrac{4}{1 + 2 \cos \theta}.$

9. $r = \dfrac{4}{1 + \cos \theta}.$

In each of Exercises 10 through 12, a conic section of eccentricity $e$ has a focus at the origin and a directrix with the given Cartesian equation. In each case, compute the distance $d$ from the focus to the directrix and determine a polar equation for the conic section. For a hyperbola, give a polar equation for each branch. Make a sketch showing the relation of the curve to its focus and directrix.

10. $e = \frac{1}{2}$;  directrix:  $3x + 4y = 25$.
11. $e = 1$;  directrix:  $4x + 3y = 25$.
12. $e = 2$;  directrix:  $x + y = 1$.
13. A comet moves in a parabolic orbit with the sun at the focus. When the comet is $10^8$ miles from the sun, a vector from the focus to the comet makes an angle of $\pi/3$ with a unit vector $N$ from the focus perpendicular to the directrix, the focus being in the negative half-plane determined by $N$.

(a) Find a polar equation for the orbit, taking the origin at the focus, and compute the smallest distance from the comet to the sun.

(b) Solve part (a) if the focus is in the positive half-plane determined by $N$.

## 13.22 Conic sections symmetric about the origin

A set of points is said to be *symmetric about the origin* if $-X$ is in the set whenever $X$ is in the set. We show next that the focus of an ellipse or hyperbola can always be placed so the conic section will be symmetric about the origin. To do this we rewrite the basic equation (13.22) as follows:

$$(13.29) \quad \|X - F\| = e\,|(X - F) \cdot N - d| = e\,|X \cdot N - F \cdot N - d| = |eX \cdot N - a|,$$

where $a = ed + eF \cdot N$. Squaring both members, we obtain

$$(13.30) \qquad \|X\|^2 - 2F \cdot X + \|F\|^2 = e^2(X \cdot N)^2 - 2eaX \cdot N + a^2.$$

If we are to have symmetry about the origin, this equation must also be satisfied when $X$ is replaced by $-X$, giving us

$$(13.31) \qquad \|X\|^2 + 2F \cdot X + \|F\|^2 = e^2(X \cdot N)^2 + 2eaX \cdot N + a^2.$$

Subtracting (13.31) from (13.30), we have symmetry if and only if

$$F \cdot X = eaX \cdot N \quad \text{or} \quad (F - eaN) \cdot X = 0.$$

This equation can be satisfied for all $X$ on the curve if and only if $F$ and $N$ are related by the equation

$$(13.32) \qquad F = eaN, \quad \text{where} \quad a = ed + eF \cdot N.$$

The relation $F = eaN$ implies $F \cdot N = ea$, giving us $a = ed + e^2a$. If $e = 1$, this last equation cannot be satisfied since $d$, the distance from the focus to the directrix, is nonzero. This means there is no symmetry about the origin for a parabola. If $e \neq 1$, we can always satisfy the relations in (13.32) by taking

$$(13.33) \qquad a = \frac{ed}{1 - e^2}, \qquad F = \frac{e^2d}{1 - e^2}\,N.$$

Note that $a > 0$ if $e < 1$ and $a < 0$ if $e > 1$. Putting $F = eaN$ in (13.30) we obtain the following.

THEOREM 13.19. *Let $C$ be a conic section with eccentricity $e \neq 1$ and with a focus $F$ at a distance $d$ from a directrix $L$. If $N$ is a unit normal to $L$ and if $F = eaN$, where $a = ed/(1 - e^2)$, then $C$ is the set of all points $X$ satisfying the equation*

$$(13.34) \qquad \|X\|^2 + e^2a^2 = e^2(X \cdot N)^2 + a^2.$$

This equation displays the symmetry about the origin since it is unchanged when $X$ is replaced by $-X$. Because of this symmetry, the ellipse and the hyperbola each have two foci, symmetrically located about the center, and two directrices, also symmetrically located about the center.

Equation (13.34) is satisfied when $X = \pm aN$. These two points are called *vertices* of the conic. The segment joining them is called the *major axis* if the conic is an ellipse, the *transverse axis* if the conic is a hyperbola.

Let $N'$ be a unit vector orthogonal to $N$. If $X = bN'$, then $X \cdot N = 0$, so Equation (13.34) is satisfied by $X = bN'$ if and only if $b^2 + e^2a^2 = a^2$. This requires $e < 1$, $b^2 = a^2(1 - e^2)$. The segment joining the points $X = \pm bN'$, where $b = a\sqrt{1 - e^2}$ is called the *minor axis* of the ellipse.

> *Note:* If we put $e = 0$ in (13.34), it becomes $\|X\| = a$, the equation of a circle of radius $a$ and center at the origin. In view of (13.33), we can consider such a circle as a limiting case of an ellipse in which $e \to 0$ and $d \to \infty$ in such a way that $ed \to a$.

## 13.23 Cartesian equations for the conic sections

To obtain Cartesian equations for the ellipse and hyperbola, we simply write (13.34) in terms of the rectangular coordinates of $X$. Choose $N = i$ (which means the directrices are vertical) and let $X = (x, y)$. Then $\|X\|^2 = x^2 + y^2$, $X \cdot N = x$, and (13.34) becomes $x^2 + y^2 + e^2a^2 = e^2x^2 + a^2$, or $x^2(1 - e^2) + y^2 = a^2(1 - e^2)$, which gives us

$$(13.35) \qquad \frac{x^2}{a^2} + \frac{y^2}{a^2(1 - e^2)} = 1.$$

This Cartesian equation represents both the ellipse ($e < 1$) and the hyperbola ($e > 1$) and is said to be in *standard form*. The foci are at the points $(ae, 0)$ and $(-ae, 0)$; the directrices are the vertical lines $x = a/e$ and $x = -a/e$.

If $e < 1$, we let $b = a\sqrt{1 - e^2}$ and write the equation of the ellipse in the standard form

$$(13.36) \qquad \frac{x^2}{a^2} + \frac{y^2}{b^2} = 1.$$

Its foci are located at $(c, 0)$ and $(-c, 0)$, where $c = ae = \sqrt{a^2 - b^2}$. An example is shown in Figure 13.14(a).

If $e > 1$, we let $b = |a|\sqrt{e^2 - 1}$ and write the equation of the hyperbola in the standard form

$$(13.37) \qquad \frac{x^2}{a^2} - \frac{y^2}{b^2} = 1.$$

Its foci are at the points $(c, 0)$ and $(-c, 0)$, where $c = |a| e = \sqrt{a^2 + b^2}$. An example is shown in Figure 13.14(b).

*Note:* Solving for $y$ in terms of $x$ in (13.37), we obtain two solutions

(13.38)
$$y = \pm \frac{b}{|a|} \sqrt{x^2 - a^2}.$$

For large positive $x$, the number $\sqrt{x^2 - a^2}$ is nearly equal to $x$, so the right member of (13.38) is nearly $\pm bx/|a|$. It is easy to prove that the difference between $y_1 = bx/|a|$ and $y_2 = b\sqrt{x^2 - a^2}/|a|$ approaches 0 as $x \to +\infty$. This difference is

$$y_1 - y_2 = \frac{b}{|a|}(x - \sqrt{x^2 - a^2}) = \frac{b}{|a|} \frac{x^2 - (x^2 - a^2)}{x + \sqrt{x^2 - a^2}} = \frac{|a| \, b}{x + \sqrt{x^2 - a^2}} < \frac{|a| \, b}{x},$$

so $y_1 - y_2 \to 0$ as $x \to +\infty$. Therefore, the line $y = bx/|a|$ is an asymptote of the hyperbola. The line $y = -bx/|a|$ is another asymptote. The hyperbola is said to approach these lines asymptotically. The asymptotes are shown in Figure 13.14(b).

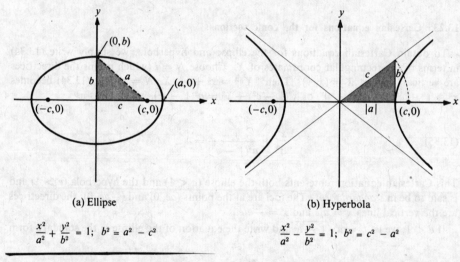

(a) Ellipse

$$\frac{x^2}{a^2} + \frac{y^2}{b^2} = 1; \quad b^2 = a^2 - c^2$$

(b) Hyperbola

$$\frac{x^2}{a^2} - \frac{y^2}{b^2} = 1; \quad b^2 = c^2 - a^2$$

FIGURE 13.14 Conic sections of eccentricity $e \neq 1$, symmetric about the origin. The foci are at $(\pm c, 0)$, where $c = |a| \, e$. The triangles relate $a$, $b$, $c$ geometrically.

The Cartesian equation for the ellipse and hyperbola will take a different form if the directrices are not vertical. For example, if the directrices are taken to be horizontal, we may take $N = j$ in Equation (13.34). Since $X \cdot N = X \cdot j = y$, we obtain a Cartesian equation like (13.35), except that $x$ and $y$ are interchanged. The standard form in this case is

(13.39)
$$\frac{y^2}{a^2} + \frac{x^2}{a^2(1 - e^2)} = 1.$$

If the conic is translated by adding a vector $X_0 = (x_0, y_0)$ to each of its points, the center will be at $(x_0, y_0)$ instead of at the origin. The corresponding Cartesian equations may be obtained from (13.35) or (13.39) by replacing $x$ by $x - x_0$ and $y$ by $y - y_0$.

To obtain a Cartesian equation for the parabola, we return to the basic equation (13.20) with $e = 1$. Take the directrix to be the vertical line $x = -c$ and place the focus at $(c, 0)$. If $X = (x, y)$, we have $X - F = (x - c, y)$, and Equation (13.20) gives us $(x - c)^2 + y^2 = |x + c|^2$. This simplifies to the standard form

(13.40)
$$y^2 = 4cx.$$

The point midway between the focus and directrix (the origin in Figure 13.15) is called the *vertex* of the parabola, and the line passing through the vertex and focus is the *axis* of the parabola. The parabola is symmetric about its axis. If $c > 0$, the parabola lies to the right of the $y$-axis, as in Figure 13.15. When $c < 0$, the curve lies to the left of the $y$-axis.

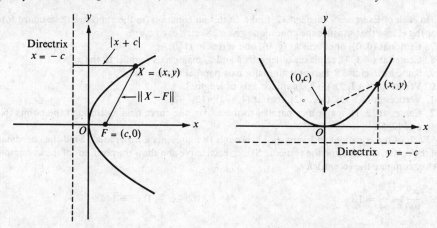

FIGURE 13.15  The parabola $y^2 = 4cx$.　　　　FIGURE 13.16  The parabola $x^2 = 4cy$.

If the axes are chosen so the focus is on the $y$-axis at the point $(0, c)$ and if the horizontal line $y = -c$ is taken as directrix, the standard form of the Cartesian equation becomes

$$x^2 = 4cy.$$

When $c > 0$ the parabola opens upward as shown in Figure 13.16. When $c < 0$, it opens downward.

If the parabola in Figure 13.15 is translated so that its vertex is at the point $(x_0, y_0)$, the corresponding equation becomes

$$(y - y_0)^2 = 4c(x - x_0).$$

The focus is now at the point $(x_0 + c, y_0)$ and the directrix is the line $x = x_0 - c$. The axis of the parabola is the line $y = y_0$.

Similarly, a translation of the parabola in Figure 13.16 leads to the equation

$$(x - x_0)^2 = 4c(y - y_0),$$

with focus at $(x_0, y_0 + c)$. The line $y = y_0 - c$ is its directrix, the line $x = x_0$ its axis.

The reader may find it amusing to prove that a parabola does not have any asymptotes.

## 13.24 Exercises

Each of the equations in Exercises 1 through 6 represents an ellipse. Find the coordinates of the center, the foci, and the vertices, and sketch each curve. Also determine the eccentricity.

1. $\dfrac{x^2}{100} + \dfrac{y^2}{36} = 1.$

4. $9x^2 + 25y^2 = 25.$

2. $\dfrac{y^2}{100} + \dfrac{x^2}{36} = 1.$

5. $4y^2 + 3x^2 = 1.$

3. $\dfrac{(x-2)^2}{16} + \dfrac{(y+3)^2}{9} = 1.$

6. $\dfrac{(x+1)^2}{16} + \dfrac{(y+2)^2}{25} = 1.$

In each of Exercises 7 through 12, find a Cartesian equation (in the appropriate standard form) for the ellipse that satisfies the conditions given. Sketch each curve.

7. Center at $(0, 0)$, one focus at $(\frac{3}{4}, 0)$, one vertex at $(1, 0)$.
8. Center at $(-3, 4)$, semiaxes of lengths 4 and 3, major axis parallel to the $x$-axis.
9. Same as Exercise 8, except with major axis parallel to the $y$-axis.
10. Vertices at $(-1, 2)$, $(-7, 2)$, minor axis of length 2.
11. Vertices at $(3, -2)$, $(13, -2)$, foci at $(4, -2)$, $(12, -2)$.
12. Center at $(2, 1)$, major axis parallel to the $x$-axis, the curve passing through the points $(6, 1)$ and $(2, 3)$.

Each of the equations in Exercises 13 through 18 represents a hyperbola. Find the coordinates of the center, the foci, and the vertices. Sketch each curve and show the positions of the asymptotes. Also, compute the eccentricity.

13. $\dfrac{x^2}{100} - \dfrac{y^2}{64} = 1.$

16. $9x^2 - 16y^2 = 144.$

14. $\dfrac{y^2}{100} - \dfrac{x^2}{64} = 1.$

17. $4x^2 - 5y^2 + 20 = 0.$

15. $\dfrac{(x+3)^2}{4} - (y-3)^2 = 1.$

18. $\dfrac{(x-1)^2}{4} - \dfrac{(y+2)^2}{9} = 1.$

In each of Exercises 19 through 23, find a Cartesian equation (in the appropriate standard form) for the hyperbola which satisfies the conditions given. Sketch each curve and show the positions of the asymptotes.

19. Center at $(0, 0)$, one focus at $(4, 0)$, one vertex at $(2, 0)$.
20. Foci at $(0, \pm\sqrt{2})$, vertices at $(0, \pm 1)$.
21. Vertices at $(\pm 2, 0)$, asymptotes $y = \pm 2x$.
22. Center at $(-1, 4)$, one focus at $(-1, 2)$, one vertex at $(-1, 3)$.
23. Center at $(2, -3)$, transverse axis parallel to one of the coordinate axes, the curve passing through $(3, -1)$ and $(-1, 0)$.
24. For what value (or values) of $C$ will the line $3x - 2y = C$ be tangent to the hyperbola $x^2 - 3y^2 = 1$?
25. The asymptotes of a hyperbola are the lines $2x - y = 0$ and $2x + y = 0$. Find a Cartesian equation for the curve if it passes through the point $(3, -5)$.

Each of the equations in Exercises 26 through 31 represents a parabola. Find the coordinates of the vertex, an equation for the directrix, and an equation for the axis. Sketch each of the curves.

26. $y^2 = -8x.$

29. $x^2 = 6y.$

27. $y^2 = 3x.$

30. $x^2 + 8y = 0.$

28. $(y-1)^2 = 12x - 6.$

31. $(x+2)^2 = 4y + 9.$

In each of Exercises 32 through 37, find a Cartesian equation (in appropriate standard form) for the parabola that satisfies the conditions given and sketch the curve.

32. Focus at $(0, -\frac{1}{4})$; equation of directrix, $y = \frac{1}{4}$.
33. Vertex at $(0, 0)$; equation of directrix, $x = -2$.
34. Vertex at $(-4, 3)$; focus at $(-4, 1)$.
35. Focus at $(3, -1)$; equation of directrix, $x = \frac{1}{2}$.
36. Axis is parallel to the $y$-axis; passes through $(0, 1)$, $(1, 0)$, and $(2, 0)$.
37. Axis is parallel to the $x$-axis; vertex at $(1, 3)$; passes through $(-1, -1)$.
38. Proceeding directly from the focal definition, find a Cartesian equation for the parabola whose focus is the origin and whose directrix is the line $2x + y = 10$.

## 13.25 Miscellaneous exercises on conic sections

1. Show that the area of the region bounded by the ellipse $x^2/a^2 + y^2/b^2 = 1$ is $ab$ times the area of a circle of radius 1.

   *Note:* This statement can be proved from general properties of the integral, without performing any integrations.

2. (a) Show that the volume of the solid of revolution generated by rotating the ellipse $x^2/a^2 + y^2/b^2 = 1$ about its major axis is $ab^2$ times the volume of a unit sphere.

   *Note:* This statement can be proved from general properties of the integral, without performing any integrations.

   (b) What is the result if the ellipse is rotated about its minor axis?
3. Find all positive numbers $A$ and $B$, $A > B$, such that the area of the region enclosed by the ellipse $Ax^2 + By^2 = 3$ is equal to the area of the region enclosed by the ellipse

$$(A + B)x^2 + (A - B)y^2 = 3 \,.$$

4. A parabolic arch has a base of length $b$ and altitude $h$. Determine the area of the region bounded by the arch and the base.
5. The region bounded by the parabola $y^2 = 8x$ and the line $x = 2$ is rotated about the $x$-axis. Find the volume of the solid of revolution so generated.
6. Two parabolas having the equations $y^2 = 2(x - 1)$ and $y^2 = 4(x - 2)$ enclose a plane region $R$.
   (a) Compute the area of $R$ by integration.
   (b) Find the volume of the solid of revolution generated by revolving $R$ about the $x$-axis.
   (c) Same as (b), but revolve $R$ about the $y$-axis.
7. Find a Cartesian equation for the conic section consisting of all points $(x, y)$ whose distance from the point $(0, 2)$ is half the distance from the line $y = 8$.
8. Find a Cartesian equation for the parabola whose focus is at the origin and whose directrix is the line $x + y + 1 = 0$.
9. Find a Cartesian equation for a hyperbola passing through the origin, given that its asymptotes are the lines $y = 2x + 1$ and $y = -2x + 3$.
10. (a) For each $p > 0$, the equation $px^2 + (p + 2)y^2 = p^2 + 2p$ represents an ellipse. Find (in terms of $p$) the eccentricity and the coordinates of the foci.
    (b) Find a Cartesian equation for the hyperbola which has the same foci as the ellipse of part (a) and which has eccentricity $\sqrt{3}$.
11. In Section 13.22 we proved that a conic symmetric about the origin satisfies the equation $\|X - F\| = |eX \cdot N - a|$, where $a = ed + eF \cdot N$. Use this relation to prove that $\|X - F\| + \|X + F\| = 2a$ if the conic is an ellipse. In other words, the sum of the distances from any point on an ellipse to its foci is constant.

12. Refer to Exercise 11. Prove that on each branch of a hyperbola the difference $\|X - F\| - \|X + F\|$ is constant.

13. (a) Prove that a similarity transformation (replacing $x$ by $tx$ and $y$ by $ty$) carries an ellipse with center at the origin into another ellipse with the same eccentricity. In other words, similar ellipses have the same eccentricity.
    (b) Prove also the converse. That is, if two concentric ellipses have the same eccentricity and major axes on the same line, then they are related by a similarity transformation.
    (c) Prove results corresponding to (a) and (b) for hyperbolas.

14. Use the Cartesian equation which represents all conics of eccentricity $e$ and center at the origin to prove that these conics are integral curves of the differential equation $y' = (e^2 - 1)x/y$.

    *Note:* Since this is a homogeneous differential equation (Section 8.25), the set of all such conics of eccentricity $e$ is invariant under a similarity transformation. (Compare with Exercise 13.)

15. (a) Prove that the collection of all parabolas is invariant under a similarity transformation. That is, a similarity transformation carries a parabola into a parabola.
    (b) Find all the parabolas similar to $y = x^2$.

16. The line $x - y + 4 = 0$ is tangent to the parabola $y^2 = 16x$. Find the point of contact.

17. (a) Given $a \neq 0$. If the two parabolas $y^2 = 4p(x - a)$ and $x^2 = 4qy$ are tangent to each other, show that the $x$-coordinate of the point of contact is determined by $a$ alone.
    (b) Find a condition on $a$, $p$, and $q$ which expresses the fact that the two parabolas are tangent to each other.

18. Consider the locus of the points $P$ in the plane for which the distance of $P$ from the point $(2, 3)$ is equal to the sum of the distances of $P$ from the two coordinate axes.
    (a) Show that the part of this locus which lies in the first quadrant is part of a hyperbola. Locate the asymptotes and make a sketch.
    (b) Sketch the graph of the locus in the other quadrants.

19. Two parabolas have the same point as focus and the same line as axis, but their vertices lie on opposite sides of the focus. Prove that the parabolas intersect orthogonally (i.e., their tangent lines are perpendicular at the points of intersection).

20. (a) Prove that the Cartesian equation

$$\frac{x^2}{a^2} + \frac{y^2}{a^2 - c^2} = 1$$

represents all conics symmetric about the origin with foci at $(c, 0)$ and $(-c, 0)$.
    (b) Keep $c$ fixed and let $S$ denote the set of all such conics obtained as $a^2$ varies over all positive numbers $\neq c^2$. Prove that every curve in $S$ satisfies the differential equation

$$xy\left(\frac{dy}{dx}\right)^2 + (x^2 - y^2 - c^2)\frac{dy}{dx} - xy = 0.$$

    (c) Prove that $S$ is self-orthogonal; that is, the set of all orthogonal trajectories of curves in $S$ is $S$ itself. [*Hint:* Replace $y'$ by $-1/y'$ in the differential equation in (b).]

21. Show that the locus of the centers of a family of circles, all of which pass through a given point and are tangent to a given line, is a parabola.

22. Show that the locus of the centers of a family of circles, all of which are tangent (externally) to a given circle and also to a given straight line, is a parabola. (Exercise 21 can be considered to be a special case.)

23. (a) A chord of length $8\,|c|$ is drawn perpendicular to the axis of the parabola $y^2 = 4cx$. Let $P$ and $Q$ be the points where the chord meets the parabola. Show that the vector from $O$ to $P$ is perpendicular to that from $O$ to $Q$.

    (b) The chord of a parabola drawn through the focus and parallel to the directrix is called the *latus rectum*. Show first that the length of the latus rectum is twice the distance from the focus to the directrix, and then show that the tangents to the parabola at both ends of the latus rectum intersect the axis of the parabola on the directrix.

24. Two points $P$ and $Q$ are said to be symmetric with respect to a circle if $P$ and $Q$ are collinear with the center, if the center is not between them, and if the product of their distances from the center is equal to the square of the radius. Given that $Q$ describes the straight line $x + 2y - 5 = 0$, find the locus of the point $P$ symmetric to $Q$ with respect to the circle $x^2 + y^2 = 4$.

# 14

# CALCULUS OF VECTOR-VALUED FUNCTIONS

## 14.1 Vector-valued functions of a real variable

This chapter combines vector algebra with the methods of calculus and describes some applications to the study of curves and to some problems in mechanics. The concept of a vector-valued function is fundamental in this study.

DEFINITION. *A function whose domain is a set of real numbers and whose range is a subset of n-space $V_n$ is called a vector-valued function of a real variable.*

We have encountered such functions in Chapter 13. For example, the line through a point $P$ parallel to a nonzero vector $A$ is the range of the vector-valued function $X$ given by

$$X(t) = P + tA$$

for all real $t$.

Vector-valued functions will be denoted by capital letters such as $F$, $G$, $X$, $Y$, etc., or by small bold-face italic letters $f$, $g$, etc. The value of a function $F$ at $t$ is denoted, as usual, by $F(t)$. In the examples we shall study, the domain of $F$ will be an interval which may contain one or both endpoints or which may be infinite.

## 14.2 Algebraic operations. Components

The usual operations of vector algebra can be applied to combine two vector-valued functions or to combine a vector-valued function with a real-valued function. If $F$ and $G$ are vector-valued functions, and if $u$ is a real-valued function, all having a common domain, we define new functions $F + G$, $uF$, and $F \cdot G$ by the equations

$$(F + G)(t) = F(t) + G(t), \qquad (uF)(t) = u(t)F(t), \qquad (F \cdot G)(t) = F(t) \cdot G(t).$$

The sum $F + G$ and the product $uF$ are vector valued, whereas the dot product $F \cdot G$ is real valued. If $F(t)$ and $G(t)$ are in 3-space, we can also define the cross product $F \times G$ by the formula

$$(F \times G)(t) = F(t) \times G(t).$$

512

The operation of composition may be applied to combine vector-valued functions with real-valued functions. For example, if $F$ is a vector-valued function whose domain includes the range of a real-valued function $u$, the composition $G = F \circ u$ is a new vector-valued function defined by the equation

$$G(t) = F[u(t)]$$

for each $t$ in the domain of $u$.

If a function $F$ has its values in $V_n$, then each vector $F(t)$ has $n$ components, and we can write

$$F(t) = (f_1(t), f_2(t), \ldots, f_n(t)) .$$

Thus, each vector-valued $F$ gives rise to $n$ real-valued functions $f_1, \ldots, f_n$ whose values at $t$ are the components of $F(t)$. We indicate this relation by writing $F = (f_1, \ldots, f_n)$, and we call $f_k$ the $k$th component of $F$.

## 14.3 Limits, derivatives, and integrals

The basic concepts of calculus, such as limit, derivative, and integral, can also be extended to vector-valued functions. We simply express the vector-valued function in terms of its components and perform the operations of calculus on the components.

DEFINITION. *If* $F = (f_1, \ldots, f_n)$ *is a vector-valued function, we define limit, derivative, and integral by the equations*

$$\lim_{t \to p} F(t) = \left( \lim_{t \to p} f_1(t), \ldots, \lim_{t \to p} f_n(t) \right) ,$$

$$F'(t) = (f_1'(t), \ldots, f_n'(t)) ,$$

$$\int_a^b F(t) \, dt = \left( \int_a^b f_1(t) \, dt, \ldots, \int_a^b f_n(t) \, dt \right) ,$$

*whenever the components on the right are meaningful.*

We also say that $F$ is *continuous, differentiable,* or *integrable* on an interval if each component of $F$ has the corresponding property on the interval.

In view of these definitions, it is not surprising to find that many of the theorems on limits, continuity, differentiation, and integration of real-valued functions are also valid for vector-valued functions. We state some of the theorems that we use in this chapter.

THEOREM 14.1. *If* $F$, $G$, *and* $u$ *are differentiable on an interval, then so are* $F + G$, $uF$, *and* $F \cdot G$, *and we have*

$$(F + G)' = F' + G', \qquad (uF)' = u'F + uF', \qquad (F \cdot G)' = F' \cdot G + F \cdot G'.$$

*If F and G have values in $V_3$, we also have*

$$(F \times G)' = F' \times G + F \times G'.$$

*Proof.* To indicate the routine nature of the proofs we discuss the formula for $(uF)'$. The proofs of the others are similar and are left as exercises for the reader.

Writing $F = (f_1, \ldots, f_n)$, we have

$$uF = (uf_1, \ldots, uf_n), \qquad (uF)' = ((uf_1)', \ldots, (uf_n)').$$

But the derivative of the $k$th component of $uF$ is $(uf_k)' = u'f_k + uf_k'$, so we have

$$(uF)' = u'(f_1, \ldots, f_n) + u(f_1', \ldots, f_n') = u'F + uF'.$$

The reader should note that the differentiation formulas in Theorem 14.1 are analogous to the usual formulas for differentiating a sum or product of real-valued functions. Since the cross product is not commutative, one must pay attention to the order of the factors in the formula for $(F \times G)'$.

The formula for differentiating $F \cdot G$ gives us the following theorem which we shall use frequently.

THEOREM 14.2. *If a vector-valued function is differentiable and has constant length on an open interval I, then $F \cdot F' = 0$ on I. In other words, $F'(t)$ is perpendicular to $F(t)$ for each t in I.*

*Proof.* Let $g(t) = \|F(t)\|^2 = F(t) \cdot F(t)$. By hypothesis, $g$ is constant on $I$, and hence $g' = 0$ on $I$. But since $g$ is a dot product, we have $g' = F' \cdot F + F \cdot F' = 2F \cdot F'$. Therefore we have $F \cdot F' = 0$.

The next theorem deals with composite functions. Its proof follows easily from Theorems 3.5 and 4.2 which contain the corresponding results for real-valued functions.

THEOREM 14.3. *Let $G = F \circ u$, where F is vector valued and u is real valued. If u is continuous at t and if F is continuous at $u(t)$, then G is continuous at t. If the derivatives $u'(t)$ and $F'[u(t)]$ exist, then $G'(t)$ also exists and is given by the chain rule,*

$$G'(t) = F'[u(t)]u'(t).$$

If a vector-valued function $F$ is continuous on a closed interval $[a, b]$, then each component is continuous and hence integrable on $[a, b]$, so $F$ is integrable on $[a, b]$. The next three theorems give basic properties of the integral of vector-valued functions. In each case, the proofs follow at once from the corresponding results for integrals of real-valued functions.

THEOREM 14.4. LINEARITY AND ADDITIVITY. *If the vector-valued functions F and G are integrable on $[a, b]$, so is $c_1F + c_2G$ for all $c_1$ and $c_2$, and we have*

$$\int_a^b (c_1F(t) + c_2G(t)) \, dt = c_1\int_a^b F(t) \, dt + c_2\int_a^b G(t) \, dt.$$

*Also, for each c in [a, b], we have*

$$\int_a^b F(t)\, dt = \int_a^c F(t)\, dt + \int_c^b F(t)\, dt\ .$$

THEOREM 14.5. FIRST FUNDAMENTAL THEOREM OF CALCULUS. *Assume F is a vector-valued function continuous on* [a, b]. *If* $c \in [a, b]$, *define the indefinite integral A to be the vector-valued function given by*

$$A(x) = \int_c^x F(t)\, dt \qquad if \quad a \le x \le b\ .$$

*Then A'(x) exists, and we have* $A'(x) = F(x)$ *for each x in* (a, b).

THEOREM 14.6. SECOND FUNDAMENTAL THEOREM OF CALCULUS. *Assume that the vector-valued function F has a continuous derivative F' on an open interval I. Then, for each choice of c and x in I, we have*

$$F(x) = F(c) + \int_c^x F'(t)\, dt\ .$$

The next theorem is an extension of the property $c \int_a^b F(t)\, dt = \int_a^b c F(t)\, dt$, with multiplication by the scalar $c$ replaced by dot multiplication by a vector $C$.

THEOREM 14.7. *If* $F = (f_1, \ldots, f_n)$ *is integrable on* [a, b], *then for every vector* $C = (c_1, \ldots, c_n)$ *the dot product* $C \cdot F$ *is integrable on* [a, b], *and we have*

$$C \cdot \int_a^b F(t)\, dt = \int_a^b C \cdot F(t)\, dt\ .$$

*Proof.* Since each component of $F$ is integrable, we have

$$C \cdot \int_a^b F(t)\, dt = \sum_{i=1}^n c_i \int_a^b f_i(t)\, dt = \int_a^b \sum_{i=1}^n c_i f_i(t)\, dt = \int_a^b C \cdot F(t)\, dt\ .$$

Now we use Theorem 14.7 in conjunction with the Cauchy-Schwarz inequality to obtain the following important property of integrals of vector-valued functions.

THEOREM 14.8. *If F and* $\|F\|$ *are integrable on* [a, b] *we have*

$$(14.1) \qquad \left\| \int_a^b F(t)\, dt \right\| \le \int_a^b \|F(t)\|\, dt\ .$$

*Proof.* Let $C = \int_a^b F(t)\, dt$. If $C = O$, then (14.1) holds trivially. Assume, then, that $C \ne O$ and apply Theorem 14.7 to get

$$(14.2) \qquad \|C\|^2 = C \cdot C = C \cdot \int_a^b F(t)\, dt = \int_a^b C \cdot F(t)\, dt\ .$$

Since the dot product $C \cdot F(t)$ is real valued, we have the inequality

$$(14.3) \qquad \int_a^b C \cdot F(t)\, dt \le \int_a^b |C \cdot F(t)|\, dt \le \int_a^b \|C\|\, \|F(t)\|\, dt \,,$$

where in the last step we used the Cauchy-Schwarz inequality, $|C \cdot F(t)| \le \|C\|\, \|F(t)\|$. Combining (14.2) and (14.3), we get

$$\|C\|^2 \le \|C\| \int_a^b \|F(t)\|\, dt \,.$$

Since $\|C\| > 0$, we can divide by $\|C\|$ to get (14.1).

## 14.4 Exercises

Compute the derivatives $F'(t)$ and $F''(t)$ for each of the vector-valued functions in Exercises 1 through 6.

1. $F(t) = (t, t^2, t^3, t^4)$.

2. $F(t) = (\cos t, \sin^2 t, \sin 2t, \tan t)$.

3. $F(t) = (\arcsin t, \arccos t)$.

4. $F(t) = 2e^t i + 3e^t j$.

5. $F(t) = \cosh t\, i + \sinh 2t\, j + e^{-3t} k$.

6. $F(t) = \log(1 + t^2)\, i + \arctan t\, j + \dfrac{1}{1 + t^2}\, k$.

7. Let $F$ be the vector-valued function given by

$$F(t) = \frac{2t}{1 + t^2} i + \frac{1 - t^2}{1 + t^2} j + k \,.$$

Prove that the angle between $F(t)$ and $F'(t)$ is constant, that is, independent of $t$.

Compute the vector-valued integrals in Exercises 8 through 11.

8. $\displaystyle\int_0^1 (t, \sqrt{t}, e^t)\, dt$.

9. $\displaystyle\int_0^{\pi/4} (\sin t, \cos t, \tan t)\, dt$.

10. $\displaystyle\int_0^1 \left( \frac{e^t}{1 + e^t} i + \frac{1}{1 + e^t} j \right) dt$.

11. $\displaystyle\int_0^1 (te^t i + t^2 e^t j + te^{-t} k)\, dt$.

12. Compute $A \cdot B$, where $A = 2i - 4j + k$ and $B = \int_0^1 (te^{2t} i + t \cosh 2t\, j + 2te^{-2t} k)\, dt$.

13. Given a nonzero vector $B$ and a vector-valued function $F$ such that $F(t) \cdot B = t$ for all $t$, and such that the angle between $F'(t)$ and $B$ is constant (independent of $t$). Prove that $F''(t)$ is orthogonal to $F'(t)$.

14. Given fixed nonzero vectors $A$ and $B$, let $F(t) = e^{2t} A + e^{-2t} B$. Prove that $F''(t)$ has the same direction as $F(t)$.

15. If $G = F \times F'$, compute $G'$ in terms of $F$ and derivatives of $F$.

16. If $G = F \cdot F' \times F''$, prove that $G' = F \cdot F' \times F'''$.

17. Prove that $\lim_{t \to p} F(t) = A$ if and only if $\lim_{t \to p} \|F(t) - A\| = 0$.

18. Prove that a vector-valued function $F$ is differentiable on an open interval $I$ if and only if for each $t$ in $I$ we have

$$F'(t) = \lim_{h \to 0} \frac{1}{h} [F(t + h) - F(t)] \,.$$

19. Prove the zero-derivative theorem for vector-valued functions. If $F'(t) = O$ for each $t$ in an open interval $I$, then there is a vector $C$ such that $F(t) = C$ for all $t$ in $I$.

20. Given fixed vectors $A$ and $B$ and a vector-valued function $F$ such that $F''(t) = tA + B$, determine $F(t)$ if $F(0) = D$ and $F'(0) = C$.

21. A differential equation of the form $Y'(x) + p(x)Y(x) = Q(x)$, where $p$ is a given real-valued function, $Q$ a given vector-valued function, and $Y$ an unknown vector-valued function, is called a first-order linear vector differential equation. Prove that if $p$ and $Q$ are continuous on an interval $I$, then for each $a$ in $I$ and each vector $B$ there is one and only one solution $Y$ which satisfies the initial condition $Y(a) = B$, and that this solution is given by the formula

$$Y(t) = Be^{-q(t)} + e^{-q(t)} \int_a^t Q(x)e^{q(x)} \, dx \, ,$$

where $q(x) = \int_a^x p(t) \, dt$.

22. A vector-valued function $F$ satisfies the equation $tF'(t) = F(t) + tA$ for each $t \geq 0$, where $A$ is a fixed vector. Compute $F''(1)$ and $F(3)$ in terms of $A$, if $F(1) = 2A$.

23. Find a vector-valued function $F$, continuous on the interval $(0, +\infty)$, such that

$$F(x) = xe^x A + \frac{1}{x} \int_1^x F(t) \, dt \, ,$$

for all $x > 0$, where $A$ is a fixed nonzero vector.

24. A vector-valued function $F$, which is never zero and has a continuous derivative $F'(t)$ for all $t$, is always parallel to its derivative. Prove that there is a constant vector $A$ and a positive real-valued function $u$ such that $F(t) = u(t)A$ for all $t$.

## 14.5 Applications to curves. Tangency

Let $X$ be a vector-valued function whose domain is an interval $I$. As $t$ runs through $I$, the corresponding function values $X(t)$ run through a set of points which we call the *graph* of the function $X$. If the function values are in 2-space or in 3-space, we can visualize the graph geometrically. For example, if $X(t) = P + tA$, where $P$ and $A$ are fixed vectors in $V_3$, with $A \neq O$, the graph of $X$ is a straight line through $P$ parallel to $A$. A more general function will trace out a more general graph, as suggested by the example in Figure 14.1. If $X$ is continuous on $I$, such a graph is called a *curve*; more specifically, the curve described by $X$. Sometimes we say that the curve is described *parametrically* by $X$. The interval $I$ is called a *parametric interval*; each $t$ in $I$ is called a *parameter*.

Properties of the function $X$ can be used to investigate geometric properties of its graph. In particular, the derivative $X'$ is related to the concept of tangency, as in the case of a real-valued function. We form the difference quotient

(14.4)
$$\frac{X(t + h) - X(t)}{h}$$

and investigate its behavior as $h \to 0$. This quotient is the product of the vector $X(t + h) - X(t)$ by the scalar $1/h$. The numerator, $X(t + h) - X(t)$, illustrated geometrically in Figure 14.2, is parallel to the vector in (14.4). If we express this difference quotient in terms of its components and let $h \to 0$, we find that

$$\lim_{h \to 0} \frac{X(t + h) - X(t)}{h} = X'(t) \, ,$$

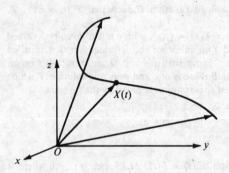

FIGURE 14.1 A curve traced out by a vector $X(t)$.

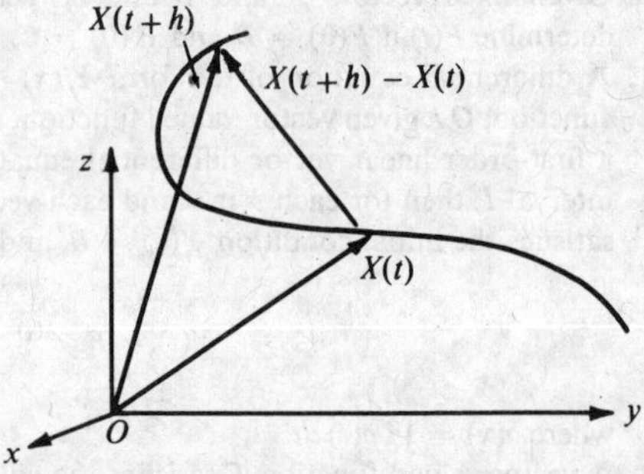

FIGURE 14.2 The vector $X(t + h) - X(t)$ is parallel to $[X(t + h) - X(t)]/h$.

assuming that the derivative $X'(t)$ exists. The geometric interpretation of this relation suggests the following definition.

DEFINITION. *Let C be a curve described by a continuous vector-valued function X. If the derivative $X'(t)$ exists and is nonzero, the straight line through $X(t)$ parallel to $X'(t)$ is called the tangent line to C at $X(t)$. The vector $X'(t)$ is called a tangent vector to C at $X(t)$.*

EXAMPLE 1. *Straight line.* For a line given by $X(t) = P + tA$, where $A \neq O$, we have $X'(t) = A$, so the tangent line at each point coincides with the graph of $X$, a property which we surely want.

EXAMPLE 2. *Circle.* If $X$ describes a circle of radius $a$ and center at a point $P$, then $\|X(t) - P\| = a$ for each $t$. The vector $X(t) - P$ is called a *radius vector;* it may be represented geometrically by an arrow from the center to the point $X(t)$. Since the radius vector has constant length, Theorem 14.2 tells us that it is perpendicular to its derivative and hence perpendicular to the tangent line. Thus, for a circle, our definition of tangency agrees with that given in elementary plane geometry.

EXAMPLE 3. *Invariance under a change of parameter.* Different functions can have the same graph. For example, suppose that $X$ is a continuous vector-valued function defined on an interval $I$ and suppose that $u$ is a real-valued function that is differentiable with $u'$ never zero on an interval $J$, and such that the range of $u$ is $I$. Then the function $Y$ defined on $J$ by the equation

$$Y(t) = X[u(t)]$$

is a continuous vector-valued function having the same graph as $X$. Two functions $X$ and $Y$ so related are called *equivalent.* They are said to provide different parametric representations of the same curve. The function $u$ is said to define a change of parameter.

The most important geometric concepts associated with a curve are those that remain invariant under a change of parameter. For example, it is easy to prove that the tangent line is invariant. If the derivative $X'[u(t)]$ exists, the chain rule shows that $Y'(t)$ also exists and is given by the formula

$$Y'(t) = X'[u(t)]u'(t).$$

The derivative $u'(t)$ is never zero. If $X'[u(t)]$ is nonzero, then $Y'(t)$ is also nonzero, so $Y'(t)$ is parallel to $X'[u(t)]$. Therefore both representations $X$ and $Y$ lead to the same tangent line at each point of the curve.

EXAMPLE 4. *Reflection properties of the conic sections.* Conic sections have reflection properties often used in the design of optical and acoustical equipment. Light rays emanating from one focus of an elliptical reflector will converge at the other focus, as shown in

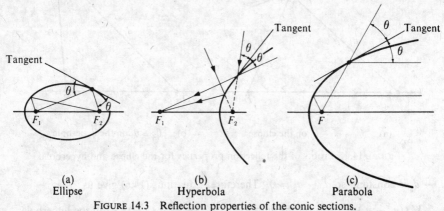

|          |           |          |
|:--------:|:---------:|:--------:|
| (a)      | (b)       | (c)      |
| Ellipse  | Hyperbola | Parabola |

FIGURE 14.3   Reflection properties of the conic sections.

Figure 14.3(a). Light rays directed toward one focus of a hyperbolic reflector will converge at the other focus, as suggested by Figure 14.3(b). In a parabolic reflector, light rays parallel to the axis converge at the focus, as shown in Figure 14.3(c). To establish these reflection properties, we need to prove that in each figure the angles labeled $\theta$ are equal. We shall do this for the ellipse and hyperbola and ask the reader to give a proof for the parabola.

Place one focus $F_1$ at the origin and let $u_1$ and $u_2$ be unit vectors having the same directions as $X$ and $X - F_2$, respectively, where $X$ is an arbitrary point on the conic. (See Figure 14.4.) If $d_1 = \|X\|$ and $d_2 = \|X - F_2\|$ are the focal distances between $X$ and the foci $F_1$ and $F_2$, respectively, we have

$$X = d_1 u_1 \quad \text{and} \quad X = d_2 u_2 + F_2.$$

Now we think of $X, u_1, u_2, d_1$, and $d_2$ as functions defined on some interval of real numbers. Their derivatives are related by the equations

(14.5) $$X' = d_1 u_1' + d_1' u_1, \qquad X' = d_2 u_2' + d_2' u_2.$$

Since $u_1$ and $u_2$ have constant length, each is perpendicular to its derivative, so Equations (14.5) give us $X' \cdot u_1 = d_1'$ and $X' \cdot u_2 = d_2'$. Adding and subtracting these relations, we find that

(14.6)        $X' \cdot (u_1 + u_2) = d_1' + d_2', \qquad X' \cdot (u_1 - u_2) = d_1' - d_2'.$

On the ellipse, $d_1 + d_2$ is constant, so $d_1' + d_2' = 0$. On each branch of the hyperbola,

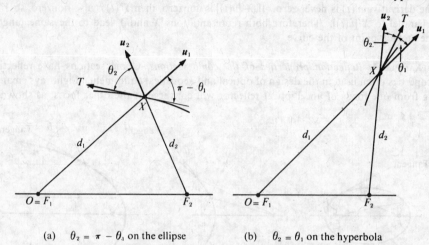

(a)    $\theta_2 = \pi - \theta_1$ on the ellipse        (b)    $\theta_2 = \theta_1$ on the hyperbola

FIGURE 14.4   Proofs of the reflection properties for the ellipse and hyperbola.

$d_1 - d_2$ is constant, so $d_1' - d_2' = 0$. Therefore, Equations (14.6) give us

$X' \cdot (u_1 + u_2) = 0$    on the ellipse,    $X' \cdot (u_1 - u_2) = 0$    on the hyperbola.

Let $T = X'/\|X'\|$ be a unit vector having the same direction as $X'$. Then $T$ is tangent to the conic, and we have

$T \cdot u_2 = -T \cdot u_1$    on the ellipse,    $T \cdot u_2 = T \cdot u_1$    on the hyperbola.

If $\theta_1$ and $\theta_2$ denote, respectively, the angles that $T$ makes with $u_1$ and $u_2$, where $0 \le \theta_1 \le \pi$ and $0 \le \theta_2 \le \pi$, these last two equations show that

$\cos \theta_2 = -\cos \theta_1$    on the ellipse,    $\cos \theta_2 = \cos \theta_1$    on the hyperbola.

Hence we have $\theta_2 = \pi - \theta_1$ on the ellipse, and $\theta_2 = \theta_1$ on the hyperbola. These relations between the angles $\theta_1$ and $\theta_2$ give the reflection properties of the ellipse and hyperbola.

## 14.6   Applications to curvilinear motion. Velocity, speed, and acceleration

Suppose a particle moves in 2-space or in 3-space in such a way that its position at time $t$ relative to some coordinate system is given by a vector $X(t)$. As $t$ varies through a time interval, the path traced out by the particle is simply the graph of $X$. Thus, the vector-valued function $X$ serves as a natural mathematical model to describe the motion. We call

$X$ the *position function* of the motion. Physical concepts such as velocity, speed, and acceleration can be defined in terms of derivatives of the position function.

In the following discussion we assume that the position function may be differentiated as often as is necessary without saying so each time.

DEFINITION. *Consider a motion described by a vector-valued function $X$. The derivative $X'(t)$ is called the velocity vector at time $t$. The length of the velocity vector, $\|X'(t)\|$, is called the speed. The second derivative of the position vector, $X''(t)$, is called the acceleration vector.*

*Notation.* Sometimes the position function $X$ is denoted by $r$, the velocity vector by $v$, the speed by $v$, and the acceleration by $a$. Thus, $v = r'$, $v = \|v\|$, and $a = v' = r''$.

If the velocity vector $X'(t)$ is visualized as a geometric vector attached to the curve at $X(t)$, we see that it lies along the tangent line. The use of the word "speed" for the length of the velocity vector will be justified in Section 14.12 where it is shown that the speed is the rate of change of arc length along the curve. This is what the speedometer of an automobile tries to measure. Thus, the length of the velocity vector tells us how fast the particle is moving at every instant, and its direction tells us which way it is going. The velocity will change if we alter either the speed or the direction of the motion (or both). The acceleration vector is a measure of this change. Acceleration causes the effect one feels when an automobile changes its speed or its direction. Unlike the velocity vector, the acceleration vector does not necessarily lie along the tangent line.

EXAMPLE 1. *Linear motion.* Consider a motion whose position vector is given by

$$r(t) = P + f(t)A,$$

where $P$ and $A$ are fixed vectors, $A \neq O$. This motion takes place along a line through $P$ parallel to $A$. The velocity, speed, and acceleration are given by

$$v(t) = f'(t)A, \qquad v(t) = \|v(t)\| = |f'(t)| \, \|A\|, \qquad a(t) = f''(t)A.$$

If $f'(t)$ and $f''(t)$ are nonzero, the acceleration vector is parallel to the velocity.

EXAMPLE 2. *Circular motion.* If a point $(x, y)$ in $V_2$ is represented by its polar coordinates $r$ and $\theta$, we have

$$x = r \cos \theta, \qquad y = r \sin \theta.$$

If $r$ is fixed, say $r = a$, and if $\theta$ is allowed to vary over any interval of length at least $2\pi$, the corresponding point $(x, y)$ traces out a circle of radius $a$ and center at the origin. If we make $\theta$ a function of time $t$, say $\theta = f(t)$, we have a motion given by the position function

$$r(t) = a \cos f(t)i + a \sin f(t)j.$$

The corresponding velocity vector is given by

$$v(t) = r'(t) = -af'(t) \sin f(t)i + af'(t) \cos f(t)j,$$

from which we find that the speed at time $t$ is

$$v(t) = \|\boldsymbol{v}(t)\| = a\,|f'(t)|\,.$$

The factor $|f'(t)| = |d\theta/dt|$ is called the *angular speed* of the particle.

An important special case occurs when $\theta = \omega t$, where $\omega$ (omega) is a positive constant. In this case, the particle starts at the point $(a, 0)$ at time $t = 0$ and moves counter-clockwise around the circle with constant angular speed $\omega$. The formulas for the position, velocity, and speed become

$$\boldsymbol{r}(t) = a\cos \omega t\,\boldsymbol{i} + a\sin \omega t\,\boldsymbol{j}\,, \qquad \boldsymbol{v}(t) = -\omega a\sin \omega t\,\boldsymbol{i} + \omega a\cos \omega t\,\boldsymbol{j}\,, \qquad v(t) = a\omega\,.$$

The acceleration vector is given by

$$\boldsymbol{a}(t) = -\omega^2 a\cos \omega t\,\boldsymbol{i} - \omega^2 a\sin \omega t\,\boldsymbol{j} = -\omega^2 \boldsymbol{r}(t)\,,$$

which shows that the acceleration is always directed opposite to the position vector. When it is visualized as a geometric vector drawn at the location of the particle, the acceleration vector is directed toward the center of the circle. Because of this, the acceleration is called *centripetal* or "center-seeking," a term originally proposed by Newton.

> *Note:* If a moving particle has mass $m$, Newton's second law of motion states that the force acting on it (due to its acceleration) is the vector $m\boldsymbol{a}(t)$, mass times acceleration. If the particle moves on a circle with constant angular speed, this is called a centripetal force because it is directed toward the center. This force is exerted by the mechanism that confines the particle to a circular orbit. The mechanism is a *string* in the case of a stone whirling in a slingshot, or *gravitational attraction* in the case of a satellite around the earth. The equal and opposite reaction (due to Newton's third law), that is, the force $-m\boldsymbol{a}(t)$, is said to be *centrifugal* or "center-fleeing."

EXAMPLE 3. *Motion on an ellipse.* Figure 14.5 shows an ellipse with Cartesian equation $x^2/a^2 + y^2/b^2 = 1$, and two concentric circles with radii $a$ and $b$. The angle $\theta$ shown in the figure is called the *eccentric angle*. It is related to the coordinates $(x, y)$ of a point on the ellipse by the equations

$$x = a\cos \theta\,, \qquad y = b\sin \theta\,.$$

As $\theta$ varies over an interval of length $2\pi$, the corresponding point $(x, y)$ traces out the ellipse. If we make $\theta$ a function of time $t$, say $\theta = f(t)$, we have a motion given by the position function

$$\boldsymbol{r}(t) = a\cos f(t)\boldsymbol{i} + b\sin f(t)\boldsymbol{j}\,.$$

If $\theta = \omega t$, where $\omega$ is a positive constant, the velocity, speed, and acceleration are given by

$$\boldsymbol{v}(t) = \omega(-a\sin \omega t\,\boldsymbol{i} + b\cos \omega t\,\boldsymbol{j})\,, \qquad v(t) = \omega(a^2\sin^2 \omega t + b^2\cos^2 \omega t)^{1/2}\,,$$

$$\boldsymbol{a}(t) = -\omega^2(a\cos \omega t\,\boldsymbol{i} + b\sin \omega t\,\boldsymbol{j}) = -\omega^2 \boldsymbol{r}(t)\,.$$

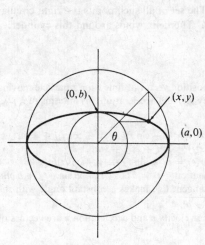

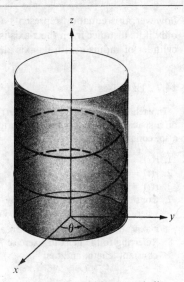

FIGURE 14.5   Motion on an ellipse.

FIGURE 14.6   Motion on a helix.

Thus, when a particle moves on an ellipse in such a way that its eccentric angle changes at a constant rate, the acceleration is centripetal.

EXAMPLE 4. *Motion on a helix.* If a point $(x, y, z)$ revolves around the $z$-axis at a constant distance $a$ from it and simultaneously moves parallel to the $z$-axis in such a way that its $z$-component is proportional to the angle of revolution, the resulting path is called a *circular helix*. An example is shown in Figure 14.6. If $\theta$ denotes the angle of revolution, we have

$$(14.7) \qquad x = a \cos \theta, \qquad y = a \sin \theta, \qquad z = b\theta,$$

where $a > 0$, and $b \neq 0$. When $\theta$ varies from 0 to $2\pi$, the $x$- and $y$-coordinates return to their original values while $z$ changes from 0 to $2\pi b$. The number $2\pi b$ is often referred to as the *pitch* of the helix.

Now suppose that $\theta = \omega t$, where $\omega$ is constant. The motion on the helix is then described by the position vector

$$r(t) = a \cos \omega t \, i + a \sin \omega t \, j + b\omega t \, k \,.$$

The corresponding velocity and acceleration vectors are given by

$$v(t) = -\omega a \sin \omega t \, i + \omega a \cos \omega t \, j + b\omega k \,, \qquad a(t) = -\omega^2 (a \cos \omega t \, i + a \sin \omega t \, j) \,.$$

Thus, when the acceleration vector is located on the helix, it is parallel to the $xy$-plane and directed toward the $z$-axis.

If we eliminate $\theta$ from the first two equations in (14.7), we obtain the Cartesian equation $x^2 + y^2 = a^2$ which we recognize as the equation of a circle in the $xy$-plane. In 3-space, however, this equation represents a surface. A point $(x, y, z)$ satisfies the equation if and only if its distance from the $z$-axis is equal to $a$. The set of all such points is a right circular cylinder of radius $a$ with its axis along the $z$-axis. The helix winds around this cylinder.

## 14.7 Exercises

In each of Exercises 1 through 6, $r(t)$ denotes the position vector at time $t$ for a particle moving on a space curve. In each case, determine the velocity $v(t)$ and acceleration $a(t)$ in terms of $i, j, k$; also, compute the speed $v(t)$.

1. $r(t) = (3t - t^3)i + 3t^2 j + (3t + t^3)k$.
2. $r(t) = \cos t\, i + \sin t\, j + e^t k$.
3. $r(t) = 3t \cos t\, i + 3t \sin t\, j + 4t k$.
4. $r(t) = (t - \sin t)i + (1 - \cos t)j + 4 \sin \dfrac{t}{2} k$.
5. $r(t) = 3t^2 i + 2t^3 j + 3t k$.
6. $r(t) = t i + \sin t\, j + (1 - \cos t)k$.

7. Consider the helix described by the vector equation $r(t) = a \cos \omega t\, i + a \sin \omega t\, j + b\omega t k$, where $\omega$ is a positive constant. Prove that the tangent line makes a constant angle with the $z$-axis and that the cosine of this angle is $b/\sqrt{a^2 + b^2}$.

8. Referring to the helix in Exercise 7, prove that the velocity $v$ and acceleration $a$ are vectors of constant length, and that

$$\frac{\|v \times a\|}{\|v\|^3} = \frac{a}{a^2 + b^2}.$$

9. Referring to Exercise 7, let $u(t)$ denote the unit vector $u(t) = \sin \omega t\, i - \cos \omega t\, j$. Prove that there are two constants $A$ and $B$ such that $v \times a = Au(t) + Bk$, and express $A$ and $B$ in terms of $a$, $b$, and $\omega$.

10. Prove that for any motion the dot product of the velocity and acceleration is half the derivative of the square of the speed:

$$v(t) \cdot a(t) = \frac{1}{2} \frac{d}{dt} v^2(t).$$

11. Let $c$ be a fixed unit vector. A particle moves in space in such a way that its position vector $r(t)$ satisfies the equation $r(t) \cdot c = e^{2t}$ for all $t$, and its velocity vector $v(t)$ makes a constant angle $\theta$ with $c$, where $0 < \theta < \frac{1}{2}\pi$.
   (a) Prove that the speed at time $t$ is $2e^{2t}/\cos \theta$.
   (b) Compute the dot product $a(t) \cdot v(t)$ in terms of $t$ and $\theta$.

12. The identity $\cosh^2 \theta - \sinh^2 \theta = 1$ for hyperbolic functions suggests that the hyperbola $x^2/a^2 - y^2/b^2 = 1$ may be represented by the parametric equations $x = a \cosh \theta$, $y = b \sinh \theta$, or what amounts to the same thing, by the vector equation $r = a \cosh \theta\, i + b \sinh \theta\, j$. When $a = b = 1$, the parameter $\theta$ may be given a geometric interpretation analogous to that which holds between $\theta$, $\sin \theta$, and $\cos \theta$ in the unit circle shown in Figure 14.7(a). Figure 14.7(b) shows one branch of the hyperbola $x^2 - y^2 = 1$. If the point $P$ has coordinates $x = \cosh \theta$ and $y = \sinh \theta$, prove that $\theta$ equals twice the area of the sector $OAP$ shaded in the figure.

   [*Hint:* Let $A(\theta)$ denote the area of sector $OAP$. Show that

$$A(\theta) = \tfrac{1}{2} \cosh \theta \sinh \theta - \int_1^{\cosh \theta} \sqrt{x^2 - 1}\, dx.$$

   Differentiate to get $A'(\theta) = \tfrac{1}{2}$.]

13. A particle moves along a hyperbola according to the equation $r(t) = a \cosh \omega t\, i + b \sinh \omega t\, j$, where $\omega$ is a constant. Prove that the acceleration is centrifugal.

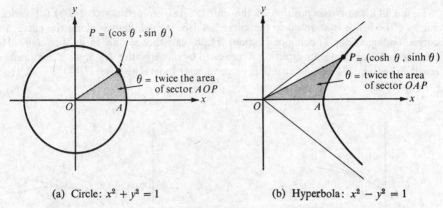

(a) Circle: $x^2 + y^2 = 1$          (b) Hyperbola: $x^2 - y^2 = 1$

FIGURE 14.7   Analogy between parameter for a circle and that for a hyperbola.

14. Prove that the tangent line at a point $X$ of a parabola bisects the angle between the line joining $X$ to the focus and the line through $X$ parallel to the axis. This gives the reflection property of the parabola. (See Figure 14.3.)

15. A particle of mass 1 moves in a plane according to the equation $r(t) = x(t)i + y(t)j$. It is attracted toward the origin by a force whose magnitude is four times its distance from the origin. At time $t = 0$, the initial position is $r(0) = 4i$ and the initial velocity is $v(0) = 6j$.
    (a) Determine the components $x(t)$ and $y(t)$ explicitly in terms of $t$.
    (b) The path of the particle is a conic section. Find a Cartesian equation for this conic, sketch the conic, and indicate the direction of motion along the curve.

16. A particle moves along the parabola $x^2 + c(y - x) = 0$ in such a way that the horizontal and vertical components of the acceleration vector are equal. If it takes $T$ units of time to go from the point $(c, 0)$ to the point $(0, 0)$, how much time will it require to go from $(c, 0)$ to the halfway point $(c/2, c/4)$?

17. Suppose a curve $C$ is described by two equivalent functions $X$ and $Y$, where $Y(t) = X[u(t)]$. Prove that at each point of $C$ the velocity vectors associated with $X$ and $Y$ are parallel, but that the corresponding acceleration vectors need not be parallel.

## 14.8 The unit tangent, the principal normal, and the osculating plane of a curve

For linear motion the acceleration vector is parallel to the velocity vector. For circular motion with constant angular speed, the acceleration vector is perpendicular to the velocity. In this section we show that for a general motion the acceleration vector is a sum of two perpendicular vectors, one parallel to the velocity and one perpendicular to the velocity. If the motion is not linear, these two perpendicular vectors determine a plane through each point of the curve called the osculating plane.

To study these concepts, we introduce the *unit tangent* vector $T$. This is another vector-valued function associated with the curve, and it is defined by the equation

$$T(t) = \frac{X'(t)}{\|X'(t)\|}$$

whenever the speed $\|X'(t)\| \neq 0$. Note that $\|T(t)\| = 1$ for all $t$.

Figure 14.8 shows the position of the unit tangent geometric vector $T(t)$ for various values of $t$ when it is attached to the curve. As the particle moves along the curve, the corresponding vector $T$, being of constant length, can change only in its direction. The tendency of $T$ to change its direction is measured by its derivative $T'$. Since $T$ has constant length, Theorem 14.2 tells us that $T$ is perpendicular to its derivative $T'$.

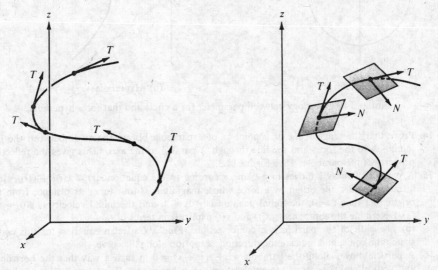

FIGURE 14.8 The unit tangent vector $T$.      FIGURE 14.9 The osculating plane.

If the motion is linear, then $T' = O$. If $T' \neq O$, the unit vector having the same direction as $T'$ is called the *principal normal* to the curve and it is denoted by $N$. Thus, $N$ is a new vector-valued function associated with the curve and it is defined by the equation

$$N(t) = \frac{T'(t)}{\|T'(t)\|}, \qquad \text{whenever} \quad \|T'(t)\| \neq 0.$$

When the two unit geometric vectors $T(t)$ and $N(t)$ are attached to the curve at the point $X(t)$, they determine a plane known as the *osculating plane* of the curve. If we choose three values of $t$, say $t_1$, $t_2$, and $t_3$, and consider the plane determined by the three points $X(t_1)$, $X(t_2)$, $X(t_3)$, it can be shown that the position of the plane approaches the position of the osculating plane at $X(t_1)$ as $t_2$ and $t_3$ approach $t_1$. Because of this, the osculating plane is often called the plane that best fits the curve at each of its points. If the curve itself is a plane curve (not a straight line), the osculating plane coincides with the plane of the curve. In general, however, the osculating plane changes with $t$. Examples are illustrated in Figure 14.9.

The next theorem shows that the acceleration vector is a sum of two vectors, one parallel to $T$ and one parallel to $T'$.

THEOREM 14.9.    *For a motion described by a vector-valued function* **r**, *let* $v(t)$ *denote the speed at time* $t$, $v(t) = \|r'(t)\|$. *Then the acceleration vector* **a** *is a linear combination of* $T$ *and* $T'$ *given by the formula*

(14.8)                         $$a(t) = v'(t)T(t) + v(t)T'(t).$$

*If* $T'(t) \neq O$, *we also have*

(14.9)                        $$a(t) = v'(t)T(t) + v(t)\,\|T'(t)\|\,N(t).$$

*Proof.*    The formula defining the unit tangent gives us

$$v(t) = v(t)T(t).$$

Differentiating this product, we find that

$$a(t) = v'(t)T(t) + v(t)T'(t),$$

which proves (14.8). To prove (14.9), we use the definition of $N$ to write $T'(t) = \|T'(t)\| N(t)$.

This theorem shows that the acceleration vector always lies in the osculating plane. An example is shown in Figure 14.10. The coefficients of $T(t)$ and $N(t)$ in (14.9) are called, respectively, the *tangential* and *normal components* of the acceleration. A change in speed contributes to the tangential component, whereas a change in direction contributes to the normal component.

For a plane curve, the length of $T'(t)$ has an interesting geometric interpretation. Since $T$ is a unit vector, we may write

$$T(t) = \cos \alpha(t)i + \sin \alpha(t)j,$$

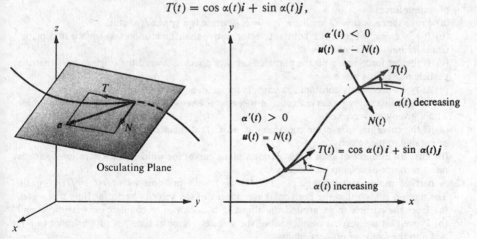

FIGURE 14.10    The acceleration vector lies
in the osculating plane

FIGURE 14.11    The angle of inclination of the
tangent vector of a plane curve.

where $\alpha(t)$ denotes the angle between the tangent vector and the positive $x$-axis, as shown in Figure 14.11. Differentiating, we find that

$$T'(t) = -\sin \alpha(t)\,\alpha'(t)\boldsymbol{i} + \cos \alpha(t)\,\alpha'(t)\boldsymbol{j} = \alpha'(t)\boldsymbol{u}(t),$$

where $\boldsymbol{u}(t)$ is a unit vector. Therefore $\|T'(t)\| = |\alpha'(t)|$ and this shows that $\|T'(t)\|$ is a measure of the rate of change of the angle of inclination of the tangent vector. When $\alpha'(t) > 0$, the angle is increasing, and hence $\boldsymbol{u}(t) = N(t)$. When $\alpha'(t) < 0$, the angle is decreasing and, in this case, $\boldsymbol{u}(t) = -N(t)$. The two cases are illustrated in Figure 14.11. Note that the angle of inclination of $\boldsymbol{u}(t)$ is $\alpha(t) + \frac{1}{2}\pi$ since we have

$$\boldsymbol{u}(t) = -\sin \alpha(t)\boldsymbol{i} + \cos \alpha(t)\boldsymbol{j} = \cos\left(\alpha(t) + \frac{\pi}{2}\right)\boldsymbol{i} + \sin\left(\alpha(t) + \frac{\pi}{2}\right)\boldsymbol{j}.$$

## 14.9 Exercises

Exercises 1 through 6 below refer to the motions described in Exercises 1 through 6, respectively, of Section 14.7. For the value of $t$ specified, (a) express the unit tangent $T$ and the principal normal $N$ in terms of $\boldsymbol{i}, \boldsymbol{j}, \boldsymbol{k}$; (b) express the acceleration $\boldsymbol{a}$ as a linear combination of $T$ and $N$.

1. $t = 2$.      3. $t = 0$.      5. $t = 1$.
2. $t = \pi$.      4. $t = \pi$.      6. $t = \frac{1}{4}\pi$.

7. Prove that if the acceleration vector is always zero, the motion is linear.
8. Prove that the normal component of the acceleration vector is $\|\boldsymbol{v} \times \boldsymbol{a}\|/\|\boldsymbol{v}\|$.
9. For each of the following statements about a curve traced out by a particle moving in 3-space, either give a proof or exhibit a counter example.
   (a) If the velocity is constant, the curve lies in a plane.
   (b) If the speed is constant, the curve lies in a plane.
   (c) If the acceleration is constant, the curve lies in a plane.
   (d) If the velocity is perpendicular to the acceleration, the curve lies in a plane.
10. A particle of unit mass with position vector $r(t)$ at time $t$ is moving in space under the actions of certain forces.
    (a) Prove that $\boldsymbol{r} \times \boldsymbol{a} = O$ implies $\boldsymbol{r} \times \boldsymbol{v} = \boldsymbol{c}$, where $\boldsymbol{c}$ is a constant vector.
    (b) If $\boldsymbol{r} \times \boldsymbol{v} = \boldsymbol{c}$, where $\boldsymbol{c}$ is a constant vector, prove that the motion takes place in a plane. Consider both $\boldsymbol{c} \neq O$ and $\boldsymbol{c} = O$.
    (c) If the net force acting on the particle is always directed toward the origin, prove that the particle moves in a plane.
    (d) Is $\boldsymbol{r} \times \boldsymbol{v}$ necessarily constant if a particle moves in a plane?
11. A particle moves along a curve in such a way that the velocity vector makes a constant angle with a given unit vector $\boldsymbol{c}$.
    (a) If the curve lies in a plane containing $\boldsymbol{c}$, prove that the acceleration vector is either zero or parallel to the velocity.
    (b) Give an example of such a curve (not a plane curve) for which the acceleration vector is never zero nor parallel to the velocity.
12. A particle moves along the ellipse $3x^2 + y^2 = 1$ with position vector $r(t) = f(t)\boldsymbol{i} + g(t)\boldsymbol{j}$. The motion is such that the horizontal component of the velocity vector at time $t$ is $-g(t)$.
    (a) Does the particle move around the ellipse in a clockwise or counterclockwise direction?
    (b) Prove that the vertical component of the velocity vector at time $t$ is proportional to $f(t)$ and find the factor of proportionality.
    (c) How much time is required for the particle to go once around the ellipse?
13. A plane curve $C$ in the first quadrant has a negative slope at each of its points and passes

through the point $(\frac{3}{2}, 1)$. The position vector $r$ from the origin to any point $(x, y)$ on $C$ makes an angle $\theta$ with $i$; and the velocity vector makes an angle $\phi$ with $i$, where $0 < \theta < \frac{1}{2}\pi$, and $0 < \phi < \frac{1}{2}\pi$. If $3 \tan \phi = 4 \cot \theta$ at each point of $C$, find a Cartesian equation for $C$ and sketch the curve.

14. A line perpendicular to the tangent line of a plane curve is called a normal line. If the normal line and a vertical line are drawn at any point of a certain plane curve $C$, they cut off a segment of length 2 on the $x$-axis. Find a Cartesian equation for this curve if it passes through the point $(1, 2)$. Two solutions are possible.

15. Given two fixed nonzero vectors $A$ and $B$ making an angle $\theta$ with each other, where $0 < \theta < \pi$. A motion with position vector $r(t)$ at time $t$ satisfies the differential equation

$$r'(t) = A \times r(t)$$

and the initial condition $r(0) = B$.
(a) Prove that the acceleration $a(t)$ is orthogonal to $A$.
(b) Prove that the speed is constant and compute this speed in terms of $A$, $B$, and $\theta$.
(c) Make a sketch of the curve, showing its relation to the vectors $A$ and $B$.

16. This exercise describes how the unit tangent and the principal normal are affected by a change of parameter. Suppose a curve $C$ is described by two equivalent functions $X$ and $Y$, where $Y(t) = X[u(t)]$. Denote the unit tangent for $X$ by $T_X$ and that for $Y$ by $T_Y$.
(a) Prove that at each point of $C$ we have $T_Y(t) = T_X[u(t)]$ if $u$ is strictly increasing, but that $T_Y(t) = -T_X[u(t)]$ if $u$ is strictly decreasing. In the first case, $u$ is said to *preserve orientation*; in the second case, $u$ is said to *reverse orientation*.
(b) Prove that the corresponding principal normal vectors $N_X$ and $N_Y$ satisfy $N_Y(t) = N_X[u(t)]$ at each point of $C$. Deduce that the osculating plane is invariant under a change of parameter.

## 14.10 The definition of arc length

Various parts of calculus and analytic geometry refer to the arc length of a curve. Before we can study the properties of the length of a curve we must agree on a *definition* of arc length. The purpose of this section is to formulate such a definition. This will lead, in a natural way, to the construction of a function (called the arc-length function) which measures the length of the path traced out by a moving particle at every instant of its motion. Some of the basic properties of this function are discussed in Section 14.12. In particular, we shall prove that for most curves that arise in practice this function may be expressed as the integral of the speed.

To arrive at a definition of what we mean by the length of a curve, we proceed as though we had to measure this length with a straight yardstick. First, we mark off a number of points on the curve which we use as vertices of an inscribed polygon. (An example is shown in Figure 14.12.) Then, we measure the total length of this polygon with our yardstick and consider this as an approximation to the length of the curve. We soon observe that some polygons "fit" the curve better than others. In particular, if we start with a polygon $P_1$, and construct a new inscribed polygon $P_2$ by adding more vertices to those of $P_1$, it is clear that the length of $P_2$ will be larger than that of $P_1$, as suggested in Figure 14.13. In the same way we can form more and more polygons with successively larger and larger lengths.

On the other hand, our intuition tells us that the length of any inscribed polygon should not exceed that of the curve (since a straight line is the shortest path between two points).

In other words, when we arrive at a definition for the length of a curve, it should be a number which is an *upper bound* to the lengths of all inscribed polygons. Therefore, it certainly seems reasonable to define the length of the curve to be the *least upper bound* of the lengths of all possible inscribed polygons.

For most curves that arise in practice, this definition gives us a useful and reasonable way to assign a length to a curve. Surprisingly enough, however, there are certain pathological cases where this definition is not applicable. There are curves for which there is *no* upper bound to the lengths of the inscribed polygons. (An example is given in Exercise

FIGURE 14.12   A curve with an inscribed polygon.

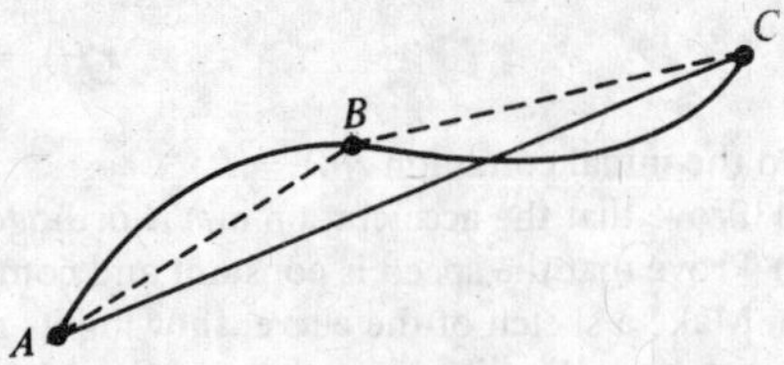

FIGURE 14.13   The polygon *ABC* has a
length greater than the polygon *AC*.

22 in Section 14.13.) Therefore it becomes necessary to classify all curves into two categories: those which have a length, and those which do not. The former are called *rectifiable curves*, the latter, *nonrectifiable*.

To formulate these ideas in analytic terms, we begin with a curve in 3-space or in 2-space described by a vector-valued function $r$, and we consider the portion of the curve traced out by $r(t)$ as $t$ varies over an interval $[a, b]$. At the outset, we only assume that $r$ is continuous on the parametric interval. Later we shall add further restrictions.

Consider now any partition $P$ of the interval $[a, b]$, say

$$P = \{t_0, t_1, \ldots, t_n\}, \qquad \text{where} \quad a = t_0 < t_1 < \cdots < t_n = b.$$

Denote by $\pi(P)$ the polygon whose vertices are the points $r(t_0), r(t_1), \ldots, r(t_n)$, respectively. (An example with $n = 6$ is shown in Figure 14.14.) The sides of this polygon have lengths

$$\|r(t_1) - r(t_0)\|, \ \|r(t_2) - r(t_1)\|, \ldots, \ \|r(t_n) - r(t_{n-1})\|.$$

Therefore, the length of the polygon $\pi(P)$, which we denote by $|\pi(P)|$, is the sum

$$|\pi(P)| = \sum_{k=1}^{n} \|r(t_k) - r(t_{k-1})\|.$$

DEFINITION.   *If there exists a positive number M such that*

(14.10)                                 $$|\pi(P)| \le M$$

*for all partitions P of* [a, b], *then the curve is said to be rectifiable and its arc length, denoted by* $\Lambda(a, b)$, *is defined to be the least upper bound of the set of all numbers* $|\pi(P)|$. *If there is no such M, the curve is called nonrectifiable.*

Note that if an $M$ exists satisfying (14.10), then, for every partition $P$, we have

$$(14.11) \qquad |\pi(P)| \leq \Lambda(a, b) \leq M ,$$

since the least upper bound cannot exceed any upper bound.

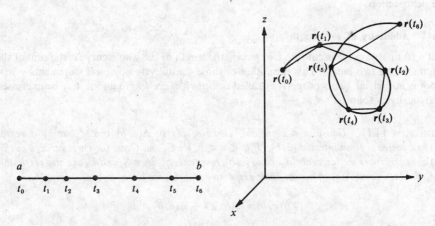

FIGURE 14.14 A partition of $[a, b]$ into six subintervals and the corresponding inscribed polygon.

It is easy to prove that a curve is rectifiable whenever its velocity vector $v$ is continuous on the parametric interval $[a, b]$. In fact, the following theorem tells us that in this case we may use the integral of the speed as an upper bound for all numbers $|\pi(P)|$.

THEOREM 14.10. *Denote by* $v(t)$ *the velocity vector of the curve with position vector* $r(t)$ *and let* $v(t) = \|v(t)\|$ *denote the speed. If $v$ is continuous on* $[a, b]$, *the curve is rectifiable and its length* $\Lambda(a, b)$ *satisfies the inequality*

$$(14.12) \qquad \Lambda(a, b) \leq \int_a^b v(t) \, dt .$$

*Proof.* For each partition $P$ of $[a, b]$, we have

$$|\pi(P)| = \sum_{k=1}^n \|r(t_k) - r(t_{k-1})\| = \sum_{k=1}^n \left\| \int_{t_{k-1}}^{t_k} r'(t) \, dt \right\|$$

$$= \sum_{k=1}^n \left\| \int_{t_{k-1}}^{t_k} v(t) \, dt \right\| \leq \sum_{k=1}^n \int_{t_{k-1}}^{t_k} \|v(t)\| \, dt = \int_a^b v(t) \, dt ,$$

the inequality being a consequence of Theorem 14.8. This shows that we have

$$|\pi(P)| \le \int_a^b v(t)\, dt$$

for all partitions $P$, and hence the number $\int_a^b v(t)\, dt$ is an upper bound for the set of all numbers $|\pi(P)|$. This proves that the curve is rectifiable and, at the same time, it tells us that the length $\Lambda(a, b)$ cannot exceed the integral of the speed.

In a later section we shall prove that the inequality in (14.12) is, in fact, an *equality*. The proof of this fact will make use of the *additivity* of arc length, a property described in the next section.

## 14.11  Additivity of arc length

If a rectifiable curve is cut into two pieces, the length of the whole curve is the sum of the lengths of the two parts. This is another of those "intuitively obvious" statements whose proof is not trivial. This property is called *additivity of arc length* and it may be expressed analytically as follows.

THEOREM 14.11.  *Consider a rectifiable curve of length $\Lambda(a, b)$ traced out by a vector $r(t)$ as $t$ varies over an interval $[a, b]$. If $a < c < b$, let $C_1$ and $C_2$ be the curves traced out by $r(t)$ as $t$ varies over the intervals $[a, c]$ and $[c, b]$, respectively. Then $C_1$ and $C_2$ are also rectifiable and, if $\Lambda(a, c)$ and $\Lambda(c, b)$ denote their respective lengths, we have*

$$\Lambda(a, b) = \Lambda(a, c) + \Lambda(c, b)\,.$$

*Proof.*  Let $P_1$ and $P_2$ be arbitrary partitions of $[a, c]$ and $[c, b]$, respectively. The points in $P_1$ taken together with those in $P_2$ give us a new partition $P$ of $[a, b]$ for which we have

(14.13)                    $|\pi(P_1)| + |\pi(P_2)| = |\pi(P)| \le \Lambda(a, b)\,.$

This shows that $|\pi(P_1)|$ and $|\pi(P_2)|$ are bounded by $\Lambda(a, b)$, and hence $C_1$ and $C_2$ are rectifiable. From (14.13), we also have

$$|\pi(P_1)| \le \Lambda(a, b) - |\pi(P_2)|\,.$$

Now, keep $P_2$ fixed and let $P_1$ vary over all possible partitions of $[a, c]$. Since the number $\Lambda(a, b) - |\pi(P_2)|$ is an upper bound for all numbers $|\pi(P_1)|$, it cannot be less than their least upper bound, which is $\Lambda(a, c)$. Hence, we have $\Lambda(a, c) \le \Lambda(a, b) - |\pi(P_2)|$ or, what is the same thing,

$$|\pi(P_2)| \le \Lambda(a, b) - \Lambda(a, c)\,.$$

This shows that $\Lambda(a, b) - \Lambda(a, c)$ is an upper bound for all the sums $|\pi(P_2)|$, and since it cannot be less than their least upper bound, $\Lambda(c, b)$, we have $\Lambda(c, b) \le \Lambda(a, b) - \Lambda(a, c)$. In other words, we have

(14.14)                    $\Lambda(a, c) + \Lambda(c, b) \le \Lambda(a, b)\,.$

Next we prove the reverse inequality. We begin with any partition $P$ of $[a, b]$. If we adjoin the point $c$ to $P$, we obtain a partition $P_1$ of $[a, c]$ and a partition $P_2$ of $[c, b]$ such that

$$|\pi(P)| \leq |\pi(P_1)| + |\pi(P_2)| \leq \Lambda(a, c) + \Lambda(c, b).$$

This shows that $\Lambda(a, c) + \Lambda(c, b)$ is an upper bound for all numbers $|\pi(P)|$. Since this cannot be less than the least upper bound, we must have

$$\Lambda(a, b) \leq \Lambda(a, c) + \Lambda(c, b).$$

This inequality, along with (14.14), implies the additive property.

## 14.12 The arc-length function

Suppose a curve is the path traced out by a position vector $r(t)$. A natural question to ask is this: How far has the particle moved along the curve at time $t$? To discuss this question, we introduce the *arc-length function s*, defined as follows:

$$s(t) = \Lambda(a, t) \quad \text{if} \quad t > a, \quad s(a) = 0.$$

The statement $s(a) = 0$ simply means we are assuming the motion begins when $t = a$.

The theorem on additivity enables us to derive some important properties of $s$. For example, we have the following.

THEOREM 14.12. *For any rectifiable curve, the arc-length function $s$ is monotonically increasing on $[a, b]$. That is, we have*

$$(14.15) \qquad s(t_1) \leq s(t_2) \quad \text{if} \quad a \leq t_1 < t_2 \leq b.$$

*Proof.* If $a \leq t_1 < t_2 \leq b$, we have

$$s(t_2) - s(t_1) = \Lambda(a, t_2) - \Lambda(a, t_1) = \Lambda(t_1, t_2),$$

where the last equality comes from additivity. Since $\Lambda(t_1, t_2) \geq 0$, this proves (14.15).

Next we shall prove that the function $s$ has a derivative at each interior point of the parametric interval and that this derivative is equal to the speed of the particle.

THEOREM 14.13. *Let $s$ denote the arc-length function associated with a curve and let $v(t)$ denote the speed at time $t$. If $v$ is continuous on $[a, b]$, then the derivative $s'(t)$ exists for each $t$ in $(a, b)$ and is given by the formula*

$$(14.16) \qquad s'(t) = v(t).$$

*Proof.* Define $f(t) = \int_a^t v(u) \, du$. We know that $f'(t) = v(t)$ because of the first fundamental theorem of calculus. We shall prove that $s'(t) = v(t)$. For this purpose we form the difference quotient

(14.17)
$$\left\| \frac{r(t+h) - r(t)}{h} \right\|.$$

Suppose first that $h > 0$. The line segment joining the points $r(t)$ and $r(t + h)$ may be thought of as a polygon approximating the arc joining these two points. Therefore, because of (14.11), we have

$$\|r(t + h) - r(t)\| \leq \Lambda(t, t + h) = s(t + h) - s(t).$$

Using this in (14.17) along with the inequality (14.12) of Theorem 14.10 we have

$$\left\| \frac{r(t+h) - r(t)}{h} \right\| \leq \frac{s(t+h) - s(t)}{h} \leq \frac{1}{h} \int_t^{t+h} v(u)\, du = \frac{f(t+h) - f(t)}{h}.$$

A similar argument shows that these inequalities are also valid for $h < 0$. If we let $h \to 0$, the difference quotient on the extreme left approaches $\|r'(t)\| = v(t)$ and that on the extreme right approaches $f'(t) = v(t)$. It follows that the quotient $[s(t + h) - s(t)]/h$ also approaches $v(t)$. But this means that $s'(t)$ exists and equals $v(t)$, as asserted.

Theorem 14.13 conforms with our intuitive notion of speed as the distance per unit time being covered during the motion.

Using (14.16) along with the second fundamental theorem of calculus, we can compute arc length by integrating the speed. Thus, the distance traveled by a particle during a time interval $[t_1, t_2]$ is

$$s(t_2) - s(t_1) = \int_{t_1}^{t_2} s'(t)\, dt = \int_{t_1}^{t_2} v(t)\, dt.$$

In particular, when $t_1 = a$ and $t_2 = b$, we obtain the following integral for arc length:

$$\Lambda(a, b) = \int_a^b v(t)\, dt.$$

EXAMPLE 1. *Length of a circular arc.* To compute the length of an arc of a circle of radius $a$, we may imagine a particle moving along the circle according to the equation $r(t) = a \cos t\, i + a \sin t\, j$. The velocity vector is $v(t) = -a \sin t\, i + a \cos t\, j$ and the speed is $v(t) = a$. Integrating the speed over an interval of length $\theta$, we find that the length of arc traced out is $a\theta$. In other words, the length of a circular arc is proportional to the angle it subtends; the constant of proportionality is the radius of the circle. For a unit circle we have $a = 1$, and the arc length is exactly equal to the angular measure.

EXAMPLE 2. *Length of the graph of a real-valued function.* The graph of a real-valued function $f$ defined on an interval $[a, b]$ can be treated as a curve with position vector $r(t)$ given by

$$r(t) = ti + f(t)j.$$

The corresponding velocity vector is $v(t) = i + f'(t)j$, and the speed is

$$v(t) = \|v(t)\| = \sqrt{1 + [f'(t)]^2}.$$

Therefore, the arc length of the graph of $f$ above a subinterval $[a, x]$ is given by the integral

(14.18) $$s(x) = \int_a^x v(t)\, dt = \int_a^x \sqrt{1 + [f'(t)]^2}\, dt\,.$$

## 14.13 Exercises

In Exercises 1 through 9, find the length of the path traced out by a particle moving on a curve according to the given equation during the time interval specified in each case.

1. $r(t) = a(1 - \cos t)i + a(t - \sin t)j, \qquad 0 \le t \le 2\pi, \quad a > 0$.

2. $r(t) = e^t \cos t\, i + e^t \sin t\, j, \qquad 0 \le t \le 2$.

3. $r(t) = a(\cos t + t \sin t)i + a(\sin t - t \cos t)j, \qquad 0 \le t \le 2\pi, \quad a > 0$.

4. $r(t) = \dfrac{c^2}{a} \cos^3 t\, i + \dfrac{c^2}{b} \sin^3 t\, j, \qquad 0 \le t \le 2\pi, \quad c^2 = a^2 - b^2, \quad 0 < b < a$.

5. $r(t) = a(\sinh t - t)i + a(\cosh t - 1)j, \qquad 0 \le t \le T, \quad a > 0$.

6. $r(t) = \sin t\, i + t\, j + (1 - \cos t)k \qquad (0 \le t \le 2\pi)$.

7. $r(t) = t\, i + 3t^2 j + 6t^3 k \qquad (0 \le t \le 2)$.

8. $r(t) = t\, i + \log(\sec t)j + \log(\sec t + \tan t)k \qquad (0 \le t \le \tfrac{1}{4}\pi)$.

9. $r(t) = a \cos \omega t\, i + a \sin \omega t\, j + b\omega k \qquad (t_0 \le t \le t_1)$.

10. Find an integral similar to that in (14.18) for the length of the graph of an equation of the form $x = g(y)$, where $g$ has a continuous derivative on an interval $[c, d]$.

11. A curve has the equation $y^2 = x^3$. Find the length of the arc joining $(1, -1)$ to $(1, 1)$.

12. Two points $A$ and $B$ on a unit circle with center at $O$ determine a circular sector $AOB$. Prove that the arc $AB$ has a length equal to twice the area of the sector.

13. Set up integrals for the lengths of the curves whose equations are (a) $y = e^x$, $0 \le x \le 1$; (b) $x = t + \log t$, $y = t - \log t$, $1 \le t \le e$. Show that the second length is $\sqrt{2}$ times the first one.

14. (a) Set up the integral which gives the length of the curve $y = c \cosh(x/c)$ from $x = 0$ to $x = a$ ($a > 0, c > 0$).
    (b) Show that $c$ times the length of this curve is equal to the area of the region bounded by $y = c \cosh(x/c)$, the $x$-axis, the $y$-axis, and the line $x = a$.
    (c) Evaluate this integral and find the length of the curve when $a = 2$.

15. Show that the length of the curve $y = \cosh x$ joining the points $(0, 1)$ and $(x, \cosh x)$ is $\sinh x$ if $x > 0$.

16. A nonnegative function $f$ has the property that its ordinate set over an arbitrary interval has an area proportional to the arc length of the graph above the interval. Find $f$.

17. Use the vector equation $r(t) = a \sin t\, i + b \cos t\, j$, where $0 < b < a$, to show that the circumference $L$ of an ellipse is given by the integral

$$L = 4a \int_0^{\pi/2} \sqrt{1 - e^2 \sin^2 t}\, dt\,,$$

where $e = \sqrt{a^2 - b^2}/a$. (The number $e$ is the eccentricity of the ellipse.) This is a special case of an integral of the form

$$E(k) = \int_0^{\pi/2} \sqrt{1 - k^2 \sin^2 t}\, dt\,,$$

called an *elliptic integral of the second kind*, where $0 \le k < 1$. The numbers $E(k)$ have been tabulated for various values of $k$.

18. If $0 < b < 4a$, let $r(t) = a(t - \sin t)i + a(1 - \cos t)j + b \sin \frac{1}{2}t\,k$. Show that the length of the path traced out from $t = 0$ to $t = 2\pi$ is $8aE(k)$, where $E(k)$ has the meaning given in Exercise 17 and $k^2 = 1 - (b/4a)^2$.

19. A particle moves with position vector

$$r(t) = tA + t^2 B + 2(\tfrac{2}{3}t)^{3/2}\,A \times B\,,$$

where $A$ and $B$ are two fixed unit vectors making an angle of $\pi/3$ radians with each other. Compute the speed of the particle at time $t$ and find how long it takes for it to move a distance of 12 units of arc length from the initial position $r(0)$.

20. (a) When a circle rolls (without slipping) along a straight line, a point on the circumference traces out a curve called a *cycloid*. If the fixed line is the $x$-axis and if the tracing point $(x, y)$ is originally at the origin, show that when the circle rolls through an angle $\theta$ we have

$$x = a(\theta - \sin \theta)\,, \qquad y = a(1 - \cos \theta)\,,$$

where $a$ is the radius of the circle. These serve as parametric equations for the cycloid.

(b) Referring to part (a), show that $dy/dx = \cot \frac{1}{2}\theta$ and deduce that the tangent line of the cycloid at $(x, y)$ makes an angle $\frac{1}{2}(\pi - \theta)$ with the $x$-axis. Make a sketch and show that the tangent line passes through the highest point on the circle.

21. Let $C$ be a curve described by two equivalent functions $X$ and $Y$, where $Y(t) = X[u(t)]$ for $c \le t \le d$. If the function $u$ which defines the change of parameter has a continuous derivative in $[c, d]$ prove that

$$\int_{u(c)}^{u(d)} \| X'(u) \|\, du = \int_{c}^{d} \| Y'(t) \|\, dt\,,$$

and deduce that the arc length of $C$ is invariant under such a change of parameter.

22. Consider the plane curve whose vector equation is $r(t) = ti + f(t)j$, where

$$f(t) = t \cos \left( \frac{\pi}{2t} \right) \quad \text{if} \quad t \ne 0\,, \qquad f(0) = 0\,.$$

Consider the following partition of the interval $[0, 1]$:

$$P = \left\{ 0, \frac{1}{2n}, \frac{1}{2n - 1}, \cdots, \frac{1}{3}, \frac{1}{2}, 1 \right\}.$$

Show that the corresponding inscribed polygon $\pi(P)$ has length

$$|\pi(P)| > 1 + \frac{1}{2} + \frac{1}{3} + \cdots + \frac{1}{2n}$$

and deduce that this curve is nonrectifiable.

## 14.14 Curvature of a curve

For a straight line the unit tangent vector $T$ does not change its direction, and hence $T' = O$. If the curve is not a straight line, the derivative $T'$ measures the tendency of the tangent to change its direction. The rate of change of the unit tangent *with respect to arc length* is called the *curvature vector* of the curve. We denote this by $dT/ds$, where $s$ represents arc length. The chain rule, used in conjunction with the relation $s'(t) = v(t)$, tells us that the curvature vector $dT/ds$ is related to the "time" derivative $T'$ by the equation

$$\frac{dT}{ds} = \frac{dt}{ds}\frac{dT}{dt} = \frac{1}{s'(t)}\,T'(t) = \frac{1}{v(t)}\,T'(t).$$

Since $T'(t) = \|T'(t)\|\,N(t)$, we obtain

(14.19) 
$$\frac{dT}{ds} = \frac{\|T'(t)\|}{v(t)}\,N(t)\,,$$

which shows that the curvature vector has the same direction as the principal normal $N(t)$. The scalar factor which multiplies $N(t)$ in (14.19) is a nonnegative number called the *curvature* of the curve at $t$ and it is denoted by $\kappa(t)$ ($\kappa$ is the Greek letter kappa). Thus the curvature $\kappa(t)$, defined to be the *length of the curvature vector*, is given by the following formula:

(14.20) 
$$\kappa(t) = \frac{\|T'(t)\|}{v(t)}\,.$$

EXAMPLE 1. *Curvature of a circle.* For a circle of radius $a$, given by $r(t) = a\cos t\,i + a\sin t\,j$, we have $v(t) = -a\sin t\,i + a\cos t\,j$, $v(t) = a$, $T(t) = -\sin t\,i + \cos t\,j$, and $T'(t) = -\cos t\,i - \sin t\,j$. Hence we have $\|T'(t)\| = 1$ so $\kappa(t) = 1/a$. This shows that a circle has constant curvature. The reciprocal of the curvature is the radius of the circle.

When $\kappa(t) \neq 0$, its reciprocal is called the *radius of curvature* and is denoted by $\rho(t)$ ($\rho$ is the Greek letter rho). That circle in the osculating plane with radius $\rho(t)$ and center at the tip of the curvature vector is called the *osculating circle*. It can be shown that the osculating circle is the limiting position of circles passing through three nearby points on the curve as two of the points approach the third. Because of this property, the osculating circle is often called the circle that "best fits the curve" at each of its points.

EXAMPLE 2. *Curvature of a plane curve.* For a plane curve, we have seen that $\|T'(t)\| = |\alpha'(t)|$, where $\alpha(t)$ is the angle the tangent vector makes with the positive $x$-axis, as shown in Figure 14.11. From the chain rule, we have $\alpha'(t) = d\alpha/dt = (d\alpha/ds)(ds/dt) = v(t)d\alpha/ds$, so Equation (14.20) implies

$$\kappa(t) = \left|\frac{d\alpha}{ds}\right|.$$

In other words, the curvature of a plane curve is the absolute value of the rate of change of $\alpha$ with respect to arc length. It measures the change of direction per unit distance along the curve.

EXAMPLE 3. *Plane curves of constant curvature.* If $d\alpha/ds$ is a nonzero constant, say $d\alpha/ds = a$, then $\alpha = as + b$, where $b$ is a constant. Hence, if we use the arc length $s$ as a parameter, we have $T = \cos(as + b)\boldsymbol{i} + \sin(as + b)\boldsymbol{j}$. Integrating, we find that $\boldsymbol{r} = (1/a) \sin(as + b)\boldsymbol{i} - (1/a) \cos(as + b)\boldsymbol{j} + A$, where $A$ is a constant vector. Therefore $\|\boldsymbol{r} - A\| = 1/|a|$, so the curve is a circle (or an arc of a circle) with center at $A$ and radius $1/|a|$. This proves that a plane curve of constant curvature $\kappa \neq 0$ is a circle (or an arc of a circle) with radius $1/\kappa$.

Now we prove a theorem which relates the curvature to the velocity and acceleration.

THEOREM 14.14. *For any motion with velocity* $\boldsymbol{v}(t)$, *speed* $v(t)$, *acceleration* $\boldsymbol{a}(t)$, *and curvature* $\kappa(t)$, *we have*

(14.21) $$\boldsymbol{a}(t) = v'(t)T(t) + \kappa(t)v^2(t)N(t).$$

*This formula, in turn, implies*

(14.22) $$\kappa(t) = \frac{\|\boldsymbol{a}(t) \times \boldsymbol{v}(t)\|}{v^3(t)}.$$

*Proof.* To prove (14.21), we rewrite (14.20) in the form $\|T'(t)\| = \kappa(t)v(t)$, which gives us $T'(t) = \kappa(t)v(t)N(t)$. Substituting this expression for $T'(t)$ in Equation (14.8), we obtain (14.21).

To prove (14.22), we form the cross product $\boldsymbol{a}(t) \times \boldsymbol{v}(t)$, using (14.21) for $\boldsymbol{a}(t)$ and the formula $\boldsymbol{v}(t) = v(t)T(t)$ for the velocity. This gives us

(14.23) $$\boldsymbol{a} \times \boldsymbol{v} = v'vT \times T + \kappa v^3 N \times T = \kappa v^3 N \times T$$

since $T \times T = O$. If we take the length of each member of (14.23) and note that

$$\|N \times T\| = \|N\| \|T\| \sin \tfrac{1}{2}\pi = 1,$$

we obtain $\|\boldsymbol{a} \times \boldsymbol{v}\| = \kappa v^3$, which proves (14.22).

In practice it is fairly easy to compute the vectors $\boldsymbol{v}$ and $\boldsymbol{a}$ (by differentiating the position vector $\boldsymbol{r}$); hence Equation (14.22) provides a useful method for computing the curvature. This method is usually simpler than determining the curvature from its definition.

For a straight line we have $\boldsymbol{a} \times \boldsymbol{v} = O$, so the curvature is everywhere zero. A curve with a small curvature at a point has a large radius of curvature there and hence does not differ much from a straight line in the immediate vicinity of the point. Thus the curvature is a measure of the tendency of a curve to deviate from a straight line.

## 14.15 Exercises

1. Refer to the curves described in Exercises 1 through 6 of Section 14.9 and in each case determine the curvature $\kappa(t)$ for the value of $t$ indicated.
2. A helix is described by the position function $\boldsymbol{r}(t) = a \cos \omega t\, \boldsymbol{i} + a \sin \omega t\, \boldsymbol{j} + b\omega t\boldsymbol{k}$. Prove that it has constant curvature $\kappa = a/(a^2 + b^2)$.

3. Two fixed unit vectors $A$ and $B$ make an angle $\theta$ with each other, where $0 < \theta < \pi$. A particle moves on a space curve in such a way that its position vector $r(t)$ and velocity $v(t)$ are related by the equation $v(t) = A \times r(t)$. If $r(0) = B$, prove that the curve has constant curvature and compute this curvature in terms of $\theta$.

4. A point moves in space according to the vector equation

$$r(t) = 4 \cos t\, i + 4 \sin t\, j + 4 \cos t\, k\,.$$

(a) Show that the path is an ellipse and find a Cartesian equation for the plane containing this ellipse.

(b) Show that the radius of curvature is $\rho(t) = 2\sqrt{2}\,(1 + \sin^2 t)^{3/2}$.

5. For the curve whose vector equation is $r(t) = e^t i + e^{-t} j + \sqrt{2}\, t\, k$, show that the curvature is $\kappa(t) = \sqrt{2}/(e^t + e^{-t})^2$.

6. (a) For a plane curve described by the equation $r(t) = x(t)i + y(t)j$, show that the curvature is given by the formula

$$\kappa(t) = \frac{|x'(t)y''(t) - y'(t)x''(t)|}{\{[x'(t)]^2 + [y'(t)]^2\}^{3/2}}\,.$$

(b) If a plane curve has the Cartesian equation $y = f(x)$, show that the curvature at the point $(x, f(x))$ is

$$\frac{|f''(x)|}{\{1 + [f'(x)]^2\}^{3/2}}\,.$$

7. If a point moves so that the velocity and acceleration vectors always have constant lengths, prove that the curvature is constant at all points of the path. Express this constant in terms of $\|a\|$ and $\|v\|$.

8. If two plane curves with Cartesian equations $y = f(x)$ and $y = g(x)$ have the same tangent at a point $(a, b)$ and the same curvature at that point, prove that $|f''(a)| = |g''(a)|$.

9. For certain values of the constants $a$ and $b$, the two curves with Cartesian equations $y = ax(b - x)$ and $(x + 2)y = x$ intersect at only one point $P$, have a common tangent line at $P$, and have the same curvature at $P$.

(a) Find all $a$ and $b$ which satisfy all these conditions.

(b) For each possible choice of $a$ and $b$ satisfying the given conditions, make à sketch of the two curves. Show how they intersect at $P$.

10. (a) Prove that the radius of curvature of a parabola is smallest at its vertex.

(b) Given two fixed unit vectors $A$ and $B$ making an angle $\theta$ with each other, where $0 < \theta < \pi$. The curve with position vector $r(t) = tA + t^2B$ is a parabola lying in the plane spanned by $A$ and $B$. Determine (in terms of $A$, $B$, and $\theta$) the position vector of the vertex of this parabola. You may use the property of the parabola stated in part (a).

11. A particle moves along a plane curve with constant speed 5. It starts at the origin at time $t = 0$ with initial velocity $5j$, and it never goes to the left of the $y$-axis. At every instant the curvature of the path is $\kappa(t) = 2t$. Let $\alpha(t)$ denote the angle that the velocity vector makes with the positive $x$-axis at time $t$.

(a) Determine $\alpha(t)$ explicitly as a function of $t$.

(b) Determine the velocity $v(t)$ in terms of $i$ and $j$.

12. A particle moves along a plane curve with constant speed 2. The motion starts at the origin when $t = 0$ and the initial velocity $v(0)$ is $2i$. At every instant it is known that the curvature $\kappa(t) = 4t$. Find the velocity when $t = \frac{1}{4}\sqrt{\pi}$ if the curve never goes below the $x$-axis.

## 14.16 Velocity and acceleration in polar coordinates

Sometimes it is more natural to describe the points on a plane curve by polar coordinates rather than rectangular coordinates. Since the rectangular coordinates $(x, y)$ are related to the polar coordinates $r$ and $\theta$ by the equations

$$x = r \cos \theta, \qquad y = r \sin \theta,$$

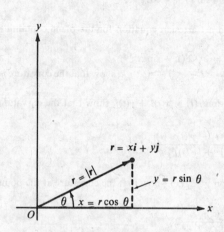

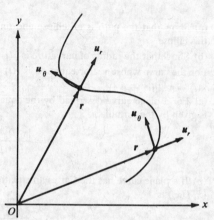

FIGURE 14.15  Polar coordinates.

FIGURE 14.16  The unit vectors $u_r$ and $u_\theta$.

the position vector $r = x\boldsymbol{i} + y\boldsymbol{j}$ joining the origin to $(x, y)$ is given by

$$\boldsymbol{r} = r \cos \theta \, \boldsymbol{i} + r \sin \theta \, \boldsymbol{j} = r(\cos \theta \, \boldsymbol{i} + \sin \theta \, \boldsymbol{j}),$$

where $r = \|\boldsymbol{r}\|$. This relation is illustrated in Figure 14.15.

The vector $\cos \theta \, \boldsymbol{i} + \sin \theta \, \boldsymbol{j}$ is a vector of unit length having the same direction as $\boldsymbol{r}$. This unit vector is usually denoted by $\boldsymbol{u}_r$ and the foregoing equation is written as follows:

$$\boldsymbol{r} = r\boldsymbol{u}_r, \qquad \text{where} \quad \boldsymbol{u}_r = \cos \theta \, \boldsymbol{i} + \sin \theta \, \boldsymbol{j}.$$

It is convenient to introduce also a unit vector $\boldsymbol{u}_\theta$, perpendicular to $\boldsymbol{u}_r$, which is defined as follows:

$$\boldsymbol{u}_\theta = \frac{d\boldsymbol{u}_r}{d\theta} = -\sin \theta \, \boldsymbol{i} + \cos \theta \, \boldsymbol{j}.$$

Note that we have

$$\frac{d\boldsymbol{u}_\theta}{d\theta} = -\cos \theta \, \boldsymbol{i} - \sin \theta \, \boldsymbol{j} = -\boldsymbol{u}_r.$$

In the study of plane curves, the two unit vectors $\boldsymbol{u}_r$ and $\boldsymbol{u}_\theta$ play the same roles in polar coordinates as the unit vectors $\boldsymbol{i}$ and $\boldsymbol{j}$ in rectangular coordinates. Figure 14.16 shows the unit vectors $\boldsymbol{u}_r$ and $\boldsymbol{u}_\theta$ attached to a curve at some of its points.

Now suppose the polar coordinates $r$ and $\theta$ are functions of $t$, say $r = f(t)$, $\theta = g(t)$. We shall derive formulas for expressing the velocity and acceleration in terms of $u_r$ and $u_\theta$. For the position vector, we have

$$r = ru_r = f(t)u_r.$$

Since $\theta$ depends on the parameter $t$, the same is true of the unit vector $u_r$ and we must take this into account when we compute the velocity vector. Thus we have

$$v = \frac{dr}{dt} = \frac{d(ru_r)}{dt} = \frac{dr}{dt}u_r + r\frac{du_r}{dt}.$$

Using the chain rule, we may express $du_r/dt$ in terms of $u_\theta$ by writing

$$(14.24) \qquad \frac{du_r}{dt} = \frac{d\theta}{dt}\frac{du_r}{d\theta} = \frac{d\theta}{dt}u_\theta,$$

and the equation for the velocity vector becomes

$$(14.25) \qquad v = \frac{dr}{dt}u_r + r\frac{d\theta}{dt}u_\theta.$$

The scalar factors $dr/dt$ and $rd\theta/dt$ multiplying $u_r$ and $u_\theta$ are called, respectively, the *radial* and *transverse components* of velocity.

Since $u_r$ and $u_\theta$ are orthogonal unit vectors, we find that

$$v \cdot v = \left(\frac{dr}{dt}\right)^2 + \left(r\frac{d\theta}{dt}\right)^2,$$

so the speed $v$ is given by the formula

$$v = \sqrt{\left(\frac{dr}{dt}\right)^2 + \left(r\frac{d\theta}{dt}\right)^2}.$$

Differentiating both sides of (14.25), we find that the acceleration vector is given by

$$a = \left(\frac{d^2r}{dt^2}u_r + \frac{dr}{dt}\frac{du_r}{dt}\right) + \left(r\frac{d^2\theta}{dt^2}u_\theta + \frac{dr}{dt}\frac{d\theta}{dt}u_\theta + r\frac{d\theta}{dt}\frac{du_\theta}{dt}\right)$$

The derivative $du_r/dt$ may be expressed in terms of $u_\theta$ by (14.24). We may similarly express the derivative of $u_\theta$ by the equation

$$\frac{du_\theta}{dt} = \frac{d\theta}{dt}\frac{du_\theta}{d\theta} = -\frac{d\theta}{dt}u_r.$$

This leads to the following formula which expresses $a$ in terms of its radial and transverse components:

$$(14.26) \qquad a = \left(\frac{d^2r}{dt^2} - r\left(\frac{d\theta}{dt}\right)^2\right)u_r + \left(r\frac{d^2\theta}{dt^2} + 2\frac{dr}{dt}\frac{d\theta}{dt}\right)u_\theta .$$

When $\theta = t$, the curve may be described by the polar equation $r = f(\theta)$. In this case, the formulas for velocity, speed, and acceleration simplify considerably, and we obtain

$$v = \frac{dr}{d\theta}u_r + ru_\theta , \qquad v = \sqrt{\left(\frac{dr}{d\theta}\right)^2 + r^2} , \qquad a = \left(\frac{d^2r}{d\theta^2} - r\right)u_r + 2\frac{dr}{d\theta}u_\theta .$$

## 14.17 Plane motion with radial acceleration

The acceleration vector is said to be *radial* if the transverse component in Equation (14.26) is always zero. This component is equal to

$$r\frac{d^2\theta}{dt^2} + 2\frac{dr}{dt}\frac{d\theta}{dt} = \frac{1}{r}\frac{d}{dt}\left(r^2\frac{d\theta}{dt}\right) .$$

Therefore, the acceleration is radial if and only if $r^2\, d\theta/dt$ is constant.

Plane motion with radial acceleration has an interesting geometric interpretation in terms of area. Denote by $A(t)$ the area of the region swept out by the position vector from a fixed time, say $t = a$, to a later time $t$. An example is the shaded region shown in Figure 14.17. We shall prove that the time rate of change of this area is exactly equal to $\frac{1}{2}r^2\, d\theta/dt$. That is, we have

$$(14.27) \qquad A'(t) = \frac{1}{2}r^2\frac{d\theta}{dt} .$$

From this it follows that the acceleration vector is radial if and only if the position vector sweeps out area at a constant rate.

To prove (14.27), we assume that it is possible to eliminate $t$ from the two equations $r = f(t)$, $\theta = g(t)$, and thereby express $r$ as a function of $\theta$, say $r = R(\theta)$. This means that there is a real-valued function $R$ such that $R[g(t)] = f(t)$. Then the shaded region in Figure 14.17 is the radial set of $R$ over the interval $[g(a), g(t)]$. By Theorem 2.6, the area of this region is given by the integral

$$A(t) = \tfrac{1}{2}\int_{g(a)}^{g(t)} R^2(\theta)\, d\theta .$$

Differentiating this integral by the first fundamental theorem of calculus and the chain rule, we find that

$$A'(t) = \frac{1}{2}R^2[g(t)]g'(t) = \frac{1}{2}f^2(t)g'(t) = \frac{1}{2}r^2\frac{d\theta}{dt} ,$$

which proves (14.27).

## 14.18  Cylindrical coordinates

If the $x$- and $y$-coordinates of a point $P = (x, y, z)$ in 3-space are replaced by polar coordinates $r$ and $\theta$, then the three numbers $r$, $\theta$, $z$ are called *cylindrical coordinates* for the point $P$. The nonnegative number $r$ now represents the distance from the $z$-axis to the point $P$, as indicated in Figure 14.18. Those points in space for which $r$ is constant are at a fixed distance from the $z$-axis and therefore lie on a circular cylinder (hence the name *cylindrical* coordinates).

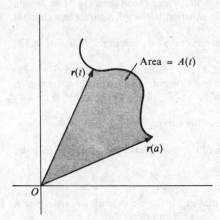

FIGURE 14.17  The position vector sweeps out area at the rate $A'(t) = \dfrac{1}{2} r^2 \dfrac{d\theta}{dt}$.

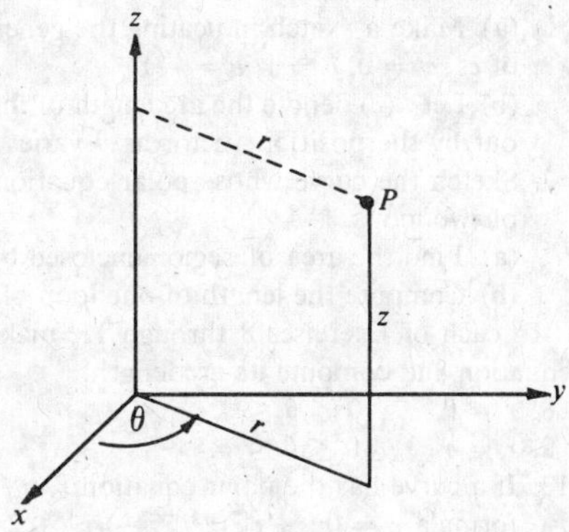

FIGURE 14.18  Cylindrical coordinates.

To discuss *space* curves in cylindrical coordinates, the equation for the position vector $r$ must be replaced by one of the form

$$r = r u_r + z(t)k .$$

Corresponding formulas for the velocity and acceleration vectors are obtained by merely adding the terms $z'(t)k$ and $z''(t)k$, respectively, to the right-hand members of the two-dimensional formulas in (14.25) and (14.26).

## 14.19  Exercises

1. A particle moves in a plane so that its position at time $t$ has polar coordinates $r = t$, $\theta = t$. Find formulas for the velocity $v$, the acceleration $a$, and the curvature $\kappa$ at any time $t$.

2. A particle moves in space so that its position at time $t$ has cylindrical coordinates $r = t$, $\theta = t$, $z = t$. It traces out a curve called a *conical helix*.
   (a) Find formulas for the velocity $v$, the acceleration $a$, and the curvature $\kappa$ at time $t$.
   (b) Find a formula for determining the angle between the velocity vector and the generator of the cone at each point of the curve.

3. A particle moves in space so that its position at time $t$ has cylindrical coordinates $r = \sin t$, $\theta = t$, $z = \log \sec t$, where $0 \le t < \frac{1}{2}\pi$.

(a) Show that the curve lies on the cylinder with Cartesian equation $x^2 + (y - \frac{1}{2})^2 = \frac{1}{4}$.

(b) Find a formula (in terms of $t$) for the angle which the velocity vector makes with $\boldsymbol{k}$.

4. If a curve is given by a polar equation $r = f(\theta)$, where $a \leq \theta \leq b \leq a + 2\pi$, prove that its arc length is

$$\int_a^b \sqrt{r^2 + \left(\frac{dr}{d\theta}\right)^2} \, d\theta \, .$$

5. The curve described by the polar equation $r = a(1 + \cos \theta)$, where $a > 0$ and $0 \leq \theta \leq 2\pi$, is called a *cardiod*. Draw a graph of the cardiod $r = 4(1 + \cos \theta)$ and compute its arc length.

6. A particle moves along a plane curve whose polar equation is $r = e^{c\theta}$, where $c$ is a constant and $\theta$ varies from 0 to $2\pi$.

(a) Make a sketch indicating the general shape of the curve for each of the following values of $c$: $c = 0$, $c = 1$, $c = -1$.

(b) Let $L(c)$ denote the arc length of the curve and let $a(c)$ denote the area of the region swept out by the position vector as $\theta$ varies from 0 to $2\pi$. Compute $L(c)$ and $a(c)$ in terms of $c$.

7. Sketch the curve whose polar equation is $r = \sin^2 \theta$, $0 \leq \theta \leq 2\pi$, and show that it consists of two loops.

(a) Find the area of region enclosed by one loop of the curve.

(b) Compute the length of one loop of the curve.

In each of Exercises 8 through 11, make a sketch of the plane curve having the given polar equation and compute its arc length.

8. $r = \theta$, $\quad 0 \leq \theta \leq \pi$.

9. $r = e^\theta$, $\quad 0 \leq \theta \leq \pi$.

10. $r = 1 + \cos \theta$, $\quad 0 \leq \theta \leq \pi$.

11. $r = 1 - \cos \theta$, $\quad 0 \leq \theta \leq 2\pi$.

12. If a curve has the polar equation $r = f(\theta)$, show that its radius of curvature $\rho$ is given by the formula $\rho = (r^2 + r'^2)^{3/2}/|r^2 - rr'' + 2r'^2|$, where $r' = f'(\theta)$ and $r'' = f''(\theta)$.

13. For each of the curves in Exercises 8 through 11, compute the radius of curvature for the value of $\theta$ indicated.

(a) Arbitrary $\theta$ in Exercise 8.

(b) Arbitrary $\theta$ in Exercise 9.

(c) $\theta = \frac{1}{4}\pi$ in Exercise 10.

(d) $\theta = \frac{1}{2}\pi$ in Exercise 11.

14. Let $\phi$ denote the angle, $0 \leq \phi \leq \pi$, between the position vector and the velocity vector of a curve. If the curve is expressed in polar coordinates, prove that $v \sin \phi = r$ and $v \cos \phi = dr/d\theta$, where $v$ is the speed.

15. A missile is designed to move directly toward its target. Due to mechanical failure, its direction in actual flight makes a fixed angle $\alpha \neq 0$ with the line from the missile to the target. Find the path if it is fired at a fixed target. Discuss how the path varies with $\alpha$. Does the missile ever reach the target? (Assume the motion takes place in a plane.)

16. Due to a mechanical failure, a ground crew has lost control of a missile recently fired. It is known that the missile will proceed at a constant speed on a straight course of unknown direction. When the missile is 4 miles away, it is sighted for an instant and lost again. Immediately an anti-missile missile is fired with a constant speed three times that of the first missile. What should be the course of the second missile in order for it to overtake the first one? (Assume both missiles move in the same plane.)

17. Prove that if a homogeneous first-order differential equation of the form $y' = f(x, y)$ is rewritten in polar coordinates, it reduces to a separable equation. Use this method to solve $y' = (y - x)/(y + x)$.

18. A particle (moving in space) has velocity vector $\boldsymbol{v} = \omega \boldsymbol{k} \times \boldsymbol{r}$, where $\omega$ is a positive constant and $\boldsymbol{r}$ is the position vector. Prove that the particle moves along a circle with constant angular speed $\omega$. (The angular speed is defined to be $|d\theta/dt|$, where $\theta$ is the polar angle at time $t$.)

19. A particle moves in a plane perpendicular to the $z$-axis. The motion takes place along a circle with center on this axis.

(a) Show that there is a vector $\boldsymbol{\omega}(t)$ parallel to the $z$-axis such that

$$v(t) = \boldsymbol{\omega}(t) \times r(t),$$

where $r(t)$ and $v(t)$ denote the position and velocity vectors at time $t$. The vector $\boldsymbol{\omega}(t)$ is called the *angular velocity* vector and its magnitude $\omega(t) = \|\boldsymbol{\omega}(t)\|$ is called the *angular speed*.

(b) The vector $\boldsymbol{\alpha}(t) = \boldsymbol{\omega}'(t)$ is called the *angular acceleration* vector. Show that the acceleration vector $a(t)$ [$= v'(t)$] is given by the formula

$$a(t) = [\boldsymbol{\omega}(t) \cdot r(t)]\boldsymbol{\omega}(t) - \omega^2(t)r(t) + \boldsymbol{\alpha}(t) \times r(t).$$

(c) If the particle lies in the $xy$-plane and if the angular speed $\omega(t)$ is constant, say $\omega(t) = \omega$, prove that the acceleration vector $a(t)$ is centripetal and that, in fact, $a(t) = -\omega^2 r(t)$.

20. A body is said to undergo a *rigid motion* if, for every pair of particles $p$ and $q$ in the body, the distance $\|r_p(t) - r_q(t)\|$ is independent of $t$, where $r_p(t)$ and $r_q(t)$ denote the position vectors of $p$ and $q$ at time $t$. Prove that for a rigid motion in which each particle $p$ rotates about the $z$-axis we have $v_p(t) = \boldsymbol{\omega}(t) \times r_p(t)$, where $\boldsymbol{\omega}(t)$ is the same for each particle, and $v_p(t)$ is the velocity of particle $p$.

## 14.20 Applications to planetary motion

By analyzing the voluminous data on planetary motion accumulated up to 1600, the German astronomer Johannes Kepler (1571–1630) tried to discover the mathematical laws governing the motions of the planets. There were six known planets at that time and, according to the Copernican theory, their orbits were thought to lie on concentric spherical shells about the sun. Kepler attempted to show that the radii of these shells were linked up with the five regular solids of geometry. He proposed an ingenious idea that the solar system was designed something like a Chinese puzzle. At the center of the system he placed the sun. Then, in succession, he arranged the six concentric spheres that can be inscribed and circumscribed around the five regular solids—the octahedron, icosahedron, dodecahedron, tetrahedron, and cube, in respective order (from inside out). The innermost sphere, inscribed in the regular octahedron, corresponded to Mercury's path. The next sphere, which circumscribed the octahedron and inscribed the icosahedron, corresponded to the orbit of Venus. Earth's orbit lay on the sphere around the icosahedron and inside the dodecahedron, and so on, the outermost sphere, containing Jupiter's orbit, being circumscribed around the cube. Although this theory seemed correct to within five percent, astronomical observations at that time were accurate to a percentage error much smaller than this, and Kepler finally realized that he had to modify this theory. After much further study it occurred to him that the observed data concerning the orbits corresponded more to *elliptical* paths than the circular paths of the Copernican system. After several more years of unceasing effort, Kepler set forth three famous laws, empirically discovered, which explained all the astronomical phenomena known at that time. They may be stated as follows:

*Kepler's first law*: Planets move in ellipses with the sun at one focus.

*Kepler's second law*: The position vector from the sun to a planet sweeps out area at a constant rate.

*Kepler's third law*: The square of the period of a planet is proportional to the cube of its mean distance from the sun.

> *Note*: By the *period* of a planet is meant the time required to go once around the elliptical orbit. The *mean distance* from the sun is one half the length of the major axis of the ellipse.

The formulation of these laws from a study of astronomical tables was a remarkable achievement. Nearly 50 years later, Newton proved that all three of Kepler's laws are consequences of his own second law of motion and his celebrated universal law of gravitation. In this section we shall use vector methods to show how Kepler's laws may be deduced from Newton's.

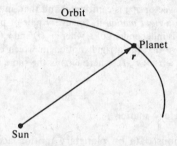

FIGURE 14.19 The position vector from the sun to a planet.

Assume we have a fixed sun of mass $M$ and a moving planet of mass $m$ attracted to the sun by a force $F$. (We neglect the influence of all other forces.) Newton's second law of motion states that

$$(14.28) \qquad F = ma,$$

where $a$ is the acceleration vector of the moving planet. Denote by $r$ the position vector from the sun to the planet (as in Figure 14.19), let $r = \|r\|$, and let $u_r$ be a unit vector with the same direction as $r$, so that $r = ru_r$. The universal law of gravitation states that

$$F = -G \frac{mM}{r^2} u_r,$$

where $G$ is a constant. Combining this with (14.28), we obtain

$$(14.29) \qquad a = -\frac{GM}{r^2} u_r,$$

which tells us that the acceleration is *radial*. In a moment we shall prove that the orbit lies in a plane. Once we know this, it follows at once from the results of Section 14.17 that the position vector sweeps out area at a constant rate.

To prove that the path lies in a plane we use the fact that $r$ and $a$ are parallel. If we introduce the velocity vector $v = dr/dt$, we have

$$r \times a = r \times \frac{dv}{dt} + v \times v = r \times \frac{dv}{dt} + \frac{dr}{dt} \times v = \frac{d}{dt}(r \times v) \, .$$

Since $r \times a = O$, this means that $r \times v$ is a constant vector, say $r \times v = c$.

If $c = O$, the position vector $r$ is parallel to $v$ and the motion is along a straight line. Since the path of a planet is not a straight line, we must have $c \neq O$. The relation $r \times v = c$ shows that $r \cdot c = 0$, so the position vector lies in a plane perpendicular to $c$. Since the acceleration is radial, $r$ sweeps out area at a constant rate. This proves Kepler's second law.

It is easy to prove that this constant rate is exactly half the length of the vector $c$. In fact, if we use polar coordinates and express the velocity in terms of $u_r$ and $u_\theta$ as in Equation (14.25), we find that

(14.30) $$c = r \times v = (ru_r) \times \left( \frac{dr}{dt} u_r + r \frac{d\theta}{dt} u_\theta \right) = r^2 \frac{d\theta}{dt} u_r \times u_\theta \, ,$$

and hence $\|c\| = |r^2 \, d\theta/dt|$. By (14.27) this is equal to $2|A'(t)|$, where $A'(t)$ is the rate at which the radius vector sweeps out area.

Kepler's second law is illustrated in Figure 14.20. The two shaded regions, which are swept out by the position vector in equal time intervals, have equal areas.

We shall prove next that the path is an ellipse. First of all, we form the cross product $a \times c$, using (14.29) and (14.30), and we find that

$$a \times c = \left( -\frac{GM}{r^2} u_r \right) \times \left( r^2 \frac{d\theta}{dt} u_r \times u_\theta \right) = -GM \frac{d\theta}{dt} u_r \times (u_r \times u_\theta) = GM \frac{d\theta}{dt} u_\theta \, .$$

Since $a = dv/dt$ and $u_\theta = du_r/d\theta$, the foregoing equation for $a \times c$ can also be written as follows:

$$\frac{d}{dt}(v \times c) = \frac{d}{dt}(GMu_r) \, .$$

Integration gives us

$$v \times c = GMu_r + b \, ,$$

where $b$ is another constant vector. We can rewrite this as follows:

(14.31) $$v \times c = GM(u_r + e) \, ,$$

where $GMe = b$. We shall combine this with (14.30) to eliminate $v$ and obtain an equation for $r$. For this purpose we dot multiply both sides of (14.30) by $c$ and both sides of (14.31) by $r$. Equating the two expressions for the scalar triple product $r \cdot v \times c$, we are led to the equation

(14.32) $$GMr(1 + e \cos \phi) = c^2 \, ,$$

where $e = \|e\|$, $c = \|c\|$, and $\phi$ represents the angle between the constant vector $e$ and the radius vector **r**. (See Figure 14.21.) If we let $d = c^2/(GMe)$, Equation (14.32) becomes

(14.33)    $$r = \frac{ed}{e \cos \phi + 1} \quad \text{or} \quad r = e(d - r \cos \phi)$$

By Theorem 13.18, this is the polar equation of a conic section with eccentricity $e$ and a focus at the sun. Figure 14.21 shows the directrix drawn perpendicular to **e** at a distance $d$ from the sun. The distance from the planet to the directrix is $d - r \cos \phi$, and the ratio

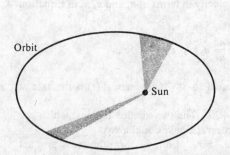

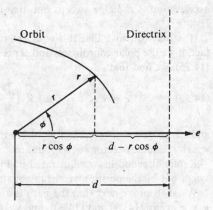

FIGURE 14.20.  Kepler's second law. The two shaded regions, swept out in equal time intervals, have equal areas.

FIGURE 14.21.  The ratio $r/(d - r \cos \phi)$ is the eccentricity $e = \|\mathbf{e}\|$.

$r/(d - r \cos \phi)$ is the eccentricity $e$. The conic is an ellipse if $e < 1$, a parabola if $e = 1$, and a hyperbola if $e > 1$. Since planets are known to move on closed paths, the orbit under consideration must be an ellipse. This proves Kepler's first law.

Finally, we deduce Kepler's third law. Suppose the ellipse has major axis of length $2a$ and minor axis of length $2b$. Then the area of the ellipse is $\pi ab$. Let $T$ be the time it takes for the planet to go once around the ellipse. Since the position vector sweeps out area at the rate $\frac{1}{2}c$, we have $\frac{1}{2}cT = \pi ab$, or $T = 2\pi ab/c$. We wish to prove that $T^2$ is proportional to $a^3$.

From Section 13.22 we have $b^2 = a^2(1 - e^2)$, $ed = a(1 - e^2)$, so

$$c^2 = GMed = GMa(1 - e^2),$$

and hence we have

$$T^2 = \frac{4\pi^2 a^2 b^2}{c^2} = \frac{4\pi^2 a^4(1 - e^2)}{GMa(1 - e^2)} = \frac{4\pi^2}{GM} a^3.$$

Since $T^2$ is a constant times $a^3$, this proves Kepler's third law.

## 14.21  Miscellaneous review exercises

1. Let $r$ denote the vector from the origin to an arbitrary point on the parabola $y^2 = x$, let $\alpha$ be the angle that $r$ makes with the tangent line, $0 \le \alpha \le \pi$, and let $\theta$ be the angle that $r$ makes with the positive $x$-axis, $0 \le \theta \le \pi$. Express $\alpha$ in terms of $\theta$.

2. Show that the vector $T = yi + 2cj$ is tangent to the parabola $y^2 = 4cx$ at the point $(x, y)$, and that the vector $N = 2ci - yj$ is perpendicular to $T$.

   [*Hint:*  Write a vector equation for the parabola, using $y$ as a parameter.]

3. Prove that an equation of the line of slope $m$ that is tangent to the parabola $y^2 = 4cx$ can be written in the form $y = mx + c/m$. What are the coordinates of the point of contact?

4. (a) Solve Exercise 3 for the parabola $(y - y_0)^2 = 4c(x - x_0)$.
   (b) Solve Exercise 3 for the parabola $x^2 = 4cy$ and, more generally, for the parabola $(x - x_0)^2 = 4c(y - y_0)$.

5. Prove that an equation of the line that is tangent to the parabola $y^2 = 4cx$ at the point $(x_1, y_1)$ can be written in the form $y_1 y = 2c(x + x_1)$.

6. Solve Exercise 5 for each of the parabolas described in Exercise 4.

7. (a) Let $P$ be a point on the parabola $y = x^2$. Let $Q$ be the point of intersection of the normal line at $P$ with the $y$-axis. What is the limiting position of $Q$ as $P$ tends to the $y$-axis?
   (b) Solve the same problem for the curve $y = f(x)$, where $f'(0) = 0$.

8. Given that the line $y = c$ intersects the parabola $y = x^2$ at two points. Find the radius of the circle passing through these two points and through the vertex of the parabola. The radius you determine depends on $c$. What happens to this radius as $c \to 0$?

9. Prove that a point $(x_0, y_0)$ is *inside*, *on*, or *outside* the ellipse $x^2/a^2 + y^2/b^2 = 1$ according as $x_0^2/a^2 + y_0^2/b^2$ is *less than, equal to*, or *greater than* 1.

10. Given an ellipse $x^2/a^2 + y^2/b^2 = 1$. Show that the vectors $T$ and $N$ given by

$$T = -\frac{y}{b^2}i + \frac{x}{a^2}j, \qquad N = \frac{x}{a^2}i + \frac{y}{b^2}j$$

are, respectively, *tangent* and *normal* to the ellipse when placed at the point $(x, y)$. If the eccentric angle of $(x_0, y_0)$ is $\theta_0$, show that the tangent line at $(x_0, y_0)$ has the Cartesian equation

$$\frac{x}{a}\cos\theta_0 + \frac{y}{b}\sin\theta_0 = 1 .$$

11. Show that the tangent line to the ellipse $x^2/a^2 + y^2/b^2 = 1$ at the point $(x_0, y_0)$ has the equation $x_0 x/a^2 + y_0 y/b^2 = 1$.

12. Prove that the product of the perpendicular distances from the foci of an ellipse to any tangent line is constant, this constant being the square of the length of half the minor axis.

13. Two tangent lines are drawn to the ellipse $x^2 + 4y^2 = 8$, each parallel to the line $x + 2y = 7$. Find the points of tangency.

14. ·A circle passes through both foci of an ellipse and is tangent to the ellipse at two points. Find the eccentricity of the ellipse.

15. Let $V$ be one of the two vertices of a hyperbola whose transverse axis has length $2a$ and whose eccentricity is 2. Let $P$ be a point on the same branch as $V$. Denote by $A$ the area of the region bounded by the hyperbola and the line segment $VP$, and let $r$ be the length of $VP$.
    (a) Place the coordinate axes in a convenient position and write an equation for the hyperbola.
    (b) Express the area $A$ as an integral and, without attempting to evaluate this integral, show that $Ar^{-3}$ tends to a limit as the point $P$ tends to $V$. Find this limit.

16. Show that the vectors $T = (y/b^2)\mathbf{i} + (x/a^2)\mathbf{j}$ and $N = (x/a^2)\mathbf{i} - (y/b^2)\mathbf{j}$ are, respectively, tangent and normal to the hyperbola $x^2/a^2 - y^2/b^2 = 1$ if placed at the point $(x, y)$ on the curve.

17. Show that the tangent line to the hyperbola $x^2/a^2 - y^2/b^2 = 1$ at the point $(x_0, y_0)$ is given by the equation $x_0 x/a^2 - y_0 y/b^2 = 1$.

18. The normal line at each point of a curve and the line from that point to the origin form an isosceles triangle whose base is on the $x$-axis. Show that the curve is a hyperbola.

19. The normal line at a point $P$ of a curve intersects the $x$-axis at $X$ and the $y$-axis at $Y$. Find the curve if each $P$ is the mid-point of the corresponding line segment $XY$ and if the point $(4, 5)$ is on the curve.

20. Prove that the product of the perpendicular distances from an arbitrary point on a hyperbola to its asymptotes is constant.

21. A curve is given by a polar equation $r = f(\theta)$. Find $f$ if an arbitrary arc joining two distinct points of the curve has arc length proportional to (a) the angle subtended at the origin; (b) the difference of the radial distances from the origin to its endpoints; (c) the area of the sector formed by the arc and the radii to its endpoints.

22. If a curve in 3-space is described by a vector-valued function $r$ defined on a parametric interval $[a, b]$, prove that the scalar triple product $r'(t) \cdot r(a) \times r(b)$ is zero for at least one $t$ in $(a, b)$. Interpret this result geometrically.

# 15

# LINEAR SPACES

## 15.1 Introduction

Throughout this book we have encountered many examples of mathematical objects that can be added to each other and multiplied by real numbers. First of all, the real numbers themselves are such objects. Other examples are real-valued functions, the complex numbers, infinite series, vectors in $n$-space, and vector-valued functions. In this chapter we discuss a general mathematical concept, called a *linear space*, which includes all these examples and many others as special cases.

Briefly, a linear space is a set of elements of any kind on which certain operations (called *addition* and *multiplication by numbers*) can be performed. In defining a linear space, we do not specify the nature of the elements nor do we tell how the operations are to be performed on them. Instead, we require that the operations have certain properties which we take as axioms for a linear space. We turn now to a detailed description of these axioms.

## 15.2 The definition of a linear space

Let $V$ denote a nonempty set of objects, called *elements*. The set $V$ is called a linear space if it satisfies the following ten axioms which we list in three groups.

*Closure axioms*

AXIOM 1. CLOSURE UNDER ADDITION. *For every pair of elements $x$ and $y$ in $V$ there corresponds a unique element in $V$ called the sum of $x$ and $y$, denoted by $x + y$.*

AXIOM 2. CLOSURE UNDER MULTIPLICATION BY REAL NUMBERS. *For every $x$ in $V$ and every real number $a$ there corresponds an element in $V$ called the product of $a$ and $x$, denoted by $ax$.*

*Axioms for addition*

AXIOM 3. COMMUTATIVE LAW. *For all $x$ and $y$ in $V$, we have $x + y = y + x$.*

AXIOM 4. ASSOCIATIVE LAW. *For all $x, y,$ and $z$ in $V$, we have $(x + y) + z = x + (y + z)$.*

551

AXIOM 5.   EXISTENCE OF ZERO ELEMENT.   *There is an element in V, denoted by O, such that*

$$x + O = x \quad \text{for all } x \text{ in } V.$$

AXIOM 6.   EXISTENCE OF NEGATIVES.   *For every x in V, the element* $(-1)x$ *has the property*

$$x + (-1)x = O$$

*Axioms for multiplication by numbers*

AXIOM 7.   ASSOCIATIVE LAW.   *For every x in V and all real numbers a and b, we have*

$$a(bx) = (ab)x.$$

AXIOM 8.   DISTRIBUTIVE LAW FOR ADDITION IN $V$.   *For all x and y in V and all real a, we have*

$$a(x + y) = ax + ay.$$

AXIOM 9.   DISTRIBUTIVE LAW FOR ADDITION OF NUMBERS.   *For all x in V and all real a and b, we have*

$$(a + b)x = ax + bx.$$

AXIOM 10.   EXISTENCE OF IDENTITY.   *For every x in V, we have* $1x = x$.

Linear spaces, as defined above, are sometimes called *real* linear spaces to emphasize the fact that we are multiplying the elements of $V$ by real numbers. If *real number* is replaced by *complex number* in Axioms 2, 7, 8, and 9, the resulting structure is called a *complex linear space*. Sometimes a linear space is referred to as a *linear vector space* or simply a *vector space*; the numbers used as multipliers are also called *scalars*. A real linear space has real numbers as scalars; a complex linear space has complex numbers as scalars. Although we shall deal primarily with examples of real linear spaces, all the theorems are valid for complex linear spaces as well. When we use the term linear space without further designation, it is to be understood that the space can be real or complex.

### 15.3   Examples of linear spaces

If we specify the set $V$ and tell how to add its elements and how to multiply them by numbers, we get a concrete example of a linear space. The reader can easily verify that each of the following examples satisfies all the axioms for a real linear space.

EXAMPLE 1. Let $V = \mathbf{R}$, the set of all real numbers, and let $x + y$ and $ax$ be ordinary addition and multiplication of real numbers.

EXAMPLE 2. Let $V = \mathbf{C}$, the set of all complex numbers, define $x + y$ to be ordinary addition of complex numbers, and define $ax$ to be multiplication of the complex number $x$ by the real number $a$. Even though the elements of $V$ are complex numbers, this is a real linear space because the scalars are real.

EXAMPLE 3. Let $V = V_n$, the vector space of all $n$-tuples of real numbers, with addition and multiplication by scalars defined in the usual way in terms of components.

EXAMPLE 4. Let $V$ be the set of all vectors in $V_n$ orthogonal to a given nonzero vector $N$. If $n = 2$, this linear space is a line through $O$ with $N$ as a normal vector. If $n = 3$, it is a plane through $O$ with $N$ as normal vector.

The following examples are called *function spaces*. The elements of $V$ are real-valued functions, with addition of two functions $f$ and $g$ defined in the usual way:

$$(f + g)(x) = f(x) + g(x)$$

for every real $x$ in the intersection of the domains of $f$ and $g$. Multiplication of a function $f$ by a real scalar $a$ is defined as follows: $af$ is that function whose value at each $x$ in the domain of $f$ is $af(x)$. The zero element is the function whose values are everywhere zero. The reader can easily verify that each of the following sets is a function space.

EXAMPLE 5. The set of all functions defined on a given interval.

EXAMPLE 6. The set of all polynomials.

EXAMPLE 7. The set of all polynomials of degree $\leq n$, where $n$ is fixed. (Whenever we consider this set it is understood that the zero polynomial is also included.) The set of all polynomials of degree *equal* to $n$ is not a linear space because the closure axioms are not satisfied. For example, the sum of two polynomials of degree $n$ need not have degree $n$.

EXAMPLE 8. The set of all functions continuous on a given interval. If the interval is $[a, b]$, we denote this space by $C(a, b)$.

EXAMPLE 9. The set of all functions differentiable at a given point.

EXAMPLE 10. The set of all functions integrable on a given interval.

EXAMPLE 11. The set of all functions $f$ defined at 1 with $f(1) = 0$. The number 0 is essential in this example. If we replace 0 by a nonzero number $c$, we violate the closure axioms.

EXAMPLE 12. The set of all solutions of a homogeneous linear differential equation $y'' + ay' + by = 0$, where $a$ and $b$ are given constants. Here again 0 is essential. The set of solutions of a nonhomogeneous differential equation does not satisfy the closure axioms.

These examples and many others illustrate how the linear space concept permeates algebra, geometry, and analysis. When a theorem is deduced from the axioms of a linear space, we obtain, in one stroke, a result valid for each concrete example. By unifying diverse examples in this way we gain a deeper insight into each. Sometimes special knowledge of one particular example helps to anticipate or interpret results valid for other examples and reveals relationships which might otherwise escape notice.

## 15.4 Elementary consequences of the axioms

The following theorems are easily deduced from the axioms for a linear space.

THEOREM 15.1. UNIQUENESS OF THE ZERO ELEMENT. *In any linear space there is one and only one zero element.*

*Proof.* Axiom 5 tells us that there is at least one zero element. Suppose there were two, say $O_1$ and $O_2$. Taking $x = O_1$ and $O = O_2$ in Axiom 5, we obtain $O_1 + O_2 = O_1$. Similarly, taking $x = O_2$ and $O = O_1$, we find $O_2 + O_1 = O_2$. But $O_1 + O_2 = O_2 + O_1$ because of the commutative law, so $O_1 = O_2$.

THEOREM 15.2. UNIQUENESS OF NEGATIVE ELEMENTS. *In any linear space every element has exactly one negative. That is, for every $x$ there is one and only one $y$ such that $x + y = O$.*

*Proof.* Axiom 6 tells us that each $x$ has at least one negative, namely $(-1)x$. Suppose $x$ has two negatives, say $y_1$ and $y_2$. Then $x + y_1 = O$ and $x + y_2 = O$. Adding $y_2$ to both members of the first equation and using Axioms 5, 4, and 3, we find that

$$y_2 + (x + y_1) = y_2 + O = y_2,$$

and

$$y_2 + (x + y_1) = (y_2 + x) + y_1 = O + y_1 = y_1 + O = y_1.$$

Therefore $y_1 = y_2$, so $x$ has exactly one negative, the element $(-1)x$.

*Notation.* The negative of $x$ is denoted by $-x$. The difference $y - x$ is defined to be the sum $y + (-x)$.

The next theorem describes a number of properties which govern elementary algebraic manipulations in a linear space.

THEOREM 15.3. *In a given linear space, let $x$ and $y$ denote arbitrary elements and let $a$ and $b$ denote arbitrary scalars. Then we have the following properties:*
 (a) $0x = O$.
 (b) $aO = O$.
 (c) $(-a)x = -(ax) = a(-x)$.
 (d) *If $ax = O$, then either $a = 0$ or $x = O$.*
 (e) *If $ax = ay$ and $a \neq 0$, then $x = y$.*
 (f) *If $ax = bx$ and $x \neq O$, then $a = b$.*
 (g) $-(x + y) = (-x) + (-y) = -x - y$.
 (h) $x + x = 2x,\ x + x + x = 3x$, *and in general,* $\sum_{i=1}^{n} x = nx$.

We shall prove (a), (b), and (c) and leave the proofs of the other properties as exercises.

*Proof of* (a). Let $z = 0x$. We wish to prove that $z = O$. Adding $z$ to itself and using Axiom 9, we find that

$$z + z = 0x + 0x = (0 + 0)x = 0x = z.$$

Now add $-z$ to both members to get $z = O$.

*Proof of* (b). Let $z = aO$, add $z$ to itself, and use Axiom 8.

*Proof of* (c). Let $z = (-a)x$. Adding $z$ to $ax$ and using Axiom 9, we find that

$$z + ax = (-a)x + ax = (-a + a)x = 0x = O,$$

so $z$ is the negative of $ax$, $z = -(ax)$. Similarly, if we add $a(-x)$ to $ax$ and use Axiom 8 and property (b), we find that $a(-x) = -(ax)$.

## 15.5 Exercises

In Exercises 1 through 28, determine whether each of the given sets is a real linear space, if addition and multiplication by real scalars are defined in the usual way. For those that are not, tell which axioms fail to hold. The functions in Exercises 1 through 17 are real-valued. In Exercises 3, 4, and 5, each function has domain containing 0 and 1. In Exercises 7 through 12, each domain contains all real numbers.

1. All rational functions.
2. All rational functions $f/g$, with the degree of $f \leq$ the degree of $g$ (including $f = 0$).
3. All $f$ with $f(0) = f(1)$.
4. All $f$ with $2f(0) = f(1)$.
5. All $f$ with $f(1) = 1 + f(0)$.
6. All step functions defined on $[0, 1]$.
7. All $f$ with $f(x) \to 0$ as $x \to +\infty$.
8. All even functions.
9. All odd functions.
10. All bounded functions.
11. All increasing functions.
12. All functions with period $2\pi$.
13. All $f$ integrable on $[0, 1]$ with $\int_0^1 f(x)\,dx = 0$.
14. All $f$ integrable on $[0, 1]$ with $\int_0^1 f(x)\,dx \geq 0$.
15. All $f$ satisfying $f(x) = f(1 - x)$ for all $x$.
16. All Taylor polynomials of degree $\leq n$ for a fixed $n$ (including the zero polynomial).
17. All solutions of a linear second-order homogeneous differential equation $y'' + P(x)y' + Q(x)y = 0$, where $P$ and $Q$ are given functions, continuous everywhere.
18. All bounded real sequences.
19. All convergent real sequences.
20. All convergent real series.
21. All absolutely convergent real series.
22. All vectors $(x, y, z)$ in $V_3$ with $z = 0$.
23. All vectors $(x, y, z)$ in $V_3$ with $x = 0$ or $y = 0$.
24. All vectors $(x, y, z)$ in $V_3$ with $y = 5x$.
25. All vectors $(x, y, z)$ in $V_3$ with $3x + 4y = 1$, $z = 0$.
26. All vectors $(x, y, z)$ in $V_3$ which are scalar multiples of $(1, 2, 3)$.
27. All vectors $(x, y, z)$ in $V_3$ whose components satisfy a system of three linear equations of the form:

$$a_{11}x + a_{12}y + a_{13}z = 0, \qquad a_{21}x + a_{22}y + a_{23}z = 0, \qquad a_{31}x + a_{32}y + a_{33}z = 0.$$

28. All vectors in $V_n$ that are linear combinations of two given vectors $A$ and $B$.

29. Let $V = \mathbf{R}^+$, the set of positive real numbers. Define the "sum" of two elements $x$ and $y$ in $V$ to be their product $x \cdot y$ (in the usual sense), and define "multiplication" of an element $x$ in $V$ by a scalar $c$ to be $x^c$. Prove that $V$ is a real linear space with 1 as the zero element.

30. (a) Prove that Axiom 10 can be deduced from the other axioms.
    (b) Prove that Axiom 10 cannot be deduced from the other axioms if Axiom 6 is replaced by Axiom 6': For every $x$ in $V$ there is an element $y$ in $V$ such that $x + y = O$.

31. Let $S$ be the set of all ordered pairs $(x_1, x_2)$ of real numbers. In each case determine whether or not $S$ is a linear space with the operations of addition and multiplication by scalars defined as indicated. If the set is not a linear space, indicate which axioms are violated.
    (a) $(x_1, x_2) + (y_1, y_2) = (x_1 + y_1, x_2 + y_2)$,     $a(x_1, x_2) = (ax_1, 0)$.
    (b) $(x_1, x_2) + (y_1, y_2) = (x_1 + y_1, 0)$,     $a(x_1, x_2) = (ax_1, ax_2)$.
    (c) $(x_1, x_2) + (y_1, y_2) = (x_1, x_2 + y_2)$,     $a(x_1, x_2) = (ax_1, ax_2)$.
    (d) $(x_1, x_2) + (y_1, y_2) = (|x_1 + x_2|, |y_1 + y_2|)$,     $a(x_1, x_2) = (|ax_1|, |ax_2|)$.

32. Prove parts (d) through (h) of Theorem 15.3.

## 15.6 Subspaces of a linear space

Given a linear space $V$, let $S$ be a nonempty subset of $V$. If $S$ is also a linear space, with the same operations of addition and multiplication by scalars, then $S$ is called a *subspace* of $V$. The next theorem gives a simple criterion for determining whether or not a subset of a linear space is a subspace.

THEOREM 15.4. *Let $S$ be a nonempty subset of a linear space $V$. Then $S$ is a subspace if and only if $S$ satisfies the closure axioms.*

*Proof.* If $S$ is a subspace, it satisfies all the axioms for a linear space, and hence, in particular, it satisfies the closure axioms.

Now we show that if $S$ satisfies the closure axioms it satisfies the others as well. The commutative and associative laws for addition (Axioms 3 and 4) and the axioms for multiplication by scalars (Axioms 7 through 10) are automatically satisfied in $S$ because they hold for all elements of $V$. It remains to verify Axioms 5 and 6, the existence of a zero element in $S$, and the existence of a negative for each element in $S$.

Let $x$ be any element of $S$. ($S$ has at least one element since $S$ is not empty.) By Axiom 2, $ax$ is in $S$ for every scalar $a$. Taking $a = 0$, it follows that $0x$ is in $S$. But $0x = O$, by Theorem 15.3(a), so $O \in S$, and Axiom 5 is satisfied. Taking $a = -1$, we see that $(-1)x$ is in $S$. But $x + (-1)x = O$ since both $x$ and $(-1)x$ are in $V$, so Axiom 6 is satisfied in $S$. Therefore $S$ is a subspace of $V$.

DEFINITION. *Let $S$ be a nonempty subset of a linear space $V$. An element $x$ in $V$ of the form*

$$x = \sum_{i=1}^{k} c_i x_i,$$

*where $x_1, \ldots, x_k$ are all in $S$ and $c_1, \ldots, c_k$ are scalars, is called a finite linear combination of elements of $S$. The set of all finite linear combinations of elements of $S$ satisfies the closure axioms and hence is a subspace of $V$. We call this the subspace spanned by $S$, or the* *linear span of S, and denote it by $L(S)$. If S is empty, we define $L(S)$ to be $\{O\}$, the set consisting of the zero element alone.*

Different sets may span the same subspace. For example, the space $V_2$ is spanned by each of the following sets of vectors: $\{i, j\}$, $\{i, j, i + j\}$, $\{O, i, -i, j, -j, i + j\}$. The space of all polynomials $p(t)$ of degree $\leq n$ is spanned by the set of $n + 1$ polynomials

$$\{1, t, t^2, \ldots, t^n\}.$$

It is also spanned by the set $\{1, t/2, t^2/3, \ldots, t^n/(n + 1)\}$, and by $\{1, (1 + t), (1 + t)^2, \ldots, (1 + t)^n\}$. The space of all polynomials is spanned by the infinite set of polynomials $\{1, t, t^2, \ldots\}$.

A number of questions arise naturally at this point. For example, which spaces can be spanned by a finite set of elements? If a space can be spanned by a finite set of elements, what is the smallest number of elements required? To discuss these and related questions, we introduce the concepts of *dependence, independence, bases,* and *dimension.* These ideas were encountered in Chapter 12 in our study of the vector space $V_n$. Now we extend them to general linear spaces.

## 15.7 Dependent and independent sets in a linear space

DEFINITION. *A set S of elements in a linear space V is called dependent if there is a finite set of distinct elements in S, say $x_1, \ldots, x_k$, and corresponding set of scalars $c_1, \ldots, c_k$, not all zero, such that*

$$\sum_{i=1}^{k} c_i x_i = O.$$

*The set S is called independent if it is not dependent. In this case, for all choices of distinct elements $x_1, \ldots, x_k$ in S and scalars $c_1, \ldots, c_k$,*

$$\sum_{i=1}^{k} c_i x_i = O \qquad implies \qquad c_1 = c_2 = \cdots = c_k = 0.$$

Although dependence and independence are properties of sets of elements, we also apply these terms to the elements themselves. For example, the elements in an independent set are called independent elements.

If $S$ is a finite set, the foregoing definition agrees with that given in Chapter 12 for the space $V_n$. However, the present definition is not restricted to finite sets.

EXAMPLE 1. If a subset $T$ of a set $S$ is dependent, then $S$ itself is dependent. This is logically equivalent to the statement that every subset of an independent set is independent.

EXAMPLE 2. If one element in $S$ is a scalar multiple of another, then $S$ is dependent.

EXAMPLE 3. If $O \in S$, then $S$ is dependent.

EXAMPLE 4. The empty set is independent.

Many examples of dependent and independent sets of vectors in $V_n$ were discussed in Chapter 12. The following examples illustrate these concepts in function spaces. In each case the underlying linear space $V$ is the set of all real-valued functions defined on the real line.

EXAMPLE. 5. Let $u_1(t) = \cos^2 t$, $u_2(t) = \sin^2 t$, $u_3(t) = 1$ for all real $t$. The Pythagorean identity shows that $u_1 + u_2 - u_3 = O$, so the three functions $u_1$, $u_2$, $u_3$ are dependent.

EXAMPLE 6. Let $u_k(t) = t^k$ for $k = 0, 1, 2, \ldots$, and $t$ real. The set $S = \{u_0, u_1, u_2, \ldots\}$ is independent. To prove this, it suffices to show that for each $n$ the $n + 1$ polynomials $u_0, u_1, \ldots, u_n$ are independent. A relation of the form $\sum c_k u_k = O$ means that

$$(15.1) \qquad \sum_{k=0}^{n} c_k t^k = 0$$

for all real $t$. When $t = 0$, this gives $c_0 = 0$. Differentiating (15.1) and setting $t = 0$, we find that $c_1 = 0$. Repeating the process, we find that each coefficient $c_k$ is zero.

EXAMPLE 7. If $a_1, \ldots, a_n$ are distinct real numbers, the $n$ exponential functions

$$u_1(x) = e^{a_1 x}, \ldots, u_n(x) = e^{a_n x}$$

are independent. We can prove this by induction on $n$. The result holds trivially when $n = 1$. Therefore, assume it is true for $n - 1$ exponential functions and consider scalars $c_1, \ldots, c_n$ such that

$$(15.2) \qquad \sum_{k=1}^{n} c_k e^{a_k x} = 0.$$

Let $a_M$ be the largest of the $n$ numbers $a_1, \ldots, a_n$. Multiplying both members of (15.2) by $e^{-a_M x}$, we obtain

$$(15.3) \qquad \sum_{k=1}^{n} c_k e^{(a_k - a_M) x} = 0.$$

If $k \neq M$, the number $a_k - a_M$ is negative. Therefore, when $x \to +\infty$ in Equation (15.3), each term with $k \neq M$ tends to zero and we find that $c_M = 0$. Deleting the $M$th term from (15.2) and applying the induction hypothesis, we find that each of the remaining $n - 1$ coefficients $c_k$ is zero.

THEOREM 15.5. *Let $S$ be an independent set consisting of $k$ elements in a linear space $V$ and let $L(S)$ be the subspace spanned by $S$. Then every set of $k + 1$ elements in $L(S)$ is dependent.*

*Proof.* When $V = V_n$, Theorem 15.5 reduces to Theorem 12.8. If we examine the proof of Theorem 12.8, we find that it is based only on the fact that $V_n$ is a linear space and not on any other special property of $V_n$. Therefore the proof given for Theorem 12.8 is valid for any linear space $V$.

## 15.8 Bases and dimension

DEFINITION. *A finite set S of elements in a linear space V is called a finite basis for V if S is independent and spans V. The space V is called finite dimensional if it has a finite basis, or if V consists of O alone. Otherwise V is called infinite dimensional.*

THEOREM 15.6. *Let V be a finite-dimensional linear space. Then every finite basis for V has the same number of elements.*

*Proof.* Let $S$ and $T$ be two finite bases for $V$. Suppose $S$ consists of $k$ elements and $T$ consists of $m$ elements. Since $S$ is independent and spans $V$, Theorem 15.5 tells us that every set of $k + 1$ elements in $V$ is dependent. Therefore, every set of more than $k$ elements in $V$ is dependent. Since $T$ is an independent set, we must have $m \leq k$. The same argument with $S$ and $T$ interchanged shows that $k \leq m$. Therefore $k = m$.

DEFINITION. *If a linear space V has a basis of n elements, the integer n is called the dimension of V. We write $n = \dim V$. If $V = \{O\}$, we say V has dimension 0.*

EXAMPLE 1. The space $V_n$ has dimension $n$. One basis is the set of $n$ unit coordinate vectors.

EXAMPLE 2. The space of all polynomials $p(t)$ of degree $\leq n$ has dimension $n + 1$. One basis is the set of $n + 1$ polynomials $\{1, t, t^2, \ldots, t^n\}$. Every polynomial of degree $\leq n$ is a linear combination of these $n + 1$ polynomials.

EXAMPLE 3. The space of solutions of the differential equation $y'' - 2y' - 3y = 0$ has dimension 2. One basis consists of the two functions $u_1(x) = e^{-x}$, $u_2(x) = e^{3x}$. Every solution is a linear combination of these two.

EXAMPLE 4. The space of all polynomials $p(t)$ is infinite-dimensional. Although the infinite set $\{1, t, t^2, \ldots\}$ spans this space, no *finite* set of polynomials spans the space.

THEOREM 15.7. *Let V be a finite-dimensional linear space with $\dim V = n$. Then we have the following:*
(a) *Any set of independent elements in V is a subset of some basis for V.*
(b) *Any set of n independent elements is a basis for V.*

*Proof.* The proof of (a) is identical to that of part (b) of Theorem 12.10. The proof of (b) is identical to that of part (c) of Theorem 12.10.

Let $V$ be a linear space of dimension $n$ and consider a basis whose elements $e_1, \ldots, e_n$ are taken in a given order. We denote such an ordered basis as an $n$-tuple $(e_1, \ldots, e_n)$.

If $x \in V$, we can express $x$ as a linear combination of these basis elements:

$$(15.4) \qquad x = \sum_{i=1}^{n} c_i e_i .$$

The coefficients in this equation determine an $n$-tuple of numbers $(c_1, \ldots, c_n)$ that is uniquely determined by $x$. In fact, if we have another representation of $x$ as a linear combination of $e_1, \ldots, e_n$, say $x = \sum_{i=1}^{n} d_i e_i$, then by subtraction from (15.4), we find that $\sum_{i=1}^{n} (c_i - d_i)e_i = O$. But since the basis elements are independent, this implies $c_i = d_i$ for each $i$, so we have $(c_1; \ldots, c_n) = (d_1, \ldots, d_n)$.

The components of the ordered $n$-tuple $(c_1, \ldots, c_n)$ determined by Equation (15.4) are called *the components of x relative to the ordered basis* $(e_1, \ldots, e_n)$.

## 15.9 Exercises

In each of Exercises 1 through 10, let $S$ denote the set of all vectors $(x, y, z)$ in $V_3$ whose components satisfy the condition given. Determine whether $S$ is a subspace of $V_3$. If $S$ is a subspace, compute dim $S$.

1. $x = 0$.
2. $x + y = 0$.
3. $x + y + z = 0$.
4. $x = y$.
5. $x = y = z$.

6. $x = y$ or $x = z$.
7. $x^2 - y^2 = 0$.
8. $x + y = 1$.
9. $y = 2x$ and $z = 3x$.
10. $x + y + z = 0$ and $x - y - z = 0$.

Let $P_n$ denote the linear space of all real polynomials of degree $\leq n$, where $n$ is fixed. In each of Exercises 11 through 20, let $S$ denote the set of all polynomials $f$ in $P_n$ satisfying the condition given. Determine whether or not $S$ is a subspace of $P_n$. If $S$ is a subspace, compute dim $S$.

11. $f(0) = 0$.
12. $f'(0) = 0$.
13. $f''(0) = 0$.
14. $f(0) + f'(0) = 0$.
15. $f(0) = f(1)$.

16. $f(0) = f(2)$.
17. $f$ is even.
18. $f$ is odd.
19. $f$ has degree $\leq k$, where $k < n$, or $f = 0$.
20. $f$ has degree $k$, where $k < n$, or $f = 0$.

21. In the linear space of all real polynomials $p(t)$, describe the subspace spanned by each of the following subsets of polynomials and determine the dimension of this subspace.
    (a) $\{1, t^2, t^4\}$;    (b) $\{t, t^3, t^5\}$;    (c) $\{t, t^2\}$;    (d) $\{1 + t, (1 + t)^2\}$.
22. In this exercise, $L(S)$ denotes the subspace spanned by a subset $S$ of a linear space $V$. Prove each of the statements (a) through (f).
    (a) $S \subseteq L(S)$.
    (b) If $S \subseteq T \subseteq V$ and if $T$ is a subspace of $V$, then $L(S) \subseteq T$. This property is described by saying that $L(S)$ is the *smallest* subspace of $V$ which contains $S$.
    (c) A subset $S$ of $V$ is a subspace of $V$ if and only if $L(S) = S$.
    (d) If $S \subseteq T \subseteq V$, then $L(S) \subseteq L(T)$.
    (e) If $S$ and $T$ are subspaces of $V$, then so is $S \cap T$.
    (f) If $S$ and $T$ are subsets of $V$, then $L(S \cap T) \subseteq L(S) \cap L(T)$.
    (g) Give an example in which $L(S \cap T) \neq L(S) \cap L(T)$.
23. Let $V$ be the linear space consisting of all real-valued functions defined on the real line. Determine whether each of the following subsets of $V$ is dependent or independent. Compute the dimension of the subspace spanned by each set.
    (a) $\{1, e^{ax}, e^{bx}\}, a \neq b$.
    (b) $\{e^{ax}, xe^{ax}\}$.
    (c) $\{1, e^{ax}, xe^{ax}\}$.
    (d) $\{e^{ax}, xe^{ax}, x^2 e^{ax}\}$.

(e) $\{e^x, e^{-x}, \cosh x\}$.  (h) $\{1, \cos 2x, \sin^2 x\}$.

(f) $\{\cos x, \sin x\}$.  (i) $\{\sin x, \sin 2x\}$.

(g) $\{\cos^2 x, \sin^2 x\}$.  (j) $\{e^x \cos x, e^{-x} \sin x\}$.

24. Let $V$ be a finite-dimensional linear space, and let $S$ be a subspace of $V$. Prove each of the following statements.

(a) $S$ is finite dimensional and $\dim S \leq \dim V$.

(b) $\dim S = \dim V$ if and only if $S = V$.

(c) Every basis for $S$ is part of a basis for $V$.

(d) A basis for $V$ need not contain a basis for $S$.

## 15.10 Inner products, Euclidean spaces. Norms

In ordinary Euclidean geometry, those properties that rely on the possibility of measuring lengths of line segments and angles between lines are called *metric* properties. In our study of $V_n$, we defined lengths and angles in terms of the dot product. Now we wish to extend these ideas to more general linear spaces. We shall introduce first a generalization of the dot product, which we call an *inner product*, and then define length and angle in terms of the inner product.

The dot product $x \cdot y$ of two vectors $x = (x_1, \ldots, x_n)$ and $y = (y_1, \ldots, y_n)$ in $V_n$ was defined in Chapter 12 by the formula

$$(15.5) \qquad x \cdot y = \sum_{i=1}^{n} x_i y_i \,.$$

In a general linear space, we write $(x, y)$ instead of $x \cdot y$ for inner products, and we define the product axiomatically rather than by a specific formula. That is, we state a number of properties we wish inner products to satisfy and we regard these properties as *axioms*.

DEFINITION. *A real linear space $V$ is said to have an inner product if for each pair of elements $x$ and $y$ in $V$ there corresponds a unique real number $(x, y)$ satisfying the following axioms for all choices of $x, y, z$ in $V$ and all real scalars $c$.*

(1) $(x, y) = (y, x)$    (*commutativity, or symmetry*).

(2) $(x, y + z) = (x, y) + (x, z)$    (*distributivity, or linearity*).

(3) $c(x, y) = (cx, y)$    (*associativity, or homogeneity*).

(4) $(x, x) > 0$    *if*  $x \neq O$    (*positivity*).

A real linear space with an inner product is called a *real Euclidean space*.

*Note:*  Taking $c = 0$ in (3), we find that $(O, y) = 0$ for all $y$.

In a complex linear space, an inner product $(x, y)$ is a complex number satisfying the same axioms as those for a real inner product, except that the symmetry axiom is replaced by the relation

$$(1') \qquad (x, y) = \overline{(y, x)},$$

where $\overline{(y, x)}$ denotes the complex conjugate of $(y, x)$. In the homogeneity axiom, the scalar multiplier $c$ can be any complex number. From the homogeneity axiom and $(1')$, we get the companion relation

$$(x, cy) = \overline{(cy, x)} = \bar{c}\overline{(y, x)} = \bar{c}(x, y).$$

A complex linear space with an inner product is called a *complex Euclidean space*. (Sometimes the term *unitary space* is also used.) One example is complex vector space $V_n(\mathbf{C})$ discussed briefly in Section 12.16.

Although we are interested primarily in examples of real Euclidean spaces, the theorems of this chapter are valid for complex Euclidean spaces as well. When we use the term Euclidean space without further designation, it is to be understood that the space can be real or complex.

The reader should verify that each of the following satisfies all the axioms for an inner product.

EXAMPLE 1. In $V_n$ let $(x, y) = x \cdot y$, the usual dot product of $x$ and $y$.

EXAMPLE 2. If $x = (x_1, x_2)$ and $y = (y_1, y_2)$ are any two vectors in $V_2$, define $(x, y)$ by the formula

$$(x, y) = 2x_1y_1 + x_1y_2 + x_2y_1 + x_2y_2.$$

This example shows that there may be more than one inner product in a given linear space.

EXAMPLE 3. Let $C(a, b)$ denote the linear space of all real-valued functions continuous on an interval $[a, b]$. Define an inner product of two functions $f$ and $g$ by the formula

$$(f, g) = \int_a^b f(t)g(t)\, dt.$$

This formula is analogous to Equation (15.5) which defines the dot product of two vectors in $V_n$. The function values $f(t)$ and $g(t)$ play the role of the components $x_i$ and $y_i$, and integration takes the place of summation.

EXAMPLE 4. In the space $C(a, b)$, define

$$(f, g) = \int_a^b w(t)f(t)g(t)\, dt,$$

where $w$ is a fixed positive function in $C(a, b)$. The function $w$ is called a *weight function*. In Example 3 we have $w(t) = 1$ for all $t$.

EXAMPLE 5. In the linear space of all real polynomials, define

$$(f, g) = \int_0^\infty e^{-t}f(t)g(t)\, dt.$$

Because of the exponential factor, this improper integral converges for every choice of polynomials $f$ and $g$.

THEOREM 15.8. *In a Euclidean space V, every inner product satisfies the Cauchy–Schwarz inequality*:

$$|(x, y)|^2 \leq (x, x)(y, y) \quad \text{for all } x \text{ and } y \text{ in } V.$$

*Moreover, the equality sign holds if and only if x and y are dependent.*

*Proof.* When we proved the corresponding result for vectors in $V_n$ (Theorem 12.3), we were careful to point out that the proof was a consequence of the properties of the dot product listed in Theorem 12.2 and did not depend on the particular definition used to deduce these properties. Therefore, the very same proof is valid in any real Euclidean space. When we apply this proof in a complex Euclidean space, we obtain the inequality $(x, y)(y, x) \leq (x, x)(y, y)$, which is the same as the Cauchy-Schwarz inequality since

$$(x, y)(y, x) = (x, y)\overline{(x, y)} = |(x, y)|^2.$$

EXAMPLE. Applying Theorem 15.8 to the space $C(a, b)$ with the inner product $(f, g) = \int_a^b f(t)g(t)\, dt$, we find that the Cauchy-Schwarz inequality becomes

$$\left(\int_a^b f(t)g(t)\, dt\right)^2 \leq \left(\int_a^b f^2(t)\, dt\right)\left(\int_a^b g^2(t)\, dt\right).$$

The inner product can be used to introduce the metric concept of length in any Euclidean space.

DEFINITION. *In a Euclidean space V, the nonnegative number $\|x\|$ defined by the equation*

$$\|x\| = (x, x)^{1/2}$$

*is called the norm of the element x.*

When the Cauchy-Schwarz inequality is expressed in terms of norms, it becomes

$$|(x, y)| \leq \|x\| \, \|y\|.$$

Since it may be possible to define an inner product in many different ways, the norm of an element will depend on the choice of inner product. This lack of uniqueness is to be expected. It is analogous to the fact that we can assign different numbers to measure the length of a given line segment, depending on the choice of scale or unit of measurement. The next theorem gives fundamental properties of norms that do not depend on the choice of inner product.

THEOREM 15.9. *In a Euclidean space, every norm has the following properties for all elements x and y and all scalars c:*
  (a) $\|x\| = 0$   *if*   $x = O$.
  (b) $\|x\| > 0$   *if*   $x \neq O$   *(positivity)*.
  (c) $\|cx\| = |c| \, \|x\|$   *(homogeneity)*.
  (d) $\|x + y\| \leq \|x\| + \|y\|$   *(triangle inequality)*.
  *The equality sign holds in* (d) *if $x = O$, if $y = O$, or if $y = cx$ for some $c > 0$.*

*Proof.*  Properties (a), (b) and (c) follow at once from the axioms for an inner product. To prove (d), we note that

$$\|x + y\|^2 = (x + y, x + y) = (x, x) + (y, y) + (x, y) + (y, x)$$
$$= \|x\|^2 + \|y\|^2 + (x, y) + \overline{(x, y)}.$$

The sum $(x, y) + \overline{(x, y)}$ is real. The Cauchy-Schwarz inequality shows that $|(x, y)| \leq \|x\| \, \|y\|$ and $|\overline{(x, y)}| \leq \|x\| \, \|y\|$, so we have

$$\|x + y\|^2 \leq \|x\|^2 + \|y\|^2 + 2\|x\| \, \|y\| = (\|x\| + \|y\|)^2.$$

This proves (d). When $y = cx$, where $c > 0$, we have

$$\|x + y\| = \|x + cx\| = (1 + c)\|x\| = \|x\| + \|cx\| = \|x\| + \|y\|.$$

DEFINITION.  *In a real Euclidean space $V$, the angle between two nonzero elements $x$ and $y$ is defined to be that number $\theta$ in the interval $0 \leq \theta \leq \pi$ which satisfies the equation*

$$(15.6) \qquad\qquad \cos \theta = \frac{(x, y)}{\|x\| \, \|y\|}.$$

*Note:*  The Cauchy-Schwarz inequality shows that the quotient on the right of (15.6) lies in the interval $[-1, 1]$, so there is exactly one $\theta$ in $[0, \pi]$ whose cosine is equal to this quotient.

## 15.11  Orthogonality in a Euclidean space

DEFINITION.  *In a Euclidean space $V$, two elements $x$ and $y$ are called orthogonal if their inner product is zero. A subset $S$ of $V$ is called an orthogonal set if $(x, y) = 0$ for every pair of distinct elements $x$ and $y$ in $S$. An orthogonal set is called orthonormal if each of its elements has norm 1.*

The zero element is orthogonal to every element of $V$; it is the only element orthogonal to itself. The next theorem shows a relation between orthogonality and dependence.

THEOREM 15.10.  *In a Euclidean space $V$, every orthogonal set of nonzero elements is independent. In particular, in a finite-dimensional Euclidean space with dim $V = n$, every orthogonal set consisting of $n$ nonzero elements is a basis for $V$.*

*Proof.*  Let $S$ be an orthogonal set of nonzero elements in $V$, and suppose some finite linear combination of elements of $S$ is zero, say

$$\sum_{i=1}^{k} c_i x_i = O,$$

where each $x_i \in S$. Taking the dot product of each member with $x_1$ and using the fact that $(x_1, x_i) = 0$ if $i \neq 1$, we find that $c_1(x_1, x_1) = 0$. But $(x_1, x_1) \neq 0$ since $x_1 \neq O$ so $c_1 = 0$. Repeating the argument with $x_1$ replaced by $x_j$, we find that each $c_j = 0$. This proves that $S$ is independent. If dim $V = n$ and if $S$ consists of $n$ elements, Theorem 15.7(b) shows that $S$ is a basis for $V$.

EXAMPLE. In the real linear space $C(0, 2\pi)$ with the inner product $(f, g) = \int_0^{2\pi} f(x)g(x)\,dx$, let $S$ be the set of trigonometric functions $\{u_0, u_1, u_2, \ldots\}$ given by

$$u_0(x) = 1, \qquad u_{2n-1}(x) = \cos nx, \qquad u_{2n}(x) = \sin nx, \qquad \text{for} \quad n = 1, 2, \ldots.$$

If $m \neq n$, we have the orthogonality relations

$$\int_0^{2\pi} u_n(x)u_m(x)\,dx = 0,$$

so $S$ is an orthogonal set. Since no member of $S$ is the zero element, $S$ is independent. The norm of each element of $S$ is easily calculated. We have $(u_0, u_0) = \int_0^{2\pi} dx = 2\pi$ and, for $n \geq 1$, we have

$$(u_{2n-1}, u_{2n-1}) = \int_0^{2\pi} \cos^2 nx\,dx = \pi, \qquad (u_{2n}, u_{2n}) = \int_0^{2\pi} \sin^2 nx\,dx = \pi.$$

Therefore, $\|u_0\| = \sqrt{2\pi}$ and $\|u_n\| = \sqrt{\pi}$ for $n \geq 1$. Dividing each $u_n$ by its norm, we obtain an orthonormal set $\{\varphi_0, \varphi_1, \varphi_2, \ldots\}$ where $\varphi_n = u_n/\|u_n\|$. Thus, we have

$$\varphi_0(x) = \frac{1}{\sqrt{2\pi}}, \qquad \varphi_{2n-1}(x) = \frac{\cos nx}{\sqrt{\pi}}, \qquad \varphi_{2n}(x) = \frac{\sin nx}{\sqrt{\pi}}, \qquad \text{for} \quad n \geq 1.$$

In Section 15.13 we shall prove that every finite-dimensional Euclidean space has an orthogonal basis. The next theorem shows how to compute the components of an element relative to such a basis.

THEOREM 15.11. *Let $V$ be a finite-dimensional Euclidean space with dimension $n$, and assume that $S = \{e_1, \ldots, e_n\}$ is an orthogonal basis for $V$. If an element $x$ is expressed as a linear combination of the basis elements, say*

$$(15.7) \qquad x = \sum_{i=1}^{n} c_i e_i,$$

*then its components relative to the ordered basis $(e_1, \ldots, e_n)$ are given by the formulas*

$$(15.8) \qquad c_j = \frac{(x, e_j)}{(e_j, e_j)} \qquad \text{for} \quad j = 1, 2, \ldots, n.$$

*In particular, if $S$ is an orthonormal basis, each $c_j$ is given by*

$$(15.9) \qquad c_j = (x, e_j).$$

*Proof.* Taking the inner product of each member of (15.7) with $e_j$, we obtain

$$(x, e_j) = \sum_{i=1}^{n} c_i(e_i, e_j) = c_j(e_j, e_j)$$

since $(e_i, e_j) = 0$ if $i \neq j$. This implies (15.8), and when $(e_j, e_j) = 1$, we obtain (15.9).

If $\{e_1, \ldots, e_n\}$ is an orthonormal basis, Equation (15.7) can be written in the form

(15.10)
$$x = \sum_{i=1}^{n} (x, e_i)e_i.$$

The next theorem shows that in a finite-dimensional Euclidean space with an orthonormal basis the inner product of two elements can be computed in terms of their components.

THEOREM 15.12. *Let $V$ be a finite-dimensional Euclidean space of dimension $n$, and assume that $\{e_1, \ldots, e_n\}$ is an orthonormal basis for $V$. Then for every pair of elements $x$ and $y$ in $V$, we have*

(15.11)
$$(x, y) = \sum_{i=1}^{n} (x, e_i)(\overline{y, e_i}) \qquad (Parseval's\ formula).$$

*In particular, when $x = y$, we have*

(15.12)
$$\|x\|^2 = \sum_{i=1}^{n} |(x, e_i)|^2.$$

*Proof.* Taking the inner product of both members of Equation (15.10) with $y$ and using the linearity property of the inner product, we obtain (15.11). When $x = y$, Equation (15.11) reduces to (15.12).

*Note:* Equation (15.11) is named in honor of M. A. Parseval (circa 1776–1836), who obtained this type of formula in a special function space.

## 15.12 Exercises

1. Let $x = (x_1, \ldots, x_n)$ and $y = (y_1, \ldots, y_n)$ be arbitrary vectors in $V_n$. In each case, determine whether $(x, y)$ is an inner product for $V_n$ if $(x, y)$ is defined by the formula given. In case $(x, y)$ is not an inner product, tell which axioms are not satisfied.

(a) $(x, y) = \sum_{i=1}^{n} x_i |y_i|$.

(b) $(x, y) = \left| \sum_{i=1}^{n} x_i y_i \right|$.

(c) $(x, y) = \sum_{i=1}^{n} x_i \sum_{j=1}^{n} y_j$.

(d) $(x, y) = \left( \sum_{i=1}^{n} x_i^2 y_i^2 \right)^{1/2}$.

(e) $(x, y) = \sum_{i=1}^{n} (x_i + y_i)^2 - \sum_{i=1}^{n} x_i^2 - \sum_{i=1}^{n} y_i^2$.

2. Suppose we retain the first three axioms for a real inner product (symmetry, linearity, and

homogeneity) but replace the fourth axiom by a new axiom (4'): $(x, x) = 0$ if and only if $x = O$. Prove that either $(x, x) > 0$ for all $x \neq O$ or else $(x, x) < 0$ for all $x \neq O$.

[*Hint:* Assume $(x, x) > 0$ for some $x \neq O$ and $(y, y) < 0$ for some $y \neq O$. In the space spanned by $\{x, y\}$, find an element $z \neq O$ with $(z, z) = 0$.]

Prove that each of the statements in Exercises 3 through 7 is valid for all elements $x$ and $y$ in a real Euclidean space.

3. $(x, y) = 0$ if and only if $\|x + y\| = \|x - y\|$.
4. $(x, y) = 0$ if and only if $\|x + y\|^2 = \|x\|^2 + \|y\|^2$.
5. $(x, y) = 0$ if and only if $\|x + cy\| \geq \|x\|$ for all real $c$.
6. $(x + y, x - y) = 0$ if and only if $\|x\| = \|y\|$.
7. If $x$ and $y$ are nonzero elements making an angle $\theta$ with each other, then

$$\|x - y\|^2 = \|x\|^2 + \|y\|^2 - 2 \|x\| \|y\| \cos \theta .$$

8. In the real linear space $C(1, e)$, define an inner product by the equation

$$(f, g) = \int_1^e (\log x) f(x) g(x) \, dx .$$

   (a) If $f(x) = \sqrt{x}$, compute $\|f\|$.
   (b) Find a linear polynomial $g(x) = a + bx$ that is orthogonal to the constant function $f(x) = 1$.
9. In the real linear space $C(-1, 1)$, let $(f, g) = \int_{-1}^1 f(t) g(t) \, dt$. Consider the three functions $u_1$, $u_2$, $u_3$ given by

$$u_1(t) = 1 , \qquad u_2(t) = t , \qquad u_3(t) = 1 + t .$$

   Prove that two of them are orthogonal, two make an angle $\pi/3$ with each other, and two make an angle $\pi/6$ with each other.
10. In the linear space $P_n$ of all real polynomials of degree $\leq n$, define

$$(f, g) = \sum_{k=0}^n f\left(\frac{k}{n}\right) g\left(\frac{k}{n}\right) .$$

   (a) Prove that $(f, g)$ is an inner product for $P_n$.
   (b) Compute $(f, g)$ when $f(t) = t$ and $g(t) = at + b$.
   (c) If $f(t) = t$, find all linear polynomials $g$ orthogonal to $f$.
11. In the linear space of all real polynomials, define $(f, g) = \int_0^\infty e^{-t} f(t) g(t) \, dt$.
   (a) Prove that this improper integral converges absolutely for all polynomials $f$ and $g$.
   (b) If $x_n(t) = t^n$ for $n = 0, 1, 2, \ldots$, prove that $(x_n, x_m) = (m + n)!$.
   (c) Compute $(f, g)$ when $f(t) = (t + 1)^2$ and $g(t) = t^2 + 1$.
   (d) Find all linear polynomials $g(t) = a + bt$ orthogonal to $f(t) = 1 + t$.
12. In the linear space of all real polynomials, determine whether or not $(f, g)$ is an inner product if $(f, g)$ is defined by the formula given. In case $(f, g)$ is not an inner product, indicate which axioms are violated. In (c), $f'$ and $g'$ denote derivatives.

   (a) $(f, g) = f(1)g(1)$.
   
   (b) $(f, g) = \left| \int_0^1 f(t) g(t) \, dt \right|$.
   
   (c) $(f, g) = \int_0^1 f'(t) g'(t) \, dt$.
   
   (d) $(f, g) = \left( \int_0^1 f(t) \, dt \right) \left( \int_0^1 g(t) \, dt \right)$.

13. Let $V$ consist of all infinite sequences $\{x_n\}$ of real numbers for which the series $\sum x_n^2$ converges. If $x = \{x_n\}$ and $y = \{y_n\}$ are two elements of $V$, define

$$(x, y) = \sum_{n=1}^{\infty} x_n y_n .$$

(a) Prove that this series converges absolutely.
   [*Hint:* Use the Cauchy-Schwarz inequality to estimate the sum $\sum_{n=1}^{M} |x_n y_n|$.]
(b) Prove that $V$ is a linear space with $(x, y)$ as an inner product.
(c) Compute $(x, y)$ if $x_n = 1/n$ and $y_n = 1/(n + 1)$ for $n \geq 1$.
(d) Compute $(x, y)$ if $x_n = 2^n$ and $y_n = 1/n!$ for $n \geq 1$.

14. Let $V$ be the set of all real functions $f$ continuous on $[0, +\infty)$ and such that the integral $\int_0^{\infty} e^{-t} f^2(t)\, dt$ converges. Define $(f, g) = \int_0^{\infty} e^{-t} f(t) g(t)\, dt$.
(a) Prove that the integral for $(f, g)$ converges absolutely for each pair of functions $f$ and $g$ in $V$.
   [*Hint:* Use the Cauchy-Schwarz inequality to estimate the integral $\int_0^{M} e^{-t} |f(t) g(t)|\, dt$.]
(b) Prove that $V$ is a linear space with $(f, g)$ as an inner product.
(c) Compute $(f, g)$ if $f(t) = e^{-t}$ and $g(t) = t^n$, where $n = 0, 1, 2, \ldots$ .

15. In a complex Euclidean space, prove that the inner product has the following properties for all elements $x$, $y$ and $z$, and all complex $a$ and $b$.
(a) $(ax, by) = a\bar{b}(x, y)$.     (b) $(x, ay + bz) = \bar{a}(x, y) + \bar{b}(x, z)$.

16. Prove that the following identities are valid in every Euclidean space.
(a) $\|x + y\|^2 = \|x\|^2 + \|y\|^2 + (x, y) + (y, x)$.
(b) $\|x + y\|^2 - \|x - y\|^2 = 2(x, y) + 2(y, x)$.
(c) $\|x + y\|^2 + \|x - y\|^2 = 2\|x\|^2 + 2\|y\|^2$.

17. Prove that the space of all complex-valued functions continuous on an interval $[a, b]$ becomes a unitary space if we define an inner product by the formula

$$(f, g) = \int_a^b w(t) f(t) \overline{g(t)}\, dt ,$$

where $w$ is a fixed positive function, continuous on $[a, b]$.

## 15.13 Construction of orthogonal sets. The Gram-Schmidt process

Every finite-dimensional linear space has a finite basis. If the space is Euclidean, we can always construct an *orthogonal* basis. This result will be deduced as a consequence of a general theorem whose proof shows how to construct orthogonal sets in any Euclidean space, finite or infinite dimensional. The construction is called the *Gram-Schmidt orthogonalization process*, in honor of J. P. Gram (1850–1916) and E. Schmidt (1845–1921).

THEOREM 15.13.   ORTHOGONALIZATION THEOREM.   *Let* $x_1, x_2, \ldots,$ *be a finite or infinite sequence of elements in a Euclidean space* $V$, *and let* $L(x_1, \ldots, x_k)$ *denote the subspace spanned by the first* $k$ *of these elements. Then there is a corresponding sequence of elements* $y_1, y_2, \ldots,$ *in* $V$ *which has the following properties for each integer* $k$:
(a) *The element* $y_k$ *is orthogonal to every element in the subspace* $L(y_1, \ldots, y_{k-1})$.
(b) *The subspace spanned by* $y_1, \ldots, y_k$ *is the same as that spanned by* $x_1, \ldots, x_k$:

$$L(y_1, \ldots, y_k) = L(x_1, \ldots, x_k) .$$

(c) *The sequence* $y_1, y_2, \ldots$, *is unique, except for scalar factors. That is, if* $y_1', y_2', \ldots$, *is another sequence of elements in V satisfying properties* (a) *and* (b), *then for each k there is a scalar* $c_k$ *such that* $y_k' = c_k y_k$.

*Proof.* We construct the elements $y_1, y_2, \ldots$, by induction. To start the process, we take $y_1 = x_1$. Now assume we have constructed $y_1, \ldots, y_r$ so that (a) and (b) are satisfied when $k = r$. Then we define $y_{r+1}$ by the equation

$$(15.13) \qquad\qquad y_{r+1} = x_{r+1} - \sum_{i=1}^{r} a_i y_i,$$

where the scalars $a_1, \ldots, a_r$ are to be determined. For $j \leq r$, the inner product of $y_{r+1}$ with $y_j$ is given by

$$(y_{r+1}, y_j) = (x_{r+1}, y_j) - \sum_{i=1}^{r} a_i(y_i, y_j) = (x_{r+1}, y_j) - a_j(y_j, y_j),$$

since $(y_i, y_j) = 0$ if $i \neq j$. If $y_j \neq O$, we can make $y_{r+1}$ orthogonal to $y_j$ by taking

$$(15.14) \qquad\qquad a_j = \frac{(x_{r+1}, y_j)}{(y_j, y_j)}.$$

If $y_j = O$, then $y_{r+1}$ is orthogonal to $y_j$ for any choice of $a_j$, and in this case we choose $a_j = 0$. Thus, the element $y_{r+1}$ is well defined and is orthogonal to each of the earlier elements $y_1, \ldots, y_r$. Therefore, it is orthogonal to every element in the subspace

$$L(y_1, \ldots, y_r).$$

This proves (a) when $k = r + 1$.

To prove (b) when $k = r + 1$, we must show that $L(y_1, \ldots, y_{r+1}) = L(x_1, \ldots, x_{r+1})$, given that $L(y_1, \ldots, y_r) = L(x_1, \ldots, x_r)$. The first $r$ elements $y_1, \ldots, y_r$ are in

$$L(x_1, \ldots, x_r)$$

and hence they are in the larger subspace $L(x_1, \ldots, x_{r+1})$. The new element $y_{r+1}$ given by (15.13) is a difference of two elements in $L(x_1, \ldots, x_{r+1})$ so it, too, is in $L(x_1, \ldots, x_{r+1})$. This proves that

$$L(y_1, \ldots, y_{r+1}) \subseteq L(x_1, \ldots, x_{r+1}).$$

Equation (15.13) shows that $x_{r+1}$ is the sum of two elements in $L(y_1, \ldots, y_{r+1})$ so a similar argument gives the inclusion in the other direction:

$$L(x_1, \ldots, x_{r+1}) \subseteq L(y_1, \ldots, y_{r+1}).$$

This proves (b) when $k = r + 1$. Therefore both (a) and (b) are proved by induction on $k$.

Finally we prove (c) by induction on $k$. The case $k = 1$ is trivial. Therefore, assume (c) is true for $k = r$ and consider the element $y'_{r+1}$. Because of (b), this element is in

$$L(y_1, \ldots, y_{r+1}),$$

so we can write

$$y'_{r+1} = \sum_{i=1}^{r+1} c_i y_i = z_r + c_{r+1} y_{r+1},$$

where $z_r \in L(y_1, \ldots, y_r)$. We wish to prove that $z_r = O$. By property (a), both $y'_{r+1}$ and $c_{r+1} y_{r+1}$ are orthogonal to $z_r$. Therefore, their difference, $z_r$, is orthogonal to $z_r$. In other words, $z_r$ is orthogonal to itself, so $z_r = O$. This completes the proof of the orthogonalization theorem.

In the foregoing construction, suppose we have $y_{r+1} = O$ for some $r$. Then (15.13) shows that $x_{r+1}$ is a linear combination of $y_1, \ldots, y_r$, and hence of $x_1, \ldots, x_r$, so the elements $x_1, \ldots, x_{r+1}$ are dependent. In other words, if the first $k$ elements $x_1, \ldots, x_k$ are independent, then the corresponding elements $y_1, \ldots, y_k$ are *nonzero*. In this case the coefficients $a_i$ in (15.13) are given by (15.14), and the formulas defining $y_1, \ldots, y_k$ become

$$(15.15) \quad y_1 = x_1, \qquad y_{r+1} = x_{r+1} - \sum_{i=1}^{r} \frac{(x_{r+1}, y_i)}{(y_i, y_i)} y_i \qquad \text{for} \quad r = 1, 2, \ldots, k - 1.$$

These formulas describe the Gram-Schmidt process for constructing an orthogonal set of nonzero elements $y_1, \ldots, y_k$ which spans the same subspace as a given independent set $x_1, \ldots, x_k$. In particular, if $x_1, \ldots, x_k$ is a basis for a finite-dimensional Euclidean space, then $y_1, \ldots, y_k$ is an orthogonal basis for the same space. We can also convert this to an orthonormal basis by *normalizing* each element $y_i$, that is, by dividing it by its norm. Therefore, as a corollary of Theorem 15.13 we have the following.

THEOREM 15.14. *Every finite-dimensional Euclidean space has an orthonormal basis.*

If $x$ and $y$ are elements in a Euclidean space, with $y \neq O$, the element

$$\frac{(x, y)}{(y, y)} y$$

is called the *projection of $x$ along $y$*. In the Gram-Schmidt process (15.15), we construct the element $y_{r+1}$ by subtracting from $x_{r+1}$ the projection of $x_{r+1}$ along each of the earlier elements $y_1, \ldots, y_r$. Figure 15.1 illustrates the construction geometrically in the vector space $V_3$.

EXAMPLE 1. In $V_4$, find an orthonormal basis for the subspace spanned by the three vectors $x_1 = (1, -1, 1, -1)$, $x_2 = (5, 1, 1, 1)$, and $x_3 = (-3, -3, 1, -3)$.

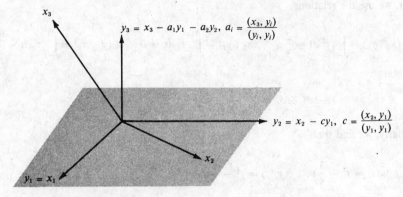

FIGURE 15.1 The Gram-Schmidt process in $V_3$. An orthogonal set $\{y_1, y_2, y_3\}$ is constructed from a given independent set $\{x_1, x_2, x_3\}$.

*Solution.* Applying the Gram-Schmidt process, we find

$$y_1 = x_1 = (1, -1, 1, -1),$$

$$y_2 = x_2 - \frac{(x_2, y_1)}{(y_1, y_1)} y_1 = x_2 - y_1 = (4, 2, 0, 2),$$

$$y_3 = x_3 - \frac{(x_3, y_1)}{(y_1, y_1)} y_1 - \frac{(x_3, y_2)}{(y_2, y_2)} y_2 = x_3 - y_1 + y_2 = (0, 0, 0, 0).$$

Since $y_3 = O$, the three vectors $x_1, x_2, x_3$ must be dependent. But since $y_1$ and $y_2$ are nonzero, the vectors $x_1$ and $x_2$ are independent. Therefore $L(x_1, x_2, x_3)$ is a subspace of dimension 2. The set $\{y_1, y_2\}$ is an orthogonal basis for this subspace. Dividing each of $y_1$ and $y_2$ by its norm we get an orthonormal basis consisting of the two vectors

$$\frac{y_1}{\|y_1\|} = \frac{1}{2}(1, -1, 1, -1) \qquad \text{and} \qquad \frac{y_2}{\|y_2\|} = \frac{1}{\sqrt{6}}(2, 1, 0, 1).$$

EXAMPLE 2. *The Legendre polynomials.* In the linear space of all polynomials, with the inner product $(x, y) = \int_{-1}^{1} x(t) y(t) \, dt$, consider the infinite sequence $x_0, x_1, x_2, \ldots,$ where $x_n(t) = t^n$. When the orthogonalization theorem is applied to this sequence it yields another sequence of polynomials $y_0, y_1, y_2, \ldots,$ first encountered by the French mathematician A. M. Legendre (1752–1833) in his work on potential theory. The first few polynomials are easily calculated by the Gram-Schmidt process. First of all, we have $y_0(t) = x_0(t) = 1$. Since

$$(y_0, y_0) = \int_{-1}^{1} dt = 2 \qquad \text{and} \qquad (x_1, y_0) = \int_{-1}^{1} t \, dt = 0,$$

we find that

$$y_1(t) = x_1(t) - \frac{(x_1, y_0)}{(y_0, y_0)} y_0(t) = x_1(t) = t.$$

Next, we use the relations

$$(x_2, y_0) = \int_{-1}^{1} t^2 \, dt = \frac{2}{3}, \qquad (x_2, y_1) = \int_{-1}^{1} t^3 \, dt = 0, \qquad (y_1, y_1) = \int_{-1}^{1} t^2 \, dt = \frac{2}{3}$$

to obtain

$$y_2(t) = x_2(t) - \frac{(x_2, y_0)}{(y_0, y_0)} y_0(t) - \frac{(x_2, y_1)}{(y_1, y_1)} y_1(t) = t^2 - \frac{1}{3}.$$

Similarly, we find that

$$y_3(t) = t^3 - \frac{3}{5} t, \qquad y_4(t) = t^4 - \frac{6}{7} t^2 + \frac{3}{35}, \qquad y_5(t) = t^5 - \frac{10}{9} t^3 + \frac{5}{21} t.$$

We shall encounter these polynomials again in Volume II in our further study of differential equations, and we shall prove that

$$y_n(t) = \frac{n!}{(2n)!} \frac{d^n}{dt^n} (t^2 - 1)^n.$$

The polynomials $P_n$ given by

$$P_n(t) = \frac{(2n)!}{2^n (n!)^2} y_n(t) = \frac{1}{2^n n!} \frac{d^n}{dt^n} (t^2 - 1)^n$$

are known as the *Legendre polynomials*. The polynomials in the corresponding orthonormal sequence $\varphi_0, \varphi_1, \varphi_2, \ldots$, given by $\varphi_n = y_n / \|y_n\|$ are called the *normalized Legendre polynomials*. From the formulas for $y_0, \ldots, y_5$ given above, we find that

$$\varphi_0(t) = \frac{1}{\sqrt{2}}, \qquad \varphi_1(t) = \sqrt{\frac{3}{2}} t, \qquad \varphi_2(t) = \frac{1}{2}\sqrt{\frac{5}{2}} (3t^2 - 1), \qquad \varphi_3(t) = \frac{1}{2}\sqrt{\frac{7}{2}} (5t^3 - 3t),$$

$$\varphi_4(t) = \frac{1}{8}\sqrt{\frac{9}{2}} (35t^4 - 30t^2 + 3), \qquad \varphi_5(t) = \frac{1}{8}\sqrt{\frac{11}{2}} (63t^5 - 70t^3 + 15t).$$

## 15.14   Orthogonal complements.   Projections

Let $V$ be a Euclidean space and let $S$ be a finite-dimensional subspace. We wish to consider the following type of approximation problem: *Given an element x in V, to determine an element in S whose distance from x is as small as possible.* The distance between two elements $x$ and $y$ is defined to be the norm $\|x - y\|$.

Before discussing this problem in its general form, we consider a special case, illustrated in Figure 15.2. Here $V$ is the vector space $V_3$ and $S$ is a two-dimensional subspace, a plane through the origin. Given $x$ in $V$, the problem is to find, in the plane $S$, that point $s$ nearest to $x$.

If $x \in S$, then clearly $s = x$ is the solution. If $x$ is not in $S$, then the nearest point $s$ is obtained by dropping a perpendicular from $x$ to the plane. This simple example suggests an approach to the general approximation problem and motivates the discussion that follows.

DEFINITION. *Let S be a subset of a Euclidean space V. An element in V is said to be orthogonal to S if it is orthogonal to every element of S. The set of all elements orthogonal to S is denoted by $S^\perp$ and is called "S perpendicular."*

It is a simple exercise to verify that $S^\perp$ is a subspace of $V$, whether or not $S$ itself is one. In case $S$ is a subspace, then $S^\perp$ is called the *orthogonal complement* of $S$.

EXAMPLE. If $S$ is a plane through the origin, as shown in Figure 15.2, then $S^\perp$ is a line through the origin perpendicular to this plane. This example also gives a geometric interpretation for the next theorem.

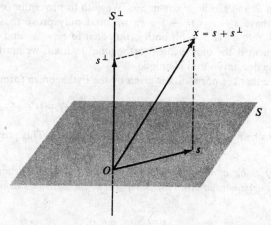

FIGURE 15.2  Geometric interpretation of the orthogonal decomposition theorem in $V_3$.

THEOREM 15.15.  ORTHOGONAL DECOMPOSITION THEOREM.  *Let V be a Euclidean space and let S be a finite-dimensional subspace of V. Then every element x in V can be represented uniquely as a sum of two elements, one in S and one in $S^\perp$. That is, we have*

(15.16) $$x = s + s^\perp, \quad where \quad s \in S \quad and \quad s^\perp \in S^\perp.$$

*Moreover, the norm of x is given by the Pythagorean formula*

(15.17) $$\|x\|^2 = \|s\|^2 + \|s^\perp\|^2.$$

*Proof.*  First we prove that an orthogonal decomposition (15.16) actually exists. Since $S$ is finite-dimensional, it has a finite orthonormal basis, say $\{e_1, \ldots, e_n\}$. Given $x$, define the elements $s$ and $s^\perp$ as follows:

(15.18) $$s = \sum_{i=1}^{n} (x, e_i)e_i, \quad s^\perp = x - s.$$

Note that each term $(x, e_i)e_i$ is the projection of $x$ along $e_i$. The element $s$ is the sum of the projections of $x$ along each basis element. Since $s$ is a linear combination of the basis elements, $s$ lies in $S$. The definition of $s^\perp$ shows that Equation (15.16) holds. To prove that $s^\perp$ lies in $S^\perp$, we consider the inner product of $s^\perp$ and any basis element $e_j$. We have

$$(s^\perp, e_j) = (x - s, e_j) = (x, e_j) - (s, e_j).$$

But from (15.18), we find that $(s, e_j) = (x, e_j)$, so $s^\perp$ is orthogonal to $e_j$. Therefore $s^\perp$ is orthogonal to every element in $S$, which means that $s^\perp \in S^\perp$.

Next we prove that the orthogonal decomposition (15.16) is unique. Suppose that $x$ has two such representations, say

(15.19) $$x = s + s^\perp \quad \text{and} \quad x = t + t^\perp,$$

where $s$ and $t$ are in $S$, and $s^\perp$ and $t^\perp$ are in $S^\perp$. We wish to prove that $s = t$ and $s^\perp = t^\perp$. From (15.19), we have $s - t = t^\perp - s^\perp$, so we need only prove that $s - t = O$. But $s - t \in S$ and $t^\perp - s^\perp \in S^\perp$ so $s - t$ is both orthogonal to $t^\perp - s^\perp$ and equal to $t^\perp - s^\perp$. Since the zero element is the only element orthogonal to itself, we must have $s - t = O$. This shows that the decomposition is unique.

Finally, we prove that the norm of $x$ is given by the Pythagorean formula. We have

$$\|x\|^2 = (x, x) = (s + s^\perp, s + s^\perp) = (s, s) + (s^\perp, s^\perp),$$

the remaining terms being zero since $s$ and $s^\perp$ are orthogonal. This proves (15.17).

DEFINITION. *Let $S$ be a finite-dimensional subspace of a Euclidean space $V$, and let $\{e_1, \ldots, e_n\}$ be an orthonormal basis for $S$. If $x \in V$, the element $s$ defined by the equation*

$$s = \sum_{i=1}^{n} (x, e_i)e_i$$

*is called the projection of $x$ on the subspace $S$.*

We prove next that the projection of $x$ on $S$ is the solution to the approximation problem stated at the beginning of this section.

## 15.15 Best approximation of elements in a Euclidean space by elements in a finite-dimensional subspace

THEOREM 15.16. APPROXIMATION THEOREM. *Let $S$ be a finite-dimensional subspace of a Euclidean space $V$, and let $x$ be any element of $V$. Then the projection of $x$ on $S$ is nearer to $x$ than any other element of $S$. That is, if $s$ is the projection of $x$ on $S$, we have*

$$\|x - s\| \leq \|x - t\|$$

*for all $t$ in $S$; the equality sign holds if and only if $t = s$.*

*Proof.* By Theorem 15.15 we can write $x = s + s^\perp$, where $s \in S$ and $s^\perp \in S^\perp$. Then, for any $t$ in $S$, we have

$$x - t = (x - s) + (s - t).$$

Since $s - t \in S$ and $x - s = s^\perp \in S^\perp$, this is an orthogonal decomposition of $x - t$, so its norm is given by the Pythagorean formula

$$\|x - t\|^2 = \|x - s\|^2 + \|s - t\|^2.$$

But $\|s - t\|^2 \geq 0$, so we have $\|x - t\|^2 \geq \|x - s\|^2$, with equality holding if and only if $s = t$. This completes the proof.

EXAMPLE 1. *Approximation of continuous functions on* $[0, 2\pi]$ *by trigonometric polynomials.* Let $V = C(0, 2\pi)$, the linear space of all real functions continuous on the interval $[0, 2\pi]$, and define an inner product by the equation $(f, g) = \int_0^{2\pi} f(x)g(x)\, dx$. In Section 15.11 we exhibited an orthonormal set of trigonometric functions $\varphi_0, \varphi_1, \varphi_2, \ldots$, where

$$(15.20) \qquad \varphi_0(x) = \frac{1}{\sqrt{2\pi}}, \qquad \varphi_{2k-1}(x) = \frac{\cos kx}{\sqrt{\pi}}, \qquad \varphi_{2k}(x) = \frac{\sin kx}{\sqrt{\pi}}, \qquad \text{for } k \geq 1.$$

The $2n + 1$ elements $\varphi_0, \varphi_1, \ldots, \varphi_{2n}$ span a subspace $S$ of dimension $2n + 1$. The elements of $S$ are called *trigonometric polynomials*.

If $f \in C(0, 2\pi)$, let $f_n$ denote the projection of $f$ on the subspace $S$. Then we have

$$(15.21) \qquad f_n = \sum_{k=0}^{2n} (f, \varphi_k)\varphi_k, \qquad \text{where} \quad (f, \varphi_k) = \int_0^{2\pi} f(x)\varphi_k(x)\, dx.$$

The numbers $(f, \varphi_k)$ are called *Fourier coefficients* of $f$. Using the formulas in (15.20), we can rewrite (15.21) in the form

$$(15.22) \qquad f_n(x) = \tfrac{1}{2}a_0 + \sum_{k=1}^{n} (a_k \cos kx + b_k \sin kx),$$

where

$$a_k = \frac{1}{\pi} \int_0^{2\pi} f(x) \cos kx \, dx, \qquad b_k = \frac{1}{\pi} \int_0^{2\pi} f(x) \sin kx \, dx$$

for $k = 0, 1, 2, \ldots, n$. The approximation theorem tells us that the trigonometric polynomial in (15.22) approximates $f$ better than any other trigonometric polynomial in $S$, in the sense that the norm $\|f - f_n\|$ is as small as possible.

EXAMPLE 2. *Approximation of continuous functions on* $[-1, 1]$ *by polynomials of degree* $\leq n$. Let $V = C(-1, 1)$, the space of real continuous functions on $[-1, 1]$, and let $(f, g) = \int_{-1}^1 f(x)g(x)\, dx$. The $n + 1$ normalized Legendre polynomials $\varphi_0, \varphi_1, \ldots, \varphi_n$, introduced in Section 15.13, span a subspace $S$ of dimension $n + 1$ consisting of all polynomials of degree $\leq n$. If $f \in C(-1, 1)$, let $f_n$ denote the projection of $f$ on $S$. Then we have

$$f_n = \sum_{k=0}^{n} (f, \varphi_k)\varphi_k, \quad \text{where} \quad (f, \varphi_k) = \int_{-1}^{1} f(t)\varphi_k(t) \, dt .$$

This is the polynomial of degree $\leq n$ for which the norm $\|f - f_n\|$ is smallest. For example, when $f(x) = \sin \pi x$, the coefficients $(f, \varphi_k)$ are given by

$$(f, \varphi_k) = \int_{-1}^{1} \sin \pi t \, \varphi_k(t) \, dt .$$

In particular, we have $(f, \varphi_0) = 0$ and

$$(f, \varphi_1) = \int_{-1}^{1} \sqrt{\frac{3}{2}} t \sin \pi t \, dt = \sqrt{\frac{3}{2}} \frac{2}{\pi} .$$

Therefore the linear polynomial $f_1(t)$ which is nearest to $\sin \pi t$ on $[-1, 1]$ is

$$f_1(t) = \sqrt{\frac{3}{2}} \frac{2}{\pi} \varphi_1(t) = \frac{3}{\pi} t .$$

Since $(f, \varphi_2) = 0$, this is also the nearest quadratic approximation.

## 15.16 Exercises

1. In each case, find an orthonormal basis for the subspace of $V_3$ spanned by the given vectors.
   (a) $x_1 = (1, 1, 1)$, $\quad x_2 = (1, 0, 1)$, $\quad x_3 = (3, 2, 3)$.
   (b) $x_1 = (1, 1, 1)$, $\quad x_2 = (-1, 1, -1)$, $\quad x_3 = (1, 0, 1)$.
2. In each case, find an orthonormal basis for the subspace of $V_4$ spanned by the given vectors.
   (a) $x_1 = (1 \ 1, 0, 0)$, $\quad x_2 = (0, 1, 1, 0)$, $\quad x_3 = (0, 0, 1, 1)$, $\quad x_4 = (1, 0, 0, 1)$.
   (b) $x_1 = (1, 1, 0, 1)$, $\quad x_2 = (1, 0, 2, 1)$, $\quad x_3 = (1, 2, -2, 1)$.
3. In the real linear space $C(0, \pi)$, with inner product $(x, y) = \int_0^{\pi} x(t)y(t) \, dt$, let $x_n(t) = \cos nt$ for $n = 0, 1, 2, \dots$ . Prove that the functions $y_0, y_1, y_2, \dots$, given by

$$y_0(t) = \frac{1}{\sqrt{\pi}} \quad \text{and} \quad y_n(t) = \sqrt{\frac{2}{\pi}} \cos nt \quad \text{for} \quad n \geq 1,$$

   form an orthonormal set spanning the same subspace as $x_0, x_1, x_2, \dots$ .
4. In the linear space of all real polynomials, with inner product $(x, y) = \int_0^1 x(t)y(t) \, dt$, let $x_n(t) = t^n$ for $n = 0, 1, 2, \dots$ . Prove that the functions

$$y_0(t) = 1, \quad y_1(t) = \sqrt{3}\,(2t - 1), \quad y_2(t) = \sqrt{5}\,(6t^2 - 6t + 1)$$

   form an orthonormal set spanning the same subspace as $\{x_0, x_1, x_2\}$.

5. Let $V$ be the linear space of all real functions $f$ continuous on $[0, +\infty)$ and such that the integral $\int_0^\infty e^{-t} f^2(t)\, dt$ converges. Define $(f, g) = \int_0^\infty e^{-t} f(t) g(t)\, dt$, and let $y_0, y_1, y_2, \ldots,$ be the set obtained by applying the Gram-Schmidt process to $x_0, x_1, x_2, \ldots,$ where $x_n(t) = t^n$ for $n \geq 0$. Prove that $y_0(t) = 1, y_1(t) = t - 1, y_2(t) = t^2 - 4t + 2, y_3(t) = t^3 - 9t^2 + 18t - 6$.

6. In the real linear space $C(1, 3)$ with inner product $(f, g) = \int_1^3 f(x) g(x)\, dx$, let $f(x) = 1/x$ and show that the constant polynomial $g$ nearest to $f$ is $g = \frac{1}{2} \log 3$. Compute $\|g - f\|^2$ for this $g$.

7. In the real linear space $C(0, 2)$ with inner product $(f, g) = \int_0^2 f(x) g(x)\, dx$, let $f(x) = e^x$ and show that the constant polynomial $g$ nearest to $f$ is $g = \frac{1}{2}(e^2 - 1)$. Compute $\|g - f\|^2$ for this $g$.

8. In the real linear space $C(-1, 1)$ with inner product $(f, g) = \int_{-1}^1 f(x) g(x)\, dx$, let $f(x) = e^x$ and find the linear polynomial $g$ nearest to $f$. Compute $\|g - f\|^2$ for this $g$.

9. In the real linear space $C(0, 2\pi)$ with inner product $(f, g) = \int_0^{2\pi} f(x) g(x)\, dx$, let $f(x) = x$. In the subspace spanned by $u_0(x) = 1, u_1(x) = \cos x, u_2(x) = \sin x$, find the trigonometric polynomial nearest to $f$.

10. In the linear space $V$ of Exercise 5, let $f(x) = e^{-x}$ and find the linear polynomial that is nearest to $f$.

# 16

# LINEAR TRANSFORMATIONS AND MATRICES

## 16.1 Linear transformations

One of the ultimate goals of analysis is a comprehensive study of functions whose domains and ranges are subsets of linear spaces. Such functions are called *transformations, mappings,* or *operators.* This chapter treats the simplest examples, called *linear* transformations, which occur in all branches of mathematics. Properties of more general transformations are often obtained by approximating them by linear transformations.

First we introduce some notation and terminology concerning arbitrary functions. Let $V$ and $W$ be two sets. The symbol

$$T : V \to W$$

will be used to indicate that $T$ is a function whose domain is $V$ and whose values are in $W$. For each $x$ in $V$, the element $T(x)$ in $W$ is called the *image of x under T,* and we say that $T$ maps $x$ onto $T(x)$. If $A$ is any subset of $V$, the set of all images $T(x)$ for $x$ in $A$ is called the *image of A under T* and is denoted by $T(A)$. The image of the domain $V$, $T(V)$, is the range of $T$.

Now we assume that $V$ and $W$ are linear spaces having the same set of scalars, and we define a linear transformation as follows.

DEFINITION. *If V and W are linear spaces, a function T: V → W is called a linear transformation of V into W if it has the following two properties:*

(a) $T(x + y) = T(x) + T(y)$     *for all x and y in V,*
(b) $T(cx) = cT(x)$     *for all x in V and all scalars c.*

These properties are verbalized by saying that $T$ preserves addition and multiplication by scalars. The two properties can be combined into one formula which states that

$$T(ax + by) = aT(x) + bT(y)$$

for all $x$, $y$ in $V$ and all scalars $a$ and $b$. By induction, we also have the more general relation

$$T\left(\sum_{i=1}^{n} a_i x_i\right) = \sum_{i=1}^{n} a_i T(x_i)$$

for any $n$ elements $x_1, \dots, x_n$ in $V$ and any $n$ scalars $a_1, \dots, a_n$.

578

The reader can easily verify that the following examples are linear transformations.

EXAMPLE 1. *The identity transformation.* The transformation $T: V \to V$, where $T(x) = x$ for each $x$ in $V$, is called the identity transformation and is denoted by $I$ or by $I_V$.

EXAMPLE 2. *The zero transformation.* The transformation $T: V \to V$ which maps each element of $V$ onto $O$ is called the zero transformation and is denoted by $O$.

EXAMPLE 3. *Multiplication by a fixed scalar c.* Here we have $T: V \to V$, where $T(x) = cx$ for all $x$ in $V$. When $c = 1$, this is the identity transformation. When $c = 0$, it is the zero transformation.

EXAMPLE 4. *Linear equations.* Let $V = V_n$ and $W = V_m$. Given $mn$ real numbers $a_{ik}$, where $i = 1, 2, \ldots, m$ and $k = 1, 2, \ldots, n$, define $T : V_n \to V_m$ as follows: $T$ maps each vector $x = (x_1, \ldots, x_n)$ in $V_n$ onto the vector $y = (y_1, \ldots, y_m)$ in $V_m$ according to the equations

$$y_i = \sum_{k=1}^{n} a_{ik} x_k \quad \text{for} \quad i = 1, 2, \ldots, m.$$

EXAMPLE 5. *Inner product with a fixed element.* Let $V$ be a real Euclidean space. For a fixed element $z$ in $V$, define $T : V \to \mathbf{R}$ as follows: If $x \in V$, then $T(x) = (x, z)$, the inner product of $x$ with $z$.

EXAMPLE 6. *Projection on a subspace.* Let $V$ be a Euclidean space and let $S$ be a finite-dimensional subspace of $V$. Define $T : V \to S$ as follows: If $x \in V$, then $T(x)$ is the projection of $x$ on $S$.

EXAMPLE 7. *The differentiation operator.* Let $V$ be the linear space of all real functions $f$ differentiable on an open interval $(a, b)$. The linear transformation which maps each function $f$ in $V$ onto its derivative $f'$ is called the differentiation operator and is denoted by $D$. Thus, we have $D : V \to W$, where $D(f) = f'$ for each $f$ in $V$. The space $W$ consists of all derivatives $f'$.

EXAMPLE 8. *The integration operator.* Let $V$ be the linear space of all real functions continuous on an interval $[a, b]$. If $f \in V$, define $g = T(f)$ to be that function in $V$ given by

$$g(x) = \int_a^x f(t)\, dt \quad \text{if} \quad a \le x \le b.$$

This transformation $T$ is called the integration operator.

## 16.2 Null space and range

In this section, $T$ denotes a linear transformation of a linear space $V$ into a linear space $W$.

THEOREM 16.1. *The set $T(V)$ (the range of $T$) is a subspace of $W$. Moreover, $T$ maps the zero element of $V$ onto the zero element of $W$.*

*Proof.* To prove that $T(V)$ is a subspace of $W$, we need only verify the closure axioms. Take any two elements of $T(V)$, say $T(x)$ and $T(y)$. Then $T(x) + T(y) = T(x + y)$, so $T(x) + T(y)$ is in $T(V)$. Also, for any scalar $c$ we have $cT(x) = T(cx)$, so $cT(x)$ is in $T(V)$. Therefore, $T(V)$ is a subspace of $W$. Taking $c = 0$ in the relation $T(cx) = cT(x)$, we find that $T(O) = O$.

DEFINITION. *The set of all elements in V that T maps onto O is called the null space of T and is denoted by N(T). Thus, we have*

$$N(T) = \{x \mid x \in V \text{ and } T(x) = O\}.$$

*The null space is sometimes called the kernel of T.*

THEOREM 16.2. *The null space of T is a subspace of V.*

*Proof.* If $x$ and $y$ are in $N(T)$, then so are $x + y$ and $cx$ for all scalars $c$, since

$$T(x + y) = T(x) + T(y) = O \qquad \text{and} \qquad T(cx) = cT(x) = O.$$

The following examples describe the null spaces of the linear transformations given in Section 16.1.

EXAMPLE 1. *Identity transformation.* The null space is $\{O\}$, the subspace consisting of the zero element alone.

EXAMPLE 2. *Zero transformation.* Since every element of $V$ is mapped onto zero, the null space is $V$ itself.

EXAMPLE 3. *Multiplication by a fixed scalar c.* If $c \neq 0$, the null space contains only $O$. If $c = 0$, the null space is $V$.

EXAMPLE 4. *Linear equations.* The null space consists of all vectors $(x_1, \ldots, x_n)$ in $V_n$ for which

$$\sum_{k=1}^{n} a_{ik} x_k = 0 \qquad \text{for} \quad i = 1, 2, \ldots, m.$$

EXAMPLE 5. *Inner product with a fixed element z.* The null space consists of all elements in $V$ orthogonal to $z$.

EXAMPLE 6. *Projection on a subspace S.* If $x \in V$, we have the unique orthogonal decomposition $x = s + s^{\perp}$ (by Theorem 15.15). Since $T(x) = s$, we have $T(x) = O$ if and only if $x = s^{\perp}$. Therefore, the null space is $S^{\perp}$, the orthogonal complement of $S$.

EXAMPLE 7. *Differentiation operator.* The null space consists of all functions that are constant on the given interval.

EXAMPLE 8. *Integration operator.* The null space contains only the zero function.

### 16.3 Nullity and rank

Again in this section $T$ denotes a linear transformation of a linear space $V$ into a linear space $W$. We are interested in the relation between the dimensionality of $V$, of the null space $N(T)$, and of the range $T(V)$. If $V$ is finite-dimensional, then the null space is also finite-dimensional since it is a subspace of $V$. The dimension of $N(T)$ is called the *nullity* of $T$. In the next theorem, we prove that the range is also finite-dimensional; its dimension is called the *rank* of $T$.

THEOREM 16.3. NULLITY PLUS RANK THEOREM. *If $V$ is finite-dimensional, then $T(V)$ is also finite-dimensional, and we have*

$$(16.1) \qquad \dim N(T) + \dim T(V) = \dim V.$$

*In other words, the nullity plus the rank of a linear transformation is equal to the dimension of its domain.*

*Proof.* Let $n = \dim V$ and let $e_1, \ldots, e_k$ be a basis for $N(T)$, where $k = \dim N(T) \leq n$. By Theorem 15.7, these elements are part of some basis for $V$, say the basis

$$(16.2) \qquad e_1, \ldots, e_k, e_{k+1}, \ldots, e_{k+r},$$

where $k + r = n$. We shall prove that the $r$ elements

$$(16.3) \qquad T(e_{k+1}), \ldots, T(e_{k+r})$$

form a basis for $T(V)$, thus proving that $\dim T(V) = r$. Since $k + r = n$, this also proves (16.1).

First we show that the $r$ elements in (16.3) span $T(V)$. If $y \in T(V)$, we have $y = T(x)$ for some $x$ in $V$, and we can write $x = c_1 e_1 + \cdots + c_{k+r} e_{k+r}$. Hence, we have

$$y = T(x) = \sum_{i=1}^{k+r} c_i T(e_i) = \sum_{i=1}^{k} c_i T(e_i) + \sum_{i=k+1}^{k+r} c_i T(e_i) = \sum_{i=k+1}^{k+r} c_i T(e_i)$$

since $T(e_1) = \cdots = T(e_k) = O$. This shows that the elements in (16.3) span $T(V)$.

Now we show that these elements are independent. Suppose that there are scalars $c_{k+1}, \ldots, c_{k+r}$ such that

$$\sum_{i=k+1}^{k+r} c_i T(e_i) = O.$$

This implies that

$$T\left( \sum_{i=k+1}^{k+r} c_i e_i \right) = O$$

so the element $x = c_{k+1} e_{k+1} + \cdots + c_{k+r} e_{k+r}$ is in the null space $N(T)$. This means there are scalars $c_1, \ldots, c_k$ such that $x = c_1 e_1 + \cdots + c_k e_k$, so we have

$$x - x = \sum_{i=1}^{k} c_i e_i - \sum_{i=k+1}^{k+r} c_i e_i = O.$$

But since the elements in (16.2) are independent, this implies that all the scalars $c_i$ are zero. Therefore, the elements in (16.3) are independent.

*Note:* If $V$ is infinite-dimensional, then at least one of $N(T)$ or $T(V)$ is infinite-dimensional. A proof of this fact is outlined in Exercise 30 of Section 16.4.

## 16.4  Exercises

In each of Exercises 1 through 10, a transformation $T: V_2 \to V_2$ is defined by the formula given for $T(x, y)$, where $(x, y)$ is an arbitrary point in $V_2$. In each case determine whether $T$ is linear. If $T$ is linear, describe its null space and range, and compute its nullity and rank.

1. $T(x, y) = (y, x)$.
2. $T(x, y) = (x, -y)$.
3. $T(x, y) = (x, 0)$.
4. $T(x, y) = (x, x)$.
5. $T(x, y) = (x^2, y^2)$.
6. $T(x, y) = (e^x, e^y)$.
7. $T(x, y) = (x, 1)$.
8. $T(x, y) = (x + 1, y + 1)$.
9. $T(x, y) = (x - y, x + y)$.
10. $T(x, y) = (2x - y, x + y)$.

Do the same as above for each of Exercises 11 through 15 if the transformation $T: V_2 \to V_2$ is described as indicated.

11. $T$ rotates every point through the same angle $\phi$ about the origin. That is, $T$ maps a point with polar coordinates $(r, \theta)$ onto the point with polar coordinates $(r, \theta + \phi)$, where $\phi$ is fixed. Also, $T$ maps $O$ onto itself.
12. $T$ maps each point onto its reflection with respect to a fixed line through the origin.
13. $T$ maps every point onto the point $(1, 1)$.
14. $T$ maps each point with polar coordinates $(r, \theta)$ onto the point with polar coordinates $(2r, \theta)$. Also, $T$ maps $O$ onto itself.
15. $T$ maps each point with polar coordinates $(r, \theta)$ onto the point with polar coordinates $(r, 2\theta)$. Also, $T$ maps $O$ onto itself.

Do the same as above in each of Exercises 16 through 23 if a transformation $T: V_3 \to V_3$ is defined by the formula given for $T(x, y, z)$, where $(x, y, z)$ is an arbitrary point of $V_3$.

16. $T(x, y, z) = (z, y, x)$.
17. $T(x, y, z) = (x, y, 0)$.
18. $T(x, y, z) = (x, 2y, 3z)$.
19. $T(x, y, z) = (x, y, 1)$.
20. $T(x, y, z) = (x + 1, y + 1, z - 1)$.
21. $T(x, y, z) = (x + 1, y + 2, z + 3)$.
22. $T(x, y, z) = (x, y^2, z^3)$.
23. $T(x, y, z) = (x + z, 0, x + y)$.

In each of Exercises 24 through 27, a transformation $T: V \to V$ is described as indicated. In each case, determine whether $T$ is linear. If $T$ is linear, describe its null space and range, and compute the nullity and rank when they are finite.

24. Let $V$ be the linear space of all real polynomials $p(x)$ of degree $\leq n$. If $p \in V$, $q = T(p)$ means that $q(x) = p(x + 1)$ for all real $x$.
25. Let $V$ be the linear space of all real functions differentiable on the open interval $(-1, 1)$. If $f \in V$, $g = T(f)$ means that $g(x) = xf'(x)$ for all $x$ in $(-1, 1)$.
26. Let $V$ be the linear space of all real functions continuous on $[a, b]$. If $f \in V$, $g = T(f)$ means that

$$g(x) = \int_a^b f(t) \sin(x - t)\, dt \quad \text{for} \quad a \leq x \leq b.$$

27. Let $V$ be the space of all real functions twice differentiable on an open interval $(a, b)$. If $y \in V$, define $T(y) = y'' + Py' + Qy$, where $P$ and $Q$ are fixed constants.
28. Let $V$ be the linear space of all real convergent sequences $\{x_n\}$. Define a transformation

$T: V \to V$ as follows: If $x = \{x_n\}$ is a convergent sequence with limit $a$, let $T(x) = \{y_n\}$, where $y_n = a - x_n$ for $n \geq 1$. Prove that $T$ is linear and describe the null space and range of $T$.

29. Let $V$ denote the linear space of all real functions continuous on the interval $[-\pi, \pi]$. Let $S$ be that subset of $V$ consisting of all $f$ satisfying the three equations

$$\int_{-\pi}^{\pi} f(t)\, dt = 0\,, \qquad \int_{-\pi}^{\pi} f(t) \cos t\, dt = 0\,, \qquad \int_{-\pi}^{\pi} f(t) \sin t\, dt = 0\,.$$

(a) Prove that $S$ is a subspace of $V$.
(b) Prove that $S$ contains the functions $f(x) = \cos nx$ and $f(x) = \sin nx$ for each $n = 2, 3, \ldots$.
(c) Prove that $S$ is infinite-dimensional.

Let $T: V \to V$ be the linear transformation defined as follows: If $f \in V$, $g = T(f)$ means that

$$g(x) = \int_{-\pi}^{\pi} \{1 + \cos(x - t)\} f(t)\, dt\,.$$

(d) Prove that $T(V)$, the range of $T$, is finite-dimensional and find a basis for $T(V)$.
(e) Determine the null space of $T$.
(f) Find all real $c \neq 0$ and all nonzero $f$ in $V$ such that $T(f) = cf$. (Note that such an $f$ lies in the range of $T$.)

30. Let $T: V \to W$ be a linear transformation of a linear space $V$ into a linear space $W$. If $V$ is infinite-dimensional, prove that at least one of $T(V)$ or $N(T)$ is infinite-dimensional.

[*Hint:* Assume dim $N(T) = k$, dim $T(V) = r$, let $e_1, \ldots, e_k$ be a basis for $N(T)$ and let $e_1, \ldots, e_k, e_{k+1}, \ldots, e_{k+n}$ be independent elements in $V$, where $n > r$. The elements $T(e_{k+1}), \ldots, T(e_{k+n})$ are dependent since $n > r$. Use this fact to obtain a contradiction.]

## 16.5 Algebraic operations on linear transformations

Functions whose values lie in a given linear space $W$ can be added to each other and can be multiplied by the scalars in $W$ according to the following definition.

DEFINITION. *Let $S: V \to W$ and $T: V \to W$ be two functions with a common domain $V$ and with values in a linear space $W$. If $c$ is any scalar in $W$, we define the sum $S + T$ and the product $cT$ by the equations*

(16.4) $$(S + T)(x) = S(x) + T(x)\,, \qquad (cT)(x) = cT(x)$$

*for all $x$ in $V$.*

We are especially interested in the case where $V$ is also a linear space having the same scalars as $W$. In this case we denote by $\mathscr{L}(V, W)$ the set of all linear transformations of $V$ into $W$.

If $S$ and $T$ are two linear transformations in $\mathscr{L}(V, W)$, it is an easy exercise to verify that $S + T$ and $cT$ are also linear transformations in $\mathscr{L}(V, W)$. More than this is true. With the operations just defined, the set $\mathscr{L}(V, W)$ itself becomes a new linear space. The zero transformation serves as the zero element of this space, and the transformation $(-1)T$

is the negative of $T$. It is a straightforward matter to verify that all ten axioms for a linear space are satisfied. Therefore, we have the following.

THEOREM 16.4. *The set $\mathscr{L}(V, W)$ of all linear transformations of $V$ into $W$ is a linear space with the operations of addition and multiplication by scalars defined as in* (16.4).

A more interesting algebraic operation on linear transformations is *composition* or *multiplication* of transformations. This operation makes no use of the algebraic structure of a linear space and can be defined quite generally as follows.

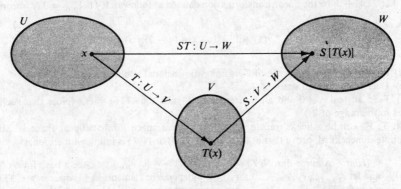

FIGURE 16.1   Illustrating the composition of two transformations.

DEFINITION.  *Let* $U$, $V$, $W$ *be sets. Let* $T: U \to V$ *be a function with domain* $U$ *and values in* $V$, *and let* $S: V \to W$ *be another function with domain* $V$ *and values in* $W$. *Then the composition* $ST$ *is the function* $ST: U \to W$ *defined by the equation*

$$(ST)(x) = S[T(x)] \qquad \text{for every } x \text{ in } U.$$

Thus, to map $x$ by the composition $ST$, we first map $x$ by $T$ and then map $T(x)$ by $S$. This is illustrated in Figure 16.1.

Composition of real-valued functions has been encountered repeatedly in our study of calculus, and we have seen that the operation is, in general, not commutative. However, as in the case of real-valued functions, composition does satisfy an associative law.

THEOREM 16.5.  *If* $T: U \to V$, $S: V \to W$, *and* $R: W \to X$ *are three functions, then we have*

$$R(ST) = (RS)T.$$

*Proof.*  Both functions $R(ST)$ and $(RS)T$ have domain $U$ and values in $X$. For each $x$ in $U$, we have

$$[R(ST)](x) = R[(ST)(x)] = R[S[T(x)]] \qquad \text{and} \qquad [(RS)T](x) = (RS)[T(x)] = R[S[T(x)]],$$

which proves that $R(ST) = (RS)T$.

DEFINITION. *Let* $T: V \to V$ *be a function which maps $V$ into itself. We define integral powers of $T$ inductively as follows*:

$$T^0 = I, \qquad T^n = TT^{n-1} \quad for \quad n \geq 1.$$

Here $I$ is the identity transformation. The reader may verify that the associative law implies the law of exponents $T^m T^n = T^{m+n}$ for all nonnegative integers $m$ and $n$.

The next theorem shows that the composition of *linear* transformations is again linear.

THEOREM 16.6. *If $U, V, W$ are linear spaces with the same scalars, and if $T: U \to V$ and $S: V \to W$ are linear transformations, then the composition $ST: U \to W$ is linear.*

*Proof.* For all $x, y$ in $U$ and all scalars $a$ and $b$, we have

$$(ST)(ax + by) = S[T(ax + by)] = S[aT(x) + bT(y)] = aST(x) + bST(y).$$

Composition can be combined with the algebraic operations of addition and multiplication of scalars in $\mathscr{L}(V, W)$ to give us the following.

THEOREM 16.7. *Let $U, V, W$ be linear spaces with the same scalars, assume $S$ and $T$ are in $\mathscr{L}(V, W)$, and let $c$ be any scalar.*
(a) *For any function $R$ with values in $V$, we have*

$$(S + T)R = SR + TR \qquad and \qquad (cS)R = c(SR).$$

(b) *For any linear transformation $R: W \to U$, we have*

$$R(S + T) = RS + RT \qquad and \qquad R(cS) = c(RS).$$

The proof is a straightforward application of the definition of composition and is left as an exercise.

## 16.6 Inverses

In our study of real-valued functions we learned how to construct new functions by inversion of monotonic functions. Now we wish to extend the process of inversion to a more general class of functions.

Given a function $T$, our goal is to find, if possible, another function $S$ whose composition with $T$ is the identity transformation. Since composition is in general not commutative, we have to distinguish between $ST$ and $TS$. Therefore we introduce two kinds of inverses which we call left and right inverses.

DEFINITION. *Given two sets $V$ and $W$ and a function $T: V \to W$. A function $S: T(V) \to V$ is called a left inverse of $T$ if $S[T(x)] = x$ for all $x$ in $V$, that is, if*

$$ST = I_V,$$

*where $I_V$ is the identity transformation on $V$. A function $R : T(V) \to V$ is called a right inverse of $T$ if $T[R(y)] = y$ for all $y$ in $T(V)$, that is, if*

$$TR = I_{T(V)},$$

*where $I_{T(V)}$ is the identity transformation on $T(V)$.*

EXAMPLE. *A function with no left inverse but with two right inverses.* Let $V = \{1, 2\}$ and let $W = \{0\}$. Define $T : V \to W$ as follows: $T(1) = T(2) = 0$. This function has two right inverses $R : W \to V$ and $R' : W \to V$ given by

$$R(0) = 1, \qquad R'(0) = 2.$$

It cannot have a left inverse $S$ since this would require

$$1 = S[T(1)] = S(0) \qquad \text{and} \qquad 2 = S[T(2)] = S(0).$$

This simple example shows that left inverses need not exist and that right inverses need not be unique.

Every function $T : V \to W$ has at least one right inverse. In fact, each $y$ in $T(V)$ has the form $y = T(x)$ for at least one $x$ in $V$. If we select one such $x$ and define $R(y) = x$, then $T[R(y)] = T(x) = y$ for each $y$ in $T(V)$, so $R$ is a right inverse. Nonuniqueness may occur because there may be more than one $x$ in $V$ which maps onto a given $y$ in $T(V)$. We shall prove presently (in Theorem 16.9) that if each $y$ in $T(V)$ is the image of *exactly one* $x$ in $V$, then right inverses are unique.

First we prove that if a left inverse exists it is unique and, at the same time, is a right inverse.

THEOREM 16.8. *A function $T : V \to W$ can have at most one left inverse. If $T$ has a left inverse $S$, then $S$ is also a right inverse.*

*Proof.* Assume $T$ has two left inverses, $S : T(V) \to V$ and $S' : T(V) \to V$. Choose any $y$ in $T(V)$. We shall prove that $S(y) = S'(y)$. Now $y = T(x)$ for some $x$ in $V$, so we have

$$S[T(x)] = x \qquad \text{and} \qquad S'[T(x)] = x,$$

since both $S$ and $S'$ are left inverses. Therefore $S(y) = x$ and $S'(y) = x$, so $S(y) = S'(y)$ for all $y$ in $T(V)$. Therefore $S = S'$ which proves that left inverses are unique.

Now we prove that every left inverse $S$ is also a right inverse. Choose any element $y$ in $T(V)$. We shall prove that $T[S(y)] = y$. Since $y \in T(V)$, we have $y = T(x)$ for some $x$ in $V$. But $S$ is a left inverse, so

$$x = S[T(x)] = S(y).$$

Applying $T$, we get $T(x) = T[S(y)]$. But $y = T(x)$, so $y = T[S(y)]$, which completes the proof.

The next theorem characterizes all functions having left inverses.

THEOREM 16.9. *A function* $T: V \to W$ *has a left inverse if and only if* $T$ *maps distinct elements of* $V$ *onto distinct elements of* $W$; *that is, if and only if, for all* $x$ *and* $y$ *in* $V$,

(16.5) $$x \neq y \quad \text{implies} \quad T(x) \neq T(y).$$

*Note:* Condition (16.5) is equivalent to the statement

(16.6) $$T(x) = T(y) \quad \text{implies} \quad x = y.$$

A function $T$ satisfying (16.5) or (16.6) for all $x$ and $y$ in $V$ is said to be *one-to-one* on $V$.

*Proof.* Assume $T$ has a left inverse $S$, and assume that $T(x) = T(y)$. We wish to prove that $x = y$. Applying $S$, we find $S[T(x)] = S[T(y)]$. Since $S[T(x)] = x$ and $S[T(y)] = y$, this implies $x = y$. This proves that a function with a left inverse is one-to-one on its domain.

Now we prove the converse. Assume $T$ is one-to-one on $V$. We shall exhibit a function $S: T(V) \to V$ which is a left inverse of $T$. If $y \in T(V)$, then $y = T(x)$ for some $x$ in $V$. By (16.6), there is *exactly one* $x$ in $V$ for which $y = T(x)$. Define $S(y)$ to be this $x$. That is, we define $S$ on $T(V)$ as follows:

$$S(y) = x \quad \text{means that} \quad T(x) = y.$$

Then we have $S[T(x)] = x$ for each $x$ in $V$, so $ST = I_V$. Therefore, the function $S$ so defined is a left inverse of $T$.

DEFINITION. *Let* $T: V \to W$ *be one-to-one on* $V$. *The unique left inverse of* $T$ (*which we know is also a right inverse*) *is denoted by* $T^{-1}$. *We say that* $T$ *is invertible, and we call* $T^{-1}$ *the inverse of* $T$.

The results of this section refer to arbitrary functions. Now we apply these ideas to linear transformations.

## 16.7 One-to-one linear transformations

In this section, $V$ and $W$ denote linear spaces with the same scalars, and $T: V \to W$ denotes a linear transformation in $\mathscr{L}(V, W)$. The linearity of $T$ enables us to express the one-to-one property in several equivalent forms.

THEOREM 16.10. *Let* $T: V \to W$ *be a linear transformation in* $\mathscr{L}(V, W)$. *Then the following statements are equivalent.*
  (a) *$T$ is one-to-one on $V$.*
  (b) *$T$ is invertible and its inverse* $T^{-1}: T(V) \to V$ *is linear.*
  (c) *For all* $x$ *in* $V$, $T(x) = O$ *implies* $x = O$. *That is, the null space* $N(T)$ *contains only the zero element of* $V$.

*Proof.* We shall prove that (a) implies (b), (b) implies (c), and (c) implies (a). First assume (a) holds. Then $T$ has an inverse (by Theorem 16.9), and we must show that $T^{-1}$ is linear. Take any two elements $u$ and $v$ in $T(V)$. Then $u = T(x)$ and $v = T(y)$ for some $x$ and $y$ in $V$. For any scalars $a$ and $b$, we have

$$au + bv = aT(x) + bT(y) = T(ax + by),$$

since $T$ is linear. Hence, applying $T^{-1}$, we have

$$T^{-1}(au + bv) = ax + by = aT^{-1}(u) + bT^{-1}(v),$$

so $T^{-1}$ is linear. Therefore (a) implies (b).

Next assume that (b) holds. Take any $x$ in $V$ for which $T(x) = O$. Applying $T^{-1}$, we find that $x = T^{-1}(O) = O$, since $T^{-1}$ is linear. Therefore, (b) implies (c).

Finally, assume (c) holds. Take any two elements $u$ and $v$ in $V$ with $T(u) = T(v)$. By linearity, we have $T(u - v) = T(u) - T(v) = O$, so $u - v = O$. Therefore, $T$ is one-to-one on $V$, and the proof of the theorem is complete.

When $V$ is finite-dimensional, the one-to-one property can be formulated in terms of independence and dimensionality, as indicated by the next theorem.

THEOREM 16.11. *Let* $T: V \to W$ *be a linear transformation in* $\mathscr{L}(V, W)$ *and assume that* $V$ *is finite-dimensional, say* $\dim V = n$. *Then the following statements are equivalent.*

(a) $T$ *is one-to-one on* $V$.

(b) *If* $e_1, \ldots, e_p$ *are independent elements in* $V$, *then* $T(e_1), \ldots, T(e_p)$ *are independent elements in* $T(V)$.

(c) $\dim T(V) = n$.

(d) *If* $\{e_1, \ldots, e_n\}$ *is a basis for* $V$, *then* $\{T(e_1), \ldots, T(e_n)\}$ *is a basis for* $T(V)$.

*Proof.* We shall prove that (a) implies (b), (b) implies (c), (c) implies (d), and (d) implies (a). Assume (a) holds. Let $e_1, \ldots, e_p$ be independent elements of $V$ and consider the elements $T(e_1), \ldots, T(e_p)$ in $T(V)$. Suppose that

$$\sum_{i=1}^{p} c_i T(e_i) = O$$

for certain scalars $c_1, \ldots, c_p$. By linearity, we obtain

$$T\left(\sum_{i=1}^{p} c_i e_i\right) = O, \quad \text{and hence} \quad \sum_{i=1}^{p} c_i e_i = O$$

since $T$ is one-to-one. But $e_1, \ldots, e_p$ are independent, so $c_1 = \cdots = c_p = 0$. Therefore (a) implies (b).

Now assume (b) holds. Let $\{e_1, \ldots, e_n\}$ be a basis for $V$. By (b), the $n$ elements $T(e_1), \ldots, T(e_n)$ in $T(V)$ are independent. Therefore, $\dim T(V) \geq n$. But, by Theorem 16.3, we have $\dim T(V) \leq n$. Therefore $\dim T(V) = n$, so (b) implies (c).

Next, assume (c) holds and let $\{e_1, \ldots, e_n\}$ be a basis for $V$. Take any element $y$ in $T(V)$. Then $y = T(x)$ for some $x$ in $V$, so we have

$$x = \sum_{i=1}^{n} c_i e_i, \quad \text{and hence} \quad y = T(x) = \sum_{i=1}^{n} c_i T(e_i).$$

Therefore $\{T(e_1), \ldots, T(e_n)\}$ spans $T(V)$. But we are assuming $\dim T(V) = n$, so $\{T(e_1), \ldots, T(e_n)\}$ is a basis for $T(V)$. Therefore (c) implies (d).

Finally, assume (d) holds. We will prove that $T(x) = O$ implies $x = O$. Let $\{e_1, \ldots, e_n\}$ be a basis for $V$. If $x \in V$, we may write

$$x = \sum_{i=1}^{n} c_i e_i, \quad \text{and hence} \quad T(x) = \sum_{i=1}^{n} c_i T(e_i).$$

If $T(x) = O$, then $c_1 = \cdots = c_n = 0$, since the elements $T(e_1), \ldots, T(e_n)$ are independent. Therefore $x = O$, so $T$ is one-to-one on $V$. Thus, (d) implies (a) and the proof is complete.

## 16.8 Exercises

1. Let $V = \{0, 1\}$. Describe all functions $T: V \to V$. There are four altogether. Label them as $T_1, T_2, T_3, T_4$ and make a multiplication table showing the composition of each pair. Indicate which functions are one-to-one on $V$ and give their inverses.

2. Let $V = \{0, 1, 2\}$. Describe all functions $T: V \to V$ for which $T(V) = V$. There are six altogether. Label them as $T_1, \ldots, T_6$ and make a multiplication table showing the composition of each pair. Indicate which functions are one-to-one on $V$, and give their inverses.

In each of Exercises 3 through 12, a function $T: V_2 \to V_2$ is defined by the formula given for $T(x, y)$, where $(x, y)$ is an arbitrary point in $V_2$. In each case determine whether $T$ is one-to-one on $V_2$. If it is, describe its range $T(V_2)$; for each point $(u, v)$ in $T(V_2)$, let $(x, y) = T^{-1}(u, v)$ and give formulas for determining $x$ and $y$ in terms of $u$ and $v$.

3. $T(x, y) = (y, x)$.
4. $T(x, y) = (x, -y)$.
5. $T(x, y) = (x, 0)$.
6. $T(x, y) = (x, x)$.
7. $T(x, y) = (x^2, y^2)$.

8. $T(x, y) = (e^x, e^y)$.
9. $T(x, y) = (x, 1)$.
10. $T(x, y) = (x + 1, y + 1)$.
11. $T(x, y) = (x - y, x + y)$.
12. $T(x, y) = (2x - y, x + y)$.

In each of Exercises 13 through 20, a function $T: V_3 \to V_3$ is defined by the formula given for $T(x, y, z)$, where $(x, y, z)$ is an arbitrary point in $V_3$. In each case, determine whether $T$ is one-to-one on $V_3$. If it is, describe its range $T(V_3)$; for each point $(u, v, w)$ in $T(V_3)$, let $(x, y, z) = T^{-1}(u, v, w)$ and give formulas for determining $x$, $y$, and $z$ in terms of $u$, $v$, and $w$.

13. $T(x, y, z) = (z, y, x)$.
14. $T(x, y, z) = (x, y, 0)$.
15. $T(x, y, z) = (x, 2y, 3z)$.
16. $T(x, y, z) = (x, y, x + y + z)$.

17. $T(x, y, z) = (x + 1, y + 1, z - 1)$.
18. $T(x, y, z) = (x + 1, y + 2, z + 3)$.
19. $T(x, y, z) = (x, x + y, x + y + z)$.
20. $T(x, y, z) = (x + y, y + z, x + z)$.

21. Let $T: V \to V$ be a function which maps $V$ into itself. Powers are defined inductively by the formulas $T^0 = I$, $T^n = TT^{n-1}$ for $n \geq 1$. Prove that the associative law for composition implies the law of exponents: $T^m T^n = T^{m+n}$. If $T$ is invertible, prove that $T^n$ is also invertible and that $(T^n)^{-1} = (T^{-1})^n$.

In Exercises 22 through 25, $S$ and $T$ denote functions with domain $V$ and values in $V$. In general, $ST \neq TS$. If $ST = TS$, we say that $S$ and $T$ *commute*.

22. If $S$ and $T$ commute, prove that $(ST)^n = S^n T^n$ for all integers $n \geq 0$.

23. If $S$ and $T$ are invertible, prove that $ST$ is also invertible and that $(ST)^{-1} = T^{-1}S^{-1}$. In other words, the inverse of $ST$ is the composition of inverses, taken in reverse order.

24. If $S$ and $T$ are invertible and commute, prove that their inverses also commute.

25. Let $V$ be a linear space. If $S$ and $T$ commute, prove that

$$(S + T)^2 = S^2 + 2ST + T^2 \qquad \text{and} \qquad (S + T)^3 = S^3 + 3S^2T + 3ST^2 + T^3 \, .$$

Indicate how these formulas must be altered if $ST \neq TS$.

26. Let $S$ and $T$ be the linear transformations of $V_3$ into $V_3$ defined by the formulas $S(x, y, z) = (z, y, x)$ and $T(x, y, z) = (x, x + y, x + y + z)$, where $(x, y, z)$ is an arbitrary point of $V_3$.
    (a) Determine the image of $(x, y, z)$ under each of the following transformations: $ST$, $TS$, $ST - TS$, $S^2$, $T^2$, $(ST)^2$, $(TS)^2$, $(ST - TS)^2$.
    (b) Prove that $S$ and $T$ are one-to-one on $V_3$ and find the image of $(u, v, w)$ under each of the following transformations: $S^{-1}$, $T^{-1}$, $(ST)^{-1}$, $(TS)^{-1}$.
    (c) Find the image of $(x, y, z)$ under $(T - I)^n$ for each $n \geq 1$.

27. Let $V$ be the linear space of all real polynomials $p(x)$. Let $D$ denote the differentiation operator and let $T$ denote the integration operator which maps each polynomial $p$ onto the polynomial $q$ given by $q(x) = \int_0^x p(t)\, dt$. Prove that $DT = I$ but that $TD \neq I$. Describe the null space and range of $TD$.

28. Let $V$ be the linear space of all real polynomials $p(x)$. Let $D$ denote the differentiation operator and let $T$ be the linear transformation that maps $p(x)$ onto $xp'(x)$.
    (a) Let $p(x) = 2 + 3x - x^2 + 4x^3$ and determine the image of $p$ under each of the following transformations: $D$, $T$, $DT$, $TD$, $DT - TD$, $T^2D^2 - D^2T^2$.
    (b) Determine those $p$ in $V$ for which $T(p) = p$.
    (c) Determine those $p$ in $V$ for which $(DT - 2D)(p) = O$.
    (d) Determine those $p$ in $V$ for which $(DT - TD)^n(p) = D^n(p)$.

29. Let $V$ and $D$ be as in Exercise 28 but let $T$ be the linear transformation that maps $p(x)$ onto $xp(x)$. Prove that $DT - TD = I$ and that $DT^n - T^nD = nT^{n-1}$ for $n \geq 2$.

30. Let $S$ and $T$ be in $\mathscr{L}(V, V)$ and assume that $ST - TS = I$. Prove that $ST^n - T^nS = nT^{n-1}$ for all $n \geq 1$.

31. Let $V$ be the linear space of all real polynomials $p(x)$. Let $R$, $S$, $T$ be the functions which map an arbitrary polynomial $p(x) = c_0 + c_1x + \cdots + c_nx^n$ in $V$ onto the polynomials $r(x)$, $s(x)$, and $t(x)$, respectively, where

$$r(x) = p(0), \qquad s(x) = \sum_{k=1}^{n} c_k x^{k-1}, \qquad t(x) = \sum_{k=0}^{n} c_k x^{k+1} \, .$$

    (a) Let $p(x) = 2 + 3x - x^2 + x^3$ and determine the image of $p$ under each of the following transformations: $R$, $S$, $T$, $ST$, $TS$, $(TS)^2$, $T^2S^2$, $S^2T^2$, $TRS$, $RST$.
    (b) Prove that $R$, $S$, and $T$ are linear and determine the null space and range of each.
    (c) Prove that $T$ is one-to-one on $V$ and determine its inverse.
    (d) If $n \geq 1$, express $(TS)^n$ and $S^nT^n$ in terms of $I$ and $R$.

32. Refer to Exercise 28 of Section 16.4. Determine whether $T$ is one-to-one on $V$. If it is, describe its inverse.

## 16.9 Linear transformations with prescribed values

If $V$ is finite-dimensional, we can always construct a linear transformation $T: V \to W$ with prescribed values at the basis elements of $V$, as described in the next theorem.

THEOREM 16.12. *Let* $e_1, \ldots, e_n$ *be a basis for an n-dimensional linear space* $V$. *Let* $u_1, \ldots, u_n$ *be n arbitrary elements in a linear space* $W$. *Then there is one and only one linear transformation* $T: V \to W$ *such that*

$$(16.7) \qquad T(e_k) = u_k \quad for \quad k = 1, 2, \ldots, n.$$

*This* $T$ *maps an arbitrary element* $x$ *in* $V$ *as follows:*

$$(16.8) \qquad If \quad x = \sum_{k=1}^{n} x_k e_k, \quad then \quad T(x) = \sum_{k=1}^{n} x_k u_k.$$

*Proof.* Every $x$ in $V$ can be expressed uniquely as a linear combination of $e_1, \ldots, e_n$, the multipliers $x_1, \ldots, x_n$ being the components of $x$ relative to the ordered basis $(e_1, \ldots, e_n)$. If we define $T$ by (16.8), it is a straightforward matter to verify that $T$ is linear. If $x = e_k$ for some $k$, then all components of $x$ are 0 except the $k$th, which is 1, so (16.8) gives $T(e_k) = u_k$, as required.

To prove that there is only one linear transformation satisfying (16.7), let $T'$ be another and compute $T'(x)$. We find that

$$T'(x) = T'\left(\sum_{k=1}^{n} x_k e_k\right) = \sum_{k=1}^{n} x_k T'(e_k) = \sum_{k=1}^{n} x_k u_k = T(x).$$

Since $T'(x) = T(x)$ for all $x$ in $V$, we have $T' = T$, which completes the proof.

EXAMPLE. Determine the linear transformation $T: V_2 \to V_2$ which maps the basis elements $i = (1, 0)$ and $j = (0, 1)$ as follows:

$$T(i) = i + j, \qquad T(j) = 2i - j.$$

*Solution.* If $x = x_1 i + x_2 j$ is an arbitrary element of $V_2$, then $T(x)$ is given by

$$T(x) = x_1 T(i) + x_2 T(j) = x_1(i + j) + x_2(2i - j) = (x_1 + 2x_2)i + (x_1 - x_2)j.$$

## 16.10 Matrix representations of linear transformations

Theorem 16.12 shows that a linear transformation $T: V \to W$ of a finite-dimensional linear space $V$ is completely determined by its action on a given set of basis elements $e_1, \ldots, e_n$. Now, suppose the space $W$ is also finite-dimensional, say dim $W = m$, and let $w_1, \ldots, w_m$ be a basis for $W$. (The dimensions $n$ and $m$ may or may not be equal.) Since $T$ has values in $W$, each element $T(e_k)$ can be expressed uniquely as a linear combination of the basis elements $w_1, \ldots, w_m$, say

$$T(e_k) = \sum_{i=1}^{m} t_{ik} w_i,$$

where $t_{1k}, \ldots, t_{mk}$ are the components of $T(e_k)$ relative to the ordered basis $(w_1, \ldots, w_m)$.

We shall display the $m$-tuple $(t_{1k}, \ldots, t_{mk})$ vertically, as follows:

(16.9)

$$\begin{bmatrix} t_{1k} \\ t_{2k} \\ \cdot \\ \cdot \\ \cdot \\ t_{mk} \end{bmatrix} .$$

This array is called a *column vector* or a *column matrix*. We have such a column vector for each of the $n$ elements $T(e_1), \ldots, T(e_n)$. We place them side by side and enclose them in one pair of brackets to obtain the following rectangular array:

$$\begin{bmatrix} t_{11} & t_{12} & \cdots & t_{1n} \\ t_{21} & t_{22} & \cdots & t_{2n} \\ \cdot & \cdot & & \cdot \\ \cdot & \cdot & & \cdot \\ \cdot & \cdot & & \cdot \\ t_{m1} & t_{m2} & \cdots & t_{mn} \end{bmatrix}$$

This array is called a *matrix* consisting of $m$ *rows* and $n$ *columns*. We call it an $m$ by $n$ matrix, or an $m \times n$ matrix. The first row is the $1 \times n$ matrix $(t_{11}, t_{12}, \ldots, t_{1n})$. The $m \times 1$ matrix displayed in (16.9) is the $k$th column. The scalars $t_{ik}$ are indexed so the first subscript $i$ indicates the *row*, and the second subscript $k$ indicates the *column* in which $t_{ik}$ occurs. We call $t_{ik}$ the *ik-entry* or the *ik-element* of the matrix. The more compact notation

$$(t_{ik}), \qquad \text{or} \qquad (t_{ik})_{i,k=1}^{m,n} ,$$

is also used to denote the matrix whose *ik*-entry is $t_{ik}$.

Thus, every linear transformation $T$ of an $n$-dimensional space $V$ into an $m$-dimensional space $W$ gives rise to an $m \times n$ matrix $(t_{ik})$ whose columns consist of the components of $T(e_1), \ldots, T(e_n)$ relative to the basis $(w_1, \ldots, w_m)$. We call this the *matrix representation* of $T$ relative to the given choice of ordered bases $(e_1, \ldots, e_n)$ for $V$ and $(w_1, \ldots, w_m)$ for $W$. Once we know the matrix $(t_{ik})$, the components of any element $T(x)$ relative to the basis $(w_1, \ldots, w_m)$ can be determined as described in the next theorem.

THEOREM 16.13. *Let $T$ be a linear transformation in $\mathscr{L}(V, W)$, where $\dim V = n$ and $\dim W = m$. Let $(e_1, \ldots, e_n)$ and $(w_1, \ldots, w_m)$ be ordered bases for $V$ and $W$, respectively, and let $(t_{ik})$ be the $m \times n$ matrix whose entries are determined by the equations*

(16.10)
$$T(e_k) = \sum_{i=1}^{m} t_{ik} w_i , \qquad for \quad k = 1, 2, \ldots, n .$$

*Then an arbitrary element*

(16.11)
$$x = \sum_{k=1}^{n} x_k e_k$$

*in V with components* $(x_1, \ldots, x_n)$ *relative to* $(e_1, \ldots, e_n)$ *is mapped by T onto the element*

(16.12)
$$T(x) = \sum_{i=1}^{m} y_i w_i$$

*in W with components* $(y_1, \ldots, y_m)$ *relative to* $(w_1, \ldots, w_m)$. *The* $y_i$ *are related to the components of x by the linear equations*

(16.13)
$$y_i = \sum_{k=1}^{n} t_{ik} x_k \qquad for \quad i = 1, 2, \ldots, m.$$

*Proof.* Applying $T$ to each member of (16.11) and using (16.10), we obtain

$$T(x) = \sum_{k=1}^{n} x_k T(e_k) = \sum_{k=1}^{n} x_k \sum_{i=1}^{m} t_{ik} w_i = \sum_{i=1}^{m} \left( \sum_{k=1}^{n} t_{ik} x_k \right) w_i = \sum_{i=1}^{m} y_i w_i ,$$

where each $y_i$ is given by (16.13). This completes the proof.

Having chosen a pair of bases $(e_1, \ldots, e_n)$ and $(w_1, \ldots, w_m)$ for $V$ and $W$, respectively, every linear transformation $T: V \to W$ has a matrix representation $(t_{ik})$. Conversely, if we start with any $mn$ scalars arranged as a rectangular matrix $(t_{ik})$ and choose a pair of ordered bases for $V$ and $W$, then it is easy to prove that there is exactly one linear transformation $T: V \to W$ having this matrix representation. We simply define $T$ at the basis elements of $V$ by the equations in (16.10). Then, by Theorem 16.12, there is one and only one linear transformation $T: V \to W$ with these prescribed values. The image $T(x)$ of an arbitrary point $x$ in $V$ is then given by Equations (16.12) and (16.13).

EXAMPLE 1. *Construction of a linear transformation from a given matrix.* Suppose we start with the 2 × 3 matrix

$$\begin{bmatrix} 3 & 1 & -2 \\ 1 & 0 & 4 \end{bmatrix}.$$

Choose the usual bases of unit coordinate vectors for $V_3$ and $V_2$. Then the given matrix represents a linear transformation $T: V_3 \to V_2$ which maps an arbitrary vector $(x_1, x_2, x_3)$ in $V_3$ onto the vector $(y_1, y_2)$ in $V_2$ according to the linear equations

$$y_1 = 3x_1 + x_2 - 2x_3 .$$

$$y_2 = x_1 + 0x_2 + 4x_3 .$$

EXAMPLE 2. *Construction of a matrix representation of a given linear transformation.* Let $V$ be the linear space of all real polynomials $p(x)$ of degree $\leq 3$. This space has dimension 4, and we choose the basis $(1, x, x^2, x^3)$. Let $D$ be the differentiation operator which maps each polynomial $p(x)$ in $V$ onto its derivative $p'(x)$. We can regard $D$ as a linear transformation of $V$ into $W$, where $W$ is the 3-dimensional space of all real polynomials of degree $\leq 2$. In $W$ we choose the basis $(1, x, x^2)$. To find the matrix representation of $D$

relative to this choice of bases, we transform (differentiate) each basis element of $V$ and express it as a linear combination of the basis elements of $W$. Thus, we find that

$$D(1) = 0 = 0 + 0x + 0x^2, \qquad D(x) = 1 = 1 + 0x + 0x^2,$$

$$D(x^2) = 2x = 0 + 2x + 0x^2, \qquad D(x^3) = 3x^2 = 0 + 0x + 3x^2.$$

The coefficients of these polynomials determine the *columns* of the matrix representation of $D$. Therefore, the required representation is given by the following $3 \times 4$ matrix:

$$\begin{bmatrix} 0 & 1 & 0 & 0 \\ 0 & 0 & 2 & 0 \\ 0 & 0 & 0 & 3 \end{bmatrix}.$$

To emphasize that the matrix representation depends not only on the basis elements but also on their order, let us reverse the order of the basis elements in $W$ and use, instead, the ordered basis $(x^2, x, 1)$. Then the basis elements of $V$ are transformed into the same polynomials obtained above, but the components of these polynomials relative to the new basis $(x^2, x, 1)$ appear in reversed order. Therefore, the matrix representation of $D$ now becomes

$$\begin{bmatrix} 0 & 0 & 0 & 3 \\ 0 & 0 & 2 & 0 \\ 0 & 1 & 0 & 0 \end{bmatrix}.$$

Let us compute a third matrix representation for $D$, using the basis $(1, 1 + x, 1 + x + x^2, 1 + x + x^2 + x^3)$ for $V$, and the basis $(1, x, x^2)$ for $W$. The basis elements of $V$ are transformed as follows:

$$D(1) = 0, \qquad D(1 + x) = 1, \qquad D(1 + x + x^2) = 1 + 2x,$$

$$D(1 + x + x^2 + x^3) = 1 + 2x + 3x^2,$$

so the matrix representation in this case is

$$\begin{bmatrix} 0 & 1 & 1 & 1 \\ 0 & 0 & 2 & 2 \\ 0 & 0 & 0 & 3 \end{bmatrix}.$$

## 16.11  Construction of a matrix representation in diagonal form

Since it is possible to obtain different matrix representations of a given linear transformation by different choices of bases, it is natural to try to choose the bases so that the resulting matrix will have a particularly simple form. The next theorem shows that we can make all the entries 0 except possibly along the diagonal starting from the upper left-hand corner of the matrix. Along this diagonal there will be a string of ones followed by zeros, the number of ones being equal to the rank of the transformation. A matrix $(t_{ik})$ with all entries $t_{ik} = 0$ when $i \neq k$ is said to be a *diagonal matrix.*

THEOREM 16.14. *Let V and W be finite-dimensional linear spaces, with* $\dim V = n$ *and* $\dim W = m$. *Assume* $T \in \mathscr{L}(V, W)$ *and let* $r = \dim T(V)$ *denote the rank of T. Then there exists a basis* $(e_1, \ldots, e_n)$ *for V and a basis* $(w_1, \ldots, w_m)$ *for W such that*

$$(16.14) \qquad T(e_i) = w_i \quad \text{for} \quad i = 1, 2, \ldots, r,$$

*and*

$$(16.15) \qquad T(e_i) = O \quad \text{for} \quad i = r + 1, \ldots, n.$$

*Therefore, the matrix* $(t_{ik})$ *of T relative to these bases has all entries zero except for the r diagonal entries*

$$t_{11} = t_{22} = \cdots = t_{rr} = 1.$$

*Proof.* First we construct a basis for $W$. Since $T(V)$ is a subspace of $W$ with $\dim T(V) = r$, the space $T(V)$ has a basis of $r$ elements in $W$, say $w_1, \ldots, w_r$. By Theorem 15.7, these elements form a subset of some basis for $W$. Therefore we can adjoin elements $w_{r+1}, \ldots, w_m$ so that

$$(16.16) \qquad (w_1, \ldots, w_r, w_{r+1}, \ldots, w_m)$$

is a basis for $W$.

Now we construct a basis for $V$. Each of the first $r$ elements $w_i$ in (16.16) is the image of at least one element in $V$. Choose one such element in $V$ and call it $e_i$. Then $T(e_i) = w_i$ for $i = 1, 2, \ldots, r$ so (16.14) is satisfied. Now let $k$ be the dimension of the null space $N(T)$. By Theorem 16.3 we have $n = k + r$. Since $\dim N(T) = k$, the space $N(T)$ has a basis consisting of $k$ elements in $V$ which we designate as $e_{r+1}, \ldots, e_{r+k}$. For each of these elements, Equation (16.15) is satisfied. Therefore, to complete the proof, we must show that the ordered set

$$(16.17) \qquad (e_1, \ldots, e_r, e_{r+1}, \ldots, e_{r+k})$$

is a basis for $V$. Since $\dim V = n = r + k$, we need only show that these elements are independent. Suppose that some linear combination of them is zero, say

$$(16.18) \qquad \sum_{i=1}^{r+k} c_i e_i = O.$$

Applying $T$ and using Equations (16.14) and (16.15), we find that

$$\sum_{i=1}^{r+k} c_i T(e_i) = \sum_{i=1}^{r} c_i w_i = O.$$

But $w_1, \ldots, w_r$ are independent, and hence $c_1 = \cdots = c_r = 0$. Therefore, the first $r$ terms in (16.18) are zero, so (16.18) reduces to

$$\sum_{i=r+1}^{r+k} c_i e_i = O.$$

But $e_{r+1}, \ldots, e_{r+k}$ are independent since they form a basis for $N(T)$, and hence $c_{r+1} = \cdots = c_{r+k} = 0$. Therefore, all the $c_i$ in (16.18) are zero, so the elements in (16.17) form a basis for $V$. This completes the proof.

EXAMPLE. We refer to Example 2 of Section 16.10, where $D$ is the differentiation operator which maps the space $V$ of polynomials of degree $\leq 3$ into the space $W$ of polynomials of degree $\leq 2$. In this example, the range $T(V) = W$, so $T$ has rank 3. Applying the method used to prove Theorem 16.14, we choose any basis for $W$, for example the basis $(1, x, x^2)$. A set of polynomials in $V$ which map onto these elements is given by $(x, \frac{1}{2}x^2, \frac{1}{3}x^3)$. We extend this set to get a basis for $V$ by adjoining the constant polynomial 1, which is a basis for the null space of $D$. Therefore, if we use the basis $(x, \frac{1}{2}x^2, \frac{1}{3}x^3, 1)$ for $V$ and the basis $(1, x, x^2)$ for $W$, the corresponding matrix representation for $D$ has the diagonal form

$$\begin{bmatrix} 1 & 0 & 0 & 0 \\ 0 & 1 & 0 & 0 \\ 0 & 0 & 1 & 0 \end{bmatrix}.$$

## 16.12 Exercises

In all exercises involving the vector space $V_n$, the usual basis of unit coordinate vectors is to be chosen unless another basis is specifically mentioned. In exercises concerned with the matrix of a linear transformation $T: V \to W$ where $V = W$, we take the same basis in both $V$ and $W$ unless another choice is indicated.

1. Determine the matrix of each of the following linear transformations of $V_n$ into $V_n$:
   (a) the identity transformation,
   (b) the zero transformation,
   (c) multiplication by a fixed scalar $c$.
2. Determine the matrix for each of the following projections.
   (a) $T: V_3 \to V_2$,   where $T(x_1, x_2, x_3) = (x_1, x_2)$.
   (b) $T: V_3 \to V_2$,   where $T(x_1, x_2, x_3) = (x_2, x_3)$.
   (c) $T: V_5 \to V_3$,   where $T(x_1, x_2, x_3, x_4, x_5) = (x_2, x_3, x_4)$.
3. A linear transformation $T: V_2 \to V_2$ maps the basis vectors $i$ and $j$ as follows:

   $$T(i) = i + j, \qquad T(j) = 2i - j.$$

   (a) Compute $T(3i - 4j)$ and $T^2(3i - 4j)$ in terms of $i$ and $j$.
   (b) Determine the matrix of $T$ and of $T^2$.
   (c) Solve part (b) if the basis $(i, j)$ is replaced by $(e_1, e_2)$, where $e_1 = i - j$, $e_2 = 3i + j$.
4. A linear transformation $T: V_2 \to V_2$ is defined as follows: Each vector $(x, y)$ is reflected in the $y$-axis and then doubled in length to yield $T(x, y)$. Determine the matrix of $T$ and of $T^2$.
5. Let $T: V_3 \to V_3$ be a linear transformation such that

   $$T(k) = 2i + 3j + 5k, \qquad T(j + k) = i, \qquad T(i + j + k) = j - k.$$

(a) Compute $T(i + 2j + 3k)$ and determine the nullity and rank of $T$.

(b) Determine the matrix of $T$.

6. For the linear transformation in Exercise 5, choose both bases to be $(e_1, e_2, e_3)$, where $e_1 = (2, 3, 5)$, $e_2 = (1, 0, 0)$, $e_3 = (0, 1, -1)$, and determine the matrix of $T$ relative to the new bases.

7. A linear transformation $T: V_3 \rightarrow V_2$ maps the basis vectors as follows: $T(i) = (0, 0)$, $T(j) = (1, 1)$, $T(k) = (1, -1)$.

(a) Compute $T(4i - j + k)$ and determine the nullity and rank of $T$.

(b) Determine the matrix of $T$.

(c) Use the basis $(i, j, k)$ in $V_3$ and the basis $(w_1, w_2)$ in $V_2$, where $w_1 = (1, 1)$, $w_2 = (1, 2)$. Determine the matrix of $T$ relative to these bases.

(d) Find bases $(e_1, e_2, e_3)$ for $V_3$ and $(w_1, w_2)$ for $V_2$ relative to which the matrix of $T$ will be in diagonal form.

8. A linear transformation $T: V_2 \rightarrow V_3$ maps the basis vectors as follows: $T(i) = (1, 0, 1)$, $T(j) = (-1, 0, 1)$.

(a) Compute $T(2i - 3j)$ and determine the nullity and rank of $T$.

(b) Determine the matrix of $T$.

(c) Find bases $(e_1, e_2)$ for $V_2$ and $(w_1, w_2, w_3)$ for $V_3$ relative to which the matrix of $T$ will be in diagonal form.

9. Solve Exercise 8 if $T(i) = (1, 0, 1)$ and $T(j) = (1, 1, 1)$.

10. Let $V$ and $W$ be linear spaces, each with dimension 2 and each with basis $(e_1, e_2)$. Let $T: V \rightarrow W$ be a linear transformation such that

$$T(e_1 + e_2) = 3e_1 + 9e_2, \qquad T(3e_1 + 2e_2) = 7e_1 + 23e_2.$$

(a) Compute $T(e_2 - e_1)$ and determine the nullity and rank of $T$.

(b) Determine the matrix of $T$ relative to the given basis.

(c) Use the basis $(e_1, e_2)$ for $V$ and find a new basis of the form $(e_1 + ae_2, 2e_1 + be_2)$ for $W$, relative to which the matrix of $T$ will be in diagonal form.

In the linear space of all real-valued functions, each of the following sets is independent and spans a finite-dimensional subspace $V$. Use the given set as a basis for $V$ and let $D: V \rightarrow V$ be the differentiation operator. In each case, find the matrix of $D$ and of $D^2$ relative to this choice of basis.

11. $(\sin x, \cos x)$.

12. $(1, x, e^x)$.

13. $(1, 1 + x, 1 + x + e^x)$.

14. $(e^x, xe^x)$.

15. $(-\cos x, \sin x)$.

16. $(\sin x, \cos x, x \sin x, x \cos x)$.

17. $(e^x \sin x, e^x \cos x)$.

18. $(e^{2x} \sin 3x, e^{2x} \cos 3x)$.

19. Choose the basis $(1, x, x^2, x^3)$ in the linear space $V$ of all real polynomials of degree $\leq 3$. Let $D$ denote the differentiation operator and let $T: V \rightarrow V$ be the linear transformation which maps $p(x)$ onto $xp'(x)$. Relative to the given basis, determine the matrix of each of the following transformations: (a) $T$; (b) $DT$; (c) $TD$; (d) $TD - DT$; (e) $T^2$; (f) $T^2D^2 - D^2T^2$.

20. Refer to Exercise 19. Let $W$ be the image of $V$ under $TD$. Find bases for $V$ and for $W$ relative to which the matrix of $TD$ is in diagonal form.

## 16.13 Linear spaces of matrices

We have seen how matrices arise in a natural way as representations of linear transformations. Matrices can also be considered as objects existing in their own right, without necessarily being connected to linear transformations. As such, they form another class of mathematical objects on which algebraic operations can be defined. The connection with linear transformations serves as motivation for these definitions, but this connection will be ignored for the moment.

Let $m$ and $n$ be two positive integers, and let $I_{m,n}$ be the set of all pairs of integers $(i, j)$ such that $1 \leq i \leq m$, $1 \leq j \leq n$. Any function $A$ whose domain is $I_{m,n}$ is called an $m \times n$ *matrix*. The function value $A(i, j)$ is called the *ij-entry* or *ij-element* of the matrix and will be denoted also by $a_{ij}$. It is customary to display all the function values in a rectangular array consisting of $m$ rows and $n$ columns, as follows:

$$\begin{bmatrix} a_{11} & a_{12} & \cdots & a_{1n} \\ a_{21} & a_{22} & \cdots & a_{2n} \\ \cdot & \cdot & & \cdot \\ \cdot & \cdot & & \cdot \\ \cdot & \cdot & & \cdot \\ a_{m1} & a_{m2} & \cdots & a_{mn} \end{bmatrix}.$$

The elements $a_{ij}$ may be arbitrary objects of any kind. Usually they will be real or complex numbers, but sometimes it is convenient to consider matrices whose elements are other objects, for example, functions. We also denote matrices by the more compact notation

$$A = (a_{ij})_{i,j=1}^{m,n} \quad \text{or} \quad A = (a_{ij}).$$

If $m = n$, the matrix is said to be a *square matrix*. A $1 \times n$ matrix is called a *row matrix*; an $m \times 1$ matrix is called a *column matrix*.

Two functions are equal if and only if they have the same domain and take the same function value at each element in the domain. Since matrices are functions, two matrices $A = (a_{ij})$ and $B = (b_{ij})$ are equal if and only if they have the same number of rows, the same number of columns, and equal entries $a_{ij} = b_{ij}$ for each pair $(i, j)$.

Now we assume the entries are numbers (real or complex) and we define addition of matrices and multiplication by scalars by the same method used for any real- or complex-valued functions.

DEFINITION. *If* $A = (a_{ij})$ *and* $B = (b_{ij})$ *are two* $m \times n$ *matrices and if* $c$ *is any scalar, we define matrices* $A + B$ *and* $cA$ *as follows:*

$$A + B = (a_{ij} + b_{ij}), \quad cA = (ca_{ij}).$$

*The sum is defined only when* $A$ *and* $B$ *have the same size.*

EXAMPLE. If

$$A = \begin{bmatrix} 1 & 2 & -3 \\ -1 & 0 & 4 \end{bmatrix} \quad \text{and} \quad B = \begin{bmatrix} 5 & 0 & 1 \\ 1 & -2 & 3 \end{bmatrix},$$

then we have

$$A + B = \begin{bmatrix} 6 & 2 & -2 \\ 0 & -2 & 7 \end{bmatrix}, \quad 2A = \begin{bmatrix} 2 & 4 & -6 \\ -2 & 0 & 8 \end{bmatrix}, \quad (-1)B = \begin{bmatrix} -5 & 0 & -1 \\ -1 & 2 & -3 \end{bmatrix}.$$

We define the zero matrix $O$ to be the $m \times n$ matrix all of whose elements are 0. With these definitions, it is a straightforward exercise to verify that the collection of all $m \times n$ matrices is a linear space. We denote this linear space by $M_{m,n}$. If the entries are real numbers, the space $M_{m,n}$ is a real linear space. If the entries are complex, $M_{m,n}$ is a complex linear space. It is also easy to prove that this space has dimension $mn$. In fact, a basis for $M_{m,n}$ consists of the $mn$ matrices having one entry equal to 1 and all others equal to 0. For example, the six matrices

$$\begin{bmatrix} 1 & 0 & 0 \\ 0 & 0 & 0 \end{bmatrix}, \begin{bmatrix} 0 & 1 & 0 \\ 0 & 0 & 0 \end{bmatrix}, \begin{bmatrix} 0 & 0 & 1 \\ 0 & 0 & 0 \end{bmatrix}, \begin{bmatrix} 0 & 0 & 0 \\ 1 & 0 & 0 \end{bmatrix}, \begin{bmatrix} 0 & 0 & 0 \\ 0 & 1 & 0 \end{bmatrix}, \begin{bmatrix} 0 & 0 & 0 \\ 0 & 0 & 1 \end{bmatrix},$$

form a basis for the set of all $2 \times 3$ matrices.

## 16.14 Isomorphism between linear transformations and matrices

We return now to the connection between matrices and linear transformations. Let $V$ and $W$ be finite-dimensional linear spaces with dim $V = n$ and dim $W = m$. Choose a basis $(e_1, \ldots, e_n)$ for $V$ and a basis $(w_1, \ldots, w_m)$ for $W$. In this discussion, these bases are kept fixed. Let $\mathscr{L}(V, W)$ denote the linear space of all linear transformations of $V$ into $W$. If $T \in \mathscr{L}(V, W)$, let $m(T)$ denote the matrix of $T$ relative to the given bases. We recall that $m(T)$ is defined as follows.

The image of each basis element $e_k$ is expressed as a linear combination of the basis elements in $W$:

$$(16.19) \qquad T(e_k) = \sum_{i=1}^{m} t_{ik} w_i \qquad \text{for} \quad k = 1, 2, \ldots, n.$$

The scalar multipliers $t_{ik}$ are the $ik$-entries of $m(T)$. Thus, we have

$$(16.20) \qquad m(T) = (t_{ik})_{i,k=1}^{m,n}.$$

Equation (16.20) defines a new function $m$ whose domain is $\mathscr{L}(V, W)$ and whose values are matrices in $M_{m,n}$. Since every $m \times n$ matrix is the matrix $m(T)$ for some $T$ in $\mathscr{L}(V, W)$, the range of $m$ is $M_{m,n}$. The next theorem shows that the transformation $m: \mathscr{L}(V, W) \to M_{m,n}$ is linear and one-to-one on $\mathscr{L}(V, W)$.

THEOREM 16.15. ISOMORPHISM THEOREM. *For all $S$ and $T$ in $\mathscr{L}(V, W)$ and all scalars $c$, we have*

$$m(S + T) = m(S) + m(T) \qquad and \qquad m(cT) = cm(T).$$

*Moreover,*

$$m(S) = m(T) \qquad implies \qquad S = T,$$

*so $m$ is one-to-one on $\mathscr{L}(V, W)$.*

*Proof.* The matrix $m(T)$ is formed from the multipliers $t_{ik}$ in (16.19). Similarly, the matrix $m(S)$ is formed from the multipliers $s_{ik}$ in the equations

$$(16.21) \qquad S(e_k) = \sum_{i=1}^{m} s_{ik} w_i \qquad \text{for} \quad k = 1, 2, \ldots, n.$$

Since we have

$$(S + T)(e_k) = \sum_{i=1}^{m} (s_{ik} + t_{ik}) w_i \qquad \text{and} \qquad (cT)(e_k) = \sum_{i=1}^{m} (ct_{ik}) w_i,$$

we obtain $m(S + T) = (s_{ik} + t_{ik}) = m(S) + m(T)$ and $m(cT) = (ct_{ik}) = cm(T)$. This proves that $m$ is linear.

To prove that $m$ is one-to-one, suppose that $m(S) = m(T)$, where $S = (s_{ik})$ and $T = (t_{ik})$. Equations (16.19) and (16.21) show that $S(e_k) = T(e_k)$ for each basis element $e_k$, so $S(x) = T(x)$ for all $x$ in $V$, and hence $S = T$.

> *Note:* The function $m$ is called an *isomorphism*. For a given choice of bases, $m$ establishes a one-to-one correspondence between the set of linear transformations $\mathscr{L}(V, W)$ and the set of $m \times n$ matrices $M_{m,n}$. The operations of addition and multiplication by scalars are preserved under this correspondence. The linear spaces $\mathscr{L}(V, W)$ and $M_{m,n}$ are said to be *isomorphic*. Incidentally, Theorem 16.11 shows that the domain of a one-to-one linear transformation has the same dimension as its range. Therefore, $\dim \mathscr{L}(V, W) = \dim M_{m,n} = mn$.

If $V = W$ and if we choose the same basis in both $V$ and $W$, then the matrix $m(I)$ which corresponds to the identity transformation $I: V \to V$ is an $n \times n$ diagonal matrix with each diagonal entry equal to 1 and all others equal to 0. This is called the *identity* or *unit matrix* and is denoted by $I$ or by $I_n$.

## 16.15 Multiplication of matrices

Some linear transformations can be multiplied by means of composition. Now we shall define multiplication of matrices in such a way that the product of two matrices corresponds to the composition of the linear transformations they represent.

We recall that if $T: U \to V$ and $S: V \to W$ are linear transformations, their composition $ST: U \to W$ is a linear transformation given by

$$ST(x) = S[T(x)] \qquad \text{for all } x \text{ in } U.$$

Suppose that $U$, $V$, and $W$ are finite-dimensional, say

$$\dim U = n, \qquad \dim V = p, \qquad \dim W = m.$$

Choose bases for $U$, $V$, and $W$. Relative to these bases, the matrix $m(S)$ is an $m \times p$ matrix, the matrix $T$ is a $p \times n$ matrix, and the matrix of $ST$ is an $m \times n$ matrix. The following definition of matrix multiplication will enable us to deduce the relation $m(ST) = m(S)m(T)$. This extends the isomorphism property to products.

DEFINITION.   *Let A be any m × p matrix, and let B be any p × n matrix, say*

$$A = (a_{ij})_{i,j=1}^{m,p} \quad and \quad B = (b_{ij})_{i,j=1}^{p,n}.$$

*Then the product AB is defined to be the m × n matrix C = $(c_{ij})$ whose ij-entry is given by*

(16.22)  $$c_{ij} = \sum_{k=1}^{p} a_{ik}b_{kj}.$$

*Note:* The product $AB$ is not defined unless the number of columns of $A$ is equal to the number of rows of $B$.

If we write $A_i$ for the *i*th row of $A$, and $B^j$ for the *j*th column of $B$, and think of these as *p*-dimensional vectors, then the sum in (16.22) is simply the dot product $A_i \cdot B^j$. In other words, the *ij*-entry of $AB$ is the dot product of the *i*th row of $A$ with the *j*th column of $B$:

$$AB = (A_i \cdot B^j)_{i,j=1}^{m,n}.$$

Thus, matrix multiplication can be regarded as a generalization of the dot product.

EXAMPLE 1. Let $A = \begin{bmatrix} 3 & 1 & 2 \\ -1 & 1 & 0 \end{bmatrix}$ and $B = \begin{bmatrix} 4 & 6 \\ 5 & -1 \\ 0 & 2 \end{bmatrix}$. Since $A$ is $2 \times 3$ and $B$ is $3 \times 2$,

the product $AB$ is the $2 \times 2$ matrix

$$AB = \begin{bmatrix} A_1 \cdot B^1 & A_1 \cdot B^2 \\ A_2 \cdot B^1 & A_2 \cdot B^2 \end{bmatrix} = \begin{bmatrix} 17 & 21 \\ 1 & -7 \end{bmatrix}.$$

The entries of $AB$ are computed as follows:

$A_1 \cdot B^1 = 3 \cdot 4 + 1 \cdot 5 + 2 \cdot 0 = 17,$      $A_1 \cdot B^2 = 3 \cdot 6 + 1 \cdot (-1) + 2 \cdot 2 = 21,$

$A_2 \cdot B^1 = (-1) \cdot 4 + 1 \cdot 5 + 0 \cdot 0 = 1,$      $A_2 \cdot B^2 = (-1) \cdot 6 + 1 \cdot (-1) + 0 \cdot 2 = -7.$

EXAMPLE 2. Let

$$A = \begin{bmatrix} 2 & 1 & -3 \\ 1 & 2 & 4 \end{bmatrix} \quad and \quad B = \begin{bmatrix} -2 \\ 1 \\ 2 \end{bmatrix}.$$

Here $A$ is $2 \times 3$ and $B$ is $3 \times 1$, so $AB$ is the $2 \times 1$ matrix given by

$$AB = \begin{bmatrix} A_1 \cdot B^1 \\ A_2 \cdot B^1 \end{bmatrix} = \begin{bmatrix} -9 \\ 8 \end{bmatrix},$$

since $A_1 \cdot B^1 = 2 \cdot (-2) + 1 \cdot 1 + (-3) \cdot 2 = -9$ and $A_2 \cdot B^1 = 1 \cdot (-2) + 2 \cdot 1 + 4 \cdot 2 = 8$.

EXAMPLE 3. If $A$ and $B$ are both square matrices of the same size, then both $AB$ and $BA$ are defined. For example, if

$$A = \begin{bmatrix} 1 & 2 \\ -1 & 1 \end{bmatrix} \quad \text{and} \quad B = \begin{bmatrix} 3 & 4 \\ 5 & 2 \end{bmatrix},$$

we find that

$$AB = \begin{bmatrix} 13 & 8 \\ 2 & -2 \end{bmatrix}, \quad BA = \begin{bmatrix} -1 & 10 \\ 3 & 12 \end{bmatrix}.$$

This example shows that in general $AB \neq BA$. If $AB = BA$, we say $A$ and $B$ *commute*.

EXAMPLE 4. If $I_p$ is the $p \times p$ identity matrix, then $I_p A = A$ for every $p \times n$ matrix $A$, and $BI_p = B$ for every $m \times p$ matrix $B$. For example,

$$\begin{bmatrix} 1 & 0 & 0 \\ 0 & 1 & 0 \\ 0 & 0 & 1 \end{bmatrix} \begin{bmatrix} 2 \\ 3 \\ 4 \end{bmatrix} = \begin{bmatrix} 2 \\ 3 \\ 4 \end{bmatrix}, \quad \begin{bmatrix} 1 & 2 & 3 \\ 4 & 5 & 6 \end{bmatrix} \begin{bmatrix} 1 & 0 & 0 \\ 0 & 1 & 0 \\ 0 & 0 & 1 \end{bmatrix} = \begin{bmatrix} 1 & 2 & 3 \\ 4 & 5 & 6 \end{bmatrix}.$$

Now we prove that the matrix of a composition $ST$ is the product of the matrices $m(S)$ and $m(T)$.

THEOREM 16.16. *Let $T: U \to V$ and $S: V \to W$ be linear transformations, where $U$, $V$, $W$ are finite-dimensional linear spaces. Then, for a fixed choice of bases, the matrices of $S$, $T$, and $ST$ are related by the equation*

$$m(ST) = m(S)m(T).$$

*Proof.* Assume dim $U = n$, dim $V = p$, dim $W = m$. Let $(u_1, \ldots, u_n)$ be a basis for $U$, $(v_1, \ldots, v_p)$ a basis for $V$, and $(w_1, \ldots, w_m)$ a basis for $W$. Relative to these bases, we have

$$m(S) = (s_{ij})_{i,j=1}^{m,p}, \quad \text{where} \quad S(v_k) = \sum_{i=1}^{m} s_{ik}w_i \quad \text{for} \quad k = 1, 2, \ldots, p,$$

and

$$m(T) = (t_{ij})_{i,j=1}^{p,n}, \quad \text{where} \quad T(u_j) = \sum_{k=1}^{p} t_{kj}v_k \quad \text{for} \quad j = 1, 2, \ldots, n.$$

Therefore, we have

$$ST(u_j) = S[T(u_j)] = \sum_{k=1}^{p} t_{kj}S(v_k) = \sum_{k=1}^{p} t_{kj} \sum_{i=1}^{m} s_{ik}w_i = \sum_{i=1}^{m} \left( \sum_{k=1}^{p} s_{ik}t_{kj} \right) w_i,$$

so we find that

$$m(ST) = \left( \sum_{k=1}^{p} s_{ik}t_{kj} \right)_{i,j=1}^{m,n} = m(S)m(T).$$

We have already noted that matrix multiplication does not always satisfy the commutative law. The next theorem shows that it does satisfy the associative and distributive laws.

THEOREM 16.17. ASSOCIATIVE AND DISTRIBUTIVE LAWS FOR MATRIX MULTIPLICATION.
*Given matrices A, B, C.*

(a) *If the products $A(BC)$ and $(AB)C$ are meaningful, we have*

$$A(BC) = (AB)C \quad \text{(associative law)}.$$

(b) *Assume A and B are of the same size. If AC and BC are meaningful, we have*

$$(A + B)C = AC + BC \quad \text{(right distributive law)},$$

*whereas if CA and CB are meaningful, we have*

$$C(A + B) = CA + CB \quad \text{(left distributive law)}.$$

*Proof.* These properties can be deduced directly from the definition of matrix multiplication, but we prefer the following type of argument. Introduce finite-dimensional linear spaces $U$, $V$, $W$, $X$ and linear transformations $T: U \to V$, $S: V \to W$, $R: W \to X$ such that, for a fixed choice of bases, we have

$$A = m(R), \qquad B = m(S), \qquad C = m(T).$$

By Theorem 16.16, we have $m(RS) = AB$ and $m(ST) = BC$. From the associative law for composition, we find that $R(ST) = (RS)T$. Applying Theorem 16.16 once more to this equation, we obtain $m(R)m(ST) = m(RS)m(T)$ or $A(BC) = (AB)C$, which proves (a). The proof of (b) can be given by a similar type of argument.

DEFINITION. *If A is a square matrix, we define integral powers of A inductively as follows:*

$$A^0 = I, \qquad A^n = AA^{n-1} \quad \text{for } n \geq 1.$$

## 16.16 Exercises

1. If $A = \begin{bmatrix} 1 & -4 & 2 \\ -1 & 4 & -2 \end{bmatrix}$, $B = \begin{bmatrix} 1 & 2 \\ -1 & 3 \\ 5 & -2 \end{bmatrix}$, $C = \begin{bmatrix} 2 & 2 \\ 1 & -1 \\ 1 & -3 \end{bmatrix}$, compute $B + C$, $AB$,

$BA$, $AC$, $CA$, $A(2B - 3C)$.

2. Let $A = \begin{bmatrix} 0 & 1 \\ 0 & 2 \end{bmatrix}$. Find all $2 \times 2$ matrices $B$ such that (a) $AB = O$; (b) $BA = O$.

3. In each case find $a$, $b$, $c$, $d$ to satisfy the given equation.

(a) $\begin{bmatrix} 0 & 0 & 1 & 0 \\ 1 & 0 & 0 & 0 \\ 0 & 1 & 0 & 0 \\ 0 & 0 & 0 & 1 \end{bmatrix} \begin{bmatrix} a \\ b \\ c \\ d \end{bmatrix} = \begin{bmatrix} 1 \\ 9 \\ 6 \\ 5 \end{bmatrix}$; (b) $\begin{bmatrix} a & b & c & d \\ 1 & 4 & 9 & 2 \end{bmatrix} \begin{bmatrix} 1 & 0 & 2 & 0 \\ 0 & 0 & 1 & 1 \\ 0 & 1 & 0 & 0 \\ 0 & 0 & 1 & 0 \end{bmatrix} = \begin{bmatrix} 1 & 0 & 6 & 6 \\ 1 & 9 & 8 & 4 \end{bmatrix}$.

4. Calculate $AB - BA$ in each case.

(a) $A = \begin{bmatrix} 1 & 2 & 2 \\ 2 & 1 & 2 \\ 1 & 2 & 3 \end{bmatrix}, \quad B = \begin{bmatrix} 4 & 1 & 1 \\ -4 & 2 & 0 \\ 1 & 2 & 1 \end{bmatrix};$

(b) $A = \begin{bmatrix} 2 & 0 & 0 \\ 1 & 1 & 2 \\ -1 & 2 & 1 \end{bmatrix}, \quad B = \begin{bmatrix} 3 & 1 & -2 \\ 3 & -2 & 4 \\ -3 & 5 & 11 \end{bmatrix}.$

5. If $A$ is a square matrix, prove that $A^n A^m = A^{m+n}$ for all integers $m \geq 0, n \geq 0$.

6. Let $A = \begin{bmatrix} 1 & 1 \\ 0 & 1 \end{bmatrix}$. Verify that $A^2 = \begin{bmatrix} 1 & 2 \\ 0 & 1 \end{bmatrix}$ and compute $A^n$.

7. Let $A = \begin{bmatrix} \cos\theta & -\sin\theta \\ \sin\theta & \cos\theta \end{bmatrix}$. Verify that $A^2 = \begin{bmatrix} \cos 2\theta & -\sin 2\theta \\ \sin 2\theta & \cos 2\theta \end{bmatrix}$ and compute $A^n$.

8. Let $A = \begin{bmatrix} 1 & 1 & 1 \\ 0 & 1 & 1 \\ 0 & 0 & 1 \end{bmatrix}$. Verify that $A^2 = \begin{bmatrix} 1 & 2 & 3 \\ 0 & 1 & 2 \\ 0 & 0 & 1 \end{bmatrix}$. Compute $A^3$ and $A^4$. Guess a general

formula for $A^n$ and prove it by induction.

9. Let $A = \begin{bmatrix} 1 & 0 \\ -1 & 1 \end{bmatrix}$. Prove that $A^2 = 2A - I$ and compute $A^{100}$.

10. Find all $2 \times 2$ matrices $A$ such that $A^2 = O$.

11. (a) Prove that a $2 \times 2$ matrix $A$ commutes with every $2 \times 2$ matrix if and only if $A$ commutes with each of the four matrices

$$\begin{bmatrix} 1 & 0 \\ 0 & 0 \end{bmatrix}, \quad \begin{bmatrix} 0 & 1 \\ 0 & 0 \end{bmatrix}, \quad \begin{bmatrix} 0 & 0 \\ 1 & 0 \end{bmatrix}, \quad \begin{bmatrix} 0 & 0 \\ 0 & 1 \end{bmatrix}.$$

(b) Find all such matrices $A$.

12. The equation $A^2 = I$ is satisfied by each of the $2 \times 2$ matrices

$$\begin{bmatrix} 1 & 0 \\ 0 & 1 \end{bmatrix}, \quad \begin{bmatrix} 1 & 0 \\ c & -1 \end{bmatrix}, \quad \begin{bmatrix} 1 & b \\ 0 & -1 \end{bmatrix},$$

where $b$ and $c$ are arbitrary real numbers. Find all $2 \times 2$ matrices $A$ such that $A^2 = I$.

13. If $A = \begin{bmatrix} 2 & -1 \\ -2 & 3 \end{bmatrix}$ and $B = \begin{bmatrix} 7 & 6 \\ 9 & 8 \end{bmatrix}$, find $2 \times 2$ matrices $C$ and $D$ such that $AC = B$
and $DA = B$.

14. (a) Verify that the algebraic identities

$$(A + B)^2 = A^2 + 2AB + B^2 \quad \text{and} \quad (A + B)(A - B) = A^2 - B^2$$

do not hold for the $2 \times 2$ matrices $A = \begin{bmatrix} 1 & -1 \\ 0 & 2 \end{bmatrix}$ and $B = \begin{bmatrix} 1 & 0 \\ 1 & 2 \end{bmatrix}$.

(b) Amend the right-hand members of these identities to obtain formulas valid for all square matrices $A$ and $B$.

(c) For which matrices $A$ and $B$ are the identities valid as stated in (a)?

### 16.17 Systems of linear equations

Let $A = (a_{ij})$ be a given $m \times n$ matrix of numbers, and let $c_1, \ldots, c_m$ be $m$ further numbers. A set of $m$ equations of the form

$$(16.23) \qquad \sum_{k=1}^{n} a_{ik}x_k = c_i \qquad \text{for} \quad i = 1, 2, \ldots, m,$$

is called a *system of $m$ linear equations in $n$ unknowns*. Here $x_1, \ldots, x_n$ are regarded as unknown. A *solution* of the system is any $n$-tuple of numbers $(x_1, \ldots, x_n)$ for which all the equations are satisfied. The matrix $A$ is called the *coefficient-matrix* of the system.

Linear systems can be studied with the help of linear transformations. Choose the usual bases of unit coordinate vectors in $V_n$ and in $V_m$. The coefficient-matrix $A$ determines a linear transformation, $T: V_n \to V_m$, which maps an arbitrary vector $x = (x_1, \ldots, x_n)$ in $V_n$ onto the vector $y = (y_1, \ldots, y_m)$ in $V_m$ given by the $m$ linear equations

$$y_i = \sum_{k=1}^{n} a_{ik}x_k \qquad \text{for} \quad i = 1, 2, \ldots, m.$$

Let $c = (c_1, \ldots, c_m)$ be the vector in $V_m$ whose components are the numbers appearing in system (16.23). This system can be written more simply as

$$T(x) = c.$$

The system has a solution if and only if $c$ is in the range of $T$. If exactly one $x$ in $V_n$ maps onto $c$, the system has exactly one solution. If more than one $x$ maps onto $c$, the system has more than one solution.

EXAMPLE 1. *A system with no solution.* The system $x + y = 1$, $x + y = 2$ has no solution. The sum of two numbers cannot be both 1 and 2.

EXAMPLE 2. *A system with exactly one solution.* The system $x + y = 1$, $x - y = 0$ has exactly one solution: $(x, y) = (\frac{1}{2}, \frac{1}{2})$.

EXAMPLE 3. *A system with more than one solution.* The system $x + y = 1$, consisting of one equation in two unknowns, has more than one solution. Any two numbers whose sum is 1 gives a solution.

With each linear system (16.23), we can associate another system

$$\sum_{k=1}^{n} a_{ik}x_k = 0 \qquad \text{for} \quad i = 1, 2, \ldots, m,$$

obtained by replacing each $c_i$ in (16.23) by 0. This is called the *homogeneous system* corresponding to (16.23). If $c \neq O$, system (16.23) is called a *nonhomogeneous system*. A vector $x$ in $V_n$ will satisfy the homogeneous system if and only if

$$T(x) = O,$$

where $T$ is the linear transformation determined by the coefficient-matrix. The homogeneous system always has one solution, namely $x = O$, but it may have others. The set of solutions of the homogeneous system is the null space of $T$. The next theorem describes the relation between solutions of the homogeneous system and those of the nonhomogeneous system.

THEOREM 16.18.    *Assume the nonhomogeneous system* (16.23) *has a solution, say b.*
(a) *If a vector x is a solution of the nonhomogeneous system, then the vector $v = x - b$ is a solution of the corresponding homogeneous system.*
(b) *If a vector v is a solution of the homogeneous system, then the vector $x = v + b$ is a solution of the nonhomogeneous system.*

*Proof.*  Let $T: V_n \to V_m$ be the linear transformation determined by the coefficient-matrix, as described above. Since $b$ is a solution of the nonhomogeneous system we have $T(b) = c$. Let $x$ and $v$ be two vectors in $V_n$ such that $v = x - b$. Then we have

$$T(v) = T(x - b) = T(x) - T(b) = T(x) - c\,.$$

Therefore $T(x) = c$ if and only if $T(v) = O$. This proves both (a) and (b).

This theorem shows that the problem of finding all solutions of a nonhomogeneous system splits naturally into two parts: (1) Finding all solutions $v$ of the homogeneous system, that is, determining the null space of $T$; and (2) finding one particular solution $b$ of the nonhomogeneous system. By adding $b$ to each vector $v$ in the null space of $T$, we thereby obtain all solutions $x = v + b$ of the nonhomogeneous system.

Let $k$ denote the dimension of $N(T)$ (the nullity of $T$). If we can find $k$ *independent* solutions $v_1, \ldots, v_k$ of the homogeneous system, they will form a basis for $N(T)$, and we can obtain every $v$ in $N(T)$ by forming all possible linear combinations

$$v = t_1 v_1 + \cdots + t_k v_k\,,$$

where $t_1, \ldots, t_k$ are arbitrary scalars. This linear combination is called the *general solution of the homogeneous system*. If $b$ is one particular solution of the nonhomogeneous system, then all solutions $x$ are given by

$$x = b + t_1 v_1 + \cdots + t_k v_k\,.$$

This linear combination is called the *general solution of the nonhomogeneous system*. Theorem 16.18 can now be restated as follows.

THEOREM 16.19.    *Let $T: V_n \to V_m$ be the linear transformation such that $T(x) = y$, where* $x = (x_1, \ldots, x_n)$, $y = (y_1, \ldots, y_m)$ *and*

$$y_i = \sum_{k=1}^{n} a_{ik} x_k \quad for \quad i = 1, 2, \ldots, m\,.$$

*Let k denote the nullity of T. If $v_1, \ldots, v_k$ are k independent solutions of the homogeneous system $T(x) = O$, and if b is one particular solution of the nonhomogeneous system $T(x) = c$, then the general solution of the nonhomogeneous system is*

$$x = b + t_1 v_1 + \cdots + t_k v_k,$$

*where $t_1, \ldots, t_k$ are arbitrary scalars.*

This theorem does not tell us how to decide if a nonhomogeneous system has a particular solution $b$, nor does it tell us how to determine solutions $v_1, \ldots, v_k$ of the homogeneous system. It does tell us what to expect when the nonhomogeneous system has a solution. The following example, although very simple, illustrates the theorem.

EXAMPLE. The system $x + y = 2$ has for its associated homogeneous system the equation $x + y = 0$. Therefore, the null space consists of all vectors in $V_2$ of the form $(t, -t)$, where $t$ is arbitrary. Since $(t, -t) = t(1, -1)$, this is a one-dimensional subspace of $V_2$ with basis $(1, -1)$. A particular solution of the nonhomogeneous system is $(0, 2)$. Therefore the general solution of the nonhomogeneous system is given by

$$(x, y) = (0, 2) + t(1, -1) \qquad \text{or} \qquad x = t, \qquad y = 2 - t,$$

where $t$ is arbitrary.

## 16.18 Computation techniques

We turn now to the problem of actually computing the solutions of a nonhomogeneous linear system. Although many methods have been developed for attacking this problem, all of them require considerable computation if the system is large. For example, to solve a system of ten equations in as many unknowns can require several hours of hand computation, even with the aid of a desk calculator.

We shall discuss a widely-used method, known as the Gauss-Jordan elimination method, which is relatively simple and can be easily programmed for high-speed electronic computing machines. The method consists of applying three basic types of operations on the equations of a linear system:

(1) *Interchanging two equations;*
(2) *Multiplying all the terms of an equation by a nonzero scalar;*
(3) *Adding to one equation a multiple of another.*

Each time we perform one of these operations on the system we obtain a new system having exactly the same solutions. Two such systems are called *equivalent*. By performing these operations over and over again in a systematic fashion we finally arrive at an equivalent system which can be solved by inspection.

We shall illustrate the method with some specific examples. It will then be clear how the method is to be applied in general.

EXAMPLE 1. *A system with a unique solution.* Consider the system

$$2x - 5y + 4z = -3$$
$$x - 2y + \phantom{4}z = 5$$
$$x - 4y + 6z = 10 .$$

This particular system has a unique solution, $x = 124$, $y = 75$, $z = 31$, which we shall obtain by the Gauss-Jordan elimination process. To save labor we do not bother to copy the letters $x$, $y$, $z$ and the equals sign over and over again, but work instead with the *augmented matrix*

(16.24)
$$\begin{bmatrix} 2 & -5 & 4 & -3 \\ 1 & -2 & 1 & 5 \\ 1 & -4 & 6 & 10 \end{bmatrix}$$

obtained by adjoining the right-hand members of the system to the coefficient matrix. The three basic types of operations mentioned above are performed on the rows of the augmented matrix and are called *row operations*. At any stage of the process we can put the letters $x$, $y$, $z$ back again and insert equals signs along the vertical line to obtain equations. Our ultimate goal is to arrive at the augmented matrix

(16.25)
$$\begin{bmatrix} 1 & 0 & 0 & 124 \\ 0 & 1 & 0 & 75 \\ 0 & 0 & 1 & 31 \end{bmatrix}$$

after a succession of row operations. The corresponding system of equations is $x = 124$, $y = 75$, $z = 31$, which gives the desired solution.

The first step is to obtain a 1 in the upper left-hand corner of the matrix. We can do this by interchanging the first row of the given matrix (16.24) with either the second or third row. Or, we can multiply the first row by $\frac{1}{2}$. Interchanging the first and second rows, we get

$$\begin{bmatrix} 1 & -2 & 1 & 5 \\ 2 & -5 & 4 & -3 \\ 1 & -4 & 6 & 10 \end{bmatrix}.$$

The next step is to make all the remaining entries in the first column equal to zero, leaving the first row intact. To do this we multiply the first row by $-2$ and add the result to the second row. Then we multiply the first row by $-1$ and add the result to the third row. After these two operations, we obtain

(16.26)
$$\begin{bmatrix} 1 & -2 & 1 & 5 \\ 0 & -1 & 2 & -13 \\ 0 & -2 & 5 & 5 \end{bmatrix}.$$

Now we repeat the process on the smaller matrix $\begin{bmatrix} -1 & 2 & -13 \\ -2 & 5 & 5 \end{bmatrix}$ which appears adjacent to the two zeros. We can obtain a 1 in *its* upper left-hand corner by multiplying the second row of (16.26) by $-1$. This gives us the matrix

$$\begin{bmatrix} 1 & -2 & 1 & 5 \\ 0 & 1 & -2 & 13 \\ 0 & -2 & 5 & 5 \end{bmatrix}.$$

Multiplying the second row by 2 and adding the result to the third, we get

(16.27)
$$\begin{bmatrix} 1 & -2 & 1 & | & 5 \\ 0 & 1 & -2 & | & 13 \\ 0 & 0 & 1 & | & 31 \end{bmatrix}.$$

At this stage, the corresponding system of equations is given by

$$x - 2y + z = 5$$
$$y - 2z = 13$$
$$z = 31.$$

These equations can be solved in succession, starting with the third one and working backwards, to give us

$$z = 31, \qquad y = 13 + 2z = 13 + 62 = 75, \qquad x = 5 + 2y - z = 5 + 150 - 31 = 124.$$

Or, we can continue the Gauss–Jordan process by making all the entries zero above the diagonal elements in the second and third columns. Multiplying the second row of (16.27) by 2 and adding the result to the first row, we obtain

$$\begin{bmatrix} 1 & 0 & -3 & | & 31 \\ 0 & 1 & -2 & | & 13 \\ 0 & 0 & 1 & | & 31 \end{bmatrix}.$$

Finally, we multiply the third row by 3 and add the result to the first row, and then multiply the third row by 2 and add the result to the second row to get the matrix in (16.25).

EXAMPLE 2. *A system with more than one solution.* Consider the following system of 3 equations in 5 unknowns:

(16.28)
$$2x - 5y + 4z + \phantom{1}u - v = -3$$
$$x - 2y + \phantom{1}z - \phantom{1}u + v = 5$$
$$x - 4y + 6z + 2u - v = 10.$$

The corresponding augmented matrix is

$$\begin{bmatrix} 2 & -5 & 4 & 1 & -1 & | & -3 \\ 1 & -2 & 1 & -1 & 1 & | & 5 \\ 1 & -4 & 6 & 2 & -1 & | & 10 \end{bmatrix}.$$

The coefficients of $x$, $y$, $z$ and the right-hand members are the same as those in Example 1.

If we perform the same row operations used in Example 1, we finally arrive at the augmented matrix

$$\begin{bmatrix} 1 & 0 & 0 & -16 & 19 & | & 124 \\ 0 & 1 & 0 & -9 & 11 & | & 75 \\ 0 & 0 & 1 & -3 & 4 & | & 31 \end{bmatrix}.$$

The corresponding system of equations can be solved for $x$, $y$, and $z$ in terms of $u$ and $v$, giving us

$$x = 124 + 16u - 19v$$
$$y = 75 + 9u - 11v$$
$$z = 31 + 3u - 4v.$$

If we let $u = t_1$ and $v = t_2$, where $t_1$ and $t_2$ are arbitrary real numbers, and determine $x$, $y$, $z$ by these equations, the vector $(x, y, z, u, v)$ in $V_5$ given by

$$(x, y, z, u, v) = (124 + 16t_1 - 19t_2, 75 + 9t_1 - 11t_2, 31 + 3t_1 - 4t_2, t_1, t_2)$$

is a solution. By separating the parts involving $t_1$ and $t_2$, we can rewrite this as follows:

$$(x, y, z, u, v) = (124, 75, 31, 0, 0) + t_1(16, 9, 3, 1, 0) + t_2(-19, -11, -4, 0, 1).$$

This equation gives the general solution of the system. The vector $(124, 75, 31, 0, 0)$ is a particular solution of the nonhomogeneous system (16.28). The two vectors $(16, 9, 3, 1, 0)$ and $(-19, -11, -4, 0, 1)$ are solutions of the corresponding homogeneous system. Since they are independent, they form a basis for the space of all solutions of the homogeneous system.

EXAMPLE 3. *A system with no solution.* Consider the system

(16.29)
$$2x - 5y + 4z = -3$$
$$x - 2y + z = 5$$
$$x - 4y + 5z = 10.$$

This system is almost identical to that of Example 1 except that the coefficient of $z$ in the third equation has been changed from 6 to 5. The corresponding augmented matrix is

$$\begin{bmatrix} 2 & -5 & 4 & | & -3 \\ 1 & -2 & 1 & | & 5 \\ 1 & -4 & 5 & | & 10 \end{bmatrix}.$$

Applying the same row operations used in Example 1 to transform (16.24) into (16.27), we arrive at the augmented matrix

(16.30)
$$\begin{bmatrix} 1 & -2 & 1 & | & 5 \\ 0 & 1 & -2 & | & 13 \\ 0 & 0 & 0 & | & 31 \end{bmatrix}.$$

When the bottom row is expressed as an equation, it states that $0 = 31$. Therefore the original system has no solution since the two systems (16.29) and (16.30) are equivalent.

In each of the foregoing examples, the number of equations did not exceed the number of unknowns. If there are more equations than unknowns, the Gauss–Jordan process is still applicable. For example, suppose we consider the system of Example 1, which has the solution $x = 124$, $y = 75$, $z = 31$. If we adjoin a new equation to this system which is also satisfied by the same triple, for example, the equation $2x - 3y + z = 54$, then the elimination process leads to the augmented matrix

$$\begin{bmatrix} 1 & 0 & 0 & 124 \\ 0 & 1 & 0 & 75 \\ 0 & 0 & 1 & 31 \\ 0 & 0 & 0 & 0 \end{bmatrix}$$

with a row of zeros along the bottom. But if we adjoin a new equation which is not satisfied by the triple (124, 75, 31), for example the equation $x + y + z = 1$, then the elimination process leads to an augmented matrix of the form

$$\begin{bmatrix} 1 & 0 & 0 & 124 \\ 0 & 1 & 0 & 75 \\ 0 & 0 & 1 & 31 \\ 0 & 0 & 0 & a \end{bmatrix},$$

where $a \neq 0$. The last row now gives a contradictory equation $0 = a$ which shows that the system has no solution.

## 16.19 Inverses of square matrices

Let $A = (a_{ij})$ be a square $n \times n$ matrix. If there is another $n \times n$ matrix $B$ such that $BA = I$, where $I$ is the $n \times n$ identity matrix, then $A$ is called *nonsingular* and $B$ is called a *left inverse* of $A$.

Choose the usual basis of unit coordinate vectors in $V_n$ and let $T: V_n \to V_n$ be the linear transformation with matrix $m(T) = A$. Then we have the following.

THEOREM 16.20. *The matrix $A$ is nonsingular if and only if $T$ is invertible. If $BA = I$, then $B = m(T^{-1})$.*

*Proof.* Assume that $A$ is nonsingular and that $BA = I$. We shall prove that $T(x) = O$ implies $x = O$. Given $x$ such that $T(x) = O$, let $X$ be the $n \times 1$ column matrix formed from the components of $x$. Since $T(x) = O$, the matrix product $AX$ is an $n \times 1$ column matrix consisting of zeros, so $B(AX)$ is also a column matrix of zeros. But $B(AX) = (BA)X = IX = X$, so every component of $x$ is 0. Therefore, $T$ is invertible, and the equation $TT^{-1} = I$ implies that $m(T)m(T^{-1}) = I$ or $Am(T^{-1}) = I$. Multiplying on the left by $B$, we find $m(T^{-1}) = B$. Conversely, if $T$ is invertible, then $T^{-1}T$ is the identity transformation so $m(T^{-1})m(T)$ is the identity matrix. Therefore $A$ is nonsingular and $m(T^{-1})A = I$.

All the properties of invertible linear transformations have their counterparts for non-singular matrices. In particular, left inverses (if they exist) are unique, and every left inverse is also a right inverse. In other words, if $A$ is nonsingular and $BA = I$, then $AB = I$. We call $B$ the *inverse* of $A$ and denote it by $A^{-1}$. The inverse $A^{-1}$ is also nonsingular and *its* inverse is $A$.

Now we show that the problem of actually determining the entries of the inverse of a nonsingular matrix is equivalent to solving $n$ separate nonhomogeneous linear systems.

Let $A = (a_{ij})$ be nonsingular and let $A^{-1} = (b_{ij})$ be its inverse. The entries of $A$ and $A^{-1}$ are related by the $n^2$ equations

$$(16.31) \qquad \sum_{k=1}^{n} a_{ik} b_{kj} = \delta_{ij},$$

where $\delta_{ij} = 1$ if $i = j$, and $\delta_{ij} = 0$ if $i \neq j$. For each fixed choice of $j$, we can regard this as a nonhomogeneous system of $n$ linear equations in $n$ unknowns $b_{1j}, b_{2j}, \ldots, b_{nj}$. Since $A$ is nonsingular, each of these systems has a unique solution, the $j$th column of $B$. All these systems have the same coefficient-matrix $A$ and differ only in their right members. For example, if $A$ is a $3 \times 3$ matrix, there are 9 equations in (16.31) which can be expressed as 3 separate linear systems having the following augmented matrices:

$$\begin{bmatrix} a_{11} & a_{12} & a_{13} & 1 \\ a_{21} & a_{22} & a_{23} & 0 \\ a_{31} & a_{32} & a_{33} & 0 \end{bmatrix}, \quad \begin{bmatrix} a_{11} & a_{12} & a_{13} & 0 \\ a_{21} & a_{22} & a_{23} & 1 \\ a_{31} & a_{32} & a_{33} & 0 \end{bmatrix}, \quad \begin{bmatrix} a_{11} & a_{12} & a_{13} & 0 \\ a_{21} & a_{22} & a_{23} & 0 \\ a_{31} & a_{32} & a_{33} & 1 \end{bmatrix}.$$

If we apply the Gauss–Jordan process, we arrive at the respective augmented matrices

$$\begin{bmatrix} 1 & 0 & 0 & b_{11} \\ 0 & 1 & 0 & b_{21} \\ 0 & 0 & 1 & b_{31} \end{bmatrix}, \quad \begin{bmatrix} 1 & 0 & 0 & b_{12} \\ 0 & 1 & 0 & b_{22} \\ 0 & 0 & 1 & b_{32} \end{bmatrix}, \quad \begin{bmatrix} 1 & 0 & 0 & b_{13} \\ 0 & 1 & 0 & b_{23} \\ 0 & 0 & 1 & b_{33} \end{bmatrix}.$$

In actual practice we exploit the fact that all three systems have the same coefficient-matrix and solve all three systems at once by working with the enlarged matrix

$$\begin{bmatrix} a_{11} & a_{12} & a_{13} & 1 & 0 & 0 \\ a_{21} & a_{22} & a_{23} & 0 & 1 & 0 \\ a_{31} & a_{32} & a_{33} & 0 & 0 & 1 \end{bmatrix}.$$

The elimination process then leads to

$$\begin{bmatrix} 1 & 0 & 0 & b_{11} & b_{12} & b_{13} \\ 0 & 1 & 0 & b_{21} & b_{22} & b_{23} \\ 0 & 0 & 1 & b_{31} & b_{32} & b_{33} \end{bmatrix}.$$

The matrix on the right of the vertical line is the required inverse. The matrix on the left of the line is the $3 \times 3$ identity matrix.

It is not necessary to know in advance whether $A$ is nonsingular. If $A$ is *singular* (not nonsingular), we can still apply the Gauss–Jordan method, but somewhere in the process one of the diagonal elements will become zero, and it will not be possible to transform $A$ to the identity matrix.

## 16.20   Exercises

Apply the Gauss–Jordan elimination process to each of the following systems. If a solution exists, determine the general solution.

1. $x + y + 3z = 5$
   $2x - y + 4z = 11$
   $\phantom{2x} -y + z = 3.$

2. $3x + 2y + z = 1$
   $5x + 3y + 3z = 2$
   $x + y - z = 1.$

3. $3x + 2y + z = 1$
   $5x + 3y + 3z = 2$
   $7x + 4y + 5z = 3.$

4. $3x + 2y + z = 1$
   $5x + 3y + 3z = 2$
   $7x + 4y + 5z = 3$
   $x + y - z = 0.$

5. $3x - 2y + 5z + u = 1$
   $x + y - 3z + 2u = 2$
   $6x + y - 4z + 3u = 7.$

6. $x + y - 3z + u = 5$
   $2x - y + z - 2u = 2$
   $7x + y - 7z + 3u = 3.$

7. $x + y + 2z + 3u + 4v = 0$
   $2x + 2y + 7z + 11u + 14v = 0$
   $3x + 3y + 6z + 10u + 15v = 0.$

8. $x - 2y + z + 2u = -2$
   $2x + 3y - z - 5u = 9$
   $4x - y + z - u = 5$
   $5x - 3y + 2z + u = 3.$

9. Prove that the system $x + y + 2z = 2$, $2x - y + 3z = 2$, $5x - y + az = 6$, has a unique solution if $a \neq 8$. Find all solutions when $a = 8$.

10. (a) Determine all solutions of the system

$$5x + 2y - 6z + 2u = -1$$
$$x - y + z - u = -2.$$

(b) Determine all solutions of the system

$$5x + 2y - 6z + 2u = -1$$
$$x - y + z - u = -2$$
$$x + y + z = 6.$$

11. This exercise tells how to determine all nonsingular $2 \times 2$ matrices. Prove that

$$\begin{bmatrix} a & b \\ c & d \end{bmatrix} \begin{bmatrix} d & -b \\ -c & a \end{bmatrix} = (ad - bc)I.$$

Deduce that $\begin{bmatrix} a & b \\ c & d \end{bmatrix}$ is nonsingular if and only if $ad - bc \neq 0$, in which case its inverse is

$$\frac{1}{ad - bc} \begin{bmatrix} d & -b \\ -c & a \end{bmatrix}.$$

Determine the inverse of each of the matrices in Exercises 12 through 16.

12. $\begin{bmatrix} 2 & 3 & 4 \\ 2 & 1 & 1 \\ -1 & 1 & 2 \end{bmatrix}$.

15. $\begin{bmatrix} 1 & 2 & 3 & 4 \\ 0 & 1 & 2 & 3 \\ 0 & 0 & 1 & 2 \\ 0 & 0 & 0 & 1 \end{bmatrix}$.

13. $\begin{bmatrix} 1 & 2 & 2 \\ 2 & -1 & 1 \\ 1 & 3 & 2 \end{bmatrix}$.

14. $\begin{bmatrix} 1 & -2 & 1 \\ -2 & 5 & -4 \\ 1 & -4 & 6 \end{bmatrix}$.

16. $\begin{bmatrix} 0 & 1 & 0 & 0 & 0 & 0 \\ 2 & 0 & 2 & 0 & 0 & 0 \\ 0 & 3 & 0 & 1 & 0 & 0 \\ 0 & 0 & 1 & 0 & 2 & 0 \\ 0 & 0 & 0 & 3 & 0 & 1 \\ 0 & 0 & 0 & 0 & 2 & 0 \end{bmatrix}$.

## 16.21 Miscellaneous exercises on matrices

1. If a square matrix has a row of zeros or a column of zeros, prove that it is singular.
2. For each of the following statements about $n \times n$ matrices, give a proof or exhibit a counter example.
   (a) If $AB + BA = O$, then $A^2B^3 = B^3A^2$.
   (b) If $A$ and $B$ are nonsingular, then $A + B$ is nonsingular.
   (c) If $A$ and $B$ are nonsingular, then $AB$ is nonsingular.
   (d) If $A$; $B$, and $A + B$ are nonsingular, then $A - B$ is nonsingular.
   (e) If $A^3 = O$, then $A - I$ is nonsingular.
   (f) If the product of $k$ matrices $A_1 \cdots A_k$ is nonsingular, then each matrix $A_i$ is nonsingular.
3. If $A = \begin{bmatrix} 1 & 2 \\ 5 & 4 \end{bmatrix}$, find a nonsingular matrix $P$ such that $P^{-1}AP = \begin{bmatrix} 6 & 0 \\ 0 & -1 \end{bmatrix}$.
4. The matrix $A = \begin{bmatrix} a & i \\ i & b \end{bmatrix}$, where $i^2 = -1$, $a = \frac{1}{2}(1 + \sqrt{5})$, and $b = \frac{1}{2}(1 - \sqrt{5})$, has the property that $A^2 = A$. Describe completely all $2 \times 2$ matrices $A$ with complex entries such that $A^2 = A$.
5. If $A^2 = A$, prove that $(A + I)^k = I + (2^k - 1)A$.
6. The special theory of relativity makes use of a set of equations of the form $x' = a(x - vt)$, $y' = y$, $z' = z$, $t' = a(t - vx/c^2)$.) Here $v$ represents the velocity of a moving object, $c$ the speed of light, and $a = c/\sqrt{c^2 - v^2}$, where $|v| < c$. The linear transformation which maps the two-dimensional vector $(x, t)$ onto $(x', t')$ is called a *Lorentz transformation*. Its matrix relative to the usual bases is denoted by $L(v)$ and is given by

$$L(v) = a \begin{bmatrix} 1 & -v \\ -vc^{-2} & 1 \end{bmatrix}.$$

Note that $L(v)$ is nonsingular and that $L(0) = I$. Prove that $L(v)L(u) = L(w)$, where $w = (u + v)c^2/(uv + c^2)$. In other words, the product of two Lorentz transformations is another Lorentz transformation.

7. If we interchange the rows and columns of a rectangular matrix $A$, the new matrix so obtained is called the *transpose* of $A$ and is denoted by $A^t$. For example, if we have

$$A = \begin{bmatrix} 1 & 2 & 3 \\ 4 & 5 & 6 \end{bmatrix}, \quad \text{then} \quad A^t = \begin{bmatrix} 1 & 4 \\ 2 & 5 \\ 3 & 6 \end{bmatrix}.$$

Prove that transposes have the following properties:
(a) $(A^t)^t = A$.     (b) $(A + B)^t = A^t + B^t$.     (c) $(cA)^t = cA^t$.
(d) $(AB)^t = B^t A^t$.     (e) $(A^t)^{-1} = (A^{-1})^t$     if     $A$ is nonsingular.

8. A square matrix $A$ is called an orthogonal matrix if $AA^t = I$. Verify that the $2 \times 2$ matrix $\begin{bmatrix} \cos\theta & -\sin\theta \\ \sin\theta & \cos\theta \end{bmatrix}$ is orthogonal for each real $\theta$. If $A$ is any $n \times n$ orthogonal matrix, prove that its rows, considered as vectors in $V_n$, form an orthonormal set.

9. For each of the following statements about $n \times n$ matrices, give a proof or else exhibit a counter example.
(a) If $A$ and $B$ are orthogonal, then $A + B$ is orthogonal.
(b) If $A$ and $B$ are orthogonal, then $AB$ is orthogonal.
(c) If $A$ and $AB$ are orthogonal, then $B$ is orthogonal.

10. *Hadamard matrices*, named for Jacques Hadamard (1865–1963), are those $n \times n$ matrices with the following properties:
  I. Each entry is 1 or $-1$.
  II. Each row, considered as a vector in $V_n$, has length $\sqrt{n}$.
  III. The dot product of any two distinct rows is 0.
Hadamard matrices arise in certain problems in geometry and the theory of numbers, and they have been applied recently to the construction of optimum code words in space communication. In spite of their apparent simplicity, they present many unsolved problems. The main unsolved problem at this time is to determine all $n$ for which an $n \times n$ Hadamard matrix exists. This exercise outlines a partial solution.
(a) Determine all $2 \times 2$ Hadamard matrices (there are exactly 8).
(b) This part of the exercise outlines a simple proof of the following theorem: *If $A$ is an $n \times n$ Hadamard matrix, where $n > 2$, then $n$ is a multiple of* 4. The proof is based on two very simple lemmas concerning vectors in $n$-space. Prove each of these lemmas and apply them to the rows of Hadamard matrix to prove the theorem.

LEMMA 1.   *If $X, Y, Z$ are orthogonal vectors in $V_n$, then we have*

$$(X + Y) \cdot (X + Z) = \|X\|^2.$$

LEMMA 2.   *Write $X = (x_1, \ldots, x_n)$, $Y = (y_1, \ldots, y_n)$, $Z = (z_1, \ldots, z_n)$. If each component $x_i, y_i, z_i$ is either 1 or $-1$, then the product $(x_i + y_i)(x_i + z_i)$ is either 0 or 4.*

# ANSWERS TO EXERCISES

*Introduction*

*I 1.4  Exercises (page 8)

1. (a) $\frac{2}{3}b^3$   (b) $b^3$   (c) $\frac{1}{12}b^3$   (d) $\frac{2}{3}b^3 + b$   (e) $\frac{1}{3}ab^3 + bc$
2. (c) $\frac{1}{4}ab^4 + bc$

3. (b) $s_n < \dfrac{b^{k+1}}{k+1} < S_n$   (c) $\dfrac{ab^{k+1}}{k+1} + bc$

I 2.5  Exercises (page 15)

1. $A = \{1, -1\}, B = \{1\}, C = \{1\}, D = \{2\}, E = \{1, -17\},$
   $F = \{1, -17, -8 + \sqrt{47}, -8 - \sqrt{47}\}.$
2. $A \subseteq A, B \subseteq A, B \subseteq B, B \subseteq C, B \subseteq E, B \subseteq F, C \subseteq A, C \subseteq B, C \subseteq C, C \subseteq E, C \subseteq F,$
   $D \subseteq D, E \subseteq E, E \subseteq F, F \subseteq F.$ (Not counting "proper" inclusions.)
3. (a) True   (b) True   (c) False   (d) True   (e) False   (f) False
4. (a) True   (b) True   (c) True   (d) True   (e) False   (f) False
5. $\varnothing, \{1\}, \{2\}, \{3\}, \{4\}, \{1, 2\}, \{1, 3\}, \{1, 4\}, \{2, 3\}, \{2, 4\}, \{3, 4\}, \{1, 2, 3\}, \{1, 2, 4\}, \{1, 3, 4\},$
   $\{2, 3, 4\}, S$
6. (a) False   (b) False   (c) False   (d) True   (e) False   (f) False
   (g) True   (h) False   (i) True
17. (c) $A \subset C$   (d) Yes   (e) No

I 4.4  Exercises (page 35)

2. $1 - 4 + 9 - 16 + \cdots + (-1)^{n+1}n^2 = (-1)^{n+1}(1 + 2 + 3 + \cdots + n)$

3. $1 + \dfrac{1}{2} + \dfrac{1}{4} + \cdots + \dfrac{1}{2^n} = 2 - \dfrac{1}{2^n}$

4. $\left(1 - \dfrac{1}{2}\right)\left(1 - \dfrac{1}{3}\right) \cdots \left(1 - \dfrac{1}{n}\right) = \dfrac{1}{n}$

5. $\dfrac{n+1}{2n}$

6. (b) $A(1)$ is false   (c) $1 + 2 + \cdots + n < \dfrac{(2n+1)^2}{8}$

7. $n_1 = 3$

I 4.7  Exercises (page 39)

1. (a) 10   (b) 15   (c) 170   (d) 288   (e) 36   (f) $\frac{5}{6}$
8. (b) $n + 1$

617

9.  Constant $= 2$
11. (a) True    (b) False    (c) False    (d) False    (e) False    (f) False

12. $\dfrac{n}{n+1}$

**I 4.9   Exercises (page 43)**

2.  $(a_1, b_2), (a_2, b_5), (a_3, b_7), (a_4, b_{10}), (a_5, b_3), (a_6, b_8), (a_7, b_9), (a_8, b_4), (a_9, b_6), (a_{10}, b_1)$
3.  (a) False    (b) True    (c) True    (d) False    (e) False

**\*I 4.10   Miscellaneous exercises involving induction (page 44)**

1.  (a) 10    (b) 1    (c) 7    (d) 21    (e) 680    (f) 1
2.  (b) 17    (c) 9    (d) No

5.  $\displaystyle\prod_{k=1}^{0} a_k = 1; \quad \prod_{k=1}^{n+1} a_k = a_{n+1} \cdot \prod_{k=1}^{n} a_k$

8.  $2^n$
9.  True if each $a_k \geq 0$
11. $n \geq 4$

## Chapter 1

**1.5   Exercises (page 56)**

1.  $f(2) = 3, f(-2) = -1, -f(2) = -3, f(\frac{1}{2}) = \frac{3}{2}, 1/f(2) = \frac{1}{3}, f(a+b) = a + b + 1,$
    $f(a) + f(b) = a + b + 2, f(a)f(b) = ab + a + b + 1$
2.  $f(2) + g(2) = 2, f(2) - g(2) = 4, f(2)g(2) = -3, f(2)/g(2) = -3, f[g(2)] = 0,$
    $g[f(2)] = -2, f(a) + g(-a) = 2 + 2a, f(t)g(-t) = (1 + t)^2$
3.  $\varphi(0) = 4, \varphi(1) = 2, \varphi(2) = 2, \varphi(3) = 2, \varphi(-1) = 6, \varphi(-2) = 8, t = 1.$
4.  (a) All $x$    (b) All $x$ and $y$    (c) All $x$ and $h$    (d) All $y$    (e) All $t$
    (f) All $a$
5.  (a) $|x| \leq 2$    (b) $|y| \leq 1$    (c) $|t| \geq \frac{1}{2}$    (d) $0 \leq a \leq 4$    (e) $|s| \leq 4$
    (f) $|x| \leq 2, \ x \neq 0$
6.  (b) $\{x \mid 0 \leq x \leq 1\}$    (c) $\{x \mid 2 \leq x \leq 4\}$    (d) Domain is empty
7.  Intersect when $x = 0, 1, -1$
8.  Intersect when $x = -1, -3$
10. (a) $p(x) = 1$    (b) $p(x) = \frac{1}{2}x(x-1) + 1$    (c) $p(x) = ax(x-1) + 1$, $a$ arbitrary
    (d) $p(x) = ax(x-1) + b$, $a$ and $b$ arbitrary
11. (a) $p(x) = ax(1-x) + b$, $a$ and $b$ arbitrary    (b) $p(x) = c$, $c$ arbitrary
    (c) $p(x) = ax$, $a$ arbitrary    (d) $p(x) = c$, $c$ arbitrary

12. (a) $\displaystyle\sum_{k=0}^{2n} \binom{2n}{k} x^k$    (b) $\displaystyle\sum_{k=0}^{n} x^k$    (c) $\displaystyle\sum_{k=0}^{2^{n+1}-1} x^k$

**1.11   Exercises (page 63)**

5.  $[nx] = \displaystyle\sum_{k=0}^{n-1} \left[ x + \dfrac{k}{n} \right]$

**1.15   Exercises (page 70)**

1.  (a) 2    (b) 4    (c) 6    (d) 4    (e) 6    (f) $-6$
2.  One example: $s(x) = \frac{5}{2}$ if $0 \leq x < 2$, $s(x) = -1$ if $2 \leq x \leq 5$

5. (b) $2 \sum_{k=1}^{8} k(\sqrt{k+1} - \sqrt{k}) = 2(21 - 3\sqrt{2} - \sqrt{3} - \sqrt{5} - \sqrt{6} - \sqrt{7})$

6. (c) $x = 1, x = \frac{5}{2}$

7. (a) 13

10. (a) $f(3) = 1, f(4) = -1, f[f(3)] = 0$    (b) $p = 14, p = 15$

11. (a), (d), (e)

12. (a), (b), (c)

## 1.26 Exercises (page 83)

| | | | | | | | |
|---|---|---|---|---|---|---|---|
| 1. | 9 | 6. | 2 | 11. | $\frac{21}{8}$ | 16. | $\frac{62}{27}$ |
| 2. | 18 | 7. | 0 | 12. | 18 | 17. | $-78$ |
| 3. | 16 | 8. | 0 | 13. | $\frac{1}{3}$ | 18. | $\frac{2592}{35}$ |
| 4. | 0 | 9. | 6 | 14. | $-\frac{1}{3}$ | 19. | $5^6/21$ |
| 5. | 1 | 10. | 11 | 15. | 2 | 20. | $-2^{11}/11$ |

21. (a) $0, \frac{3}{2}$    (b) $0$

22. (a) $\frac{5}{6}$    (b) $c/2$

23. $p(x) = 6x - 6x^2$

24. $p(x) = 4x + 8x^2 + 3x^3$

27. $(1/A) \int_{Aa+B}^{Ab+B} f(x)\, dx$ if $A \neq 0$;    $(b - a)f(B)$ if $A = 0$.

## Chapter 2

## 2.4 Exercises (page 94)

| | | | |
|---|---|---|---|
| 1. | $\frac{32}{3}$ | 9. | $\frac{1}{4}(5\sqrt{5} - 3)$ |
| 2. | $\frac{32}{3}$ | 10. | $\frac{7}{4}$ |
| 3. | $\frac{4}{3}$ | 11. | $\frac{7}{3}$ |
| 4. | $\frac{4}{3}$ | 12. | $\frac{7}{3}$ |
| 5. | $\frac{1}{12}$ | 13. | $\dfrac{9\sqrt{3} - 1}{27}$ |
| 6. | $\dfrac{4\sqrt{2}}{3} - \dfrac{3\sqrt[3]{2}}{2} + \dfrac{1}{12}$ | 14. | 5 |
| 7. | $\dfrac{4\sqrt{2}}{3} - \dfrac{3\sqrt[3]{2}}{2} + \dfrac{1}{6}$ | 15. | $c = \frac{1}{2}'$ |
| 8. | $\frac{1}{3}(10 - 4\sqrt{2})$ | 16. | $a = -2$ |

17. (a) $9\pi/2$    (b) $\pi/2$    (c) $-6\pi$

## 2.8 Exercises (page 104)

*Note:* In Exercises 1 through 13, $n$ denotes an arbitrary integer.

1. (b) $\frac{1}{2}\pi + n\pi$

2. (a) $\frac{1}{2}\pi + 2n\pi$    (b) $2n\pi$    (c) $\frac{3}{2}\pi + 2n\pi$    (d) $(2n + 1)\pi$

6. $\tan(x + y) = \dfrac{\tan x + \tan y}{1 - \tan x \tan y}$ ;    $\cot(x + y) = \dfrac{\cot x \cot y - 1}{\cot x + \cot y}$

7. $A = \frac{3}{2}, B = \frac{3}{2}\sqrt{3}$

8. $A = C \cos \alpha, B = C \sin \alpha$

9. $C = (A^2 + B^2)^{1/2}$. If $A^2 + B^2 \neq 0$, choose $\alpha$ so that $\cos \alpha = A/C$, $\sin \alpha = B/C$. If $A = B = 0$, choose any $\alpha$.

10. $C = 2\sqrt{2}, \alpha = 5\pi/4$
11. $C = \sqrt{2}, \alpha = -\pi/4$
12. $\frac{1}{4}\pi + n\pi$
13. $\frac{1}{2}\pi + 2n\pi;\ \pi + 2n\pi$
17. (a) $1 - \frac{1}{2}\sqrt{3}$  (b) $1 - \frac{1}{2}\sqrt{2}$  (c) $\frac{1}{2}$  (d) 1  (e) 2  (f) 0  (g) 0
    (h) $\frac{1}{2}(\sqrt{3} - \sqrt{2})$
18. $\frac{1}{2}\pi^2 + 2$                              21. $2\sqrt{2} - 2$
19. $1 + \pi^3/24$                               22. $\frac{1}{2}\pi$
20. 0                                              23. $\sqrt{3} + \pi/6$
24. $\sqrt{3} + \frac{1}{2}x + \sin x + \pi/6$ if $0 \le x \le 2\pi/3;\ 2\sqrt{3} - \frac{1}{2}x - \sin x + 5\pi/6$ if $2\pi/3 \le x \le \pi$
25. $(x^6 - x^3)/3 + \cos x - \cos(x^2)$
26. 1
27. 1

## 2.11  Exercises (page 110)

5. $4\pi^3/3$              9. $8\pi$              13. 2
6. $\pi$                  10. $\pi/8$             14. $3\pi/2$
7. $2\pi$                 11. $\pi/2$             15. $9\pi/2$
8. $4\pi$                 12. 2

## 2.13  Exercises (page 114)

1. $\pi c^2 b^3/3$         5. $\pi^2/2$          9. $3\pi/10$         13. $(\frac{32}{3} - 4\sqrt{3})\pi r^3$
2. $\pi/2$                6. $\pi^2/4$          10. $\pi/2$          14. $a = \frac{4}{3}$
3. $2\pi/3$               7. $\pi^2$            11. $2\pi\sqrt{3}$   15. $16\sqrt{3}/3$
4. $33\pi/5$              8. $\pi/2$            12. $\frac{6}{5}$    16. $4a^5/5$

17. $\dfrac{h}{6}(B_1 + 4M + B_2)$

18. (a) $8\pi/5$   (b) $2\pi$   (c) $10\pi/3$   (d) $16\pi/15$

## 2.15  Exercises (page 116)

1. 60 ft-lb                                    5. 3750 ft-lb
2. 125 joules;  0.8 meter                      6. 5000 ft-lb
3. (a) 441 joules   (b) 425 joules             7. 20,000 ft-lb
4. $a = 3, b = -2$                             8. 21,800 ft-lb

## 2.17  Exercises (page 119)

1. $(a^2 + ab + b^2)/3$                     6. $2/\pi$
2. $\frac{7}{12}$                          7. $2/\pi$
3. $\frac{4}{3}$                           8. $1/\pi$
4. $\frac{45}{28}$                         9. $\frac{1}{2}$
5. $2/\pi$                                 10. $\frac{1}{2}$
11. $c = a/\sqrt{3};\ c = a/(n + 1)^{1/n}$
12. (a) $w(x) = x$   (b) $w(x) = x^2$   (c) $w(x) = x^3$
14. All three
16. (a) $L/2$   (b) $L^3/3$  (c) $L/\sqrt{3}$
17. (a) $7L/12$   (b) $5L^3/8$   (c) $\sqrt{15}\,L/6$
18. (a) $2L/3$   (b) $L^4/4$   (c) $\sqrt{2}\,L/2$
19. (a) $11L/18$   (b) $31L^4/192$   (c) $\sqrt{62}\,L/12$

20. (a) $3L/4$ (b) $L^5/5$ (c) $\sqrt{15}\,L/5$
21. (a) $21L/32$ (b) $19L^5/240$ (c) $\sqrt{190}\,L/20$
22. $\rho(x) = x^2$ for $0 \le x \le L$ gives $\bar{x} = 3L/4$
23. (a) $6/\pi$ (b) $3\sqrt{2}/2$
24. $T = 2\pi$ sec; $80\sqrt{3}$

## 2.19 Exercises (page 124)

1. $x + x^2/2 + x^3/3$
2. $2y + 2y^2 + 8y^3/3$
3. $\frac{5}{6} + 2x + 2x^2 + 8x^3/3$
4. $-2x + 2x^2 - x^3$
5. $(3x^5 + 5x^3 + 136)/15$
6. $x^{10}/5 + 2x^6/3 - x^5/5 - 2x^3/3 + x^2 - x$
7. $x + \frac{2}{3}x^{3/2} - \frac{5}{3}$
8. $\frac{2}{3}(x^3 - x^{3/2}) + \frac{4}{5}(x^{5/2} - x^{5/4})$
9. $\sin x$
10. $\frac{1}{2}x^2 + \sin(x^2)$
11. $\frac{1}{2}x^2 - \frac{1}{2}x + \cos(x^2) - \cos x$
12. $\frac{1}{3}(x^3 - \cos 3x + 1)$
13. $\frac{1}{3}(x^6 - x^3 + \cos 3x - \cos(3x^2))$
14. $\frac{1}{2}y^2 + \frac{1}{2}y - \frac{1}{4}\sin 2y$
15. $2\sin\dfrac{x}{2} - \frac{1}{2}\cos 2x + \frac{1}{2}$
16. $\frac{3}{4}(x + \pi) + \sin x + \frac{1}{4}\sin 2x$
17. $0, \pm\sqrt{2}$
18. (c) $P(x) = \frac{1}{2}(x - [x])^2 - \frac{1}{2}(x - [x])$ (d) $\frac{1}{12}$
20. (b) $g(2) = 2A, g(5) = 5A$ (c) $A = 0$

## Chapter 3

## 3.6 Exercises (page 138)

1. $\frac{1}{4}$
2. $-1$
3. $4$
4. $1$
5. $2t$
6. $-1$
7. $1$
8. $0$
9. $0$
10. $0$
11. $1$
12. $-1$
13. $1$
14. $-1$

22. $a = (\sin c - b)/c$ if $c \ne 0$; if $c = 0$ there is no solution unless $b = 0$, in which case any $a$ will do.
23. $a = (2\cos c - b)/c^2$ if $c \ne 0$; if $c = 0$ there is no solution unless $b = 2$, in which case any $a$ will do.
24. The tangent is continuous everywhere except at $x = \frac{1}{2}\pi + n\pi$, where $n$ is any integer; the cotangent is continuous everywhere except at $x = n\pi$, where $n$ is any integer.
25. $f(x) \to 1$ as $x \to 0$. Define $f(0) = 1$ for continuity at 0.
28. No
29. No
30. $f(x) \to 0$ as $x \to 0$. Define $f(0) = 0$ for continuity at 0.
32. $f(x) \to 0$ as $x \to 0$. Define $f(0) = 0$ for continuity at 0.

**3.8  Exercises (page 142)**

1.  $x^2 - 1$, all $x$
2.  $(x - 1)^2$, all $x$
3.  $|x|$, all $x$
4.  0, defined only at $x = 0$
5.  $x, x \geq 0$

6.  $-x, x \geq 0$
7.  $\sin \sqrt{x}, x \geq 0$
8.  $\sqrt{\sin x}, 2k\pi \leq x \leq (2k + 1)\pi, k$ an integer
9.  $\sqrt{x + \sqrt{x}}, x > 0$
10.  $\sqrt{x + \sqrt{x} + \sqrt{x + \sqrt{x}}}, x > 0$

11.  $-3$     13. 1     15. 1     17. 0     19. 1
12.  $\sqrt{3}$     14. 1     16. 2     18. 2     20. $\frac{1}{2}$
21.  $x^2$ if $x \geq 0$; 0 if $x < 0$
22.  1 if $1 \leq |x| \leq \sqrt{3}$; 0 otherwise
23.  $x^2$ if $x \geq 0$; 0 if $x < 0$

**3.15  Exercises (page 149)**

1.  $g(y) = y - 1$; all $y$
2.  $g(y) = \frac{1}{2}(y - 5)$; all $y$
3.  $g(y) = 1 - y$; all $y$
4.  $g(y) = y^{1/3}$; all $y$
5.  $g(y) = y$ if $y < 1$; $\sqrt{y}$ if $1 \leq y \leq 16$; $(y/8)^2$ if $y > 16$

**3.20  Exercises (page 155)**

3.  0.099 669 rounded off in the sixth decimal place

*Chapter* 4

**4.6  Exercises (page 167)**

1.  $f'(0) = 1, f'(\frac{1}{2}) = 0, f'(1) = -1, f'(-10) = -19$
2.  (a) 1, $-2$     (b) 0, $-1$     (c) 3, $-4$
3.  $2x + 3$
4.  $4x^3 + \cos x$
5.  $4x^3 \sin x + x^4 \cos x$
6.  $-1/(x + 1)^2$
7.  $-2x/(x^2 + 1)^2 + 5x^4 \cos x - x^5 \sin x$
8.  $-1/(x - 1)^2$
9.  $\sin x/(2 + \cos x)^2$
10.  $-\dfrac{2x^5 + 9x^4 + 8x^3 + 3x^2 + 2x - 3}{(x^4 + x^2 + 1)^2}$
11.  $\dfrac{1 - 2(\sin x + \cos x)}{(2 - \cos x)^2}$
12.  $\dfrac{\sin x + x \cos x}{1 + x^2} - \dfrac{2x^2 \sin x}{(1 + x^2)^2}$
13.  (b) $v_0/32$ sec     (c) $-v_0$ ft/sec     (d) 16 ft/sec; 160 ft/sec; $16T$ ft/sec
     (f) $f(t) = v_0 t - 10t^2$ is one example
14.  $3x^2$, where $x$ is the length of an edge
16.  $\frac{1}{2}x^{-1/2}$

17. $\dfrac{-1}{2\sqrt{x}(1 + \sqrt{x})^2}$

18. $\frac{3}{2}x^{1/2}$

19. $-\frac{3}{2}x^{-5/2}$

20. $\frac{1}{2}x^{-1/2} + \frac{1}{3}x^{-2/3} + \frac{1}{4}x^{-3/4}$

21. $-\frac{1}{2}x^{-3/2} - \frac{1}{3}x^{-4/3} - \frac{1}{4}x^{-5/4}$

22. $\dfrac{1 - x}{2\sqrt{x}(1 + x)^2}$

23. $\dfrac{2 + \sqrt{x}}{2(1 + \sqrt{x})^2}$

26. $\sec x(1 + 2\tan^2 x)$

27. $x \sec^2 x + \tan x$

28. $-(x^{-2} + 4x^{-3} + 9x^{-4})$

29. $\dfrac{2(1 + x^2)}{(1 - x^2)^2}$

30. $\dfrac{2(1 - 2x)}{(1 - x + x^2)^2}$

31. $\dfrac{x \cos x - \sin x}{x^2}$

32. $-\dfrac{1 + \cos x}{(x + \sin x)^2}$

33. $\dfrac{ad - bc}{(cx + d)^2}$

34. $-\dfrac{(2x^2 + 3)\sin x + 4x \cos x}{(2x^2 + 3)^2}$

35. $\dfrac{(2ax + b)(\sin x + \cos x) + (ax^2 + bx + c)(\sin x - \cos x)}{1 + \sin 2x}$

36. $a = d = 1; \ b = c = 0$

37. $a = c = e = 0; \ b = f = 2; \ d = -1$

38. (a) $\dfrac{nx^{n+1} - (n + 1)x^n + 1}{(x - 1)^2}$

(b) $\dfrac{n^2 x^{n+3} - (2n^2 + 2n - 1)x^{n+2} + (n + 1)^2 x^{n+1} - x^2 - x}{(x - 1)^3}$

## 4.9  Exercises (page 173)

1. 1, 3
2. (a) $-1, \frac{1}{2}$    (b) $-\frac{1}{2}, 0$    (c) $-2, \frac{3}{2}$
3. $(2n + 1)\pi$, where $n$ is any integer
4. $a = -2, b = 4$
5. $a = 1, b = 0, c = -1$
6. (a) $x_1 + x_2 + a$    (b) $\frac{1}{2}(x_1 + x_2)$
7. Tangent at $(3, -3)$; also intersect at $(0, 0)$
8. $m = -2, b = -2, a = \frac{1}{2}, c = \frac{3}{8}$
9. $a = 2c, b = -c^2$

10. $a = \dfrac{3}{2c}, b = -\dfrac{1}{2c^3}$

11. $a = \cos c, b = \sin c - c \cos c$

12. $-\dfrac{1}{\sqrt{x}(1 + \sqrt{x})^2}; \quad \dfrac{1 + 3\sqrt{x}}{2(x + \sqrt{x})^3}; \quad -\dfrac{3}{4}\dfrac{1 + 4\sqrt{x} + 5x}{\sqrt{x}(x + \sqrt{x})^4}$

13. $a = -4, \ b = 5, \ c = -1, \ d = -2$

14. (a) $\dfrac{15}{4}$    (b) 2    (c) $\frac{1}{2}$

15. (a) True    (b) True    (c) False if $f'(a) \neq 0$. Limit is $2f'(a)$
   (d) False if $f'(a) \neq 0$. Limit is $\frac{1}{2}f'(a)$

16. (a) $D^*(f + g) = (1 + g/f)D^*f + (1 + f/g)D^*g$ when $f(x)$ and $g(x)$ are not $0$;

$\quad\quad D^*(f \cdot g) = g^2 \, D^*f + f^2 \, D^*g$;

$\quad\quad D^*(f/g) = (g^2 \, D^*f - f^2 \, D^*g)/g^4$ when $g(x) \neq 0$

(b) $D^*f(x) = 2f(x) \, Df(x)$

(c) $f(x) = c$ for all $x$

## 4.12  Exercises (page 179)

1. $-2 \cos x(1 + 2 \sin x)$

2. $x/\sqrt{1 + x^2}$

3. $(2x^3 - 4x) \sin x^2 - 2x \cos x^2 + 2 \sin x^3 + 6x^3 \cos x^3$

4. $-\sin 2x \cos (\cos 2x)$

5. $n \sin^{n-1} x \cos (n + 1)x$

6. $\cos x \cos (\sin x) \cos [\sin (\sin x)]$

7. $\dfrac{2 \sin x(\cos x \sin x^2 - x \sin x \cos x^2)}{\sin^2 x^2}$

8. $2/(\sin^2 x)$

9. $-\dfrac{16 \cos 2x}{\sin^3 2x}$

10. $\dfrac{1 + 2x^2}{\sqrt{1 + x^2}}$

11. $4(4 - x^2)^{-3/2}$

12. $\dfrac{2x^2}{1 - x^6}\left(\dfrac{1 + x^3}{1 - x^3}\right)^{1/3}$

13. $-(1 + x^2)^{-3/2}$

14. $\dfrac{1 + 2\sqrt{x} + 4\sqrt{x} \, g(x)}{8\sqrt{x} \, g(x)\sqrt{x + g(x)}}$, where $g(x) = \sqrt{x + \sqrt{x}}$

15. $\dfrac{6 + 3x + 8x^2 + 4x^3 + 2x^4 + 3x^5}{(2 + x^2)^{1/2}(3 + x^3)^{2/3}}$

16. $f'(x) = (x + 1)^{-2}$;  $g'(x) = (2x + 1)^{-2}$

17.

| $x$ | $h(x)$ | $h'(x)$ | $k(x)$ | $k'(x)$ |
|-----|--------|---------|--------|---------|
| 0 | 0 | −10 | 0 | 5 |
| 1 | 1 | 5 | 1 | 12 |
| 2 | 2 | 4 | 2 | −10 |
| 3 | 3 | 12 | 3 | 4 |

18.

| $x$ | $g'(x)$ | $g''(x)$ |
|-----|---------|----------|
| 0 | 0 | 0 |
| 1 | 3 | 10 |
| 2 | 30 | 36 |

19. (a) $2xf'(x^2)$
    (b) $[f'(\sin^2 x) - f'(\cos^2 x)] \sin 2x$
    (c) $f'[f(x)]f'(x)$
    (d) $f'(x)f'[f(x)]f'\{f[f(x)]\}$
20. (a) 75 cm³/sec  (b) 300 cm³/sec  (c) $3x^2$ cm³/sec
21. 400 mph
22. (a) $20\sqrt{5}$ ft/sec  (b) $50\sqrt{2}$ ft/sec
23. 7.2 mi/hr
24. (a) and (b)  $5/(4\pi)$ ft/min
25. $c = 1 + 36\pi$
26. $dV/dh = 75\pi$ ft³/ft;  $dr/dt = 1/(15\pi)$ ft/sec
27. $\dfrac{66}{7}$ cm²/sec
28. $n = 33$
29. (a)  $x = \frac{1}{2}, \ y = \frac{1}{4}$  (b) $\frac{1}{2}\sqrt{3}$

## 4.15 Exercises (page 186)

3. (b)  $c = \frac{1}{2}, \ c = \sqrt{2}$
6. (a)  $\theta = \frac{1}{2}, \ \theta \to \frac{1}{2}$

   (b)  $\theta = \dfrac{x + \frac{1}{3}h}{x + \sqrt{x^2 + xh + \frac{1}{3}h^2}}$;  $\theta \to \frac{1}{2}$ if $x > 0$

7. (b)  $f$ has at most $k + r$ zeros in $[a, b]$

## 4.19 Exercises (page 191)

1. (a) $\frac{3}{2}$  (b) $f$ decreases if $x < \frac{3}{2}$; increases if $x > \frac{3}{2}$  (c) $f'$ increases for all $x$
2. (a) $\pm\frac{2}{3}\sqrt{3}$  (b) $f$ increases if $|x| > \frac{2}{3}\sqrt{3}$; decreases if $|x| < \frac{2}{3}\sqrt{3}$
   (c) $f'$ increases if $x > 0$; decreases if $x < 0$
3. (a) $\pm 1$  (b) $f$ increases if $|x| > 1$; decreases if $|x| < 1$
   (c) $f'$ increases if $x > 0$; decreases if $x < 0$
4. (a) 1, 3  (b) $f$ increases if $x < 1$ or if $x > 3$; decreases if $1 < x < 3$
   (c) $f'$ increases if $x > 2$; decreases if $x < 2$
5. (a) 1  (b) $f$ increases if $x > 1$; decreases if $x < 1$  (c) $f'$ increases for all $x$
6. (a) none  (b) $f$ increases if $x < 0$; decreases if $x > 0$
   (c) $f'$ increases if $x < 0$, or if $x > 0$
7. (a) $2^{1/3}$  (b) $f$ increases if $x < 0$, or if $x > 2^{1/3}$; decreases if $0 < x < 2^{1/3}$
   (c) $f'$ increases if $x < 0$, or if $x > 0$
8. (a) 2  (b) $f$ increases if $x < 1$, or if $1 < x < 2$; decreases if $2 < x < 3$, or if $x > 3$
   (c) $f'$ increases if $x < 1$, or if $x > 3$; decreases if $1 < x < 3$
9. (a) $\pm 1$  (b) $f$ increases if $|x| < 1$; decreases if $|x| > 1$
   (c) $f'$ increases if $-\sqrt{3} < x < 0$, or if $x > \sqrt{3}$; decreases if $x < -\sqrt{3}$, or if $0 < x < \sqrt{3}$
10. (a) 0  (b) $f$ increases if $x < -3$ or if $-3 < x < 0$; decreases if $0 < x < 3$, or if $x > 3$
    (c) $f'$ increases if $|x| > 3$; decreases if $|x| < 3$

*Note.* In Exercises 11, 12, and 13, $n$ denotes an arbitrary integer.

11. (a) $\frac{1}{2}n\pi$  (b) $f$ increases if $n\pi < x < (n + \frac{1}{2})\pi$; decreases if $(n - \frac{1}{2})\pi < x < n\pi$
    (c) $f'$ increases if $(n - \frac{1}{4})\pi < x < (n + \frac{1}{4})\pi$; decreases if $(n + \frac{1}{4})\pi < x < (n + \frac{3}{4})\pi$
12. (a) $2n\pi$  (b) $f$ increases for all $x$
    (c) $f'$ increases if $2n\pi < x < (2n + 1)\pi$; decreases if $(2n - 1)\pi < x < 2n\pi$

13.   (a)  $(2n + \frac{1}{2})\pi$    (b)  $f$ increases for all $x$
     (c)  $f'$ increases if $(2n + \frac{1}{2})\pi < x < (2n + \frac{3}{2})\pi$;  decreases if $(2n - \frac{1}{2})\pi < x < (2n + \frac{1}{2})\pi$

14.   (a)  0    (b)  $f$ increases if $x > 0$; decreases if $x < 0$    (c)  $f'$ increases for all $x$

## 4.21  Exercises (page 194)

2.  $\frac{1}{4}L$ ft wide, $\frac{1}{2}L$ ft long

3.  Width $\frac{1}{2}\sqrt{2A}$, length $\sqrt{2A}$

7.  $\sqrt{2}\,L$

10.  $r = \frac{1}{2}h = R/\sqrt{2}$

12.  $r = \frac{1}{2}R,\ \ h = \frac{1}{2}H$

13.  $r = 2R/3,\ \ h = H/3$

14.  $h = \frac{4}{3}R,\ \ r = \frac{2}{3}\sqrt{2}\,R$

15.  A rectangle whose base is twice the altitude

16.  Isosceles trapezoid, lower base the diameter, upper base equal to the radius

17.   (a)  $6\frac{2}{3}, 6\frac{2}{3}, \frac{5}{3}$
     (b)  $8 + 2\sqrt{7}, 2 + 2\sqrt{7}, 5 - \sqrt{7}$

18.  $\sqrt{5}$

19.   (a)  $20\sqrt{3}$ mi/hr;  \$10.39
     (b)  $40\sqrt{2}$ mi/hr;  \$16.97
     (c)  60 mi/hr;  \$22.00
     (d)  60 mi/hr;  \$27.00
     (e)  60 mi/hr;  \$32.00

20.  $\pi/4$

21.  Crease $= \frac{9}{2}\sqrt{3}$ inches;  angle $= \arctan \frac{1}{2}\sqrt{2}$

22.   (a)  max $= 3\sqrt{3}\,r$;  min $= 4r$
     (b)  $\frac{1}{4}L$

23.  Rectangle has base $4P/(3\pi + 8)$, altitude $P(4 + \pi)/(6\pi + 16)$

24.  $V = 48\pi$ for $0 \le h < 2$;  $V = 4\pi(4 + h)^3/(9h)$ for $h \ge 2$

26.  $A = 2(\frac{24}{7})^{7/2}$

27.  $m(t) = 0$ if $t^2 \ge \frac{1}{3}$;  $m(t) = t^2 - \frac{1}{3}$ if $t^2 \le \frac{1}{3}$

## ★4.23  Exercises (page 201)

1.  $\dfrac{\partial f}{\partial x} = 4x^3 - 8xy^2$;  $\dfrac{\partial f}{\partial y} = 4y^3 - 8x^2y$;  $\dfrac{\partial^2 f}{\partial x^2} = 12x^2 - 8y^2$;  $\dfrac{\partial^2 f}{\partial y^2} = 12y^2 - 8x^2$;

   $\dfrac{\partial^2 f}{\partial x\,\partial y} = \dfrac{\partial^2 f}{\partial y\,\partial x} = -16xy$

2.  $f_x = \sin(x + y) + x\cos(x + y)$;  $f_y = x\cos(x + y)$;  $f_{yy} = -x\sin(x + y)$;
   $f_{xx} = 2\cos(x + y) - x\sin(x + y)$;  $f_{xy} = f_{yx} = \cos(x + y) - x\sin(x + y)$

3.  $D_1 f = y + y^{-1}$;  $D_2 f = x - xy^{-2}$;  $D_{1,1}f = 0$;  $D_{2,2}f = 2xy^{-3}$;  $D_{1,2}f = D_{2,1}f = 1 - y^{-2}$

4.  $f_x = x(x^2 + y^2)^{-1/2}$;  $f_y = y(x^2 + y^2)^{-1/2}$;  $f_{xx} = y^2(x^2 + y^2)^{-3/2}$;
   $f_{yy} = x^2(x^2 + y^2)^{-3/2}$;  $f_{xy} = f_{yx} = -xy(x^2 + y^2)^{-3/2}$

5.  $f_{yy} = 6x^2y\cos(x^2y^3) - 9x^4y^4\sin(x^2y^3)$;
   $f_{xy} = f_{yx} = 6xy^2\cos(x^2y^3) - 6x^3y^5\sin(x^2y^3)$

6.  $f_{xy} = f_{yx} = 6\cos(2x - 3y)\cos[\cos(2x - 3y)] + 6\sin^2(2x - 3y)\sin[\cos(2x - 3y)]$

7.  $\dfrac{\partial^2 f}{\partial x\,\partial y} = \dfrac{\partial^2 f}{\partial y\,\partial x} = -2(x + y)(x - y)^{-3}$;  $\dfrac{\partial^2 f}{\partial x^2} = 4y(x - y)^{-3}$;  $\dfrac{\partial^2 f}{\partial y^2} = 4x(x - y)^{-3}$

8.  $f_{xx} = -3xy^2(x^2 + y^2)^{-5/2}$;  $f_{yy} = -x(x^2 - 2y^2)(x^2 + y^2)^{-5/2}$;
   $f_{xy} = f_{yx} = y(2x^2 - y^2)(x^2 + y^2)^{-5/2}$

## Chapter 5

**5.5  Exercises (page 208)**

1. $\frac{5}{4}(b^4 - a^4)$
2. $\frac{4}{5}(b^5 - a^5) + 6(a^2 - b^2)$
3. $\frac{1}{5}(b^5 - a^5) + \frac{1}{4}(b^4 - a^4) - (b^2 - a^2) - 2(b - a)$
4. $\frac{1}{2}(b^2 - a^2) - \left(\frac{1}{b} - \frac{1}{a}\right) + \frac{3}{2}\left(\frac{1}{b^2} - \frac{1}{a^2}\right)$
5. $(b - a) + \frac{4}{3}(b^{3/2} - a^{3/2}) + \frac{1}{2}(b^2 - a^2)$
6. $\sqrt{2}(b^{3/2} - a^{3/2})$
7. $\frac{2}{5}(b^{5/2} - a^{5/2}) - 2(b^{3/2} - a^{3/2}) + 7(b^{1/2} - a^{1/2})$
8. $\frac{3}{2}(b^{4/3} - a^{4/3} - b^{2/3} + a^{2/3})$
9. $\frac{1}{3}(b^6 - a^6) - 3(\cos b - \cos a)$
10. $\frac{3}{7}(b^{7/3} - a^{7/3}) - 5(\sin b - \sin a)$
14. $f(\frac{1}{4}\pi) = \frac{1}{2}\pi$; $f'(\frac{1}{4}\pi) = 2 - \pi$
15. $f(t) = -\sin t$; $c = \pi/3$
16. $f(t) = \sin t - 1$; $c = 0$
17. $f(x) = 2x^{15}$; $c = -\frac{1}{9}$
18. $p(x) = 3 + \frac{1}{2}x + \frac{1}{4}x^2$
19. $f''(1) = 2$; $f'''(1) = 5$
20. (a)  $(1 + x^2)^{-3}$  (b)  $2x(1 + x^4)^{-3}$  (c)  $2x(1 + x^4)^{-3} - 3x^2(1 + x^6)^{-3}$
21. $\dfrac{2x^{13}}{1 + x^8} - \dfrac{3x^{20}}{1 + x^{12}}$
22. (a)  16  (b)  $1 + \frac{3}{2}\sqrt{2}$  (c)  $(36)^{1/3}$  (d)  $\frac{1}{5}$
23. $f(a) = a(3 - \cos a)^{1/2}$
24. (a)  $-\pi$  (b)  $1 - \pi$  (c)  0  (d)  $-\pi^2$  (e)  $3\pi/2$
25. (a)  $\pi - \frac{1}{2}$  (b)  $\frac{1}{2}$  (c)  $\frac{1}{2} + (\pi - \frac{1}{2})(t - 1)$  (d)  $\frac{1}{2}(t - 1) + (\pi - \frac{1}{2})(t - 1)^2/2$
26. (a)  None  (b)  One example is $f(x) = x + x^2$  (c)  None
    (d)  One example is $f(x) = 1 + x + x^2$ for $x \geq 0$, $f(x) = 1/(1 - x)$ for $x \leq 0$
28. (a) implies $\alpha$ and $\delta$;  (b) implies $\alpha$;  (c) implies $\alpha$ and $\gamma$;  (d) implies $\alpha$ and $\delta$;
    (e) implies $\alpha$, $\delta$, and $\epsilon$.

**5.8  Exercises (page 216)**

1. $\frac{1}{3}(2x + 1)^{3/2} + C$
2. $(\frac{2}{45})(1 + 3x)^{5/2} - (\frac{2}{27})(1 + 3x)^{3/2} + C$
3. $\frac{2}{7}(x + 1)^{7/2} - \frac{4}{5}(x + 1)^{5/2} + \frac{2}{3}(x + 1)^{3/2} + C$
4. $-\frac{2}{27}$
5. $-\dfrac{1}{4(x^2 + 2x + 2)^2} + C$
6. $\frac{1}{3}\cos^3 x - \cos x + C$
7. $\frac{3}{7}(z - 1)^{7/3} + \frac{3}{4}(z - 1)^{4/3} + C$
8. $-\frac{1}{2}\csc^2 x + C$
9. $\frac{8}{3} - \sqrt{3}$
10. $\dfrac{1}{3 + \cos x} + C$
11. $\dfrac{2}{\sqrt{\cos x}} + C$
12. $2(\cos 2 - \cos 3)$
13. $-\dfrac{\cos x^n}{n} + C$
14. $-\frac{1}{3}\sqrt{1 - x^6} + C$
15. $\frac{4}{9}(1 + t)^{9/4} - \frac{4}{5}(1 + t)^{5/4} + C$
16. $x(x^2 + 1)^{-1/2} + C$
17. $\frac{1}{40}(8x^3 + 27)^{5/3} + C$
18. $\frac{3}{2}(\sin x - \cos x)^{2/3} + C$
19. $2\sqrt{1 + \sqrt{1 + x^2}} + C$
20. $-\frac{5}{2}(x - 1)^{2/5} + C$

### 5.10 Exercises (page 220)

1. $\sin x - x \cos x + C$
2. $2x \sin x + 2 \cos x - x^2 \cos x + C$
3. $x^3 \sin x + 3x^2 \cos x - 6x \sin x - 6 \cos x + C$
4. $-x^3 \cos x + 3x^2 \sin x + 6x \cos x - 6 \sin x + C$
5. $\frac{1}{2} \sin^2 x + C$
6. $\frac{1}{8} \sin 2x - \frac{1}{4}x \cos 2x + C$
15. (b) $(5\pi/32)a^6$
17. $\frac{2}{3}(3\sqrt{31} + \sqrt{3} - 11.35)$
18. $\tan x - x; \quad \frac{1}{3} \tan^3 x - \tan x + x$
19. $-\cot x - x; \quad -\frac{1}{3} \cot^3 x + \cot x + x$
20. (a) $n = 4$ \qquad (b) $2$

### *5.11 Miscellaneous review exercises (page 222)

1. $g^{(k)}(0) = 0$ if $0 \le k \le n - 1$; $g^{(n)}(0) = n!$
2. $6x^5 - 15x^4 + 10x^3 + 1$
6. $3$
7. $\frac{67}{5}$
9. $y = 16x^2/9$
10. (b) $f'(0) = 0$
11. $-\frac{2}{5} \cos 5x + \frac{3}{25} \sin 5x - \frac{3}{5}x \cos 5x$
12. $\frac{1}{3}(1 + x^2)^{3/2}$
13. $-3^{10}/20$
14. $37/8281$
15. $\frac{1}{30}(1 + x^5)^6$
16. $1/265650$
17. $\cos \frac{1}{2} - \cos 1$
18. $[12(x - 1)^{1/2} - 24] \sin (x - 1)^{1/4} - 4[(x - 1)^{3/4} - 6(x - 1)^{1/4}] \cos (x - 1)^{1/4}$
19. $\frac{1}{4} \sin^2 x^2$
20. $-\frac{2}{9}(1 + 3 \cos^2 x)^{3/2}$
22. $a = 9, \quad b = \frac{27}{2}$
23. $\frac{8}{15}, \quad \frac{16}{35}, \quad \frac{128}{315}, \quad \frac{256}{693}$
24. $\frac{1}{13}x^{13} + \frac{1}{6}x^{12} + \frac{1}{11}x^{11}$
26. $3$
27. $\frac{1}{2}\left(\frac{1}{2} + \frac{1}{\pi + 2} - A\right)$
34. (a) $p(x) = -x^2 + x - 1$
35. (a) $P_1(x) = x - \frac{1}{2}; \quad P_2(x) = x^2 - x + \frac{1}{6}; \quad P_3(x) = x^3 - \frac{3}{2}x^2 + \frac{1}{2}x;$
    $P_4(x) = x^4 - 2x^3 + x^2 - \frac{1}{30}; \quad P_5(x) = x^5 - \frac{5}{2}x^4 + \frac{5}{3}x^3 - \frac{1}{6}x$

## Chapter 6

### 6.9 Exercises (page 236)

1. (a) $1$ \qquad (b) $(a + b)/(1 + ab)$
2. (a) $0$ \qquad (b) $\dfrac{e - 1}{e + 1}$ \qquad (c) $4$ \qquad (d) $\dfrac{(e^2 - 1)^2}{4e^2}$
3. Increasing if $0 < x < e$, decreasing if $x > e$; convex if $x > e^{3/2}$, concave if $0 < x < e^{3/2}$

4.  $(2x)/(1 + x^2)$

5.  $x/(1 + x^2)$

6.  $x/(x^2 - 4)$

7.  $1/(x \log x)$

8.  $(2/x) + 1/(x \log x)$

9.  $x/(x^4 - 1)$

15. $-1/(x \log^2 x)$

16. $\frac{1}{3} \log |2 + 3x| + C$

17. $x \log^2 |x| - 2x \log |x| + 2x + C$

18. $\frac{1}{2}x^2 \log |x| - \frac{1}{4}x^2 + C$

19. $\frac{1}{2}x^2 \log^2 |x| - \frac{1}{2}x^2 \log |x| + \frac{1}{4}x^2 + C$

20. 3

21. $\log |\sin x| + C$

22. $\dfrac{x^{n-1}}{n + 1} \log |ax| - \dfrac{x^{n+1}}{(n + 1)^2} + C$ if $n \neq -1$; $\frac{1}{2} \log^2 |ax| + C$ if $n = -1$

23. $\dfrac{x^3}{3} \left(\log^2 |x| - \frac{2}{3} \log |x| + \frac{2}{9}\right) + C$

24. $\log |\log x| + C$

25. $-2$

26. $\frac{2}{3}(-2 + \log |x|)\sqrt{1 + \log |x|} + C$

27. $\dfrac{x^4}{4} \log^3 |x| - \frac{3}{16}x^4 \log^2 |x| + \frac{3}{32}x^4 \log |x| - \frac{3}{128}x^4 + C$

34. $4 \log x$

35. $3 + 3 \log x.$

36. $a \log a$

10. $\dfrac{n(x + \sqrt{1 + x^2})^n}{\sqrt{1 + x^2}}$

11. $1/[2(1 + \sqrt{x + 1})]$

12. $\log (x + \sqrt{x^2 + 1})$

13. $1/(a - bx^2)$

14. $2 \sin (\log x)$

## 6.17 Exercises (page 248)

1.  $3e^{3x-1}$

2.  $8xe^{4x^2}$

3.  $-2xe^{-x^2}$

4.  $\dfrac{e^{\sqrt{x}}}{2\sqrt{x}}$

5.  $-\dfrac{e^{1/x}}{x^2}$

13. $e^x(x - 1) + C$

14. $-e^{-x}(x + 1) + C$

15. $e^x(x^2 - 2x + 2) + C$

16. $-\frac{1}{2}e^{-2x}(x^2 + x + \frac{1}{2}) + C$

17. $2(\sqrt{x} - 1)e^{\sqrt{x}} + C$

24. $a^a x^{a^a - 1} + ax^{a-1}a^{x^a} \log a + a^x a^{a^x}(\log a)^2$

25. $1/[x \log x \log (\log x)]$

26. $e^x(1 + e^{2x})^{-1/2}$

27. $x^x x^{x^x}\left[\dfrac{1}{x} + \log x + (\log x)^2\right]$

28. $(\log x)^x\left(\log \log x + \dfrac{1}{\log x}\right)$

6.  $2^x \log 2$

7.  $2^{1+x^2}x \log 2$

8.  $(\cos x)e^{\sin x}$

9.  $-(\sin 2x)e^{\cos^2 x}$

10. $1$

11. $e^x e^{e^x}$

12. $e^x e^{e^x} e^{e^{e^x}}$

18. $-\frac{1}{2}(x^2 + 1)e^{-x^2} + C$

19. $b = e^a$, $a$ arbitrary

21. $x^x(1 + \log x)$

22. $1 + (1 + 2x + 2x^2)e^{x^2}$

23. $4(e^x + e^{-x})^{-2}$

29.  $2x^{-1+\log x} \log x$

30.  $\dfrac{(\log x)^{x-1}}{x^{1+\log x}} [x - 2(\log x)^2 + x \log x \log (\log x)]$

31.  $(\sin x)^{1+\cos x} [\cot^2 x - \log (\sin x)] - (\cos x)^{1+\sin x} [\tan^2 x - \log (\cos x)]$

32.  $x^{-2+1/x}(1 - \log x)$

33.  $\dfrac{54x - 36x^2 + 4x^3 + 2x^4}{3(1 - x)^2(3 - x)^{2/3}(3 + x)^{5/3}}$

34.  $\displaystyle\prod_{i=1}^{n} (x - a_i)^{b_i} \sum_{k=1}^{n} \dfrac{b_k}{x - a_k}$

### 6.19   Exercises (page 251)

16.  $\frac{5}{3}$

17.  $\frac{3}{4}$

18.  $\sinh x = \frac{5}{12}, \cosh x = \frac{13}{12}$

19.  $\frac{37}{12}$

20.  $\frac{24}{25}$

### 6.22   Exercises (page 256)

12.  $\dfrac{1}{\sqrt{4 - x^2}}$  if  $|x| < 2$

13.  $\dfrac{1}{\sqrt{1 + 2x - x^2}}$  if  $|x - 1| < \sqrt{2}$

14.  $\dfrac{1}{|x| \sqrt{x^2 - 1}}$  if  $|x| > 1$

15.  $\dfrac{\cos x}{|\cos x|}$  if  $x \neq (k + \frac{1}{2})\pi, k$ an integer

16.  $\dfrac{\sqrt{x}}{2(1 + x)}$  if  $x \geq 0$

17.  $\dfrac{1 + x^4}{1 + x^6}$

18.  $-\dfrac{2x}{|x| (1 + x^2)}$  if  $x \neq 0$

19.  $\dfrac{\sin 2x}{\sin^4 x + \cos^4 x}$  if  $x \neq (k + \frac{1}{2})\pi$

20.  $\dfrac{1}{2(1 + x^2)}$

21.  $\dfrac{\cos x + \sin x}{\sqrt{\sin 2x}}$  if  $k\pi < x < (k + \frac{1}{2})\pi$

22.  $\dfrac{x}{|x| \sqrt{1 - x^2}}$  if  $0 < |x| < 1$

23.  $1/(1 + x^2)$  if  $x \neq 1$

24.  $\dfrac{4x}{\sqrt{1 - x^4}(\arccos x^2)^3}$  if  $|x| < 1$

25.  $\dfrac{1}{2x \sqrt{x - 1} \arccos (1/\sqrt{x})}$  if  $x > 1$

27.  $\dfrac{3x}{(1 - x^2)^2} + \dfrac{(1 + 2x^2) \arcsin x}{(1 - x^2)^{5/2}}$

29.  $\arcsin \dfrac{x}{|a|} + C$

30.  $\arcsin \dfrac{x + 1}{\sqrt{2}} + C$

31.  $\dfrac{1}{a} \arctan \dfrac{x}{a} + C$

32.  $\dfrac{1}{a} \sqrt{\dfrac{a}{b}} \arctan \left( \sqrt{\dfrac{b}{a}} x \right) + C$  if  $ab > 0$;

$\dfrac{a}{2 |a| \sqrt{-ab}} \log \left| \dfrac{\sqrt{|a|} + x \sqrt{|b|}}{\sqrt{|a|} - x \sqrt{|b|}} \right| + C$  if  $ab < 0$

33. $\dfrac{2}{\sqrt{7}} \arctan \dfrac{2x-1}{\sqrt{7}} + C$

34. $\frac{1}{2}[(1+x^2)\arctan x - x] + C$

35. $\dfrac{x^3}{3} \arccos x - \dfrac{2+x^2}{9} \sqrt{1-x^2} + C$

36. $\frac{1}{2}(1+x^2)(\arctan x)^2 - x \arctan x + \frac{1}{2}\log(1+x^2) + C$

37. $(1+x)\arctan \sqrt{x} - \sqrt{x} + C$

38. $(\arctan \sqrt{x})^2 + C$

39. $\frac{1}{2}(\arcsin x + x\sqrt{1-x^2}) + C$

40. $\dfrac{(x-1)e^{\arctan x}}{2\sqrt{1+x^2}} + C$

41. $\dfrac{(x+1)e^{\arctan x}}{2\sqrt{1+x^2}} + C$

42. $\dfrac{1}{2}\left(\arctan x - \dfrac{x}{1+x^2}\right) + C$

43. $\arctan e^x + C$

44. $\frac{1}{2}\log(1+e^{-2x}) - \dfrac{\operatorname{arccot} e^x}{e^x} + C$

45. $a \arcsin \dfrac{x}{a} - \sqrt{a^2 - x^2} + C$

46. $\dfrac{2(b-a)}{|b-a|} \arcsin \sqrt{\dfrac{x-a}{b-a}} + C$

47. $\frac{1}{4}|b-a|(b-a)\arcsin \sqrt{\dfrac{x-a}{b-a}} + \frac{1}{4}\sqrt{(x-a)(b-x)}\,[2x-(a+b)] + C$

## 6.25  Exercises (page 267)

1. $\log|x-2| + \log|x+5| + C$

2. $\frac{1}{2}\log \left| \dfrac{(x+2)^4}{(x+1)(x+3)^3} \right| + C$

3. $-\dfrac{1}{3(x-1)} + \frac{2}{9}\log \left| \dfrac{x-1}{x+2} \right| + C$

4. $\frac{1}{2}x^2 - x + \log \left| \dfrac{x^3(x+2)}{x-1} \right| + C$

5. $\log|x+1| - \dfrac{3}{(2x+1)^2} + \dfrac{3}{2x+1} + C$

6. $2\log|x-1| + \log(x^2+x+1) + C$

7. $x + \frac{1}{3}\arctan x - \frac{8}{3}\arctan(x/2) + C$

8. $2\log|x| - \log|x+1| + C$

9. $\log|x| - \frac{1}{2}\log(x^2+1) + \dfrac{1}{2(x^2+1)} + C$

10. $\dfrac{9x^2+50x+68}{4(x+2)(x+3)^2} + \frac{1}{8}\log \left| \dfrac{(x+1)(x+2)^{16}}{(x+3)^{17}} \right| + C$

11. $\dfrac{1}{x+1} + \log|x+1| + C$

12. $\frac{1}{2}\log|x^2-1| - \log|x| + C$

13. $x + \frac{4}{5}\log|x-2| - \frac{9}{5}\log|x+3| + C$

14. $\log|x-2| - \dfrac{4}{x-2} + C$

15. $\dfrac{1}{2-x} - \arctan(x-2) + C$

16. $4 \log |x + 1| - \frac{3}{2} \log |x| - \frac{5}{2} \log |x + 2| + C$

17. $\frac{1}{4} \log \left| \dfrac{x + 1}{x - 1} \right| - \dfrac{x}{2(x^2 - 1)} + C$

18. $\frac{1}{3} \log \dfrac{(x - 1)^2}{x^2 + x + 1} + C$

19. $\log |x| + \dfrac{1}{x^2 + 1} + C$

20. $\dfrac{1}{4x} + \dfrac{1}{4x^2} + \dfrac{1}{8} \log \left| \dfrac{x - 2}{x} \right| + C$

21. $\log \dfrac{|x|}{\sqrt{1 + x^2}} - x + \arctan x + C$

22. $\frac{1}{4} \log |(x - 1)/(x + 1)| - \frac{1}{2} \arctan x + C$

23. $\dfrac{1}{4\sqrt{2}} \log \dfrac{x^2 + x\sqrt{2} + 1}{x^2 - x\sqrt{2} + 1} + \dfrac{1}{2\sqrt{2}} \arctan \dfrac{x\sqrt{2}}{1 - x^2} + C$

24. $(x^2 + 2x + 2)^{-1} + \arctan (x + 1) + C$

25. $-x/(x^5 + x \cdot + 1) + C$

26. $\dfrac{1}{\sqrt{5}} \arctan \dfrac{1 + 3 \tan (x/2)}{\sqrt{5}} + C$

27. $\dfrac{2}{\sqrt{1 - a^2}} \arctan \left( \sqrt{\dfrac{1 - a}{1 + a}} \tan \dfrac{x}{2} \right) + C$

28. $\dfrac{1}{\sqrt{a^2 - 1}} \log \left| \dfrac{a + \cos x + \sqrt{a^2 - 1} \sin x}{1 + a \cos x} \right| + C$

29. $x - \frac{1}{2}\sqrt{2} \arctan (\sqrt{2} \tan x) + C$

30. $\dfrac{1}{ab} \arctan \left( \dfrac{a}{b} \tan x \right) + C$

31. $-\dfrac{\cos x}{a(a \sin x + b \cos x)} + C$

32. $(\pi/4) - \frac{1}{2} \log 2$

33. $\frac{1}{2} x \sqrt{3 - x^2} + \frac{3}{2} \arcsin \left( \dfrac{x}{\sqrt{3}} \right) + C$

34. $-\sqrt{3 - x^2} + C$

35. $\sqrt{3 - x^2} - \sqrt{3} \log \left( \dfrac{\sqrt{3 - x^2} + \sqrt{3}}{x} \right) + C$

36. $\sqrt{x^2 + x} + \frac{1}{2} \log (2\sqrt{x^2 + x} + 2x + 1) + C$

37. $\frac{1}{2} x \sqrt{x^2 + 5} + \frac{5}{2} \log (x + \sqrt{x^2 + 5}) + C$

38. $\sqrt{x^2 + x + 1} - \frac{1}{2} \log (2x + 1 + 2\sqrt{x^2 + x + 1}) + C$

39. $\log (2x + 1 + 2\sqrt{x^2 + 1}) + C$

40. $-\dfrac{\sqrt{2 - x - x^2}}{x} + \dfrac{\sqrt{2}}{4} \log \left( \dfrac{\sqrt{2 - x - x^2}}{x} - \dfrac{\sqrt{2}}{4} \right) - \arcsin \left( \dfrac{2x + 1}{3} \right) + C$

## 6.26  Miscellaneous review exercises (page 268)

1.  $f(x) + f(1/x) = \frac{1}{2}(\log x)^2$

2.  $f(x) = \log \sqrt{3/(2 + \cos x)}$

4.  1

5.  (a)  $-\frac{7}{12}$    (b)  $V = \int_1^4 \frac{\pi(4x + 2)}{x(x + 1)(x + 2)}\, dx$

6.  (a)  $x \geq 1$    (c)  $F(ax) - F(a);\;\; F(x) - \dfrac{e^x}{x} + e;\;\; xe^{1/x} - e - F\!\left(\dfrac{1}{x}\right)$

7.  (a)  No such function    (b)  $-2^x \log 2$    (c)  $\frac{1}{2}x \pm 1$

9.  (a)  $g(3x) = 3e^{2x}g(x)$    (b)  $g(nx) = ne^{(n-1)x}g(x)$    (c)  2    (d)  $C = 2$

10.  $f(x) = b^{x/a}g(x)$,   where $g$ is periodic with period $a$

12.  (a)  $-Ae^{-a}$    (b)  $\frac{1}{2}A$    (c)  $A + 1 - \frac{1}{2}e$    (d)  $e \log 2 - A$

13.  (b)  $c_0 + nc_1 + n(n - 1)c_2 + n(n - 1)(n - 2)c_3$

(c)  If $p(x) = \displaystyle\sum_{k=0}^{m} c_k x^k$, then $f^{(n)}(0) = \displaystyle\sum_{k=0}^{m} k!\binom{n}{k}c_k$

16.  (a)  $\frac{2}{3}x^2(x + |x|)$

(b)  $x - \frac{1}{3}x^3$ if $|x| \leq 1$;  $x - \frac{1}{2}x\,|x| + \dfrac{1}{6}\dfrac{|x|}{x}$ if $|x| > 1$

(c)  $1 - e^{-x}$ if $x \geq 0$;  $e^x - 1$ if $x < 0$

(d)  $x$ if $|x| \leq 1$;  $\frac{1}{3}x^3 + \dfrac{2}{3}\dfrac{|x|}{x}$ if $|x| > 1$

17.  $f(x) = \sqrt{(2x + 1)/\pi}$

18.  (a)  $\frac{1}{2}(1 - e^{-2t})$    (b)  $\frac{1}{4}\pi(1 - e^{-4t})$    (c)  $\frac{1}{2}\pi[1 - e^{-2t}(2t + 1)]$    (d)  $\pi$

19.  (a)  $\log 3 - 2 \log 2$    (b)  No real $x$ exists

20.  (a)  True    (b)  False    (c)  True    (d)  False if $x < 0$

25.  (d)  $\displaystyle\int_0^x e^{-t}t^n\, dt = n!e^{-x}\left(e^x - \sum_{k=0}^{n}\frac{x^k}{k!}\right)$

27.  (a)  $f(t) = 2\sqrt{t} - 1$ if $t > 0$
(b)  $f(t) = t - \frac{1}{2}t^2 + \frac{1}{2}$ if $0 \leq t \leq 1$
(c)  $f(t) = t - \frac{1}{3}t^3 + \frac{1}{3}$ if $|t| \leq 1$
(d)  $f(t) = t$ if $t \leq 0$;  $f(t) = e^t - 1$ if $t > 0$

28.  (b)  $C_n = -2\displaystyle\sum_{k=1}^{n}\frac{(k - 1)!}{\log^k 2}$    (c)  $b = \log 2$    (d)  $e^2 \operatorname{Li}(e^{2x-2})$

29.  $g(y) = -e^y$;  all $y$

30.  (b)  constant $= \frac{3}{2}$


## Chapter 7

## 7.8  Exercises (page 284)

8.  (b)  $\dfrac{55\sqrt{2}}{672} + R$,   where  $|R| \leq \dfrac{\sqrt{2}}{7680} < 2 \cdot 10^{-4}$

9.  $0.9461 + R$,   where  $|R| < 2 \cdot 10^{-4}$

## 7.11  Exercises (page 290)

1. $1 + x \log 2 + \frac{1}{2}x^2 \log^2 2$
2. $\cos 1 + (\cos 1 - \sin 1)(x - 1) - \frac{1}{2}(2 \sin 1 + \cos 1)(x - 1)^2 + \frac{1}{6}(\sin 1 - 3 \cos 1)(x - 1)^3$
3. $x - x^2 - \dfrac{x^3}{6} + \dfrac{x^4}{2} - \dfrac{59x^5}{120} + \dfrac{x^6}{8}$
4. $a = 0, \quad b = 1, \quad c = -\frac{1}{2}$

5. $-\frac{2}{3}$        10. $1$         15. $\frac{1}{6}$        20. $-2$        25. $-e/2$
6. $a/b$         11. $1$         16. $-1$        21. $\frac{1}{6} \log a$        26. $e^{-1/2}$
7. $\frac{2}{3}$         12. $\log a/\log b$        17. $-1$        22. $\frac{1}{6}$        27. $e^{1/6}$
8. $-\frac{1}{6}$        13. $\frac{1}{3}$         18. $\frac{1}{6}$         23. $1/e$         28. $\frac{1}{2}$
9. $\frac{1}{2}$         14. $\frac{1}{2}$         19. $1$         24. $e^3$         29. $\frac{1}{2}$

30. $a = 2; \quad \text{limit} = \frac{3}{2}$
33. $f(0) = 0; \quad f'(0) = 0; \quad f''(0) = 4; \quad \text{limit} = e^2$

## 7.13  Exercises (page 295)

1. $\frac{14}{3}$         5. $(a/b)^2$        9. $1$
2. $-2$         6. $\frac{1}{6}$        10. $-\frac{1}{3}$
3. $\frac{1}{3}$         7. $1/\sqrt{2a}$        11. $n(n + 1)/2$
4. $-\frac{1}{6}$        8. $-2$         12. $\frac{1}{3}(a^2 - b^2)/(a^2b^2)$

13. $6 \text{ as } x \to 0; \quad 4/\pi \text{ as } x \to \pi/2$
14. $a = -3; \quad b = \frac{9}{2}$
15. $a = 4; \quad b = 1$
16. (a) $T(x) = \tan \frac{1}{2}x - \frac{1}{2} \sin x$    (b) $S(x) = \frac{1}{2}x - \frac{1}{2} \sin x$    (c) $\frac{3}{2}$
17. $tE/L$
18. $-\dfrac{At \cos kt}{2k}$

## 7.17  Exercises (page 303)

1. $0$         8. $e/2$        15. $0$         22. $1$
2. $1$         9. $+\infty$        16. $1$         23. $e^e$
3. $\frac{1}{3}$         10. $1$         17. $-1$        24. $e^{2/\pi}$
4. $1/\sqrt{b}$        11. $0$         18. $1$         25. $-\frac{1}{2}$
5. $\frac{1}{24}$         12. $0$         19. $e$         26. $\log 2$
6. $1$         13. $\frac{1}{2}$         20. $1$         27. $\frac{1}{2}$
7. $0$         14. $0$         21. $1/e$        28. $c = \frac{1}{8}; \quad \text{limit} = \frac{7}{8}$

29. $\frac{1}{2}$
30. $c = 1; \quad \text{limit} = \frac{1}{2}\sqrt{3}$
32. (b) $11.55$ years    (c) $11.67$ years

*Chapter 8*

## 8.5  Exercises (page 311)

1. $y = e^{3x} - e^{2x}$

2. $y = \frac{2}{3}x^2 + \frac{1}{3}x^5$

3. $y = 4 \cos x - 2 \cos^2 x$

4. $y = x^2 - 2 + 2e^{-x^2/2}$
5. $x = \frac{1}{3}e^{2t} + \frac{2}{3}e^{-t}$
6. $y = (x + C)/\sin x$

7. $y = \dfrac{1}{2}\left(1 + \dfrac{1}{x}\right)(C - e^{-x^2})$

8. $y = \sin x + C/\sin x$

9. $y = \left(\dfrac{x - 2}{x - 3}\right)^2\left(x + \dfrac{1}{x - 2} + C\right)$

10. $y = xT(x) + Cx$
11. $f(x) = 1 + \log x$
12. Only the function given

14. $y = (\sqrt{2}e^{2x} + e^{2x} - e^x)^2$
15. $y = 1/(x^2 - x + 2 - e^{-x})$
16. $y = (x^3 - x)^2$
17. $y = 1/(x^2 + x - x^2 \log x)$

18. (a) $y = \left(\dfrac{e^x + e^{2-x}}{2x}\right)^{1/2}$  (b) $y = -\left(\dfrac{e^x + e^{2-x}}{2x}\right)^{1/2}$  (c) $y^2 = \dfrac{\sinh x}{x}$

20. (a) $y = \dfrac{Ce^{3x} + 2}{Ce^{3x} - 1}$ with $C = \dfrac{b+2}{b-1}$  (b) $y = \dfrac{e^{3x} + 2C}{e^{3x} - C}$ with $C = \dfrac{b-1}{b+2}$

## 8.7 Exercises (page 319)

1. $100(1 - 2^{-1/16}) = 4.2$ percent
2. Four times the initial amount
3. (a) $T = (\log n)/k$  (b) $w(t) = (b - t)/(b - a)$
4. $256(1 - e^{-t/8})$ if $0 \le t \le 10$;  $16 + 166e^{20-2t}$ if $t \ge 10$
6. $v \to \sqrt{mg/k}$

7. (c) 54.5 min  (d) $T = \dfrac{1}{10k}[1 + (600 - t)k + (1400k - 1)e^{-kt}]$

8. $55°$
9. 19.5 lb
10. 54.7 lb
13. For Equation (8.20), $x = x_0 e^{k(t-t_0)}$;  for Equation (8.22), $\alpha = Mk$

15. $x = M\left[1 + \exp\left(-M\int_{t_0}^t k(u)\, du\right)\right]^{-1}$

16. (a) 200 million  (b) 217 million
17. (a) 0.026 per year  (b) 0.011 per year;  260 million;  450 million
18. $dx/dt = kx(1 - at)$;  $x = x_0 e^{k(t-at^2/2)}$;  curve (d)

## 8.14 Exercises (page 328)

1. $y = c_1 e^{2x} + c_2 e^{-2x}$
2. $y = c_1 \cos 2x + c_2 \sin 2x$
3. $y = c_1 + c_2 e^{4x}$
4. $y = c_1 + c_2 e^{-4x}$
5. $y = e^x(c_1 \cos \sqrt{2}x + c_2 \sin \sqrt{2}x)$
6. $y = c_1 e^x + c_2 e^{-3x}$
7. $y = e^x(c_1 \cos x + c_2 \sin x)$
8. $y = e^x(c_1 \cos 2x + c_2 \sin 2x)$
9. $y = e^{-x}(c_1 + c_2 x)$
10. $y = e^x(c_1 + c_2 x)$
11. $y = \frac{5}{3} - \frac{2}{3}e^{-3x/2}$
12. $y = -\cos(5x - 15)$

13. $y = \dfrac{a}{2}e^{b(x-1)} + \dfrac{b}{2}e^{a(x-1)}$, where $a = 2 - \sqrt{5}, b = 2 + \sqrt{5}$

14. $y = 2e^{-2x}(\cos x + \sin x)$
15. $u(x) = \frac{1}{2}e^{2x-\pi} \sin 5x$;  $v(x) = \frac{5}{6}e^{-2x-\pi} \sin 3x$
16. $u(x) = 6(e^{4x} - e^{-x})/5$;  $v(x) = e^x - e^{-5x}$
17. $k = n^2\pi^2$;  $f_k(x) = C \sin n\pi x$  $(n = 1, 2, 3, \ldots)$
19. (b) No  (c) If $k \ne 0$ the condition is $a_1 - a_2 \ne n\pi/k$
20. (a) $y'' - y = 0$
    (b) $y'' - 4y' + 4y = 0$
    (c) $y'' + y' + \frac{5}{4}y = 0$
    (d) $y'' + 4y = 0$
    (e) $y'' - y = 0$

**8.17 Exercises (page 333)**

1. $y = c_1 e^x + c_2 e^{-x} - x$
2. $y = c_1 e^x + c_2 - 2x - x^2 - \frac{1}{3}x^3$
3. $y = c_1 e^{-x} + c_2 + \frac{1}{3}x^3$
4. $y = e^x(c_1 \cos \sqrt{2}x + c_2 \sin \sqrt{2}x) - \frac{8}{27} + \frac{2}{9}x + \frac{2}{3}x^2 + \frac{1}{3}x^3$
5. $y = c_1 e^x + c_2 e^{4x} + \frac{9}{32} + \frac{1}{8}x + \frac{1}{4}x^2$
6. $y = c_1 e^{2x} + c_2 e^{-3x} - \frac{7}{12} + \frac{1}{2}x - x^2 - \frac{1}{3}x^3$
7. $y = (c_1 + \frac{1}{4}x)e^{2x} + c_2 e^{-2x}$
8. $y = c_1 \cos 2x + c_2 \sin 2x + \frac{1}{8}e^{-2x}$
9. $y = c_1 e^{-2x} + (c_2 + \frac{1}{3}x)e^x$
10. $y = c_1 e^{-2x} + c_2 e^x + \frac{1}{4}e^{2x}$
11. $y = c_1 e^{-2x} + (c_2 + \frac{1}{3}x)e^x + \frac{1}{4}e^{2x}$
12. $y = (c_1 + c_2 x + \frac{1}{3}x^3)e^x + x + 2$
13. $y = (c_1 + c_2 x - \log|x|)e^{-x}$
14. $y = c_1 \sin x + (c_1 + \log|\csc x + \cot x|)\cos x - 2$
15. $y = c_1 e^x + c_2 e^{-x} + (e^x - e^{-x})\log(1 + e^x) - xe^x - 1$
16. $y = (c_1 + \frac{1}{3}x)e^x + \frac{1}{6}e^{-x} + c_2 e^{-2x} - \frac{1}{6} - \frac{1}{3}(e^x + e^{-2x})\log(1 + e^x)$
17. $y = \begin{cases} (c_1 + c_2 x)e^{-3x} & \text{if } x < 1 \text{ or } x > 2, \\ (a + bx)e^{-3x} + \frac{1}{9} & \text{if } 1 \le x \le 2 \end{cases}$
18. $y = c_1 e^{3x} + c_2 e^{-3x} + \frac{1}{6}xe^{3x}$
19. $y = (c_1 - \frac{1}{6}x)\cos 3x + (c_2 - \frac{1}{18})\sin 3x$
20. $y = (c_1 - \frac{1}{2}x)\cos x + c_2 \sin x$
21. $y = c_1 \cos x + (c_2 + \frac{1}{2}x)\sin x$
22. $y = c_1 \cos 2x + c_2 \sin 2x + x \cos x + \frac{2}{3}\sin x$
23. $y = c_1 \cos 2x + c_2 \sin 2x + x \sin x - \frac{2}{3}\cos x$
24. $y = c_1 + c_2 e^{3x} - \frac{1}{5}e^{2x}(3 \sin x + \cos x)$
25. $y = c_1 \sin x + c_2 \cos x + \frac{1}{40}e^{2x}(3 \sin 3x - \cos 3x)$

**8.19 Exercises (page 339)**

1. $2\sqrt{2}$
2. $\pm 140\pi$
3. $A = C$, $m = k$, $\beta = \alpha - \frac{1}{2}\pi$
4. $y = 3 \cos 4\pi x$
5. $C = (y_0^2 + v_0^2)^{1/2}$
6. $y = \frac{1}{3}\sqrt{6}$, $y'' = -12y = -4\sqrt{6}$
7. $y = -A \sin \dfrac{\pi x}{3}$, where $A$ is positive
8. $I(t) = \begin{cases} \sin t + 1 - \cos t & \text{if } 0 \le t \le 2\pi, \\ \sin t & \text{if } t \ge 2\pi \end{cases}$
9. (a) $1/(2\pi\sqrt{2})$    (b) $R < \sqrt{2}$
10. $r(t) = \frac{1}{2}gt^2 - ct + c\left(t - \dfrac{w}{k}\right)\log\left(1 - \dfrac{kt}{w}\right)$
11. $r(t) = ct + c\left(\dfrac{w}{k} - t\right)\log\left(1 - \dfrac{kt}{w}\right)$
12. $r(t) = \dfrac{wv_0}{k}\log\dfrac{w}{w - kt}$

## 8.22 Exercises (page 344)

1. $y' + \frac{2}{3} = 0$
2. $y' + 2y = 0$
3. $yy' - x = 0$
4. $xy' + y = 0$
5. $2xy' - y = 0$

6. $(x^2 - y^2 - 1)y' - 2xy = 0$
7. $(x - 1)y' - xy = 0$
8. $(x^2 - 4)y' - y = 0$
9. $y' + y \tan x = 0$
10. $\sqrt{1 - x^2}\, y' + y^2 + 1 = 0$

11. $(x^2 - y^2 - 1)y' - 2xy = 0$
12. $(x^2 + 2xy - y^2 - 2)y' - y^2 - 2xy + x^2 + 2 = 0$
14. $x + y = -1$ is both an integral curve and an isocline
15. $y = Cx + C^2$; envelope: $y = -\frac{1}{4}x^2$

## 8.24 Exercises (page 347)

1. $y^3 = \frac{3}{4}x^4 + C$
2. $\cos x = Ce^{1/\cos y}$
3. $y(C + \log |x + 1|) = 1$
4. $y - 2 = C(y - 1)e^x$
5. $y^2 + 2\sqrt{1 - x^2} = C$

6. $y = C(x - 1)e^x$
7. $\arctan y + \arcsin x = C$
8. $(1 + y^2)(1 + x^2) = Cx^2$
9. $y^4(x + 2) = C(x - 2)$
10. $1 + y^2 = Cx^2 e^{x^2}$

11. $(y + \frac{1}{2})e^{-2y} = e^x(\cos x - \sin x) + C$
12. $x^2 - 1 = C(y^2 + 1)$
13. $f(x) = 2e^{x-1}$
14. $f(x) = \sqrt{5x^2 + 1}$
15. $f(x) = -\log(1 + x^2)$
16. $f(x) = \pm 1$; $f(x) = \sin(x + C)$; also, those continuous functions whose graphs may be obtained by piecing together portions of the curves $y = \sin(x + C)$ with portions of the lines $y = \pm 1$. One such example is $f(x) = -1$ for $x \le 0$, $f(x) = \sin(x - \frac{1}{2}\pi)$ for $0 \le x \le 3\pi$, $f(x) = 1$ for $x \ge 3\pi$
17. $f(x) = C$
18. $f(x) = Ae^{x/C}$
19. $f(x) = 0$
20. $f(x) = 0$

## 8.26 Exercises (page 350)

2. $x^2 + y^2 = C$
3. $y = x \log |Cx|$
4. $x^2 + y^2 = Cx^4$
5. $y^2 = C(x^2 + y^2)^3$
6. $x^2 + 2Cy = C^2$, $C > 0$
7. $y(Cx^2 - 1) = x$
8. $\arctan \dfrac{x}{y} + \log |y| = C$

9. $\dfrac{y}{x} - \dfrac{x}{y} + \log \dfrac{y^3}{x} = C$
10. $\tan \dfrac{y}{2x} = Cx$
11. $(x + y)^3 = Cx^4 y^4$

## 8.28 Miscellaneous review exercises (page 355)

1. $3x - 2y = C$
2. $x^2 - y^2 = C$
3. $x^2 + y^2 - Cx + 1 = 0$
4. $2x^2 + y^2 = C$
5. $2y^2 - x^2 = C$
6. $y^2 = x + C$

7. $xy = C$
8. $y^2 - \log(\sin^2 x) = C$
9. $(x - C)^2 + y^2 = C^2 - 1$
10. $x^2 + y^2 - C(x + y) + 2 = 0$
11. $y = -2x \log x$

12. $y = -\dfrac{1}{k} x \log x$

13. $f(x) = Cx^n$, or $f(x) = Cx^{1/n}$

14. $f(x) = Cx^{n/2}$, or $f(x) = Cx^{1/(2n)}$

15. $y = \dfrac{6}{\pi} \dfrac{x}{x^3 + 2}$

16. $y = \tfrac{3}{2}(1 - e^{x-1})$; $\; b = \dfrac{3}{2e} - 3$

17. $y = -6x^2 + 5x + 1$

18. $59.6 \sec$

20. $\dfrac{2\pi R^2 \sqrt{h}}{9A_0}$ sec, where $R$ is the radius of the base and $h$ is the height of the cone (in feet)

21. $y = e^x$

22. $y^3 = -\tfrac{1}{3}x + Cx^{-1/2}$ for $x > 0$, or $y^3 = -\tfrac{1}{3}x$ for all $x$

23. $m = -1$; $\; y^2 \log|y| = \tfrac{1}{2}e^{-2x} + Cy^2$

24. (a) $a = 0, b = \tfrac{1}{4}$ (b) $f(x) = 2x^{1/2}$

25. (b) $y = e^{4x} - e^{-x^3/3}$

26. (a) $1/(t + 1)$ grams in $t$ years (b) $1 \text{ gm}^{-1}\text{yr}^{-1}$

27. $[1 - \tfrac{1}{2}(2 - \sqrt{2})t]^2$ grams in $t$ years; $\; 2 + \sqrt{2}$ years

28. (a) $365e^{-2.65t}$ citizens in $t$ years (b) $365(1 - e^{-2.65t})$ fatalities in $t$ years

29. $6.96 \text{ mi/sec} = 25,056 \text{ mi/hr}$

30. (a) Relative minimum at 0 (b) $a = \tfrac{2}{3}, b = \tfrac{20}{9}$ (d) $\tfrac{2}{3}$

31. (b) Minimum (c) $\tfrac{1}{2}$

# Chapter 9

## 9.6 Exercises (page 365)

1. (a) $2i$ (b) $-i$ (c) $\tfrac{1}{2} - \tfrac{1}{2}i$ (d) $18 + i$ (e) $-\tfrac{1}{5} + \tfrac{3}{5}i$ (f) $1 + i$
   (g) $0$ (h) $1 + i$

2. (a) $\sqrt{2}$ (b) $5$ (c) $1$ (d) $1$ (e) $\sqrt{2}$ (f) $\sqrt{65}$

3. (a) $r = 2, \theta = \tfrac{1}{2}\pi$ (b) $r = 3, \theta = -\tfrac{1}{2}\pi$ (c) $r = 1, \theta = \pi$ (d) $r = 1, \theta = 0$
   (e) $r = 2\sqrt{3}, \theta = 5\pi/6$ (f) $r = 1, \theta = \tfrac{1}{4}\pi$ (g) $r = 2\sqrt{2}, \theta = \tfrac{1}{4}\pi$
   (h) $r = 2\sqrt{2}, \theta = -\tfrac{1}{4}\pi$ (i) $r = \tfrac{1}{2}\sqrt{2}, \theta = -\tfrac{1}{4}\pi$ (j) $r = \tfrac{1}{2}, \theta = -\tfrac{1}{2}\pi$

4. (a) $y = 0, x$ arbitrary (b) $x > 0, y = 0$ (c) All $x$ and $y$ (d) $x = 0$, $y$ arbitrary; or $y = 0, x$ arbitrary (e) $x = 1, y = 0$ (f) $x = 1, y = 0$

## 9.10 Exercises (page 371)

1. (a) $i$ (b) $-2i$ (c) $-3$ (d) $1$ (e) $1 + i$ (f) $(1 + i)/\sqrt{2}$
   (g) $\sqrt{2}\,i$ (h) $-i$

2. (a) $y = 0, x$ arbitrary (b) $x = y = 0$ (c) $x = 0, y = (2n + 1)\pi$, where $n$ is any integer (d) $x = 1, y = \tfrac{1}{2}\pi + 2n\pi$, where $n$ is any integer

3. (b) $z = 2n\pi i$, where $n$ is any integer

6. $c_{-k} = \tfrac{1}{2}(a_{-k} + ib_{-k})$ for $k = 1, 2, \ldots, n$

8. (c) $\tfrac{1}{2}\sqrt{3} + \tfrac{1}{2}i, \; -\tfrac{1}{2}\sqrt{3} + \tfrac{1}{2}i, \; -i$
   (d) $a + bi, \; -a - bi, \; -b + ai, \; b - ai$, where $a = \tfrac{1}{2}\sqrt{2 + \sqrt{2}}$ and $b = \tfrac{1}{2}\sqrt{2 - \sqrt{2}}$
   (e) $a - bi, \; -a + bi, \; b + ai, \; -b - ai$, where $a$ and $b$ are as in (d)

11. (a) $1, e^{-\pi/2}, e^{-\pi}$ (c) $-\pi < \arg(z_1) + \arg(z_2) \le \pi$

13. $B = A/(b - \omega^2 + a\omega i)$

*Chapter* 10

**10.4  Exercises (page 382)**

| | | | | | | | | |
|---|---|---|---|---|---|---|---|---|
| 1. | (a) | Converges | (b) | 0 | 12. | (a) | Converges | (b) $\frac{1}{3}$ |
| 2. | (a) | Converges | (b) | $-1$ | 13. | (a) | Converges | (b) 0 |
| 3. | (a) | Diverges | | | 14. | (a) | Converges | (b) 0 |
| 4. | (a) | Converges | (b) | $\frac{1}{5}$ | 15. | (a) | Converges | (b) 0 |
| 5. | (a) | Converges | (b) | 0 | 16. | (a) | Converges | (b) 0 |
| 6. | (a) | Diverges | | | 17. | (a) | Converges | (b) $e^2$ |
| 7. | (a) | Converges | (b) | 0 | 18. | (a) | Diverges | |
| 8. | (a) | Diverges | | | 19. | (a) | Converges | (b) 0 |
| 9. | (a) | Converges | (b) | 1 | 20. | (a) | Diverges | |
| 10. | (a) | Diverges | | | 21. | (a) | Converges | (b) 0 |
| 11. | (a) | Converges | (b) | 0 | 22. | (a) | Diverges | |

23. $N > 1/\epsilon$
24. $N > 1/\epsilon$
25. $N > 1/\epsilon$
26. $N > 1/\epsilon$
27. $N > \sqrt{2/\epsilon}$
28. $N > \dfrac{\log \epsilon}{\log (9/10)}$

34. (c)  Let $s_n = \dfrac{b-a}{n} \sum_{k=0}^{n-1} f\left(a + k\,\dfrac{b-a}{n}\right)$, and define $t_n$ similarly as a sum from 1 to $n$. Both

    sequences $\{s_n\}$ and $\{t_n\}$ converge to the integral $\int_a^b f(x)\,dx$.

**10.9  Exercises (page 391)**

22. (a) 1    (b) $2e - 3$    (c) $e + 1$
23. (b) 5
24. (a) Identical    (b) Not identical    (c) Not identical    (d) Identical

**\*10.10  Exercises on decimal expansions (page 393)**

1. $\frac{4}{9}$
2. $\frac{51}{99}$
3. $\frac{200}{99}$
4. $\frac{41}{333}$
5. $\frac{1}{7}$

**10.14  Exercises (page 398)**

| | | | |
|---|---|---|---|
| 1. | Divergent | 8. | Convergent |
| 2. | Convergent | 9. | Divergent |
| 3. | Convergent | 10. | Convergent |
| 4. | Convergent | 11. | Divergent |
| 5. | Convergent | 12. | Convergent |
| 6. | Convergent | 13. | Divergent |
| 7. | Convergent | 14. | Convergent |

15. Convergent for $s > 1$;  divergent for $s \leq 1$
16. Convergent
17. Convergent
18. Convergent

### 10.16   Exercises (page 402)

1.  Convergent
2.  Convergent
3.  Convergent
4.  Divergent
5.  Divergent
6.  Divergent
7.  Divergent
8.  Convergent
9.  Convergent
10. Divergent
11. Convergent
12. Divergent
13. Convergent
14. Convergent if $0 < r < 1$, or when $x = k\pi$, $k$ any integer

### 10.20   Exercises (page 409)

1.  Conditionally convergent
2.  Conditionally convergent
3.  Divergent for $s \le 0$; conditionally convergent for $0 < s \le 1$; absolutely convergent for $s > 1$
4.  Absolutely convergent
5.  Absolutely convergent
6.  Absolutely convergent
7.  Divergent
8.  Divergent
9.  Divergent
10. Conditionally convergent
11. Absolutely convergent
12. Divergent
13. Absolutely convergent
14. Absolutely convergent
15. Divergent
16. Absolutely convergent
17. Absolutely convergent
18. Absolutely convergent
19. Conditionally convergent
20. Conditionally convergent
21. Divergent
22. Conditionally convergent
23. Divergent
24. Conditionally convergent
25. Divergent for $s \le 0$; conditionally convergent for $0 < s \le 1$; absolutely convergent for $s > 1$
26. Absolutely convergent
27. Absolutely convergent
28. Divergent
29. Absolutely convergent
30. Absolutely convergent
31. Absolutely convergent
32. Absolutely convergent
33. $z = 0$
34. All $z$
35. All $z$ satisfying $|z| < 3$
36. All $z$
37. All $z$ except negative integers
38. All $z \ne 1$ satisfying $|z| \le 1$
39. $|z| < e^{-1/85}$
40. All $z$
41. All $z \ne 0$ satisfying $0 \le |z - 1| \le 1$
42. All $z \ne -1$ satisfying $|2z + 3| \le 1$
43. All $z = x + iy$ with $x \ge 0$
44. All $z$ satisfying $|2 + 1/z| > 1$
45. All $z$ satisfying $|2 + 1/z| > 1$
46. All $z \ne 0$
47. $|x - k\pi| \le \pi/4$, $k$ any integer
48. $|x - k\pi| \le \pi/6$, $k$ any integer

### 10.22   Miscellaneous review exercises (page 414)

1.  (a)  0
    (b)  Converges if $c \le 1$; limit is 0 if $c < 1$; limit is 1 if $c = 1$; diverges if $c > 1$
2.  (a)  1     (b)  The larger of $a$ and $b$
3.  $\frac{1}{3}a_1 + \frac{2}{3}a_2$
4.  $\frac{1}{2}(1 + \sqrt{5})$
5.  0
7.  Divergent
8.  Convergent if $s < \frac{1}{2}$; divergent if $s \ge \frac{1}{2}$
9.  Convergent

10. Divergent
11. Divergent
14. $c \leq 3$
15. $a \geq 3$
17. When $a \geq -1$, limit is $\dfrac{a+1}{a+2}$ ; when $a \leq -1$, limit is $0$

**10.24  Exercises (page 420)**

1. Divergent
2. Convergent
3. Convergent
4. Convergent
5. Convergent

6. Convergent
7. Convergent
8. Convergent
9. Divergent
10. Convergent if $s > 1$; divergent if $s \leq 1$

11. $C = \frac{1}{2}$; integral has value $\frac{1}{4} \log \frac{5}{4}$
12. $C = \frac{1}{2}$; integral has value $\frac{1}{4} \log \frac{8}{3}$
13. $C = \frac{1}{2}\sqrt{2}$; integral has value $\dfrac{3}{\sqrt{2}} \log \sqrt{2}$
14. $a = b = 2e - 2$
15. $a = 1$;  $b = 1 - \dfrac{\sqrt{3}}{\pi}$
16. (b)  Both diverge
17. (c)  Diverges

## Chapter 11

**11.7  Exercises (page 430)**

1. $r = 2$;  convergent for $|z| < 2$
2. $r = 2$;  convergent for $|z| \leq 2, z \neq 2$
3. $r = 2$;  convergent for $|z + 3| \leq 2, z \neq -1$
4. $r = \frac{1}{2}$;  convergent for $|z| \leq \frac{1}{2}$
5. $r = \frac{1}{2}$;  convergent for $|z| < \frac{1}{2}$
6. $r = e$;  convergent for $|z| < e$
7. $r = 1$;  convergent for $|z + 1| \leq 1$
8. $r = +\infty$
9. $r = 4$;  convergent for $|z| < 4$
10. $r = 1$;  convergent for $|z| < 1$
11. $r = 1$
12. $r = 1/e$
13. $r = +\infty$ if $a = k\pi$, $k$ an integer;  $r = 1$ if $a \neq k\pi$
14. $r = e^{-a}$
15. $r = \max(a, b)$
16. $r = \min(1/a, 1/b)$

**11.13  Exercises (page 438)**

1. $|x| < 1$;  $1/(1 + x^2)$
2. $|x| < 3$;  $1/(3 - x)$
3. $|x| < 1$;  $x/(1 - x)^2$
4. $|x| < 1$;  $-x/(1 + x)^2$

5. $|x| < \frac{1}{2}$; $\dfrac{1}{1 + 2x} + \dfrac{\log(1 + 2x)}{2x}$

6. $-\frac{1}{2} \le x < \frac{1}{2}$; $-\log(1 - 2x)$

7. $-2 \le x < 2$; $\dfrac{2}{x} \arctan \dfrac{x}{2}$

8. All $x$; $e^{-x^3}$

9. All $x$; $x^{-3}(e^x - 1 - x - \frac{1}{2}x^2)$ if $x \ne 0$, $0$ if $x = 0$

10. All $x$; $\dfrac{e^{x-1} - x}{(x - 1)^2}$ if $x \ne 1$; $\frac{1}{2}$ if $x = 1$

22. $-\dfrac{\sqrt{2}\, 2^{97}}{98!}$

23. $a_0 = 4\sqrt{2}$, $a_1 = 0$, $a_2 = 5\sqrt{2}$, $a_3 = 0$, $a_4 = \frac{15}{8}\sqrt{2}$

## 11.16  Exercises (page 443)

1. $a_{n+2} = \dfrac{(n + 3)(n - 2)}{(n + 2)(n + 1)} a_n$ for $n \ge 0$; $f(x) = 1 - 3x^2$

2. $a_{n+2} = \dfrac{(n + 4)(n - 3)}{(n + 2)(n + 1)} a_n$ for $n \ge 0$; $f(x) = 2x - \dfrac{10}{3} x^3$

3. All $x$

4. All $x$

5. All $x$; $a = 1$, $b = 0$

6. All $x$; $f(x) = e^{x^2}$

7. All $x$; $f(x) = e^x - x - 1$

8. All $x$; $f(x) = \cos 2x$

9. All $x$; $f(x) = x + \sinh 3x$

12. $y = 1 + x + x^2 + \frac{4}{3}x^3 + \cdots$

13. $y = x + \frac{1}{4}x^4 + \frac{1}{14}x^7 + \frac{23}{1120}x^{10} + \cdots$

14. $y = \frac{1}{2}x^2 + \frac{1}{12}x^5 + \frac{1}{060}x^8 + \frac{7}{8800}x^{11} + \cdots$

15. $y = \displaystyle\sum_{n=0}^{\infty} \dfrac{\alpha^n x^n}{n!}$

16. $y = c_0\left(1 + \displaystyle\sum_{n=1}^{\infty} \dfrac{x^{3n}}{(2 \cdot 3)(5 \cdot 6) \cdots [(3n - 1) \cdot (3n)]}\right)$

$\qquad\qquad + c_1\left(x + \displaystyle\sum_{n=1}^{\infty} \dfrac{x^{3n+1}}{(3 \cdot 4)(6 \cdot 7) \cdots [(3n) \cdot (3n + 1)]}\right)$

17. $y = c_0\left(1 + \displaystyle\sum_{n=1}^{\infty} \dfrac{(-1)^n x^{2n}}{2 \cdot 4 \cdots (2n)}\right) + c_1 \displaystyle\sum_{n=1}^{\infty} \dfrac{(-1)^{n+1} x^{2n-1}}{1 \cdot 3 \cdots (2n - 1)}$

18. $a_1 = -1$, $a_2 = 0$, $a_3 = \frac{2}{3}$; $f(x) = (x + 1)e^{-2x}$

19. $a_5 = 0$, $a_6 = -\dfrac{7}{8!}$; $f(x) = \dfrac{\sin x}{x} + \dfrac{\cos x - 1}{x^2}$ if $x \ne 0$; $f(0) = \frac{1}{2}$; $f(\pi) = -2/\pi^2$

20. (c) $\sqrt{2} = 1.4142135623$

21. (b) $\sqrt{3} = 1.732050807568877$

Chapter 12

**12.4 Exercises (page 450)**

1. (a) $(5, 0, 9)$ (b) $(-3, 6, 3)$ (c) $(3, -1, 4)$ (d) $(-7, 24, 21)$ (e) $(0, 0, 0)$
5. $x = \frac{1}{5}(3c_1 - c_2), \quad y = \frac{1}{5}(2c_2 - c_1)$
6. (a) $(x + z, x + y + z, x + y)$ (c) $x = 2, \quad y = 1, \quad z = -1$
7. (a) $(x + 2z, x + y + z, x + y + z)$ (b) One example: $x = -2, \quad y = z = 1$
8. (a) $(x + z, x + y + z, x + y, y)$ (c) $x = -1, \quad y = 4, \quad z = 2$
12. The diagonals of a parallelogram bisect each other

**12.8 Exercises (page 456)**

1. (a) $-6$ (b) $2$ (c) $6$ (d) $0$ (e) $4$
2. (a) $(A \cdot B)C = (21, 28, -35)$ (b) $A \cdot (B + C) = 64$ (c) $(A + B) \cdot C = 72$

   (d) $A(B \cdot C) = (30, 60, -105)$ (e) $A/(B \cdot C) = \left(\dfrac{2}{15}, \dfrac{4}{15}, \dfrac{-7}{15}\right)$

5. One example: $(1, -5, -3)$
6. One example: $x = -2, \quad y = 1$
7. $C = \frac{4}{9}(-1, -2, 2), \quad D = \frac{1}{9}(22, -1, 10)$

8. $C = \frac{1}{11}(1, 2, 3, 4, 5), \quad D = \left(\dfrac{5}{11}, \dfrac{7}{44}, \dfrac{1}{33}, \dfrac{-5}{88}, \dfrac{-7}{55}\right)$

9. (a) $\sqrt{74}$ (b) $\sqrt{14}$ (c) $\sqrt{53}$ (d) $5$
10. (a) $(1, -1)$ or $(-1, 1)$ (b) $(1, 1)$ or $(-1, -1)$ (c) $(3, 2)$ or $(-3, -2)$
    (d) $(b, -a)$ or $(-b, a)$

11. (a) $\dfrac{1}{\sqrt{42}}(4, -1, 5)$ (b) $\dfrac{1}{\sqrt{14}}(-2, -3, 1)$ (c) $\dfrac{1}{\sqrt{2}}(1, 0, 1)$

    (d) $\dfrac{1}{\sqrt{42}}(-5, -4, -1)$ (e) $\dfrac{1}{\sqrt{42}}(-1, -5, 4)$

12. $A$ and $B$, $C$ and $D$, $C$ and $E$, $D$ and $E$
13. (a) $(2, -1)$ and $(-2, 1)$ (b) $(2, 1)$ and $(-2, -1)$ (c) $(1, 2)$ and $(-1, -2)$
    (d) $(1, 2)$ and $(-1, -2)$
14. One example: $C = (8, 1, 1)$
15. One example: $C = (1, -5, -3)$
16. $P = \frac{11}{25}(3, 4), \quad Q = \frac{2}{25}(-4, 3)$
17. $P = \frac{5}{2}(1, 1, 1, 1), \quad Q = \frac{1}{2}(-3, -1, 1, 3)$

18. $\pm \dfrac{1}{\sqrt{2}}(0, 1, 1)$

20. The sum of the squares of the sides of any parallelogram is equal to the sum of the squares of the diagonals.
22. $4; \quad 12\sqrt{2}$

23. $C = \frac{1}{11}(1, 2, 3, 4, 5), \quad D = \dfrac{1}{11}\left(10, \dfrac{7}{2}, \dfrac{2}{3}, \dfrac{-5}{4}, \dfrac{-14}{5}\right)$

24. $C = tA, \quad D = B - tA, \quad$ where $\quad t = (A \cdot B)/(A \cdot A)$

**12.11 Exercises (page 460)**

1. $\frac{11}{9}B$
2. $\frac{5}{2}B$

3. (a) $\dfrac{6}{7}, \dfrac{3}{7}, \dfrac{-2}{7}$  (b) $\left(\dfrac{6}{7}, \dfrac{3}{7}, \dfrac{-2}{7}\right)$ and $\left(\dfrac{-6}{7}, \dfrac{-3}{7}, \dfrac{2}{7}\right)$

5. $0, \sqrt{\tfrac{35}{41}}, \sqrt{\tfrac{6}{41}}$

6. $7\pi/8$

8. $\pi/6$

9. $0$

10. (b) Equation holds for all $x$ and $y$ if $\cos\theta = 1$; if $\cos\theta \neq 1$ the only solution is $x = y = 0$

14. All except (b).

17. (c) All except Theorem 12.4(a).

18. (a) All

## 12.15 Exercises (page 467)

1. (a) $x = y = \tfrac{1}{2}$  (b) $x = -\tfrac{1}{2}, \; y = \tfrac{1}{2}$  (c) $x = 4, \; y = -1$
   (d) $x = 1, \; y = 6$

2. $x = \tfrac{1}{4}, \; y = \tfrac{7}{8}$

3. $x = 3, \; y = -4$

7. All $t \neq 0$

9. (c) $7i - 4(i + j)$

10. (b) $j = B - A, \quad k = \tfrac{1}{3}(C - B)$  (c) $\tfrac{1}{3}(15A - 14B + 5C)$

11. $\{A\}, \{B\}, \{C\}, \{D\}, \{A, B\}, \{A, C\}, \{A, D\}, \{B, C\}, \{C, D\}$

12. (a) Independent  (b) One example: $D = A$  (c) One example: $E = (0, 0, 0, 1)$
    (d) For the choice $E = (0, 0, 0, 1)$, we have $X = 2A + B - C + 3E$

13. (c) $t = 0, \sqrt{2}, -\sqrt{2}$

14. (a) $\{(1, 0, 1, 0), (0, 1, 0, 1), (2, 0, -1, 0)\}$  (b) The set given  (c) The set given

17. $\{(0, 1, 1), (1, 1, 1), (0, 1, 0)\}, \quad \{(0, 1, 1), (1, 1, 1), (0, 0, 1)\}$

18. $\{(1, 1, 1, 1), (0, 1, 1, 1), (0, 0, 1, 1), (0, 0, 0, 1)\}$,
    $\{(1, 1, 1, 1), (0, 1, 1, 1), (0, 1, 0, 0), (0, 0, 1, 0)\}$

19. $L(U) = L(T) = L(S)$

20. One example: $A = \{E_1, \ldots, E_n\}, \quad B = \{E_1 + E_2, E_2 + E_n, \ldots, E_{n-1} + E_n, E_n + E_1\}$

## 12.17 Exercises (page 470)

1. (a) $-1 - i$  (b) $-1 + i$  (c) $1 - i$  (d) $-1 + i$  (e) $-1 - i$
   (f) $2 - i$  (g) $-i$  (h) $-1 + 2i$  (i) $-3 - 2i$  (j) $2i$

2. One example: $(1 + i, -5 - 3i, 1 - 3i)$

8. $\pi/3$

9. $3A - B + 2C$

## Chapter 13

## 13.5 Exercises (page 477)

1. (b), (d), and (e)

2. (a) and (e)

3. (c), (d), and (e)

4. (b), (e), and (f)

5. (a) No  (b) No  (c) No

6. $A, B, C, D, F$ are collinear

7. Intersect at $(5, 9, 13)$

8. (b) No

9. (a) $9t^2 + 8t + 9$  (b) $\tfrac{1}{3}\sqrt{65}$

## 13.8 Exercises (page 482)

1. (c) and (e)
2. (a), (b), and (c)
3. (a) $x = 1 + t$, $y = 2 + s + t$, $z = 1 + 4t$
   (b) $x = s + t$, $y = 1 + s$, $z = s + 4t$
4. (a) $(1, 2, 0)$ and $(2, -3, -3)$   (b) $M = \{(1, 2, 0) + s(1, 1, 2) + t(-2, 4, 1)\}$
6. (a), (b), and (c) $x - 2y + z = -3$
7. (a) $(0, -2, -1)$ and $(-1, -2, 2)$
   (b) $M = \{(0, -2, -1) + s(-1, 0, 3) + t(3, 3, 6)\}$
8. Two examples: $(-5, 2, 6)$ and $(-14, 3, 17)$
9. (a) Yes   (b) Two examples: $(1, 0, -1)$ and $(-1, 0, 1)$
10. $(-2, \frac{5}{2}, -\frac{7}{2})$
11. (a), (b) and (c) No
13. $x - y = -1$

## 13.11 Exercises (page 487)

1. (a) $(-2, 3, -1)$   (b) $(4, -5, 3)$   (c) $(4, -4, 2)$   (d) $(8, 10, 4)$
   (e) $(8, 3, -7)$   (f) $(10, 11, 5)$   (g) $(-2, -8, -12)$   (h) $(2, -2, 0)$
   (i) $(-2, 0, 4)$

2. (a) $\pm \dfrac{1}{\sqrt{26}}(-4, 3, 1)$   (b) $\pm -\dfrac{1}{\sqrt{2054}}(-41, -18, 7)$   (c) $\pm \dfrac{1}{\sqrt{6}}(1, 2, 1)$

3. (a) $\frac{15}{2}$   (b) $\frac{3}{2}\sqrt{35}$   (c) $\frac{1}{2}\sqrt{3}$
4. $8i + j - 2k$
6. (b) $\cos \theta$ is negative   (c) $\sqrt{5}$
9. (a) One solution is $B = -i - 3k$   (b) $i - j - k$ is the only solution
11. (a) Three possibilities; $D = B + C - A = (0, 0, 2)$, $D = A + C - B = (4, -2, 2)$,
    $D = A + B - C = (-2, 2, 0)$   (b) $\frac{1}{2}\sqrt{6}$
12. $-4$; $8\sqrt{3}$; $-\frac{1}{2}\sqrt{3}$

## 13.14 Exercises (page 491)

1. (a) 96   (b) 27   (c) $-84$
2. 0, $\sqrt{2}$, $-\sqrt{2}$
3. 2
6. (a) $(2b - 1)i + bj + ck$, where $b$ and $c$ are arbitrary   (b) $-\frac{1}{5}i + \frac{2}{5}j$
11. $-3i + 2j + 5k$
14. (b) 2
15. (b) $\sqrt{2005/41}$
17. $x = 1$, $y = -1$, $z = 2$
18. $x = 1$, $y = -1$, $z = 2$
19. $x = 1$, $y = 4$, $z = 1$

## 13.17 Exercises (page 496)

1. (a) $(-7, 2, -2)$   (b) $-7x + 2y - 2z = 0$   (c) $-7x + 2y - 2z = -9$
2. (a) $(\frac{1}{3}, \frac{2}{3}, -\frac{2}{3})$   (b) $-7, -\frac{7}{2}, \frac{7}{2}$   (c) $\frac{7}{3}$   (d) $(-\frac{7}{9}, -\frac{14}{9}, \frac{14}{9})$
3. $3x - y + 2z = -5$; $9/\sqrt{14}$
4. (b) $\frac{19}{18}\sqrt{6}$
5. (a) $(1, 2, -2)$   (b) $x + 2y - 2z = 5$   (c) $\frac{5}{3}$
6. $10x - 3y - 7z + 17 = 0$
7. Two angles: $\pi/3$ and $2\pi/3$

8. $x + 2y + 9z + 55 = 0$

9. $X(t) = (2, 1, -3) + t(4, -3, 1)$

10. (b) $N = (1, 3, -2)$     (c) $t = 1$     (d) $2x + 3y + 2z + 15 = 0$
    (e) $x + 3y - 2z + 19 = 0$

11. $x + \sqrt{2}\,y + z = 2 + \sqrt{2}$

12. 6

13. $\dfrac{1}{\sqrt{122}}\,(7, -8, -3)$

14. $x - y + z = 2$

15. $(\frac{3}{2}, 0, \frac{1}{2})$

17. $X(t) = (1, 2, 3) + t(1, -2, 1)$

19. (b) $P = -\frac{1}{25}(5, -14, 2)$

## 13.21  Exercises (page 503)

3. $r = ed/(1 - e\sin\theta)$;   $r = -ed/(1 + e\sin\theta)$

4. $e = 1$,  $d = 2$

5. $e = \frac{1}{2}$,  $d = 6$

6. $e = \frac{1}{3}$,  $d = 6$

7. $e = 2$,  $d = 1$

8. $e = 2$,  $d = 2$

9. $e = 1$,  $d = 4$

10. $d = 5$,  $r = 25/(10 + 3\cos\theta + 4\sin\theta)$

11. $d = 5$,  $r = 25/(5 + 4\cos\theta + 3\sin\theta)$

12. $d = \frac{1}{2}\sqrt{2}$,  $r = 1/(\cos\theta + \sin\theta + \frac{1}{2}\sqrt{2})$,  $r = 1/(\cos\theta + \sin\theta - \frac{1}{2}\sqrt{2})$

13. (a) $r = 1.5 \times 10^8/(1 + \cos\theta)$;  $7.5 \times 10^7$ miles   (b) $r = 5 \times 10^7/(1 - \cos\theta)$;
    $2.5 \times 10^7$ miles

## 13.24  Exercises (page 508)

1. Center at $(0, 0)$;  foci at $(\pm 8, 0)$;  vertices at $(\pm 10, 0)$;  $e = \frac{4}{5}$

2. Center at $(0, 0)$;  foci at $(0, \pm 8)$;  vertices at $(0, \pm 10)$;  $e = \frac{4}{5}$

3. Center at $(2, -3)$;  foci at $(2 \pm \sqrt{7}, -3)$;  vertices at $(6, -3), (-2, -3)$;  $e = \sqrt{7}/4$

4. Center at $(0, 0)$;  foci at $(\pm \frac{4}{3}, 0)$;  vertices at $(\pm \frac{5}{3}, 0)$;  $e = \frac{4}{5}$

5. Center at $(0, 0)$;  foci at $(\pm \sqrt{3}/6, 0)$;  vertices at $(\pm\sqrt{3}/3, 0)$;  $e = \frac{1}{2}$

6. Center at $(-1, -2)$;  foci at $(-1, 1), (-1, -5)$;  vertices at $(-1, 3), (-1, -7)$;  $e = \frac{3}{5}$

7. $7x^2 + 16y^2 = 7$

8. $\dfrac{(x + 3)^2}{16} + \dfrac{(y - 4)^2}{9} = 1$

9. $\dfrac{(x + 3)^2}{9} + \dfrac{(y - 4)^2}{16} = 1$

10. $\dfrac{(x + 4)^2}{9} + (y - 2)^2 = 1$

11. $\dfrac{(x - 8)^2}{25} + \dfrac{(y + 2)^2}{9} = 1$

12. $\dfrac{(x - 2)^2}{16} + \dfrac{(y - 1)^2}{4} = 1$

13. Center at $(0, 0)$;  foci at $(\pm 2\sqrt{41}, 0)$;  vertices at $(\pm 10, 0)$;  $e = \sqrt{41}/5$

14. Center at $(0, 0)$;  foci at $(0, \pm 2\sqrt{41})$;  vertices at $(0, \pm 10)$;  $e = \sqrt{41}/5$

15. Center at $(-3, 3)$;  foci at $(-3 \pm \sqrt{5}, 3)$;  vertices at $(-1, 3), (-5, 3)$;  $e = \sqrt{5}/2$

16. Center at $(0, 0)$;   foci at $(\pm 5, 0)$;   vertices at $(\pm 4, 0)$;   $e = 5/4$
17. Center at $(0, 0)$;   foci at $(0, \pm 3)$;   vertices at $(0, \pm 2)$;   $e = \frac{3}{2}$
18. Center at $(1, -2)$;   foci at $(1 \pm \sqrt{13}, -2)$; vertices at $(3, -2), (-1, -2)$;   $e = \frac{1}{2}\sqrt{13}$
19. $\dfrac{x^2}{4} - \dfrac{y^2}{12} = 1$
20. $y^2 - x^2 = 1$
21. $\dfrac{x^2}{4} - \dfrac{y^2}{16} = 1$
22. $(y - 4)^2 - \dfrac{(x + 1)^2}{3} = 1$
23. $\dfrac{8(y + 3)^2}{27} - \dfrac{5(x - 2)^2}{27} = 1$
24. $\pm\sqrt{\frac{23}{3}}$
25. $4x^2 - y^2 = 11$
26. Vertex at $(0, 0)$;   directrix $x = 2$;   axis $y = 0$
27. Vertex at $(0, 0)$;   directrix $x = -\frac{3}{4}$;   axis $y = 0$
28. Vertex at $(\frac{1}{2}, 1)$;   directrix $x = -\frac{5}{2}$;   axis $y = 1$
29. Vertex at $(0, 0)$;   directrix $y = -\frac{3}{2}$;   axis $x = 0$
30. Vertex at $(0, 0)$;   directrix $y = 2$;   axis $x = 0$
31. Vertex at $(-2, -\frac{9}{4})$;   directrix $y = -\frac{13}{4}$;   axis $x = -2$
32. $x^2 = -y$
33. $y^2 = 8x$
34. $(x + 4)^2 = -8(y - 3)$
35. $(y + 1)^2 = 5(x - \frac{7}{4})$
36. $(x - \frac{3}{2})^2 = 2(y + \frac{1}{8})$
37. $(y - 3)^2 = -8(x - 1)$
38. $x^2 - 4xy + 4y^2 + 40x + 20y - 100 = 0$

## 13.25   Miscellaneous exercises on conic sections (page 509)

3. $B > 0$,   $A = \frac{1}{2}(1 + \sqrt{5})B$
4. $\frac{2}{3}bh$
5. $16\pi$
6. (a) $\frac{8}{3}$   (b) $2\pi$   (c) $48\pi/5$
7. $x^2/12 + y^2/16 = 1$
8. $x^2 - 2xy + y^2 - 2x - 2y = 1$
9. $y^2 - 4x^2 - 4y + 4x = 0$
10. (a)   $e = \sqrt{2/(p + 2)}$;   foci at $(\sqrt{2}, 0)$ and $(-\sqrt{2}, 0)$   (b)   $6x^2 - 3y^2 = 4$
15. (b)   $y = Cx^2$,   $C \neq 0$
16. $(4, 8)$
17. (a)   $x = \frac{4}{3}a$   (b)   $27pq^2 = 4a^3$
18. $(x - \frac{2}{5})^2 + (y - \frac{4}{5})^2 = \frac{4}{5}$

## *Chapter* 14

## 14.4   Exercises (page 516)

1. $F'(t) = (1, 2t, 3t^2 + 4t^3)$;   $F''(t) = (0, 2, 6t, 12t^2)$
2. $F'(t) = (-\sin t, \sin 2t, 2\cos 2t, \sec^2 t)$;   $F''(t) = (-\cos t, 2\cos 2t, -4\sin 2t, 2\sec^2 t \tan t)$
3. $F'(t) = ((1 - t^2)^{-1/2}, -(1 - t^2)^{-1/2})$;   $F''(t) = (t(1 + t^2)^{-3/2}, -t(1 + t^2)^{-3/2})$

4. $F'(t) = (2e^t, 3e^t); \quad F''(t) = (2e^t, 3e^t)$

5. $F'(t) = (\sinh t, 2\cosh 2t, -3e^{-3t}); \quad F''(t) = (\cosh t, 4\sinh 2t, 9e^{-3t})$

6. $F'(t) = (2t/(1 + t^2), 1/(1 + t^2), -2t/(1 + t^2));$
   $F''(t) = ((2 - 2t^2)/(1 + t^2)^2, -2t/(1 + t^2)^2, (6t^2 - 2)/(1 + t^2)^3)$

8. $(\frac{1}{2}, \frac{2}{3}, e - 1)$

9. $(1 - \frac{1}{2}\sqrt{2}, \frac{1}{2}\sqrt{2}, \log \frac{1}{2}\sqrt{2})$

10. $\left( \log \dfrac{1 + e}{2}, 1 - \log \dfrac{1 + e}{2} \right)$

11. $(1, e - 2, 1 - 2/e)$

12. $0$

15. $G'(t) = F(t) \times F''(t)$

20. $F(t) = \frac{1}{6}t^3 A + \frac{1}{2}t^2 B + tC + D$

22. $F''(1) = A, \quad F(3) = (6 + 3\log 3)A$

23. $F(x) = e^x(x + 1)A - eA$

## 14.7 Exercises (page 524)

1. $v(t) = (3 - 3t^2)i + 6tj + (3 + 3t^2)k; \quad a(t) = -6ti + 6j + 6tk; \quad v(t) = 3\sqrt{2}(1 + t^2)$

2. $v(t) = -\sin t\, i + \cos t\, j + e^t k; \quad a(t) = -\cos t\, i - \sin t\, j + e^t k; \quad v(t) = (1 + e^{2t})^{1/2}$

3. $v(t) = 3(\cos t - t\sin t)i + 3(\sin t + t\cos t)j + 4k; \quad a(t) = -3(2\sin t + t\cos t)i + 3(2\cos t - t\sin t)j; \quad v(t) = (9t^2 + 25)^{1/2}$

4. $v(t) = (1 - \cos t)i + \sin t\, j + 2\cos \dfrac{t}{2} k; \quad a(t) = \sin t\, i + \cos t\, j - \sin \dfrac{t}{2} k; \quad v(t) = 2$

5. $v(t) = 6ti + 6t^2 j + 3k; \quad a(t) = 6i + 12tj; \quad v(t) = 6t^2 + 3$

6. $v(t) = i + \cos t\, j + \sin t\, k; \quad a(t) = -\sin t\, j + \cos t\, k; \quad v(t) = \sqrt{2}$

9. $A = ab\omega^3, \quad B = a^2\omega^3$

11. (b) $8e^{4t}/\cos^2 \theta$

15. (a) $x(t) = 4\cos 2t, \quad y(t) = 3\sin 2t$ \quad (b) $x^2/16 + y^2/9 = 1$

16. $3T/4$

## 14.9 Exercises (page 528)

1. (a) $T = \frac{1}{10}\sqrt{2}(-3i + 4j + 5k); \quad N = -\frac{4}{5}i - \frac{3}{5}j$ \quad (b) $a = 12\sqrt{2}\, T + 6N$

2. (a) $T = -(1 + e^{2\pi})^{-1/2}j + e^\pi(1 + e^{2\pi})^{-1/2}k; \quad N = \dfrac{(1 + e^{2\pi})i + e^{2\pi}j + e^\pi k}{(1 + e^{2\pi})^{1/2}(1 + 2e^{2\pi})^{1/2}}$

   (b) $a = (1 + e^{2\pi})^{-1/2}[e^{2\pi}T + (1 + 2e^{2\pi})^{1/2}N]$

3. (a) $T = \frac{3}{5}i + \frac{4}{5}k; \quad N = j$ \quad (b) $a = 6N$

4. (a) $T = i; \quad N = -\frac{1}{2}\sqrt{2}(j + k);$ \quad (b) $a = \sqrt{2}\, N$

5. (a) $T = \frac{1}{3}(2i + 2j + k); \quad N = \frac{1}{3}(i + 2j - 2k)$ \quad (b) $a = 12T + 6N$

6. (a) $T = \frac{1}{2}\sqrt{2}\, i + \frac{1}{2}j + \frac{1}{2}k; \quad N = -\frac{1}{2}\sqrt{2}j + \frac{1}{2}\sqrt{2}\, k$ \quad (b) $a = N$

9. Counter example for (b) and (d): motion on a helix

11. One example: $r(t) = 2\int e^{2t}\cos t\, dt\, i + 2\int e^{2t}\sin t\, dt\, j + e^{2t}k; \quad v(t)$ makes a constant angle with $k$, but $a(t)$ is never zero nor parallel to $v(t)$

12. (a) Counterclockwise \quad (b) $3$ \quad (c) $2\pi/\sqrt{3}$

13. $x^2/3 + y^2/4 = 1$

14. $y^2 = 4x; \quad y^2 = 8 - 4x$

15. (b) $\|A\| \|B\| \sin \theta$

## 14.13 Exercises (page 535)

1. $8a$

2. $\sqrt{2}(e^2 - 1)$

3. $2\pi^2 a$

4. $4(a^3 - b^3)/(ab)$

5. $2a\left(\cosh\dfrac{T}{2}\sqrt{\cosh T} - 1\right) - \sqrt{2}\,a\log\left(\dfrac{\sqrt{2}\cosh(T/2) + \sqrt{\cosh T}}{1 + \sqrt{2}}\right)$

6. $2\sqrt{2}\,\pi$

7. 50

8. $\sqrt{2}\log(1 + \sqrt{2})$

9. $|\omega|\sqrt{a^2 + b^2}\,(t_1 - t_0)$

10. $\int_c^d \sqrt{1 + [g'(y)]^2}\,dy$

11. $\dfrac{26\sqrt{13} - 16}{27}$

13. (a) $\displaystyle\int_0^1 \sqrt{1 + e^{2x}}\,dx$   (b) $\displaystyle\int_1^e \sqrt{2 + \dfrac{2}{t^2}}\,dt$

14. (c) $c\sinh\dfrac{2}{c}$

16. $f(x) = k\cosh\left(\dfrac{x}{k} + C\right)$,  or $f(x) = k$

19. $v(t) = 1 + 2t$;  3 units of time

## 14.15  Exercises (page 538)

1. (1) $\frac{1}{75}$   (2) $(1 + 2e^{2\pi})^{1/2}(1 + e^{2\pi})^{-3/2}$   (3) $\frac{6}{25}$   (4) $\frac{1}{4}\sqrt{2}$   (5) $\frac{2}{27}$   (6) $\frac{1}{2}$

3. $\dfrac{1}{\|B\|\sin\theta}$

4. (a) $x = z$

7. $\kappa = \|a\|/\|v\|^2$

9. $a = \frac{1}{4}$,  $b = 2$;  intersect at $(0, 0)$

10. Vertex at $-\frac{1}{2}\cos\theta\,A + \frac{1}{4}\cos^2\theta\,B$

11. (a) $\alpha(t) = \frac{1}{2}\pi - 5t^2$   (b) $v(t) = 5\sin 5t^2\,i + 5\cos 5t^2\,j$

12. $\sqrt{2}\,i + \sqrt{2}\,j$

## 14.19  Exercises (page 543)

1. $v(t) = u_r + tu_\theta$;  $a(t) = -tu_r + 2u_\theta$;  $\kappa(t) = (2 + t^2)(1 + t^2)^{-3/2}$

2. (a) $v(t) = u_r + tu_\theta + k$;  $a(t) = -tu_r + 2u_\theta$;  $\kappa(t) = (t^4 + 5t^2 + 8)^{1/2}(2 + t^2)^{-3/2}$
   (b) $\arccos\sqrt{2/(2 + t^2)}$

3. (b) $\frac{1}{2}\pi - t$

5. 32

6. (b) $L(c) = \dfrac{\sqrt{1 + c^2}}{c}(e^{2\pi c} - 1)$ if $c \neq 0$;  $L(0) = 2\pi$.   $a(c) = \dfrac{e^{4\pi c} - 1}{4c}$ if $c \neq 0$;  $a(0) = \pi$

7. (a) $3\pi/16$   (b) $2 + \frac{1}{3}\sqrt{3}\log(2 + \sqrt{3})$

8. $\frac{1}{2}\pi(\pi^2 + 1)^{1/2} + \frac{1}{2}\log(\pi + \sqrt{\pi^2 + 1})$

9. $\sqrt{2}\,(e^\pi - 1)$

10. 4

11. 8

13.  (a) $(\theta^2 + 1)^{3/2}/(\theta^2 + 2)$   (b) $\sqrt{2}\,e^\theta$   (c) $\frac{2}{3}\sqrt{2 + \sqrt{2}}$   (d) $\frac{2}{3}\sqrt{2}$

15.  $r = r_0 e^{-\theta \cot \alpha}$; target at origin, missile starts at $r = r_0$, $\theta = 0$; $\alpha$ denotes the angle, $0 < \alpha < \pi$, determined by $v$ and $-r$; for $0 < \alpha < \pi/2$ the path is a spiral for which $r \to 0$ as $\theta$ increases indefinitely; for $\alpha = \pi/2$ it is a circle about the origin; for $\pi/2 < \alpha < \pi$ it is a spiral for which $r$ increases indefinitely as $\theta$ increases indefinitely.

16.  Use as positive $x$-axis the line from position sighted four miles away to ground crew. Proceed three miles along this line (to allow for the possibility that the missile is returning to base) and then follow the spiral $r = e^{\theta/\sqrt{8}}$

17.  $\log \sqrt{x^2 + y^2} + \arctan (y/x) = C$

## 14.21  Miscellaneous review exercises (page 549)

1.  $\tan \alpha = \tan \theta/(2 + \tan^2 \theta)$
3.  $(c/m^2, 2c/m)$
4.  (a)  $y - y_0 = m(x - x_0) + c/m$;   tangent at $(x_0 + c/m^2, y_0 + 2c/m)$
     (b)  $y - y_0 = m(x - x_0) - cm^2$;   tangent at $(x_0 + 2cm, y_0 + cm^2)$
6.  $(y_1 - y_0)(y - y_0) = 2c(x + x_1 - 2x_0)$;   $x_1 y = 2y_1 x - x_1 y_1$;
     $(x_1 - x_0)(y - y_0) = 2(y_1 - y_0)(x - x_0) - (x_1 - x_0)(y_1 - y_0)$
7.  (a)  $(0, \frac{1}{2})$

     (b)  Write $Q = (0, b(x))$. If $f''(0) \neq 0$ then $b(x) \to f(0) + \dfrac{1}{f''(0)}$ as $x \to 0$.

     Otherwise, $|b(x)| \to +\infty$ as $x \to 0$.

8.  $r = \dfrac{1 + c}{2} \to \dfrac{1}{2}$ as $c \to 0$

13.  $(2, 1), (-2, -1)$
14.  $\frac{1}{2}\sqrt{2}$
15.  $3x^2 - y^2 = 3a^2$;   $\dfrac{A(r)}{r^3} \to \dfrac{1}{36a}$

21.  (a)  $f(\theta) = k \sin (\theta + C)$,   or $f(\theta) = k$
     (b)  $f(\theta) = Ce^{\theta/\sqrt{k^2 - 1}}$,   where $k^2 > 1$
     (c)  $f(\theta) = (2/k) \sec (\theta + C)$,   or $f(\theta) = 2/k$

## Chapter 15

## 15.5  Exercises (page 555)

| 1. | Yes | 8. | Yes | 15. | Yes | 22. | Yes |
|----|-----|----|-----|-----|-----|-----|-----|
| 2. | Yes | 9. | Yes | 16. | Yes | 23. | No |
| 3. | Yes | 10. | Yes | 17. | Yes | 24. | Yes |
| 4. | Yes | 11. | No | 18. | Yes | 25. | No |
| 5. | No | 12. | Yes | 19. | Yes | 26. | Yes |
| 6. | Yes | 13. | Yes | 20. | Yes | 27. | Yes |
| 7. | Yes | 14. | No | 21. | Yes | 28. | Yes |

31.  (a)  No   (b)  No   (c)  No   (d)  No

## 15.9  Exercises (page 560)

| 1. | Yes; 2 | 5. | Yes; 1 | 9. | Yes; 1 | 13. | Yes; $n$ |
|----|--------|----|--------|----|--------|-----|----------|
| 2. | Yes; 2 | 6. | No | 10. | Yes; 1 | 14. | Yes; $n$ |
| 3. | Yes; 2 | 7. | No | 11. | Yes; $n$ | 15. | Yes; $n$ |
| 4. | Yes; 2 | 8. | No | 12. | Yes; $n$ | 16. | Yes; $n$ |

17. Yes; $\dim = 1 + \frac{1}{2}n$ if $n$ is even, $\frac{1}{2}(n + 1)$ if $n$ is odd
18. Yes; $\dim = \frac{1}{2}n$ if $n$ is even, $\frac{1}{2}(n + 1)$ if $n$ is odd
19. Yes; $k + 1$
20. No
21. (a) $\dim = 3$    (b) $\dim = 3$    (c) $\dim = 2$    (d) $\dim = 2$
23. (a) If $a \neq 0$ and $b \neq 0$, set is independent, $\dim = 3$; if one of $a$ or $b$ is zero, set is dependent, $\dim = 2$    (b) Independent, $\dim = 2$    (c) If $a \neq 0$, independent, $\dim = 3$; if $a = 0$, dependent, $\dim = 2$    (d) Independent; $\dim = 3$    (e) Dependent; $\dim = 2$    (f) Independent; $\dim = 2$    (g) Independent; $\dim = 2$    (h) Dependent; $\dim = 2$    (i) Independent; $\dim = 2$    (j) Independent; $\dim = 2$

## 15.12 Exercises (page 566)

1. (a) No    (b) No    (c) No    (d) No    (e) Yes
8. (a) $\frac{1}{2}\sqrt{e^2 + 1}$    (b) $g(x) = b\left(x - \dfrac{e^2 + 1}{4}\right)$, $b$ arbitrary
10. (b) $\dfrac{(n + 1)(2n + 1)}{6n}\,a + \dfrac{n + 1}{2}\,b$    (c) $g(t) = a\left(t - \dfrac{2n + 1}{3n}\right)$, $a$ arbitrary
11. (c) 43    (d) $g(t) = a(1 - \frac{2}{3}t)$, $a$ arbitrary
12. (a) No    (b) No    (c) No    (d) No
13. (c) 1    (d) $e^2 - 1$
14. (c) $n!/2^{n+1}$

## 15.16 Exercises (page 576)

1. (a) and (b) $\frac{1}{3}\sqrt{3}\,(1, 1, 1)$,    $\frac{1}{6}\sqrt{6}\,(1, -2, 1)$
2. (a) $\frac{1}{2}\sqrt{2}\,(1, 1, 0, 0)$,    $\frac{1}{6}\sqrt{6}\,(-1, 1, 2, 0)$,    $\frac{1}{6}\sqrt{3}\,(1, -1, 1, 3)$
    (b) $\frac{1}{3}\sqrt{3}\,(1, 1, 0, 1)$,    $\dfrac{1}{\sqrt{42}}\,(1, -2, 6, 1)$
6. $\frac{2}{3} - \frac{1}{2}\log^2 3$
7. $e^2 - 1$
8. $\frac{1}{2}(e - e^{-1}) + \dfrac{3}{e}\,x$;    $1 - 7e^{-2}$
9. $\pi - 2\sin x$
10. $\frac{3}{4} - \frac{1}{4}x$

## Chapter 16

## 16.4 Exercises (page 582)

1. Linear; nullity 0, rank 2
2. Linear; nullity 0, rank 2
3. Linear; nullity 1, rank 1
4. Linear; nullity 1, rank 1
5. Nonlinear
6. Nonlinear
7. Nonlinear
8. Nonlinear
9. Linear; nullity 0, rank 2
10. Linear; nullity 0, rank 2
11. Linear; nullity 0, rank 2
12. Linear; nullity 0, rank 2
13. Nonlinear
14. Linear; nullity 0, rank 2
15. Nonlinear
16. Linear; nullity 0, rank 3
17. Linear; nullity 1, rank 2
18. Linear; nullity 0, rank 3
19. Nonlinear
20. Nonlinear
21. Nonlinear
22. Nonlinear
23. Linear; nullity 1, rank 2
24. Linear; nullity 0, rank $n + 1$

25. Linear;  nullity 1, rank infinite          26.  Linear;  nullity infinite, rank 2
27. Linear;  nullity 2, rank infinite
28. $N(T)$ is the set of constant sequences; $T(V)$ is the set of sequences with limit 0
29. (d) $\{1, \cos x, \sin x\}$ is a basis for $T(V)$; $\dim T(V) = 3$      (e)  $N(T) = S$      (f) If $T(f) =$
    $cf$ with $c \neq 0$, then $c \in T(V)$ so we have $f(x) = c_1 + c_2 \cos x + c_3 \sin x$; if $c_1 = 0$, then
    $c = \pi$ and $f(x) = c_1 \cos x + c_2 \sin x$, where $c_1$, $c_2$ are not both zero but otherwise arbitrary;
    if $c_1 \neq 0$, then $c = 2\pi$ and $f(x) = c_1$, where $c_1$ is nonzero but otherwise arbitrary.

## 16.8  Exercises (page 589)

3.  Yes;  $x = v$,  $y = u$
4.  Yes;  $x = u$,  $y = -v$
5.  No
6.  No
7.  No
8.  Yes;  $x = \log u$,  $y = \log v$
9.  No
10. Yes;  $x = u - 1$,  $y = v - 1$
11. Yes;  $x = \frac{1}{2}(v + u)$,  $y = \frac{1}{2}(v - u)$
12. Yes;  $x = \frac{1}{3}(v + u)$,  $y = \frac{1}{3}(2v - u)$
13. Yes;  $x = w$,  $y = v$,  $z = u$
14. No
15. Yes;  $x = u$,  $y = \frac{1}{2}v$,  $z = \frac{1}{3}w$
16. Yes;  $x = u$,  $y = v$,  $z = w - u - v$
17. Yes;  $x = u - 1$,  $y = v - 1$,  $z = w + 1$
18. Yes;  $x = u - 1$,  $y = v - 2$,  $z = w - 3$
19. Yes;  $x = u$,  $y = v - u$,  $z = w - v$
20. Yes;  $x = \frac{1}{2}(u - v + w)$,  $y = \frac{1}{2}(v - w + u)$;  $z = \frac{1}{2}(w - u + v)$
25. $(S + T)^2 = S^2 + ST + TS + T^2$;
    $(S + T)^3 = S^3 + TS^2 + STS + S^2T + ST^2 + TST + T^2S + T^3$
26. (a)  $(ST)(x, y, z) = (x + y + z, x + y, x)$;  $(TS)(x, y, z) = (z, z + y, z + y + x)$;
    $(ST - TS)(x, y, z) = (x + y, x - z, -y - z)$;  $S^2(x, y, z) = (x, y, z)$;
    $T^2(x, y, z) = (x, 2x + y, 3x + 2y + z)$;
    $(ST)^2(x, y, z) = (3x + 2y + z, 2x + 2y + z, x + y + z)$;
    $(TS)^2(x, y, z) = (x + y + z, x + 2y + 2z, x + 2y + 3z)$;
    $(ST - TS)^2 = (2x + y - z, x + 2y + z, -x + y + 2z)$;
    (b)  $S^{-1}(u, v, w) = (w, v, u)$;  $T^{-1}(u, v, w) = (u, v - u, w - v)$;
    $(ST)^{-1}(u, v, w) = (w, v - w, u - v)$;  $(TS)^{-1}(u, v, w) = (w - v, v - u, u)$
    (c)  $(T - I)(x, y, z) = (0, x, x + y)$;  $(T - I)^2(x, y, z) = (0, 0, x)$;
    $(T - I)^n(x, y, z) = (0, 0, 0)$  if  $n \geq 3$
28. (a)  $Dp(x) = 3 - 2x + 12x^2$;  $Tp(x) = 3x - 2x^2 + 12x^3$;  $(DT)p(x) = 3 - 4x + 36x^2$;
    $(TD)p(x) = -2x + 24x^2$;  $(DT - TD)p(x) = 3 - 2x + 12x^2$;
    $(T^2D^2 - D^2T^2)p(x) = 8 - 192x$      (b)  $p(x) = ax$, $a$ an arbitrary scalar
    (c)  $p(x) = ax^2 + b$, $a$ and $b$ arbitrary scalars      (d)  All $p$ in $V$
31. (a)  $Rp(x) = 2$;  $Sp(x) = 3 - x + x^2$;  $Tp(x) = 2x + 3x^2 - x^3 + x^4$;
    $(ST)p(x) = 2 + 3x - x^2 + x^3$;  $(TS)p(x) = 3x - x^2 + x^3$;  $(TS)^2p(x) = 3x - x^2 + x^3$;
    $(T^2S^2)p(x) = -x^2 + x^3$;  $(S^2T^2)p(x) = 2 + 3x - x^2 + x^3$;  $(TRS)p(x) = 3x$;
    $(RST)p(x) = 2$
    (b)  $N(R) = \{p \mid p(0) = 0\}$;  $R(V) = \{p \mid p$ is constant$\}$;  $N(S) = \{p \mid p$ is constant$\}$;
    $S(V) = V$;  $N(T) = \{O\}$;  $T(V) = \{p \mid p(0) = 0\}$      (c)  $T^{-1} = S$
    (d)  $(TS)^n = I - R$;  $S^nT^n = I$
32. $T$ is not one-to-one on $V$ because it maps all constant sequences onto the same sequence

**16.12**   **Exercises (page 596)**

1.   (a)   The identity matrix $I = (\delta_{jk})$, where $\delta_{jk} = 1$ if $j = k$, and $\delta_{jk} = 0$ if $j \neq k$
     (b)   The zero matrix $O = (a_{jk})$ where each entry $a_{jk} = 0$
     (c)   The matrix $(c\delta_{jk})$, where $(\delta_{jk})$ is the identity matrix of part (a)

2.   (a) $\begin{bmatrix} 1 & 0 & 0 \\ 0 & 1 & 0 \end{bmatrix}$    (b) $\begin{bmatrix} 0 & 1 & 0 \\ 0 & 0 & 1 \end{bmatrix}$    (c) $\begin{bmatrix} 0 & 1 & 0 & 0 & 0 \\ 0 & 0 & 1 & 0 & 0 \\ 0 & 0 & 0 & 1 & 0 \end{bmatrix}$

3.   (a)   $-5i + 7j, \quad 9i - 12j$
     (b) $\begin{bmatrix} 1 & 2 \\ 1 & -1 \end{bmatrix}, \begin{bmatrix} 3 & 0 \\ 0 & 3 \end{bmatrix}$    (c) $\begin{bmatrix} -\frac{7}{4} & -\frac{1}{4} \\ \frac{1}{4} & \frac{7}{4} \end{bmatrix}, \begin{bmatrix} 3 & 0 \\ 0 & 3 \end{bmatrix}$

4.   $\begin{bmatrix} -2 & 0 \\ 0 & 2 \end{bmatrix}, \begin{bmatrix} 4 & 0 \\ 0 & 4 \end{bmatrix}$

5.   (a)   $3i + 4j + 4k$; nullity 0, rank 3    (b) $\begin{bmatrix} -1 & -1 & 2 \\ 1 & -3 & 3 \\ -1 & -5 & 5 \end{bmatrix}$

6.   $\begin{bmatrix} 2 & 0 & -2 \\ 1 & -1 & 1 \\ 2 & 1 & 0 \end{bmatrix}$

7.   (a)   $T(4i - j + k) = (0, -2)$; nullity 1, rank 2    (b) $\begin{bmatrix} 0 & 1 & 1 \\ 0 & 1 & -1 \end{bmatrix}$
     (c) $\begin{bmatrix} 0 & 1 & 3 \\ 0 & 0 & -2 \end{bmatrix}$    (d)   $e_1 = j, \quad e_2 = k, \quad e_3 = i, \quad w_1 = (1, 1), \quad w_2 = (1, -1)$

8.   (a)   $(5, 0, -1)$; nullity 0, rank 2    (b) $\begin{bmatrix} 1 & -1 \\ 0 & 0 \\ 1 & 1 \end{bmatrix}$
     (c)   $e_1 = i, \quad e_2 = i + j, \quad w_1 = (1, 0, 1), \quad w_2 = (0, 0, 2), \quad w_3 = (0, 1, 0)$

9.   (a)   $(-1, -3, -1)$; nullity 0, rank 2    (b) $\begin{bmatrix} 1 & 1 \\ 0 & 1 \\ 1 & 1 \end{bmatrix}$
     (c)   $e_1 = i, \quad e_2 = j - i, \quad w_1 = (1, 0, 1), \quad w_2 = (0, 1, 0), \quad w_3 = (0, 0, 1)$

10.   (a)   $e_1 - e_2$; nullity 0, rank 2    (b) $\begin{bmatrix} 1 & 2 \\ 5 & 4 \end{bmatrix}$    (c)   $a = 5, \quad b = 4$

11.   $\begin{bmatrix} 0 & -1 \\ 1 & 0 \end{bmatrix}, \begin{bmatrix} -1 & 0 \\ 0 & -1 \end{bmatrix}$

12.   $\begin{bmatrix} 0 & 1 & 0 \\ 0 & 0 & 0 \\ 0 & 0 & 1 \end{bmatrix}, \begin{bmatrix} 0 & 0 & 0 \\ 0 & 0 & 0 \\ 0 & 0 & 1 \end{bmatrix}$

13.   $\begin{bmatrix} 0 & 1 & 1 \\ 0 & 0 & -1 \\ 0 & 0 & 1 \end{bmatrix}, \begin{bmatrix} 0 & 0 & 0 \\ 0 & 0 & -1 \\ 0 & 0 & 1 \end{bmatrix}$

14. $\begin{bmatrix} 1 & 1 \\ 0 & 1 \end{bmatrix}$, $\begin{bmatrix} 1 & 2 \\ 0 & 1 \end{bmatrix}$

15. $\begin{bmatrix} 0 & -1 \\ 1 & 0 \end{bmatrix}$, $\begin{bmatrix} -1 & 0 \\ 0 & -1 \end{bmatrix}$

16. $\begin{bmatrix} 0 & -1 & 1 & 0 \\ 1 & 0 & 0 & 1 \\ 0 & 0 & 0 & -1 \\ 0 & 0 & 1 & 0 \end{bmatrix}$, $\begin{bmatrix} -1 & 0 & 0 & -2 \\ 0 & -1 & 2 & 0 \\ 0 & 0 & -1 & 0 \\ 0 & 0 & 0 & -1 \end{bmatrix}$

17. $\begin{bmatrix} 1 & -1 \\ 1 & 1 \end{bmatrix}$, $\begin{bmatrix} 0 & -2 \\ 2 & 0 \end{bmatrix}$

18. $\begin{bmatrix} 2 & -3 \\ 3 & 2 \end{bmatrix}$, $\begin{bmatrix} -5 & -12 \\ 12 & -5 \end{bmatrix}$

19. (a) $\begin{bmatrix} 0 & 0 & 0 & 0 \\ 0 & 1 & 0 & 0 \\ 0 & 0 & 2 & 0 \\ 0 & 0 & 0 & 3 \end{bmatrix}$ (b) $\begin{bmatrix} 0 & 1 & 0 & 0 \\ 0 & 0 & 4 & 0 \\ 0 & 0 & 0 & 9 \\ 0 & 0 & 0 & 0 \end{bmatrix}$ (c) $\begin{bmatrix} 0 & 0 & 0 & 0 \\ 0 & 0 & 2 & 0 \\ 0 & 0 & 0 & 6 \\ 0 & 0 & 0 & 0 \end{bmatrix}$

(d) $\begin{bmatrix} 0 & -1 & 0 & 0 \\ 0 & 0 & -2 & 0 \\ 0 & 0 & 0 & -3 \\ 0 & 0 & 0 & 0 \end{bmatrix}$ (e) $\begin{bmatrix} 0 & 0 & 0 & 0 \\ 0 & 1 & 0 & 0 \\ 0 & 0 & 4 & 0 \\ 0 & 0 & 0 & 9 \end{bmatrix}$ (f) $\begin{bmatrix} 0 & 0 & -8 & 0 \\ 0 & 0 & 0 & -48 \\ 0 & 0 & 0 & 0 \\ 0 & 0 & 0 & 0 \end{bmatrix}$

20. Choose $(x^3, x^2, x, 1)$ as a basis for $V$, and $(x^2, x)$ as a basis for $W$. Then the matrix of $TD$ is

$\begin{bmatrix} 6 & 0 & 0 & 0 \\ 0 & 2 & 0 & 0 \end{bmatrix}$

## 16.16 Exercises (page 603)

1. $B + C = \begin{bmatrix} 3 & 4 \\ 0 & 2 \\ 6 & -5 \end{bmatrix}$, $AB = \begin{bmatrix} 15 & -14 \\ -15 & 14 \end{bmatrix}$, $BA = \begin{bmatrix} -1 & 4 & -2 \\ -4 & 16 & -8 \\ 7 & -28 & 14 \end{bmatrix}$,

$AC = \begin{bmatrix} 0 & 0 \\ 0 & 0 \end{bmatrix}$, $CA = \begin{bmatrix} 0 & 0 & 0 \\ 2 & -8 & 4 \\ 4 & -16 & 8 \end{bmatrix}$, $A(2B - 3C) = \begin{bmatrix} 30 & -28 \\ -30 & 28 \end{bmatrix}$

2. (a) $\begin{bmatrix} a & b \\ 0 & 0 \end{bmatrix}$, $a$ and $b$ arbitrary (b) $\begin{bmatrix} -2a & a \\ -2b & b \end{bmatrix}$, $a$ and $b$ arbitrary

3. (a) $a = 9$, $b = 6$, $c = 1$, $d = 5$ (b) $a = 1$, $b = 6$, $c = 0$, $d = -2$

4. (a) $\begin{bmatrix} -9 & -2 & -10 \\ 6 & 14 & 8 \\ -7 & 5 & -5 \end{bmatrix}$ (b) $\begin{bmatrix} -3 & 5 & -4 \\ 0 & 3 & 24 \\ 12 & -27 & 0 \end{bmatrix}$

6. $A^n = \begin{bmatrix} 1 & n \\ 0 & 1 \end{bmatrix}$

7. $A^n = \begin{bmatrix} \cos n\theta & -\sin n\theta \\ \sin n\theta & \cos n\theta \end{bmatrix}$.

8. $A^n = \begin{bmatrix} 1 & n & \dfrac{n(n+1)}{2} \\ 0 & 1 & n \\ 0 & 0 & 1 \end{bmatrix}$

9. $\begin{bmatrix} 1 & 0 \\ -100 & 1 \end{bmatrix}$

10. $\begin{bmatrix} a & b \\ c & -a \end{bmatrix}$, where $b$ and $c$ are arbitrary, and $a$ is any solution of the equation $a^2 = -bc$

11. (b) $\begin{bmatrix} a & 0 \\ 0 & a \end{bmatrix}$, where $a$ is arbitrary

12. $\begin{bmatrix} 1 & 0 \\ 0 & 1 \end{bmatrix}$, $\begin{bmatrix} -1 & 0 \\ 0 & -1 \end{bmatrix}$, and $\begin{bmatrix} a & b \\ c & -a \end{bmatrix}$, where $b$ and $c$ are arbitrary and $a$ is any solution of the equation $a^2 = 1 - bc$

13. $C = \begin{bmatrix} \frac{15}{2} & \frac{13}{2} \\ 8 & 7 \end{bmatrix}$, $D = \begin{bmatrix} \frac{33}{4} & \frac{19}{4} \\ \frac{43}{4} & \frac{25}{4} \end{bmatrix}$

14. (b) $(A + B)^2 = A^2 + AB + BA + B^2$; $(A + B)(A - B) = A^2 + BA - AB - B^2$
    (c) For those which commute

## 16.20 Exercises (page 613)

1. $(x, y, z) = (\frac{8}{5}, -\frac{7}{5}, \frac{3}{5})$
2. No solution
3. $(x, y, z) = (1, -1, 0) + t(-3, 4, 1)$
4. $(x, y, z) = (1, -1, 0) + t(-3, 4, 1)$
5. $(x, y, z, u) = (1, 1, 0, 0) + t(1, 14, 5, 0)$
6. $(x, y, z, u) = (1, 8, 0, -4) + t(2, 7, 3, 0)$
7. $(x, y, z, u, v) = t_1(-1, 1, 0, 0, 0) + t_2(-1, 0, 3, -3, 1)$
8. $(x, y, z, u) = (1, 1, 1, -1) + t_1(-1, 3, 7, 0) + t_2(4, 9, 0, 7)$
9. $(x, y, z) = (\frac{4}{3}, \frac{2}{3}, 0) + t(5, 1, -3)$
10. (a) $(x, y, z, u) = (1, 6, 3, 0) + t_1(4, 11, 7, 0) + t_2(0, 0, 0, 1)$
    (b) $(x, y, z, u) = (\frac{3}{11}, 4, \frac{19}{11}, 0) + t(4, -11, 7, 22)$

12. $\begin{bmatrix} -1 & 2 & 1 \\ 5 & -8 & -6 \\ -3 & 5 & 4 \end{bmatrix}$

14. $\begin{bmatrix} 14 & 8 & 3 \\ 8 & 5 & 2 \\ 3 & 2 & 1 \end{bmatrix}$

13. $\begin{bmatrix} -\frac{5}{3} & \frac{2}{3} & \frac{4}{3} \\ -1 & 0 & 1 \\ \frac{7}{3} & -\frac{1}{3} & -\frac{5}{3} \end{bmatrix}$

15. $\begin{bmatrix} 1 & -2 & 1 & 0 \\ 0 & 1 & -2 & 1 \\ 0 & 0 & 1 & -2 \\ 0 & 0 & 0 & 1 \end{bmatrix}$

$$16. \quad \begin{bmatrix} 0 & \frac{1}{2} & 0 & -1 & 0 & 1 \\ 1 & 0 & 0 & 0 & 0 & 0 \\ 0 & 0 & 0 & 1 & 0 & -1 \\ -3 & 0 & 1 & 0 & 0 & 0 \\ 0 & 0 & 0 & 0 & 0 & \frac{1}{2} \\ 9 & 0 & -3 & 0 & 1 & 0 \end{bmatrix}$$

## 16.21 Miscellaneous exercises on matrices (page 614)

3. $P = \begin{bmatrix} 2 & 1 \\ 5 & -1 \end{bmatrix}$

4. $\begin{bmatrix} 0 & 0 \\ 0 & 0 \end{bmatrix}$, $\begin{bmatrix} 1 & 0 \\ 0 & 1 \end{bmatrix}$, and $\begin{bmatrix} a & b \\ c & 1-a \end{bmatrix}$, where $b$ and $c$ are arbitrary and $a$ is any solution of the quadratic equation $a^2 - a + bc = 0$

10. (a) $\begin{bmatrix} 1 & 1 \\ -1 & 1 \end{bmatrix}$, $\begin{bmatrix} 1 & 1 \\ 1 & -1 \end{bmatrix}$, $\begin{bmatrix} -1 & 1 \\ 1 & 1 \end{bmatrix}$, $\begin{bmatrix} 1 & -1 \\ 1 & 1 \end{bmatrix}$, $\begin{bmatrix} -1 & -1 \\ 1 & -1 \end{bmatrix}$, $\begin{bmatrix} -1 & -1 \\ -1 & 1 \end{bmatrix}$, $\begin{bmatrix} 1 & -1 \\ -1 & -1 \end{bmatrix}$, $\begin{bmatrix} -1 & 1 \\ -1 & -1 \end{bmatrix}$

# INDEX